The Great Alaska Earthquake of 1964

COMMITTEE ON THE ALASKA EARTHQUAKE
OF THE
DIVISION OF EARTH SCIENCES
NATIONAL RESEARCH COUNCIL

ENGINEERING

NATIONAL ACADEMY OF SCIENCES
WASHINGTON, D.C.
1973

THE GREAT ALASKA EARTHQUAKE OF 1964

Geology

Seismology and Geodesy

Hydrology

Biology

Oceanography and Coastal Engineering

Engineering

Human Ecology

Summary and Recommendations

Available from
Printing and Publishing Office
National Academy of Sciences
2101 Constitution Avenue
Washington, D.C. 20418

ISBN 0-309-01606-1

Library of Congress Catalog Card Number 68-60037

Printed in the United States of America

FRONTISPIECE   Remains of the collapsed six-story Four Seasons apartment building in Anchorage. U.S. Army Corps of Engineers photograph.

Foreword

Soon after the Alaska earthquake of March 27, 1964, President Lyndon B. Johnson wrote to Donald F. Hornig, his Special Assistant for Science and Technology:

It is important we learn as many lessons as possible from the disastrous Alaskan earthquake. A scientific understanding of the events that occurred may make it possible to anticipate future earthquakes, there and elsewhere, so as to cope with them more adequately.

I, therefore, request that your office undertake to assemble a comprehensive scientific and technical account of the Alaskan earthquake and its effects. . . .

In defining the scientific and technical questions involved and the related informational requirements for collection and assessment, I hope that you will be able to enlist the aid of the National Academy of Sciences. . . .

In discussions that followed, the Academy was requested by Dr. Hornig to establish the Committee on the Alaska Earthquake, to be charged with three principal tasks—to evaluate efforts being made to gather scientific and engineering information about the earthquake and its effects, to encourage the filling of gaps in the record, and to compile and publish a comprehensive report on the earthquake.

Under the chairmanship of Konrad B. Krauskopf of Stanford University, a twelve-man committee was formed of specialists from related scientific and technical disciplines. Their first meeting was held on June 15, 1964.

The resulting documents, prepared by the Committee and its seven specialized panels, constitute perhaps the most comprehensive and detailed account of an earthquake yet compiled. The Committee has attempted to compile from the available information and analysis a useful resource for present and future scholars in this field. As a result of the present study, much that is new and useful has been learned about earthquakes as well as about natural disasters in general.

In addition to the membership of the central committee, the work of several hundred scientists and engineers is represented in the Committee's report. Many of these are staff members of government agencies that have gathered facts and data about the earthquake and its effects; others are from universities and nongovernmental scientific organizations with an interest in earthquake-related research. Their help and cooperation in making this report possible is deeply appreciated.

PHILIP HANDLER
President
National Academy of Sciences

v

COMMITTEE ON THE ALASKA EARTHQUAKE

KONRAD B. KRAUSKOPF, *Chairman*; Stanford University, 1964–
HUGO BENIOFF, California Institute of Technology, 1964
EARL F. COOK, Texas A&M University, 1968–
DOAK C. COX, University of Hawaii, 1964–
ERNEST DOBROVOLNY, U.S. Geological Survey, 1964–
EDWIN B. ECKEL, The Geological Society of America, 1965–
JAMES GILLULY, U.S. Geological Survey, 1964–1965
RICHARD P. GOLDTHWAIT, The Ohio State University, 1964–
J. EUGENE HAAS, University of Colorado, 1968–
GEORGE Y. HARRY, JR., National Oceanic and Atmospheric Administration, 1965–
HAROLD D. HAUF, Consultant, Sun City, Arizona, 1964–
GEORGE W. HOUSNER, California Institute of Technology, 1964–
ROBERT W. KATES, Clark University, 1964–
H. BOLTON SEED, University of California, Berkeley, 1964–
DON TOCHER, National Oceanic and Atmospheric Administration, 1964–

Ex Officio

M. KING HUBBERT, U.S. Geological Survey and Stanford University, 1964–1965
J. HOOVER MACKIN, University of Texas, 1965–1967
JOHN R. BORCHERT, University of Minnesota, 1967–1969
GORDON J. F. MACDONALD, University of California, Santa Barbara, 1969–1970
JOHN C. MAXWELL, University of Texas, 1970–1972
ALLAN V. COX, Stanford University, 1972–

LIAISON
REPRESENTATIVES

S. THEODORE ALGERMISSEN, National Oceanic and Atmospheric Administration, 1964–
WALTER S. BAER, Office of Science and Technology, 1967–1968
GEORGE E. BECRAFT, U.S. Geological Survey, 1970–
WILLIAM E. BENSON, National Science Foundation, 1964–
RUDOLPH A. BLACK, Advanced Research Projects Agency, 1967–
THOMAS R. CASEY, Office of Emergency Preparedness, 1970–1971
JOHN M. DeNOYER, Department of Defense, 1966–1967
ROBERT A. FROSCH, Department of Defense, 1964–1966
GEORGE O. GATES, U.S. Geological Survey, 1964–1970
GEORGE A. KOLSTAD, Atomic Energy Commission, 1968–
JAMES L. LEWIS, Office of Emergency Preparedness, 1968–1970
NED A. OSTENSO, Office of Naval Research, 1970–
DAVID Z. ROBINSON, Office of Science and Technology, 1965–1967
CARL H. SAVIT, Office of Science and Technology, 1970–1971
JOHN S. STEINHART, Office of Science and Technology, 1968–1969
LEONARD S. WILSON, Army Research Office, 1968–1970
VALENTINE ZADNIK, Army Research Office, 1971–
ARTHUR J. ZEIZEL, Department of Housing and Urban Development, 1970–

Preface

South central Alaska (Figure 1), including Prince William Sound and the Aleutian area, is one of the world's most active seismic regions. On March 27, 1964, at about 5:36 p.m. local time (0336, or 3:36 a.m. GMT, March 28), an earthquake of unusual severity struck the Prince William Sound area. Seismologists record earthquake occurrences in Greenwich mean time (GMT). The U.S. Coast and Geodetic Survey, therefore, uses 03h 36m 14.0 ± 0.2s GMT, March 28, 1964, as the time of the earthquake. The coordinates of the epicenter of the main shock have been calculated as lat. $61.04° ± 0.05°$ N and long. $147.73° ± 0.07°$ W, and the focus was within a few tens of kilometers of the surface. Not only was this earthquake of large magnitude (between 8.3 and 8.6 on the Richter scale, on which the greatest known earthquake is 8.9), but its duration (3 to 4 minutes) and the area of its damage zone ($50,000$ mi^2) were extraordinary. Probably twice as much energy was released by the Alaska earthquake as by the one that rocked San Francisco in 1906.

The shock was felt over $500,000$ mi^2. A tsunami (a train of long waves impulsively generated, in this case by movement of the sea floor) or "tidal wave" swept from the Gulf of Alaska across the length of the Pacific and lapped against Antarctica. Water levels in wells as far away as South Africa jumped abruptly, and shock-induced waves were generated in the Gulf of Mexico. An atmospheric pressure wave caused by the earthquake was recorded at La Jolla, California, more than 2,000 mi away. Seismic surface waves, with periods of many seconds, moved the ground surface of most of the North American continent by as much as 2 in.

The magnitude of the earthquake can be calculated only from teleseismic records, and its duration can be estimated only from eyewitness accounts, because no seismic instruments capable of recording strong ground motion were in Alaska at the time. The range of uncertainty in the magnitude calculations (8.3–8.6) is far greater in terms of energy release than the figures suggest; from the most generally ac-cepted relation of magnitude to energy release, it can be calculated that magnitude 8.6 represents approximately twice the energy release of magnitude 8.3.

Measured crustal deformation was more extensive than the deformation related to any known previous earthquake. Areas of uplift and subsidence were separated by a line of zero land-level change trending both southwestward and eastward from the vicinity of the epicenter, about 80 mi east-southeast of Anchorage; this line parallels the major tectonic features of the region. Areas north and northwest of the zero line subsided as much as 7.5 ft; areas south and southeast rose, over wide areas, as much as 6 ft. Locally the uplift was much greater: 38 ft on Montague Island and more than 50 ft on the sea floor southwest of the island. The zone of uplift was along the continental margin of the Aleutian Trench. Not only was the earth's crust displaced vertically, but horizontal movements of tens of feet took place, in which the landmass moved southeastward relative to the ocean floor. The area of crustal deformation was more than 100,000 mi^2.

The mechanism of the earthquake remains to some extent uncertain. Fault-plane solutions for the main shock and the principal aftershocks, of which there were 10 of magnitudes greater than 6.0 within 24 hours after the initial shock, are consistent either with thrusting of the continent over the ocean floor along a plane dipping 5°–15° north or northwest, or with downward slip of the continent along a near-vertical plane; in either case the strike of the fault is northeast in the vicinity of Kodiak Island to east in Prince William Sound, parallel to the dominant tectonic trend. Although the fault-plane solutions do not permit an unambiguous decision between the two possible planes, several other lines of evidence strongly favor the low-angle thrust alternative.

The strong ground motion induced many snowslides, rockfalls, and landslides, both subaerial and submarine. The submarine landslides created local sea waves or tsunamis,

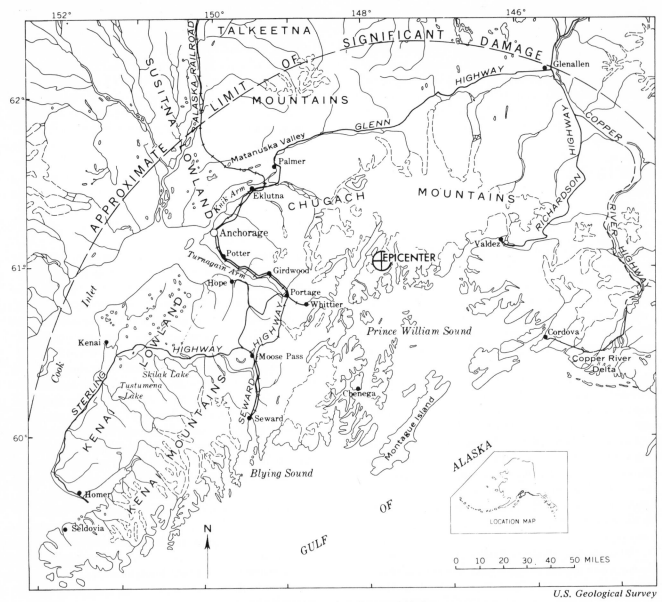

FIGURE 1 Map of south central Alaska.

U.S. Geological Survey

which, together with the major tsunami generated by the crustal deformation, smashed port and harbor facilities, covered sessile organisms and salmon-spawning beds with silt, disturbed and killed salmon fry, leveled forests, and caused saltwater invasion of many coastal freshwater lakes.

The tectonic elevation and depression caused extensive damage to the biota of coastal forests, migratory-bird nesting grounds, salmon-spawning waters and gravels, as well as shellfish habitats, and initiated long-term changes in littoral and stream morphology. Clams, barnacles, algae, and many other marine and littoral organisms perished in areas of up-

lift. Spawning beds, trees, and other vegetation were destroyed in areas of depression.

Except for the major tsunami, which caused extensive damage in British Columbia and took 16 lives in Oregon and California, violence to man and his structures was restricted to the area of tectonic land-level change. Tsunamis, major and local, took the most lives. Landslides caused the most damage.

The number of lives lost in Alaska, 115, was very small for an earthquake of this magnitude. Factors that contributed to the light loss of life were the sparse population, the fortuitous timing of the earthquake, a low tide, the absence of fire in residential and business areas, the generally clement weather, and the fact that the earthquake occurred during the off-season for fishing. The earthquake came on the evening of a holiday, when the schools were empty and most offices deserted, but when most people were still wearing their warm clothing. The low tide and the absence of fishermen and cannery workers mitigated the destruction and loss of life from tsunamis.

Public and private property loss was over $300 million. Hundreds of homes were destroyed. A multistory apartment building (fortunately not occupied), a department store, and other buildings in Anchorage collapsed. Oil storage tanks at Valdez, Seward, and Whittier ruptured and burned. Many other structures were destroyed or damaged. Most of downtown Kodiak was inundated by the major tsunami.

Damage to surface transportation facilities was extensive. The Alaska Railroad lost its port facility at Whittier, its docks at Seward, and numerous bridges on the Kenai Peninsula. Many highway bridges, especially on the Seward and Copper River highways, were damaged. Many port and harbor facilities, especially at Seward, Valdez, Kodiak, Whittier, Cordova, and Homer, were destroyed.

The earthquake crippled Alaska's economy because nearly half the people of the state live within the damage area and because the land- and sea-transport facilities on which the economy depends were knocked out.

Relief came quickly. The extensive military establishment proved a great source of strength in implementing emergency measures designed to reduce the loss of life, to ease immediate suffering, and to restore needed services promptly. Financial assistance for relief purposes was provided immediately by the Office of Emergency Planning under provisions of the Federal Disaster Act.

Recovery was rapid. Of major importance in the reconstruction effort was a congressional program to provide additional federal aid not possible under existing authority. This program was recommended by the Federal Reconstruction and Development Planning Commission for Alaska, a unique body appointed by President Lyndon B. Johnson on April 2, 1964. The additional aid included transitional grants to maintain essential public services; an increase in the federal share of highway reconstruction costs; a decrease in the local share of urban renewal projects; debt adjustments on existing federal loans; federal purchase of state bonds; and grants for a state mortgage-forgiveness program. An estimated $330 million of government and private funds financed Alaska's recovery from the earthquake.

The Alaska earthquake is the best documented and most thoroughly studied earthquake in history. Attempts have been made to draw lessons from both the physical event and the human experience. Strong-motion seismographs and accelerographs were installed in Alaska shortly after the earthquake, providing a basis for study of the stronger aftershocks. The tsunami warning system for the North Pacific was greatly improved within a few months, mainly by establishment of three new seismograph stations in south central Alaska as the basic elements in the system. Risk maps for Anchorage, Homer, Seward, and Valdez, based upon extensive geological studies, were prepared by the Scientific and Engineering Task Force of the Reconstruction Commission and were used discriminatingly as a basis for federal aid to reconstruction and as guides to future builders. The entire town of Valdez was relocated. Communities and state and professional organizations in seismic areas outside Alaska reexamined codes and programs related to earthquake hazard in light of the Alaska experience. Finally, the Alaska earthquake turned the nation's attention again, and sharply, to the problems of improving the elements of a national natural-disaster policy: zoning and construction codes; prediction and warning systems; rescue and relief organizations; disaster-data collection and analysis; and disaster insurance and reconstruction aids.

Thus the earthquake had many facets. It was a natural scientific experiment on a grand scale, providing data on a variety of long-standing problems regarding the mechanism and effects of earthquakes. It served as a test of man-made structures under extreme conditions, and as a guide to improvements in the location and design of such structures to make them better able to withstand seismic shocks. It was an object lesson in human response to disaster, pointing the way to increased effectiveness of warning systems, of emergency measures during disasters, and of relief and recovery operations.

The charge to the Committee on the Alaska Earthquake was made to ensure that as much technical and scientific information as possible would be wrung from the earthquake experience and that the results would be assembled into a comprehensive report. At its first meeting the Committee decided that its initial task of evaluating and encouraging efforts to gather scientific and technical information could best be carried out by panels representing the major disciplines involved in the data-gathering: engineering, geography (human ecology), geology, hydrology, oceanography, and seismology. Biology, at first included within oceanography, was later made the basis of a separate panel.

As information for a comprehensive report accumulated, it became clear that the report itself could most appropriately follow the panel structure. Accordingly, this report appears in eight volumes, seven put together by the separate panels and a summary volume prepared by the full Committee.

In the early meetings of the Committee, and especially as it became apparent that many of the physical-science and some of the engineering aspects of the earthquake would be treated comprehensively in government publications and individual studies, there was considerable discussion of the appropriate content of the Committee's final report.

The Committee finally decided that the advantages of having available, under one cover and in one place in a library, a truly comprehensive report on the earthquake would justify the expense of duplicating some material already published. In addition, the Committee agreed, a complete report would provide a better basis for the inclusion of cross-disciplinary papers, for pointing out lessons learned from the Alaska experience, and for making recommendations designed to reduce the loss of life and property in subsequent major earthquakes.

As a model for its work, the Committee could look back to the classic report on the 1906 San Francisco earthquake, published by the Carnegie Institution in 1908. To emulate the comprehensiveness of this magnificent report seemed possible, but not the unity and coherence that it gained from the encyclopedic knowledge of its editor and principal author, A. C. Lawson. The breadth and depth of scientific interest in earthquakes have increased so greatly since 1906 that no one man can hope to master, as Lawson did, a great part of existing technical knowledge on all aspects of earthquakes. A report today must necessarily have many authors and must reflect in its length and diversity the extraordinary development of disciplines and instruments over the past half century.

Despite the Committee's attempt to make the report broadly comprehensive, there are unfortunate and obvious gaps in the record, mainly in those subject-matter fields not included in the work of government agencies. Such gaps are identified in the appropriate volumes of the report.

Apart from these gaps, the report covers a wide variety of subjects in engineering, natural science, and social science. Ranging from seismology to human ecology, it sets forth what is known about the structure of the earth's crust in south central Alaska, especially in relation to possible earthquake mechanisms and to tsunami generation; describes the effects of the earthquake on geologic processes, rocks, and soils; outlines the seismic history of Alaska and gives the seismic parameters of the earthquake; presents the results of energy-release, strain-release, and focal-mechanism studies of the main shock and aftershocks; describes the effects of the earthquake on groundwater and surface-water bodies and on glaciers and snowfields; discusses the generation, propagation, and effects of earthquake-induced tsunamis; describes immediate as well as long-term effects on plants and animals of abrupt land elevation and depression and of slides and tsunamis; sets forth in detail, with analyses, the response of man-made structures to the earthquake; chronicles in narrative form both the physical and human events of the earth-

quake; describes the impact of the earthquake on individuals, communities, and organizations; and puts forward recommendations that range from geologic mapping for hazard zoning, through methods of assuring site-suited earthquake-resistant construction, to means of improving the human response to disaster.

This volume on engineering is one of the eight that make up the report. Its objective is to provide information that will be of use to engineers, research workers, and public officials in making earthquakes less destructive. The practical purposes of studying destructive earthquakes are to make clear the nature of the damaging effects, why they occurred, and how they might have been avoided, hence to ensure greater public safety and welfare during future earthquakes.

Reports on some aspects of earthquake damage to the works of man have been prepared for many previous earthquakes in the United States, but in this volume for the first time an attempt is made to provide an engineering study giving as complete coverage as possible of the destructive effects of a great earthquake. Although the earthquake shook a large area with damaging intensity, fortunately the area was not densely populated, and therefore the damage wrought and the losses suffered were small compared to what they might have been. In consequence, the engineering information that could be gathered was not complete, for there was no large city in the area and no extensive industrial development. Nevertheless, a detailed study of the Alaska earthquake experience will make possible an extrapolation to the consequences of a major earthquake striking a large metropolitan area.

The Alaska event, so to speak, was an engineering experiment on a large scale in which many kinds of structures built on many kinds of foundation material were subjected to great deforming forces. Unfortunately, from an engineering standpoint the preparation for the experiment was gravely deficient in that no instruments had been installed capable of recording the ground motion during the earthquake; hence, this important engineering information is lacking. One of the major engineering recommendations is that strong-motion recording instruments in adequate numbers be set up in all earthquake-prone areas of the United States so that the crucial data missing from the Alaska record may be obtained during future earthquakes.

Some aspects of the earthquake pertinent to engineering are treated in other volumes of the report. The effects of earthquake-generated tsunamis on structures near the coast are described in the volume on Oceanography and Coastal Engineering. Landslides and other results of foundation instability are described and analyzed from a geologic point of view in the Geology volume. Economic questions relating to earthquake damage are treated in the Human Ecology volume.

From a human point of view, loss of life and destruction of property are the most important and most dreaded consequences of a great earthquake. Both can be minimized by good engineering in the location, design, and construction of the structures in which men live and work. The large amount of engineering study devoted to the Alaska earthquake and recorded in the pages of this Engineering volume will be more than justified if it aids in improving criteria for engineering design in areas where major earthquakes can be expected.

KONRAD B. KRAUSKOPF
Stanford University

Acknowledgments

The Committee on the Alaska Earthquake and the Panel on Engineering are particularly indebted to the National Science Foundation, the former U.S. Coast and Geodetic Survey, the U.S. Geological Survey, the Office of Emergency Preparedness, the Army Research Office, the Atomic Energy Commission, the Advanced Research Projects Agency, the Office of Naval Research, Defense Civil Preparedness Agency, and the Department of Transportation for support of the Committee under Contract NSF C-310, T.O. 89; to the Department of Housing and Urban Development for similar support under Contract H-1229; to the Bureau of Land Management, Bureau of Indian Affairs, Bureau of Sport Fisheries and Wildlife, National Park Service, and the U.S. Geological Survey for special support; to the National Science Foundation for publication support under Contract NSF C-310, T.O. 208; and to the United States Air Force Academy for the temporary assignment of Lt. Paul C. Jennings to assist the Panel on Engineering in 1964.

The Committee and Panel greatly appreciate the time and effort provided by Ray W. Clough (Chairman), Tor L. Brekke, Anil K. Chopra, Joseph Penzien, and Robert L. Wiegel of the Department of Civil Engineering, University of California, Berkeley; Glen V. Berg of the Department of Civil Engineering, University of Michigan; Robert D. Darragh of Dames and Moore, San Francisco; and Anestis S. Veletsos of the Department of Civil Engineering, Rice University, for their comments and suggestions as reviewers and members of a special National Academy of Engineering review committee that was arranged in conjunction with the Division of Earth Sciences.

The Panel thanks the various government and private organizations that made available the time of the authors whose works make up the volume. Special recognition is due the California Institute of Technology; the University of Michigan; the University of Southern California; the University of Alaska; the University of California at Berkeley; the former U.S. Coast and Geodetic Survey; the former Environmental Science Services Administration; the National Oceanic and Atmospheric Administration; the U.S. Geological Survey; The Geological Society of America; the U.S. Army Corps of Engineers; and the U.S. Bureau of Reclamation for making it possible for some of their personnel to serve as Panel members, liaison members, authors, and reviewers. Similarly, the Panel expresses its appreciation to Stanford University, the California Institute of Technology, Texas A&M University, the University of Hawaii, the U.S. Geological Survey, The Geological Society of America; The Ohio State University, the University of Colorado, the former U.S. Bureau of Commercial Fisheries, the National Oceanic and Atmospheric Administration, the University of Southern California, Clark University, the University of California at Berkeley, the former U.S. Coast and Geodetic Survey, and the former Environmental Science Services Administration for making available their personnel for service on the parent Committee; and also to the Office of Science and Technology, the National Science Foundation, the Army Research Office, the Advanced Research Projects Agency, the former U.S. Coast and Geodetic Survey, the former Environmental Science Services Administration, the National Oceanic and Atmospheric Administration, the U.S. Geological Survey, the Office of Emergency Preparedness, the Atomic Energy Commission, the Office of Naval Research, and the Department of Housing and Urban Development for the time and assistance provided by their liaison representatives to the Committee.

The Panel is grateful to the University of Idaho, the U.S. Geological Survey, and Emory University for making the services of editors and indexers available; to John S. Petrie for checking galley and page proofs; to the U.S. Army Corps of Engineers for assistance with maps and illustrations; to the U.S. Army and the U.S. Air Force for transportation to the affected areas; and to the California Institute of Technology for furnishing a meeting place for the Panel.

Since 1964, reorganizations within federal agencies and departments have involved several of the Committee's supporting agencies. On July 13, 1965, the U.S. Coast and Geodetic Survey (USC&GS) and other component agencies were combined to form the Environmental Science Services Administration (ESSA) under the Department of Commerce. On October 3, 1970, ESSA, together with several other organizations, became the National Oceanic and Atmospheric Administration (NOAA), also under the Department of Commerce. Elements of the Department of the Interior's Bureau of Commercial Fisheries became the National Marine Fisheries Service of NOAA. Although the Bureau of Commercial Fisheries, the Coast and Geodetic Survey, and the Environmental Science Services Administration no longer exist as organizations, their names are used for historical accuracy, as is that of the Office of Emergency Preparedness on October 21, 1968. Similarly, the Office of Civil Defense became the Defense Civil Preparedness Agency on May 5, 1972.

Contents

III.   DAMAGE AND REPAIR

General Introduction, Conclusions, and Recommendations

When a destructive earthquake strikes, all the works of man are affected by ground shaking; some structures and facilities are further damaged by land subsidence or elevation, by land slumping and sliding, by tsunamis, and by fires. A complete account of the 1964 Alaska earthquake would include descriptions of the damage and repair of each structure and facility, as well as summaries of the gross effects of the earthquake. The preparation of such a report would be a tremendous and difficult task, unlike any that has ever been attempted. Damage reports of past U.S. earthquakes have been compiled by only a few persons with limited time and funds; these reports have therefore been very selective in their coverage.

The unusual circumstances of the March 27, 1964, Alaska earthquake, however, have made possible a relatively comprehensive report. Although the earthquake produced strong shaking and was very destructive, it occurred in a region whose total population was only about 140,000; the number of communities, structures, and facilities was consequently very small compared to that in the State of California, for example, and the overall effect of the earthquake is relatively easy to grasp. The Alaska region presented samples of almost all types of communities and facilities: inland and waterfront, on ocean and inland waters, and on mountain and plain; it had facilities for transportation by highway, railroad, water, and air; and it contained important military installations in addition to civilian communities. This great variety of structures and environment make the lessons to be learned from the Alaska earthquake applicable to a broad spectrum of the activities of man.

The Alaska earthquake of March 27, 1964, interests en-

gineers greatly because it provides valuable information on matters relating to the safety and welfare of the public during and following destructive ground shaking. Some of the more obvious lessons learned from this event led to immediate changes in the earthquake provisions of the building codes, but the total body of information obtained from the earthquake covers such a broad spectrum that much study and analysis is required to clarify the lessons that can be learned. Every engineer, planner, or government official concerned with public safety and welfare during earthquakes and with minimizing the cost of providing earthquake protection can learn much from a study of the Alaska earthquake.

A Richter magnitude of 8.4 classifies the Alaska shock as among the world's great earthquakes. The magnitudes of several great earthquakes have been recorded as follows:

Alaska 1964	8.4
Chile 1960	8.4
Tokyo 1923	8.2
San Francisco 1906	8.2

The Alaska earthquake released approximately twice as much energy as the 1906 San Francisco earthquake, and it shook an area of approximately 75,000 mi^2 with potentially damaging intensity. Much of this area was covered by coastal waters, so that the elevation and subsidence of the earth's crust in the region of the causative fault not only adversely affected harbor facilities but also generated tsunamis (seismic sea waves). These tsunamis, which were responsible for most of the loss of life, caused death and severe damage in waterfront communities not only in Alaska but as far away as Crescent City, California. The tsunamis and the damage they caused are described in the Oceanography and Coastal Engineering volume, which contains a portion of the engineering report on the Alaska earthquake.

Most of the waterfront communities in the affected area were established on outwash plains built up of alluvial materials that proved to be unusually susceptible to earthquake-

1

induced soil failures. Some unexpectedly large landslides caused loss of life and severe damage. The tsunamis and the earthslides were prominent engineering features of the earthquake, and they emphasized the great potential for destruction inherent in these seismic hazards.

The large area affected by strong ground shaking, approximately 500 × 150 mi, had a population of only 140,000, making the potential for damage relatively small, particularly compared to the population of 14,000,000 or more that would have been affected had such an earthquake occurred in California. The reader of this report, therefore, should keep in mind a multiplying factor of 10–100 when translating the Alaska experience to more highly developed parts of the country. The total cost of the earthquake is estimated to have been in the range of $350 million to $500 million, making the per capita cost $2,500 to $3,500, which agrees well with the per capita costs of the 1906 San Francisco earthquake ($3,500) and the 1933 Long Beach earthquake ($2,500) when expressed in 1969 dollars. A figure of $3,000 per capita is therefore a useful number for estimating the cost of a strong earthquake in an urban environment in the United States. This per capita loss extrapolated to a population of 14,000,000 gives $42 billion, which shows that the total damage loss in Alaska was very small for an earthquake of such large magnitude. The number of lives lost (131) was also unexpectedly small for so large an earthquake, but it appears to have been mainly chance that kept this number small.

Most of the significant damage to structures occurred in Anchorage, the largest city in Alaska, with a population of 47,000 in addition to approximately the same number of people living on contiguous military bases (see Figure 1). The plain on which Anchorage is situated is more than 100 ft above sea level, and the bluffs at the ocean shore and adjacent to stream beds were surprisingly susceptible to extensive landslides during the ground shaking.

The experience of the Alaska earthquake can be used to forecast what could happen if a magnitude 8+ earthquake were to occur near Los Angeles, San Francisco, or Seattle. More significantly, the Alaskan experience can indicate the steps that should be taken to make cities in seismic regions safer and more resistant to damage.

THE WORK OF THE PANEL ON ENGINEERING

The objectives of the Panel on Engineering were to collect data of engineering significance and to make them available for future study and, where appropriate, to analyze these data and to draw conclusions of practical significance. The Alaska earthquake was so large and the funding available for studies was so small that the Panel obviously could not itself undertake the collection of data and the preparation

of papers for a complete engineering report. Panel members therefore agreed to prepare papers dealing with some specific features of the earthquake, although the major portion of the report would have to be prepared by others. Because the Army Corps of Engineers District Office in Anchorage was deeply involved in the reconstruction effort, it was requested to prepare the pertinent information in a form suitable for this report. Part III of this volume contains papers prepared by engineers in the Corps' Alaska District Office who both experienced the earthquake and were responsible for much of the rebuilding. These papers describe damage and reconstruction at military facilities and at civilian facilities whose reconstruction was financed, in part, by federal rehabilitation programs. Papers on damage to bridge foundations and on nonstructural damage were prepared under contract with the Corps of Engineers and these are also included in this volume.

Our report complements the U.S. Geological Survey report (1970) on the Alaska earthquake, which focuses on the geological aspects of the earthquake, and the U.S. Coast and Geodetic Survey (1967) report, volume 2A of which was "prepared essentially for design and structural engineers." The problems posed by destructive earthquakes and the studies needed to solve them are also discussed in the National Academy of Engineering report, *Earthquake Engineering Research* (Committee on Earthquake Engineering Research, 1969).

George W. Housner and Paul C. Jennings jointly planned and organized this engineering report on the Alaska earthquake and did the technical editing. This first attempt at a comprehensive engineering report on a U.S. earthquake at first encountered difficulties because the appropriate procedures and methods of funding had not been established. An investigation of an earthquake is more difficult and costly to organize in Alaska than, for example, in California. The investigation of a magnitude 8.4 earthquake is a much bigger task than the investigation of a magnitude 6.4 shock, if only because of the much greater land area involved. For these reasons, the effort that went into investigating the engineering aspects of the Alaska earthquake was not as large during the first year of the project as would have been desirable.

It is obvious, in retrospect, that there should be three different kinds of engineering report on a destructive earthquake. One report should be prepared from the point of view of engineering design and should contain information of immediate practical value. A second, prepared from the point of view of earthquake-engineering research, should contain data and analyses appropriate for deducing conclusions of practical value that are not immediately obvious. A third should relate to the needs of government officials responsible for planning protection against earthquakes and for executing relief operations following a disaster;

such a report should deal mainly with the social and economic implications of the damage and should present all data that might be pertinent to mitigating future earthquake disasters.

The following conclusions and recommendations briefly summarize the engineering lessons learned from or reinforced by the Alaska earthquake (Committee on the Alaska Earthquake, 1969). They represent a synthesis of the conclusions of general interest from all the contributors to this volume, but not all the detailed conclusions and recommendations that appear in the individual papers have been included. General conclusions are discussed first; specific suggestions for the practice of earthquake engineering have been grouped together in the final section.

CONCLUSIONS AND GENERAL RECOMMENDATIONS

The task of making cities resistant to earthquakes involves not only technical but also social problems. Destructive earthquakes occur infrequently in any one location, and the probability of occurrence of a great earthquake is less than the probability of a moderately damaging earthquake; society must therefore decide how large an investment it is willing to make to avoid loss of life and injury and to minimize earthquake damage in rare events. It is generally agreed in the United States that there should be no deaths caused by earthquakes. There is no economic justification, however, for requiring all structures to be designed to withstand, without any damage, the strongest possible ground shaking if, for example, this is an event that takes place once in 500 years. It would be advisable to invest less in earthquake resistance if the investment meant only a modest reduction of damage in the event of this ground shaking once in 500 years. The main problem to be solved is one of economics: How large an initial cost is justified to reduce damage in future earthquakes? Once the danger of loss of life and injury has been ruled out, the evaluation of the cost of various degrees of earthquake protection as compared to the monetary value of the damage prevented should be recognized as the basic social problem involved with earthquakes, and an effort that is commensurate with the importance of the problem should be directed toward its solution. Even if it were financially justified, to run the risk of a rare event leading to disastrous hardship is not socially justified.

At present, this economic decision is made indirectly by building owners, local government officials, practicing engineers, legislators, and the business community, prompted by the occurrence or nonoccurrence of destructive earthquakes and by the consequent degree of political pressure for greater public safety or for reducing costs. To make a more rational decision, the answers to the following questions should be known:

1. When and where, in a probabilistic sense, will earthquakes of various magnitudes occur in the future, and what is the nature of the ground shaking to be expected from them?

2. How can design and construction best protect the populace and ensure against failure of important structures, and yet allow controlled damage in the event of very strong shaking?

3. What is the cost of providing the resistance as compared to the cost of repairing the damage?

The present state of knowledge concerning these three questions is not adequate for making a rational economic decision, and studies should be undertaken to improve it. In addition, cost–benefit ratios should be estimated on the basis of present knowledge for regions of different seismicity and for different construction costs.

The general public and business leaders should be informed of the nature of the earthquake hazard in their communities, a hazard that depends on many technical and nontechnical factors in addition to the expected frequency of occurrence of strong ground shaking. These factors include potential landslides, the number and locations of old buildings and old dams, the condition of the water-supply system, the type of construction, the climate, and the population distribution. To accurately and completely assess the earthquake hazard to a community would require much study, but major cities in seismic areas should nevertheless try to assess this hazard, as they have in Japan. In addition, local and state governments in seismic regions should plan for the occurrence of future destructive earthquakes and should take steps to minimize their harmful effects.

Related to the hazard problem is the question of earthquake insurance. The present status of earthquake insurance is unsatisfactory; there is inadequate coverage because the rates are too high and policies are not readily available. A more efficient and widely used form of earthquake insurance, perhaps utilizing public as well as private resources, should be developed.

Earthquake-resistant design and construction in Anchorage was similar to that in other earthquake-prone states such as Washington and California. In fact, many of the Anchorage buildings had been designed or checked by Washington and California engineers, and the earthquake resistance of buildings in Anchorage was not significantly different from that of buildings in similar cities in California and Washington. There are buildings in these states similar to the collapsed and damaged buildings in Anchorage, a situation that should warn us that in seismic areas many buildings, both new and old, have inadequate earthquake

FIGURE 1   Map of the city of Anchorage, Alaska, also showing the location of Elmendorf Air Force Base. The Fort Richardson Military Reservation is to the east of Elmendorf AFB.

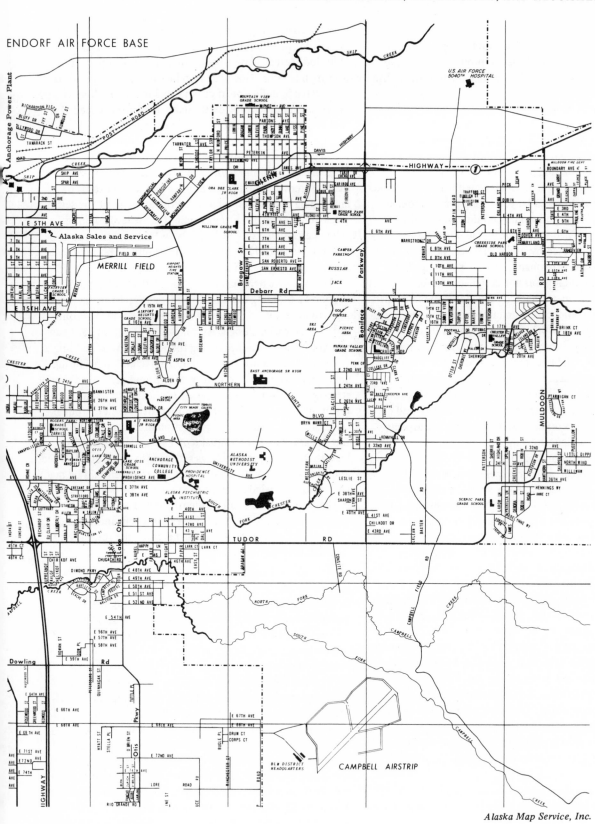

Alaska Map Service, Inc.

resistance. The existence of old buildings that were not designed to resist earthquakes represents a major hazard to the public. It is recommended that communities take steps to identify these structures and to reduce the hazards to life and limb.

Current seismic building codes are not adequate to provide a reasonable assurance that structures designed and built in strict compliance with the codes will not be severely damaged in a moderate-to-strong earthquake. The Four Seasons apartment building was a new six-story structure, designed and constructed in accordance with the earthquake provisions of the building code, yet during the earthquake it collapsed completely and would certainly have killed nearly everyone in it had it been occupied. Severe and costly damage was also sustained by other relatively new buildings in Anchorage. On the other hand, the five-story Hillside Manor apartment building was not designed according to the building code; it was, in fact, designed in complete variance with accepted engineering practice, but it survived without collapsing and without injuring any of its occupants. It was severely damaged, to be sure, and later had to be demolished as a total loss, but it provided safety for its occupants and in this sense behaved better than did the supposedly well-designed Four Seasons building. This comparison indicates that accepted engineering practice and existing building codes do not cover all significant aspects of the earthquake-design problem.

From an engineering and scientific point of view, an earthquake is a full-scale seismic experiment. Some $350 million has been expended on repair and restoration after the Alaska earthquake, but no preparation had been made before the event to record earthquake-engineering data. It should be recognized that the occurrence of earthquakes provides an opportunity to record valuable data, and appropriate preparations should be made before they occur.

The most significant loss to engineers that resulted from this lack of preparation was that no recordings of earthquake ground motions or of building or soil-structure response were obtained in Alaska during the 1964 shock; hence, there is no scientific information on the shaking that caused the damage. The great value that such records would have had emphasizes the need for installing suitable recording instruments in seismic areas. To avoid repetition of this irretrievable loss, appropriate recording instruments should be installed in all areas where earthquakes are a problem. To understand the effects of the earthquake on structures and soil masses, it is essential to know the true motion of the ground.

The Modified Mercalli Intensity Scale provides a concise way of describing human and other responses to the shaking and the nature of the damage; however, the intensity of motion indicated by a grade on the standard Modified Mercalli Scale is not an acceptable substitute for instru-

mental records of ground and building shaking. The damage in the Alaska earthquake clearly showed that the Modified Mercalli Intensity is not suitable for many engineering purposes. This scale is indicative of damage but is not a reliable indicator of ground shaking. A method of assessing and describing earthquake intensities is needed that is directly meaningful to engineering design.

The Alaska earthquake was especially noteworthy for the occurrence of landslides involving the movement of large masses of ground with the resulting destruction of many homes and buildings. Similar potential hazards of landsliding and soil liquefaction exist in many of the seismic areas in the country. For example, the great Mississippi valley earthquake of 1812 near New Madrid, Missouri, produced large landslides similar to the Fourth Avenue slide in Anchorage and many instances of soil liquefaction.

The Alaska earthquake emphasized that the ground that supports a building must be considered as part of the building structure, and its behavior must be taken into account in the engineering design. Although this situation has been recognized so far as supporting the weight of the building is concerned, it has not been widely appreciated that during an earthquake the vibrations of the ground produce dynamic stresses in the soil. These stresses may cause dynamic failure resulting in large landslides as during the Alaska earthquake, or resulting in large-scale liquefaction of the soil as during the Niigata, Japan, earthquake of 1964, when the soil so lost its strength that buildings settled into the ground, tilted, and overturned. A strong investigative effort should be made to develop knowledge about the dynamic behavior of soils so that the problems can be identified and appropriate counter-measures employed. Research is very much needed on these and other features of the earthquake response of soils and soil structures.

Reliable and meaningful seismic-zoning maps that indicate seismic hazards and expected intensities of ground shaking could be of great value for engineering planning and design. Seismic-zoning maps made in the past, however, have not been entirely satisfactory from the standpoint of engineering. In fact, in the present state of knowledge, nobody knows how to make a completely satisfactory engineering seismic-zoning map. The potential value of such maps makes it highly desirable to develop the knowledge needed to prepare them, on both large and small scales.

After any disaster, it is important to learn which features of the situation were responsible for the disaster and which errors and deficiencies had hazardous consequences. Following a destructive earthquake, the significant facts are very difficult to establish. Precisely how was the engineering design made? Was the construction in conformity with the design? What was the precise cause of the collapse? What weaknesses existed? It is difficult for an individual to establish the facts because information may not be made available, because a sufficiently thorough inspection of the collapsed or damaged structure cannot be made, or because legal aspects may interfere. Many different viewpoints and contradictory statements are therefore circulated and published after the earthquake, creating an atmosphere of uncertainty about what did happen and why. Following an earthquake in which there were collapses or damage hazardous to life and limb, it would be desirable for a blue-ribbon governmental panel of unimpeachable character to make an investigation, hold hearings, and prepare a report that makes clear the causes of the hazardous conditions.

In recent years, numerous destructive earthquakes in other parts of the world have emphasized the international nature of the problem. For a solution, cooperation among nations will be required. Many developing nations are in seismically active regions, and in their technical and industrial development they often undertake major engineering projects such as dams, power plants, or large factories that expose them to catastrophic economic loss and social disaster in the event of a major failure. With this exposure ever increasing, prudence requires that earthquake risk be considered in the design and construction of such facilities. This cannot be accomplished from outside the country; an awareness of the risk and a capacity for earthquake-resistant design and construction must be built up within the nation itself. To aid in creating the required internal technical and scientific capacities, it is recommended that technical and financial assistance be made available for programs of instruction and research in seismology and earthquake engineering at some of the universities or technological institutes in these nations and also for establishing strong-motion seismograph stations there to increase the probability of obtaining records of future destructive earthquakes.

The Alaska earthquake has shown very clearly that the overall level of effort in earthquake-engineering research has not been sufficient to meet the demands of engineering practice. Research work in government and university laboratories must be strengthened to provide the necessary answers to problems in earthquake engineering and to train the rapidly increasing numbers of competent young engineers that are needed by industry and other elements of society.

The presence of the military installations was an especially important factor in the reconstruction and recovery; the Alaska earthquake was the first in which the federal government had played such a major role in the rehabilitation of a stricken region. Relatively large amounts of money were made available, and numerous government agencies participated in the effort. Large military installations were a source of organized manpower with technical training, backed up by equipment and supplies, and ready to play an active role in the reconstruction and rehabilitation. The assistance provided by the federal government was the chief factor in the rapid recovery of the afflicted region. The precedent set in coping with this earthquake will probably serve as a model for government actions in the event of future destructive shocks.

The Alaska District Office of the Army Corps of Engineers in Anchorage, with a large and active group of civilian engineers and technicians whose training and experience prepared them to undertake the task of rebuilding, played a major role in the reconstruction effort. The office was assigned the responsibility for most of the reconstruction for which government funds were used, and this included a wide variety of civilian, as well as military, structures and facilities. For many of these, the Alaska District Office had been responsible for the original design and construction and therefore was in a particularly favorable position to assess the nature and cause of the damage. The Alaska District Office had records of the exact costs of repair for those structures and facilities for whose reconstruction it was responsible.

The Committee on the Alaska Earthquake recommended that the Corps of Engineers prepare a report, setting down the most important data about the 1964 Alaska earthquake that had been amassed by the Alaska District Office, so that the information could be published in the National Academy of Sciences report on the earthquake.

The papers in Part III of this volume are based on the Alaska District Office report. These papers give a detailed account of damage, repair, and costs that has never before been available for an earthquake. The publication of this information sets a precedent that should be followed by the Corps of Engineers and other organizations when involved in future major disasters. A significant conclusion to be drawn from these papers is that the major cost of an earthquake, contrary to popular belief, lies not so much in spectacular damage to major structures, such as high-rise buildings and long-span bridges, as it does in moderate damage to a large number of smaller and more ordinary structures and facilities.

RECOMMENDATIONS FOR BUILDING STRUCTURES

Earthquake-engineering design aims at making structures strong enough to withstand ground shaking without hazard to the public. Damage to buildings falls into two main categories: structural and architectural. The first is damage to the structural elements that provide strength to the building; the second is damage to partitions, ceilings, light fixtures, elevators, mechanical equipment, and other items that are the responsibility of the architect rather than the structural engineer. The cost of repairing architectural earthquake damage in Alaska was much greater than the cost of repairing structural damage, even for completely collapsed structures, because architectural elements usually represent two thirds of the total cost of a building. It was obvious that much of the architectural damage could have been avoided if some simple precautions had been taken at the time the building was designed. Some of this damage was hazardous—for example, the falling of light fixtures and the toppling of partition walls. The effects of possible earthquake forces and motions on nonstructural elements should be taken into account when a building is designed. Research aimed at the development of useful guides to design is needed.

The excessive damage sustained by the multistory buildings in Anchorage demonstrates that more accurate and reliable methods of structural analysis need to be developed and introduced into engineering practice. Special attention should be given to improvements that can be introduced now, and studies should be made to develop others that can be introduced in the near future. These improvements will undoubtedly depend heavily on the capabilities and use of digital computers; eventually a computer analysis of the dynamics of every new major structure in seismic areas of the country should be made.

It is recommended, too, that studies be made to develop seismic-building-code provisions that would use dynamic principles directly, instead of the currently used concept of equivalent static forces. Response spectrum concepts and modal properties of the structure might be employed.

The collapse of the Four Seasons apartment building, which was designed and constructed according to the requirements of the building code, shows that the code does not ensure safety against collapse for new buildings. Careful studies should be made of building-code requirements to eliminate the possibility of collapse or very serious damage. Particular examination should be given to new and different types of construction, such as core-wall structures like the Four Seasons, lift-slab structures, and precast structures.

Improved codes, by themselves, are not sufficient to ensure satisfactory performance during earthquakes. Good construction practice and quality materials are also necessary. To achieve these ends and to ensure that the intent of the design is achieved requires competent supervision by experienced engineers familiar with the structural design. All too often in past earthquakes, including the Alaska shock, the earthquake response of structures has revealed weaknesses that would not have passed competent inspection.

The extensive and costly damage sustained by the three 14-story buildings in Anchorage, as well as the serious damage and collapse of multistory concrete buildings in the 1967 Caracas, Venezuela, earthquake, indicate that more research is needed on the dynamic behavior of structures when stressed beyond the elastic limit into a damaged state. More research is especially needed on concrete-frame structures. In particular, reliable methods of assessing the factor of safety against collapse are needed.

Most of the hospitals in the strongly shaken region were damaged sufficiently so as not to be usable at the end of the earthquake, just when the need for their facilities was greatest. In seismic regions, special considerations should be given to the design of hospitals, buildings designated for emergency shelters, and buildings that house organizations and equipment relied on to cope with a disaster so that they will be functional after an earthquake.

RECOMMENDATIONS FOR SOILS AND SOIL STRUCTURES

The effects of the Alaska earthquake on soils were major features of this event. Landslides were particularly destructive, and they focused attention on the great damage potential of unstable soils during earthquakes. Special research should be directed toward solving the problems of soils in earthquakes because soil problems are encountered in many parts of the United States and the rest of the world.

Perhaps the most striking feature of the damage caused by soil failures was the initiating role of the liquefaction of sandy deposits. The major landslides at Valdez, Seward, and Kenai Lake have been attributed to liquefaction of gravelly sands, the Fourth Avenue, L Street and Government Hill slides have been attributed to liquefaction of sand seams, and the major slide at Turnagain Heights was caused, in large measure, by liquefaction of sand lenses. Extensive damage to railroad and highway bridges and to embankments was also caused by liquefaction of silty and sandy foundation materials. Special attention should be given to possible soil liquefaction and landsliding in the planning of cities and the siting of structures.

Gross movements of landslides in Anchorage did not begin until a minute or two after the ground shaking started. They did not, therefore, develop during the period of strongest ground shaking when soil stresses were at a maximum, but developed later as a result of loss of strength in the underlying soils caused by the sequence of earthquake motions. The influence of duration of shaking on soil behavior should be evaluated and the information disseminated to practicing engineers.

Pseudostatic methods of analysis of slope stability provide a means for comparing the merits of different embankment sections and for ensuring increased conservatism in the design on an empirical basis. There is, however, little to guide the design engineer in selecting an appropriate value for the seismic coefficient in this approach; furthermore, this method of analysis is inadequate to explain the mechanics of a considerable number of embankment failures. Satisfactory analysis of slope stability during earthquakes can only be made with dynamic analyses that consider loss in strength of soils that result from the build-up of pore-water pressures as the earthquake continues. Such analyses must include the earthquake response of the soil mass adjacent to the slope, the stress history during the earthquake of the soil elements composing the slope, the cyclic nature of the stresses induced by the earthquake, the changes in soil characteristics with time during the earthquake, and the geological details of the soil formation that may influence the mechanics of failure.

The 1964 Alaska earthquake caused severe damage to a wide variety of bridge foundations within a distance of approximately 80 mi of the zone of major energy release. The degree of severity of damage was greatly dependent on the foundation-support conditions; no cases of severe or moderate foundation displacement were reported for bridges known to be founded wholly on bedrock. The greatest concentrations of severe damage to bridge foundations occurred in regions characterized by thick deposits of saturated, cohesionless soils. Ample evidence exists of liquefaction of these materials during the earthquake, and this phenomenon probably played a major role in the development of foundation displacement and bridge damage. The design of bridge foundations in seismic areas should give special attention to the possible effects of earthquakes.

The detailed studies of soil failures caused by the Alaska earthquake have contributed greatly to the available information on soil behavior during earthquakes. Similar studies should be conducted whenever failures occur as a result of earthquake action.

During the Alaska earthquake, liquefaction of loose to medium-dense deposits of saturated sandy materials demonstrated their potential for initiating catastrophic failures. Such deposits should be treated with the utmost caution in land development in areas of high seismicity. Where major developments are already located on deposits of this kind, their vulnerability to catastrophic damage during a major earthquake should be evaluated, and, where necessary, appropriate plans for emergency action developed or remedial measures initiated.

The costs of damage resulting from soil failures in the Alaska earthquake of 1964 (such as the five major landslides in Anchorage, slope failures along the waterfront areas of Valdez and Seward, and highway and bridge damage) might be conservatively estimated at over $100 million. Scientific and technological research is urgently needed to advance the knowledge of soil behavior during earthquakes, so that failures may be avoided and vulnerable areas and structures recognized. Appropriate plans could then be made for emergency action and remedial measures.

EFFECTS ON BODIES OF WATER

The major loss of life and extensive damage during the earthquake caused by the tsunami and waves of local origin underscore the need for a better understanding of the tsu-

nami problem. In particular, we need to know how to assess the likelihood of tsunamis, the heights of the runup waves, the physical effects these waves might have, and how to cope with tsunami action. The building of nuclear power plants on the seacoast makes this problem especially important.

There is a need for economic and risk analyses of important coastal communities. These analyses should define appropriate design tsunamis and make clear the degree of existing hazard and the amount of tsunami protection that is economically justified.

RECOMMENDATIONS FOR ENGINEERING PRACTICE

The earthquake provisions of the existing national code for the design of highway structures (The American Association of State Highway Officials, 1965) should be revised in light of the complexity of modern structures and existing knowledge of earthquake ground motions. The earthquake provisions of this code are not adequate for modern practice.

The Alaska earthquake showed the need for critical evaluation of the resistance of older earth dams in seismic parts of the country. The damage sustained by the dam at Eklutna and the damage to earth dams and hydraulic structures caused by other major earthquakes (Resources Agency of the State of California, 1967) indicates that this is a serious problem that has not been adequately faced. The Eklutna dam, northeast of Anchorage, was shaken moderately by the earthquake. This old, relatively small earth dam was at first thought to have received only minor damage. More thorough investigation indicated, however, that the damage was much more serious, and a new dam has now superseded the old one. If the dam had been closer to the center of the earthquake, it probably would have failed. Hundreds of old earth dams in seismic areas of the United States are also in danger of failing if shaken strongly. These hazardous dams should be brought to modern standards of safety, or their use should be restricted. Development of reliable methods for evaluating the earthquake resistance of old earth dams is urgently needed. Research to develop more reliable methods of earthquake design for new earth dams should also be undertaken. An important part of such a program should be the placing of strong-motion accelerographs and other suitable instruments on dams and in their vicinity to record earthquake motions. The failure of a dam can be such a tremendous catastrophe that special efforts to increase its safety are justified.

Although, at present, most dams are constructed of earth rather than of concrete, many old concrete dams are still in use. The earthquake resistance of concrete dams is poorly understood and should be studied.

The Alaska earthquake demonstrated again that oil tanks are special earthquake hazards because of the combustible contents. Communities such as Whittier, Seward, and Valdez had oil tanks in locations that were affected by tsunami action, and a number of the tanks were damaged enough to release and ignite the contents. Such fires are potentially catastrophic, and precautions should be taken to avoid them. Special consideration should be given to the possibility of tsunami hazard in the location of oil tanks; furthermore, piping connections, valves, and so forth, should be placed so as to avoid damage from floating objects and consequent release of the contents.

Several oil tanks, some of them in Anchorage, were damaged and collapsed because of ground shaking. The earthquake design of these tanks was not adequate to resist the earthquake forces imposed on them. Because of the potential holocaust that can result from damage to oil and gasoline tanks, it is recommended that large fluid-storage tanks be designed to resist the actual forces expected during earthquakes without danger of collapse or damage that will release the contents. Existing tanks containing flammable liquids that are found to be in danger of collapse during strong earthquakes should be strengthened or provisions should be made to contain all the liquid in the event of collapse. The design of any containment structure for such hazardous tanks must take into consideration possible seiching in the containment structure, and the occurrence of appreciable fluid velocities on collapse, as well as give special attention to piping and connections.

The establishment of a model building code for waterfront areas susceptible to tsunami action is recommended to regulate the planning, design, and construction of buildings and facilities. The control of damage sustained from tsunamis depends on details of locating, designing, and protecting structures. It would be of great value if available information were collected and incorporated in a model building code to guide the development of waterfront communities.

One of the most hazardous, yet most easily remedied, aspects of earthquakes is the damage to architectural features of buildings. To minimize the hazard from this damage, the seismic provisions of the Uniform Building Code should be expanded to specify the minimum earthquake forces to be resisted by light fixtures, electrical and mechanical equipment-mounting systems, and other appurtenances not covered by the present code. To complement modifications of the building code, a handbook of recommended practice for earthquake-resistant design of nonstructural features of buildings should be prepared.

As a measure to increase public safety, it is recommended that emergency lighting and power systems in seismic areas meet the following requirements:

1. Emergency lighting systems, sufficient for safe egress, should be provided in all buildings over one story in height,

with the exception of single-family dwellings.

2. Emergency power systems in all hospitals and all buildings open to the public that are over six stories high should include power for operating at least one elevator.

3. All components of emergency lighting and power systems should be capable of resisting a lateral force greater than 50 percent of the weight of the component.

Building codes in seismic areas should require the installation of strong-motion earthquake recorders in major buildings. Section 91.2396e and Rule of General Application No. 6516 of the Los Angeles Building Code can serve as examples to other governmental agencies. Dams, nuclear reactors, and other structures whose failure might endanger the public safety should also be instrumented.

Special seismic-hazard maps of cities should be prepared that designate areas exposed to potential hazard from landslides, soil liquefaction, and subsidence in the event of strong ground shaking. These maps should be freely available to the public and should call to public attention the need for special consideration on the part of prospective buyers, builders, and dwellers, Ordinances should be passed requiring such investigations to be made by qualified experts before sites are purchased or plans are made for schools and other important public buildings. The California State Legislature passed such a measure in 1967.

Primarily because of the hazard of earthquake-caused fires, but also to avoid unnecessary hardship to the public, the utility departments of cities in the seismic areas of the country should evaluate the earthquake resistance of essential utility systems and modify them as needed to provide adequate earthquake resistance. The shutoff mechanisms installed in the gas-distributing system in Anchorage demonstrated their value in reducing the fire hazard after the earthquake. Similarly, the necessity of an emergency water-supply system was made clear in the San Francisco earthquake of 1906. In other seismic areas, especially in southern California, a high fire hazard exists in low-density residential areas during a large part of the year. The possibility of earthquake-caused fires in these areas should not be ignored.

After the Alaska earthquake, and before the preparation of this part of the report, destructive earthquakes occurred in Japan, Chile, Peru, and in southern California at the edge of the Los Angeles metropolitan area. In the short time since 1964, nearly all the above recommendations and conclusions have been reinforced by the occurrence of the type of earthquake damage their implementation is intended to reduce.

RECOVERY FROM THE EARTHQUAKE

The recovery from the 1964 Alaska earthquake was rapid and complete: First, funds were channeled into the disaster area by the federal government; second, the discovery of an

FIGURE 2 View of Anchorage from the top of the Anchorage-Westward Hotel, looking southwest over Fourth Avenue (1970). The nine-story Captain Cook Hotel in the right background was constructed after the earthquake. It fronts on Fourth Avenue and is just east of the graben of the L Street side.

G. W. Housner

oil field on the northern slope of Alaska had a great economic effect.

In the summer of 1970, we made a special trip to Alaska to make a final assessment of the recovery. The city of Anchorage had an air of prosperity (Figure 2); there was little evidence of the earthquake except for a signboard at the location of the Fourth Avenue slide that explained the "earthquake buttress area." The stability of this slide area was improved by the placement of earth buttresses, and the area was regraded and turned into a large parking lot (Figures 3 and 4). The eastern portion of the Turnagain slide had been bulldozed flat and public arguments were in progress to decide whether it should be subdivided for houses or be made into a park (Figure 5). The surface traces of the graben behind the L Street slide were no longer visible, and a number of new structures have been built close to its former location.

The 14-story Mt. McKinley and 1200 L Street apartment buildings had been repaired, and both were occupied (Figures 3 and 6). A new Penney Building had been constructed

P. C. Jennings

FIGURE 3 Looking east along Fourth Avenue, across the site of the Fourth Avenue slide in Anchorage. The slide area has been regraded, repaired, and partly reoccupied; 14-story Mt. McKinley apartment building is visible in the left background.

FIGURE 4 Looking northeast over the top of the Fourth Avenue slide. The slope was buttressed and the area was turned into a parking lot. The repaired power plant can be seen in the background.

G. W. Housner

on the site of the original building. The West Anchorage High School was reduced to a one-story building and is again in use (Figure 7).

Several new buildings have been constructed in Anchorage since the earthquake, including some that serve as headquarters for oil companies active in Alaska. The nine-story Captain Cook Hotel has been constructed on the corner of Fourth Avenue and K Street, a couple of hundred feet east of the graben behind the L Street slide (see Figure 1).

A new 14-story concrete-block bearing-wall hotel of novel design has also been built (Figure 8).

In the town of Seward, new dock and harbor facilities have been constructed to replace those destroyed by the earthquake.

Valdez has been rebuilt at a new location (Figure 9), with a population of the new town about the same as that of the old town (approximately 700). The town was laid out for a much larger number and at first the extra vacant

P. C. Jennings

FIGURE 5 Looking northwest over the Turnagain slide area, which has been bulldozed smooth. Proposals have been made to convert it into a public park. Some of the effects of the slide are visible in the left background.

FIGURE 6   The rebuilt and reoccupied 1200 L Street apartment building in Anchorage. The extensive cracking of the walls was repaired with gunite concrete and with epoxy cement.

G. W. Housner

lots were not sold. More recently, the selection of Valdez as the southern terminus of the Trans-Alaska pipeline resulted in the sale of most of the lots. Hopes are high that industrial facilities will be constructed and permanent jobs provided. In 1970, the first section of the 48-in.-diameter pipe for the Trans-Alaska pipeline was being unloaded at the dock of new Valdez and trucked to the vicinity of old Valdez for temporary storage. To eliminate any occupancy of old Valdez, the homes were condemned and destroyed in 1970.

The general impression obtained in Anchorage, Seward, and Valdez was clearly one of relative prosperity. Although the 1964 earthquake was not forgotten, there seemed to be no exceptional concern or apprehension about future earthquakes.

GEORGE W. HOUSNER
PAUL C. JENNINGS
California Institute of Technology

P. C. Jennings

FIGURE 7   West Anchorage High School. The second story was removed and the remainder of the building reconstructed in accordance with the zone 3 earthquake requirements of the *Uniform Building Code*.

G. W. Housner

FIGURE 8 A new 14-story concrete-block bearing-wall hotel under construction in Anchorage.

REFERENCES

American Association of State Highway Officials, 1965. Standard specifications for highway bridges (ninth edition). Washington: American Association of State Highway Officials.

Committee on the Alaska Earthquake, 1969. Toward reduction of losses from earthquakes: Conclusions from the Great Alaska Earthquake of 1964. An advance report. Washington: National Academy of Sciences. 34 p.

Committee on Earthquake Engineering Research, 1969. Earthquake engineering research. A report to the National Science Foundation prepared by the National Academy of Engineering, Division of Engineering. Springfield, Virginia: Clearinghouse for Federal Scientific and Technical Information. 313 p.

Resources Agency of the State of California, 1967. Earthquake damage to hydraulic structures in California. Bulletin No. 116-3. Sacramento: Department of Water Resources.

U.S. Coast and Geodetic Survey, 1967. The Prince William Sound, Alaska, earthquake of 1964 and aftershocks. Fergus J. Wood, editor-in-chief. Volume II-A: Research studies—Engineering seismology. Washington: Government Printing Office. 392 p.

U.S. Geological Survey, 1970. The Alaska earthquake, March 27, 1964. U.S. Geological Survey Professional Papers 541–546. Washington: Government Printing Office.

P. C. Jennings

FIGURE 9 Civic buildings in the new town of Valdez. New residences can be seen in the background.

I
GROUND
MOTIONS
AND BEHAVIOR
OF SOILS

Introduction

The Alaska earthquake was especially notable for the great length of the fault segment along which slippage occurred, the extensive tectonic displacements, the unusually large area that experienced strong ground shaking, and the remarkable movements of ground that included numerous large and destructive landslides and extensive areas of sandboils. These features were so much more impressive than similar phenomena observed in other U.S. earthquakes that documentation of available information is especially important for the benefit of strong-motion seismologists, earthquake engineers, and soils engineers.

In the paper by Donald E. Hudson and William K. Cloud "Seismological Background for Engineering Studies of the Earthquake," the fault movement, tectonic displacements, and magnitude of the earthquake are discussed. The authors also present an intensity map and the aftershock records of the earthquake and describe the strong shaking of the main shock.

George W. Housner and Paul C. Jennings in "Reconstituted Earthquake Ground Motion at Anchorage" found that because no strong-motion instruments were in operation in Alaska at the time of the earthquake, no records were obtained of the main shock. An accelerograph, flown in by the U.S. Coast and Geodetic Survey the day after the earthquake, was not set up in time to record the only aftershock that produced moderately strong shaking in Anchorage. Later, over a dozen accelerographs were installed in Alaska, but so far none of these has recorded even moderately strong ground shaking. In this study, the information available on the ground motion at Anchorage and on ground motion in general is combined to synthesize an accelerogram that represents statistically the earthquake shaking.

Ronald F. Scott puts into perspective the various soil phenomena produced by the earthquake in his summary description "Behavior of Soils during the Earthquake," which introduces the papers that deal with specific soil behavior.

H. Bolton Seed's paper "Landslides Caused by Soil Liquefaction" was prepared for the Committee on the Alaska Earthquake and designed to bring into focus the general problem of landslides related to soil liquefaction. He uses as examples some of the large, destructive slides in Anchorage.

The paper by H. Bolton Seed and Stanley D. Wilson gives a detailed description of the Turnagain Heights landslide. This extensive landslide destroyed many houses and caused some loss of life; it is therefore important that engineers and building officials understand why and how the slide occurred.

William L. Shannon and David E. Hilts describe the submarine landslide at Seward, a slide that generated a large water wave and was responsible for extensive damage and loss of life. Slides of this kind pose a serious problem to waterfront communities where the submarine soil conditions are similar to those at Seward.

The paper by James K. Mitchell, William N. Houston, and George Yamane discusses the sensitivity and geotechnical properties of Bootlegger Cove Clay. In that clay of this type was involved in numerous landslides, technical information on its properties is particularly important.

"Sandblows and Liquefaction," by Ronald F. Scott and Kenneth A. Zuckerman, presents information on a simple but striking experiment that demonstrates some features of sand boils and the associated liquefaction. The appearance of sand boils after the Alaska earthquake was a symptom of deep-seated disturbance of soil. When this kind of disturbance occurs under a structure, it can cause serious damage.

In "Performance of Bridge Foundations," during the earthquake, Grant A. Ross, H. Bolton Seed, and Ralph R. Migliaccio describe the extensive damage to bridges, caused chiefly by sliding and lurching of the soft soil that supported the bridges or that formed their abutments. Such soil motions were so prevalent that they clearly pose a severe earthquake problem for bridges in Alaska.

GEORGE W. HOUSNER
PAUL C. JENNINGS
California Institute of Technology

DONALD E. HUDSON
CALIFORNIA INSTITUTE OF TECHNOLOGY
WILLIAM K. CLOUD*
U.S. COAST AND GEODETIC SURVEY

Seismological Background for Engineering Studies of the Earthquake

ABSTRACT: The Alaska earthquake has provided much seismological information of direct interest to earthquake engineers for an interpretation of structural damage. It has also revealed significant deficiencies in knowledge that should be remedied by vigorous research programs.

It has been shown that the earthquake was a multiple event consisting of several shocks distributed over a wide region. The location of the major event, of magnitude 8.4, cannot be determined accurately, but it could well have been at a considerable distance from the initial epicenter. This uncertainty about the location of the main source of energy release complicates an interpretation of damage patterns described by the isoseismal map of earthquake intensities.

An important deficiency in the information available is the lack of any measurements of strong ground motion because of the absence of suitable instrumentation in the area. After the earthquake, a network of strong-motion accelerographs was established in Alaska.

The ground acceleration at Anchorage, where major structural damage occurred, was probably in the range 0.1–0.2 g. The duration of heavy ground shaking was about 1½ minutes, with strong ground motions persisting for several minutes.

Although many studies of the mechanism of the earthquake have been made, it has so far not been possible to develop an unambiguous picture of the fault motion. From the general pattern of tectonic deformation and aftershock distributions, however, the main outlines of the process are clear and known in sufficient detail to assist in an engineering interpretation of damage.

In the Alaska earthquake, it was possible for the first time to relate the generation of a tsunami to measurable patterns of tectonic displacements.

*Now with the University of California at Berkeley.

The Alaska earthquake of March 27, 1964, was one of the major events in seismologic history. Its various seismological and geophysical aspects have been studied in great detail and have been extensively reported in technical literature. This paper summarizes information from these specialized seismological studies that have a direct bearing on the interpretation of the earthquake from the point of view of engineering.

The earthquake engineer, with his primary interest in the development of earthquake-resistant design, requires information of the following basic types: (a) the location of regions of high energy release or of significant tectonic deformation in relation to damaged engineering works; (b) a comparison of the magnitude, time-duration, and frequency characteristics of the earthquake with those of other earthquakes for which structural damage studies have been made; (c) a description of the destructive ground motions in the epicentral region, including the acceleration-time history, special conditions of faulting, fault creep, elevations and subsidences, and consolidations; and (d) knowledge of any special conditions of local geology, soils, and so forth, that might modify in a significant way the damaging ground motions or the interpretation of structural damage.

Unfortunately, it is not possible to supply all the required information on the great Alaska earthquake; however, the knowledge that is available helps a great deal in understanding the essential features of the event. In addition to summarizing this knowledge, this chapter indicates certain missing elements of information and suggests means of improving the supply of information in future earthquakes.

SEISMIC HISTORY OF ALASKA

Alaska has long been known as a region of high seismicity: As an important segment of the circum-Pacific belt of earthquakes, the Aleutian–Alaskan arc accounts for a significant portion of the seismic energy released each year throughout the globe (Gutenberg and Richter, 1954). About 6 percent of the large shallow earthquakes of the world occur in this region.

Although the first recorded earthquake in Alaska was in 1788, accurate information on epicentral locations first became available during the present century. Figure 1 shows the epicenters of all earthquakes with a magnitude greater than 6 that occurred in the region from 1899 to 1964. Within 1,000 km of the epicenter of the 1964 earthquake, in the immediate area of Prince William Sound, six earthquakes with a magnitude greater than 8, 19 earthquakes with magnitudes between 7 and 8, and 57 earthquakes with magnitudes between 6 and 7 have occurred (U.S. Coast and Geodetic Survey, 1966). Since 1912, three earthquakes with a magnitude greater than 7 have occurred within 100 km of the epicenter of the 1964 earthquake.

GEOLOGICAL SETTING

The Aleutian–Alaskan arc is one of the classic tectonic structures exhibiting most of the defining features of Pacific-type arcs, which have been summarized by Richter (1958) as: a deep oceanic trench; a line of epicenters of shallow earthquakes, negative gravity anomalies, and a submarine ridge or chain of small islands; a belt of positive gravity anomalies and epicenters of intermediate-depth earthquakes; the principal structural arc, often marked by active or recently extinct volcanoes; and an inner structural belt of older volcanoes and deeper earthquakes.

Although detailed geologic mapping has been difficult in Alaska, a number of major fault systems have been recognized, mostly from geomorphic evidence. In general, it has not been possible to correlate earthquake-epicenter patterns with these major fault systems; however, in certain cases a close relation between specific earthquakes and known faults

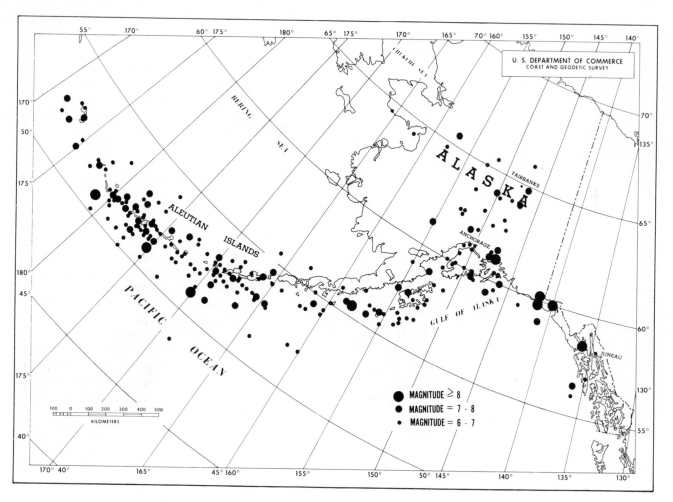

FIGURE 1   Alaska earthquakes of magnitude > 6.0 from 1899 to 1964.

can be established. The two great Yakutat Bay earthquakes of September 1899 (magnitude $M > 8$) probably involved motions along the Chugach–St. Elias fault, which is in the same general tectonic region as Prince William Sound (U.S. Coast and Geodetic Survey, 1966). The Lituya Bay earthquake of July 10, 1958, involved primarily a strike-slip movement along the Fairweather fault, which extends southeast of the Chugach–St. Elias fault. Horizontal fault movements of as much as 21½ ft were measured at one point on this fault (Tocher, 1960).

SEISMIC ZONING OF ALASKA

Alaska was not included on the 1948 Seismic-Probability Map of the United States published by the U.S. Coast and Geodetic Survey, or on the 1951 revision, nor was it included on the maps or in discussions presented by Richter (1959) in his study of the seismic regionalization of the

United States. In 1950, the U.S. Coast and Geodetic Survey prepared a seismic-probability map of Alaska (Figure 2), which, apparently was never published in any form or given an official status. This map was made available, however, as a guide to engineers considering seismic zoning problems in Alaska.

In 1950, Anchorage adopted the Uniform Building Code of the Pacific Coast Building Officials Conference, which embodies earthquake lateral-force provisions. The city, just at the beginning of a period of major development, increased in population from about 10,000 in 1950 to some 44,000 in 1960. It thus happened that almost all the major construction of the city was carried out under the provisions of a building code that included standard earthquake-resistant provisions. Although the unofficial 1950 seismic-probability map of Figure 2 indicates that Anchorage was in a zone 3 region, the decision was made at the adoption of the building code in 1950 to use zone 2 earthquake rating for lateral-force determinations. In 1955,

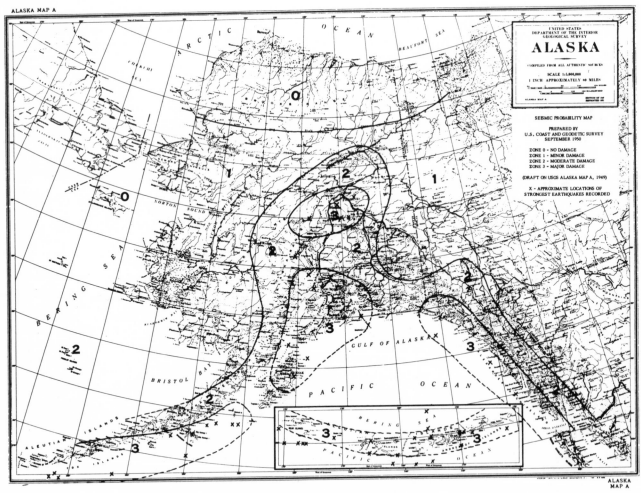

FIGURE 2 Seismic-probability map for Alaska.

the Anchorage City Council, at the urging of structural engineers, increased the lateral-force requirements to zone 3.

From 1950 to 1961, plans for all major structures in Anchorage were checked for compliance with horizontal-force requirements by structural engineers of the International Conference of Building Officials. From 1961, plans were checked by officials of the local Anchorage Building Department.

The situation in Anchorage is thus of unusual interest from the standpoint of seismic zoning and building-code provisions. In general, it could be concluded that there had been an effective flow of information from seismology to structural engineering, and that the past knowledge of the high seismicity of the area had been translated into practical terms in the form of the legal requirements of a locally enforced building code.

EPICENTRAL LOCATION

The revised epicentral location of the main shock of the March 27, 1964, earthquake, as determined by the U.S. Coast and Geodetic Survey (1969), is 61.04±0.05°N and 147.73±0.07°W. If the indicated standard errors and the spread of the preliminary calculations (U.S. Coast and Geodetic Survey, 1964; Von Hake and Cloud, 1966) are taken into consideration, the location of the epicenter can be said to be known within about 10 mi.

The epicenter calculations were based on readings from 119 stations throughout the world, including 67 standard stations of the World-Wide Network of Standard Seismographs (WWNSS), which had 95 stations operating at the time of the earthquake (U.S. Coast and Geodetic Survey, 1966).

Because the earthquake has been shown to be a multiple event, with the main source of energy release at a considerable distance from the epicenter of the first event of the sequence as determined above (Wyss and Brune, 1967, and Seismology and Geodesy volume), the standard epicentral location is even less significant than usual as an indication of the origin of energy release. This point will be discussed in more detail in a later section on the mechanism of the earthquake.

FOCAL DEPTH

The U.S. Coast and Geodetic Survey (1964) preliminary report gives the focal depth as 20 km and indicates that for computational purposes the depth has been restrained to 20 km. In a later report, the U.S. Coast and Geodetic Survey (1966) gives the depth in one table as "about 21 km" and in another place as 33 km. Von Hake and Cloud (1966)

give the depth as 33 km. Later references to the earthquake have regarded the depth as lying between 20 and 50 km (Stauder and Bollinger, 1966, and Seismology and Geodesy volume). For engineering considerations, the depth of focus should perhaps be said to be within 10–30 mi.

Earthquake engineers should note that although the uncertainties concerning epicentral location and depth of focus are not large, they involve distances that are not necessarily small compared to the approximately 80 mi between Anchorage and the epicenter. Because the main source of energy release may be about 100 mi from the initial epicenter, it is clear that great caution must be used in the interpretation of such factors as the relation between distance and magnitude of ground shaking (Wyss and Brune, 1967).

MAGNITUDE OF THE MAIN SHOCK

A summary of the magnitude determinations that have been reported for the main shock is given in Table 1. There is an essential agreement on the magnitude—which, perhaps, should be specified as $M = 8.4$. Because the magnitude scale is logarithmic, a difference of 0.3 on the magnitude scale corresponds to a factor of 2 in ground amplitude.

The magnitude of the Alaska earthquake of March 27, 1964, is more accurately known than that of several smaller

TABLE 1 Magnitude Determinations for the Main Shock Alaska Earthquake of March 28, 1964

Station	Magnitude	Reference	Remarks
Pasadena	8.4	USC&GS[a] (1964)	
Pasadena	8.5	C. F. Richter (1966)[b]	
Berkeley	8½–8¾	USC&GS (1964)	
Palisades	8.6	USC&GS (1964)	
USC&GS	8.5	USC&GS (1964)	Albuquerque Wood–Anderson
		Von Hake and Cloud (1966)	P-phase, Washington
USC&GS	8.4	USC&GS (1966)	
USC&GS	8.3	USC&GS (1967)	Revised
USC&GS	8.3	USC&GS (1969)	Revised, final
Collmberg	8.8	BCIS[c] (1964)	
Kew	8.7	BCIS (1964)	
Matsushiro	8.0	BCIS (1964)	
Moscow	8¼	BCIS (1964)	
Athens	8.5	BCIS (1964)	
Uppsala	8.5	BCIS (1964)	
Prague	8.5	BCIS (1964)	

[a] U.S. Coast and Geodetic Survey.
[b] Personal communication.
[c] Bureau Centrale Internationale Séismologique, Strasbourg, March 1964.

earthquakes for which larger ranges have been reported (Table 2). The magnitude of the Alaska earthquake is compared to those of other well-known earthquakes in Table 3.

Earthquake engineers should note that there are several ways to calculate the magnitude of earthquakes; the waves used, the travel path, and the station corrections employed may significantly affect the results (Table 2). The magnitudes of Table 3 are based primarily on the information given by Richter (1958; personal communication, 1966) and are believed to be comparable on the basis of a common definition and data-processing technique as far as is feasible.

Determination of the magnitude of the Alaska earthquake is complicated by the multiple shocks (Wyss and Brune, 1967); these shocks also make it difficult to correlate magnitude and total energy released.

AFTERSHOCK STUDIES

The Alaska earthquake was followed by a long series of aftershocks that gradually diminished in number and size over a period of several months according to a pattern that has been commonly observed for large earthquakes (U.S. Coast and Geodetic Survey, 1964; Algermissen, 1966b; Benioff, 1951). Within 24 hours of the main shock, 10 aftershocks of magnitude exceeding $M = 6$ occurred.

Immediately after the main shock, portable seismological stations were flown into the area to establish a local network for the accurate determination of aftershock epicenters. The first station was operational by 9:30 a.m. AST, March 30, and the network of seven temporary stations shown in Figure 3 was operating by April 12; the stations at Homer and Valdez were added June 30 and August 2, respectively (U.S. Coast and Geodetic Survey, 1966). By introducing such a local network, the locations of aftershock epicenters can be much more accurately determined than

TABLE 2   Magnitude Determinations for Recent Damaging Earthquakes as Reported by Stations or Organizations Listed

Agadir, 1960		Skopje, 1963		Niigata, 1964	
Station	Magnitude	Station	Magnitude	Station	Magnitude
Prague	5½–5¾	USC&GS	5¾–6	USC&GS	7¼–7½
Strasbourg	5¾–6	Palisades	5.5	Pasadena	7.4
Moscow	5¾	Berkeley	5.5–5.75	Palisades	7¼
Zagreb	5.6	Moscow	5.75–6.0	Japan	7.5
Kew	5.7	Athens	6.0		
USC&GS	6¼	Uppsala	6.5		
Pasadena	5.8	Rome	6.6		
		Pasadena	5.9		

TABLE 3   Magnitudes of Some Well-Known Damaging Earthquakes[a]

Location	Date	Magnitude
Agadir, Morocco	1960	5.8
Skopje, Yugoslavia	1963	5.9
Santa Barbara, California	1925	6.3
Long Beach, California	1937	6.3
Hebgen Lake, Montana	1959	7.1
Niigata, Japan	1964	7.4
Kern County, California	1952	7.7
San Francisco, California	1906	8.3
Tokyo, Japan	1923	8.3
Chile	1960	8.4
Alaska	1964	8.5
Assam, India	1950	8.7

[a]Based on personal communication from C. F. Richter (1966).

the location of the main shock, which had to be located by information from distant stations that were not necessarily disposed in the most favorable directions. Because of this local network, the accuracy of determination of the aftershock epicenters is about 2 mi, compared to the 10 mi of the main shock.

Figure 4 shows the location of the larger aftershocks of the earthquake. During the 4 months following the earth-

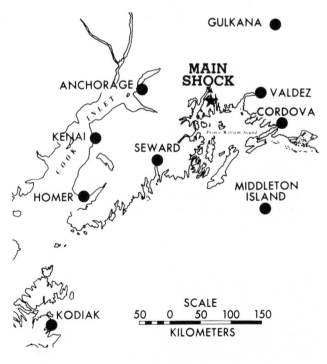

FIGURE 3   Temporary Seismograph Network installed by the U.S. Coast and Geodetic Survey to monitor aftershocks of the Prince William Sound, Alaska, earthquake of 1964.

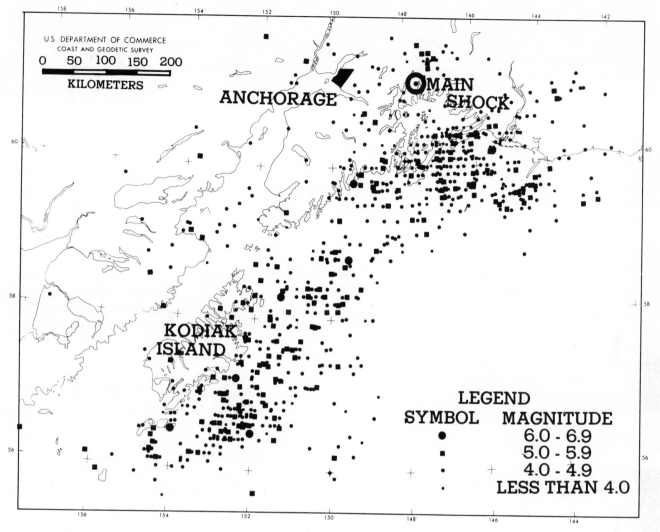

FIGURE 4   Larger aftershocks of the Prince William Sound earthquake.

quake, there were 174 earthquakes with $M \geqslant 5$ that extended over an area approximately 200 mi wide by 600 mi long (Algermissen, 1966b). The largest aftershocks were of magnitude 6.6. These figures may be compared to those for the Chile earthquake of 1960, which had a main shock of $M = 8.4$, about the same size as the Alaska earthquake. In Chile, the main shock had been preceded the day before by three earthquakes of $M = 7.5$ and one of $M = 7.8$. It was followed during the next 8 months by two earthquakes exceeding $M = 7$ and at least 10 earthquakes exceeding $M = 6.5$ (St.-Amand, 1961).

As a measure of the immensely increased seismic activity associated with such aftershock sequences, the 174 aftershocks of the Alaska earthquake of $M \geqslant 5$ that occurred within 4 months is compared to only two earthquakes of $M \geqslant 5$ in all California during the whole of 1964 (Algermissen, 1966b).

The magnitude distribution of the aftershocks of the Alaska earthquake for the period March 28 to September 4, 1964, is shown in Figure 5 (Algermissen, 1966b). A study of the strain released by the aftershocks (Press and Jackson, 1965, and Seismology and Geodesy volume), based on an estimated 12,000 aftershocks of $M \geqslant 3.5$ that occurred during a 69-day period following the earthquake, indicated that the main shock accounted for about one fourth of the total strain release; during the first day about one half of the total strain was released.

The local network makes it possible to determine the depth of focus of the aftershocks considerably more accurately than that of the main shock. Figure 6 shows the distribution of aftershock foci with depth, across a typical section of the aftershock zone. The average depth of focus of the aftershocks is about 12 mi.

An accurate location of the aftershock foci is of great

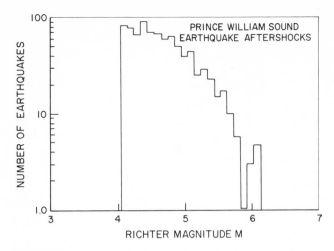

FIGURE 5 Magnitude distribution of aftershocks of the Alaska earthquake. After Algermissen (1966b).

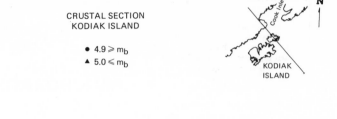

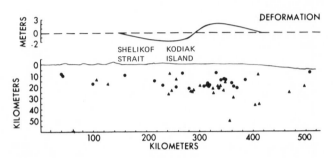

FIGURE 6 Depth distribution of aftershock foci, Alaska earthquake (Algermissen, 1966b). The m_b notation refers to body-wave magnitude.

significance in understanding the basic mechanism of the earthquake. No single piece of seismologic, geologic, or geodetic evidence can decisively pin down the earthquake mechanism for the main shock; hence, all contributing factors that can throw light on the extent, direction, or depth of the event must be carefully examined.

EARTHQUAKE INTENSITY

In the absence of direct measurements of the strong ground motions associated with the Alaska earthquake, a careful assessment of the earthquake intensity assumes particular importance.

Earthquake intensity is a subjective evaluation of the effects of an earthquake on people, on man-made structures, and on the earth. By grouping typical effects into twelve classes, from I, "not felt," to XII, "damage nearly total," it is possible to assign a rough rating to a particular area. The intensity ratings should be regarded as a shorthand substitute for the detailed description of earthquake effects reported from field investigations. These intensity scales make it possible to summarize preliminary data in the concise form of a map. It should not be forgotten that the basic field descriptions themselves must inevitably contain much more information than the intensity rating.

An abridged version of the Modified Mercalli Intensity Scale of 1931, used by the U.S. Coast and Geodetic Survey (Wood and Neumann, 1931), is given in Table 4 along with correlations to the older Rossi-Forel Scale of 1883. The intensity ratings are most meaningful when they can be made by a field-survey team that can make a detailed personal inspection of all the areas involved. Because such a detailed study is often not feasible, a questionnaire or report form is

usually sent to many persons in the area who are supposed capable of a critical assessment. By a judicious balance of various opinions, it is usually possible to achieve a reasonably consistent overall picture.

Figure 7 shows a new version of the postcard questionnaire that was adopted by the U.S. Coast and Geodetic Survey in March 1966. The general procedure used by the U.S. Coast and Geodetic Survey for the Alaska earthquake follows (Townshend and Cloud, 1965):

1. One thousand questionnaire forms were sent to all parts of Alaska and to parts of Canada; 400 replies were received.

2. Reconnaissance flights were made from Fairbanks to Anchorage, Valdez, Seward, Kodiak, Cordova, and intermediate locations immediately after the earthquake.

3. As many reports as possible were obtained from other organizations and from newspapers.

4. Field investigations were made, especially in the Anchorage area, by Survey consultants and by personnel flown in from San Francisco, Washington, and Albuquerque.

5. Reports were obtained from Survey ship personnel and aerial-photography crews.

For the evaluation of intensity and the preparation of the isoseismal map, the preceding accumulated information was sent to the U.S. Coast and Geodetic Survey's Seismological Field Survey Office in San Francisco. There the intensity ratings were made by Mrs. Nina H. Scott, who, from 1950 to 1964, had prepared the isoseismal maps for Pacific Coast

TABLE 4   Modified Mercalli Intensity Scale of 1931 (Abridged)

Intensity	Characteristics	Intensity	Characteristics
I.	Not felt, except by a very few under especially favorable circumstances. (I, Rossi-Forel Scale)		or badly designed structures. Some chimneys broken. Noticed by persons driving motorcars. (VIII, Rossi-Forel Scale)
II.	Felt only by a few persons at rest, especially on upper floors of buildings. Delicately suspended objects may swing. (I to II, Rossi-Forel Scale)	VIII.	Damage slight in specially designed structures; considerable in ordinary substantial buildings with partial collapse; great in poorly built structures. Panel walls thrown out of frame structures. Fall of chimneys, factory stacks, columns, monuments, walls. Heavy furniture overturned. Sand and mud ejected in small amounts. Changes in well water. Persons driving motorcars disturbed. (VIII+ to IX−, Rossi-Forel Scale)
III.	Felt quite noticeably indoors, especially on upper floors of buildings, but many people do not recognize it as an earthquake. Standing motorcars may rock slightly. Vibration like passing of truck. Duration estimated. (III, Rossi-Forel Scale)	IX.	Damage considerable in specially designed structures; well-designed frame structures thrown out of plumb; great in substantial buildings, with partial collapse. Buildings shifted off foundations. Ground cracked conspicuously. (IX+, Rossi-Forel Scale)
IV.	During the day, felt indoors by many, outdoors by few. At night, some awakened. Dishes, windows, doors disturbed; walls make creaking sound. Sensation like heavy truck striking building. Standing motorcars rocked noticeably. (IV to V, Rossi-Forel Scale)	X.	Some well-built wooden structures destroyed; most masonry and frame structures destroyed with foundations; ground badly cracked. Rails bent. Landslides considerable from river banks and steep slopes. Shifted sand and mud. Water splashed (slopped) over banks. (X, Rossi-Forel Scale)
V.	Felt by nearly everyone; many awakened. Some dishes, windows, etc., broken; a few instances of cracked plaster; unstable objects overturned. Disturbance of trees, poles, and other tall objects sometimes noticed. Pendulum clocks may stop. (V to VI, Rossi-Forel Scale)	XI.	Few, if any, [masonry] structures remain standing. Bridges destroyed. Broad fissures in ground. Underground pipelines completely out of service. Earth slumps and land slips in soft ground. Rails bent greatly.
VI.	Felt by all; many frightened and run outdoors. Some heavy furniture moved; a few instances of fallen plaster or damaged chimneys. Damage slight. (VI to VII, Rossi-Forel Scale)	XII.	Damage total. Waves seen on ground surfaces. Lines of sight and level distorted. Objects thrown upward into air.
VII.	Everyone runs outdoors. Damage negligible in buildings of good design and construction; slight to moderate in well-built ordinary structures; considerable in poorly built		

earthquakes that were published in the *Quarterly Abstracts of Earthquake Reports*, issued by the U.S. Coast and Geodetic Survey. These are the isoseismal maps finally published in a simplified form in the annual summary reports *United States Earthquakes*. The isoseismal map originally prepared in this way for the Alaska earthquake is reproduced in Figure 8. Later, a revised preliminary isoseismal map was published (Townshend and Cloud, 1965) (Figure 9). The final form of the isoseismal map published in *United States Earthquakes–1964*, is shown in Figure 10 (Von Hake and Cloud, 1966). The variations between the three isoseismal maps reflect differences in the interpretation of the field data and indicate generally the amount of detail that should be read into such maps.

The basic deficiencies and inaccuracies of all current intensity scales are well known and have been discussed in detail in many publications (Richter, 1958). The difficulty of finding comparable structures or of properly assessing the actual characteristics of existing structures has often been noted. The Alaska earthquake posed several special

problems in the evaluation of intensities. The sparse population and the nonuniform distribution of people and structures made it very difficult to get information from large regions of the shaken area. Difficulties of transportation, communication, and access further complicated the task. In addition, the many cases of large-scale land movements, such as landslides, slumping, and cracking, tended to increase evaluation difficulties. There is evidence that in some regions relatively small ground shaking was responsible for large-scale landslide phenomena, which, in turn, resulted in many damage anomalies. A further important factor is that the intensity scale does not distinguish between long-period and short-period seismic-wave effects. In Anchorage, for example, there were cases of modern multistory buildings with long-period responses that suffered major damage, whereas adjacent structures with short-period responses were not damaged, even though they involved relatively weak elements, such as brick chimneys. In port areas, it is also necessary to distinguish carefully between wave damage and ground-shaking damage. It is obviously difficult to in-

FORM **C&GS-680**
(3-66)

U.S. DEPARTMENT OF COMMERCE
ENVIRONMENTAL SCIENCE SERVICES ADMINISTRATION   Budget Bureau No. 41-RO 13.5:
COAST AND GEODETIC SURVEY   Approval Expires June 30, 1970

EARTHQUAKE REPORT

1. An earthquake was felt ☐ ; not felt ☐

   Time _____ A.M.

   Date of shock _____

   _____ P.M.

If felt, please supply information below *(Underline appropriate words or fill spaces.)*
If not felt, please sign and return card, which requires no postage.

2. YOUR LOCATION DURING EARTHQUAKE

a. **City, County, State** (Exact location in city or rural area at time of shock is important.)

b. **Ground:**

Rocky, gravelly, loose, compact, marshy, filled in, or _____

Level, sloping, steep, or _____

c. **If inside, type of construction**

Wood, brick, stone, or _____

d. **Quality of construction**

New, old, well built, poorly built, or _____

e. **No. of floors in building**

f. **Observer's floor**

g. **Activity when earthquake occurred:**

Walking, sitting, lying down, sleeping

h. **If outside, you, others were:**

Quiet, active

3. EFFECTS ON POPULATION

a. **Felt by:**

Very few, several, many, all (in your home) (in community)

b. **Awakened:**

No one, few, many, all (in your home) (in community)

c. **Frightened:**

No one, few, many, all (in your home) (in community); general panic

5. RELATED SOUNDS

a. **Rattling of windows, doors, dishes, etc.** _____

b. **Creaking of building** (Describe) _____

c. **Earth noises:** Faint, moderate, loud _____

5. PHYSICAL EFFECTS AND DAMAGE

a. **Outside:**

(1) Trees and bushes shaken, vehicles rocked, etc. _____

(2) Ground cracked; landslides; water disturbed, etc. _____

(3) Chimneys, tombstones, elevated water tanks, etc., cracked, twisted,

    overturned _____

(4) Other effects _____

b. **Buildings:**

(1) Hanging objects swung moderately, violently. Direction _____

(2) Small objects shifted, overturned, fell _____

(3) Furniture shifted, overturned, broken _____

(4) Plaster cracked, broken, fell _____

(5) Windows cracked _____

(6) Structural elements of brick, wood, or _____

    Damage slight, moderate, great _____

Signature and address of observer

Additional information will be appreciated. Use space on reverse side.

USCOMM-DC 36414-P66

FIGURE 7   Standard postcard earthquake report questionnaire of the U.S. Coast and Geodetic Survey.

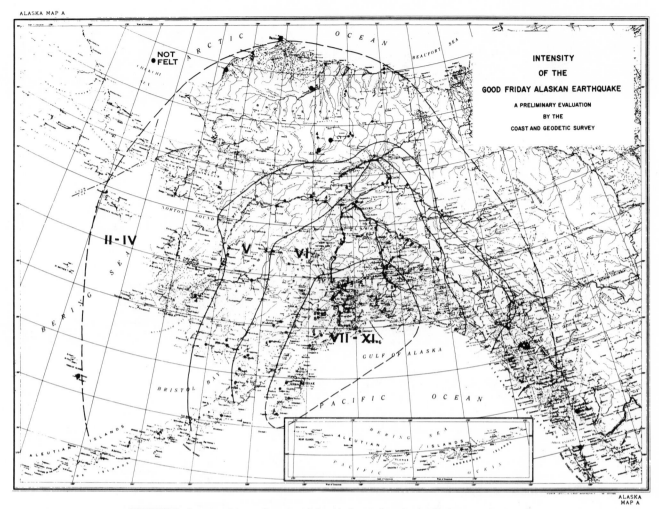

FIGURE 8   Isoseismal intensity map of the Alaska earthquake (preliminary evaluation I).

corporate such refinement into the definitions of the intensity scale, without making it so complicated that its primary purpose is defeated.

A reexamination of the intensity-scale definitions, especially at the higher intensities, is evidently needed. The whole philosophy of the design and use of such intensity scales should be revised in terms of modern instrumental seismology. Evidence from recent California earthquakes, for example, has shown that surface faulting can be associated with earthquakes of much smaller magnitude than had hitherto been supposed. The Parkfield earthquake of June 27, 1967, which had a magnitude of $M=5.5$, was associated with surface faulting over a distance of some 23 mi (Brown and others, 1967). This same earthquake also showed that large-peak ground accelerations (as high as 0.4–0.5 g) did not cause significant damage to ordinary structures in the near vicinity (Harding and others, 1966). Even more striking was the Imperial, California, earthquake of March 4, 1966, in which some 6 mi of surface faulting

were associated with an $M=3.6$ earthquake (Brune and Allen, 1967). Features such as ground cracking should therefore not always be associated with high intensity levels. Ground-motion measurements made during the Niigata earthquake of June 16, 1964, indicated that moderate ground shaking of peak acceleration of about 0.1 g was responsible for massive consolidation of the ground with resultant major structural damage (International Institute of Seismology and Earthquake Engineering, 1965). In this case, a special characteristic of the local soil was responsible for the extent of the damage, and this would have been a difficult factor to account for properly in an intensity assessment.

GROUND-MOTION MEASUREMENTS

The seismograph nearest to the epicenter of the main shock was at College, Alaska, almost 250 mi away, where the U.S.

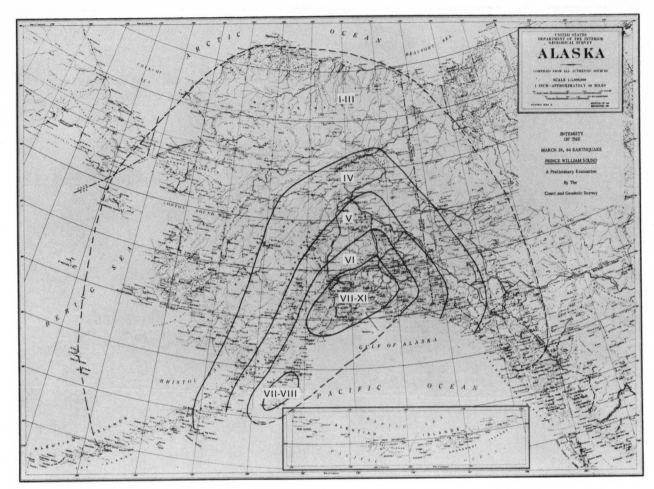

FIGURE 9   Isoseismal intensity map of the Alaska earthquake (preliminary evaluation II).

Coast and Geodetic Survey operates a standard station as a part of the WWNSS. The sensitive seismographs at the College station were, of course, off scale for a very considerable period, and no direct measurements of the ground motion in the region of damage are available.

The failure to obtain any measurements of the damaging ground motion is most unfortunate, but not unexpected. The network of strong-motion accelerographs that are required for such strong-motion measurements is far from adequate (Hudson, 1963, 1965). Before the earthquake, the U.S. Coast and Geodetic Survey Pacific Coast Network had included about 100 such instruments, concentrated mostly in the Los Angeles and the San Francisco regions of California. Figure 11 shows the 1967 network, including the 15 strong-motion accelerographs installed in Alaska after the earthquake. This figure may be compared with the U.S. seismic-probability map of Figure 12, which indicates the regions of highest seismic risk. It will be seen that there is a considerable amount of zone 3 (highest seismic risk) area

that is not covered by strong-motion instruments. Although the high seismicity of Alaska has long been known and the nature of the seismic risk accurately assessed in 1950, no proposals were made for the installation of strong-motion accelerographs in Alaska before the 1964 earthquake. In view of the limited number of instruments available, it was apparently considered that neither the economic investment in the state nor the value of the scientific information that might be obtained would justify the installation of accelerographs in Alaska.

STRONG-MOTION ACCELEROGRAPHS

The present inadequate facilities for measuring the damaging ground motion of earthquakes, strikingly dramatized by the Alaska earthquake, pose major problems for earthquake engineering. Without a knowledge of the damaging ground motion, engineers cannot put the subject of earthquake-

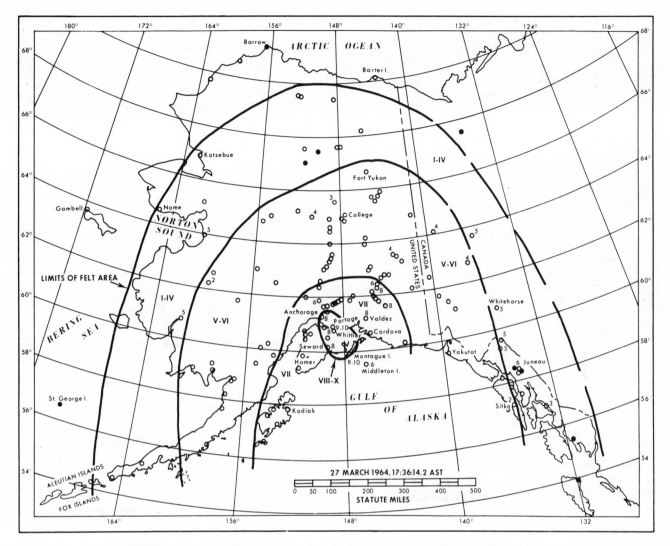

FIGURE 10 Isoseismal intensity map of the Alaska earthquake (Von Hake and Cloud, 1966).

resistant design on a rational and scientific foundation; as a result, progress is slow.

This is a worldwide problem, for only in Japan and in certain regions of California do strong-motion instruments exist in anything like sufficient numbers. During the 1957–1966 decade, the world has been devastated by a series of destructive earthquakes: Mexico, 1957; Chile, 1960; Agadir, Morocco, 1960; Iran, 1962; Skopje, Yugoslavia, 1963; Alaska, 1964; Turkey, 1966. Not one single measurement of destructive ground motion is available for any of these earthquakes.

This lack of information on strong ground motion is not a consequence of any lack of knowledge of how to obtain such information. Since the early 1930's, suitable instruments have been available, and the standard accelerograph that has been developed and used in California by the U.S. Coast and Geodetic Survey has proved to be entirely satis-

factory. Comparable instruments have been available commercially for some time in several countries, and there is considerable literature on the use of such instruments and on the interpretation of the results (Cloud, 1964; Hudson, 1963, 1965; Halverson, 1965). Since 1933, when the Long Beach earthquake supplied the first ground-acceleration record, the U.S. Coast and Geodetic Survey Pacific Coast Network has recorded all important earthquakes that occurred in the continental Pacific Coast states, so that the general principles involved in setting up a strong-motion network are well understood.

Two main difficulties block the adequate development of strong-motion instrumentation. The first difficulty is financial; the objection to the relatively high cost of the equipment and the large number of instruments that would be required to cover the regions of high seismic risk could perhaps be offset by a more comprehensive analysis of the

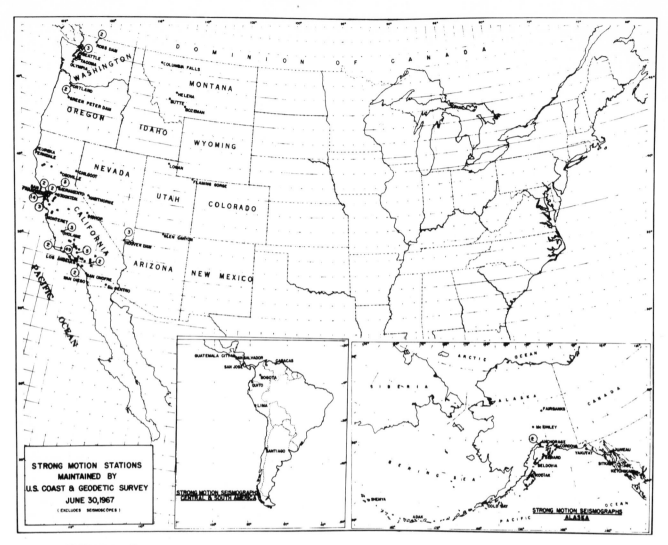

FIGURE 11   Strong-motion accelerograph stations maintained by the U.S. Coast and Geodetic Survey, June 30, 1967.

economics of earthquake damage. The second difficulty is organizational. Because strong-motion seismology falls between pure seismology and earthquake engineering, it may suffer the fate of many interdisciplinary fields and be neglected by both sides. It is often supposed that the international network of seismological stations, established by seismologists for the study of earthquakes, is adequate for the measurement of strong ground motions; in actuality, however, the instruments in these seismological stations are not able or designed to measure such motions.

Because of improper organization, it has not been possible to plan a comprehensive instrumentation network that would reduce the cost of the instruments by producing them in larger quantities. The network has grown so slowly that the accelerographs have been virtually handmade in small lots, at an inevitably high cost.

The United States has, of course, a direct interest in im-

proving the coverage of such strong-motion instrumentation in other parts of the world. Fortunately, great earthquakes do not occur very often, and in any one country the chance of obtaining records of large earthquake ground motion is small. There is good evidence that great earthquakes all over the world have many similar features; recordings from one seismic area are therefore of direct interest to all other regions. Because some 25 different countries have suffered loss of life from earthquakes during this century, the advantages of international cooperation in this field are obvious.

MAIN-SHOCK AND AFTERSHOCK MEASUREMENTS

At the time of the main shock, the nearest strong-motion accelerographs in operation were in Washington, some

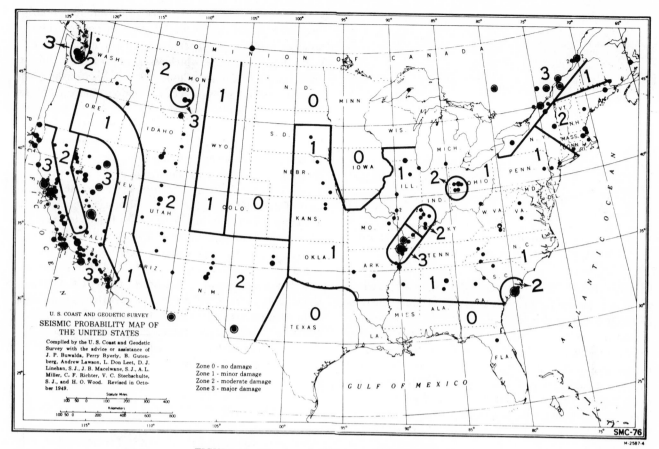

FIGURE 12 Seismic-probability map of the United States.

1,300 mi from the epicenter. It was surprising that the Tacoma accelerograph was triggered at this distance by the main shock. The reason the Tacoma accelerograph started when similar instruments in Olympia and Seattle did not is, presumably, that at Tacoma the starting pendulum had been adjusted to a more sensitive position.

Figure 13 shows the record obtained from the Tacoma accelerograph. The only measurable traces were those from the Carder displacement pendulums, which have a natural period of about 4 seconds. The short-period accelerograph elements with 0.06-second elements did not show any visible motion. The motion recorded by the 4-second pendulums was of a sufficiently long period so that the ground accelerations could be approximated, and the maximum ground accelerations at Tacoma were found to be 0.0008 g—much below the levels for significant structural damage or even for human perceptibility.

An estimate of the ground acceleration at Anchorage can

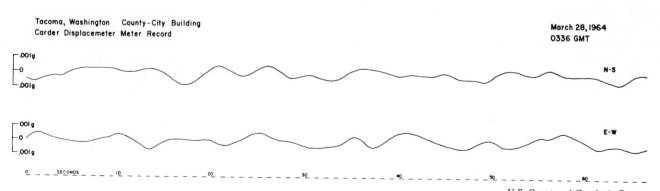

FIGURE 13   Record obtained from Tacoma accelerograph during Alaska earthquake.

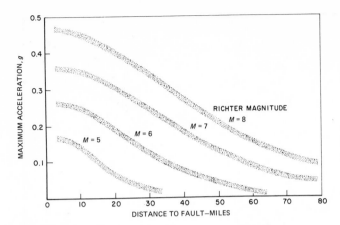

FIGURE 14   Maximum earthquake ground acceleration vs. Richter magnitude and distance from fault. After Housner (1965).

be obtained from the curves prepared by Housner (1965), who has examined the problem of ground shaking caused by destructive earthquakes from information based on recorded ground accelerations. If the curves of Figure 14 are used and the uncertainty in the distance from Anchorage to the main source of seismic energy is taken into consideration, the ground acceleration at Anchorage would probably fall in the range 0.1–0.2 g. This can be compared to other estimates of maximum ground acceleration based on the same fundamental strong-motion data of about 0.15 g (Cloud, 1963, 1967).

The peak acceleration alone is a very inadequate description of the damaging potential of an earthquake. The duration and the frequency content of the ground motion are equally important. A 0.1 to 0.2 g acceleration at the relatively large epicentral distance of Anchorage, at which much of the short-period motion would have attenuated to a low level, represents a more damaging situation in some respects than a similar acceleration peak close to the epicenter associated with a shorter-period motion.

Immediately after the earthquake, two strong-motion accelerographs were flown to Alaska and were temporarily installed in Anchorage. Figure 15 shows an accelerogram obtained from an aftershock measured at Elmendorf Air Force Base, Anchorage, which was strongly felt but did little or no additional damage (Cloud, 1967). This aftershock was located about 75 mi N70°E of the station, compared to the 70 mi N110°E for the main shock.

Because the aftershock of Figure 15 originated close to the epicenter of the main shock and was presumably part of the same general phenomenon, it might be expected to share some of the frequency characteristics of the main shock. Figure 16 shows a Fourier spectrum curve for one component of the Anchorage aftershock. Although there is no assurance that it bears any special resemblance to the Fourier spectrum of the main shock, a similarity is not unlikely. The aftershock spectrum definitely shows that components below 0.5 second are reduced. This is consistent with the observation of damage caused by the main shock in Anchorage, which indicates relatively less damage to low-period structures than to longer-period structures. It will be noted that the aftershock spectrum shows no evidence of major peaking that might be associated with certain special ground conditions.

DURATION OF HEAVY GROUND SHAKING

All observers agree that the duration of strong shaking seemed very long—perhaps several minutes. The best evidence of the actual duration is afforded by a tape recording made during the earthquake in Anchorage by Mr. Robert A. Pate. A description of the circumstances under which the recording was made, together with a 33 1/3-rpm disk reproducing the tape, has been given by Steinbrugge (1967). At the time of the earthquake, Mr. Pate was about to record a taped message and on first feeling the shaking he started the machine and began to talk. Within 2 to 3 seconds after he begins to speak, the background noise indi-

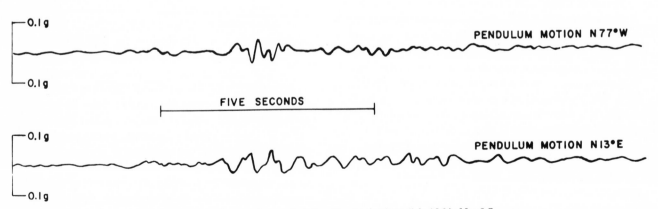

FIGURE 15   Accelerograph record of the aftershock of April 3, 1964; M = 5.7.

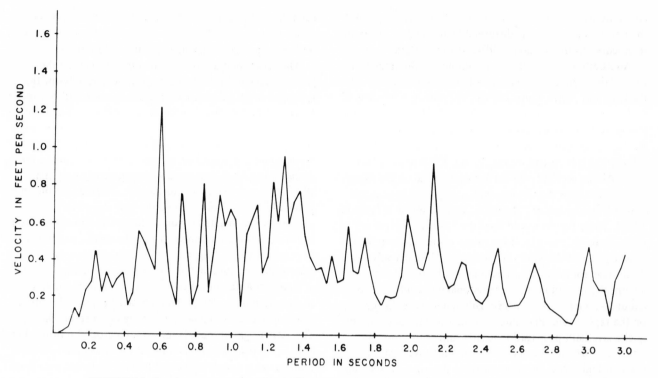

FIGURE 16   Fourier spectrum curve for N77°W component of the aftershock of April 3, 1964, Anchorage.

cates a heavy shaking. The background noise seems to be the result of pictures rattling on the walls, cabinet doors banging, furniture shifting back and forth, and a general creaking and rattling of the wooden-frame structure of the house. The amount of noise is surprising in view of the small amount of damage caused, which apparently consisted of one glass broken in the bathroom.

The comparative intensity of the background noise as it increased, decreased, and then increased again, should give an accurate objective indication of the duration of heavy shaking. The interesting comments made by Mr. Pate give additional information that aids in the interpretation of the noise.

A careful timing of the background noise made during repeated listenings gives the following sequence, from the time the background noise becomes distinctly perceptible (within 2 to 3 seconds of the start of the tape): Noise builds up steadily to a maximum after about 20 seconds; noise diminishes slowly, until it has practically ceased after about 35 seconds; noise gradually builds up again to approximately its former maximum after about 50 seconds; noise gradually decreases, ceasing after about 80–85 seconds. The total period of heavy shaking therefore lasted about 1½ minutes with a brief pause after the first ½ minute.

After the period of heavy shaking, there was a longer period in which the ground motions were still of an alarming magnitude: After 80–85 seconds, background noise

practically ceases; after 2 minutes 40 seconds, "still shaking"; after 3 minutes, "still swaying back and forth"; after 3 minutes 40 seconds, "still shaking a little." At this point, Mr. Pate left his house and visited his neighbors, apparently feeling that for the time being, at least, the earthquake was over.

This information indicates that, what appears to be a discrepancy between the numerous subjective reports of ground-shaking duration of many minutes and the deduction from the effects on structures, the duration was of about 1 minute and was roughly comparable to past earthquake experiences, is mainly the difference between a strongly perceptible ground motion and a damaging ground motion (Housner, 1965).

Another potential source of information on the time duration of the ground shaking are the records obtained on various recording instruments such as those used in industrial and power plants. Most of these instruments record on a 24-hour basis and have a relatively slow time scale on which it is difficult to resolve minutes. The effects of the earthquake on the timing mechanism are also difficult to assess. One usable record of this type was obtained from an outside air-temperature-recording gage located at Whittier, Alaska, about 45 mi from the epicenter (Kachadoorian, 1965). Although the dynamic characteristics of the device are not specified, it can be clearly seen from the 24-hour record that the mechanism was strongly disturbed for several minutes. The amount of this time that might represent the natural motion of the disturbed instrument in returning to an equilibrium position is difficult to ascertain.

Another line of evidence that illuminates the time duration of the ground shaking comes from a consideration of the length of faulting involved and the probable velocity of fault propagation (Steinbrugge, 1967). Analysis of measurements of the Chile earthquake of 1960 indicated fault-fracture-propagation velocities of 3–4 km/sec (Benioff and others, 1961; Press and others, 1961). The length of faulting in Alaska is about 800 km as estimated from the extent of the aftershock distribution and about 650 km as determined from the spectra of surface waves (Press and Jackson, 1965). These figures would limit the total time duration from 2½ to 4½ minutes. If the origin of the waves at a particular place on the fault is considered to be relatively near Anchorage for only about one third of the total fault length, the time duration of heavy shaking would then be about 1–1½ minutes, which roughly coincides with the time on the tape record. Preliminary studies of the Alaska earthquake give fault-propagation results similar to those obtained for the Chile earthquake. One such investigation (Toksöz and others, 1965) indicates a propagation velocity of 3 km/sec and a fault-rupture distance of about 600 km, which would correspond to a total of 2–3 minutes of shaking.

ESTIMATES OF ANCHORAGE GROUND MOTION

In the absence of measurements, there has been a good deal of speculation about the damaging ground motions associated with the Alaska earthquake. Although it is well known that the psychological effects of an earthquake almost inevitably lead to exaggerated subjective evaluations of ground motion and duration, many of these highly colored stories are often repeated in responsible technical reports. The spectacular nature of the damage associated with some of the Anchorage landslides gave rise at first to the notion that ground motions of an entirely unprecedented nature must have been involved. This does not seem to have been the case. All quantitative evidence points clearly to the conclusion that the ground accelerations and time durations were consistent with those of past earthquakes having similar magnitudes and extent of faulting (Housner, 1965). Detailed calculations of the effects of typical earthquake ground motion on specific Anchorage structures have shown that the observed damage can be accounted for by assumed ground motion compatible with that measured and inferred in past earthquakes (Clough and Benuska, 1966; Benuska and Clough, 1973, this volume). For example, calculations made on an oil tank damaged during the earthquake showed that a maximum ground ac-

celeration of 0.20 g and an assumed velocity–response-spectrum value of 2.0 ft/sec would be consistent with the observed damage (Hanson, 1973, this volume).

The same conclusion is reached by considering the ground accelerations necessary to cause landslides of the type that occurred at Anchorage (Shannon & Wilson, Inc., 1964). Although there are many uncertainties in estimating the dynamic properties of soils and in accounting for mechanisms of sliding, it is evident that large ground accelerations would not always be necessary. In fact, some of the slopes in the Anchorage area were apparently only marginally stable under static conditions (Shannon & Wilson, Inc., 1964; Miller and Dobrovolny, 1959).

The recent Niigata, Japan, earthquake of June 16, 1964, had some interesting similarities to the Alaska earthquake. In certain areas of Niigata, a large-scale soil liquefaction occurred that resulted in extensive tilting of buildings because of foundation failures. Fortunately, it happened that a strong-motion accelerograph recorded the ground motions just before and during failure in a region of severe damage. The accelerograph records show that a ground motion that built up to 0.1 g and lasted only about 6 seconds was sufficient to cause the dynamic soil failures (International Institute of Seismology and Earthquake Engineering, 1965; Strong-Motion Earthquake Observation Committee, 1964).

ORIGIN OF THE SEISMIC DISTURBANCE

From the preceding information, it is evident that an important factor in the engineering interpretation of earthquake damage is the distance from the structure to the origin of the seismic disturbance. Not only must these distances be known to make meaningful comparisons between damage at various points and for different earthquakes, but the frequency spectrum of the ground motions also depends significantly on distance.

Neither the epicenter nor the hypocenter of an earthquake is necessarily, or even likely to be, the effective source of the damaging seismic waves for large earthquakes. The epicenter is defined as the point on the surface of the earth vertically above the region in which the earthquake motions are initiated. The actual extent of crustal deformation may be such that the major sources of damaging seismic waves are much closer to a particular point of damage than is the epicenter.

If, for example, the basic mechanism consists of propagation of a fault fracture from an epicenter located near one end of the fault over distances of several hundred miles, it is evident that the distances to the fault may be much less than epicentral distances for very large regions. The distance from the epicenter alone is thus not an adequate indication of the amount or type of damage.

For the Alaska earthquake, the situation is further complicated by the fact that the earthquake was apparently a multiple event, consisting of at least six separate earthquakes that occurred within approximately 1 minute (Wyss and Brune, 1967). Because this is the first major earthquake for which adequate measurements are available for a detailed study of such multiple shocks, a brief summary of the investigation of Wyss and Brune is presented here.

MULTIPLE-SHOCK EARTHQUAKES

Large earthquakes are usually followed by a sequence of aftershocks that occur with sufficient time between them to be recognized as separate events. During the strong initial phases of an earthquake, several shocks originating in adjacent regions of the earth's crust might occur with so brief a time interval between them that the records would, in effect, be superimposed and would give the impression of one major shock. That this can happen has been verified in some detail for the Niigata, Japan, earthquake of June 16, 1964 (Miyamura and others, 1965).

Wyss and Brune have shown that the Alaska earthquake records are characterized by multiple P-phases, not predicted by travel-time curves, that can be explained only by the supposition of an overlapping sequence of shocks. By an examination of low magnification records from 80 stations over a wide range of azimuths, they have been able to recognize and to locate six separate shocks within about the first minute of the earthquake. The first five events occurred at various azimuths about the initial epicenter; the remaining event headed off southwest in the general direction of the aftershock pattern. The final event studied occurred about 72 seconds after the initial shock and was located some 250 km southwest of the initial epicenter; this corresponds to an equivalent rupture velocity of 3.5 km/sec, which is consistent with the values previously quoted.

The values of fault-propagation velocity given earlier were calculated on the basis of surface-wave data, on the assumption that fault fracture occurred as a continuous uniform propagation process. It has been pointed out, however, that such uniform processes cannot properly account for the short-period components of the radiated energy (Haskell, 1964). The multiple-earthquake concept, on the other hand, pictures the propagation as a sequence of discrete jumps. The overall equivalent rupture velocities are the same for the two concepts, but the multiple-earthquake model permits a more detailed study of the actual fracture mechanism than can be achieved by surface-wave measurements alone.

Figure 17 shows the location of the epicenter and the six events determined by Wyss and Brune to be the major components of the main shock. In view of the limited data

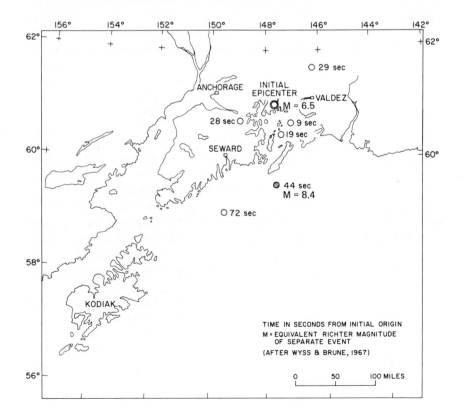

FIGURE 17 Multiple events of main shock of the Alaska Earthquake. After Wyss and Brune (1967).

available, the locations of the separate events of the multiple sequence cannot be as precise as the location of the initial epicenter. The initial shock, located at the accepted epicenter, was found to have a Richter magnitude of 6.5, whereas the 44-second event, the largest single shock of the sequence, had a magnitude of 8.4.

The magnitude figures given by Wyss and Brune are body-wave magnitudes. To make them comparable to the surface-wave magnitudes used elsewhere in this paper, they have been converted by the relationship $M_s = 1.59\ m_b - 3.97$ (Richter, 1958). These figures are consistent with the magnitude figures quoted above, which would presumably represent an integrated effect of the whole sequence. If it is assumed that the major source of energy responsible for the damaging ground shaking in the various Alaskan cities emanates from this 44-second shock, a reasonably consistent picture of the relative ground shaking at Anchorage, Valdez, and Seward emerges. If the initial epicenter, or an approximate fault trace, is considered as the origin of the damaging ground motions, it is more difficult to explain the relative pattern of ground shaking. In addition, the timing of the initial pulse and the later major pulse is consistent with the pattern of the tape-recorded noise mentioned in connection with the duration of the earthquake.

The concept of a multiple-earthquake mechanism can make important contributions to the explanation of damage patterns and is of direct interest to earthquake engineers. It seems likely that most earthquakes of the size of the Alaska shock might have such a multiple character. It was not possible to study in detail this aspect of the 1960 Chile earthquake because of a lack of suitable low-magnification records, but it is not unlikely that the Chile earthquake was also multiple. As previously mentioned, Japanese seismologists have found strong evidence that the Niigata earthquake of 1964 was multiple, and it also appears that the Fukui earthquake of 1948 was at least a double shock (Miyamura and others, 1965).

In the report of the 1906 San Francisco earthquake, H. F. Reid (1910) distinguished between two locations—the "beginning" of the shock and the "violent" shock, which he fixed roughly at some 30 mi along the fault from the initial movements. Although Reid lacked the instrumental data needed to study the details of the propagation mechanism, he was able to form a concept of the main features of the process that is probably correct.

EARTHQUAKE-MECHANISM STUDIES

Once the approximate location of the origin of the seismic disturbance is known, additional questions involving the mechanism of energy release become important for a more detailed study of the damage potential of the event. The basic problems of earthquake mechanism have been studied by many different seismological, geological, geodetic, and geophysical methods. Although great progress has been made, only relatively simple hypothetical cases can be treated so far, and the extent to which actual earthquakes can be explained reasonably completely leaves much to be desired.

In this respect, the explanations of the Alaska earthquake are representative of the current status of the subject. Although a large amount of data is available, it has not been possible to date to develop an unambiguous picture of the basic mechanism of the earthquake. The reasons for these difficulties will be outlined briefly, based to a large extent on the comprehensive report by Stauder and Bollinger (1966) on the focal mechanism of the earthquake.

Because of limitations on the basic data, only the initial event can be studied in detail. The extent to which the focal mechanisms involved in this initial event may be typical of the much broader-scale processes at work during the whole earthquake sequence will require further study.

FAULT-PLANE SOLUTIONS

According to the elastic-rebound theory, whose general principles are at present accepted by most North American seismologists and geologists, the sudden rupture of strained rocks along a fault zone and the consequent release of accumulated strain energy are the basic sources of the seismic energy. It is usually considered that the rupture begins in a particular region and then propagates along the fault at a specific velocity. It has been possible, by using simple models, to calculate the velocity of propagation of fault fractures from seismological data obtained from large earthquakes such as that in Chile in 1960.

From a measurement of the direction of first motion of various wave trains received at many different seismological stations distributed throughout the world, it is possible to calculate the orientation of two perpendicular planes that are closely related to the focal mechanism of the earthquake. If it is assumed that the basic earthquake mechanism involves motion along a plane as in the case of simple faulting, one of these calculated perpendicular planes corresponds to the fault plane. It is thus possible from such fault-plane solutions to deduce a considerable amount of information on the focal mechanism from seismological data.

Unfortunately, it is not always possible to decide which of the two perpendicular planes corresponds to the fault plane. For the main shock of the Alaska earthquake, it was possible to accurately calculate from the P-wave first-motion data one of the nodal planes (Stauder and Bollinger, 1966; Berg, 1965; Algermissen, 1966a). In this way a nodal plane with a strike azimuth of 66° and a dip 85° to the southeast has been determined. The waves generated by the main shock, however, were so large that the S-wave first arrivals were obscured, and the second nodal plane could not be directly determined. It is not possible on the basis of seismological evidence to decide whether the 66° azimuth nodal plane is a fault plane, or whether it is normal to the fault. In the first case, the fault motion would be primarily dip-slip on a near-vertical fault; in the second, the fault motion would be a low-angle thrust. These two possibilities are indicated in Figure 18.

In an attempt to resolve the ambiguity, a careful study was made of a number of the aftershocks (Stauder and Bollinger, 1966). Because the aftershocks record much smaller amplitudes, S-wave first-motion directions could be determined as well as the P-wave arrivals, and it was possible to determine both nodal planes accurately. A close relation was found between the focal mechanisms of the aftershocks and the main shock. It is not possible to decide which of the two nodal planes is the fault plane for the aftershocks any more than it is possible for the main shock. It was concluded that, on seismological evidence alone, it

would not be possible to decide whether the main fault motion was near-vertical or overthrust.

One reason for the importance of such a decision for engineering purposes is illustrated in Figure 18. If a city were located at point A, it would be much closer to the overthrust fault plane than to the vertical fault plane, although the epicentral distance might be the same in both cases. The mechanism involved may thus have a major influence on the most basic distance parameters. Fortunately, the location of Anchorage probably involves no major difference between the two planes, although this cannot be established with certainty.

The fault-plane solutions would be expected to indicate fault directions compatible with the aftershock distribution pattern. Figure 4 shows that the general trend of the aftershock region has an azimuth of about 35°, which agrees roughly with the tectonic trend of the region. The approximately vertical P-wave-located nodal plane, however, has a well-determined azimuth of 66°, which suggests that the near-vertical nodal plane is not the fault plane.

A similar conclusion is reached from a consideration of

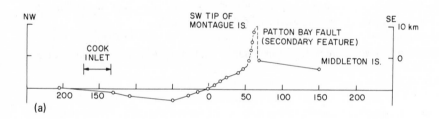

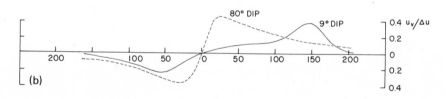

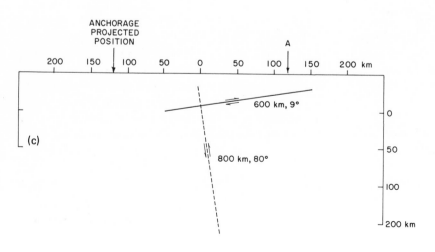

FIGURE 18 Correlation of assumed fault models and tectonic displacements. (a) Measured tectonic displacements of free surface; after Plafker (1965) and Stauder and Bollinger (1966). (b) Ratio of computed vertical displacement to fault slip; after Savage and Hastie (1966). (c) Assumed fault models giving vertical displacements in (b) above.

the depth of focus and nodal-plane solutions for a sequence of aftershocks. This also tends to suggest that the faulting is of the shallow-dipping overthrust type (Stauder and Bollinger, 1966).

TECTONIC DEFORMATION

Other important information relating to the basic mechanism of the earthquake comes from a consideration of the tectonic deformation of the region. Figure 19 shows the major regions of tectonic uplift and subsidence in the epicentral and aftershock region (Plafker, 1965). Comparison to Figure 4 shows that the axis of the tectonic deformation corresponds well to the aftershock pattern.

In the upper portion of Figure 18, a vertical cross section of the region along the line A–A in Figure 19 shows the vertical uplifts and subsidences (Plafker, 1965; Stauder and Bollinger, 1966). By the dislocation theory, it is possible to calculate the surface displacements corresponding to faults with specified lengths, locations, and directions. Figure 18b and c show the results of such calculations for the two faults indicated, with dip angles corresponding to the two nodal planes of the fault-plane solutions (Savage and Hastie, 1966; Stauder and Bollinger, 1966). The lengths and locations of the faults with respect to the epicenter were selected to give

surface displacement patterns that would agree as well as possible with the measured tectonic displacements of Figure 18a. The near-vertical fault results in a deformed region for which the axes of maximum uplift and subsidence are too close together; in this respect, the low-angle overthrust fault again seems to agree better with measured displacements. It can perhaps also be concluded, on the basis of the general location of the regions of maximum uplift and subsidence, that the length and location of the overthrust fault shown in Figure 18c are approximately correct, and, in particular, that the left (north) end of the fault has the approximate relation as shown for Anchorage. The aftershock map of Figure 4 shows that most of the aftershocks fall on the far side of the zero axis of tectonic deformation (shown in Figure 19) from Anchorage, particularly in the north region nearest Anchorage and the epicenter. This fact also suggests that the major fault motions were progressing from the epicenter away from Anchorage.

The low-angle overthrust fault model would make the closest distance from the fault plane to Anchorage some 60 mi, which would still be consistent with the fact that the long-period structural responses in Anchorage were relatively large compared with short-period responses—a well-known characteristic of distant earthquakes.

If the general fault-location pattern of Figure 18 is correct, then the distance relation to Anchorage would not be

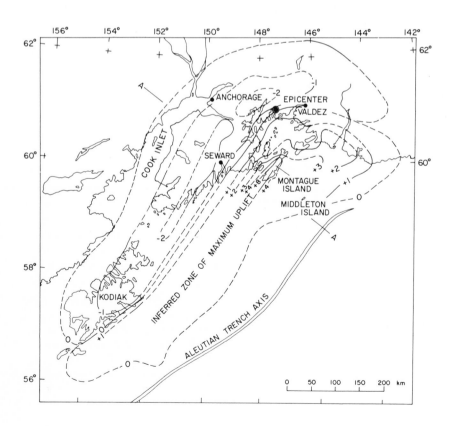

FIGURE 19 Major regions of tectonic uplift and subsidence, Alaska earthquake. After Plafker (1965).

significantly altered by a choice between the near-vertical and the overthrust fault. For certain other localities, however, the choice might be significant, illustrating the importance for engineering studies of an accurate determination of focal mechanism.

Additional studies of the geologic structure of the aftershock region have been made by seismic and echo-sounding profiling. Such investigations have defined a preexisting zone of discontinuous faults in the area, with thrust faults characterizing an east–west trending system and steep dipping faults showing a northeast trending system (von Huene and others, 1967). The relation between these faults and the 1964 earthquake is not clear. This additional information does not materially assist in deciding which fault planes were active in that earthquake.

Preliminary investigations of the horizontal crustal movements associated with the Alaska earthquake give additional support to the idea of a large-scale overthrust movement. Measurements made by the U.S. Coast and Geodetic Survey indicate horizontal motions of points on the south side of the Kenai Peninsula of as much as 70 ft in a southeast direction and similar movements of the southern tip of Montague Island of as much as 67 ft (Parkin, 1966). The relative displacements revealed by these preliminary studies have not all been entirely consistent, and additional investigations will be needed to distinguish between the effects of crustal tilting and horizontal movements that might be associated with overthrust faulting.

Discussions and studies of the focal mechanism of the Alaska earthquake are still under way. It is unlikely, however, that completely satisfactory answers will be found to some questions. In some cases, it is possible to use surface-wave determinations of direction of rupture propagation to resolve uncertainties in fault-plane solutions; on the basis of such considerations, it has been maintained that the near-vertical fault plane is indicated (Press and Jackson, 1965; Press, 1965). Other authors (Savage and Hastie, 1966; Stauder and Bollinger, 1966), however, maintain that in the Alaska earthquake the direction of rupture propagation was such that no distinction between nodal planes can be made on that basis. It appears also that no definite conclusions can be reached by a consideration of very small permanent displacements measured in Hawaii (Press, 1965; Savage and Hastie, 1966). When all the evidence is considered, the current consensus seems to be that, although the low-dip overthrust fault is the more likely hypothesis, the matter cannot be said to be settled (Stauder and Bollinger, 1966).

A complete description of the physical processes involved in the Alaska earthquake would no doubt be much more complex than is suggested by any of the simple models implied in the above investigation. Data are at hand, however, for a much more complete study of the event than has been possible for any comparable earthquake in the past. Despite this increased information, no complete description of this very complicated phenomenon can be expected. We hope that the deficiencies in the basic data for this earthquake will point the way toward improved instrumentation and investigative techniques for future earthquakes.

TSUNAMI GENERATION

Most large earthquakes involving vertical tectonic displacements under the sea generate tsunamis. Because the tectonic displacements are beneath the sea where they are difficult to detect and measure, it has not formerly been possible to relate the generation of the sea wave to a directly measurable pattern of tectonic displacements. In the Alaska earthquake, it was possible for the first time to get a direct picture of such movements because a sufficient portion of the pattern was displayed on land to permit the undersea portions to be directly inferred.

Figure 20 shows the source area of the tsunamis generated by the Alaska earthquake that was inferred from the arrival times of the initial wave (Plafker and Mayo, 1965; Spaeth and Berkman, 1969). Land is distributed so that these first arrivals outline a potential source area in a reasonably complete way. By comparing Figure 20 to the aftershock-epicenter map of Figure 4 and to the regions of tectonic uplift and subsidence of Figure 19, a consistent picture emerges of an appropriate mechanism for the generation of a tsunami.

CONCLUSIONS

Seismology has supplied a great deal of the necessary information on the Alaska earthquake of March 27, 1964, for an engineering analysis of the earthquake effects on structures. For the future development of earthquake engineering, it is perhaps more important to emphasize the facts that seismology has not been able to provide. The most important deficiencies in our information on the earthquake are the lack of measurements of the actual damaging ground motions at any point in Alaska and the uncertainty and inaccuracy of the knowledge of the locations of the maximum sources of energy release. This uncertainty makes it impossible to establish the distances of specific sites on the surface from these points of energy release.

A much more extensive network of strong-motion earthquake instrumentation in all seismic regions of the world and an improved knowledge of all aspects of the earthquake-mechanism problem will be required to solve these problems for future earthquakes.

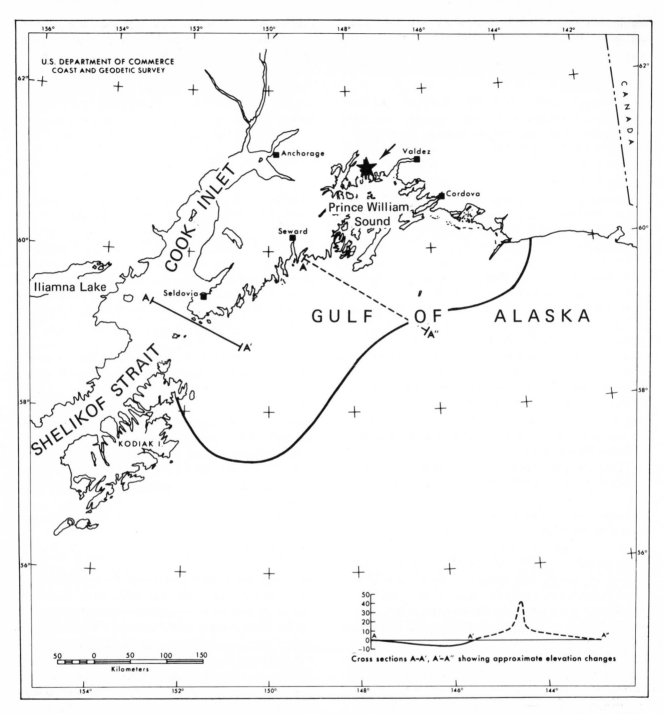

FIGURE 20   Approximate generation area of Alaska earthquake tsunami from tide station measurements (Spaeth and Berkman, 1969).

ACKNOWLEDGMENTS

The foregoing summary was completed before the publication either of the seismological volume of the study of the Alaska earthquake prepared by the Environmental Science Services Administration of the U.S. Coast and Geodetic Survey or of the seismological portion of the report being prepared for the National Academy of Sciences; hence, the results of these comprehensive studies are not included here. We should like to express our appreciation to Dr. Don Tocher of the National Oceanic and Atmospheric Administration, chairman of the Panel on Seismology of the National Academy of Sciences Committee on the Alaska Earthquake, who has checked the report for general accuracy from the seismological point of view. We should also like to thank Professors C. F. Richter of the California Institute of Technology and J. N. Brune of the University of California at

San Diego for helpful comments on earthquake magnitudes and on multiple earthquakes.

REFERENCES

Algermissen, S. T., 1966a. Mechanism of the Prince William Sound earthquake *in* ESSA Symposium on Earthquake Prediction. U.S. Department of Commerce, Environmental Science Services Administration. Washington: Government Printing Office. p. 20–25.

Algermissen, S. T., 1966b. Seismic studies in Alaska *in* ESSA Symposium on Earthquake Prediction. U.S. Department of Commerce, Environmental Science Services Administration. Washington: Government Printing Office. p. 48–52.

Benioff, Hugo, 1951. Earthquakes and rock creep. *Bulletin of the Seismological Society of America,* 41 (January), 31–62.

Benioff, Hugo, Frank Press, and S. Smith, 1961. Excitation of the free oscillations of the earth by earthquakes. *Journal of Geophysical Research*, 66 (February), 605–619.

Benuska, K. Lee, and Ray W. Clough, 1973. Dynamic analyses of building failures *in* The Great Alaska Earthquake of 1964: Engineering. NAS Pub. 1606. Washington: National Academy of Sciences.

Berg, Eduard, 1965. The Alaskan earthquake, its location and seismic setting *in* Science in Alaska, 1964: Proceedings Fifteenth Alaskan Science Conference, College, Alaska, August 31 to September 4, 1964. George Dahlgren, editor. College: Alaska Division American Association for the Advancement of Science, March 15. p. 218–232.

Brown, R. D., J. G. Wedder, R. E. Wallace, E. F. Roth, R. F. Yerkes, R. D. Castle, A. O. Waananen, R. W. Page, and J. P. Eaton, 1967. The Parkfield–Cholame, California, earthquakes of June–August 1966. U.S. Geological Survey Professional Paper 579. Washington: Government Printing Office. 66 p.

Brune, J. N., and C. R. Allen, 1967. A low-stress-drop low-magnitude earthquake with surface faulting: The Imperial, California, earthquake of March 4, 1966. *Bulletin of the Seismological Society of America*, 57 (June), 501–514.

Cloud, William K., 1963. Maximum accelerations during earthquakes. Proceedings, Primeros Jornados Chilena de Sismologia e Ingenieria Antisismica, Santiago, Chile. 14 p.

Cloud, William K., 1964. Instruments for earthquake investigation *in* Earthquake investigations in the Western United States, 1931–1964. D. S. Carder, editor. U.S. Coast and Geodetic Survey. Washington: Government Printing Office. p. 5–20.

Cloud, William K., 1967. Strong-motion and building-period measurements *in* Vol. II-A: The Prince William Sound, Alaska, earthquake of 1964 and aftershocks. Environmental Science Services Administration, U.S. Coast and Geodetic Survey. Washington: Government Printing Office. p. 319–331.

Clough, Ray W., and K. Lee Benuska, 1966. FHA study of seismic design criteria for high-rise buildings. A report for Federal Housing Administration, Technical Studies Program (HUD TS-3). Washington: T. Y. Lin and Associates (Consulting Engineers). 347 p.

Gutenberg, B., and Charles F. Richter, 1954. Seismicity of the earth and associated phenomena. Princeton: Princeton University Press. 322 p.

Halverson, H. T., 1965. The strong-motion accelerograph. Proceedings, Third World Conference on Earthquake Engineering, New Zealand. 20 p.

Hanson, Robert D., 1973. Behavior of liquid-storage tanks *in* The Great Alaska Earthquake of 1964: Engineering. NAS Pub. 1606. Washington: National Academy of Sciences.

Harding, S. T., W. Rinehart, and W. K. Cloud, 1966. The Parkfield, California, earthquake of June 27, 1966. Environmental Science Services Administration. Washington: Government Printing Office. 65 p.

Haskell, N. A., 1964. Total energy and energy spectral density of elastic wave radiation from propagating faults. *Bulletin of the Seismological Society of America*, 54 (December), 1811–1841.

Housner, George W., 1965. Intensity of earthquake ground shaking near the causative fault. Proceedings, Third World Conference on Earthquake Engineering, New Zealand. 20 p.

Hudson, Donald E., 1963. The measurement of ground motion of destructive earthquakes. *Bulletin of the Seismological Society of America*, 53 (February), 419–437.

Hudson, Donald E., 1965. Ground motion measurements in earthquake engineering. Proceedings, Symposium on Earthquake Engineering, University of British Columbia. 36 p.

International Institute of Seismology and Earthquake Engineering, 1965. The Niigata earthquake, 16 June 1964, and resulting damage to reinforced-concrete buildings. Report 1, Tokyo. 62 p.

Kachadoorian, Reuben, 1965. Effects of the earthquake of March 27, 1964, at Whittier, Alaska. U.S. Geological Survey Professional Paper 542-B. Washington: Government Printing Office. 21 p. Also *in* The Great Alaska Earthquake of 1964: Geology. NAS Pub. 1601. Washington: National Academy of Sciences, 1971. p. 439–459.

Miller, Robert D., and Ernest Dobrovolny, 1959. Surficial geology of Anchorage and vicinity, Alaska. U.S. Geological Survey Bulletin 1093. Washington: Government Printing Office. 128 p.

Miyamura, S., S. Omote, R. Teisseyre, and E. Vesanen, 1965. Multiple shocks and earthquake series pattern. *Bulletin of the International Institute of Seismology and Earthquake Engineering* (Tokyo), v. 2, p. 71–92.

Parkin, Ernest J., 1966. Alaskan surveys to determine crustal movements. Part II—horizontal displacement. Paper presented at the Annual Meeting of the American Congress on Surveying and Mapping, Washington, D.C., March 10. Rockville [Maryland]: U.S. Coast and Geodetic Survey. 15 p.

Plafker, George, 1965. Tectonic deformation associated with the 1964 Alaska earthquake. *Science*, 148 (June 25), 1675–1687.

Plafker, George, and L. R. Mayo, 1965. Tectonic deformation, subaqueous slides and destructive waves associated with the Alaskan March 27, 1964, earthquake: An interim geologic evaluation. U.S. Geological Survey Open-File Report. Menlo Park: U.S. Geological Survey. 34 p.

Press, Frank, 1965. Displacements, strains, and tilts at teleseismic distances. *Journal of Geophysical Research*, 70 (May 15), 2395–2412. Also *in* The Great Alaska Earthquake of 1964: Seismology and Geodesy. NAS Pub. 1602. Washington: National Academy of Sciences, 1972. p. 289–306.

Press, Frank, and David Jackson, 1965. Alaskan earthquake, 27 March 1964: Vertical extent of faulting and elastic strain energy release. *Science*, 147 (February 19), 867–868. Also *in* The Great Alaska Earthquake of 1964: Seismology and Geodesy. NAS Pub. 1602. Washington: National Academy of Sciences, 1972. p. 109–111.

Press, Frank, Ari Ben-Menahem, and M. Nafi Toksöz, 1961. Experimental determination of earthquake fault length and rupture velocity. *Journal of Geophysical Research*, 66 (October), 3471–3485.

Reid, H. F., 1910. The California earthquake of April 18, 1906.

Volume II: The mechanics of the earthquake. Washington: Carnegie Institution. 192 p. (Reprinted 1969).

Richter, Charles F., 1958. Elementary seismology. San Francisco: W. H. Freeman and Company. 768 p.

Richter, Charles F., 1959. Seismic regionalization. *Bulletin of the Seismological Society of America*, 49 (April), 123–162.

St.-Amand, Pierre, 1961. Los Terremotos de Mayo–Chile 1960. China Lake [Calif.]: U.S. Naval Ordnance Test Station. 39 p.

Savage, J. C., and L. M. Hastie, 1966. Surface deformation associated with dip-slip faulting. *Journal of Geophysical Research*, 71 (October 15), 4897–4904. Also *in* The Great Alaska Earthquake of 1964: Seismology and Geodesy. NAS Pub. 1602. Washington: National Academy of Sciences, 1972. p. 189–196.

Shannon & Wilson, Inc., 1964. Report on Anchorage area soil studies, Alaska, to U.S. Army Engineer District, Anchorage, Alaska, August 28. Seattle: Shannon & Wilson, Inc. 300 p.

Spaeth, Mark G., and Saul C. Berkman, 1969. The tsunami of March 28, 1964, as recorded at tide stations *in* Volume II-B,C: The Prince William Sound, Alaska, earthquake of 1964 and aftershocks. Environmental Science Services Administration, U.S. Coast and Geodetic Survey. Washington: Government Printing Office. p. 223–307.

Stauder, W., and G. A. Bollinger, 1966. The focal mechanism of the Alaska earthquake of March 28, 1964, and of its aftershock sequence. *Journal of Geophysical Research*, 71 (November 15), 5283–5296. Also *in* The Great Alaska Earthquake of 1964: Seismology and Geodesy. NAS Pub. 1602. Washington: National Academy of Sciences, 1972. p. 235–248.

Steinbrugge, Karl V., 1967. Introduction to the earthquake engineering of the 1964 Prince William Sound, Alaska, earthquake *in* Vol. II-A: The Prince William Sound, Alaska, earthquake of 1964 and aftershocks. Environmental Science Services Administration, U.S. Coast and Geodetic Survey. Washington: Government Printing Office. p. 1–6.

Strong-Motion Earthquake Observation Committee, 1964. Strong-motion earthquake records of the Niigata earthquake. Special Publication. Earthquake Research Institute, University of Tokyo.

Tocher, Don, 1960. The Alaska earthquake of July 10, 1958: Movement on the Fairweather fault and field investigations of southern epicentral region. *Bulletin of the Seismological Society of America*, 50 (April), 267–292.

Toksöz, M. Nafi, Ari Ben-Menahem, and David G. Harkrider, 1965. Source mechanism of Alaska earthquake from long-period seismic surface waves (Abstract). *Transactions, American Geophysical Union*, 46 (March), 154.

Townshend, John B., and William K. Cloud, 1965. Preliminary intensity evaluations of the Prince William Sound earthquake of March 28, 1964. Proceedings Fifteenth Alaskan Science Conference, College, Alaska, August 31 to September 4, 1964. George Dahlgren, editor. College: Alaska Division American Association for the Advancement of Science. p. 233–238.

U.S. Coast and Geodetic Survey, 1964. Preliminary report–Prince William Sound, Alaskan earthquakes March–April 1964 (second printing). Seismology Division Report. Washington: U.S. Coast and Geodetic Survey. 101 p.

U.S. Coast and Geodetic Survey, 1966. The Prince William Sound, Alaska, earthquake of 1964 and aftershocks. Fergus J. Wood, editor-in-chief. Volume I: Operational phases of the Coast and Geodetic Survey program in Alaska for the period March 27 to December 31, 1964. Washington: Government Printing Office, 263 p.

U.S. Coast and Geodetic Survey, 1969. The Prince William Sound, Alaska, earthquake of 1964 and aftershocks. Louis E. Leipold, editor-in-chief. Volume II-B,C: Research studies–seismology and marine geology. Washington: Government Printing Office. 350 p.

Von Hake, Carl A., and William K. Cloud, 1966. United States earthquakes, 1964. Environmental Science Services Administration, U.S. Coast and Geodetic Survey. Washington: Government Printing Office. 91 p.

von Huene, Roland, Richard J. Malloy, George G. Shor, Jr., and Pierre St.-Amand, 1967. Geologic structures in the aftershock region of the 1964 Alaskan earthquake. *Journal of Geophysical Research*, 72 (July 15), 3649–3660.

Wood, H. O., and F. Neumann, 1931. Modified Mercalli intensity scale of 1931. *Bulletin of the Seismological Society of America*, 21 (December), 277–283.

Wyss, Max, and James N. Brune, 1967. The Alaska earthquake of 28 March 1964: A complex multiple rupture. *Bulletin of the Seismological Society of America*, 57 (October), 1017–1023. Also *in* The Great Alaska Earthquake of 1964: Seismology and Geodesy. NAS Pub. 1602. Washington: National Academy of Sciences, 1972. p. 60-64.

GEORGE W. HOUSNER
PAUL C. JENNINGS
CALIFORNIA INSTITUTE OF TECHNOLOGY

Reconstituted Earthquake Ground Motion at Anchorage

The lack of any record of ground motion in the region of destructive shaking during the Alaska earthquake makes it difficult to evaluate precisely the engineering significance of much of the damage. The severity of the damage is a function of the character of the ground shaking and the physical properties of the structures concerned. Usually, the pertinent physical properties that a damaged structure had before the earthquake are not well known; therefore, analyses of the dynamic response of the structure to the recorded ground motion must reconcile the observed damage with the estimated properties of the structure. If ground motions are not recorded during the earthquake, such analyses are often made by using ground motions recorded during other earthquakes. In the case of the 1964 Alaska earthquake (M=8.4), however, the ground motion had certain special characteristics, such as duration of shaking, that differed from those of ground motions recorded in other earthquakes of lesser magnitudes. These differences make it difficult to perform appropriate analyses in those situations where these special characteristics are significant. The difficulty is especially serious for the landslides, where the cumulative effect of the ground shaking over the total duration is important. As accurate as possible an estimate of the nature of the ground shaking is therefore of considerable value in improving the results of dynamic analyses by providing more realistic excitation. Information is available about the ground shaking in Anchorage that can be combined with the knowledge of earthquake ground motions, in general, to construct an accelerogram that incorporates the major features of the ground shaking during the earthquake. This reconstituted ground motion can then be used in engineering analyses of the responses of soils or structures.

GENERAL PROPERTIES OF GROUND MOTIONS

It is well known from past recordings of earthquake ground motions that the free-field surface acceleration (horizontal)

ABSTRACT: To aid analysis of the dynamic response of structures to the Alaska earthquake, a simulated accelerogram of the ground motion at Anchorage was constructed by combining information from a variety of secondary observations of the motion and its effects with knowledge of general earthquake ground motions. A maximum acceleration of approximately 15 percent of gravity is indicated. The strong ground shaking lasted for about 1 minute and was followed by approximately 3 minutes of lesser shaking.

43

is a transient random function that has an initial rise time, then a phase of strong shaking, followed by a gradual decay of the amplitude of motion. The duration of shaking is a function of the magnitude of the earthquake and the distance from the causative fault. Ground accelerations of large earthquakes in the United States that were recorded close to the causative fault, on firm ground, exhibit spectral characteristics that correspond approximately to white noise over the frequency range from 0.1 to 3.0 cycles per second (cps). The frequency content of ground motion can be influenced by such factors as the distance from the causative fault, which attenuates the higher frequency components more strongly than the low frequencies; the source mechanism, which can affect both the high frequency components and the low frequency components; and the wave speeds in the local soils, especially if the upper soil layer is extremely soft. The foregoing facts, inferred from recorded shocks, permit the construction of mathematical models of earthquake motion and the generation of accelerograms that simulate recorded motions.

SPECIFIC PROPERTIES OF ANCHORAGE GROUND MOTION

Because the specific properties of the ground motion at Anchorage are discussed by Hudson and Cloud (1973, this volume), only a summary of the pertinent features will be given here. The most important information for our purposes was recorded by Mr. Robert A. Pate on a tape recorder that he was using to dictate a letter at the time of the earthquake. The tape, with added narration, was reproduced by Mr. Pate on a 7-in. 33 1/3-rpm commerical phonograph record, "Earthquake–Alaska." We listened to the original tape, which is in the possession of Mr. Pate, to verify that the record was a true duplication without excisions or inserts. The noise of furniture rattling, house creaking, and so forth, together with Mr. Pate's comments, permit the time history of the intensity of shaking to be sketched as shown in Figure 1. The initial strong phase of shaking built up to a maximum at 20 seconds from the beginning and decreased to a relatively low value at 36 seconds. The second phase of strong shaking built up to a maximum at 53 seconds, which is slightly less intense than the initial maximum. The second phase decreased to a minimum at 66 seconds, followed by a slight increase, and then by a gradual decrease. After the first 120 seconds of ground shaking, the intensity decreased, until at 220 seconds when Mr. Pate had to pay careful attention to feel that the house was "still shaking a little." This remark indicates that the ground shaking had attenuated almost to the limit of perceptibility at 4 minutes after the initial motion. Figure 1

gives an accurate description of the times of maximum and minimum intensities and shows the estimated amplitude of the intensity as a function of time.

In Anchorage, the damage to one- and two-story buildings was not great, indicating that the higher-frequency components of ground shaking (approximately 3–10 cps) were relatively attenuated. This is consistent with Anchorage being 80 mi from the epicenter and somewhat closer to the nearest portion of the slipped fault. The Tehachapi, California, earthquake of July 21, 1952, was approximately 80 mi from the center of Los Angeles, and both the building damage and the recorded ground accelerations in Los Angeles indicated a relative attenuation of higher-frequency components. On the basis of the Tehachapi earthquake and other recorded shocks, it is estimated that the maximum acceleration at a distance of 80 mi from the causative fault of a very large earthquake would be approximately 10 percent of gravity and, at 60 mi, approximately 15 percent of gravity. The observed damage at Anchorage suggests that 15 percent of gravity is a reasonable estimate of the maximum acceleration in that city.

The damage to structures that had natural periods of vibration of about 1 second, together with observations of the amplitudes of vibration of hanging pictures and other oscillating systems, indicate that response spectrum values for periods near 1 second were similar to those of the 1952 Taft, California, accelerogram and somewhat less than those of the 1940 El Centro, California, accelerograms.

From previous earthquake motions, the maximum transient ground displacement at Anchorage was estimated to be on the order of 1 ft.

The spectrum of an aftershock recorded at Anchorage (Hudson and Cloud, 1973, this volume) does not indicate any marked influence of the local soils such as would be expected of a very soft upper layer of soil, as, for example, in Mexico City.

RECONSTITUTION OF THE GROUND ACCELERATION

The simulated ground acceleration at Anchorage was constructed in the following manner:

A pair of 2-minute-long samples of a stationary random process was used as a basis. The frequency components of this motion correspond to those of typical large United States shocks (Housner and Jennings, 1964).

The high-frequency components of one 2-minute-long segment were filtered on the digital computer by effectively passing the acceleration through an oscillator that had a natural period of 0.8 seconds and a damping of 70 percent

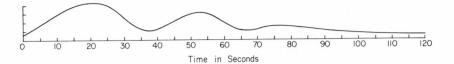

FIGURE 1   Shaping function for the amplitude of ground acceleration.

of critical. This procedure shaped the high-frequency end of the spectrum to correspond to ground motion at approximately 60 mi from the causative fault.

The acceleration was passed through a low-frequency filter with period of 10 seconds and 70 percent damping to control the maximum amplitude of the displacement obtained by double integration of the acceleration. The resulting filtered motion was shaped by multiplying it by the amplitude function shown in Figure 1; this procedure produced the 2 minutes of motion shown in Figure 2. The accelerogram was scaled so that the pseudo-velocity response spectrum had peak values, for 1 percent damping, of approximately 3 fps, as shown in Figure 3.

The second 2-minute-long segment of random function was passed through a high-frequency filter whose natural period was 1.5 seconds and whose damping was 70 percent of critical. This accounted for the fact that these motions had traveled greater distances. It was passed through the same long-period filter and was shaped by multiplying by an amplitude function that decreased linearly from the 120-second value in Figure 1 to one fourth of that value at 240 seconds.

The resulting 4-minute-long accelerogram is shown in Figure 4. The peak acceleration, which occurs near 18 seconds, is 14 percent of gravity. The maximum acceleration near the end of the 240 seconds of motion decreases to approximately 0.5 percent of gravity, but such motion would still be perceptible. The maximum acceleration of 14 percent of gravity is relatively small compared with the 33 percent of gravity recorded during the 1940 El Centro shock ($M = 7.1$), which is a reflection of the attenuation of the short-period motion at Anchorage. For periods longer than approximately 0.5 second, the motion is almost as intense as the El Centro motion. The integrated velocity and displacement are shown in Figures 5 and 6.

USE OF THE RECONSTITUTED GROUND MOTION

It is envisioned that the accelerogram will be useful to engineers wishing to estimate the response of structures to the Alaska earthquake. Punch-card decks, or printouts, for the 240-second-long accelerogram in Figure 4, digitized at intervals of one fortieth of a second, are available for such studies. It is our opinion that the actual acceleration at Anchorage could not have differed markedly from that shown in Figure 4 in those characteristics significant to structural vibrations. In a statistical sense, however, the actual details of acceleration, velocity, and displacement shown in Figures 4, 5, and 6 are not significant; other accelerograms, constructed in exactly the same way from

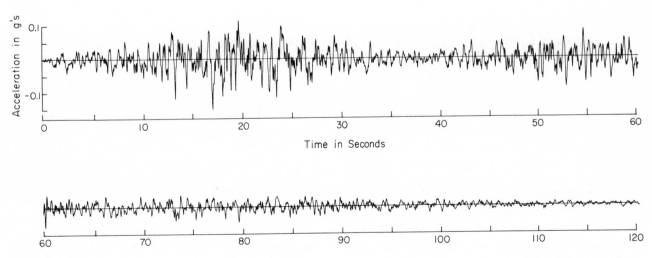

FIGURE 2   Simulated horizontal ground acceleration for the first 120 seconds of ground shaking at Anchorage, Alaska, during the earthquake.

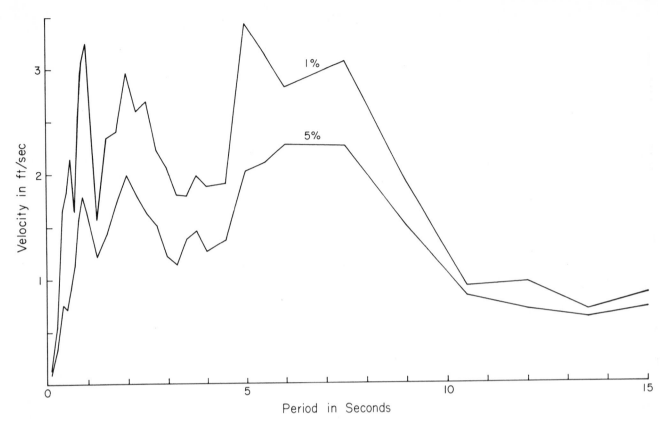

FIGURE 3   Pseudo-velocity response spectrum for the acceleration shown in Figure 2.

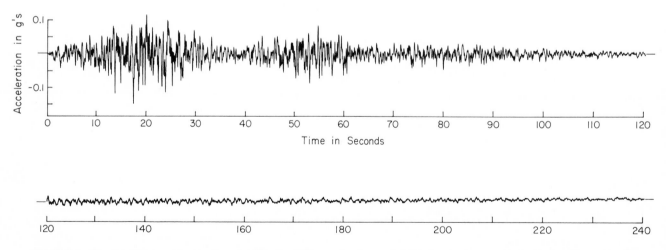

FIGURE 4   Simulated horizontal ground acceleration for 240 seconds of ground shaking at Anchorage, Alaska, during the earthquake.

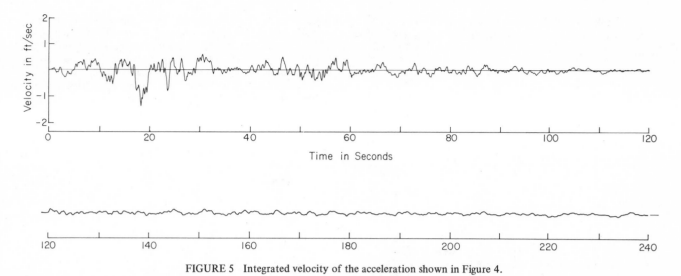

FIGURE 5   Integrated velocity of the acceleration shown in Figure 4.

different samples of the steady-state random function, would show different details and would produce statistical variations in response calculations.

SUMMARY

On the basis of a variety of facts known about the ground shaking at Anchorage, together with a knowledge of past recorded earthquake ground motions, a random function was generated that is judged to be a good estimate of the ground motion at Anchorage during the earthquake. The total duration of perceptible ground shaking is approximately 240 seconds. The strong shaking occurred during two intervals. The first and strongest shaking, with a peak acceleration of 14 percent of gravity and a duration of approximately 30 seconds, is followed by a 20-second segment

with a peak acceleration of 9 percent of gravity. Presumably these periods of shaking were caused by two major events on the causative fault. The strong shaking occurs during the first minute of motion. The last 3 minutes of motion are less strong and the acceleration decreases to a peak value of about 0.5 percent of gravity at the end.

The nature of the accelerations is such that higher frequencies (> 2 cps) are attenuated, accounting for the fact that the peak acceleration of 14 percent of gravity is not large. For lower frequencies (< 1.3 cps), the shaking is strong, comparable in intensity to the Taft, California, record of July 21, 1952, and almost as strong as the El Centro, California, record of May 18, 1940. The 60-second duration of relatively strong motion, together with the following 180 seconds of weaker motion, would, of course, make the shaking more destructive than a short earthquake of similar intensity.

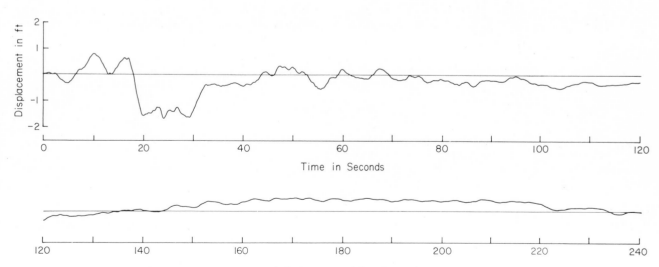

FIGURE 6   Integrated displacement of the velocity shown in Figure 5.

The reconstituted ground motion can be used to analyze the responses of structures and soils in the Anchorage area during the earthquake.

ACKNOWLEDGMENTS

We are indebted to N. C. Tsai and J. R. Born for carrying out the digital computations and to the National Science Foundation for contributing to the support of this investigation.

REFERENCES

Housner, G. W., and P. C. Jennings, 1964. Generation of artificial earthquakes. *Journal of the Engineering Mechanics Division* (American Society of Civil Engineers), 90 (February), 113–150.

Housner, G. W., and P. C. Jennings, 1970. Printout for simulated horizontal ground acceleration for 240 seconds of ground shaking at Anchorage, Alaska, during the earthquake of March 27, 1964. (Copy on file, Library, National Academy of Sciences-National Academy of Engineering, Washington, D.C.)

Hudson, D. E., and W. K. Cloud, 1973. Seismological background for engineering studies *in* The Great Alaska Earthquake of 1964: Engineering. NAS Pub. 1606. Washington: National Academy of Sciences.

Pate, Robert A. [1964]. 7 inch 33 1/3 RPM record, "Earthquake–Alaska," produced by Bob Pate, Alaskan Artifacts Enterprises [Anchorage].

RONALD F. SCOTT
CALIFORNIA INSTITUTE OF TECHNOLOGY

Behavior of Soils during the Earthquake

ABSTRACT: The adverse behavior of soils during the earthquake caused extensive damage and had the potential for causing much greater distress had the affected region been more densely populated. Large earth slides in Anchorage and subaqueous slides at Valdez and Seward damaged streets, buildings, utilities, and shoreside structures. Numerous slope and embankment failures harmed railways, highways, and particularly bridges. A variety of soil-related phenomena took place: rock avalanches and snow avalanches were observed; soil liquefaction, subsidence, and consolidation occurred; and cracks, fissures, and sand spouts developed in many places. The earthquake demonstrated once again that under these conditions the uncontrolled behavior of soils has the potential for great loss of life and extensive damage. Postearthquake studies indicate that present knowledge of the dynamic behavior of soils is not sufficient to give confidence in future earthquake-resistant design and analysis. Additional research is needed on the properties of soils in relation to earthquake hazards.

Some of the most damaging effects of the Alaska earthquake arose from the unstable behavior of certain soils. The earthquake emphasized that the undesirable response of some soils or soil states to shock or vibrations has the potential for great damage during earthquakes. This conclusion was confirmed soon afterward by the Niigata, Japan, earthquake of June 16, 1964, which caused very extensive and costly damage because of liquefaction of fine sandy soil. The behavior of soils during the Alaska earthquake has many important implications for engineers, city planners, and government officials: Large earthslides in Anchorage did much damage; underwater slides at the ports of Valdez, Seward, and Whittier, together with the water waves generated by them, destroyed port and harbor facilities and adjacent structures; rock avalanches and snow avalanches occurred in the strongly shaken area; gross movements of soft soils distorted the piers and abutments of many bridges; soil subsidence took place in many areas; and slumping and sliding developed in railway and highway fills and embankments. Many regions exhibited surface cracks, fissures, craters, and sandblows that indicated major disturbances of the soil at depth.

Detailed descriptions of the soil and geological morphology and the soil behavior in the affected area are available elsewhere; consequently, only brief summaries, with appropriate references, of these descriptions will be given here.

GEOLOGICAL AND SOIL CHARACTERISTICS

The area most affected by the earthquake comprises Prince William Sound, the Kenai Peninsula, and Kodiak Island and is a region of high mountains interrupted by steep-walled glaciated valleys and fiords (Figures 1 and 2). Rocky slopes, both above and below water, in many areas exceed 35° over substantial distances. The bedrock of the region consists of sedimentary rocks of Jurassic and late Cretaceous age. After Paleocene time, these rocks were greatly distorted and meta-

George Housner

FIGURE 1   Delta and shorefront, Whittier, Alaska. The damaged wharf and gutted oil tanks are in the foreground.

morphosed; igneous intrusions occurred during Cretaceous or Tertiary periods. Graywacke and phyllite are the predominant rocks, but unmetamorphosed sedimentary rocks occur in many areas, for example, near Anchorage and on Kodiak Island. Although largely affected by distance from the epicenter, the response of different regions to the earthquake seems to have depended, to some extent, on the local geology.

The region has been uplifted and eroded in the Tertiary and Quaternary periods. Periodic glacier advances and retreats have occurred, leaving sculptured valleys and steep-walled fiords. Deltas have built up in the fiords from glacial outwash materials. Because sediment transport was rapid, the resulting deposits are poorly consolidated. With near surface groundwater conditions and high deposition rates, the deltas in some cases may be underconsolidated from the point of view of soil mechanics. Because the deltas in many fiords form the only level ground available in areas selected for settlement, they have been used as building sites for towns, docks, and railroads. Bars or shoals in the fiords mark

the limits of glacier advance. In general, the glacial-outwash soils consist of alternate layers of silts, sands, and gravels and mixtures of these materials. Clay deposits are found locally, the most important of these in a discussion of the Alaska earthquake being the Bootlegger Cove Clay in the vicinity of Anchorage. In most areas, the soils are saturated and the water table is close to ground surface.

In the region affected by the earthquake, permafrost is not found in the sea-level soil deposits, but seasonal freezing extends to depths from 5 to 10 ft. Local variations are found because of climatic conditions, soil types, snow cover, water-table depth, and distance from a water body. At the time of the earthquake, the depth of frozen soil was close to the annual maximum, and, in some areas, thawing at the surface had barely begun. The nature of soil response to the earthquake was affected by this stiff, brittle, frozen zone.

In areas of extensive submarine soil slides, such as Valdez, Seward, and Whittier, the tide level was near the mean lower low water (MLLW) elevation on the ebb cycle at the time of the earthquake. At these locations, the change in sea level from the previous high tide was 12–13 ft; at Valdez, for example, the tide was approximately 6.2 ft below mean sea level (MSL). Thus, in the various inlets and estuaries, water levels during the earthquake were least favorable for the maintenance of the stability of soil slopes along and below the waterline.

At Anchorage, precipitation and temperature records for the winter of 1963–1964 indicate a below-normal precipitation, followed by a sharp freeze in November. Snowfall, in general, was well below normal.

The rock and soil structure in the immediate vicinity of Anchorage, Alaska, has been described in a number of papers (Cederstrom and others, 1964; Miller and Dobrovolny,

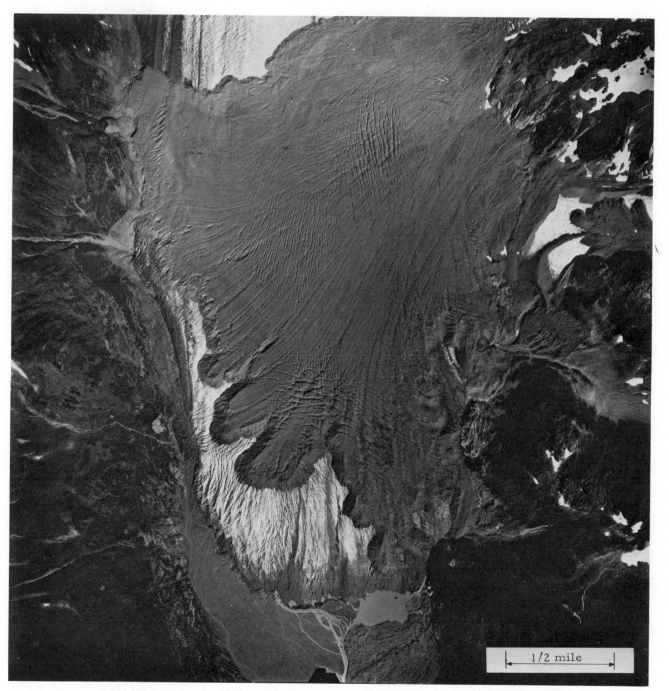

1/2 mile

Austin Post, U.S. Geological Survey

FIGURE 2   Sherman Glacier rockslide, Alaska. Photograph taken 5 years after the earthquake.

1959; Trainer and Waller, 1965). Bedrock, consisting of metamorphic rocks of pre-Cretaceous (probably Mesozoic) age, outcrops about 7 mi east of the center of Anchorage at the base of the Chugach Mountains, which are composed of these rocks. Major structures in the exposed bedrock trend approximately north–south.

In the Anchorage area, Tertiary bedrock consisting of unmetamorphosed beds of coal, shale, and sandstone, is covered to depths of several hundred feet (700–800 ft at the west power-plant well, Elmendorf A F B) by glacial and alluvial fan deposits of Pleistocene and Recent ages. Many moraine deposits are present. These soils were laid down in several periods of glaciation—the last of which covered most of the underlying material with an outwash layer of sand, gravel, or a mixture of these two varying in thickness from 10 to 60 or 70 ft. The city of Anchorage is built on this relatively dense coarse outwash soil that forms a generally level terrace 75–100 ft above M S L. Erosion by the sea along the coast and by rivers has cut into these glacial deposits to form cliffs or bluffs 50–70 ft high along the coast and adjacent to the stream channels.

The glaciated valley forming Turnagain Arm to the south and east of Anchorage is presumably filled to approximately the mean water level with similar glacial deposits and overlain by estuarine silts that form extensive mud flats. The road and railroad to Portage run along the north side of Turnagain Arm and cross regions of exposed bedrock as well as areas of estuarine, glacial, and alluvial deposits. Both routes are situated at elevations 10–50 ft above mean high water along most of the distance to Portage.

The soil profile in the Anchorage area generally consists, at the surface, of the relatively dense sandy gravel layer as deep at 100 ft in some areas, although the common depth range is 20–70 ft. This gravel layer becomes thinner to the southwest, disappearing to the northeast of the International Airport and just west of the Turnagain Heights area. The surface layer in Turnagain Heights is predominantly a fine-to-medium sand.

Under the gravel is a layered light gray silty clay containing lenses and layers of silt, sand, and sandy gravel to depths of 200–300 ft below the surface in some places. This clay, called Bootlegger Cove Clay, contains chlorite, mica, and mixed layered chlorite-montmorillonite clay minerals (Miller and Dobrovolny, 1959).

The clay layer, according to Miller and Dobrovolny (1959), outcrops along the bluffs bordering Bootlegger Cove (Turnagain area) between Chester and Ship Creeks and to the north of Ship Creek. It also is exposed on both sides of Ship Creek for a distance of about 1½ mi from the coast, making appearances along the south side of Chester Creek for ½ mi inland and along Fish Creek for about ½ mi. A thick layer of the Bootlegger Cove Clay lies under the city of Anchorage and in the Turnagain area, but it decreases in thickness toward the southeast, particularly

along Chester Creek where it disappears altogether about ½ mi east of Spenard. This clay was laid down as a rock flour in proglacial lakes or estuaries (Schmidt, 1963). Below the clay, older glacial tills are found to a depth of about 700 ft in the Anchorage area. Trainer and Waller (1965) estimate that these deposits were laid down in at least five glacial stages; the uppermost sands and gravels were deposited most recently—about 15,000 years ago. As thickness of the clay layer decreases eastward from the city, the shale bedrock underlying the till comes closer to the surface. Karlstrom (1964) believes that the clay consists of three units; a lower layer laid down in a proglacial lake, a middle layer deposited in estuaries formed in an interglacial period, and an upper layer formed in a succeeding proglacial lake.

In an analysis of the mineral content of the Bootlegger Cove Clay, Kerr and Drew (1965) report that it contains illite, chlorite, some kaolinite, fine quartz, and weathered feldspars. This differs from Miller and Dobrovolny's (1959) x-ray analysis of the clay, which showed a content of montmorillonite in the minus 2 micron fraction. Kerr and Drew point out, however, that most of the clays that they investigated were obtained from drill holes and were therefore unweathered, whereas samples used by Miller and Dobrovolny were weathered surface samples in which the original lattice minerals had altered to montmorillonite. They consider that the chlorite may also be an alteration product resulting from submarine weathering in a marine environment. They found 40–60 percent of the clay to consist of a minus 2 micron fraction, and the physical properties—water content, density, shearing strength, and thixotropy—depended on the mineral aggregate and the particle size. The mechanical behavior of the clay, its mineral content, and particle size range were similar to those of the so-called "quick" clays from Oslo, Norway, that exhibit a high degree of sensitivity to disturbance. Following the leaching theory of sensitivity of Rosenqvist (1953), Hansen (1965) has suggested that the stiffer clays accumulate in water of low salinity and more sensitive clays in waters of near-normal salinity. The present salt content of the water in the Bootlegger Cove Clay rarely exceeds 0.6 g/liter (seawater salt content is 35 g/liter). No relation was noted by Kerr and Drew (1965) between the sensitivity and the salt content of various Bootlegger Cove Clay samples. In this respect, the Anchorage clay is unlike the Norwegian marine sediments in which sensitivity is inversely proportional to the existing salt concentration of the pore water (Bjerrum, 1954; Rosenqvist, 1953). The Bootlegger Cove formation is more like the Leda Clay of Canada in which radical changes of sensitivity are observed in the absence of large changes in pore-water salt concentration (Crawford, 1961; Penner, 1963). Both the Canadian and Anchorage clays are uniformly low in salt content, whereas Norwegian clays show a wide range of salt concentration in the pore water. No definite correlation of the sensitivity of the Bootlegger Cove Clay with the mineral content of various samples was observed by Kerr and Drew (1965). The sensitivity was found to be correlated, however, with the low liquid limit and low plasticity, which is also true of the Leda Clay in Canada. Test results (Miller and Dobrovolny, 1959; Shannon & Wilson, Inc., 1964a) indicate that the Bootlegger Cove Clay has a liquid-limit water content in the range of 25–40 percent, a plastic-limit water content in the range of 18–22 percent, and a natural water content of between 20 and 25 percent, which is indicative of a clay of medium plasticity. The variation from sample to sample is caused by the content of silt present. The more sensitive clay samples have a liquid limit of about 35 percent and a plasticity index of 12 percent. The shearing strength of the clay typically decreases from a value of about 2,000 pounds per square foot (psf) at its upper surface to about 900 psf at a position 50 ft lower (at approximately MSL) and then increases again, reaching 1,200–1,300 psf at 30 ft below MSL. At some depths, the water content of the clay exceeds its liquid limit and the sensivity of the material reaches a maximum, with a remolded shearing strength as low as 40 psf.

The strength-versus-depth curves in various reports are similar to those of a normally consolidated clay that has been dried out and, consequently, overconsolidated in the upper layers. The oxidation of the upper few feet of the clay profile also points to some desiccation. The ratio of the increase in unconfined compressive shear strength with increase of effective stress in the clay below MSL is approximately 0.17 : 0.20 (Shannon & Wilson, Inc., 1964a), which is consistent with the relation for a normally consolidated clay at the plasticity index of the Bootlegger Cove Clay. The clay is therefore concluded to be normally consolidated below a depth of about MSL and to be overconsolidated above that depth. Sand and silt layers and lenses occur in the clay, and their presence is considered by Seed and Wilson (1967) to be significant in the behavior of the bluffs during the earthquake.

Where it is present, the Bootlegger Cove Clay overlies morainal till or sand and gravel layers into which most of the water wells of the area penetrate; in the absence of clay, the upper sand and gravel outwash directly overlies the geologically earlier sand and gravel moraine material. Under the sand and gravel layer, glacial till material is found up to 200 or 300 ft thick resting on bedrock.

The source of groundwater is runoff water from the mountains east of the city and infiltration from rainfall and melting snow on the ground surface. In general, groundwater flows from the mountains to the coast and moves through the more permeable soil layers. Because the clay deposit is both underlain and overlain by sand and gravel layers, available groundwater is found both above and below the clay. Springs occur in the bluffs along Cook Inlet (Miller and Dobrovolny, 1959).

As a consequence of these groundwater conditions, the pore-water pressures (static water level) in the various per-

vious layers of sand and gravel below and within the Bootlegger Cove Clay fluctuate seasonally with time delays as the water supply and withdrawals vary. The pore pressures in the sand and gravel layers within and below the Bootlegger Cove Clay could significantly affect the static and dynamic stability of all slopes and bluffs in the Anchorage area.

The mean annual temperature of Anchorage is 35.3°F; as might be expected, no permafrost is found in the winter, although, in the coarser surface materials, freezing may reach annual depths of 10 ft, with annual freezing indices ranging from 2,500- to 3,000-degree days. Extremes of 1,600- and 3,400-degree days have been recorded in a 10-year period. The thawing index is normally between 3,000- and 3,500-degree days, with extremes of 2,900- and 3,900-degree days in 10 years. At the time of the earthquake in 1964, the depth of frozen soil at Anchorage seems to have been in the range of 5–8 ft, depending on local climatic and soil conditions. Ground thawing, which usually begins at the end of March or in the first two weeks of April, had progressed, at most, to a depth of a few inches when the earthquake took place. The depth of frozen soil in the suburbs of Anchorage was greatest under highways, where the protective snow cover had been removed. Around houses and heated structures the frozen soil was thinner or nonexistent. These small changes in the prevailing depth of freeze gave rise to observable differences in the local effects of the earthquake.

Aerial photographs of the Anchorage area (Lemke, 1967, Figure 32) show evidence that slides had occurred along the bluffs in the past, but these are not known to have been associated with earthquakes. Slides had, however, occurred along the railroad tracks at Potter Hill, south of Anchorage, during previous earthquakes.

EFFECTS OF THE ALASKA EARTHQUAKE OF 1964

The main earthquake began at 5:36 p.m. AST on March 27, 1964 (03:36 GMT, March 28), had its epicenter at 61.1°N and 147.7°W (±15 km), and has been assigned a magnitude of 8.3–8.4 on the Richter scale. The depth of the focus has been estimated to be 20–50 km below the surface (U.S. Coast and Geodetic Survey, 1969). Anchorage is therefore about 80 mi distant from the epicenter in a straight line, Seward 95 mi, Portage about 45 mi, and Whittier about 35 mi distant. No seismic instrumentation was operating in the area affected by the earthquake at the time the vibrations occurred, so that no instrumental data are available on local intensity or duration of shaking. Observations by a large number of witnesses indicate, however, that the duration of perceptible shaking in the Anchorage area was unusually long, perhaps as long as 4 minutes. The record of a meter at the Whittier Power Station showed strong vibrations

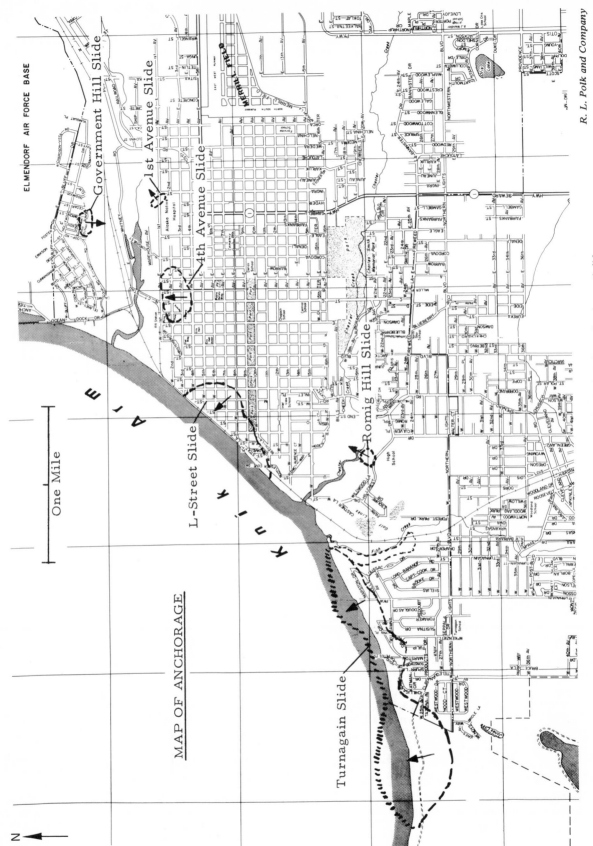

FIGURE 3 Map of city of Anchorage, showing locations of major earthslides.

R. L. Polk and Company

54

lasting several minutes (Scott, 1964). The paper "Reconstituted Ground Motion at Anchorage," by Housner and Jennings in this volume, gives the estimated intensity, duration, and frequency content of the ground motion, based on available data. The extended duration of the earthquake-generated movements seems to have had a significant effect on the behavior of the soil in the Anchorage area. The long period of strong shaking probably resulted from a related sequence of earthquake-generating ruptures, rather than by a single movement (Wyss and Brune, 1967). The main shock or sequence of shocks was followed by many aftershocks in succeeding months (USC&GS, 1969), but no significant damage resulted from these aftershocks. The major portion of the tectonic energy released in the earthquake sequence occurred during the main event or events (Press and Jackson, 1965).

SOIL BEHAVIOR

The soil responded to the earthquake vibrations in different regions in many different ways, depending on the mechanical properties of the material itself, the geometry of the ground surface and soil layers, the depth of the water table, and the intensity and duration of ground shaking. Some of the major categories of observed behavior will be briefly described in this paper, with references to those papers and reports that present the results of more detailed examinations of individual phenomena.

There was nowhere any sign of damage to a structure caused by local small-scale footing or foundation failure. All the structures affected by soil movements were in areas of large-scale ground movements caused by landslides and by slope failures.

The snow cover on the ground before the earthquake made the displacement of the surfaces of soil blocks and cracks very easy to recognize and examine on photographs. Because the upper surface of the soil was frozen to depths of as great as 10 ft, the earthquake movements caused the brittle frozen surface layers to break into slabs and blocks. Much of the observable cracking in many areas resulted from this behavior of the frozen crust.

SUBAERIAL SLIDES

The greatest damage caused by the earthquake resulted from soil slides and from the waves generated by those slides that occurred under water. Most of the damage resulting from subaerial slides took place in Anchorage and vicinity; subaqueous slides and associated waves caused extensive damage and loss of life at Valdez, Seward, and Whittier. Consequently, detailed soil-engineering investigations and studies were carried out principally in Anchorage; although uncertainties remain, the soil behavior and move-

ment mechanisms there are the best understood.

The locations of the principal earth slides that occurred in Anchorage during the earthquake are shown on Figure 3. The most spectacular landslide, involving 12.5 million yd^3 of soil, occurred at Turnagain Heights (Figures 3–6), a subdivision of Anchorage (Seed and Wilson, 1967; Shannon & Wilson, Inc., 1964a). [For comparison, the largest known earth and rock slide, whose volume was estimated at 3 billion yd^3, occurred at Sarez in the Pamirs, now Tadzhik, USSR, in 1911 (Galitzin, 1915).] The Turnagain slide was a laterally spreading landslide, a type that has been known to occur as a result of high pore pressures or of greatly reduced shearing strength in a layer or layers underlying the sliding mass. In this case, the excessive pore pressures or shear-strength reduction were probably generated by the repeated distortion of soil layers by the earthquake ground motions. The Bootlegger Cove Clay soil profile discussed here shows a minimum shearing strength at approximately MSL and also exhibits a varying, but high, sensitivity to disturbance. Consequently, the earthquake may have disturbed the clay by reducing the shearing strength of the clay and increasing the pore pressures. Alternatively, and this explanation is favored by Seed and Wilson (1967), liquefaction could have occurred first in some of the low relative-density sand layers and lenses in the clay as a result of their cyclic stressing by the earthquake vibrations. With the resulting loss of strength in these lenses, shearing would have also occurred in the adjacent clay, substantially reducing its strength.

Such spreading failures usually occur very rapidly, in minutes, and a question therefore arises about the time-sequence of movements in the Turnagain Heights slide. A number of eyewitness reports indicate that sliding at Turnagain did not begin until 1–2 minutes after ground shaking commenced. There is less unanimity as to the time at which sliding stopped. Long (1973, this volume) cites reports that the sliding stopped when the strong vibratory motions terminated. However, another paper (Hansen, 1965) remarks that sliding continued for "a full minute or more" after the earthquake ceased. From their calculations, Seed and Wilson (1967) deduce the following sequence of motions: Strong shaking commences—which results in the development of either liquefaction of sand lenses, or loss of strength in the Bootlegger Cove Clay, or both—at some distance back from the bluffs; the reduction of strength spreads until eventually, 1 or 2 minutes after the beginning of ground shaking, the bluffs fail and slide seaward; the material landward of the bluffs slides toward the sea on the liquefied and remolded layers; failure progresses inland as long as strong shaking continues. Seed and Wilson conclude therefore that the prolonged duration of strong ground motions demonstrated in the Alaska earthquake was highly significant to the nature of the soil failures that developed. If the motions had been as strong, but had lasted perhaps

Steve McCutcheon

FIGURE 4 Turnagain Heights landslide, Anchorage. Fish Creek is in the foreground.

only 45 seconds to 1 minute, they think that the failures might not have developed at all. Because of the time required for drainage of a liquefied sand zone, sliding caused by liquefaction might be expected to continue for some time after the cessation of strong ground motion. If, on the other hand, the slopes failed as the strength of a clay or other layer was exceeded, without liquefaction, sliding

should terminate with the end of shaking. It is unfortunate that circumstances preclude the resolution of this point.

Other slides in the Anchorage area are discussed and analyzed in the Shannon & Wilson, Inc. report (1964a) and by Long (this volume). Long discusses three categories of slides that were observed: rotational slumps, translatory slides, and earth flows. On some of the slides, movements

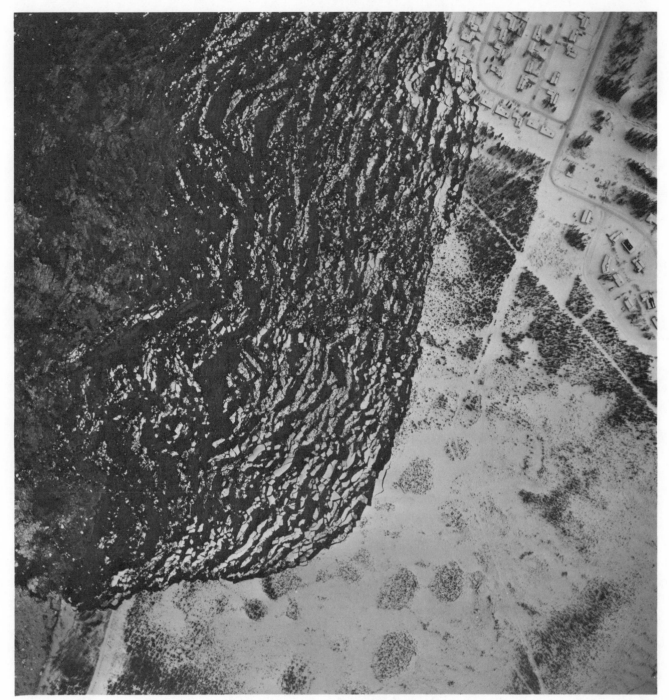

FIGURE 5   Portion of Turnagain Heights slide immediately after the earthquake.

of a few inches continued in the year following the earthquake. Of the many slides that occurred during the earthquake, all those exhibiting horizontal-translation sliding failed in soft sensitive clay or sand strata in the Bootlegger Cove Clay formation. In some places, the depth of these layers below the base of the slope resulted in some buttress-ing of the slide, thus resisting the formation of that type of failure. It was apparent that the noses or points of many steep bluffs remained stable during the earthquake, possibly because of better drainage. Long considers that shearing of the soft sensitive Bootlegger Cove Clay was primarily responsible for failure in the plane of sliding, although

FIGURE 6 Appearance of Turnagain land-slide at ground level.

George Housner

liquefaction within sand layers contributed to the failure in his opinion. He also thinks that the leaching of the clay with its influence on the clay shearing-strength sensitivity (Rosenqvist, 1953) is a process that is occurring at present as a result of seepage through the clay layers. After the sliding that occurred during this earthquake, new seepage patterns would begin, and the sensitivity of the clay in adjacent areas would then be affected, so that future earthquakes might cause sliding elsewhere. If this hypothesis is correct, the time duration of such a leaching process is important.

The presence of a frozen ground layer of varying thickness seems to have had a significant effect on the distribution of slide-related surface cracking in some areas. Long (this volume) suggests that houses in the Turnagain area behind the area of gross sliding might have been damaged differently or perhaps less had the ground been thawed at the time of the earthquake. Hansen (1965) observed that zones of weakness in the ground, such as backfilled trenches or backfills around building foundations, were particularly susceptible to cracking. Old frost cracks were reopened by the earthquake; at Turnagain Heights, the ground-surface cracks were affected by concrete curbing, streets, and garage and house foundations. Cracks were also observed at the junction of fill and existing ground material.

The Fourth Avenue (Figures 7 and 8), L Street (Figure 9) and Alaska Native Hospital slides (Shannon & Wilson, Inc., 1964a) consisted of much smaller lateral soil movements than those of the Turnagain slide. In each case, a very large mass of soil, including a part of the bluff and relatively flat slopes at the toe, moved laterally with little rotation for a distance of several feet. Because the new cliff formed be-hind the crack at the head of the slide was therefore left un-supported, it failed, causing a section behind the slide to fall down into the space provided by the lateral movement; such a subsided block is called a graben. In some areas this behavior was repeated to a diminishing extent behind the primary slide block, causing successive groups of cracks and grabens. These slopes appear to have been unstable only under the conditions imposed on them by the earthquake; that is, liquefaction was absent. Older slides are clearly visible in aerial photographs of the bluffs in the vicinity of the Native Hospital and have been discussed by Grantz and others (1964) and Hansen (1965). The slide at Government Hill in Anchorage (see Figure 10) was a rotational slide (Long, this volume). The Potter Hill slide along The Alaska Railroad is considered to have been a flow slide (Long, this volume; McCulloch and Bonilla, 1970), occurring in stratified sands that liquefied; before the earthquake, the sands had been subjected to some seepage pressures. This section of the railroad subgrade had also failed during the 1954 earthquake. At the time of the earthquake, sand issued from cracks on the surface of the bluff about 400 ft east of the edge at the Potter Hill slide. A snow slide also occurred in the Ship Creek Valley partially blocking the flow of water into the reservoir behind Ship Creek Dam for 1½ days. Although corrected in later work (Waller, 1966b), Waller and others (1965) erroneously implied that the flow in Ship Creek was reduced because the creek flowed into ground cracks caused by the earthquake. Earth slides in the Anchorage area are described in detail in Hansen (1965), Long (this volume), Seed and Wilson (1967), and Shannon & Wilson, Inc. (1964a).

Slides occurred in soils and rocks in many places that were shaken by the earthquake. A concentration of earthquake-induced slides along the southeast coast of Kodiak Island and in the neighboring offshore islands, in contrast to their scarcity elsewhere, is of particular interest (Kachadoorian and Plafker, 1967). Distribution of the slides appears to have been controlled by local morphology and structure, but may also have been related to the proximity of the area to the earthquake focal region. The maximum landslide frequency occurred in bedded rock of Tertiary age (Kachadoorian and Plafker, 1967) and seems to be related to the physical properties of the rock, which

Steve McCutcheon

FIGURE 7 Fourth Avenue landslide, Anchorage. Extensive cracking and graben intersect Fourth Avenue (top). Damage caused by ground compression at toe of slide in foreground.

FIGURE 8 Graben of Fourth Avenue land-slide as seen on Fourth Avenue.

Bureau of Land Management

contains weak materials such as clay and siltstone along which sliding can easily occur. In addition, the rocks are folded in a complex fashion and are broken by numerous faults, joints, and bedding planes. Because the material weathers easily, fairly thick accumulations of landslide-prone soil and colluvium have developed. The more rapid erosion in this kind of material has produced numerous steep-sided stream valleys that are susceptible to slope failures. It is also possible that the combination of the material properties gave rise to bigger motions or accelerations in areas underlain by Tertiary rock than in other materials. The correlation of the landslide frequency with the detailed geology in this area seems to be worth more thorough examination.

SUBAQUEOUS SLIDES

During the Alaska earthquake, subaqueous slides occurred in the low river-delta area in Valdez harbor (Coulter and Migliaccio, 1966), and submarine slides were also observed at Seward (Lemke, 1967) and Whittier (Kachadoorian, 1965). The delta and shoreline of Whittier are seen in Figure 1. Water boils, which are characteristic of submarine slides, were also observed in other parts of the Prince William Sound area.

Subaqueous slides occurred in Tokun, Charlotte, and Kushtaka lakes (Tuthill and Laird, 1966). The shores of these lakes have slopes of 10° or more in most places and an average depth of 70–120 ft. Shallower lakes, where the water was only 6 or 7 ft deep, were not subject to slides. McCulloch (1966) has studied the energy considerations involved in lake flows or slides. Lacustrine sliding occurred as far away from the epicenter as 145 mi, at Beluga Lake, 60 mi northwest of Anchorage. Lacustrine slides occurred at the east end of Kenai Lake as well as at Tazlina Lake, Beluga Lake, and Eklutna Lake and elsewhere. Long (1973, this volume) lists papers that describe these phenomena in detail.

The tide at areas of submarine failure was near the MLLW elevation on the ebb cycle, and seepage from adjacent streams and groundwater flows probably contributed excess pore pressures that caused the soil strength conditions in these subaqueous areas to deteriorate. Sliding in lakes was usually most severe near an active stream channel. Submarine sliding at Valdez began shortly after the initiation of the earthquake ground motion. The present average slope of the delta face at Valdez is 6 degrees, although slope angles of 20–30 degrees occur at some places in the upper part of the delta. Plafker and Mayo (1965) present a map showing the general distribution of the larger destructive local waves caused by subaqueous slides in Prince William Sound and part of the Kenai Peninsula. They point out that a large proportion of the casualties caused by the earthquake resulted from the combination of subaqueous slides and their associated waves, and they give detailed descriptions of a number of the larger slides.

Coulter and Migliaccio (1966) summarize the geological profile and soil properties in the Valdez area and discuss the conditions and mechanics of the subaqueous slide that swept away a section of the Valdez waterfront. At the post-earthquake waterfront, the subsidence of the ground is about 9 ft and decreases rapidly with distance from the waterfront. The tectonic information suggests that Valdez is approximately on the line of zero elevation change from tectonic movements; the subsidence indicated is caused almost entirely by consolidation and compaction of the

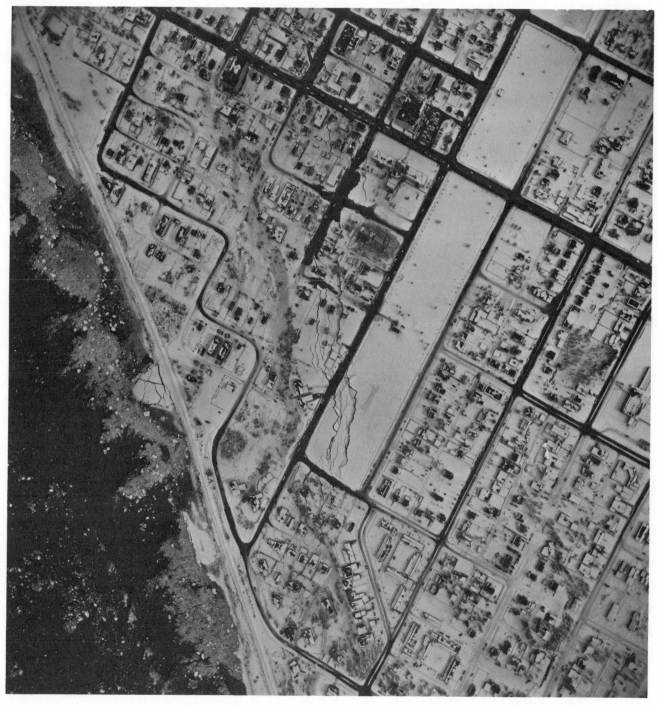

Air Photo Tech, Inc.

FIGURE 9   L Street landslide shortly after the earthquake. Cracks in the snow delineate the extent of the slide.

Steve McCutcheon

FIGURE 10   Government Hill landslide. The Government Hill School building (left foreground) was severely damaged.

underlying soil in combination with the lateral movements that followed the major slide. At the time of the earthquake, the ground at Valdez was frozen down to the water table, a depth of 4–6 ft, and this affected the development of fissures and cracks during the earthquake. Within the town, the pattern of the fissure system was complicated, as it was at Turnagain, because of the difference between frozen depths under streets that had been cleared of snow and thawed zones over pipeline sewers and foundation areas. Coulter and Migliaccio (1966) also refer to broken-ground phenomena in previous earthquakes.

The tectonic changes accompanying the earthquake will have long-term effects. The establishment of new high-water levels and sea levels has led to erosion and deposition in new areas (Kirkby and Kirkby, 1969; Stanley, 1968). In some places of submergence, erosion of cliffs that were formerly stable may lead to further slope-stability problems along shoreline bluffs.

Plafker (1969) observes that seismic vibrations triggered innumerable rockslides, avalanches, and rockfalls over an area of 100,000 mi^2 in south central Alaska. The greatest concentration of rockslides took place in the mountains encircling the epicenter, particularly in the Kenai Mountains, the Chugach Mountains north of Turnagain Arm, and the Talkeetna Mountains. Most of the rockslides involved hard sedimentary and metamorphic blocks of early Tertiary or pre-Tertiary age and, in a few cases, granitic intrusive rocks. Most of the slides occurred in remote uninhabited areas where the effects were of greater geologic and geomorphic interest than of economic interest.

Post (1967) presents a tabulation of the occurrence of earthquake-induced avalanches, all of which occurred close to glaciers, probably because glacier erosion steepens the bases of the mountains; subsequent retreat or decrease in thickness of glaciers adjacent to the mountains then exposes those mountain faces that are potentially unstable. Older rock-avalanche sites are evident in the vicinity of Anchorage. The largest of the rock avalanches, the Sherman Glacier slide, has been described by Bull and Marangunic (1967) and Plafker (1965). The extent to which the debris from the Sherman Glacier slide and other slides traversed the surface of the glacier at angles as small as ½ degree to 4 ½ degrees is shown in Figure 2; these low angles raise questions on the mechanism of a slide flow that was coherent enough to carry along some very large boulders. Shreve (1966) examined this phenomenon and suggested that the descending debris flow traps air between it and the ground or glacier surface as its angle of descent lessens. The flow then rides along on this layer of compressed, trapped air with a minimum of energy dissipation. The overall mechanism may be plausible, but its details are hard to visualize. The process by which air becomes trapped and compressed under a chaotic stream of rock fragments as the stream becomes a thin widespread layer is not clear; nor is it clear how the entrapped air can maintain its pressure under a moving mass of incoherent rock fragments without dissi-

pating through the granular material in less time than the duration of the flow. Further quantitative study of this phenomenon is necessary.

Soil and rock masses with morphological features similar to those of the slide debris on the Sherman Glacier have been observed elsewhere (Shreve, 1968), and the air-lubrication mechanism has been adduced to explain their occurrence. A region on the moon on the northeast edge of the feature Tsiolkovski, on the side of the moon facing away from the earth (Figure 11), exhibits surface features similar to those developed by the motion of the slide debris on the Sherman Glacier. Application of the air-lubrication hypothesis to the formation of this lunar area would necessitate the presence of gas during the genesis of this area. The gas may have been a transient generated volcanically or during an impact event in the lunar vacuum. Other rock avalanches during the Alaska earthquake have been described by Tuthill and Laird (1966); the air lubrication mechanism also has been suggested to account for some of their features.

Snow avalanches are common in the area, and a number

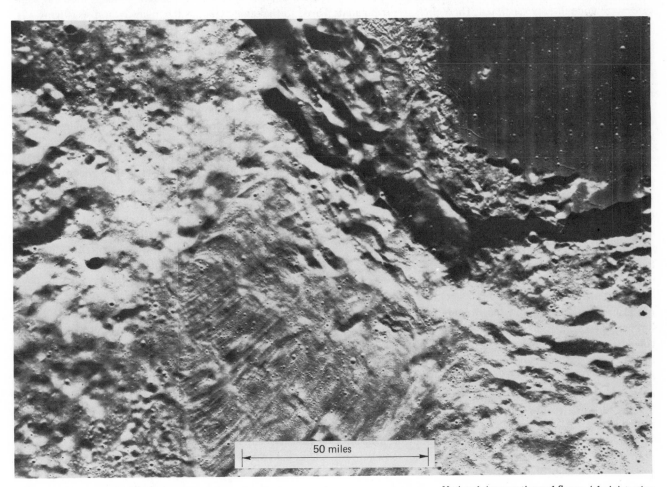

50 miles

National Aeronautics and Space Administration
FIGURE 11   Orbiter III photograph of a portion of lunar farside feature, Tsiolkovski, February 1967.

were triggered by the earthquake. Several avalanches of economic importance took place along the Anchorage–Portage road (Scott, 1964), and these were reported to have traveled further out from the toe of the slope than usual. The past winter had been one of lighter-than-normal snowfall; consequently, the presence of broken trees in some of the slides indicated that the slides had not all followed customary paths.

SOIL SUBSIDENCE AND CONSOLIDATION

Along the shores of Turnagain Arm and along the other arms and inlets of the area affected by the earthquake, considerable settlement or compaction was caused in the glacial outwash and alluvial soils by the earthquake vibrations and by tectonic movements in the basement rocks. Slumping and sliding occurred in the railroad and highway fills and embankments that had been constructed on these deposits.

During the shearing and distortion of the Bootlegger Cove Clay participating in the slide movements and possibly also of soil layers in the arms and inlets, excess pore pressures were undoubtedly generated. These pressures dissipated through drainage of the pore water after the earthquake. In all areas subject to sliding and slumping, settlements ranging from several inches to several feet occurred. These settlements continued at decreasing rates for periods that depended on the soil properties and drainage conditions. In the regions immediately behind slope failures, both lateral and vertical soil movements took place as the soil adjusted to the new stress conditions.

The decrease in pore pressures had the favorable effect of permitting the soil to consolidate and increase in strength, so that, other factors excluded, all the regions that had failed gradually increased in stability at a decreasing rate. Other factors involved in postearthquake adjustments included the drainage of surface rainfall and snowmelt into the cracks and crevices left behind the failure zones, the melting of the frozen surface layer, and the development of new erosion patterns in areas of tectonic level changes.

Sliding of zones of frozen ground was observed at various places, and settlement of the ground surface resulted both from consolidation of the underlying material aggravated by vibrations and from liquefaction as a consequence of crustal movements involving horizontal stretching of the soil surface (Long, 1973, this volume). Stretching settlement was evident landward of the Turnagain slide and behind other slides, whereas settlement from soil consolidation occurred in the Portage area and at Valdez. Settlements measured varied from 1–2 in. on shallow sand (15 ft deep) to a few feet in the Portage area on much thicker sediment.

Damage typical of that sustained by highways and bridge approaches throughout the area was evident along the Anchorage–Portage Road (Kachadoorian, 1968; Scott,

1964). The condition of the road and bridges became progressively worse closer to Portage. Up to about 10 mi from Anchorage, damage was confined to some slumping of approach fills and settling of fills away from abutments, whereas the bridges were relatively intact. Further on, large cracks were evident in the highway and in the underlying base course (frozen to a depth of several feet) as a result of the slumping of the road shoulders. At this location, most of the road bridges, which are made of reinforced concrete, supported for the most part on wooden piles, had collapsed into the streams that they crossed. In some cases, the ground movements had vibrated the bridge off the piles so that the deck fell and was impaled on the piles. The last bridge structure, about 200 ft long, at the entrance to Portage, was completely demolished (Figure 12). Failure of bridges may have resulted from liquefaction of the soils in which the bridge piers were embedded and from lateral displacements of the surface material.

The bridges on the railway, running for the most part alongside the road, were either trestle structures or consisted of steel members on wooden piles and were not damaged to the same extent as the highway bridges (Figure 12).

The effect of the earthquake on highways has been described in detail (Kachadoorian, 1968; Migliaccio, 1965). Damage to the roadways and bridges was principally caused by seismic shaking, compaction of fills and underlying sediments, lateral displacement of the roadway and bridges, fractures, landslides, avalanches, and regional tectonic subsidence (Kachadoorian, 1968). The intensity of damage was controlled primarily by the nature and depth of the soil on which the structures rested and, to a lesser extent, by the engineering characteristics of the structures themselves. Structures on bedrock were only slightly damaged, if at all, whereas those on thick sequences of alluvial sediments were slightly to severely damaged or destroyed by the shaking. Low-lying areas underlain by saturated sediments, such as the Turnagain Arm sections of the Seward–Anchorage Highway, were the most severely damaged stretches of the highway system. Along the Seward–Anchorage Highway, the sediments underlying the roadways are fine-grained, and the water table is shallow. All bridges on the Copper River Highway, except for one on bedrock, were damaged by seismic shaking. The chief cause of the damage was lateral displacement of the sediments toward a free or unrestrained face. In general, the thicker the roadway fills, the more severe was the damage.

Bridges with a relatively heavy superstructure consisting of concrete decks on wood piles were more severely damaged than those with all-wood or all-concrete decks on concrete piers. The subsidence caused both by regional tectonic effects and local soil compaction amounted to more than 13 ft in some places and caused inundation of many miles of highway by high tides. At most bridges, excessive subsi-

FIGURE 12   Destroyed road bridge, Anchorage–Portage Road near Portage, Alaska. Repairs are under way on the relatively undamaged railroad bridge.

Steve McCutcheon

dence of the approach fills caused differential displacements between the bridge and the fill. Many bridges were damaged because of the movement of their abutments toward the river as the result of partial slope failures. This kind of damage caused the partial collapse of the historic Million Dollar Bridge spanning the Copper River. Kachadoorian (1968) reports that liquefaction was responsible for both vertical and horizontal displacment of the sediments adjacent to highways.

In the area of Kodiak and the nearby islands, structural damage resulted mainly from foundation failure caused by partial liquefaction and differential settlement and cracking of unconsolidated deposits in artificial fill (Kachadoorian and Plafker, 1967). It was reported that a cannery structure split in half when it was shifted off its piling foundation; the piling was driven into beach gravel that partly liquefied during the earthquake. Local surface subsidence through compaction, flow, and sliding took place throughout the area during the earthquake. The areas of greatest subsidence were in thick, unconsolidated, saturated marine or lacustrine deposits and uncompacted man-made fills. Subsidence in some areas was accompanied by cracking of the ground and ejection of water or water-sediment mixtures.

At Homer, 2.5 ft of subsidence is thought to have resulted from consolidation of the underlying alluvium; at Snow River Valley, 18 mi north of Seward, 2–3 ft; and, in the vicinity of Portage, 4–5 ft of subsidence occurred (Grantz and others, 1964; Lemke, 1967). The vibration-induced settlements reached maximum values of 2–3 percent of the alluvial thickness. In some locations, the observed subsidence was not entirely caused by volume changes in the sediments, but developed partly from consolidation and partly as a result of lateral spreading of deposits toward creeks or river channels.

Tuthill and Laird (1966) devote a section of their paper to subsidence, which, in the Anchorage area, was about 0.6 ft maximum along the shore bluffs behind the Turnagain slide and progressively less toward the east and south. They attribute this settlement to consolidation of the unconsolidated sediments underlying the city. They noted that water levels in the sand and gravel aquifers did not rise, which indicated that compaction probably did not occur in these aquifers. They suggest that the compaction occurred in the fine sand and silt lenses in the Bootlegger Cove Clay, including those associated with the landslides. The land subsidence caused by both consolidation and tectonic movements in the Anchorage area was approximately 4 ft.

Intimately associated with settlements and subsidence in the region affected by the earthquake is the effect of the vibrations on the hydrologic regime. Waller (1966a) and Waller and others (1965) have treated this question in detail. Permanent changes in the hydrologic system at Anchorage have resulted in an apparent increase in discharge from the groundwater system and the lowering of artesian pressures. Pore pressures in the Bootlegger Cove Clay were high after the earthquake, but declined with time. Several months later, the water table in wells in which recordings were made during the earthquake was still several feet lower than the level preceding the earthquake.

Waller (1966b) gives a description of groundwater behavior over the entire area affected by the earthquake. Groundwater was drastically affected, mostly in unconsolidated aquifers, to a distance of at least 160 mi from the epicenter. The earthquake caused permanent changes in the aquifer system, and, in some places, artesian-pressure levels dropped by as much as 15 ft.

CRACKS, FISSURES, AND SANDBLOWS

A common sight during earthquakes is the ejection of sand- and silt-laden water from vents, cracks, and fissures in the ground surface. Such occurrences usually start some time after the beginning of ground motions and may continue for several minutes after the cessation of strong ground shaking. Although they have been widely noticed (Oldham, 1882), and the morphology of some events has been examined weeks or months after the earthquake, they have rarely been studied quantitatively (Housner, 1958). A variety of names has been given to the phenomena—e.g., sand spouts, sandblows, mud vents, and mud volcanoes. We refer to them here as sand spouts or sandblows.

Plafker and others (1969) found that fissured or cracked ground was widespread over an area of about 100,000 mi², reaching as far north as Fort Yukon (400 mi from the epicenter), 500 mi to the southeast to Juneau, and more than 500 mi to the west. Almost all the fissures were observed in unconsolidated sediments, particularly where the materials were saturated or where the water table was close to the surface. Fissures on deltas, outwash deposits, and beach ridges were extensive. On the Copper River Delta, fissures up to 6 ft wide and ¼ mi long were formed. Fine sand and water was ejected from many of the fissures, mainly those along the lower part of the deltas on alluvial subplains, along the shore of shallow bays, on sand dunes, and on the beach ridges. These ground fissures and sand spouts resulted in widespread minor damage to roads and underground utilities in several areas and in most of the larger communities. In general, the highways and railroads were more damaged by fissures than were the communities. Within 100 mi of the epicenter, vast quantities of sediment-laden water were ejected in most of the floodplains of the glacial fluvial valleys (Grantz and others, 1964; Waller 1966a). Waller considered a shallow water table and confinement by frost to be the requirements for the ejections, which were also commonly associated with cratering and subsidence of the unconsolidated material. Fissuring and the production of associated soil-water suspensions were also prevalent in south central Alaska (Grantz and

others, 1964; Waller, 1966b). Some fissures extended across stream floodplains, but most were on adjacent terraces parallel to the stream banks. Silt, sand, or gravel was ejected along many of the fissures and formed ridges on one or both sides as seen in the cross section in Figure 13; sometimes flows or sheets were formed extending to several feet from the fissures (Figure 14). Probably every major valley in south central Alaska showed evidence of fissures and flows. In some places, groundwater containing sand erupted to heights of about 6 ft; and in one eruption, the sand came from a sand lens about 12 ft below the surface. Enough material was removed from the ground in some locations to cause local collapse and probably general subsidence, although collapse craters generally had visible outflow channels. Some craters formed where there was no evidence of discharge, indicating either that the underlying material was compacted, or that fine material was removed by groundwater and ejected some distance from the crater. Similar observations were made in a previous Alaska earthquake (Davis, 1960). Cross sections of fissures and ejected soil are discussed by Reimnitz and Marshall (1965) and Coulter and Migliaccio (1966).

In Kodiak, several feet of subsidence occurred in some areas. It was reported that cracks formed during the earthquake ejected water as high as 6 ft. Sandblows, sand volcanoes, and cracking of the ground with sediment extrusion were observed throughout the area (Figure 14). Near Anchorage, where the water table was shallow and the overlying frozen ground was cracked by the earthquake, sandblows were produced. The ejected material in the Anchorage area shows plainly on the surface of the snow-covered ground. A motorist reported seeing sand spouts higher than his car on the road above the mouth of Chester Creek (Hansen, 1965). At Turnagain Heights, sand boils resulted from the agitation and settlement of slump blocks within the landslide. These boils built sand ridges 2–3 ft high, 3–6 ft wide, and about 100 ft long; the sand was finer grained than the adjacent outwash.

A large kidney-shaped boil near Turnagain Heights, but outside the landslide area, spread over an area of 3,000 ft² to the west of an Alaska Railroad embankment that had collapsed. On the other side of the same embankment, two other large boils appeared. Hansen (1965) thought that they may have been caused by earthquake-induced liquefaction of the underlying silty sand, which thereafter emerged at the surface when the embankment fill collapsed. Several similar, but smaller, boils also formed in the downtown area of Anchorage in the toe of the Fourth Avenue slide.

Most of the lakes in the Anchorage area, frozen at the time of the earthquake, developed distinctive patterns of peripheral ice cracks that generally extended 50–100 ft out from shore. Most of the cracks ejected water during the

FIGURE 13   Cross section through fissure and sandblow deposit.

Fred O. Jones

earthquake, and where the bottom was shallow enough, they ejected mud. Large mud fountains formed at Lake Otis, and sand boils were observed along the lower slopes of the Ship Creek Valley. In many areas, cracks opened in the soil, the largest being observed in the Portage area where they were 4–6 ft wide (Long, 1973, this volume).

Cracks were caused by earthquake movement and soil stretching in areas where lateral movements toward a free face, such as a creek or other channel, were possible. Extensive ground cracks formed in the mud flats extending north from the mouth of Ship Creek to and beyond Anchorage City Dock in an area underlain by silt, peat, muskeg, and artificial fill. Quantities of mud were extruded from large polygonal fractures in the flats northeast of the city dock. Damage was caused by cracks south of the Army Dock to the west of Ocean Dock Road (Long, 1973, this volume). An eyewitness said that at Portage water spouts continued for several minutes after seismic vibrations stopped, indicating that the sediments must have remained liquid for some time after the earthquake had ceased (Kachadoorian, 1968). Fissuring and sand boils are reported to have occurred in Forest Acres, a subdivision of Seward, and along the Snow River Valley 18 mi north of Seward (Lemke, 1967; Shannon & Wilson, Inc., 1964b).

Kachadoorian (1968) gives a very complete description of the damage to highways and roadways and includes schematic pictures of the various types of fracture that the earthquake generated in roadways. Fractures on the high-

ways were more pronounced than those on the railroad bed, although horizontal displacements were similar in both systems. The reason for the difference is that the roadway consisted of well-compacted, well-graded cohesive and frozen material, whereas the railroad ballast is a coarse, poorly graded material, unbonded by frozen soil water. The denser fill of the highway therefore fractured easily, whereas the coarse gravel of the railroad bed was not cracked.

Fractures occurred along the highway center line, where relatively thick roadway fill was underlain by fine-grained saturated sediments in swamp deposits and where the roadway was underlain by fine-grained silty sand and gravel; the water table was within 2 ft of the surface (Figure 15). Fractures occurred along the edges of almost all the highways. Normal and oblique fractures occurred on highways in a number of places. Where the highway passed over saturated fine sand and silt with an adjacent free face, a very distinct and destructive fracture system occurred as a result of the displacement of the material toward the free face. At the time of the earthquake, the roadway and ground underneath it was frozen to depths of 4–5 ft, which contributed to the clarity of many of the fractures.

Kachadoorian (1968) noticed that sand was ejected through fissures in the ground where the depth to the water table was usually less than 10 ft. The largest ejecta blanket covered the Copper River Highway over an area of at least an acre to a depth of as much as 3 ft. Kachadoorian concludes that the type of sediments on which the highway

FIGURE 14   Aerial view of sand fissures, Kodiak Island.

Fred O. Jones

rested played a major role in the amount and type of damage that the structure experienced. Highways underlain by
coarse sand and gravel were fractured substantially less than
those underlain by fine-grained sand and silt. Structures on
fine-grained sediments subsided more than those on coarse-
grained sediments. The depth of the water table is the next
most important factor controlling damage; in general, the
closer the water table is to the surface, the more damage the
highway system sustained.

Ferrians (1966) writes of permafrost that extends to
depths of 200 ft in the Copper River Basin area; it was, however, generally absent in areas in which ground cracks
formed. Permafrost is not present near large deep lakes;
consequently, ground cracks occurred locally along the
shores. Where ground cracks formed in fine-grained de-

posits, an impervious permafrost table was generally 10–20
ft below the surface.

Ground cracks can be generated by one or more of three
mechanisms: lateral extensions in regions where the soil
can move toward a free face, stresses in the horizontal
direction caused by repeated alternate compression and
extension of materials in flat-lying areas, and differential
vertical volume changes caused by the shaking and consolidation of soil materials that vary laterally in thickness
or character. For the stressed soil to crack, however, it must
possess cohesive and brittle characteristics. A dried-out fine-
grained soil will crack under these conditions; a cohesionless
sand or plastic cohesive clay may not. Over much of the
area affected by the earthquake, the necessary requirement
of brittleness was met by the frozen surface layer of soil.

It is possible, in fact, that tensile thermal stresses already existed in the frozen soil as a result of the low air temperatures prevailing before the earthquake.

A complete survey of ground cracks was made in the Martin–Bering rivers area by Tuthill and Laird (1966), who present some statistical data on their frequencies. They also give a cross section through a sandblow deposit, together with grain-size analyses of the materials sampled in different places through the cross section. All the deposits studied issued from earthquake-induced ground fractures, rather than from boils of circular symmetry. Tuthill and Laird observed that, in the earthquake-induced fountain craters, the grain size of the sediments ranged from coarse sand to medium gravel much coarser than the materials emerging from cracks. The authors conclude that the flow of water from fountains of this kind must have been greater

than that from crack vents to carry the coarser material. Most of the craters were 2–3 ft deep and 4–8 ft across. From their morphology, the craters were concluded to have been formed in less time than was required to deposit the mud-vent soil fields.

It appears likely that in level areas with the type of surface soil that does not crack during the earthquake, liquefied subsurface material will be ejected through isolated, axially symmetrical vents, forming sand blows that are essentially circular in plan form. Where the ground nature or topography is conducive to the development of surface cracks during an earthquake, liquefied soil from below will emerge through the cracks and spread laterally (Figures 13 and 14). Thus, for a given volume of liquefied subsurface soil, it seems likely that greater velocities of ejection will be achieved through circular constrictions than through

Art Kennedy

FIGURE 15 Center line crack in Seward–Anchorage Highway caused by slumping of embankment shoulders on underlying alluvium.

two-dimensional cracks. This would explain the differences in volume and grain size observed in the different surface features. In "Sandblows and Liquefaction," Scott and Zuckerman (1973, this volume) describe and discuss the mechanism of sandblows in some detail.

Several circular subsidence craters were also observed. One of these was conical, about 14 ft in diameter and 5 ft deep. It was on a strip of alluvium a few feet higher than the surrounding area and was covered by moss and a few alder shrubs that were 4–5 years old. The moss remained in a nearly normal growing position in the bottom of the cone, and no evidence could be found to indicate that water had flowed out from the depression. Other depressions were found that were 20–25 ft in diameter and about 8 ft deep; these also showed no evidence of water flows. Tuthill and Laird (1966) concluded that the subsidence craters had been formed either by the subsurface migration of fine-grained sediments away from the area of the depressions as the result of groundwater flow, or by consolidation of loosely compacted alluvium in zones perhaps formerly occupied by ice blocks.

Small mud cones, a few inches in diameter and height and several inches apart, were minor and infrequent features on top of mud-vent deposits. These cones were deposited by slowly flowing springs at the end of mud-vent deposition. Slight variation in grain size within the cones indicated that the water flow fluctuated. These mud cones may have been formed as a result of consolidation of the mud-vent material during the period immediately following the cessation of flow. The finer-grained silts or clays in the vent effluent would remain in suspension longer and would eventually settle on top of the coarser vent material. The fine sediment would then be perforated by the water driven out of the underlying coarser material as it consolidated, or as a consequence of aftershock vibrations. Thus, smaller mud vents would occur on the outwash deposits of larger sand blows or vents.

POSTEARTHQUAKE REMEDIAL MEASURES

A variety of soil drilling and testing was carried out after the earthquake in the principal area of damage to determine the soil profiles and failure conditions and to outline the requirements for remedial work (Long, 1973, this volume). These tests led to the conclusion that liquefaction of sand lenses may have played a part in the sliding of the Turnagain area. After the earthquake, an attempt was therefore made to densify any loose layers still remaining. The test took the form of setting off explosive charges located at an appropriate depth. These charges were also intended to remold the Bootlegger Cove Clay, because the relative importance of the parts played by sand-lens liquefaction and clay sensi-

tivity was uncertain. Remolding of the clay would permit it to consolidate under more or less controlled conditions.

Experiments were also carried out on electroosmotic and chemical stabilization of the clay. Stabilization by the establishment of a bulkhead of artificially frozen soil at the toe of slopes was considered. Although this was found to be feasible and might possibly have been economical, it was rejected because of associated maintenance requirements. The blasting, remolding, and electroosmotic processes were not found to be effective in the soils of the Anchorage area, and the blasting disturbed the residents. As a consequence of the stabilization studies made at the Turnagain slide, it was decided that some modifications of the slope and surface-drainage patterns, together with protection of the existing toe of the slope at the beach from erosion by waves, would be sufficient to ensure future stability of the area. Additional safety has been provided by the consolidation and strengthening of the material since the occurrence of the earthquake. In the areas of the downtown slides in Anchorage, stability has been regained by removal of soil at the toe of the slope and its replacement by compacted granular material in restraining bulkheads. The soil investigations and remedial work have been described in detail in several papers (Long, this volume; Seed and Wilson, 1967; Shannon & Wilson, Inc., 1964a, b).

SUMMARY AND CONCLUSIONS

During the Alaska earthquake, extensive damage was done by earthslides, subaqueous slides, soil subsidence and consolidation, failures of slopes and embankments, and slumping and lurching of soft soils against bridge abutments and piers. Engineers can learn a great deal from this behavior, but much remains to be learned about the dynamic behavior of soils during earthquakes. Further research is needed. The lessons to be learned from the damaging behavior of soils during the Alaska earthquake should be of particular value to city planners and government officials. Cities in seismic regions with soils whose behavior during earthquake shaking is estimated to be potentially hazardous should take appropriate steps to minimize earthquake damage.

REFERENCES

Bjerrum, Laurits, 1954. Geotechnical properties of Norwegian marine clays. *Géotechnique*, 4 (No. 2), 49–69.

Bull, Colin, and Cedomir Marangunic, 1967. The earthquake-induced slide on the Sherman Glacier, south-central Alaska, and its glaciological effects *in* Physics of snow and ice. Proceedings of the International Conference on Low Temperature Science, Sapporo, Japan, 1966, Vol. 1, Part 1. Sapporo: Institute of Low Temperature Science. p. 395–408.

Cederstrom, D. J., Frank W. Trainer, and Roger M. Waller, 1964. Geology and groundwater resources of the Anchorage area, Alaska. U.S. Geological Survey Water-Supply Paper 1773. Washington: Government Printing Office. 108 p.

Coulter, Henry W., and Ralph R. Migliaccio, 1966. Effects of the earthquake of March 27, 1964, at Valdez, Alaska. U.S. Geological Survey Professional Paper 542-C. Washington: Government Printing Office. 36 p. Also *in* The Great Alaska Earthquake of 1964: Geology. NAS Pub. 1601. Washington: National Academy of Sciences, 1971. p. 359–394.

Crawford, C. B., 1961. Engineering studies of Leda Clay soils in Canada *in* Soils in Canada. Royal Society of Canada Special Publication No. 3. Ottawa: Royal Society of Canada. p. 200–217.

Davis, T. N., 1960. Field report on the Alaska earthquakes of April 7, 1958. *Bulletin of the Seismological Society of America*, 50 (October), 489–510.

Ferrians, Oscar J., Jr., 1966. Effects of the earthquake of March 27, 1964, in the Copper River Basin area, Alaska. U.S. Geological Survey Professional Paper 543-E. Washington: Government Printing Office. 28 p. Abstract *in* The Great Alaska Earthquake of 1964: Geology. NAS Pub. 1601. Washington: National Academy of Sciences, 1971. p. 282–283.

Galitzin, B. B., 1915. Earthquake of February 18, 1911. *Comptes Rendus*, 160, 810. [Translated by O. Klotz, *Bulletin of the Seismological Society of America*, 5 (No. 4, 1915), 206–213.]

Grantz, Arthur, George Plafker, and Reuben Kachadoorian, 1964. Alaska's Good Friday earthquake, March 27, 1964: A preliminary geologic evaluation. U.S. Geological Survey Circular 491. Washington: U.S. Geological Survey. 35 p.

Hansen, Wallace R., 1965. Effects of the earthquake of March 27, 1964, at Anchorage, Alaska. U.S. Geological Survey Professional Paper 542-A. Washington: Government Printing Office. 68 p. Also *in* The Great Alaska Earthquake of 1964: Geology. NAS Pub. 1601. Washington: National Academy of Sciences, 1971. p. 289–357.

Hansen, Wallace R., Edwin B. Eckel, William E. Schaem, Robert E. Lyle, Warren George, and Genie Chance, 1966. The Alaska earthquake, March 27, 1964: Field investigations and reconstruction effort. U.S. Geological Survey Professional Paper 541. Washington: Government Printing Office. 111 p.

Housner, George W., 1958. The mechanism of sandblows. *Bulletin of the Seismological Society of America*, 48 (April), 155–161.

Kachadoorian, Reuben, 1965. Effects of the earthquake of March 27, 1964, at Whittier, Alaska. U.S. Geological Survey Professional Paper 542-B. Washington: Government Printing Office. 21 p. Also *in* The Great Alaska Earthquake of 1964: Geology. NAS Pub. 1601. Washington: National Academy of Sciences, 1971. p. 439–459.

Kachadoorian, Reuben, 1968. Effects of the earthquake of March 27, 1964, on the Alaska highway system. U.S. Geological Survey Professional Paper 545-C. Washington: Government Printing Office. 66 p. Also *in* The Great Alaska Earthquake of 1964: Geology. NAS Pub. 1601. Washington: National Academy of Sciences, 1971. p. 641–703.

Kachadoorian, Reuben, and George Plafker, 1967. Effects of the earthquake of March 27, 1964, on the communities of Kodiak and nearby islands. U.S. Geological Survey Professional Paper 542-F. Washington: Government Printing Office. 41 p. Abstract *in* The Great Alaska Earthquake of 1964: Geology. NAS Pub. 1601. Washington: National Academy of Sciences, 1971. p. 539–540.

Karlstrom, Thor N. V., 1964. Quaternary geology of the Kenai Lowland and glacial history of the Cook Inlet region, Alaska. U.S.

Geological Survey Professional Paper 443. Washington: Government Printing Office. 69 p.

Kerr, Paul F., and Isabella M. Drew, 1965. Quick clay movements, Anchorage, Alaska: A preliminary report. Air Force Cambridge Research Laboratories Scientific Report 5 (AFCRL-66-78) Bedford [Massachusetts]: U.S. Air Force, Office of Aerospace Research. 133 p.

Kirkby, M. J., and Anne V. Kirkby, 1969. Erosion and deposition on a beach raised by the 1964 earthquake, Montague Island, Alaska. U.S. Geological Survey Professional Paper 543-H. Washington: Government Printing Office. 41 p. Abstract *in* The Great Alaska Earthquake of 1964: Geology. NAS Pub. 1601. Washington: National Academy of Sciences, 1971. p. 281.

Lemke, Richard W., 1967. Effects of the earthquake of March 27, 1964, at Seward, Alaska. U.S. Geological Survey Professional Paper 542-E. Washington: Government Printing Office. 43 p. Also *in* The Great Alaska Earthquake of 1964: Geology. NAS Pub. 1601. Washington: National Academy of Sciences, 1971. p. 395–437.

Long, Erwin L., 1973. Earth slides and related soil phenomena *in* The Great Alaska Earthquake of 1964: Engineering. NAS Pub. 1606. Washington: National Academy of Sciences.

McCulloch, David S., 1966. Slide-induced waves, seiching, and ground fracturing caused by the earthquake of March 27, 1964, at Kenai Lake, Alaska. U.S. Geological Survey Professional Paper 543-A. Washington: Government Printing Office. 41 p. Also *in* The Great Alaska Earthquake of 1964: Hydrology. NAS Pub. 1603. Washington: National Academy of Sciences, 1968. p. 47–81.

McCulloch, David S., and Manuel G. Bonilla, 1970. Effects of the earthquake of March 27, 1964, on The Alaska Railroad. U.S. Geological Survey Professional Paper 545-D. Washington: Government Printing Office. 161 p. Abridged *in* The Great Alaska Earthquake of 1964: Geology. NAS Pub. 1601. Washington: National Academy of Sciences, 1971. p. 543–640.

Migliaccio, Ralph R., 1965. Earthquake damage to highways in the Valdez district, Alaska *in* Highway Research Record Number 91: Road Crown, Testing, Compaction, Soil Bitumen; The Alaska Earthquake. 7 reports. Highway Research Board, National Academy of Sciences–National Research Council. NAS Pub. 1307. Washington: National Academy of Sciences. p. 64–72.

Miller, Robert D., and Ernest Dobrovolny, 1959. Surficial geology of Anchorage and vicinity, Alaska. U.S. Geological Survey Bulletin 1093. Washington: Government Printing Office. 128 p.

Oldham, Thomas A., 1882. The Cachar earthquake of 10 January 1869. R. D. Oldham, editor. *Memoirs of Geological Survey of India* [Calcutta: Office of the Superintendent of Government Printing], 19 (Part 1), 1–98.

Penner, E., 1963. Sensitivity in Leda Clay. *Nature*, 197 (January 26), 347–348.

Plafker, George [1965]. Sherman Glacier rockslide avalanche triggered by the Alaska earthquake of March 27, 1964 (Abstract). Menlo Park, California: U.S. Geological Survey. 2 p.

Plafker, George, 1969. Tectonics of the March 27, 1964, Alaska earthquake. U.S. Geological Survey Professional Paper 543-I. Washington: Government Printing Office. 74 p. Also *in* The Great Alaska Earthquake of 1964: Geology. NAS Pub. 1601. Washington: National Academy of Sciences, 1971. p. 47–122.

Plafker, George, Reuben Kachadoorian, Edwin B. Eckel, and Lawrence R. Mayo, 1969. Effects of the earthquake of March 27, 1964, on various communities. U.S. Geological Survey Professional Paper 542-G. Washington: Government Printing Office. 50 p. Also *in* The Great Alaska Earthquake of 1964:

Geology. NAS Pub. 1601. Washington: National Academy of Sciences, 1971. p. 489–538.

Plafker, George, and Lawrence R. Mayo, 1965. Tectonic deformation, subaqueous slides, and destructive waves associated with the Alaskan March 27, 1964, earthquake: An interim geologic evaluation. U.S. Geological Survey Open-File Report. Menlo Park, California: U.S. Geological Survey. 34 p.

Post, Austin, 1967. Effects of the March 1964 Alaska earthquake on glaciers. U.S. Geological Survey Professional Paper 544-D. Washington: Government Printing Office. 42 p. Also *in* The Great Alaska Earthquake of 1964: Hydrology. NAS Pub. 1603. Washington: National Academy of Sciences, 1968. p. 266–308.

Press, Frank, and David Jackson, 1965. Alaskan earthquake, 27 March 1964: Vertical extent of faulting and elastic strain energy release. *Science*, 147 (February 19), 867–868. Also *in* The Great Alaska Earthquake of 1964: Seismology and Geodesy. NAS Pub. 1602. Washington: National Academy of Sciences, 1972. p. 109–111.

Reimnitz, Erk, and Neil F. Marshall, 1965. Effects of the Alaska earthquake and tsunami on recent deltaic sediments. *Journal of Geophysical Research*, 70 (May 15), 2363–2376. Also *in* The Great Alaska Earthquake of 1964: Geology. NAS Pub. 1601. Washington: National Academy of Sciences, 1971. p. 265–278.

Rosenqvist, I. Th., 1953. Considerations on the sensitivity of Norwegian quick clays. *Géotechnique*, 3 (March), 195–200.

Schmidt, Ruth A. M., 1963. Pleistocene marine microfauna in the Bootlegger Cove Clay, Anchorage, Alaska. *Science*, 141 (July 26), 350–351.

Scott, R. F., 1964. Report on soil mechanics and foundation engineering aspects of the Alaskan earthquake of March 27, 1964, Appendix II, *in* Report on Analysis of Earthquake Damage to Military Construction in Alaska, 27 March 1964. Washington: Engineering Division, Directorate of Military Construction, Office, Chief of Engineers, U.S. Army, June 30. 45 p.

Seed, H. Bolton, and Stanley D. Wilson, 1967. The Turnagain Heights landslide in Anchorage, Alaska. *Journal of the Soil Mechanics and Foundations Division* (American Society of Civil Engineers), 93 (September), 325–354. Also *in* The Great Alaska Earthquake of 1964: Engineering. NAS Pub. 1606. Washington: National Academy of Sciences, 1973.

Shannon & Wilson, Inc., 1964a. Report on Anchorage area soil studies, Alaska, to U.S. Army Engineer District, Anchorage, Alaska. Seattle: Shannon & Wilson, Inc. 300 p.

Shannon & Wilson, Inc., 1964b. Report on subsurface investigation for city of Seward, Alaska, and vicinity, to U.S. Army Engineer District, Anchorage, Alaska. Seattle: Shannon & Wilson, Inc. 77 p.

Shreve, Ronald L., 1966. Sherman landslide, Alaska. *Science*, 154 (December 30), 1639–1643. Also *in* The Great Alaska Earthquake of 1964: Hydrology. NAS Pub. 1603. Washington: National Academy of Sciences, 1968. p. 395–401.

Shreve, Ronald L., 1968. The Blackhawk landslide. Geological Society of America Special Paper 108. Boulder: The Geological Society of America. 47 p.

Stanley, Kirk W., 1968. Effects of the Alaska earthquake of March 27, 1964, on shore processes and beach morphology. U.S. Geological Survey Professional Paper 543-J. Washington: Government Printing Office. 21 p. Also *in* The Great Alaska Earthquake of 1964: Geology. NAS Pub. 1601. Washington: National Academy of Sciences, 1971. p. 229–249.

Trainer, Frank W., and Roger M. Waller, 1965. Subsurface stratigraphy of glacial drift at Anchorage, Alaska, *in* Geological Survey Research 1965: Short Papers in the Geological Sciences. U.S. Geological Survey Professional Paper 525-D. Washington: Government Printing Office. p. 167–174.

Tuthill, Samuel J., and Wilson M. Laird, 1966. Geomorphic effects of the earthquake of March 27, 1964, in the Martin–Bering rivers area, Alaska. U.S. Geological Survey Professional Paper 543-B. Washington: Government Printing Office. 29 p. Abstract *in* The Great Alaska Earthquake of 1964: Geology. NAS Pub. 1601. Washington: National Academy of Sciences, 1971. p. 284.

U.S. Coast and Geodetic Survey, 1967. The Prince William Sound, Alaska, earthquake of 1964 and aftershocks. Fergus J. Wood, editor-in-chief. Volume II-A: Research studies–Engineering seismology. Washington: Government Printing Office. 392 p.

U.S. Coast and Geodetic Survey, 1969. The Prince William Sound, Alaska, earthquake of 1964 and aftershocks. Louis E. Leipold, editor-in-chief. Volume II-B,C: Research studies–seismology and marine geology. Washington: Government Printing Office. 350 p.

Waller, Roger M., 1966a. Effects of the March 1964 Alaska earthquake on the hydrology of the Anchorage area. U.S. Geological Survey Professional Paper 544-B. Washington: Government Printing Office. 18 p. Also *in* The Great Alaska Earthquake of 1964: Hydrology. NAS Pub. 1603. Washington: National Academy of Sciences, 1968. p. 82–96.

Waller, Roger M., 1966b. Effects of the March 1964 Alaska earthquake on the hydrology of south-central Alaska. U.S. Geological Survey Professional Paper 544-A. Washington: Government Printing Office. 28 p. Also *in* The Great Alaska Earthquake of 1964: Hydrology. NAS Pub. 1603. Washington: National Academy of Sciences, 1968. p. 12–39.

Waller, Roger M., Harold E. Thomas, and Robert C. Vorhis, 1965. Effects of the Good Friday earthquake on water supplies. *Journal American Water Works Association*, 57 (February), 123–131.

Wyss, Max, and James N. Brune, 1967. The Alaska earthquake of 28 March 1964: A complex multiple rupture. *Bulletin of the Seismological Society of America*, 57 (October), 1017–1023. Also *in* The Great Alaska Earthquake of 1964: Seismology and Geodesy. NAS Pub. 1602. Washington: National Academy of Sciences, 1972. p. 60–64.

H. BOLTON SEED
UNIVERSITY OF CALIFORNIA, BERKELEY

Reprinted with minor changes from
Journal of the Soil Mechanics and Foundations Division
(American Society of Civil Engineers), September 1968,
"Landslides during Earthquakes Due to Soil Liquefaction"

Landslides Caused by Soil Liquefaction

ABSTRACT: The destructive landslides caused by soil liquefaction in the Alaska earthquake were a major feature of the shock. Many engineers and building officials were surprised by the amount of movement involved and the extent of the resulting damage. However, an examination of past earthquakes reveals that counterparts of the earthquake-induced landslides in Alaska can be found in earlier earthquakes elsewhere in the world. A review of 70 such slides, occurring in 37 earthquakes, shows that they have invariably been initiated in saturated sandy soils in a loose to medium-dense condition as a result of earthquakes ranging in magnitude from 5½ to 8½ and at epicentral distances ranging from several miles to several hundred miles. Only by studying such events, paying particular attention to the significant details involved, can engineers and geologists hope to develop meaningful methods of analyzing relatively simple cases of landslides caused by soil liquefaction during earthquakes or of evaluating more complex situations on the basis of appropriate experience.

The destructive landslides caused by soil liquefaction in the Alaska earthquake were very significant engineering features of the shock. Many engineers and building officials were impressed and surprised by the amount of movement involved and the resulting damage. However, an examination of past earthquakes reveals that counterparts of the earthquake-induced landslides in Alaska can be found in earlier earthquakes elsewhere in the world. It is clear that earthquake-induced landslides caused by soil liquefaction pose a major engineering problem that should be given special attention. The present paper is a review that tries to put the problem into focus and to indicate the current state of knowledge.

In the year 373/2 B.C., during a disastrous winter night, a strange thing happened in central Greece. Helice, a great and prosperous town on the north coast of the Peloponnesus, was engulfed by the waves after being levelled by a great earthquake. Not a single soul survived.... The next day two thousand men hastened to the spot to bury the dead, but they found none, for the people of Helice had been buried under the ruins and subsequently carried to the bottom of the sea, where they now lie.

This description of the destruction of Helice by Marinatos (1960) may well record the earliest known case of a major landslide resulting from soil liquefaction induced by an earthquake. Helice was located on deltaic deposits of alluvial sand between the mouths of the Selinus and Cerynites rivers and about a mile and a half from the coast. The city is now completely covered and no trace of it exists either on the ground surface or on the bottom of the sea.

The events leading to the disappearance of Helice and all its inhabitants are not immediately clear. Undoubtedly, a general subsidence of the land area occurred during the earthquake, and this alone could have led to flooding of the city. However, both Schmidt (1875) and Marinatos (1960), who made detailed studies of the event, concluded that in addition to destruction of buildings by the ground shaking and flooding caused by land subsidence, the ground slipped toward the sea, possibly as much as half a mile. Marinatos points out that ordinarily building destruction and flooding could be expected to result in some of the dead floating to the surface, where they would have been picked up by the Achaeans for burial. Only the entrapment of the inhabitants in collapsed buildings and the presence of temporarily lique-fied and flowing soils could have resulted in no one surviving and no dead being found (Marinatos, 1960). Some evidence in support of this concept is provided by the fact that

... the phenomenon was repeated, in exactly the same place though to a lesser degree, during the earthquake of December 26, 1861.... Again the soil slipped to the northeast (toward the sea) in the following way: a crack about 8 miles long and 6 ft wide ap-

peared in the earth along the foot of the mountain. A strip of plain 325 to 425 feet wide disappeared slowly under the sea along the whole eight-mile length, while the remaining part of the plain sank about six feet and showed many minor cracks and small chasms.

A map of the area, showing the extent of cracking in the 1861 earthquake, and a drawing of a part of the plain adjacent to the coast, both prepared by Schmidt (1875), are very revealing (Figures 1 and 2). Cracking of the extent indicated must necessarily have been accompanied by lateral translation of the soil, and the presence of sand craters indicates the probable liquefaction of sand deposits at some

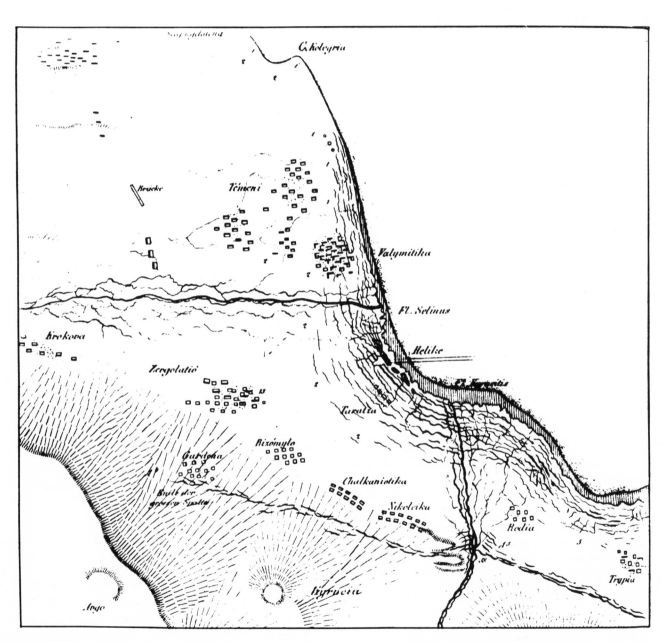

FIGURE 1 Slide area along coast and cracking of ground in vicinity of Helice caused by earthquake of 1861. After Schmidt (1875).

FIGURE 2   Sketch of area along coast after earthquake of 1861. After Schmidt (1875).

depth below the ground surface. Because the earthquake of 373 B.C. is estimated to have been about 10 times greater in intensity, the probability that landslides caused by sand liquefaction contributed to the disappearance of Helice must be considered very great.

In the following pages, we shall discuss a number of other landslides that have occurred during earthquakes due to soil liquefaction. In considering these cases, however, we should emphasize that in no phase of soil engineering is attention to detail more important than in translating experience of landslides during earthquakes. Much has been written (Shannon & Wilson, Inc., 1964; Hansen, 1965, and Geology volume), for example, of the landslides in Anchorage, Alaska, that occurred during the earthquake of March 1964. These slides are often attributed to failure of the sensitive Boot-legger Cove Clay that underlies the Anchorage area, and they are used as a dramatic example of the great vulner-ability of clay deposits to failure during earthquakes.

How different this picture would have been if the Alaska earthquake had differed in only one significant detail. Many strong earthquakes of comparable magnitude to the Alaska earthquake have caused severe ground shaking lasting for 1–1.5 minutes. The 1906 San Francisco earthquake (mag-nitude $M = 8.2$) is reported to have induced ground mo-tions lasting for only about 65 seconds. The landslides in Anchorage did not begin to develop until about 1.5–2 min-utes after the strong ground shaking started. Thus, if the duration of ground shaking in the Alaska earthquake had

been similar to that of its San Francisco predecessor of similar magnitude, the landslides probably would not have occurred at all. Strong ground shaking in the Anchorage area would have caused structural damage to buildings, and investigators would have drawn conclusions concerning the remarkable ability of slopes underlain by sensitive clay deposits to withstand earthquake effects. The significant detail that the Alaska earthquake was of particularly long duration can therefore be identified as contributing to a complete reversal in engineering experience concerning the stability of clay deposits during earthquakes. Recognition of this important detail would, however, still be an over-simplification of the actual situation. There is good evidence that the major cause of the Anchorage slides was probably liquefaction of sand layers, sand and silt seams, and lenses within the clay deposit. In spite of the great sensitivity of the clay, the chances are very high that the clay portion of the deposit would not have failed to anything like the same extent—in spite of the unusually long duration of the earth-quake ground motions—if the sand and silt layers and lenses had not first liquefied and caused it to be subjected to dis-proportionately large forces. We have here another signifi-cant detail that might well reverse completely our engineer-ing attitude toward the potential vulnerability of other clay deposits, not containing such seams and lenses, to landslides resulting from ground motions of similar intensity.

In an attempt to discern the significant details, let us now look at some of the landslides that have developed as a result of soil liquefaction during earthquakes and, by recognizing similar features in these occurrences, endeavor to draw conclusions regarding the significance of these phenomena.

PRESENT KNOWLEDGE OF SOIL LIQUEFACTION

It might be helpful first to review briefly the available knowledge of soil-liquefaction phenomena under earthquake loading conditions and the factors that influence it. During an earthquake, a soil element in an earth slope is subjected to a series of alternating shear stresses that vary in magnitude in a random fashion. In addition, a soil element under a sloping surface is subjected to an initial shear stress caused by the dead load stresses in the earth bank. Thus, depending on the relative magnitudes of the initial stress and the cyclic stresses induced by the earthquake, a soil element will be subjected to a type of loading that can be idealized as one of the forms shown in Figure 3.

If a sample of saturated sand is subjected to cyclic-loading conditions of this type, it may remain stable for a number of cycles; although pore pressures in the sample build up progressively, the saturated sand may suddenly lose all its strength. The accompanying development would be that the pore-water pressures would then equal the applied confining pressure. This complete loss of strength and the ability of the sand to undergo displacements without exhibiting resistance is known as liquefaction. An example of the liquefaction of a saturated sand under cyclic-loading conditions is shown in Figure 4. Here the sand sample, which was initially subjected to an effective confining pressure of 1 kg/cm² but no shear stresses, liquefied after about 8 cycles of a deviator stress of ±0.39 kg/cm².

Although there is much field and laboratory evidence for the liquefaction of cohesionless soils under earthquake-loading conditions, there is little evidence for similar behavior in clays. In fact, limited data appear to indicate that an increase in the clay fraction of a soil reduces the possi-

bility of liquefaction occurring. During earthquakes, the cyclic strains developed in elements of sand in the field may be not more than about 0.4 percent, whereas the strains in deposits of soft clay may be as large as 1 or 2 percent. Figures 5 and 6 show the effects of cyclic strains of these magnitudes on saturated sand and clay. In Figure 5, the application of a cyclic strain of about 0.17 percent to a sample of saturated sand—initially consolidated under a confining pressure of 1.5 kg/cm²—caused liquefaction after about 16 strain cycles (Seed and Lee, 1966). In contrast, Figure 6 shows the loss of strength of samples of San Francisco Bay mud, a slightly organic silty clay (Liquid Limit or LL = 88, Plastic Limit or PL = 43, Sensitivity = 8) after 200 strain cycles of different amplitudes (Thiers and Seed, 1968). Even 200 strain cycles with an amplitude of 2 percent caused a strength reduction of only about 5 percent. It appears therefore that liquefaction problems are not likely to develop in plastic soils.

For saturated sands, the possible development of liquefaction under cyclic loading conditions (Seed and Lee, 1966) is determined by the:

1. Magnitude of the cyclic stress or strain
2. Number of stress or strain cycles
3. Initial density
4. Confining pressure
5. Initial shear stresses acting on the sand

Figure 7 shows a typical relation between the magnitude of the cyclic stress and the number of stress cycles required to induce failure for samples of sand subjected to a confining pressure of 1 kg/cm². The larger the magnitude of the applied cyclic stresses, the fewer the number of cycles required to induce liquefaction.

The magnitude of the cyclic stresses required to induce liquefaction of a saturated sand increases rapidly with increase in initial density of the sand as illustrated by the data in Figure 8 (Lee and Seed, 1967). Although some semblance of liquefaction may be developed in relatively dense samples, it is of such a temporary nature that no significant deforma-

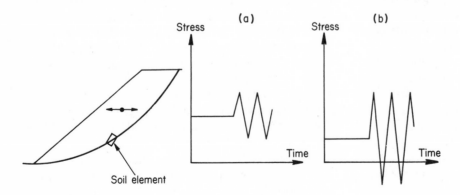

FIGURE 3 Stress conditions on soil elements under earthquake loading conditions. (a) One-directional loading with symmetrical stress pulses. (b) Two-directional loading with symmetrical stress pulses.

Test No 114
Initial void ratio = 0.87
Initial confining pressure = 2.0 kg per sq cm

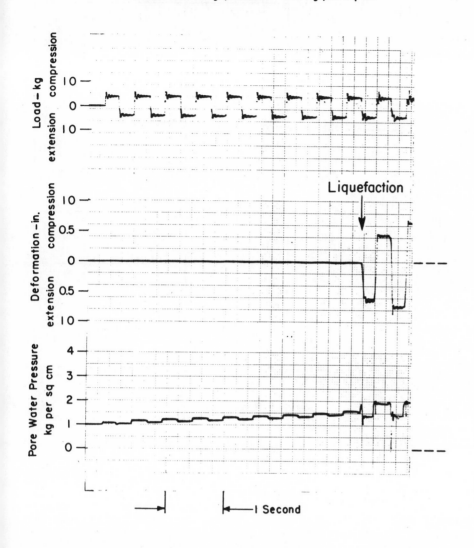

FIGURE 4   Record of a typical pulsating load test on loose sand.

tions of these materials can develop even after very large numbers of stress applications.

Other factors being equal, the higher the confining pressure on a sand, the greater the cyclic-shear stress required to induce liquefaction (Seed and Lee, 1966; Lee and Seed, 1967), as illustrated by the test data in Figure 8; thus, if the density is essentially constant, liquefaction is not likely to be initiated at abnormally great depths (e.g., 100 ft) because of the high confining pressures developed by the overburden. Liquefaction would probably develop initially above this level and possibly propagate down to great depths as a result of progressive failure.

Finally, laboratory tests show that the larger the ratio of initial shear stress to initial confining pressure acting on a horizontal surface of a soil element, the greater is the horizontal cyclic-shear stress required to induce liquefaction in

a given number of stress cycles. This result, illustrated in Figure 9, has a significant influence on the ease of liquefaction of saturated sands in the vicinity of slopes; thus, one can conclude that, other factors being equal, liquefaction will be induced more easily under level-ground conditions than in the sloping zones of a deposit.

In light of these results, let us now look at the types of materials and conditions that are known to have led to landslides resulting from soil liquefaction during earthquakes.

FLOW SLIDES

If, as a result of deformation, the pore-water pressures in a mass of cohesionless soil increase to the point where they are equal to the externally applied pressures, the soil is said

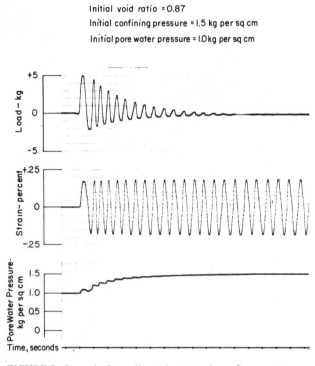

Initial void ratio = 0.87

Initial confining pressure = 1.5 kg per sq cm

Initial pore water pressure = 1.0 kg per sq cm

FIGURE 5   Record of a cyclic strain test on loose Sacramento River sand.

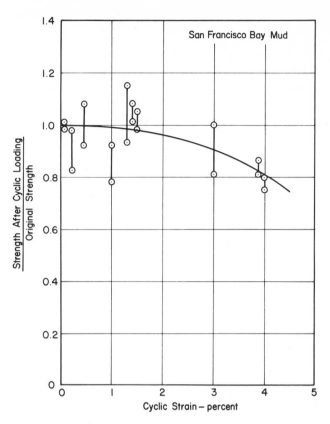

FIGURE 6   Effect of 200 uniform strain cycles on the strength of clay.

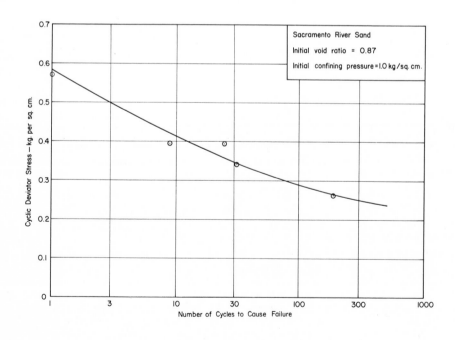

Sacramento River Sand

Initial void ratio = 0.87

Initial confining pressure = 1.0 kg/sq. cm.

FIGURE 7   Relation between cyclic stress and number of cycles required to cause failure.

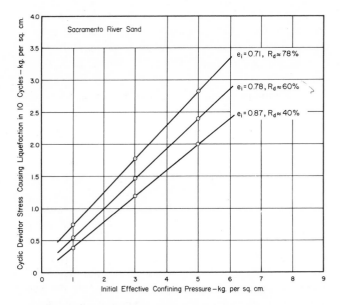

FIGURE 8 Effect of density and confining pressure on cyclic stress required to cause liquefaction.

to liquefy. Although this will normally be a temporary condition, if liquefaction occurs in a soil mass or in a zone of a soil mass that is not completely confined by adjacent deposits, the result is a lateral sliding of the mass toward the unsupported surface. If movements are extensive, the motion is termed a flow slide. However, if movements are relatively small compared to the size of the slide mass, the result is a landslide caused by liquefaction with accompanying slumping and cracking.

Slide movements caused by liquefaction but involving displacements of only limited extent have been described as follows by McCulloch and Bonilla (1967) in a review of railroad bridge damage after the 1964 Alaska earthquake:

Compression and skewing of bridges at streams produced the most dramatic demonstration of horizontal ground displacement but similar kinds of displacements were also produced by even minor topographic depressions. . . . In many cases where there was horizontal displacement there was also severe ground cracking.

The materials involved in these movements are described as ranging in composition from silt and very fine sand to gravel.

For several reasons, including those following, a slide caused by soil liquefaction may not result in deformations large enough for it to be called a flow slide:

1. In many cases, a liquefied zone may not extend all the way to a free surface; thus, sliding occurs partly through liquefied soil and partly through nonliquefied soil. In such cases, the strength of the nonliquefied soil may be sufficient to prevent sliding when the inertia forces caused by earthquake ground motions have stopped.

2. A medium-dense cohesionless soil may exhibit liquefaction over a small deformation range, but stiffen rapidly because of a tendency for dilation and an accompanying reduction in pore-water pressures if severe deformation develops (Seed and Lee, 1966); this type of soil can undergo small movements but has a self-stabilizing effect against large movements.

3. Liquefaction can only persist as long as high pore-water pressures persist in a soil; if drainage can occur

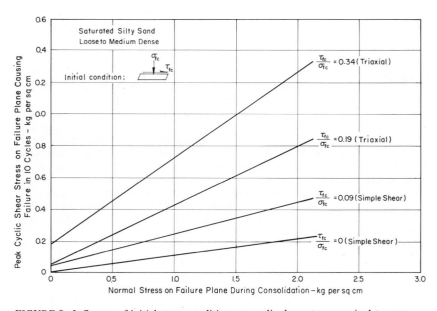

FIGURE 9 Influence of initial stress conditions on cyclic-shear stress required to cause liquefaction.

rapidly, liquefaction may persist for such a short time that large displacements are unable to develop.

On the other hand, some soils have characteristics that produce little change or lead to an increase in pore-water pressures as deformations develop. Once liquefaction occurs in these materials and the liquefied zone extends to a free surface, the extensive lateral movements characteristic of flow slides will be inevitable.

Flow slides involving extensive movements of soil masses have occurred many times as a result of the ground deformations induced by earthquakes. These slides have usually occurred in saturated sands, although a substantial number have developed in loess deposits. Besides the landslide at Helice, the earliest historical flow slides appear to be those at Fez (1755) (Lyell, 1883; Richter, 1958), and Soriano (1783) (Richter, 1958). The earliest flow slides for which a detailed account is available (Fuller, 1912) are those that occurred in the New Madrid earthquake of 1811. Descriptions of some of the better-documented flow slides are presented in the following paragraphs.

NEW MADRID EARTHQUAKE (1811)

The New Madrid (Missouri) earthquake, which occurred at 2 o'clock on the morning of December 16, 1811, caused numerous landslides along the banks of the Mississippi River. Flint (1826) describes one of these slides in the following terms:

A bursting of the earth just below the village of New Madrid arrested this mighty stream in its course and caused a reflux of its waves, by which, in a little time, a great number of boats were swept by the ascending current into the north of the bayou, carried out and left upon the dry earth,

while another observer (Fuller, 1912) reported that

as soon as he was able to look round he observed whole forests on each bank fall prostrate like soldiers grounding their arms at the word of command.

Fuller (1912) reports that "travellers reaching the Mississippi after the earthquake found the channel unrecognizable, everything being changed by the action of the shock," and Lloyd (1856), describing the experiences of another voyage, reported that "during the various shocks the banks of the Mississippi caved in by whole acres at a time."

Lyell (1849), who visited the New Madrid area some 35 years after the earthquake, noted that the river bank at that time was about a mile behind its preearthquake position over a 6-mi reach, presumably as a result of landslides at the time of the earthquake and of the erosion that had occurred in the ensuing period.

Because much of the soil in the area is loose sandy ma-

terial, and because of the prevalence of sand boils in the New Madrid area and the magnitude of the slides that occurred, it appears that they were caused primarily by the liquefaction of the saturated sand deposits by the earthquake ground motions.

In addition to sliding of the banks, Fuller's account of the earthquake also records that "many islands in the Mississippi disappeared at the time of the earthquake." Hildreth (1844) says: "The sand bars and points of islands gave way, swallowed up in the tumultuous bosom of the river." Latrobe (1836), describing the trip of the first steamer on the river, says: "The pilot, alarmed and confused, affirmed that he was lost, as he found the channel everywhere altered. . . . A large island in midchannel, which was sought by the pilot as the better alternative for anchoring, was sought in vain, having disappeared entirely." Lorenzo Dow (see p. 77, Broadhead, 1902) reports the washing away and disappearance of two islands in the New Madrid area, while Broadhead (1902) quotes, from the *St. Louis Globe-Democrat* of March 1902, an article from the papers of Aug. Warner on the disappearance of an island in the lower Mississippi, not far from Vicksburg: "In the night the earthquake came, and next morning, when the accompanying haziness disappeared, the island could no longer be seen—it had been utterly destroyed." Fuller concluded: "The disappearance of the islands, which were usually only a few feet above the water, seems to be due partly to washing and partly to the flowage of the loose incoherent, water-saturated sands of which they were composed."

KANSU EARTHQUAKE (1920)

One of the most dramatic series of flow slides in recorded history occurred during the Kansu (China) earthquake of December 16, 1920. Close and McCormick (1922) describe the events in the following terms:

Of that most remarkable series of seismic disturbances which occurred throughout the world in November and December, 1920, the most phenomenal was undoubtedly the great Kansu earthquake of the late evening of December 16. . . . Landslides that eddied like waterfalls, crevasses that swallowed houses and camel trains, and villages that were swept away under a rising sea of loose earth, were a few of the subsidiary occurrences that made the earthquake in Kansu, one of the most appalling catastrophes in history.

The area of greatest destruction, 100 by 300 miles in extent, contains ten large cities besides numerous villages. In it is the heart of the loess country . . . where the loose earth cascaded down the valleys and buried every object in its path.

It is in the loess area that the immense slides out of the terraced hills occurred, burying or carrying away villages . . . damming stream-beds and turning valleys into lakes, and accomplishing those hardly believable freaks which the natives name "the footsteps of the gods." The loss of nearly two hundred thousand lives and the total destruction of hundreds of towns and cities calls for reconstruction work on a staggering scale.

Describing the scene in one valley the authors make the following report:

> The only survivors of this valley were saved as if by a miracle—a husbandman and his two young sons, whose farmstead, instead of being buried, was caught upon the back of one of the slides, carried half a mile down the valley to where it was diverted by two streams of earth coming from other directions and, as the resultant of the two forces, was pushed another quarter of a mile up a small draw. . . . The survivors say that they felt a tremendous underground roar and felt the shock, which seemed to them to consist of a sickening swing to the north-east and a violent jerk back to the southwest, lasting half a minute. They made all ordinary efforts to save themselves, and between successive tremors following the main shock, huddled back into their homes to await the morning.
>
> Not until day dawned and they crawled out to find neighboring villages obliterated, farm lands carried away or buried, streams blocked and hills of earth towering above their compounds did they apprehend that the "hills had walked."
>
> It was in this Valley of the Dead that the most arresting freak of the cataclysm occurred. Two sections of the ancient, well-packed highway, accompanied by the tall trees which bordered it, were cut from the line of the road following the side-hill, swept hundreds of yards over the stream bed, and set, intact, upon an angle on top of the heap of loose loess.

In another valley:

> Our route through this larger valley led us past three lakes formed through the blocking of the stream by five enormous slides. . . . Some of the scooped-out places left by these slides were half a mile in width at the mouth, extending back into the hills for a mile and furnished enough dirt to cover several square miles of valley floor. . . . In each case the earth which came down bore the appearance of having shaken loose, clod from clod and grain from grain, and then cascaded like water forming vortices, swirls and all the convulsions into which a torrent might shape itself. . . . Two slides . . . coming from the sides of the valley buried a village of several hundred persons. . . .

The condition of the loess deposits at the time of this earthquake is not known, but it is clear that liquefaction occurred, if not from the development of pore-water pressures, then presumably from the development of pore-air pressures.

CHAIT EARTHQUAKE (1949)

A very similar series of events occurred under similar conditions in the Chait (USSR) earthquake ($M = 7.5$) on July 10, 1949. Extensive flow slides developed in loess deposits along the upper and middle reaches of the Surchob River and Yasman River valleys. Gubin (1960) reports that a large number of earth flows rolled down the mountain-sides, completely burying 21 villages in the Yasman River valley, eight on the right bank of the Surchob River and four more in the Obi-Kabud River valley. Figure 10 shows the extent of the flow slide areas.

A view of the earth flow that buried the village of Chait

in the Yasman River valley is shown in Figure 11. According to Gubin the slides occurred on steep mountain slopes covered with thick loess deposits that had been subjected to heavy rainfall before the earthquake. The slide material moved rapidly, and in the Yasman River valley the flow debris completely covered the bottom of the valley, forming an obstruction about 20 km long, somewhat more than 1 km wide and "several tens of meters deep."

Similar slides, but on a smaller scale, are also reported to have occurred during the earthquakes of Karatag in 1907, Chuyanchinsk in 1907, Garm in 1941, Faizabad in 1943, and Yasman in 1949 (Gubin, 1960). In most of these earthquakes, also, the loess deposits had been wetted by heavy rains preceding the earthquake.

SAN FRANCISCO (1957)

Although the preceding examples are of extensive flow slides that developed during major earthquakes, flow slides may also be induced on a smaller scale during relatively small earthquakes. This phenomenon is evidenced by the slides that occurred along the highway bordering Lake Merced in San Francisco during an earthquake of magnitude 5.3 in 1957. The highway was constructed on several feet of fill overlying a saturated loose-sand deposit; sections of the highway were carried some distance into the lake, illustrating the large lateral translations characteristic of flow slides (Figure 12).

CHILEAN EARTHQUAKE (1960)

During the Chilean earthquake of 1960, extensive failures of quay walls occurred at Puerto Montt (Duke and Leeds, 1963) as a result of liquefaction of the saturated cohesionless soils, with which they were backfilled, and resulting flow slides. Over a length of 2,000 ft, the land along the coast flowed into the sea, carrying the retaining structures with it. Quay walls, consisting typically of 16-ft reinforced-concrete sections constructed on 35 ft of high soil-filled concrete caissons, overturned completely over a length of about 900 ft; over another section 700 ft long, the reinforced-concrete upper sections overturned completely, whereas the lower caisson section tilted outwards. The fill behind the walls disappeared into the bay (Figure 13).

ALASKA EARTHQUAKE (1964)

An extensive landslide very similar to that which developed near Helice in 1861 occurred at Valdez during the Alaska earthquake of 1964 (Coulter and Migliaccio, 1966, and Geology volume). The town was located on a delta composed of silt, fine sand, and gravel, with the silt and fine sand occurring as beds and stringers within the coarser sand and

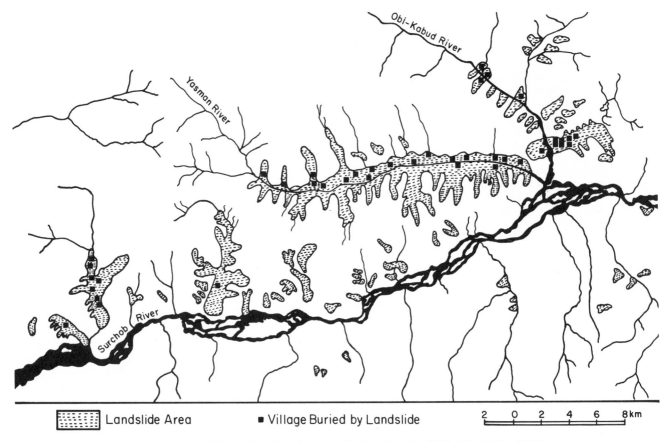

FIGURE 10   Landslides in loess deposits during Chait earthquake, 1949. After Gubin (1960).

FIGURE 11   Flow-slide debris in Yasman River valley. After Gubin (1960).

FIGURE 12   Flow slides near Lake Merced during the San Francisco earthquake of 1957.

FIGURE 13   Flow slide of backfill material during Chilean earthquake of 1960.

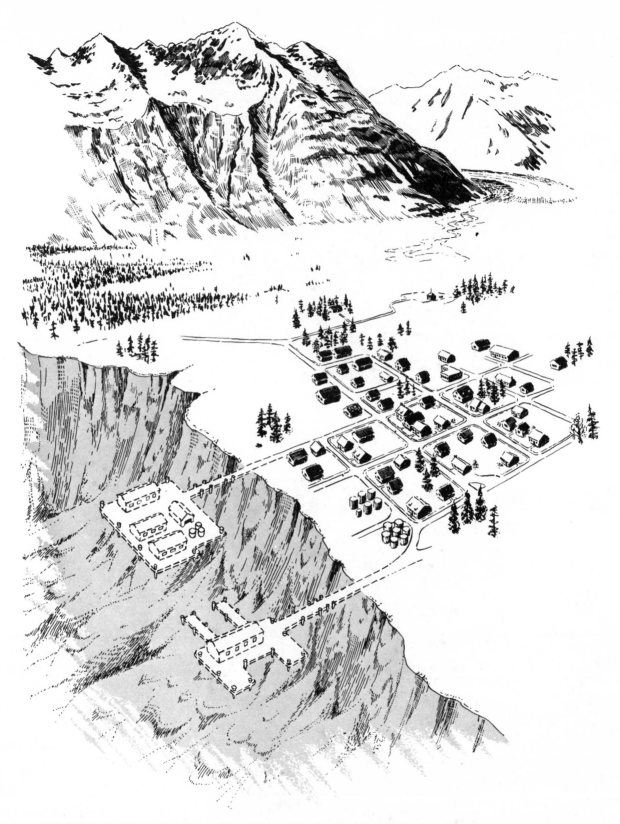

FIGURE 14   Artist's concept of flow slide at Valdez, 1964. Sketch by David Laneville, Alaska Department of Highways.

gravel deposit. The standard penetration resistance varied between about 7 and 25 blows per foot.

During the earthquake ($M = 8.4$ at an epicentral distance of about 40 mi), liquefaction of this deposit resulted in a slide, involving approximately 98 million yd³ of material, which extended inland about 500 ft and destroyed the harbor facilities and nearshore installations (Figure 14). A plan of the city is shown in Figure 15, and profiles through the slide area are shown in Figure 16. In some sections a depth of as much as 200 ft of soil was involved in the sliding, and it moved several thousand feet out into the fiord. Coulter and Migliaccio (1966) report:

The slide occurred so rapidly and with such violence that eye-witnesses on the shore were overwhelmed. Many of them have very little recollection of what actually occurred directly beneath their feet. The SS *Chena*, a converted liberty ship some 400 ft long, was discharging freight at the Valdez dock when the quake struck. The *Chena* first rose about 20 to 30 ft, then bottomed, rose, bottomed, shot forward, bottomed again and was lifted clear. . . . As the *Chena* was rising, the Valdez dock was in violent motion. Within seconds of the first tremors, the dock broke in two and the warehouses flipped forward and vanished into an extremely turbulent sea. *Chena* crew-

men watched men, women and children on the dock struggling desperately to get off or to find something to hold on to. None had time to escape. . . . The slide and its concomitant waves were responsible for the loss of 30 lives.

During the slide, approximately 500 ft were lost off the end of the north dock. The ship berths on the north and the west face of this dock each measured 325 ft. The dock held six large buildings, each approximately 50 ft wide, having an aggregate length of nearly 700 ft, and numerous smaller sheds, platforms and related structures. Almost 400 ft were lost off the end of the south dock, including a berth at the west face 200 ft long. The dock held one large building 200 by 50 feet, one smaller building and an extensive bank of freezer units. . . . A 500-foot L-shaped bulkhead between the two docks and 900 linear feet of floats in the small boat harbor were also destroyed.

Accompanying the coastal landslide was a lateral movement of land toward the shore, extending as much as 3,600 ft behind the coastline. In this zone, a general settlement resulting from soil compaction and extensive fissuring of the ground caused damage to many buildings and destruction of the sewer and water-supply systems. Large fissures were observed opening and closing along the streets. The spurting of water and suspended silt and sand from many

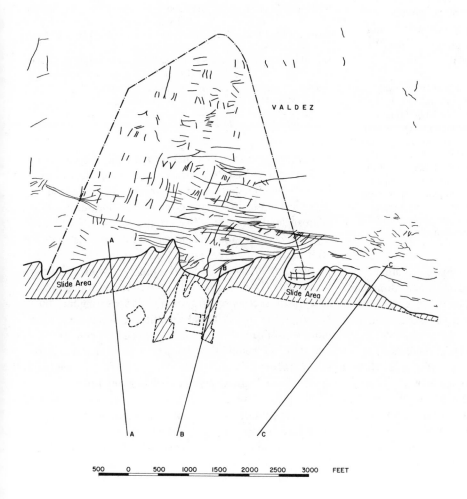

FIGURE 15 Map showing slide area and ground cracking at Valdez, Alaska. After Coulter and Migliaccio (1966).

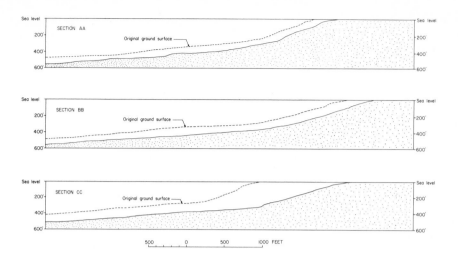

SECTION AA

Sea level

Original ground surface

SECTION BB

Sea level

Original ground surface

SECTION CC

Sea level

Original ground surface

500   0   500   1000 FEET

FIGURE 16   Profiles though slide area at Valdez, Alaska. After Coulter and Migliaccio (1966).

of the fissures indicates that the soil well behind the coast-line was also liquefied to some extent.

The positions of the ground cracks and fissures are shown in Figure 15. Measurements of the separations across fissures along Alaska Avenue from the waterfront to the east end of the town totaled more than 80 ft, whereas ground-surface settlement increased from relatively minor amounts at the east end of the town to about 9 ft near the dock area (Coulter and Migliaccio, 1966):

> The principal cause of damage to man-made structures away from the water-front was ground breakage. Approximately 40 per-cent of the homes and most of the larger commercial buildings in Valdez were seriously damaged by fissures extending under or near them. The effects to wooden buildings—the predominant type—are not readily apparent from the outside, but extensive foundation damage, which completely destroyed the structural integrity of the building, occurred in every unit intersected by fissures. The break-age of the foundations in most houses was accompanied by fractur-ing of floor joists, buckling of floors and warping and cracking of interior walls. In many houses, intersection of the foundations by fissures resulted in the pumping of large volumes of silt and sand into the cellars and crawl spaces.

Records of earthquake activity and damage at Valdez since 1898 show five previous occasions on which submarine sliding probably occurred as a result of earthquake activity (Coulter and Migliaccio, 1966). These occasions are listed in Table 1.

Slides very similar to the one at Valdez also occurred at Seward and Kenai Lake during the Alaska earthquake. The slide at Seward (Lemke, 1967, and Geology volume; Shannon, 1966), involving about 4,000 ft of shoreline, is illustrated by Figures 17 and 18, which show the dock area before and after the earthquake. The boat harbors, docks, and portions of the old shoreline completely disappeared, and railroad tracks are seen to be running directly into the water where dock facilities once stood. The slide also car-

TABLE 1   Submarine Sliding Between 1898 and 1964 at Valdez

Date of Earthquake	Observed Effect
September 3, 1899	Indications of increased depth to harbor bottom
February 14, 1908	Submarine cable breaks (Tarr and Martin, 1912)
September 21, 1911	Submarine cable breaks (Tarr and Martin, 1912)
January 31, 1912	Submarine cable breaks
February 23, 1925	Part of dock collapsed

ried away warehouses and fuel-storage tanks (Figure 18).

Seward, like Valdez, is located on a deltaic deposit of loose to medium-dense sand and gravel containing sand layers and lenses. Along the coast, the ground surface sloped at an angle of about 15°–20° into the bay. The slide move-ment in the waterfront area began about 30–45 seconds after the start of violent ground shaking, but was probably preceded by offshore sliding of submarine deposits. Eyewit-nesses state (Lemke, 1967) that the slide developed progres-sively, with successive strips of land disappearing into the bay as long as the earthquake continued. When the ground motions stopped, the slide had regressed between 50 and 500 ft inland; behind the slide scarp, the ground was intri-cately fractured for distances of 100–800 ft. The maximum depth of soil displaced by sliding was about 120 ft.

The progressive nature of the slide movements at Seward is of special interest in evaluating the mechanics of land-slide development caused by liquefaction. Because the stresses required to cause liquefaction of a saturated sand increase with the confining pressure, the extent of liquefac-tion of a deposit during an earthquake could be expected to

FIGURE 17   Shoreline at Seward before the Alaska earthquake of 1964.

be limited to a depth of about 50 ft, and a flow slide might initially involve only a limited depth of soil. Once such a layer had slid away, however, the reduction in confining pressure would permit liquefaction of the underlying layer, and this procedure could repeat progressively during an earthquake. Although there is some basis for expecting landslides caused by liquefaction to develop progressively, the slide at Seward would appear to be the first case where such a process has been definitely reported.

A detailed description of the slides at Kenai Lake has been presented by McCulloch (1966, and Hydrology volume), who described the area as follows:

Kenai Lake lies in a narrow glacially scoured trough near the center of the Kenai Peninsula in south-central Alaska. . . . The lake is about 80 miles southwest of the calculated position of the epicenter of the 1964 earthquake. The lake is about 23 miles long and averages 1 1/3 miles wide . . . the steep rock walls on either side reach altitudes of 3000 to 4000 ft. Deltas have been built up by creeks flowing down

FIGURE 18   Shoreline at Seward after the Alaska earthquake of 1964.

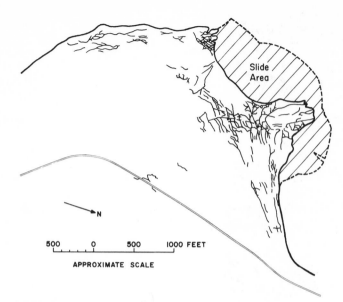

FIGURE 19   Map showing slide area and ground cracking at Lakeview Delta. After McCulloch (1966).

the steep valley walls, by rivers flowing into the eastern arm of the lake and by a river that enters the lake at the junction of the two western arms.

The earthquake triggered landslides from nine of these deltas, the largest slides being at Lakeview, Lawing, Ship Creek, and Rocky Creek. A plan of the slide area at Lakeview Delta is shown in Figure 19 and a cross section through the slide area in Figure 20 (McCulloch, 1966). The soil in the delta consists primarily of sandy gravel with sand lenses. The extensive movement of the slide debris and the associated cracking of the ground behind the slide area are again indicative of liquefaction of the deposit.

A summary of the characteristics of the four main slides is presented in Figure 21. One of the largest slides occurred where the initial slope was only about one half of that in the other delta areas, possibly because of the greater ease of soil liquefaction where initial shear stresses have lower values.

Flow slides have therefore been caused by earthquakes

ranging in magnitude from 5.3 to 8.7 and at epicentral distances ranging from zero to hundreds of miles. The types of material involved have usually been loose to medium-dense saturated sandy soils or rain-soaked loess. The details of soil density that are available show that the standard penetration resistance seems to have been less than about 20 blows per foot. The prevalence of flow slides in these materials would suggest that deposits of these types must be considered particularly vulnerable to instability during earthquakes.

The great similarity between the geologic formations and events at Valdez, Seward, and Kenai Lake during the Alaska earthquake of 1964 and those at Helice in 1861 (Figures 1, 2, 15, 17, 19) is remarkable and lends support to the belief that the loss of Helice and all its inhabitants in 373 B.C. was caused primarily by a major landslide induced by liquefaction of sandy materials during the earthquake.

SLIDES CAUSED BY LIQUEFACTION OF SAND SEAMS AND LAYERS

A secondary category of slides that might develop because of liquefaction during earthquakes is that in which the liquefaction occurs in a sand seam or thin sand layer underlying an otherwise stable mass of soil. The conditions involved in this type of slide are shown schematically in Figure 22.

The possibility of the sand seam liquefying is determined by the initial condition of the sand, by the magnitude of the cyclic stresses induced in it by the earthquake, by the initial stresses in the sand before the earthquake, by the duration of shaking, and by the possibilities for dissipation of pore-water pressures in the sand seam as they build up during an earthquake. Let us assume that the sand is unable to drain during the earthquake and that its relative density is uniform and such that liquefaction could be induced under appropriate magnitudes of cyclic stresses. Analyses of the response of earth banks to earthquake base motions indicate that the induced shear stresses are reasonably uniform along horizontal planes (Idriss and Seed, 1967). Thus the

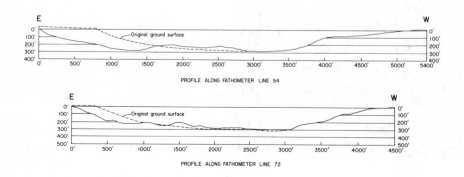

FIGURE 20   Profiles through slide area at Lakeview Delta. After McCulloch (1966).

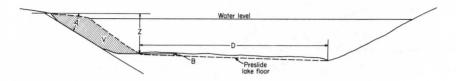

Slide	Volume (cu. yds)	Slope angle (A, in degrees)	Depth (Z, in feet)	Lake-floor slope angle (B, in degrees)	Distance of debris travel (D, in feet)
Lakeview	17,675,000	10.5	220	3	1,280
Lawing	2,171,000	20	400	2	2,100
Ship Creek	18,027,000	25	520	0	4,750
Rocky Creek	2,286,000	25	380	2.5	600

FIGURE 21 Summary of soil movements in main slide areas at Kenai Lake. After McCulloch (1966).

progress of development of liquefaction in a sand seam such as that shown in Figure 22 is likely to be influenced in large measure by the initial stresses in the seam.

Approximate values of the vertical normal stresses (σ) and horizontal shear stresses (τ) on elements of such a sand seam in a bank of soil are shown in Figure 23a. At a considerable distance behind the face of the slope the horizontal shear stress is zero. The horizontal shear stress increases, however, with increasing proximity of an element to the slope. From the point of view of development of liquefaction, the ratio τ/σ for any element is of particular interest. Values of this ratio are shown in the center section of Figure 23. The results of simple shear tests, simulating the stress conditions developed in the sand seam during an earthquake, show that the greater the ratio τ/σ before cyclic stresses are applied, the greater is the difficulty of inducing liquefaction (Figure 9).

If the sand seam is assumed to have the same characteristics as the sand used in the test program that provided the data in Figure 9, the cyclic shear stresses required to cause liquefaction of the various elements in 10 cycles of stress application will have the values shown in the lower part of Figure 23; these values correspond to the values of τ/σ for the elements shown in the center section of the figure. Conversely, if the equivalent uniform cyclic stress induced throughout the sand by the earthquake ground motions is assumed to be 500 psf, the number of cycles (N_f), required

to induce liquefaction of the various elements is also shown in the lower part of Figure 23.

From this figure, it appears that, because of the preearthquake stress conditions in some earth banks, it is more difficult to liquefy a sand seam or layer near the face of the slope than well behind the slope. In fact, it would appear that liquefaction of such a sand seam is likely to begin well behind the slope and below the crest of the slope and to progress rapidly between these zones; however, even when this liquefaction has developed, a significant portion of the seam below the surface of the slope may not yet have liquefied as a result of earthquake-induced stresses. As a consequence, lateral movement of the soil mass overlying the liquefied part of the seam would be restricted to some extent by the nonliquefied zone near the slope, and the general condition of the earth bank at this stage would be as shown in Figure 24. These considerations would suggest that the mechanics of sliding on liquefied seams might develop along the following general lines:

As liquefaction develops in the sand layer or seam, the vertically propagating shear waves from the underlying rock will be progressively damped. Ultimately, if liquefaction extends over a substantial zone behind the face of the slope, very little ground motion caused by shear wave propagation through the base would be developed in the soil above the liquefied layer; the only horizontal motions developed in this material would be those transmitted through the nonliquefied section of the sand seam near the face of the slope and ground motions transmitted through the vertical sides around the perimeter of the soil overlying the liquefied sand seam.

At this stage, a complex force pattern would develop on the soil mass adjacent to the slope, including a tendency for progressive extension of the liquefied layer as a result of stress concentrations in the nonliquefied soil. From the point of view of a landslide, however, the most critical conditions would be produced by the components of motion acting at right angles to the face of the slope. Owing to these motions, inertia forces tending to cause sliding of the soil above the liquefied sand layer might well be induced by

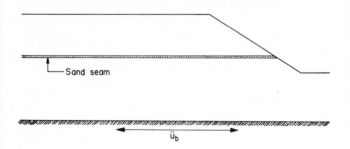

FIGURE 22 Slope underlain by saturated sand seam. $\ddot{U}_b$ is the base acceleration.

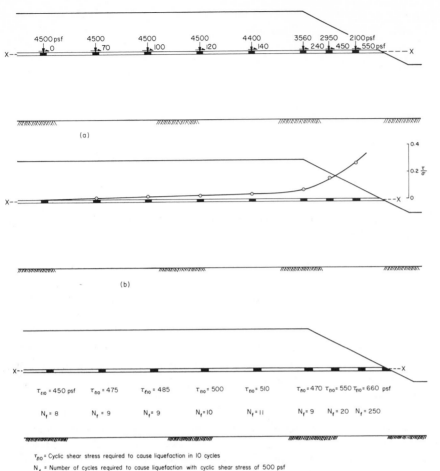

FIGURE 23 Development of liquefaction in sand seam underlying earth bank. (a) Vertical normal and horizontal shear stresses on plane XX; (b) Variation of ratio of τ/σ along plane XX; (c) cyclic stress conditions causing liquefaction.

locally generated longitudinal waves. Because the liquefied layer must necessarily terminate somewhere behind the slope, the more rigid soil adjacent to it will repeatedly hit the end of the soil mass above the liquefied layer and propagate waves through it in a horizontal direction (Figure 25). Because of the vertical components of ground motions that might also develop, it is possible that the waves generated in the upper layer could be Rayleigh waves rather than compression waves. In any case, the overall effect would be about the same.

If the waves are generated some distance behind the slope, the directions of ground accelerations caused by the longitudinal or Rayleigh waves would reverse every half wavelength (Figure 26). Furthermore, because of the relatively flat slope, there is no significant reflection of these waves at the face of the slope. Inertia forces tending to cause sliding of soil near the face of the slope could thus be generated only on a zone of soil extending about half a wavelength behind the slope.

The development of sliding might therefore be visualized

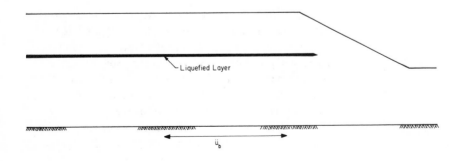

FIGURE 24 Progress of liquefaction in sand seam after period of ground shaking.

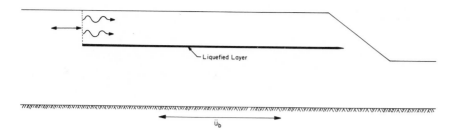

FIGURE 25 Inducement of compression waves in soil above liquefied layer.

in the following way: Liquefaction might develop in a sand seam or layer well behind a slope and extend progressively toward the face of the slope, with a nonliquefied section under the slope preventing sliding in the early stages. As the liquefied section extends, however, horizontal inertia forces of the type previously described could be developed. Ultimately, the combination of the inertia forces on a section of soil half a wavelength wide and the static lateral pressure on the back of this soil mass might become large enough to overcome the resistance provided by the nonliquefied soil under the face of the slope. And for a brief instant the soil mass will move outward. As soon as the inertia forces are reversed, however, movement will stop. A slide would thus develop as a result of a series of outward movements of a soil mass on a surface along the liquefied layer and extending through the nonliquefied section under the face of the slope. The extent of the slide mass would be determined by the configurations of the slope and the depth of the liquefied layer. Normally, it would be determined by the particular location of the half wavelength that produced maximum inertia forces on soil near the face of the slope (Figure 27). In general, the slide mass would be expected to extend a little more than half a wavelength behind the intersection of the sand seam with the face of the slope (Figure 27).

As the slide mass moved outward, downward and lateral sliding would occur on inclined failure surfaces at the back of the slide mass, resulting in a depression called a "graben"

(Figure 27). The dimensions of the graben would depend on the extent of lateral movement of the slide mass and would increase progressively with each successive displacement of the mass as the earthquake ground motions continued. Because movements of the liquefied layer would be restricted by the nonliquefied section at the outer end, however, the slide motions would cease when the ground motions stopped; they would also tend to be arrested by the stabilization of the liquefied sand as a result of the restoration of static shear stresses (Seed and Lee, 1966). Although the sliding in such cases would be induced by liquefaction of a sand seam, it would not be able to induce the extensive lateral motions characteristic of flow slides unless progressive failure or the shear displacements alone were sufficient to cause liquefaction or a substantial loss of strength of the portion of the seam near the face of the slope.

Slides of the type discussed above have occurred in a number of earthquakes. In discussing slide movements in the New Madrid earthquake of 1811, Fuller (1912) described the formation of "fissures," which consisted of narrow downfaulted blocks between parallel cracks (Figure 28). He records the existence in the New Madrid area of fissures over half a mile long, 20–30 ft wide, and as much as 15 ft deep:

In the majority of cracks of this type there was an extrusion of sand, hence the undermining cannot be due to the transfer of material to the surface through fissures in the immediate vicinity.

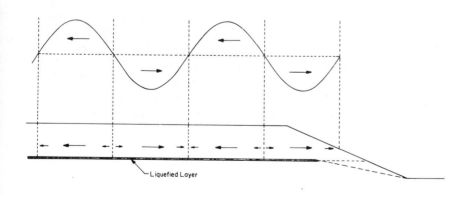

FIGURE 26 Directions of ground accelerations caused by compression waves in soil above liquefied layer.

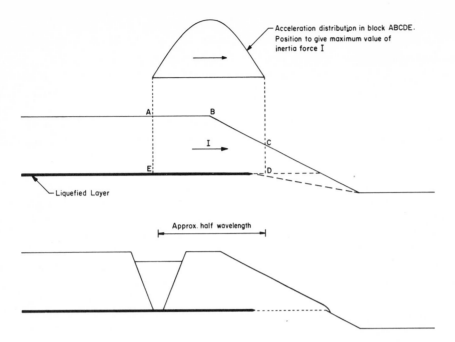

FIGURE 27   Location of slide mass overlying liquefied sand seam.

There remains the undermining by extrusion through more distant sand blows or undermining by creep of the quicksand into the rivers. From exposures in the bottom of the streams at low water it seems probable that the latter action took place to a considerable extent and it is believed that in it lies the explanation of the sinking of the blocks of the great compound fissures.

Although this mechanism is somewhat different from that previously proposed, it is remarkably similar in its essential details. Fuller (1912) presents the photograph in Figure 29 that illustrates the movement of liquefied sand during the earthquake into a crack in the overlying soil formation. Continuing this description of slides producing graben-type depressions, Fuller states:

> Skirting the edge of the bluffs in the vicinity of Reelfoot Lake, a characteristic landslide topography is almost constantly in sight from the carriage road which follows their base. . . . On climbing up the bluff the traveller sees increased confusion; sharp ridges of earth alternate with deep gashes, the whole surface locally being broken into a jumble of irregular ridges, mounds and hummocks interspersed with trench or basin-like hollows and other more irregular depressions. . . . Some of the depressions, those between parallel fissures, have the same canal-like aspect that characterizes those of the river-bottoms, but some are considerably larger, one reported by Safford being as much as 100 ft wide. Speaking of Obion County, Tennessee, Shaler says, "depressions are even now visible (1869) 100 ft deep and varying from a few feet to 100 ft wide."

These events are remarkably similar to the slides that occurred about 152 years later in Anchorage during the earthquake of March 1964. At least three major landslides (Shannon & Wilson, Inc., 1964)—the Fourth Avenue slide, the L Street slide, and the Government Hill slide—appear to have resulted from liquefaction of sand layers and the consequent formation of grabens about 100 ft wide and 15–20 ft deep. An aerial view of the Government Hill slide is shown in Figure 30 and the damage to a school building that lay across the graben is shown in Figure 31.

In the L Street slide area, a landmass about 5,000 ft long and about 1,200 ft wide moved laterally about 14 ft, resulting in the formation of a graben around the periphery of the slide. A view of the graben, which was about 10 ft deep and 100 ft wide, where it crossed a field is shown in Figure 32.

Cross sections through the slide area showing the soil conditions are given in Figures 33 and 34. The slide is believed to have resulted from liquefaction of the sand layer at about elevation 45 ft. For the section shown in Figure 33, the slide surface probably extended along the surface of the thin sand layer until it pinched out near the bluff line and then ran through the medium-stiff clay to the ground surface. For the section shown in Figure 34, the slide surface probably extended along the liquefied sand at elevation 45

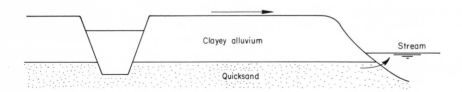

FIGURE 28   Fuller's concept of mechanics of graben formation in New Madrid earthquake of 1811.

FIGURE 29 Earthquake fissure filled with intruded sand during New Madrid earthquake of 1811. After Fuller (1912).

and, when this layer pinched out, ran along the boundary between the sand and gravel and the soft clay.

One of the prime reasons for the belief that sliding occurred in liquefied sand layers, in addition to their presence at the apparent elevation of the slide surface, is the fact that the slide movements stopped as soon as the earthquake ground motions ceased. If sliding had taken place in the soft sensitive clay, the loss of strength accompanying large displacements would have been so great that the slide mass would have shown continued instability even after the earthquake forces had ceased. Liquefied sand can stabilize quickly, however, as a result of drainage or reestablishment of static load conditions after an earthquake.

Similar movements occurred in the Fourth Avenue slide area. Here a slide mass about 1,600 ft long and 900 ft wide moved laterally about 15 ft. A cross section through the

slide is shown in Figure 35. Again a layer of saturated sand was found to exist at the apparent elevation (elevation 45–50) of the slide surface, and slide movements stopped as soon as the earthquake ground motions had abated. A sample recovered from a borehole behind the slide area showed a juxtaposition of sand and clay that could only have developed if the sand had been in a liquefied condition; this circumstance lends credence to the hypothesis that liquefaction of the sand extended well behind the bluff line.

In the slide sections shown in Figures 34 and 35, the graben is located a little more than 600 ft behind the intersection of the main slide surface with the face of the slope. For the material above the slide surface, the estimated wavelength for compression waves is about 1,200 ft, which lends some support to the hypothesis for the mechanism of slide development previously discussed. The position of the graben in Figure 33 may have been influenced by the widely different characteristics of the soil layers above the slide surface in this case.

SLIDES CAUSED BY LIQUEFACTION OF SAND LENSES

One of the most dramatic events of the Alaska earthquake of 1964 was the enormous landslide along the coastline in the Turnagain Heights area of Anchorage (Seed and Wilson, 1967, and this volume) (Figure 36). The coastline in this area was marked by bluffs some 70 ft high, sloping at about 1.5 : 1 down to the inlet. The slide extended about 8,500 ft from west to east along the bluff line, and retrogressed inland a distance of about 1,200 ft at its west end and about 600 ft at its east end. The total area within the slide zone was thus about 130 acres.

Within the slide area, the original ground surface was completely devastated by displacements that broke the ground into a complex system of ridges and depressions, producing an extremely irregular and hummocky surface. In the depressed areas between the ridges, the ground dropped an average of about 35 ft during the sliding.

Lateral movement of the soil mass during the sliding was extensive. The material from the original bluff line moved out into the bay as much as 2,000 ft in some places. The ground at the west end of the slide area was undeveloped, but that at the east end had been developed as a residential area. About 75 houses at the east end of the slide were destroyed.

Eyewitness accounts indicate that the sliding began about 2 minutes after the start of the earthquake and continued to some extent after the earthquake-induced ground motions had ceased.

The soil conditions in the east end of the slide zone are shown in Figure 37. In general, the Turnagain area (surface

FIGURE 30 Government Hill slide, Anchorage, during Alaska earthquake of 1964.

U.S. Army

elevation 70) is covered by a surface layer of sand and gravel that varies in thickness from 15–20 ft at the east end of the slide area to about 5–10 ft at the west end. The sand and gravel is underlain by a deep bed of Bootlegger Cove Clay, about 100–150 ft thick. This soil is a sensitive marine deposit of silty clay with a shear strength decreasing from about 1 ton/ft² at its surface (elevation approximately 50) to about 0.45 ton/ft² at elevation 0, and then increasing to about 0.6 ton/ft² at elevation –30; its sensitivity varies between about 5 and 30.

The clay deposit contains numerous lenses of silt and fine sand, particularly near the surface on which sliding oc-

FIGURE 31 Damage to school building in graben area of Government Hill slide.

FIGURE 32   View of graben behind L Street slide area, Anchorage.

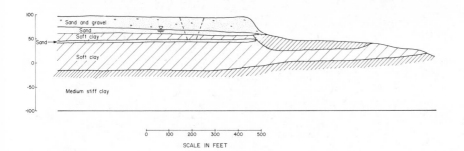

FIGURE 33   Cross section through south end of L Street slide area, Anchorage, Alaska. After Shannon & Wilson, Inc. (1964).

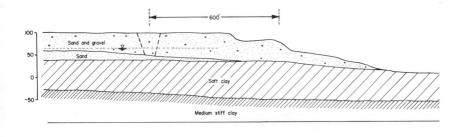

FIGURE 34   Cross section through north end of L Street slide area, Anchorage, Alaska. After Shannon & Wilson, Inc. (1964).

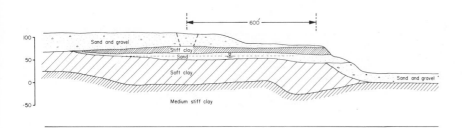

FIGURE 35   Cross section through Fourth Avenue slide area, Anchorage, Alaska. After Shannon & Wilson, Inc. (1964).

FIGURE 36   Turnagain Heights slide area, Anchorage (1964).

curred. These lenses varied in thickness from a fraction of an inch to several feet. Below the sliding surface, sand lenses were very thin and were encountered only occasionally.

To investigate the behavior of sand lenses embedded in were conducted on representative samples of the sand and clay to determine, for each of these materials, the relation

between the magnitudes of the cyclic stress and the number of cycles required to cause failure of the clay or liquefaction of the sand. The results of these tests are shown in the companion paper by Seed and Wilson (1967). In addition, a response analysis was conducted to determine the stresses and strains likely to be induced during the earthquake in the

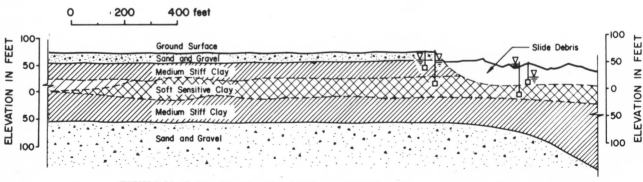

FIGURE 37   Section through east end of Turnagain Heights slide area, Anchorage (1964).

soil deposits well behind the bluff line. Values of the maximum stresses and strains throughout the deposit, as determined by the analysis, have also been presented by Seed and Wilson (1967). The presence of the sand lenses was not considered in making the analysis. However, the presence of continuous thin seams of sand throughout the clay would have little influence on the stresses developed in the deposit and the computed values of maximum stress may be considered reasonably applicable for homogeneous clay or for clay containing continuous sand seams.

By comparing the average cyclic shear stresses developed in continuous sand seams or in the clay with the strength test data for these materials, it was found that the sand could be expected to liquefy after about 12 stress cycles, which correspond to about 45 seconds of ground motions in the analysis, whereas the clay would not be expected to fail until after about 22 cycles or 1½ minutes of ground shaking.

On this basis alone, liquefaction could be expected to occur in sand seams before any significant strength loss de-

veloped in the clay. The sand occurs as lenses, however, rather than as continuous seams, and the influence of this situation must also be evaluated.

To investigate the behavior of sand lenses embedded in clay deposits during earthquakes, an analysis was made of the maximum stresses developed in a single sand lens (50 ft wide and 2 ft thick), embedded in the center of a clay deposit (50 ft thick and of infinite extent), if the base of the deposit were subjected to the ground motions recorded at Pasadena in the Kern County, California, earthquake of 1952. The geometric configuration and material properties are shown in Figure 38. To make the analysis, it was necessary to use a finite-element idealization of the soil system and the particular element arrangement used in the analysis is shown in Figure 39. By this means the stresses and strains developed at different points in the soil as a result of the base motions shown in Figure 40 can readily be determined (Clough and Chopra, 1966).

The maximum stresses developed by the earthquake ground motions along a horizontal plane through the center

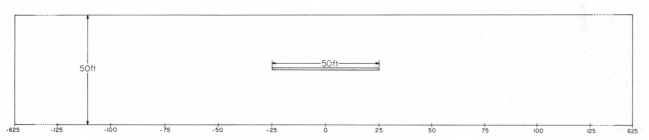

FIGURE 38   Sand lens embedded in clay layer.

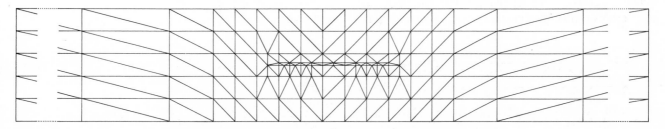

FIGURE 39   Finite-element idealization of sand lens in clay layer.

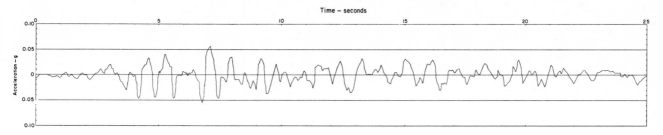

FIGURE 40   Accelerogram for Pasadena recording of 1952 Kern County earthquake.

line of the sand lens and the adjacent clay are shown in Figure 41; also shown in this figure are the stresses that would be developed along the same plane if the sand were in the form of a continuous seam rather than a lens. The discontinuity associated with the lens leads to a high stress concentration at the ends of the lens and to a corresponding reduction in stress in the adjacent clay. The very high stress values at the edges of the lens would, however, lead to liquefaction in these zones very much more rapidly than in a sand seam of the same thickness.

Liquefaction of the edges of the lens would, in turn, lead to a redistribution of stress. The maximum stresses developed in the lens for the same earthquake ground motions, if the outer 5 ft at each end of the lens were liquefied, are shown in Figure 42. The maximum stresses in the sand adjacent to the liquefied section are now higher than before.

Apparently, therefore, liquefaction during earthquakes of sand lenses embedded in clay deposits can develop progressively and rapidly from the outer edges toward the center, and liquefaction will occur considerably faster in lenses than in continuous sand seams or layers.

The development of the Turnagain Heights slide may accordingly be visualized as shown in Figure 43. Before the earthquake, the presence of numerous sand lenses in the clay between elevation 5 and 20 ft would serve to stiffen the clay and increase its stability. During the earthquake, however, the sand lenses would liquefy as a result of the stresses induced in them by the ground motions; the deposit might therefore be considered to contain water in the zones formerly occupied by the sand lenses.

As in the case of sand seams, however, the initial shear stresses in the sand lenses in the vicinity of the slope would inhibit the development of liquefaction in this area so that after a short period of earthquake ground motions, lique-

faction of sand lenses would extend well behind the bluff line, but the nonliquefied lenses near the bluffs and the surrounding clay would serve as a buttress and prevent a slide from occurring. The situation at this stage would be very similar to that outlined previously for sliding along sand seams or layers; sliding would develop in an analogous fashion, except that the slide surface would necessarily pass through the clay between adjacent liquefied lenses.

When inertia forces in the soil behind the bluff line were able to overcome the strength of the clay that formed the bluffs, a large mass of soil would begin to move on a horizontal plane, and a graben would begin to form about half a wavelength inland from the bluff line. Simultaneously, the loss of strength of the clay accompanying the horizontal displacement would lead to a continuously weakened zone all along the base of the slide mass and thus to an initial slide, of a more conventional form, at the edge of the bluffs. Once the stabilizing influences of the nonliquefied soil near the bluffs had been removed, movement would develop rapidly by sliding on the already liquefied lenses, leading to the series of ridges and depressions shown in Figure 43.

This behavior, involving the formation of a graben some distance behind the bluff line, and the simultaneous rotational sliding of sections near the bluff line would help to reconcile the somewhat conflicting reports of eyewitnesses. Typical quotations (U.S. Army Engineer District, 1964) from people in the area include the following:

"It went in one big piece."

"I looked towards the Inlet and about the first thing I saw was houses slipping over the edge of the bluff. . . . By this time the land between the bluff and where I was, which is probably two blocks, was opening up."

"I would say it progressed inward toward where I was."

"One piece went off and then another came after it."

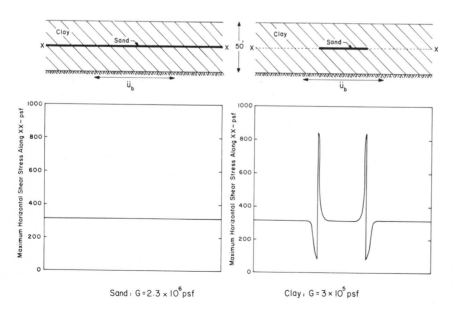

FIGURE 41   Maximum shear stresses induced in sand layer and sand lens embedded in clay deposit subjected to Pasadena ground motions from Kern County earthquake.

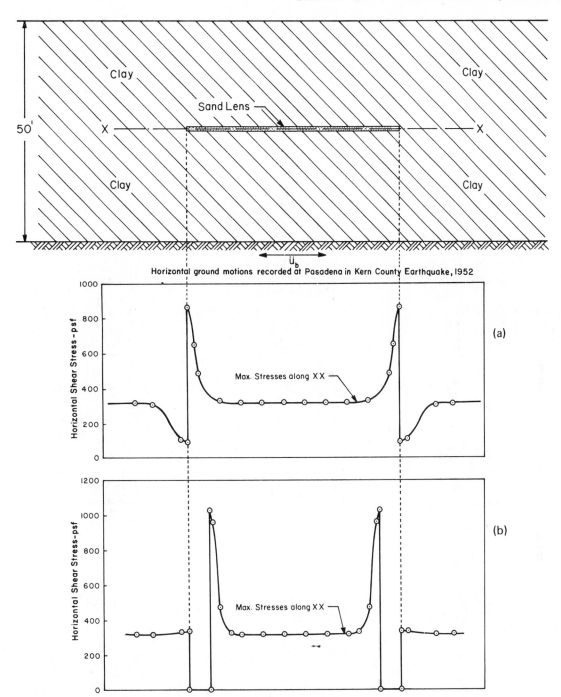

FIGURE 42   Changes in shear-stress distribution along sand lens caused by liquefaction at edges. (a) Maximum shear stresses if no liquefaction occurred in sand lens; (b) maximum shear stresses if outer 5 ft of sand lens were liquefied.

The following factors are evidence that liquefaction of sand lenses played a major role in the development of the Turnagain Heights landslide.

1. Several samples recovered from the slide area showed sand and clay intermixed in a form that could only have occurred as a result of the fluid characteristics of the sand.

2. Ridges of sand, 2–3 ft high, 3–6 ft wide, and about 100 ft long, were formed by sand boils within the slide area (Hansen, 1965, and Geology volume); a large boil, spread over an area of 3,200 ft^2, was also noted near but outside the slide area (Engineering Geology Evaluation Group, 1964).

3. A description of the slide movements by residents of a

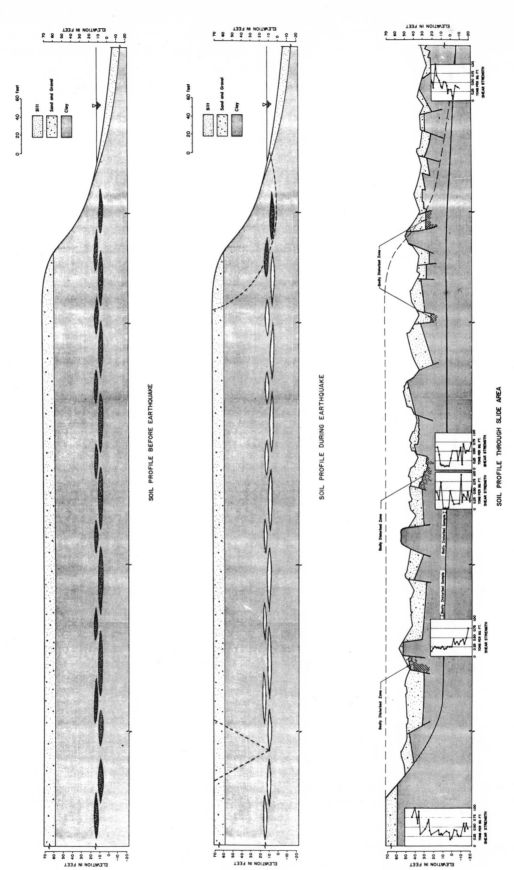

FIGURE 43 Conceptual development of Turnagain Heights landslide, Anchorage, Alaska.

100

house in the slide area during the earthquake in which they said, "The floor ripped and sand came up from below into the living room" (U.S. Army Engineer District, 1964). It is difficult to imagine such an inflow of sand except by liquefaction.

4. Although considerable evidence (lateral extension, cracking, settlement) indicates that the area behind the slide area was underlain by a severely weakened layer during the earthquake, no evidence of a weakened clay zone underlying this area was revealed by borings made several weeks after the earthquake (Shannon & Wilson, Inc., 1964).

5. Sand lenses were encountered in many borings made in the slide area, but very few were noted in borings made immediately adjacent to the slide area (U.S. Army Engineer District, 1966).

Although some of this evidence is circumstantial, it lends support to the concept that a severely weakened zone developed in the early stages of the earthquake in the area behind the bluff line and that, although this zone was a composite of sand lenses and adjacent clay, liquefaction of the sand played a significant role in its development.

Three major landslides very much resembling the Turnagain Heights landslide occurred in the valley slopes of the San Pedro River near Lake Rinihue, about 45 mi east of Valdivia, during the Chilean earthquake of 1960 (Davis and Karzulovic, 1961). The slide debris blocked the course of the river, causing the water level in the lake to rise about 80 ft above its normal level and threatening the safety of Valdivia. Controlled discharge of the impounded water

through relocated stream channels, however, prevented any loss of life and minimized property damage.

The locations of the three slides are shown in Figure 44. The smallest of the three slides (number 1) covered an area of about 35 acres and involved about 2 million yd^3 of soil; the intermediate slide (number 2) covered an area of about 75 acres and involved about 6 million yd^3 of soil; and the largest of the three slides (number 3) covered an area of about 300 acres and involved about 30 million yd^3 of soil. Figure 45 shows an aerial photo of slide areas 1 and 2.

Ancient landslides can readily be identified in this area. One of these, involving some 100 million yd^3 of material, is shown in Figure 44. Early historical records of Valdivia describe a major earthquake in December 1575 and show that at the same time the river was blocked by an enormous slide that was not breached by the impounded water for 134 days. When it was finally overtopped, however, the rapid cutting caused a catastrophic flood that destroyed a large part of Valdivia. These events may well have been repeated, with less disastrous consequences, some 385 years later.

A detailed description of the largest of the three slides that took place in 1960, a description of the soil conditions and an indication of the mechanism of failure have been presented by Davis and Karzulovic (1961). Cross sections through the slide area, before and after sliding, are shown in Figure 46. Characteristic features of the slide are the large lateral translation of the slide mass, some parts of which moved about 1,200 ft; the much smaller vertical movement of about 150 ft; and the almost horizontal position of the final ground surface in the slide area. Such a configuration

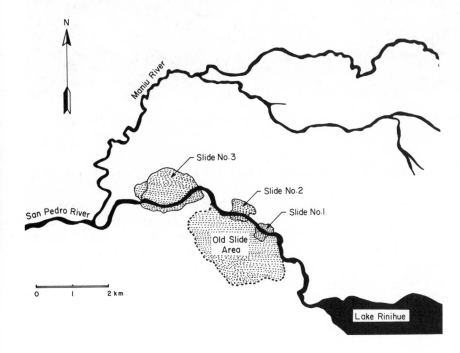

FIGURE 44 Locations of slide areas near Lake Rinihue during Chilean earthquake of 1960. After Davis and Karzulovic (1961).

FIGURE 45   Aerial photograph of slide areas 1 and 2 near Lake Rinihue, Chile, 1960. After Davis and Karzulovic (1961).

is typical of that normally associated with slides induced by liquefaction.

The soil conditions in the large slide area consisted of a surface deposit of sand and gravel, ranging from zero to about 150 ft thick, underlain by a 250-ft-thick deposit of lacustrine clay and by a deeper bed of cemented sand and gravel. Field studies indicated that the main surface of sliding was probably essentially horizontal and at a depth of about 150 ft in the lacustrine clay deposit (Figure 46).

The clay deposit itself is highly stratified, with alternating layers of silt and clay and frequent seams of fine sand. Indi-

vidual layers of silt and clay are between 2 and about 12 in. thick in the upper 100 ft of the deposit. In the zone of sliding the silt layers are from about 2 to 6 in. thick and sand seams are up to 2 in. thick. The lower half of the clay deposit was below the water table at the time of the earthquake.

During the earthquake, the slide developed in a period of several minutes, with minor sliding within the slide debris continuing after the ground motions stopped. Within the slide area, the slide debris formed a series of ridges, some of which extended for about 1,000 ft. One block of soil, about 50 acres in extent, moved virtually intact through a distance of about 1,000 ft and was set down directly above the original bed of the river.

From a detailed study of the circumstances surrounding this slide, Davis and Karzulovic (1961) concluded:

> The first strong seismic activity produced a collapse of the structure of various thin beds of highly porous silt and fine sand. This left the overlying mass of material supported entirely by a mixture of water, sand and silt which had no strength. Continued seismic activity started a large block of sediments moving towards the river. . . . As the block moved out across the river bed, smaller blocks broke off behind and, in turn, produced rotational slumping.

The extensive lateral movements associated with the slide certainly support the view that liquefaction of sand and silt layers or lenses was primarily responsible for the failure.

FAILURE OF TAILINGS DAMS

No survey of landslides caused by soil liquefaction during earthquakes would be complete without some mention of the failures that have occurred in tailings dams formed from mining wastes. The Barahona tailings dam failed during an earthquake in Chile in 1928, but the greatest number of failures of this type of structure developed during a single earthquake in Chile on March 28, 1965 (Dobry and Alvarez, 1967). The dam at the El Cobre mine, which had been built up to a height of about 100 ft, destroyed part of the village of El Cobre and caused the deaths of some 200 people. Ten other tailings dams failed or were damaged during the same earthquake.

The tailings dams typically consist of a relatively thin outer shell of sand and an inner core of saturated fine sand and siltlike material. Failure apparently developed as a result of liquefaction of the core during the earthquake, causing a failure of the outer shell that permitted the liquefied core to flow out of the dams. At El Cobre, columns of liquid were observed to shoot upward, and other evidences of liquefac-

tion in the form of vents and boils were readily apparent. The material from the dam flowed a distance of 8 mi in a period of 10–20 minutes after the breaking of the outer shell.

The tailings-dam failures in the 1965 Chilean earthquake have been described in some detail by Dobry and Alvarez (1967); the general mechanics of the failures, involving liquefaction behind the slope followed by slope failure and a rapid translation of the soil behind the slope, is not unlike that hypothesized for the Turnagain Heights and the Rinihue failures.

SLIDES CAUSED BY FOUNDATION LIQUEFACTION IN EMBANKMENTS

In addition to slides in natural deposits, much damage during earthquakes has resulted from slumping and settlement of embankments caused by liquefaction of the foundation materials on which they were constructed. Probably the most dramatic example of this type of slide was the complete failure of a portion of the Sheffield Dam during the Santa Barbara earthquake of 1926 (see following section), but numerous other examples of severe displacements of embankments have been reported. In some cases, the displacements have been caused primarily by settlement of the embankment into the underlying liquefied soil, whereas in others they have been caused by lateral spreading of the base of the embankment.

Figure 47 illustrates the behavior of a dike, built to a height of 7 ft along the bank of a canal in northern Mexico, that sank completely into the saturated sandy foundation material during the El Centro earthquake of 1940. Similar behavior along railroad embankments constructed on silty and sandy deposits in the 1964 Alaska earthquake was reported by McCulloch and Bonilla (1967):

> In some areas the whole embankment settled irregularly from about 2 to 6 ft into the underlying sediments. Comparison of design

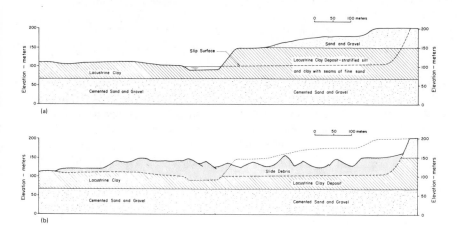

FIGURE 46 Approximate sections through large slide area near Lake Rinihue, Chile, 1960. After Davis and Karzulovic (1961). (a) Section through slide area before earthquake; (b) and after earthquake.

FIGURE 47 Settlement of dike in El Centro earthquake, 1940.

profiles with post-quake profiles across the embankment suggests that there was minor spreading of the embankment-fill, but that most of the lowering was due to a downward movement into the underlying sediment. In some places the embankment looked like a roller coaster . . . silt, sand and gravel were ejected with ground water from ground cracks at the lower places of the roller coaster.

Other embankments constructed on saturated silts suffered extensive cracking because of lateral spreading (Figure 48a). Similar behavior of embankments has been reported in the Hawkes Bay, New Zealand, earthquake of 1931 (Henderson, 1933), the Chilean earthquake of 1960 (Duke and Leeds, 1963), and the Niigata earthquake of 1964 (Yamada, 1966; Kawakami and Asada, 1966; Yokomura, 1966). The limited lateral movements of these embankments suggests that liquefaction may not have extended across the entire base of the embankments, possibly because liquefaction did not occur under the outer parts of the slopes owing to the high initial values of the shear stress/normal stress ratio (Figure 9) and relatively low induced stresses. Under these conditions, liquefaction might be visualized as developing under the central part of the embankment and beyond the toes of the slopes (Figure 48b), permitting overall slumping and cracking along the center line but without the large translations often associated with liquefied soil masses. Alternatively, the reason for the limited movements may be that the foundation soil is sufficiently dense for liquefaction to occur only over a limited deformation range (Seed and Lee, 1966).

POSTEARTHQUAKE SLIDES

Liquefaction of sand lenses may also play a significant role in the development of landslides some time after an earth-quake has occurred. This situation might develop, for example, under soil conditions similar to those shown in Figure 49, where a slope in a moderately stiff clay contains an extensive sand lens. Before the earthquake, both the clay and the sand will contribute to the stability of the slope. During an earthquake, however, the sand lens may liquefy with a complete loss of strength in this zone; nevertheless, the clay may still be strong enough to maintain stability, although the stresses induced in it will be substantially increased.

It has been shown, however, that under a sudden increase in load that is insufficient to cause immediate failure, clay soils may undergo a progressive slow-creep movement, culminating some hours, days, or weeks later in a sudden increase in deformation rate and accompanying failure (Casagrande and Wilson, 1951; Sherif, 1965). A typical example of this type of behavior in a laboratory test specimen is shown in Figure 50. Liquefaction of a sand lens in a clay bank may thus initiate a creep movement that will culminate in failure of the slope some days or weeks after the earthquake occurs.

A good example of a slide that developed some days after an earthquake is the behavior of an old slide area in Kirkwood Creek following the Hebgen Lake, Montana, earthquake of August 17, 1959 (Hadley, 1964). This slide area, about 400–800 ft wide and half a mile long, had been stable for many years and showed no significant movement for at least 5 days after the earthquake. After this time, however, it began to slide again and moved about 100 ft over a period of several weeks. The bulk of the soil mass involved was a clayey deposit, but little is known of its detailed stratigraphy. No apparent cause of the sliding, other than the earthquake, can be conceived.

A somewhat similar event may have occurred at a site on

the Baker River (Peck, 1967) after the Seattle earthquake of April 29, 1965. Again the slope involved was an area in which sliding had previously occurred, but which had apparently stabilized before the earthquake. The soils overlying bedrock consisted primarily of laminated clays and silty clays with interbedded members of fine silty sand or clean fine sand, the sand members occurring in irregular lenticular deposits. The ground surface before sliding had an average slope of about 1 : 3.

The first signs of sliding were noticed in March 1964; during the following 14 months, measures were taken to prevent the movement by installing drains. Substantial slide movements developed, nevertheless, particularly during periods of heavy rainfall. By April 10, 1965, however, the

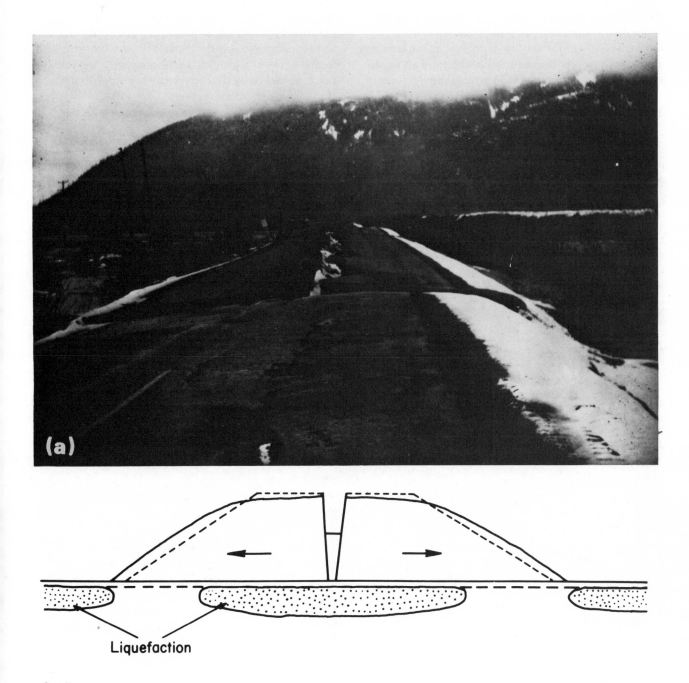

FIGURE 48   (a) Cracking of embankment constructed on saturated silt, Alaska earthquake, 1964. (b) Liquefaction of foundation soils permitting lateral spreading of the embankment.

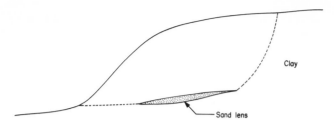

FIGURE 49   Liquefaction of sand lens leading to delayed slide.

combined effects of the drainage measures and the cessation of heavy rainfall produced a situation where, for all practical purposes, the movements had stopped entirely.

The environmental factors that might have influenced the subsequent stability of the slope are listed in Table 2.

Just before the major slide developed, rains occurred,

TABLE 2   Environmental Factors Influencing Subsequent Slope Stability at the Baker River Site Associated with the Seattle Earthquake of April 29, 1965

Date (1965)	Environmental Changes	Condition of Slide Area
April 10	—	No movement for all practical purposes
April 20–30	10-day cumulative rainfall = 2.5 in.	No significant effect
April 29	Strong earthquake	No significant effect
May 4–12	10-day cumulative rainfall = 2.0 in.	No significant effect
May 15–16	10-day cumulative rainfall = 2.6 in.	No significant effect
May 17	—	Movement observed in slide area
May 18	—	Catastrophic failure

producing a 10-day cumulative total rainfall of 2.6 in. Similar rainfalls had, however, occurred twice during the preceding 30 days with no significant effect on the slope stability. It seems possible, therefore, that the occurrence of the strong earthquake on April 29 may have introduced some new condition that might have affected the slope behavior.

Obviously, it is impossible to say that liquefaction of sand lenses caused by earthquake activity led to either of the slope failures discussed. Numerous other possible causes of the movements may be postulated, but the reports of several instances of postearthquake slope movements within several weeks of a significant earthquake raise the possibility that liquefaction of sand lenses may have contributed to the development of these events.

THE SHEFFIELD DAM FAILURE

Because of the limited knowledge and complexity of the soil conditions, few of the examples previously discussed provide an opportunity to check the applicability of analytical methods for investigating the probability of slide development during earthquakes; a notable exception is the Sheffield Dam failure during an earthquake near Santa Barbara in 1925. Although it is now some 40 years since the failure occurred, it is possible to reconstruct reasonably well the conditions existing at the time of the earthquake.

The dam was constructed in the winter of 1917 in a ravine north of the city of Santa Barbara (U.S. Army Corps of Engineers, 1949). Figure 51 shows a representative section through the dam at its maximum height. The embankment, 720 ft long and with a maximum height of about 25 ft, was constructed of soil from the reservoir excavation and compacted by routing the construction equipment over

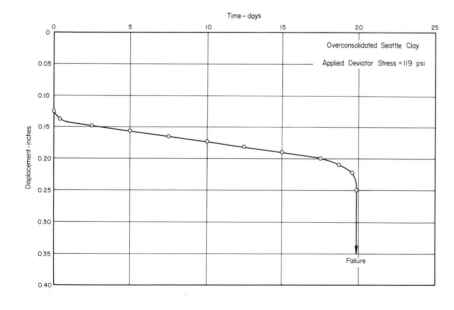

FIGURE 50   Long-term failure of stiff clay under sustained load. After Sherif (1965).

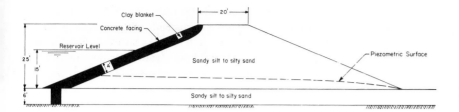

FIGURE 51   Cross section through Sheffield Dam embankment.

the fill. The body of the dam was composed of silty sand and sandy silt containing some cobbles and boulders, but the upstream slope was faced with a 4-ft-thick clay blanket that was extended as much as 10 ft into the foundation to serve as a cutoff wall; a 5-in. concrete facing overlay the clay blanket. No record of the degree of compaction of the embankment is available, but it was probably about 75–80 percent, based on the standard American Association of State Highway Officials (AASHO) compaction test. Figure 52 is a view of the dam with the reservoir empty.

The foundation soil consists of a layer of terrace alluvium, 4–10 ft thick, overlying sandstone bedrock. Drill holes made in 1949 by the Corps of Engineers showed the alluvium to consist mainly of silty sand and sandy silt containing cobbles varying from 3 to 6 in. in diameter and with some thin layers of clayey sand and gravelly, sandy clay (U.S. Army Corps of Engineers, 1949). The upper 2 ft of the foundation soil, with a relative density of about 35 percent, is somewhat looser than the underlying deposits, and it has been fairly well established that there was no formal stripping of these upper soil layers before construction of the embankment.

Before the earthquake occurred, seepage was reported near the toe of the downstream slope and in the area beyond the toe. The Santa Barbara Water Department's records state that examination after the failure indicated that there was no leakage of water through the upstream core, but that seepage around and underneath the cutoff had saturated the lower part of the main structure; it appears, therefore, that the water level in the embankment was somewhat similar to that shown in Figure 51. At the time of the earthquake, the water in the reservoir was about 15–18 ft deep.

The main shock of the earthquake occurred at 6:42 a.m. on June 29, 1925. Although no strong-motion instruments were in existence at the time, on the basis of records obtained at distant stations, the earthquake has been assigned a magnitude rating of 6.3, with an epicenter some 7 mi northwest of the dam site (Eppley, 1960).

Reliable observers report that the ground shaking in the area of the dam site had a Rossi-Forel intensity of about IX and a duration of about 15–18 seconds (Willis, 1925; Byerly, 1955). On the basis of correlations with ground accelerations developed in other earthquakes, it seems that the earthquake ground motions at the Sheffield Dam site might be approximated as follows:

FIGURE 52   Sheffield Dam before failure.

Maximum ground acceleration	0.15 g
Duration of significant shaking	15–18 seconds
Predominant frequency of accelerations	3 cps

The time history of such a ground motion might be approximated by appropriate scaling of the accelerograph record of the 1940 El Centro earthquake. This record was obtained about 7 mi from the epicenter of an earthquake of magnitude 7.0. The ground motions at the Sheffield Dam site might be expected to be somewhat similar in form but with smaller amplitudes, a slightly higher predominant frequency, and a smaller duration of shaking. They might be represented by scaling the ordinates of the El Centro record to a maximum acceleration of 0.15 g, scaling the abscissa to a predominant frequency of about 3 cps, and continuing the record for only about 15 seconds. Figure 53 shows a time history of such ground accelerations. We believe that a ground-motion record of this type provides a reasonable basis for analyzing the behavior of the Sheffield Dam.

Unfortunately, there were no eyewitnesses to the failure. From the reports of engineers (O'Shaughnessy, 1925; Nunn, 1925) who inspected the dam after the failure, however, it seems reasonable to conclude that sliding occurred near the base of the embankment, causing a section about 300 ft long to move as much as 100 ft downstream, breaking up

as it went (Figure 54). A movement of this extent was undoubtedly related in some manner to liquefaction or to a severe reduction in strength of soil near the base of the dam resulting from increases in pore-water pressure induced by the shaking caused by the earthquake.

To study the failure, a comprehensive series of strength tests have been performed on samples of silty sand obtained from the foundation deposits at the dam site and recompacted to approximately the same density as the foundation and embankment material (Seed and others, 1967). These tests included conventional consolidated-undrained static-loading tests, consolidated-undrained triaxial-compression tests under cyclic-loading conditions, and consolidated-undrained simple shear tests under cyclic-loading conditions. Together with the information on conditions at the time of failure, these data may be used as a basis for investigating the applicability of various procedures for analyzing the seismic stability of the embankment.

ANALYSES OF THE SEISMIC STABILITY OF THE DOWNSTREAM SLOPE, USING CONVENTIONAL PSEUDOSTATIC PROCEDURES

Past practice and most current practice in the analysis of embankment stability against earthquake forces involves the computation of the minimum factor of safety against

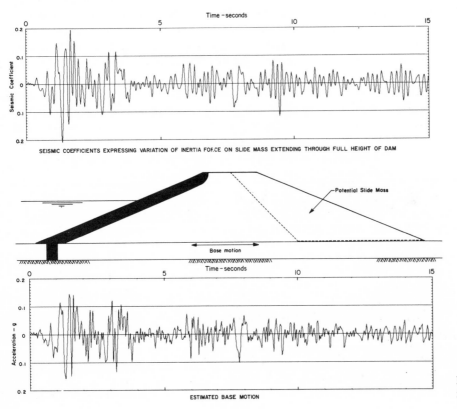

FIGURE 53   Analysis of response of Sheffield Dam to earthquake ground motions.

FIGURE 54   Sheffield Dam after failure.

sliding when a static horizontal force, intended to represent the disturbing effect of the earthquake, is included in the analysis. The analysis is treated as a static problem, and the horizontal force is expressed as the product of a seismic coefficient k and the weight W of the potential sliding mass. If the factor of safety approaches unity, the section is generally considered unsafe, although generally there is no recognized limit for the minimum acceptable factor of safety.

When a conventional pseudostatic approach of this type is used, the seismic coefficient adopted often ranges from 0.05 to 0.15. For many earth dams, a value of 0.1 has been used. Because the earthquake at Santa Barbara was by no means as strong as the largest recorded or anticipated in the western United States, its equivalent effects would presumably correspond to some intermediate value in the range of seismic coefficients used for design (for example, 0.1). This value might therefore be considered reasonable to use for

evaluating the stability of the Sheffield Dam during the 1925 Santa Barbara earthquake by conventional procedures of analysis.

Possible variations in choices of computational details make it possible to obtain a wide range of computed results using a conventional pseudostatic approach. When the most common choices of analytical details leading to essentially the lowest values for the computed factor of safety were used, it was found that, for the water-table elevation shown in Figure 51, the incorporation of a static seismic force represented by a seismic coefficient of 0.1 led to a computed factor of safety of 1.21 for the critical sliding surface shown in Figure 55; such a result would normally indicate adequate stability of the embankment.

If the soil-test data were interpreted conservatively, the water-table elevation in the embankment was taken at a conservatively high elevation, and the analysis was made with conservative choices of analytical details, the use of a

Design Assumptions	Factor of Safety
Seismic force acting at base of slice	1.21
Seismic force acting at C·G· of slice	1.32

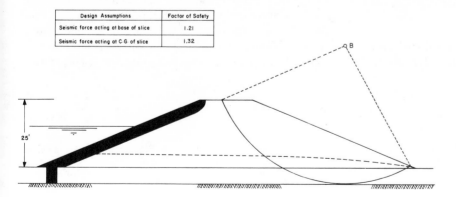

FIGURE 55   Pseudostatic analysis of embankment stability during earthquake. For conventional approach, the seismic coefficient = 0.1 and the minimum safety factor = 1.21.

seismic coefficient of 0.1 was found to give a computed factor of safety approaching 1.0 for the critical sliding surface shown in Figure 55. Alternatively, for the conditions shown in Figure 51 and average strength-test data, a seismic coefficient of 0.17 would have led to a computed factor of safety of 1.0 for the critical sliding surface. Although a failure condition could have been predicted by these means, the result would still suffer from the limitation that the computed position of the critical sliding surface bears little resemblance to that on which failure apparently took place. In fact, sliding along the critical surface indicated by a conventional pseudostatic analysis would not apparently have led to any loss of freeboard or to a movement of the embankment that could lead directly to a loss of water from the reservoir; this was clearly not the case.

If seismic coefficients of the order of 0.1–0.17 are required to predict failure of the embankment for the type of earthquake experienced by the Sheffield Dam, much higher values of the order of 0.3–0.5 would be indicated for the largest earthquakes that might be expected to occur in California and in other regions adjacent to major active faults.

This situation is somewhat worsened if computations are made to determine the seismic coefficients required to predict sliding along a surface corresponding approximately to the surface on which failure actually occurred. Figure 56 shows that for average strength-test data and the probable water-level conditions, the minimum value of the seismic coefficient that would predict failure along a sliding surface in the probable failure zone is about 0.21. Even the use of conservative strength-test data, a conservatively high water-table elevation in the embankment, and conservative choices of analytical details would still require the use of a seismic coefficient of at least 0.15 to indicate failure on a sliding surface in this zone.

The pseudostatic approach, incorporating conventional values of the seismic coefficient, does not therefore appear to provide a satisfactory basis for analyzing the observed failure of the Sheffield Dam.

ANALYSES OF THE SEISMIC STABILITY OF THE DOWNSTREAM SLOPE USING DYNAMIC-ANALYSIS PROCEDURES

Because pseudostatic approaches are apparently unsatisfactory, it is of interest to determine whether a dynamic analysis—incorporating considerations of the dynamic response of the embankment and soil-strength values determined under cyclic-loading conditions—would adequately predict the observed performance (Seed, 1966).

As a first step in applying this procedure to the Sheffield Dam, a response analysis was made to determine the time history of seismic coefficients (Seed and Martin, 1966); the inertia forces developed by the Santa Barbara earthquake were expressed on potential slide masses extending to the base of the dam. The ground motions used for the analysis were those shown in Figure 53: The dam was considered to have a variable shear modulus expressed by the relationship $G = 6 \times 10^4 \times \sigma_o{}^{1/3}$ psf, where σ_o is the average overburden pressure along a plane at any depth below the crest, and a damping ratio of 20 percent. These values are typical of those measured for silty sands at strains corresponding to those induced by the earthquake base motions.

The results of a computation of the dynamic seismic coefficients developed on a slide mass extending to the base of the dam are shown in Figure 53. The maximum value of the seismic coefficient developed was 0.19; for 8 or 9 cycles, the seismic coefficient reached values exceeding 0.10. From a study of the results shown in Figure 53, it was concluded that the effects of the earthquake were essentially equivalent to 10 cycles of a uniform cyclic seismic coefficient of about 0.15, and these values were adopted for purposes of analysis.

A comprehensive series of triaxial-compression tests was conducted to evaluate the strength and deformation characteristics of saturated specimens of the silty sand, under cyclic-loading conditions, for samples initially consolidated to different principal-stress ratios. The results of this test series are shown in Figure 57. For samples initially consolidated to principal stress ratios (K_c) of 1.0 and 1.2, failure was accompanied by sudden liquefaction of the samples.

With the help of the cyclic-loading triaxial-test data for the soil, analyses were then made of the seismic stability of the Sheffield Dam. A dynamic analysis procedure was used (Seed, 1966) and consideration was given to the initial stress conditions on soil elements in the embankment before the earthquake occurred (Lowe and Karafiath, 1959). The results of these analyses are summarized in Figures 58 and 59. The most critical surface was found to be close to that shown in Figure 58, and the corresponding factor of safety against failure by liquefaction along this surface was 1.15.

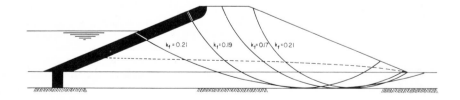

FIGURE 56 Seismic coefficients indicating failure in pseudostatic analyses. k_f = seismic coefficient for which factor of safety along sliding surface is unity.

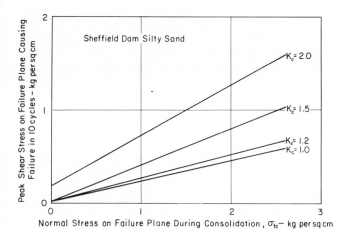

FIGURE 57 τ_{ff}/σ_{fc} (shear stress on failure plane at time failure occurs versus the normal stress on the failure plane when soil is consolidated) relations for cyclic-loading triaxial-compression tests.

puted failure condition range only from 0.19 to 0.22, compared to values greater than 0.21 for analyses of similar conditions using the pseudostatic approach. The seismic coefficient indicating failure might have been reduced to about 0.17 by considering the water level to be somewhat higher in the embankment.

Although the dynamic-analysis approach seems to provide a reasonably good evaluation of the mode of failure of the Sheffield Dam, the computed factor of safety is perhaps somewhat higher than might have been expected for a dam that failed so completely.

A critical appraisal of the analytical procedure indicates that some degree of error is inevitably introduced because of difficulties in attempting to use the triaxial-test procedure to simulate the stress conditions induced by an earthquake on relatively flat potential-failure surfaces with high static factors of safety. Major difficulties encountered in this process are as follows:

This position of the critical sliding surface and mode of failure are in good accord with the observed performance of the Sheffield Dam, although the computed factor of safety is only a little better than that indicated by the pseudostatic analyses.

As in the pseudostatic analyses, computations were also made to determine the values of the seismic coefficient (k_f), which would have led to a computed factor of safety of 1.0 against complete failure for various potential sliding surfaces. The results of these computations are shown in Figure 59. For slip surfaces intersecting the upstream slope below the water level, the seismic coefficient values that lead to a com-

1. For elements of soil on relatively flat surfaces, the shear stresses on the potential-failure planes are very low before the earthquake, yet the normal stresses on these surfaces are high and the principal stress ratios (K_c) may well be of the order of 2. The only manner in which a combination of high normal stress and low shear stress may be induced on a potential-failure surface in a conventional triaxial test is to consolidate a sample under approximately equal values of major and minor principal stress; that is, with a very low value of the principal stress ratio rather than the much higher field value. For the soil element at point B in Figure 60, for example, the initial shear stress on the horizontal

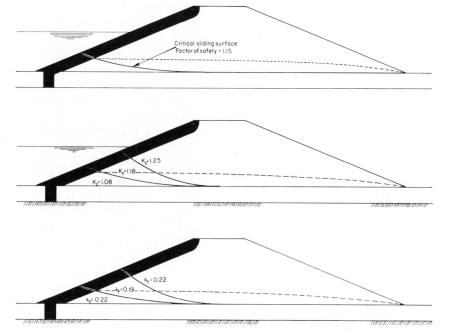

FIGURE 58 Critical sliding surface determined by dynamic analysis using cyclic-loading triaxial-compression test data.

FIGURE 59 Dynamic analysis using cyclic-loading triaxial-compression test data, where K_c = principal stress ratio before earthquake for soil elements along sliding surface, and k_f = seismic coefficient for which factor of safety along sliding surface is unity.

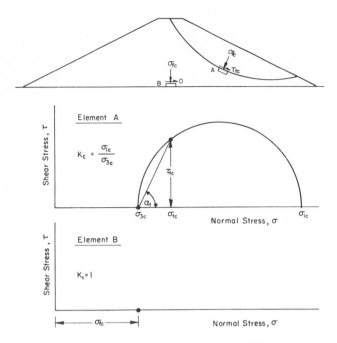

FIGURE 60   Simulation of stress conditions on soil elements in embankment. Soil element A: K_c reasonably correct; little principal stress re-orientation during earthquake and the anisotropically consolidated-undrained triaxial-compression test is adequate. Soil element B: $K_c = 1$; major principal stress re-orientation during earthquake; triaxial-compression test is adequate.

plane, which is a potential surface of sliding during an earthquake, is zero, and the triaxial test representation of this condition would involve consolidation of a sample under isotropic-stress conditions as shown in Figure 60. Yet in the embankment the soil element is consolidated under stresses corresponding closely to K_o conditions.

This discrepancy in consolidation conditions does not arise to the same extent for soil elements on surfaces with initially high shear stresses; that is, with relatively lower values of the factor of safety under static-loading conditions. The triaxial test can thus reasonably represent the preearthquake stresses on an element such as A in Figure 60, but not those on an element such as B.

2. During an earthquake, the directions of the induced principal stresses do not coincide with those existing before the earthquake. For all elements of soil in an embankment, there is therefore some re-orientation of principal stress directions during the shaking. For an element such as A in Figure 60, the degree of principal stress re-orientation when the factor of safety is reduced is relatively small; for an element such as B, however, the degree of principal stress re-orientation is substantially larger.

In a triaxial-compression test, it is not possible to effect any re-orientation of principal stress directions other than of 90 degrees. In most tests, there is no re-orientation of principal stress directions, and although this provides a rea-

sonable simulation of the deforming stress conditions on elements such as A, it does not correspond at all well with the cyclic re-orientation of principal stress directions that occurs on elements such as B, while the shaking continues during an earthquake.

Although triaxial-test procedures may be entirely adequate for investigating the seismic stability of an embankment along potential slip surfaces that are subjected to high initial shear stresses caused by static loads, they do not provide a good simulation of field loading conditions for soil elements located along relatively flat potential-slip surfaces where static shear stresses are low. For this reason, it would appear that cyclic-loading simple shear tests might provide a better basis for analyses.

The test equipment and the mechanics of sample deformations in a cyclic-loading simple shear test have been described elsewhere (Peacock and Seed, 1967). Essentially, a sample is maintained in a condition of plane strain in one horizontal direction, but it can be loaded vertically and can undergo shear strains in the other horizontal direction. Thus, it can be deformed to simulate the strains developed in soil elements subjected to plane-strain loading conditions in the field. A schematic diagram of the test equipment is shown in Figure 61.

In simple shear tests, a soil sample can be brought to initial equilibrium under any given normal stress (σ_{fc}) and any given shear stress (τ_{fc}), representing the initial stresses on a soil element on a potential failure plane in the field. Cyclic-shear stresses can then be superimposed to represent the effects of the earthquake. By determining the cyclic-shear stresses required to cause failure, the test data lead directly to a relation between the peak cyclic-shear stress causing failure in a given number of cycles (τ_{ff}) and the normal stress on a soil element before the earthquake effects were applied (σ_{fc}).

Tests can be conducted for any desired ratio of τ_{fc}/σ_{fc} with the soil sample still being subjected to an effective principal stress ratio approaching that in the field, and the major principal stress can be subjected to a cyclic re-orientation during simulated earthquake loading. Thus, the test eliminates some of the disadvantages of the triaxial-compression-test procedure with regard to the simulation of field loading conditions. Its main limitation is that, for soils showing a substantial loss in strength after failure, stress concentrations at the edges of samples tend to induce failure at average stresses somewhat lower than the peak strength. Nevertheless, if due allowance is made for this effect, the test offers considerable advantages over other testing techniques.

With appropriately corrected cyclic simple shear test data (Peacock and Seed, 1967) for the strength of the soils in the Sheffield Dam and its foundation, and the dynamic-

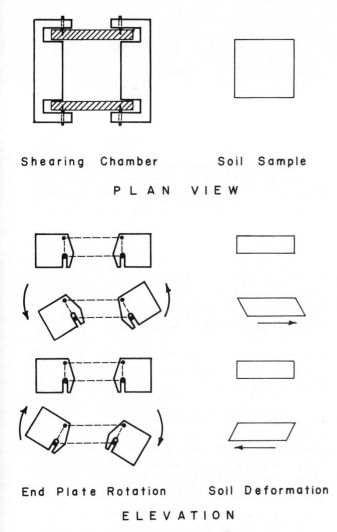

Shearing Chamber   Soil Sample

P L A N   V I E W

End Plate Rotation   Soil Deformation

E L E V A T I O N

FIGURE 61 Schematic diagram of simple shear test equipment.

analysis procedure previously described, analyses were made of the seismic stability of the dam during the Santa Barbara earthquake. The results of these analyses are shown in Figure 62. The most critical surface of sliding was found to be along the base of the dam where the computed factor of safety was only 0.75. In the analysis of an embankment failure during an earthquake, however, there is no reason why the actual factor of safety should not be less than unity, because the embankment might have failed before the sur-

face ground motions had ceased—a situation comparable to the existence of a factor of safety of unity under a smaller earthquake or a factor of safety less than unity for the full earthquake. From the extent of sliding of the Sheffield Dam, failure appears to have occurred before the ground motions had subsided.

In the cyclic-loading simple shear tests representative of the stress conditions on the critical sliding surface, the silty sand always failed as a result of liquefaction of the test specimen, with the sample showing very little deformation before the sudden onset of large strains accompanied by virtually no resistance to deformation. The dynamic analysis procedure incorporating cyclic simple shear test data thus provides a reasonable and adequate basis for understanding and evaluating the mechanics of the Sheffield Dam failure. Although this procedure is somewhat simplified for design purposes, similar results are indicated by more elaborate analyses that take into account the progressive nature of the development of soil liquefaction along the base of the embankment.

Probably the most convenient method of comparing the results of the stability-analysis procedures discussed above is to compare the values of the seismic coefficients that would have to be incorporated in them to predict failure along slip surfaces approximating that on which failure actually occurred. On the basis of the opinions of postfailure observers and the consequences of failure, this surface must have been near the base of the dam, intersecting the upstream face of the dam below the reservoir level. For all practical purposes, it can be considered to be located within the zone shown in Figure 63. For surfaces in this zone, values of the seismic coefficient (k_f) leading to a computed factor of safety of unity using the various analytical procedures are shown in Figure 63. With a pseudostatic analysis, the value of k_f would have to be in the range 0.15–0.21 even if the analysis incorporates conservative choices of analytical details; with a dynamic analysis with cyclic-loading triaxial-compression-test data, the value of k_f would be about 0.17–0.19; and with a dynamic analysis with cyclic-loading simple-shear-test data, the value of k_f would be about 0.11.

The significance of these values must be judged in light of the fact that the earthquake inducing failure was of strong but not major intensity. This probably induced a maximum ground acceleration of about 0.15 g at the dam site, a duration of shaking of about 15 seconds, and a series

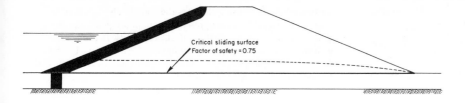

Critical sliding surface
Factor of safety = 0.75

FIGURE 62 Critical sliding surface determined by dynamic analysis using cyclic-loading simple shear test data.

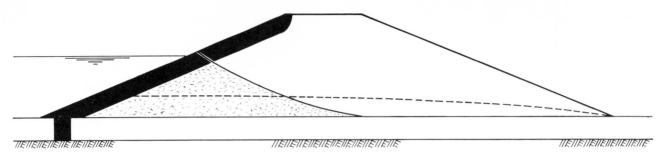

Method of Analysis	Seismic Coefficient Required to Indicate Failure for Critical Slip Surface in Probable Failure Zone (shaded)
Pseudo – static analyses using strength parameters from static loading consolidated – undrained tests (total stresses)	0.15 to 0.21
Analyses using test data from cyclic loading anisotropically consolidated – undrained triaxial compression tests (10 cycles)	0.17 to 0.19
Analyses using test data from cyclic loading simple shear tests (10 cycles)	0.11

Earthquake Characteristics: Maximum ground acceleration about 0.15g; duration of strong shaking about 15 seconds

Response Analysis: Indicates about 10 cycles with seismic coefficient equal to 0.15 for slides extending to base of embankment

FIGURE 63   Summary of analytical results.

of about 10 significant cycles of inertia forces represented by a seismic coefficient of about 0.15.

Failure of the Sheffield Dam by sliding along the base of the embankment might have resulted simply from the embankment soil being somewhat stronger than the surface layer of foundation material. This condition would not, however, significantly affect the quantitative results presented for sliding along the observed failure surface.

From the preceding discussion, it appears that the sliding of the Sheffield Dam was caused by a liquefaction failure of the loose saturated silty sand near the base of the embankment—a condition that can apparently be best predicted by procedures that incorporate the essential details of the field conditions, including consideration of the dynamic nature of the problem and the use of appropriate data from tests conducted under cyclic-loading conditions.

CONCLUSION

We have presented a discussion of the nature of soil liquefaction during earthquakes and the role of this liquefaction in the development of landslides in different types of soil formations. Particular cases have been described to illustrate the various types of slides that may occur. These cases are by no means exhaustive, however, as evidenced by the compilation of known cases of landslides during earthquakes

caused by soil liquefaction presented in Table 3. A review of the data in this table shows that these landslides have invariably been initiated by liquefaction of saturated sandy soils in a loose to medium-dense condition as a result of earthquakes ranging in magnitude from 5.5 to 8.7 and at epicentral distances ranging from several miles to several hundred miles. In this context, the landslides at Valdez, Seward, and Anchorage in the Alaska earthquake of 1964 are certainly not unique events. Rather, they are typical of the disastrous slides which may result from the ground motions induced by major earthquakes. Only by studying such events, with attention to the significant details involved, can engineers and geologists hope to develop meaningful methods of analyzing relatively simple cases of landslides caused by soil liquefaction during earthquakes or of evaluating more complex situations on the basis of appropriate experience.

ACKNOWLEDGMENTS

I am indebted to many colleagues and friends who aided in the assembly of the information presented herein. My particular thanks go to I. M. Idriss, J. N. Mathur, M. Silver, and H. Dezfulian for assistance with the analyses and computations; to K. L. Lee and P. Dunlop for information on the Sheffield Dam; to Grant A. Ross for assistance in compiling a list of previous flow slides; to I. E. Gubin and W. D. L. Finn for information about the Chait earth-

TABLE 3 Landslides Caused by Soil Liquefaction during Earthquakes

Date	Location of Earthquake	Magnitude	Location of Slide	Epicentral Distance (mi)	Type of Structure	Soil Type	Reference
373 B.C.	Helice	—	Helice	—	Coastal delta	—	Marinatos (1960)
AD 1755	Lisbon	≈ 8.7	Fez	≈ 430	—	—	Lyell (1883), Richter (1958)
1783	Calabria	—	Soriano	35	River banks	Fluvial sediments, clays with sand seams	Lyell (1883)
			Laureau	—	Hillsides	Volcanic sediments	
			Terranuova	5	River banks	Fluvial sediments	
					River banks	Fluvial sediments	
1811	New Madrid	—	Mississippi River Valley, Mo., Ark., Tenn., Ky., Ill., Ind., Vicksburg, Miss.	Major slides 30 and minor slides 140–290	River valley banks and islands	Fluvial sediments, sands to muds	Fuller (1912)
					Island	Fluvial sediments, sands to muds	
1869	Cachar	—	Barak River at Silchar	40–80	River banks	Fluvial—sand to clay	Oldham (1882), Oldham and Mallet (1872)
1886	Charleston	—	15 mi SW of Ashley River, Ashley River at Greggs	5–20 5–10	Railway fill River bank	Fluvial and deltaic sands and silts	Dutton (1889)
1897	India (Assam)	≈ 8.7	Shillong and Tutra regions	0–100	Canal banks Road embankments	Founded on alluvial plains	Oldham (1899), Richter (1958)
1899	Alaska (Yakutat)	—	Valdez	—	Submarine deposit	Deltaic and marine sediments—mainly silty sand and gravel	Coulter and Migliaccio (1966)
1902	St. Vincent	—	St. Vincent	—	Coastal delta	—	Hovey (1902)
1906	San Francisco	8.2	San Francisco area	10–30	Hillsides	—	Lawson (1908)
1907	Karatag	—	—	—	Loess slopes	Loess	Gubin (1960)
1907	Chuyanchinsk	—	—	—	Loess slopes	Loess	Gubin (1960)
1908	Alaska	—	Valdez	25	Submarine deposit	Deltaic and marine sediments—mainly silty sand and gravel	Coulter and Migliaccio (1966)
1911	Alaska	6.9	Valdez	40	Submarine deposit	Deltaic and marine sediments—mainly silty sand and gravel	Tarr and Martin (1912)
1912	Alaska	7.25	Valdez	—	Submarine deposit	Deltaic and marine sediments—mainly silty sand and gravel	Coulter and Migliaccio (1966)
1920	Kansu Province	—	Kansu Province	—	Loess slopes	Loess	Close and McCormick (1922)
1923	Kwanto (Tokyo)	8.2	Yokohama area Tokyo area	40 60	Coastal hillsides Coastal hillsides	— —	Wakimizu (1924), Hodgson (1957)
1925	Santa Barbara	6.3	Santa Barbara	7	Earth dam	Silty sand	—
1928	Chile	8.3	El Teniente	100	Tailings dam	Mining waste	Dobry and Alvarez (1967)

TABLE 3 (Continued)

Date	Location of Earthquake	Magnitude	Location of Slide	Epicentral Distance (mi)	Type of Structure	Soil Type	Reference
1933	Long Beach	6.3	Long Beach Newport Beach	20 3	Highway fills Highway fills	Fills over marshland on shore roads	Wood (1933), Richter (1958), Hodgson (1957)
1934	Bihar, Nepal	8.4	Sitamarhi to Purnea	0–80	Road and railway fills	Fluvial sediments, including sands	Roy (1939)
1935	India (now Pakistan)	7.6	Motihari	70	Lake banks	Alluvium—sand lenses	Richter (1958)
			Quetta	20–40	River banks	Alluvium—uncertain gradation	West (1936), Richter (1958)
1940	El Centro	7.0	All-American Canal	6	Canal banks	Levees and foundations of deltaic sands	G. A. Ross (personal communication)
			Alamo Canal	7–25	Canal banks	Levees and foundations of deltaic sands	
			Solfatara Canal	25–30	Canal banks	Levees and foundations of deltaic sands	
			Brawley	20	Road and railway fills	Deltaic and fluvial sands	
1941	Garm	—	—	—	Loess slopes	Loess	Gubin (1960)
1943	Faizabad	—	—	—	Loess slopes	Loess	Gubin (1960)
1948	Fukui	7.2	Fukui plain	0–15	Levees, river banks, road and railway fills	Aeolian sands, beach sands, fluvial sands and silts	Tsuya (1950), Collins and Foster (1949), Butler *et al.* (1949)
1949	Chait	7.5	Surchob and Yasman river valleys	5–25	Loess slopes	Loess	Gubin (1960)
1950	Imperial Valley	5.4	Calipatria area	1–5	Canal banks	Deltaic and aeolian sands	Wood and Heck (1966)
1954	Anchorage	6.7	Rabbit Creek	20–40	Embankment	Fill on sand	Hansen (1965)
1957	San Francisco	5.3	Lake Merced	8	Lake banks	Aeolian and beach sands	C. K. Chan (personal communication)
1959	Jaltipan	6.5	Coatzacoalcos	20	River banks, water-front fill	Fine sandy silt, uniform and loose	de Cossio (1960), Marsal (1961)
			Minatitlan–Coatzacoalcos highway	20–30	Road and bridge approach fills	Fill over marshland	
1960	Chile	8.4	Rinihue	140	River banks; highway and railway fills	Fluvial and glacial sands; foundations of fluvial and glacial gravels, sands, silts	Duke and Leeds (1963), K. L. Lee (personal communication)

116

			Puerto Mont…		Coastal terraces; sea walls and quay walls	Glaciofluvial deposits. Fill mainly sands to silty sands, loose	
				240			
			Valdivia	125	River banks	Fluvial sediments	
1964	Alaska	8.4	Anchorage	70	Coastal bluffs	Sand layers and lenses in clay deposit	Shannon & Wilson, Inc. (1964), Coulter and Migliaccio (1966)
			Valdez	40	Coastal delta	Silty sands and gravel	
			Seward	90	Coastal delta	—	
			Kenai Lake	80	Lake deltas	Deltaic sandy gravels; some sand lenses	McCulloch (1966)
1964	Niigata	7.3	Niigata area	35	Earth banks	Fluvial sand	Yamada (1966), Yokomura (1966), Kawakami and Asada (1966)
1965	Chile	7.2	El Cobre	≃25	Tailings dam	Mining waste	Dobry and Alvarez (1967)
			La Patagua	≃ 9	Tailings dam	Mining waste	
			Hierro Viejo	≃16	Tailings dam	Mining waste	
			Los Maquis	≃ 8	Tailings dam	Mining waste	
			El Cerrado	≃18	Tailings dam	Mining waste	
1965	Seattle	6.7	Capitol Lake Blvd., Olympia	38	Road causeway	Sand/gravel fill over lake and tidal sediments	G. A. Ross (personal communication)
			Union Pacific at Tumwater	38	Railway on benched slope	Cut/fill slope in outwash sands	
			Suquamish	26	Coastal bluff	Till over fine sand and silt strata	
			Port Orchard	18	Waterfront fill	Sand over beach sand and bay mud	
			E. Mercer Way, Mercer Island	10	Roadways on benched slopes	Sand on tills and outwash sands	
			Edmonds	29	Dumped fill on slope	Sandy till and refuse on till slope	
			Foster golf course, Duwamish	10	River terrace	Fluvial sands and silts	
			Victor	24	Highway fill	Sand fill at toe of coastal bluff	
1966	Parkfield	5.5	Cholame Creek north of Cholame	17	Stream banks	Fluvial sediments, sand strata, or lenses	G. A. Ross (personal communication)

quake; to C. K. Chan for photographs of landslides around Lake Merced; to C. M. Duke for photographs of the damage in the Chilean earthquake of 1960; to H. D. McNiven for advice about wave propagation; to G. R. Martin for many helpful discussions on the mechanics of sliding caused by liquefaction of sand seams; to C. R. Allen and G. W. Housner for photographs of earthquake damage; to S. Davis for information on the Rinihue landslides; to S. D. Wilson for information about the Baker River slide; to members of the staffs of the U.S. Geological Survey and the Alaska District, Corps of Engineers for information on the Alaska earthquake; to the State of California Department of Water Resources, who sponsored the study of the Sheffield Dam failure; and to many colleagues in studies of the Alaska earthquake of 1964, whose comments and advice helped to frame many of the ideas presented in the paper.

REFERENCES

Broadhead, G. C., 1902. The New Madrid earthquake. *American Geologist*, 30 (August), 76–87.

Butler, D. W., K. Muto, and K. Minami, 1949. Engineering report on the Fukui earthquake. Tokyo: General Headquarters, Far East Command, Office of the Engineer.

Byerly, Perry, 1955. Notes on the intensity of the Santa Barbara earthquake between Santa Barbara and San Luis Obispo. *Bulletin of the Seismological Society of America*, 15 (December), 279–281.

Casagrande, A., and S. D. Wilson, 1951. Effects of rate of loading on the strength of clays and shales at constant water content. *Geotechnique*, 2 (June), 251–263.

Close, U., and E. McCormick, 1922. Where the mountains walked. *The National Geographic Magazine*, 41 (May), 445–464.

Clough, R. W., and A. K. Chopra, 1966. Earthquake stress analysis in earth dams. *Journal of the Engineering Mechanics Division* (American Society of Civil Engineers), 92 (April), 197–211.

Collins, J. J., and H. L. Foster, 1949. The Fukui earthquake, Hokuriku Region, Japan, 28 June 1948. *Geology*, Vol. 1, February. Tokyo: General Headquarters, Far East Command, Office of the Engineer.

Coulter, Henry W., and Ralph R. Migliaccio, 1966. Effects of the earthquake of March 27, 1964, at Valdez, Alaska. U.S. Geological Survey Professional Paper 542-C. Washington: Government Printing Office. 36p. Also *in* The Great Alaska Earthquake of 1964: Geology. NAS Pub. 1601. Washington: National Academy of Sciences, 1971. p. 359–394.

Davis, S., and J. K. Karzulovic, 1961. Deslizamientos en el valle del rio San Pedro Provincia de Valdivia Chile. Anales de la Facultad de Ciencias Fisicales y Matematicas, Publication No. 20. Santiago: University of Chile, Institute of Geology.

de Cossio, R. D., 1960. Foundation failures during the Coatzacoalcos (Mexico) earthquake of 26 August 1959. Proceedings, Second World Conference on Earthquake Engineering, Tokyo, Japan.

Dobry, R., and L. Alvarez, 1967. Seismic failures of Chilean tailings dams. *Journal of the Soil Mechanics and Foundations Division* (American Society of Civil Engineers), 93 (November), 237–260.

Duke, C. Martin, and David J. Leeds, 1963. Response of soils, foundations, and earth structures to the Chilean earthquakes of 1960. *Bulletin of the Seismological Society of America*, 53 (February), 309–357.

Dutton, C. E., 1889. The Charleston earthquake of August 31, 1886. U.S. Geological Survey 8th Annual Report. Washington: Government Printing Office. p. 203–528.

Engineering Geology Evaluation Group, 1964. Geologic report: 27 March 1964 earthquake in Greater Anchorage area (unpublished report). Anchorage: Alaska State Housing Authority and City of Anchorage. 47 p.

Eppley, R. A., 1960. Earthquake history of the United States, Part II, No. 41-1. U.S. Coast and Geodetic Survey. Washington: Government Printing Office. 55 p.

Flint, Timothy, 1826. Recollections of the last 10 years, passed in occasional residences and journeyings, in the valley of the Mississippi, from Pittsburg and the Missouri to the Gulf of Mexico, and from Florida to the Spanish frontier. Boston: Cummings, Hillyard and Company. p. 222–228.

Fuller, M. L., 1912. The New Madrid earthquake. U.S. Geological Survey Bulletin 494. Washington: Government Printing Office. 119 p.

Gubin, I. E., 1960. Regime of seismicity on the territory of Tadjikistan. USSR Academy of Sciences Press: Moscow.

Hadley, Jarvis B., 1964. Landslides and related phenomena accompanying the Hebgen Lake earthquake of August 17, 1959 *in* The Hebgen Lake, Montana, earthquake of August 17, 1959. U.S. Geological Survey Professional Paper 435. Washington: Government Printing Office. p. 107–138.

Hansen, Wallace R., 1965. Effects of the earthquake of March 27, 1964, at Anchorage, Alaska. U.S. Geological Survey Professional Paper 542-A. Washington: Government Printing Office. 68 p. Also *in* The Great Alaska Earthquake of 1964: Geology. NAS Pub. 1601. Washington: National Academy of Sciences, 1971. p. 289–357.

Henderson, J., 1933. The geological aspects of the Hawke's Bay earthquakes. *The New Zealand Journal of Science and Technology*, 15 (July), 38–75.

Hildreth, S. P., 1844. Original contributions to the American pioneer. Cincinnati: J. S. Williams. p. 34–35.

Hodgson, J. H., 1957. Nature of faulting in large earthquakes. *Geological Society of America Bulletin*, 68 (May), 611–643.

Hovey, E. O., 1902. Martinique and St. Vincent. A preliminary report upon the eruptions of 1902. *American Museum of Natural History Bulletin*, Vol. 16, p. 333–372.

Idriss, I. M., and H. Bolton Seed, 1967. Response of earth banks during earthquakes. *Journal of the Soil Mechanics and Foundations Division* (American Society of Civil Engineers), 93 (May), 61–82.

Kawakami, F., and A. Asada, 1966. Damage to the ground and earth structures by the Niigata earthquake of June 16, 1964. *Soil and Foundation*, 6 (January), 14–30.

Latrobe, C. J., 1836. The rambler in North America. London: R. B. Seeley and W. Burnside. p. 108.

Lawson, A. C. (Chairman, California State Earthquake Investigation Commission), 1908. The California earthquake of April 18, 1906. 2 Volumes. Carnegie Institution Publication 87. Washington: Carnegie Institution of Washington. 451 p. (Reprinted 1969)

Lee, Kenneth L., and H. Bolton Seed, 1967. Cyclic stress conditions causing liquefaction of sand. *Journal of the Soil Mechanics and Foundations Division* (American Society of Civil Engineers), 93 (January), 47–70.

Lemke, Richard W., 1967. Effects of the earthquake of March 27, 1964 at Seward, Alaska. U.S. Geological Survey Professional Paper 542-E. Washington: Government Printing Office. 43 p. Also *in* The Great Alaska Earthquake of 1964: Geology. NAS Pub. 1601. Washington: National Academy of Sciences, 1971. p. 395–437.

Lloyd, J. T., 1856. Lloyd's steamboat directory. Cincinnati: J. T. Lloyd and Company. p. 325.

Lowe, J., and L. Karafiath, 1959. Stability of earth dams upon drawdown. First Pan-American Conference on Soil Mechanics and Foundation Engineering, Mexico City, Mexico, 1959.

Lyell, Sir Charles, 1849. A second visit to the United States of North America (Volume 2). London: J. Murray. p. 228–239.

Lyell, Sir Charles, 1883. Principles of geology (11th edition, Volume II). New York: Appleton and Company. 652 p.

McCulloch, David S., 1966. Slide-induced waves, seiching, and ground fracturing caused by the earthquake of March 27, 1964, at Kenai Lake, Alaska. U.S. Geological Survey Professional Paper 543-A. Washington: Government Printing Office. 41 p. Also in The Great Alaska Earthquake of 1964: Hydrology. NAS Pub. 1603. Washington: National Academy of Sciences, 1968. p. 47–81.

McCulloch, David S., and Manuel G. Bonilla, 1967. Railroad damage in the Alaska earthquake. Journal of the Soil Mechanics and Foundations Division (American Society of Civil Engineers), 93 (September), 89–100.

Marinatos, S. N., 1960. Helice submerged town of classical Greece. Archaeology, 13 (No. 3, Autumn), 186–193.

Marsal, R. J., 1961. Behavior of a sandy uniform soil during the Jaltipan earthquake, Mexico. Proceedings of the Fifth International Conference on Soil Mechanics and Foundation Engineering, Paris, France.

Nunn, Herbert, 1925. Municipal problems of Santa Barbara. Bulletin of the Seismological Society of America, 15 (December), 308–319.

Oldham, R. D., 1899. Report on the great earthquake of 12 June 1897. Memoirs of the Geological Survey of India [Calcutta: Office of the Superintendent of Government Printing], Vol. 49. 379 p.

Oldham, Thomas O., 1882. The Cachar earthquake of 10 January 1869 (R. D. Oldham, editor). Memoirs of the Geological Survey of India [Calcutta: Office of the Superintendent of Government Printing], 19 (Part 1), 1–98.

Oldham, Thomas O., and R. Mallett, 1872. Secondary effects of the earthquake of 10 January 1869 in Cachar. Geologic Society Quarterly Journal (London), Vol. 28.

O'Shaughnessy, M. M., 1925. Letter to the Editor. Engineering News Record, July 9.

Peacock, W. H., and H. Bolton Seed, 1967. Liquefaction of saturated sand under cyclic loading simple shear conditions. Berkeley: University of California, Soil Mechanics and Bituminous Research Laboratory, July.

Peck, R. B., 1967. Stability of natural slopes. Journal of the Soil Mechanics and Foundations Division (American Society of Civil Engineers), 93 (July), 403–417.

Richter, Charles F., 1958. Elementary seismology. San Francisco: W. H. Freeman and Company. 768 p.

Roy, S. C., 1939. The Bihar–Nepal earthquake of 1934: Seismometric study. Memoirs of the Geological Survey of India [Calcutta: Office of the Superintendent of Government Printing], Vol. 73.

Schmidt, J. F. J., 1875. Studien über Erdbeben. Leipzig: C. Scholtze.

Seed, H. Bolton, 1966. A method for earthquake resistant design of earth dams. Journal of the Soil Mechanics and Foundations Division (American Society of Civil Engineers), 92 (January), 13–41.

Seed, H. Bolton, and Kenneth L. Lee, 1966. Liquefaction of saturated sands during cyclic loading. Journal of the Soil Mechanics and Foundations Division (American Society of Civil Engineers), 92 (November), 105–134.

Seed, H. Bolton, and G. R. Martin, 1966. The seismic coefficient in earth dam design. Journal of the Soil Mechanics and Foundations Division (American Society of Civil Engineers), 92 (May), 25–58.

Seed, H. Bolton, and Stanley D. Wilson, 1967. The Turnagain Heights landslide, Anchorage, Alaska. Journal of the Soil Mechanics and Foundations Division (American Society of Civil Engineers), 93 (July), 325–353. Also in The Great Alaska Earthquake of 1964: Engineering. NAS Pub. 1606. Washington: National Academy of Sciences, 1973.

Seed, H. Bolton, K. L. Lee, and I. M. Idriss, 1967. An analysis of the Sheffield Dam failure. Journal of the Soil Mechanics and Foundations Division (American Society of Civil Engineers), 95 (November), 1453–1490.

Shannon, W. L., 1966. Slope failures at Seward, Alaska. Paper presented at American Society of Civil Engineers Conference on Stability and Performance of Slopes and Embankments, Berkeley, California, August.

Shannon & Wilson, Inc., 1964. Report on Anchorage area soil studies, Alaska, to U.S. Army Engineer District, Alaska, August. Seattle: Shannon & Wilson, Inc. 300 p.

Sherif, M. A., 1965. Flow and fracture properties of Seattle clays. Soil Engineering Research Series No. 1, January. Seattle: University of Washington.

Tarr, Ralph S., and Lawrence Martin, 1912. The earthquakes at Yakutat Bay, Alaska, in September, 1899. U.S. Geological Survey Professional Paper 69. Washington: Government Printing Office. 135 p.

Thiers, G. R., and H. Bolton Seed, 1968. Cyclic stress-strain characteristics of clay. Journal of the Soil Mechanics and Foundations Division (American Society of Civil Engineers), 94 (March), 555–569.

Tsuya, H., 1950. The Fukui earthquake of June 28, 1948. Report of the Special Committee for the Study of the Fukui Earthquake, Tokyo.

U.S. Army Corps of Engineers, 1949. Report on investigation of failure of Sheffield Dam, Santa Barbara. Insurance Report. Washington: U.S. Army Corps of Engineers.

U.S. Army Engineer District, 1964. Eyewitness accounts. Anchorage: U.S. Army Engineer District, Alaska.

U.S. Army Engineer District, 1966. Internal report on Turnagain earthquake slide studies. Anchorage: U.S. Army Engineer District, Alaska, April.

Wakimizu, T., 1924. Kwaguku–Tisiki. Scientific Knowledge, 4 (No. 4, April). (in Japanese)

West, W. D., 1936. Geological account of the Quetta earthquake. Transaction of the Mining Geology Institute of India, Vol. 30.

Willis, B., 1925. A study of the Santa Barbara earthquake of June 29, 1925. Bulletin of the Seismological Society of America, 15 (December), 255–278.

Wood, H. O., 1933. Preliminary report on the Long Beach earthquake. Bulletin of the Seismological Society of America, 23 (No. 2), 43–56.

Wood, H. O., and N. H. Heck, 1966. Earthquake history of the United States. U.S. Coast and Geodetic Survey. Washington: Government Printing Office.

Yamada, G., 1966. Damage to earth structures and foundations by the Niigata earthquake, June 16, 1964. Soil and Foundation, 6 (January).

Yokomura, S., 1966. The damage to river dykes and related structures caused by the Niigata earthquake. Soil and Foundation, 6 (January).

H. BOLTON SEED
UNIVERSITY OF CALIFORNIA, BERKELEY

STANLEY D. WILSON
SHANNON & WILSON, INC.

Reprinted with minor changes from
Journal of the Soil Mechanics and Foundations Division
(American Society of Civil Engineers), July 1967,
"The Turnagain Heights Landslide, Anchorage, Alaska"

Turnagain Heights Landslide

ABSTRACT: During the Alaska earthquake of March 27, 1964, a large landslide, involving a strip of coastline about 8,500 ft long and extending inland about 900 ft, occurred in the Turnagain Heights area near Anchorage. A study of the soil conditions in the slide area and an analysis of the mechanics of the landslide development led to the conclusion that the slide developed because of a loss in strength of the soils, particularly of lenses of sand, that underlay the slide area as a result of the sequence of earthquake ground motions. The mechanics of soil movement in the slide area were discovered to be complex, involving the subsidence of large blocks of soil, the lateral displacement of clay in a 25-ft-thick zone, and the simultaneous lateral translation of the slide debris on liquefied sands and silts. A relatively small margin separates catastrophic failure from a possibly adequate performance under equally strong shaking of somewhat shorter duration; for this reason, great care must be exercised in translating experiences of such failures to other areas and conditions.

DESCRIPTION OF THE SLIDE

During the Alaskan earthquake of March 27, 1964, a number of major slides occurred in the Anchorage area (Shannon & Wilson, Inc., 1964; Hansen, 1965). The largest of these slides was along the coastline in the Turnagain Heights area. A plan of the slide area is shown in Figure 1 and an aerial view of the slide is shown in Figure 2.

The coastline in this area was marked by bluffs some 70 ft high, sloping at about 1.5 : 1 down to the bay. The slide extended about 8,500 ft from west to east along the bluff line and retrogressed inward from the coast a distance of about 1,200 ft at the west end and about 600 ft at the east end. The total area within the slide zone was thus about 130 acres.

Within the slide area the original ground surface was completely broken up into a complex system of ridges and depressions, producing an extremely irregular and hummocky surface. A general view of the central part of the slide area is shown in Figure 3 and a view of the east end of the area is shown in Figure 4. In the depressed areas between the ridges, the ground dropped an average of about 35 ft during the sliding.

Lateral movement of the soil mass during the slide was extensive. The material from the original bluff line moved out into the bay as much as 2,000 ft in some places (Figure 1), and, in general, the outward movement beyond the original bluff line mirrored the extent of inland regression of the slide behind the bluff line.

The ground at the west end of the slide area was undeveloped, but that at the east end was a residential area. About 75 houses located in the east end of the slide area were destroyed; a view of some of these houses after the slide is shown in Figure 5.

A study conducted in Anchorage by the Engineering Geology Evaluation Group (1964) reveals the extent of movements of some of the houses in the slide area. The group prepared Figure 6, which shows the initial and final

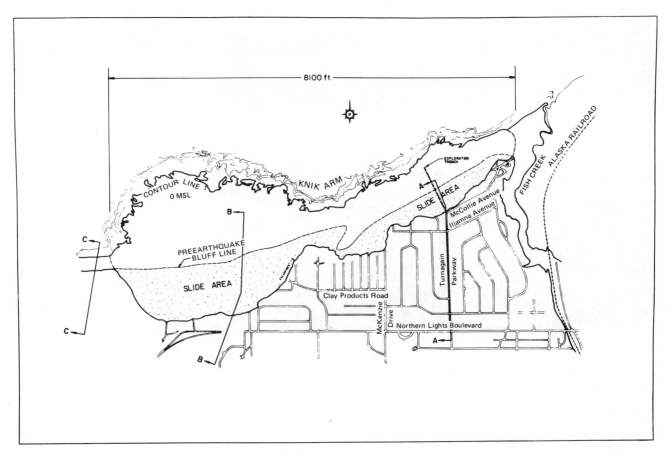

FIGURE 1 Plan of slide area.

FIGURE 2 Aerial view of Turnagain Heights landslide.

FIGURE 3 Conditions in central part of slide area.

positions of houses determined by surveys before and after the earthquake. Some of the houses moved laterally about 500 or 600 ft, usually—though not always—toward the original coastline. The transverse movement of some houses is indicative of the complex mechanism involved in the development of the slide.

Eyewitness accounts indicate that the sliding began about 2 minutes after the earthquake started and continued to some extent after the earthquake-induced ground motions had ceased. The movement seems to have started as two separate slides, one at the east end and one at the west end, which merged together as they developed and enlarged.

During the earthquake, numerous tension cracks developed in the ground behind the slide zone as a result of a general movement of the land toward the coastline. Cracking was more intensive behind the east end of the slide, and surveys in this area showed that the accumulated extension in a 2,000-ft zone extending behind the slide area amounted

FIGURE 4 Conditions in east end of slide area.

FIGURE 5 Houses destroyed by slide.

to about 3 ft. No appreciable movement occurred in this area during the 3-month period following the earthquake.

THE ALASKA EARTHQUAKE

The earthquake that caused the Turnagain Heights landslide has been rated by the U.S. Coast and Geodetic Survey as a shock of magnitude 8.5 on the revised Richter scale, with its epicenter about 80 mi east of Anchorage. Because there were no strong-motion seismograph stations in the area,

little is known about the magnitude of the ground motions induced by the earthquake. On the basis of the observed damage and related effects, however, the intensity in the Anchorage area is estimated at approximately VIII on the Modified Mercalli Scale.

One of the main features of the ground motions induced by the earthquake was their unusually long duration. At least six people were found in and outside the Anchorage area who had timed the duration of perceptible ground shaking on watches; the durations observed by these people ranged from about 4.5 to 7.5 minutes. On the basis of these

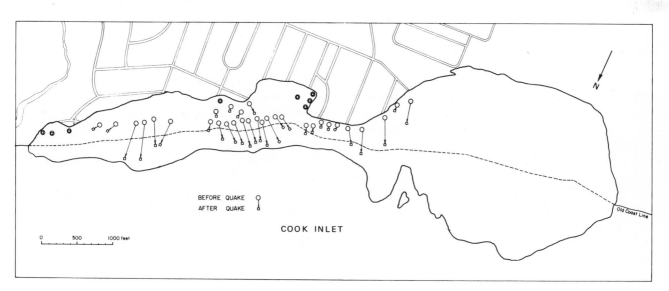

BEFORE QUAKE

AFTER QUAKE

COOK INLET

Old Coast Line

N

0   500   1000 feet

FIGURE 6 Movements of houses in slide area.

observations the duration of significant motions seems to have been at least 4 minutes.

Eyewitness reports agree, in general, that the first ground motions at Anchorage had a strong east–west component. As the shaking continued, however, the main component is said to have shifted first to a north–south direction and later to a more complex motion on which little general agreement can be obtained.

GEOLOGY OF THE ANCHORAGE AREA

The Anchorage area, located within a well-known earthquake region, occupies 150 mi² at the head of Cook Inlet in south central Alaska. The geology of the region has been discussed by Miller and Dobrovolny (1959). The city is built on lowlands, on a relatively flat plain of outwash sand and gravel underlain by Bootlegger Cove Clay. Rocks of Mesozoic and Tertiary age are overlain by unconsolidated deposits of glacial drift, mantled with wind-deposited silt. The lowlands range from sea level to 1,200 ft, with an average elevation of less that 200 ft above mean sea level. The highest point in the nearby Chugach Range is at elevation 4,301 ft.

The oldest rocks exposed in the Anchorage area are the metamorphics of the Chugach Mountains. These Mesozoic rocks are mainly greenstones, graywackes, slates, argillites, and limestones. Tertiary shales of the Matanuska formation locally compose the bedrock beneath glacial drift. The drift was deposited during the Pleistocene and consists of successions of unsorted material (till), outwash sand and gravel, estuarine or lacustrine clay, and silt beds. Undifferentiated drift and morainal and alluvial fan material have been deposited between other glacial drift and nonglacial materials, resulting in poorly defined boundaries. Nonglacial deposits include loess, alluvium, estuarine silt, dune sand, and swamp deposits.

Ablation till is fragmental and unconsolidated material that underlies outwash, lacustrine, and marine deposits. The till is thickest beneath the lowlands away from the Chugach Mountains. Deposits near the mountains contain till with subordinate outwash sediments. Till in the Anchorage area has been identified in drill cuttings on the basis of hardness and relative impermeability.

Clay and silt are present as an extensive deposit that has been designated the Bootlegger Cove Clay. It overlies some of the ground morainal till and prodelta deposits and is a blue-gray plastic clay that is relatively impermeable and easily identified. The deposit is fairly continuous, but is concealed to the north by an end moraine and pinches out elsewhere. It ranges from nothing to a thickness of more than 300 ft, averaging from 100 to 150 ft in thickness. Silty and sandy beds are found within the clay. These are slightly to moderately permeable, but for purposes of groundwater development have proved unsatisfactory. Naptowne outwash (sand and gravel) overlying the Bootlegger Cove Clay is the significant foundation material for Anchorage. This deposit is relatively shallow, so that clay is exposed in the bluff areas and the slopes are susceptible to slumping and sliding. The outwash is cross-laminated and crudely bedded. The ground-surface slopes vary gently to the southwest and the immediately underlying materials grade from coarse sand, cobbles, and boulders (toward Eagle River) to stratified sand (toward Turnagain).

The geomorphic features are primarily glacial: morainal hills, the outwash plain, the meltwater channels and depressions, lakes and swamps, and other glacial features from older ice sheets. Most of the existing land forms have resulted from ice movement, and only minor topographic modification has taken place since.

All the larger streams, except Chester Creek, rise in the Chugach Mountains and flow across the outwash plain in channels. Fed by precipitation and snowmelt, the streams are not yet fully integrated with swamps, lakes, and ponds of glacial origin. Chester and Ship creeks and their tributaries dissect the north half of Anchorage, occupying older valleys cut by larger glacier-fed streams. Campbell Creek, flowing in a deeply incised meltwater channel, extends from a glaciated mountain valley to the lowlands, where it meanders through swamps. Many swamp lakes are connected by sluggish streams, and lakes found on ground moraines are very poorly drained. Small swamps are even found in higher environments along edges of stream valleys and near hilltops. These swamps are a result of poor subsurface drainage, where relatively impervious clayey till lies underneath, restricting the downward movement of water.

SOIL CONDITIONS IN THE TURNAGAIN HEIGHTS SLIDE AREA

An extensive program of soil exploration (Shannon & Wilson, Inc., 1964) was undertaken to determine the soil conditions in the Turnagain Heights slide area. The general soil conditions determined by these investigations are shown in Figures 7–10. Figures 7 and 8 show soil profiles along sections through the east and west ends of the slide area (sections AA and BB, Figure 1). Figure 9 shows a soil profile through the area just west of the slide area where no sliding occurred (section CC, Figure 1), and Figure 10 shows a profile along an east–west section through the slide area.

In general, the Turnagain area (surface elevation $\simeq 70$ ft) is covered by a surface layer of sand and gravel that ranges in thickness from 15–20 ft at the east end of the slide area to about 5–10 ft at the west end.

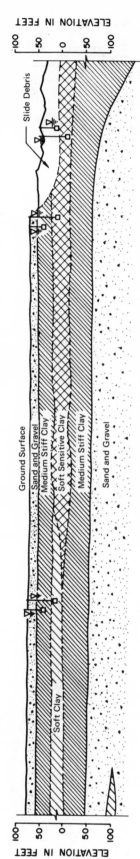

FIGURE 7 Soil profile through east end of slide area (Section AA in Figure 1).

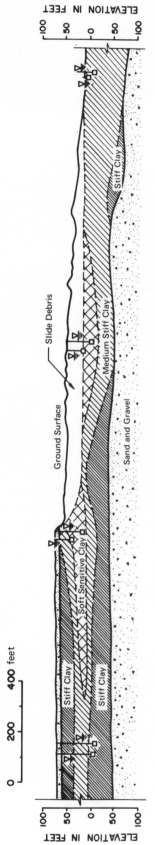

FIGURE 8 Soil profile through west end of slide area (Section BB in Figure 1).

125

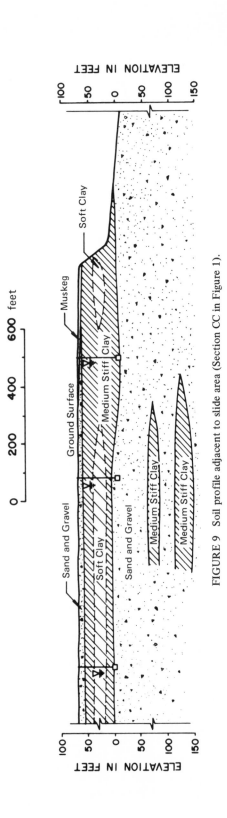

FIGURE 9 Soil profile adjacent to slide area (Section CC in Figure 1).

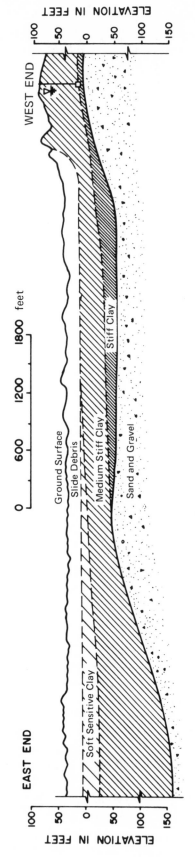

FIGURE 10 Soil profile along slide area.

126

The sand and gravel deposit is underlain by a deep bed of Bootlegger Cove Clay about 100–150 ft thick. This soil is a sensitive marine deposit of silty clay with a shear strength decreasing from about 1 ton/ft² at its surface (elevation approximately 50 ft) to about 0.45 ton/ft² at elevation 0 and then increasing again to about 0.6 ton/ft² at elevation –30 ft; its sensitivity ranges between about 5 and 30. The more sensitive samples of the clay typically have a liquid limit of about 33 and a plasticity index of 12, and are plotted just above the A-line on a plasticity chart. (A typical variation of strength with depth is illustrated by the data presented in Figure 18.)

Between elevation +25 ft and –10 ft at the east end of the slide area, and between elevation +35 ft and +10 ft at the west end of the slide area, the water content of the clay exceeds the liquid limit; in these zones, maximum sensitivity is indicated by the shear-strength determinations, which for the remolded soil is about 0.02 ton/ft². It is unfortunate that the zone of maximum sensitivity generally coincides with the zone of lowest strength for this deposit. In general, the sensitivity of the clay seems to decrease with increasing distance behind the original coastline (see profiles AA and BB in Figures 7 and 8), and the extremely sensitive clay was not found in borings made about 2,000 ft behind the original bluff line.

The clay deposit contains numerous thin strata and seams of silt and fine sand that are apparently not continuous throughout the deposit. At some points the sand strata are up to 3 ft thick; usually, however, they range from a fraction of an inch to several inches in depth. At the east end of the slide areas, frequent thin seams of fine sand were found between elevations 30 ft and 37 ft, a sand layer several feet thick was encountered near elevation 20 ft, and a number of thinner lenses were found below this, their thickness and frequency diminishing with depth; below 10 ft elevation, sand lenses were thin and were found only infrequently.

At the west end of the slide area, sand lenses were thinner and less frequently encountered than at the east end. However, the sand lenses in this part of the slide zone were commonly associated with silt lenses, which were found at frequent intervals near and above an elevation of +20 ft. Below this, they were only occasionally encountered.

Seaward of the bluff line that existed before the slide, the clay was overlain by a deposit of estuary silt that sloped gently downward away from the shoreline. This material, which would tend to liquefy during the earthquake, probably played a significant role in the development of the slide by providing a lubricated surface on which blocks of soil from the sliding mass could move outward with little resistance to motion.

A soil profile along a section CC just west of the slide area is shown in Figure 9. The extent of the zone of very

sensitive clay is much reduced in this area. In addition, the clay is somewhat stiffer than that at corresponding depths in the adjacent slide area, no sand lenses were observed in the borings above 15-ft elevation, and the total depth of clay is some 30 ft less than in the adjacent slide area. These facts possibly explain why sliding did not extend further to the west in spite of the generally similar topographic and geologic conditions in this area.

STRENGTH OF SOILS UNDER CYCLIC-LOADING CONDITIONS

Laboratory studies (Seed and Lee, 1964; Seed and Chan, 1964) were conducted to investigate the strengths of the soils in the Turnagain Heights slide area under conditions simulating those developed during the earthquake. For soil elements in the embankment some distance behind the bluffs, these conditions can be simulated approximately by simple shear tests conducted under cyclic-loading conditions.

The results of such tests performed on undistributed samples of the sensitive silty clay are shown in Figure 11. Some of these tests—modified to permit the conduct of cyclic-stress or cyclic-strain tests—were performed using the simple shear equipment developed by the Norwegian Geotechnical Institute (Bjerrum and Landva, 1966). Other tests were performed using cyclic-loading triaxial-compression procedures (Seed and Chan, 1966). Both types of test gave essentially the same results, showing that failure of this clay could be induced by cyclic stresses substantially less than the static strength of the clay under undrained-loading conditions. For 30 significant stress cycles, such as might have been developed during the earthquake, failure was induced by cyclic stresses equal to about 55 percent of the static strength; for the soft sensitive clay, which might be considered to have an *in situ* shear strength of about 850 psf, this corresponds to a cyclic-shear strength of about 470 psf.

Under cyclic loading conditions, loose and medium-dense saturated sands may fail by liquefaction. The cyclic-shear stresses required to induce liquefaction of the sand seams were investigated by tests on a typical sample taken at about 20 ft elevation at the east end of the slide area. For this purpose, the cyclic-loading triaxial-test procedure used previously by Seed and Lee (1966) was adopted; the results of such tests may be corrected to other void ratios and to confining pressures on the basis of previous data for similar materials (Seed and Lee, 1965). It is also necessary to apply a correction to the data to convert the results to those corresponding to simple shear conditions. For samples of similar sand at about 12.5 ft elevation and for the approximate *in situ* void-ratio conditions measured by field density determinations, the test data indicated the relation between cyclic-shear stress and number of stress cycles required to

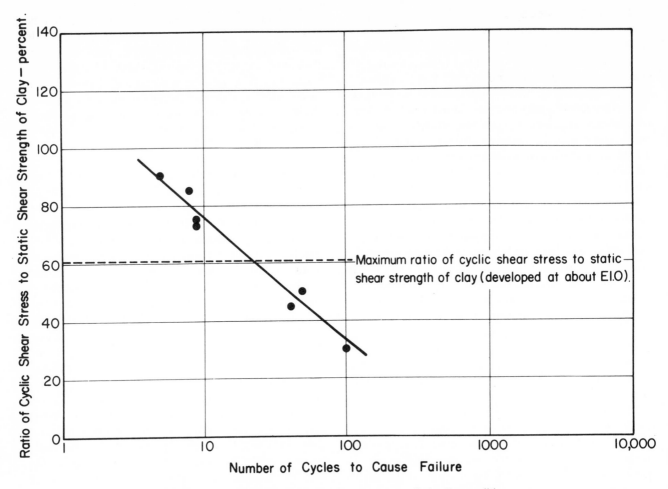

FIGURE 11   Strength of samples of silty clay under cyclic-loading conditions.

cause liquefaction shown in Figure 12. Liquefaction of the sand seams can be expected to occur in 30 cycles at a cyclic shear stress of about 420 psf, a shear stress somewhat less than that required to induce failure of the soft clay in the same number of cycles. Thus, for comparable shear stresses in the zone behind the bluffs, liquefaction might be expected in the sand before failure would develop in the clay.

INVESTIGATION OF SOIL DISPLACEMENT IN SLIDE ZONE

Several methods were used to investigate the nature of the soil displacements in the slide zone and the possible locations of slip surfaces, including the following:

CONTINUOUS-SAMPLE BORINGS

A number of borings were made from which continuous undisturbed samples were recovered to a depth of 100 ft or

more. In cases of sample loss, a supplementary boring was made adjacent to the first, and overlapping samples were extracted.

In some cases, the samples were closely examined in the field in order to detect possible zones of disturbance. Penetrometer tests and miniature vane tests were conducted at frequent intervals along a freshly exposed section of the sample to aid in this investigation, and the location of disturbed zones was facilitated by the presence of the thin horizontal silt and sand seams in the clay. Several samples were recovered in this way that showed considerable intermixing of the sand and clay, together with a much-reduced strength in the clay portion of the sample. The positions of these samples on a soil profile through the east end of the slide zone are shown in Figure 13.

For the majority of the borings, samples were shipped to the laboratory; there, they were subjected to a detailed examination involving a description of the soil, stratification, and any evidence of disturbance, augmented by determinations of Atterberg limits, natural water content, shear strength, and sensitivity at about 1-ft intervals. Shear-strength determinations were made by a torsional-vane shear device specially developed for rapid testing in this investigation (Shannon & Wilson, Inc., 1964).

Strength values varied considerably in some borings and numerous zones of extremely low strength were encountered. These zones were attributed to sample disturbance during sliding and their positions were noted in relation to other observations. The variation of shear strength with depth in several borings made along a soil profile at the east end of the slide area is shown in Figure 13. Just behind the slide area, shear strengths rarely drop below 0.3 kg/cm² (whereas in borings made in the slide area, many values are less than 0.25 kg/cm², and some are as low as 0.03 kg/cm²). The zones of very low shear strength agree well with the locations of very badly disturbed samples in the soil profile.

In the early stages of the investigation, considerable confusion was caused by the observation that borings made as little as 10–20 ft apart showed radical differences in the variation of shear-strength depth. However, subsequent interpretation of the mechanism of slide movement led to the conclusion that such variations are to be expected in slide zones of this type.

TRENCH SECTION

To throw further light on the distribution of materials in the slide area, a 1,000-ft trench extending from the back of the slide zone to some distance beyond the toe of the original bluff line was constructed through the east end of the slide zone. The trenching was accomplished in two phases; a shallow trench for access and deeper trenching to expose the surface of the clay throughout the slide profile for mapping. The depth of this trench was increased to as much as 30 ft in some places to uncover the clay that was buried under substantial depths of sand and gravel in depressions in the slide area. To take advantage of the fresh exposures, details of the stratigraphy revealed by the walls of the trench were mapped as the excavating progressed.

The distribution of the sand and gravel and the clay

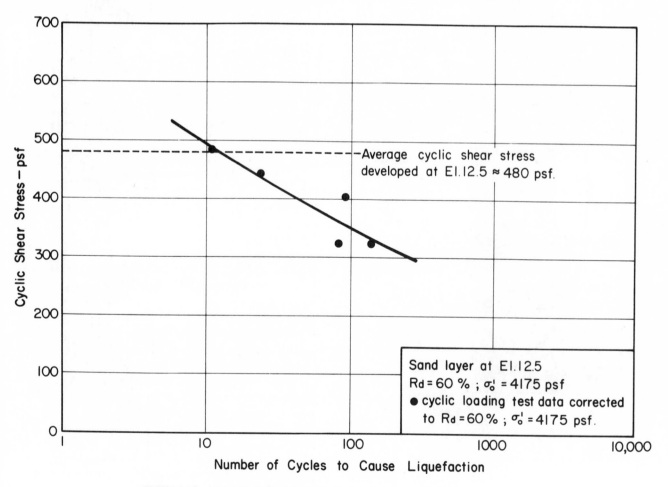

FIGURE 12 Stresses inducing liquefaction of sand under cyclic-loading conditions.

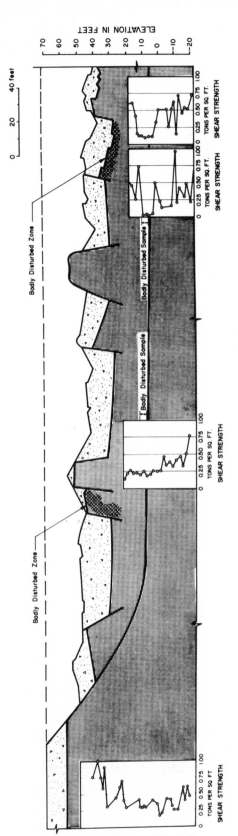

FIGURE 13 Detailed soil profile through east end of slide area.

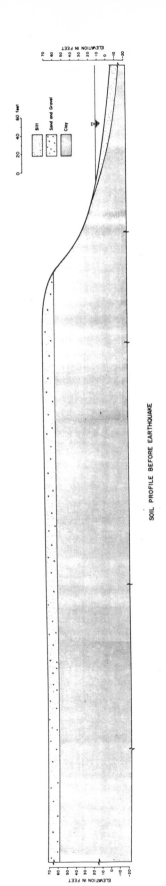

SOIL PROFILE BEFORE EARTHQUAKE

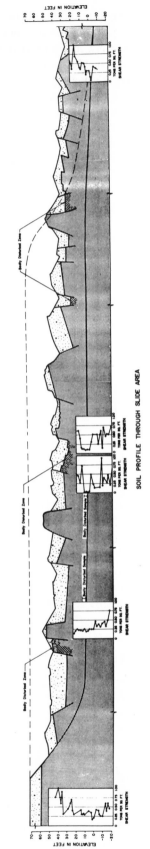

FIGURE 14 Soil profile in trench section through east end of slide area.

130

within the slide area revealed by this trench section is shown in Figure 14. The ridges of clay separated by depressed zones are readily apparent, as is the erratic distribution of the sand and gravel that originally uniformly overlaid the clay to a depth of about 15 ft. In many places the stratification of the exposed clay was relatively undisturbed, but in other zones the clay was apparently severely disturbed and disoriented. The locations of the badly disturbed zones are shown on the profile. Unless otherwise noted, the stratification was essentially parallel to the upper surface of the clay.

SURVEY OF CLAY RIDGES

The clay ridges shown in Figure 3 were a characteristic feature of the slide area. Hansen (1965) has described them as follows:

> Hundreds of sharp-crested clay ridges alternating with collapsed troughs, and oriented normal to the direction of slippage, distinguished the disruption pattern of the Turnagain Heights slide. . . . Most of the clay ridges ranged in height from about 10 to 15 ft, but a few were more than 20 ft high. They were as much as 300 ft long and were spread 50 to 150 ft apart. Their steep sides, which sloped 60° to 70°, were furrowed and grooved by slippage of one surface against another. On the average the ridges were sharper crested and more closely spaced . . . in the west end of the slide area than in the east end.

A view of a particularly well-formed ridge at the east end of the slide area is shown in Figure 15a; a view of a towering ridge in the west end of the slide area, with the original soil overburden still perched on top of it after translating several hundred feet, is shown in Figure 15b.

Observations revealed that these ridges of clay had undergone large displacements with virtually no change in inclination and with only small changes in elevation. Measurements showed that the changes in elevation of the ridges were compatible with sliding on a slip surface that had an inclination of about 4 percent downward toward the original toe of the bluff, as shown in Figure 14.

OBSERVATION IN SLIDE AREA

Reconnaissance in the west end of the slide area revealed the presence of a zone, about a quarter of an acre in extent, which was completely free of slide debris (see Figure 16) and along which sliding had apparently occurred. This zone, located on the original bluff line, had an average elevation of about +20 ft, but it sloped down with an average grade of about 15 percent toward the original toe of the bluff. The presence of this zone indicated that sliding at the west end of the slide zone occurred on surfaces above elevation +20 ft. The lower surface of sliding was, however, almost certainly deeper at the east end of the slide area.

FIGURE 15   Ridges of clay in slide area. See text for discussion.

FIGURE 16 Zone of slide area completely free of debris.

OBSERVATIONS BEHIND SLIDE AREA

After the earthquake, a survey was made of the settlement of the area behind the slide zone. Settlements up to 8 in. were found to have occurred within several hundred feet of the slide scarp; beyond this distance, settlements were much smaller. Such observations indicate a movement of soil toward the main slide area.

ANALYSIS OF TURNAGAIN HEIGHTS SLIDE

DEPTH OF SLIDE ZONE

A detailed section through the east end of the slide zone, revealed by the exploration trench and the results of tests on samples from several borings made along this section, is shown in Figure 13. Samples taken from borings within the slide area show unusually low strengths over some depth ranges, followed by a sudden marked increase in strength. The low strength values probably indicate material disturbed by sliding, and the higher values reflect the presence of undisturbed soil. The boundaries at which marked increases in strength occur may denote the position of the main sliding surface.

In two of the borings shown in Figure 13, continuous samples of soil from the slide area were critically examined in the field for evidence of severe disturbance. The presence of thin seams in the clay greatly facilitated this examination. The positions of samples evidencing severe disturbance in each of these holes are shown on Figure 13.

Because of the positions of the severely disturbed samples, the boundaries between low and high strengths of the clay, and the positions of clay zones exhibiting lower strengths than similar material at the same elevation outside the slide area, it was concluded that the main surface of sliding was probably at an elevation of about 8 ft near the back of the section. Further, it probably sloped slightly toward the toe of the original bluff line.

The logs of borings made through the center of the west end of the slide area gave some indication of a similar sliding surface at about 10-ft elevation. The debris-free zones somewhat further west, however, indicated the slide surface to be at about 20 ft elevation. Thus the main slide surface at the west end of the slide area may have varied between 10 and 20 ft elevation, reaching the higher elevations with increasing distance in the westerly direction. In the direction of sliding, the main slide surface probably had an average slope of about 4 percent behind the original bluff line, steepening to about 10 or 15 percent in this location.

STABILITY BEFORE EARTHQUAKE AND SLIDING POTENTIAL

Analyses of the stability of the bluffs along the coastline before the earthquake, made by using undrained shear strengths measured on samples obtained from adjacent areas, indicate a factor of safety of about 0.85. This method of analysis, however, has been shown previously (Bjerrum and Kjaernsli, 1957) to give values too low for the factor of safety of natural slopes consisting mostly of normally consolidated soft clay, and the low computed value is not necessarily indicative of marginal stability.

Some support for the belief that the bluffs had only

marginal stability before the earthquake is provided by their long history of sliding induced by undercutting of the toe of the slopes as a result of coastal erosion. Such slides however, are likely to be shallow and their occurrence is not necessarily indicative of potential instability along a deep-seated sliding surface.

Whatever the margin of stability may have been, it was sufficient to prevent failure of the bluff slopes as a result of accelerations induced by the following (U.S. Coast and Geodetic Survey, 1964):

1. An earthquake in 1943 of magnitude 7.3 at an epicentral distance of about 35 mi

2. An earthquake in 1951 of magnitude 6.3 at an epicentral distance of about 50 mi

3. An earthquake in 1954 of magnitude 6.5–7 at an epicentral distance of about 60 mi (This earthquake triggered a substantial slide along The Alaska Railroad at Potter Hill, about 10 mi south of Anchorage.)

4. The first 1.5 minutes of the Alaska earthquake of 1964

Thus, the margin of stability might well have been considered adequate for many purposes. It is extremely significant that if the duration of ground shaking in the 1964 earthquake had been no longer than that associated with many previous strong-motion records, the slide would not have occurred, and the bluffs would have been considered to have an adequate margin of stability to withstand an extremely strong ground motion.

In light of these facts, it is difficult to know whether detailed studies made before the earthquake would have predicted the probability of major sliding being induced by even a major earthquake at an epicentral distance of 75 mi. It is extremely doubtful that any analyses would have anticipated the extent of inland regression of the slide (1,200 ft behind a 70-ft-high slope at the west end of the slide area). It is of special interest, therefore, to examine not only the cause of the slide, but also the probable reasons for its large inland regression.

CAUSES OF SLIDE DEVELOPMENT

During a major earthquake, the maximum ground accelerations and the corresponding inertia forces that they induce in slopes invariably develop during the first 30 seconds of ground shaking. In the case of the Turnagain slide, numerous eyewitnesses report no evidence of an impending slope failure during the first 1.5 minutes of the ground motions. This seems to indicate that deformations began to develop, not during the period of application of large inertia forces at the beginning of the earthquake, but during a period of smaller inertia forces midway through the

earthquake. The only explanation for smaller inertia forces being able to induce displacements not previously induced by larger inertia forces is that the soil was in a substantially weaker condition during the period of application of the smaller forces than it was when the larger forces were developed. The primary cause of the landslide in the Turnagain area was probably the loss of strength of the soil resulting from the ground displacements induced by the earthquake; if there had been no loss of strength, the stresses induced by the earthquake would have been insufficient to cause failure. This conclusion dramatically illustrates the importance of considering the possible loss of strength of soils as a result of cyclic loading in assessing the stability of embankments during earthquakes.

REASONS FOR INLAND REGRESSION OF SLIDE ZONE

The large extent of inland regression of the slide zone may be attributed to several major factors:

Presence of Shoreline Silt Deposits

One of the prime factors leading to the large inland regression of the slide was undoubtedly the presence of a sloping layer of estuary silt at the toe of the bluff. The nature of this material can be seen in the photograph (Figure 17) taken at such an area of the coastline. During the earthquake, this silt would liquefy and thereby provide a semi-fluid sloping surface to facilitate the translation of soil masses falling onto it. Failure of the bluff by any type of slide would cause the sliding mass to be deposited on the silt and thereby continue to slide outward into the water, leaving a new exposed face that might well fail by a repetition of the same mechanism. This process would continue as long as the earthquake lasted. In fact, the slide would be able to retrogress because there was no opportunity for a buildup of slide debris at the toe of the slope to buttress the unstable condition.

Loss of Strength in Soil behind Bluff Line

The slide, as previously mentioned, must have been induced by a loss of strength in the soil underlying the bluff. The configuration of the slide area following the earthquake is indicative of sliding induced by the presence of an extremely weak zone underlying the slide area and extending back well behind the original bluff line. The probable presence of such a zone is also indicated by the following evidence:

1. The cracking and lateral extension of the surface behind the slide area in the direction of the coastline indicates movement of level ground toward the slide area. This extension could only be caused by movement along an extremely weak layer, indicating that a severely weakened zone ex-

FIGURE 17   Offshore silt deposit.

tended beyond the boundaries of the slide area, at least at the east end of the slide.

2. Settlement as much as 8 in. in the surface just behind the slide area was probably caused by movement along the weakened zone toward the slide area itself.

3. The relatively horizontal nature of the lower boundary of the slide area indicates that some characteristics of a depositional layer may have been involved in the slide movements.

Possible causes of the development of such a weakened zone are loss of strength in the clay deposits, because of the cyclic-shear stresses and strains induced in them by the earthquake, and liquefaction of sand lenses and seams, within the clay deposit, caused by the cyclic loading induced by the earthquake. A weak zone caused by either of these factors would lead to a rapid development of the slide once it had started. The possibility of such effects developing in the soil behind the bluff line is worth considering.

For this purpose, an analysis has been made to assess the likely magnitude of the stresses and strains developed in the soil during the first 1.5 minutes of ground shaking and their effects on the sand and clay deposits. The entire deposit of soil overlying the firm rock base at a depth of about 470 ft was considered to respond as a damped elastic system to horizontal base motions caused by the earthquake. The resulting soil response was computed following the procedure described by Seed and Idriss (1966).

The soil conditions, used in the analysis and shown in Figure 18, are considered representative of those existing in and behind the east end of the slide area before the earthquake. Shear moduli for use in the analysis were selected on the basis of vibration tests on undisturbed samples (Shannon & Wilson, Inc., 1964), giving due consideration to the effects of sample disturbance, amplitude of shear strains developed in the field, and the stiffening effect of sand lenses in the soft clay. A damping factor of 20 percent was chosen on the basis of previous test data and the value found to give a reasonable assessment of soil response in the Niigata earthquake (Seed and Idriss, 1966). For purposes of analysis, the entire soil deposit was treated as a series of 27 different layers. Layers 5 ft thick were used in the soft and medium clays that are of primary interest, and appropriately thicker layers were used elsewhere. Previous studies have shown that this number of layers is sufficient to give an accurate representation of the response of the deposit.

It was assumed that the base motions would be similar in form to those previously recorded on firm ground at a distance of 75 mi from a major earthquake. Accordingly, they were considered to have the same form as the accelerations recorded at Pasadena as a result of the Kern County, California, earthquake of 1952 (Figure 19). Because this earthquake had a magnitude of only 7.7 (compared to the Alaska earthquake magnitude of 8.5) and a strong-motion duration of only about 35 seconds, it was considered appropriate to increase the amplitude of the motions by a scaling factor of 1.5 and to simulate the first 2 minutes of the longer duration of the Alaska earthquake by repeating the Pasadena record three times in sequence. Thus, the record shown in Figure 19, with the ordinates multiplied by 1.5, was considered to represent 30–40 seconds of base-rock shaking in the Anchorage area during the first 2 minutes of the Alaska earthquake.

The computed response of the soil deposits to this base motion are presented in Table 1 and Figure 18. The maximum ground-surface acceleration was determined to be 0.11 g, and the fundamental period of the deposit was 2.01 seconds. These values agree well with corresponding

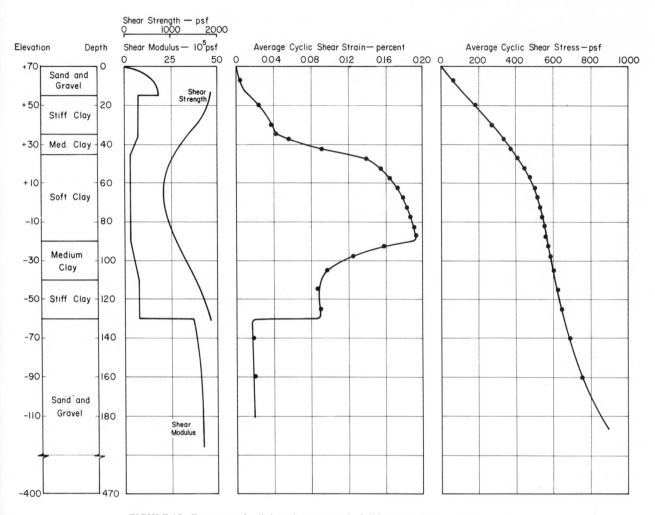

FIGURE 18   Response of soil deposit at east end of slide area to horizontal base motions.

G. W. Housner, California Institute of Technology

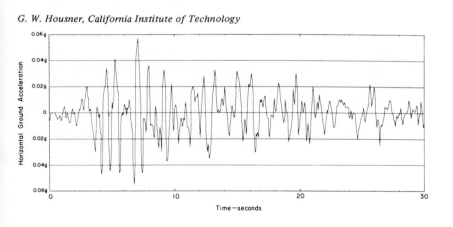

FIGURE 19   Horizontal ground accelerations at Pasadena caused by the 1952 Kern County, California, earthquake.

TABLE 1   Response Analysis of Soil Deposits

Elev.	Depth, ft	Material	Shear Strength, s_u (psf)	Shear Modulus, $\times 10^5$ (psf)	Average Cyclic Strain, %	Average Cyclic Stress, τ_c (psf)	Effective Overburden Pressure, σ_o' (psf)	Ratio τ_c/σ_o'	Ratio τ_c/s_u
62.5	7.5	Sand and gravel	–	15.1	0.0045	69	–	–	–
50	20	Stiff clay	1800	7.2	0.0255	184	2100	0.087	–
40	30	Stiff clay	1600	7.2	0.0376	271	2700	0.100	–
32.5	37.5	Medium clay	1300	5.9	0.057	335	3140	0.107	–
27.5	42.5	Medium clay	1100	4.1	0.091	375	3415	0.110	–
22.5	47.5	Soft clay	1000	2.9	0.142	414	3675	0.112	0.41
17.5	52.5	Soft clay	900	2.9	0.155	450	3925	0.114	0.50
12.5	57.5	Soft clay	870	2.9	0.165	480	4175	0.115	0.55
7.5	62.5	Soft clay	850	2.9	0.173	501	4425	0.113	0.59
2.5	67.5	Soft clay	850	2.9	0.179	519	4675	0.111	0.61
−2.5	72.5	Soft clay	860	2.9	0.183	530	4925	0.108	0.61
−7.5	77.5	Soft clay	890	2.9	0.186	540	5175	0.104	0.60
−12.5	82.5	Soft clay	950	2.9	0.191	555	5425	0.102	0.58
−17.5	87.5	Soft clay	1000	2.9	0.193	560	5675	0.099	0.56
−22.5	92.5	Medium clay	1150	3.6	0.159	572	–	–	–
−27.5	97.5	Medium clay	1250	4.7	0.125	588	–	–	–
−35	105	Medium clay	1400	6.3	0.096	605	–	–	–
−45	115	Stiff clay	1600	7.2	0.087	625	–	–	–
−55	125	Stiff clay	1800	7.2	0.090	646	–	–	–
−70	140	Sand and gravel	–	38.1	0.018	690	–	–	–
−135	205	Sand and gravel	–	42.9	0.022	930	–	–	–
−275	345	Sand and gravel	–	50.2	0.032	1620	–	–	–

values estimated by residents and by observers of the Anchorage ground shaking.

The computed variations of shear stresses developed near the top and bottom of the soft-clay layer are shown in Figure 20. The stresses near the bottom of the layer have the same form as those near the top of the layer, but they are significantly larger. At both levels, the amplitude of the stress cycles varies considerably. A careful study of these response patterns shows that it is reasonable to represent the stress history near the top of the soft clay by 10 significant cycles with an average amplitude of 415 psf and that near the bottom of the layer by the same number of stress cycles with an average amplitude of 560 psf. These average stress cycles have a period of about 1.2 seconds and occur at a rate of 10 cycles per 30–40 seconds of ground shaking.

By this procedure, the average cyclic-shear stress and shear strain were determined at all levels in the soil deposit. It is apparent that the maximum shear strains occur in the soft-clay layer, with the magnitude increasing progressively in this layer from about 0.14 percent to about 0.19 percent with increasing depth. Because of the varying shear moduli, the average cyclic-shear stress increases progressively with increasing depth in the soil deposit as indicated in Figure 18.

The values of cyclic-shear stress shown in Figure 18 together with the cyclic-loading test data presented previously, can be used to assess the possibility of strength loss in the

soil deposits behind the bluff. In making this assessment, however, it is important to recognize that the analysis was made using average shear moduli for clay layers containing sand lenses. Because the sand in such deposits will, unless it liquefies, be significantly stiffer than the surrounding clay, the stresses in the sand lenses would actually be higher than those shown on the figure, whereas the stresses on the adjacent clay would be correspondingly lower.

A loss in strength of sand during cyclic loading may develop as a result of liquefaction. Details of a method for analyzing the possibility of liquefaction developing have been presented by Seed and Idriss (1966) and Seed and Lee (1965). It has been shown that in a deposit of sand of uniform relative density, the danger of liquefaction is determined by the ratio of the cyclic-shear stress to the initial effective overburden pressure (τ_c/σ_o'); the larger the ratio, the smaller is the number of stress cycles required to induce liquefaction. Values of this ratio for the upper parts of the soil deposit are listed in Table 1. It will be seen that the ratio is a maximum at a depth of 57.5 ft, indicating that liquefaction, if it occurred at all, would be likely to develop first at about 12 ft elevation. This is not, however, a strong maximum, and initial liquefaction might be expected to occur anywhere in the range of 0- to 20-ft elevation. If liquefaction occurred, the pattern of cyclic-shear stresses would be changed, and assessments of the possibility of further liquefaction could not be made from the data in Figure 18.

The possibility of liquefaction occurring at an elevation of 12.5 ft can be assessed by comparing the magnitude of the cyclic-shear stress developed at this level with the cyclic stresses required to induce liquefaction of the sand in cyclic-loading tests for comparable initial conditions. This comparison is shown in Figure 12, which indicates that the computed average value of the shear stress developed at this elevation would induce liquefaction in about 12 stress cycles, i.e., in about 45 seconds of ground shaking. Because the actual stresses probably exceed the computed stresses, as previously noted, liquefaction of sand lenses or layers in the zone around an elevation of 12.5 ft might reasonably be expected to occur within the first 45 seconds of the earthquake.

A similar analysis can be made to determine the possibility of loss of strength in the clay. For a saturated clay, the possibility of failure is indicated by the ratio of the average cyclic-shear stress to the undrained shear strength (τ_c/s_u); in which case, the higher ratios would be more critical. The computed values of this ratio are listed in Table 1, which shows that the ratio is a maximum in the zone from +3- to −3-ft elevation. Again, however, there is no strong

maximum, and the most dangerous condition could occur in the range from +10- to −15-ft elevation.

The number of stress cycles required to induce failure at the most critical elevation can be assessed by comparing the computed ratio of τ_c/s_u with the values of this ratio required to cause failure of the clay as determined by cyclic-loading tests. This comparison is shown in Figure 11, which shows that for constant-stress conditions, failure of the clay would require about 22 stress cycles, or about 1.5 minutes of ground shaking.

On the basis of this analysis, it appears that liquefaction of the sand between an elevation of 0 and 20 ft would be likely to occur before any significant strength loss developed in the clay. Such liquefaction might be expected to have occurred in the first 45 seconds of the earthquake, so that the soft clay behind the bluff would have contained numerous lenses of liquefied sand; at a somewhat later stage, strength loss of the clay would also develop in some zones. This sequence of events is also indicated by the results of cyclic-strain tests conducted on samples of the sand and clay under conditions representative of those developed *in situ*.

It seems, therefore, that before failure occurred near the bluff line, the soil behind the bluff had developed a severely weakened and largely liquefied zone somewhere between

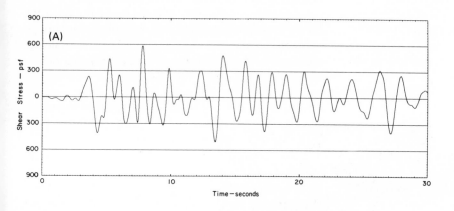

FIGURE 20 (A) Shear-stress variation near top of soft clay layer (elevation 22.5 ft).

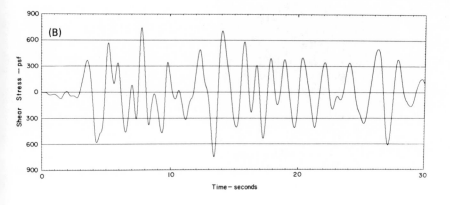

FIGURE 20 (B) Shear-stress variation near bottom of soft clay layer (elevation −17.5 ft).

0- and 20-ft elevation; once failure occurred at the bluff line, permitting movement along this weakened zone, sliding would progress rapidly and would lead to the large inland regression of the slide area. Because of the lenticular nature of the sand seams, however, the weakened zone or main slide surface would necessarily pass through clay in some section of its length, producing a composite surface on which sliding would develop. The most probable zone of sand liquefaction indicated by the analysis 0- to 20-ft elevation is in somewhat better agreement with the probable position of the base of the main slide surface (+10- to +5-ft elevation) than is the computed position of the zone of maximum weakening in the clay (+10- to –15-ft elevation).

The following evidence supports the concept that sand lenses or seams in and behind the slide area played an important role in the development of the slide:

1. Several samples recovered from the slide area showed sand and clay intermixed in a form that could only have resulted from fluid characteristics of the sand.

2. Ridges of sand, 2 to 3 ft high, 3 to 6 ft wide, and about 100 ft long were formed by sand boils within the slide area (Hansen, 1965) as shown in Figure 21. A large boil, spread over an area of 3,200 ft^2, was also noted near but outside the slide area by the Engineering Geology Evaluation Group (1964).

3. A description (U.S. Army Engineer District, 1964) of the slide movements by residents of a house in the slide area during the earthquake stated: "The floor ripped and sand came up from below into the living room." It is difficult to imagine such an inflow of sand, unless it were caused by liquefaction.

4. Although there is considerable evidence (lateral extension, cracking, settlement) that the area behind the slide area was underlain by a severely weakened layer during the earthquake, no evidence of a weakened clay zone underlying this area was revealed by borings made several weeks after the earthquake.

5. Although sand lenses were encountered in many borings made in the slide area, very few were noted in borings made immediately adjacent to the slide area (U.S. Army Engineer District, 1966).

Some of this evidence is circumstantial, but it lends support to the concept that a severely weakened zone developed in the early stages of the earthquake in the area behind the bluff line and that, although this zone was a composite of sand lenses and adjacent clay, liquefaction of the sand played a significant role in its development.

Sensitivity of Soft Clay and Duration of Ground Shaking

The large inland regression of the slide area was undoubtedly also influenced by the high sensitivity of the clay. Once sliding of a mass was initiated, this sensitivity would result in a further drastic loss of shear strength caused by remolding in the shear zones that facilitated lateral displacement. Furthermore, the extremely long duration of the earthquake (more than 4 minutes) was a prime factor in determining the extent of the movements. Once the ground motion

FIGURE 21 Ridge of sand formed by sand boil in slide area.

stopped, most of the sliding stopped, and the extent of the slide area, especially at the east end of the slide area would have been substantially increased if the earthquake had continued a little longer.

MECHANICS OF SLIDE MOVEMENT AS INDICATED BY MODEL TESTS

An examination of the ground configuration in the slide area (see Figures 2–4) makes it obvious that the sliding could not have developed solely as a result of a progressive series of conventional slides in clay along circular arcs that were directed toward the coastline. Trees and poles could be seen inclined in opposite directions—a pattern not likely to develop from repeated slides in the same direction. Furthermore, the steep-sided ridges of clay previously described, which moved large distances with little or no change in elevation, were a characteristic feature of the slide area, and the mechanism leading to their formation required clarification. Finally, it was important to develop some concept of the probable mechanism of sliding to obtain a better concept of the nature of the material in the slide area and thereby to assess its vulnerability to further sliding if another similar earthquake should occur.

To throw some light on the mechanics of slide development when clay soils are underlain by a layer of extremely weak material, a series of model tests was conducted at the University of California. A bank of clay about 4 in. high, composed of an extremely weak layer overlain by layers of stronger clay, was constructed in the approximate configuration of the bluffs in the Turnagain Heights area. The layers of clay composing the model were given different colors to facilitate observations of the slip surfaces, and the model was maintained in a stable condition during construction by supporting the face and toe of the slope with a retractable bulkhead. Thus the model might be considered to represent the conditions in the Turnagain area after a severely weakened zone had developed behind the bluff line after 30–60 seconds of the earthquake.

When the construction was completed, the retractable bulkhead supporting the model embankment was removed and sliding was allowed to develop. In a number of tests, sliding was facilitated by vibrating the model on a shaking table after withdrawal of the bulkhead. The general pattern of the slide area in the model was found to bear a close resemblance to that in the Turnagain area, with ridges of clay developing and translating through substantial distances with little change in elevation.

The model provided an excellent means of observing the mechanics of slide development. Failure was usually found to involve the sequence of movements illustrated in Figure 22 and described as follows:

1. A series of several rotational slides, starting just behind the crest of the slope and retrogressing from the slope, causes outward and downward movement of the ground surface. These slides are accompanied by extrusion of the weak layer from the toe of the slide (Figure 22a–d).

2. After several such slides, the upper layers of stronger clay, which moved laterally and downward, cut through the weak layer so that no further extrusion from the toe can occur (Figure 22d). Beyond this point, continued sliding results in the outward movement of a prismatic ridge of soil, essentially without change in elevation (Figure 22e).

3. Following the lateral translation of the ridge, extensive tension cracking develops in the clay behind the ridge, giving the impression that a wide zone of soil is affected by the movements (Figure 22f).

4. The area behind the ridge settles, forming a sloping depressed zone in which the tension cracks may separate the soil into a series of blocks. This action is well illustrated by Figure 22f and by the photograph in Figure 23, which was taken during the conduct of a model test.

5. When the outer end of the depressed zone has subsided sufficiently, a conventional type of slide movement occurs along a surface consisting of a short curved portion in the stiff clays and a substantial horizontal section along

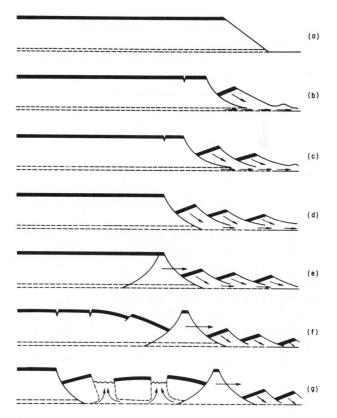

FIGURE 22 Failure mechanism observed in model tests. See text for discussion.

FIGURE 23   Formation of clay ridge during model test.

the weak layer at the base. This movement causes lateral translation and subsidence of the soil behind the ridge, forming a new scarp at the back of the slide area and a graben depression. The movement is usually accompanied by a slight heaving of the previously subsided toe of the graben area. Sometimes a separation of the slide mass into several blocks is caused by weak material squeezed to the sides of the blocks as they subside (Figure 22g).

6. During the rotation and subsidence of the stiff clay to form the new scarp line, the downward movement of the stiff clay again cuts through the weak layer so that its extrusion from the base of the hitherto unaffected area is stopped. Thus continuation of the slide, either because the base is slightly inclined or because of inertia forces induced by shaking, causes a repetition of the operations described in movements 2 to 5 and a progressive retrogression of the slide area.

One important observation made was that the formation of the prismatic ridges was only found when the weak layer was unable to extrude through the base of the slide area. Apart from the probable slope of the main sliding surface, the ridges maintain their early elevations, no material moves through them, and all the material that was originally behind the ridge remains behind it as the entire mass translates laterally. This situation provides a basis for determining the nature of the movements in the slide area. In addition, the subsidence of material to form a graben-type depression was accompanied by some sideways extrusion of underlying weak material. Subsidence and spreading of the original ground cannot possibly occur without some extrusion of material in this way.

The concepts of slide movements developed from the model tests provided a valuable key to the understanding of

the mechanism of slide development and to the analysis of the soil conditions in the slide area.

MECHANICS OF SLIDE DEVELOPMENT

On the basis of the foregoing concepts and analyses, the outlined hypothesis for the mechanics of the Turnagain Heights landslide can be developed:

1. Possibly because of the greater depth of clay near the bluff line, which would give the material in this area a longer period of vibration and a reduced response, the soil composing the bluffs was sufficiently strong to withstand about 2 minutes of ground shaking before failure developed.

2. As long as the bluffs remained stable, the soil behind them was buttressed against lateral movement. During the first minute or so of the earthquake, however, liquefaction of sand lenses occurred at about 5- to 20-ft elevation at the east end of the slide area and at 15- to 25-ft elevation at the west end of the slide area. This created a severely weakened zone that extended backward from the temporarily stable bluffs some considerable distance inland.

3. Finally, as a result of inertia forces and loss of strength in the soils, failure developed near the bluffs by a conventional slide mechanism. The slide mass slipped outward into the water by sliding on the surface of the sloping silt deposit, leaving the slide surface exposed and permitting the development of a second slide of the same type.

4. After one or more such slides had occurred, the sliding surface merged into the previously weakened zone behind the original bluff line. At this stage, the mode of failure changed to a form similar to that shown in Figure 22. Failure progressed rapidly, which resulted in the development of ridges of clay throughout the slide area and in badly dis-

integrated depressed zones between the ridges. At this stage, the main surface of sliding was the zone that had been severely weakened by liquefaction of sand lenses, but the sliding also involved extensive shear zones in the clay. Remolding of the clay between lenses and elsewhere during sliding resulted in a substantial quantity of very weak clay in the slide zone.

5. The severely weakened zone facilitated translation of soil in the slide zone; once slide debris had passed beyond the bluff line, it slipped rapidly outward along the sloping surface of the offshore silt deposit.

6. Sliding continued as long as the earthquake lasted, but movements were rapidly arrested once the ground motions stopped, partly because the offshore silt deposit was stabilized, sand deposits in the slide zone were stabilized, and inertia forces were eliminated. The substantial volume of remolded clay in and near the slide zone, however, permitted a continuation of sliding to some extent after the ground motions had stopped.

With this hypothesis and the pattern of slide development indicated by the model tests, it is possible to reconstruct the mechanics of failure leading to the configuration of material in the trench section through the east end of the slide area shown in Figure 24. Because no material moves through the ridges of clay, the volume of soil between ridge material after sliding must be the same as the volume between ridges before sliding. The initial positions of the ridges can be determined by finding the lateral spacing required to recompress the soil into its original thickness; the probable vertical positions of the intervening soil blocks can then be determined from a comparison of their dimensions, the available space between the initial positions of the clay ridges, and the initial position of the well-defined boundary between the clay and the overlying sand and gravel outwash.

By this procedure, the probable initial positions of blocks of soil in the slide zone were reconstructed as shown in Figure 24(B). In the space between the slide scarp and the first clay ridge (block 4), the volume of material indicates that this clay ridge must have been initially in the position shown in the reconstructed section. The probable position of block 1 can be determined by sliding it back along the slide scarp until the outwash and clay boundary is in the correct initial position. Soil block 2 is then found to fit into the space between block 1 and the clay ridge; it, therefore, appears that the soil occupying space 3 in the slide section (A) must have been extruded laterally from the space below block 2 in the reconstructed section. This explanation agrees with the observation that the clay in space 3 was very badly disturbed during construction of the trench (see Figure 14).

This procedure leads to the fully reconstructed section (B) shown in Figure 24 and indicates that the clay ridges

underwent large lateral translations during the sliding; ridge 18 moved a distance of 240 ft. These displacements are very similar to the observed movements of houses in the slide area shown in Figure 6. The slide reconstruction also indicates that failure involved the displacement of large zones of clay in the depth range from +5- to +30-ft elevation. Thus the condition of the clay within the slide area would be expected to vary enormously; at some sections, it would be relatively undisturbed except for a small depth near the main failure zone, whereas in others it would consist of a thick layer—down to approximately +5-ft elevation—of displaced and badly disturbed material. This condition would explain why two borings in the slide area, made only 10–20 ft apart, but with one passing through block 2 in Figure 24 and the other passing through section 3, might show radically different strength variations in the clay.

CONCLUSION

The following conclusions have evolved from this study of the Turnagain Heights landslide, which occurred during the Alaska earthquake:

1. The nature of the Bootlegger Cove Clay formation is very complex, involving sand and silt lenses and seams distributed throughout a silty clay and ranging in sensitivity from 5 to 30. It is very difficult to analyze the behavior of such deposits, even under static loading, and still more difficult under earthquake-loading conditions.

2. Because no measurements of the ground motions developed at Anchorage during the earthquake are available, analyses of the soil behavior must be based on estimates of motions made by observers in the area. To provide a basis for analyses of soil behavior, it is extremely important that efforts be made to establish strong-motion accelerographs in areas likely to suffer major damage during earthquakes.

3. The landslide at Turnagain Heights did not begin until about 1.5–2 minutes after the earthquake had started. Probably, therefore, it did not develop during the period of maximum ground motions, but as a result of the loss of strength in the underlying soils that resulted from the sequence of earthquake motions.

4. The extensive inland regression of the slide was probably due in large measure to liquefaction of sand lenses and weakening of clay soil over a zone extending well behind the original bluff line. The presence of an offshore deposit of silt that facilitated removal of slide debris from the toe of the slide area, the high sensitivity of the clay, and the unusually long duration of the earthquake were also factors contributing to this regression.

5. Sliding was accompanied by large lateral translation of material and by the development of numerous character-

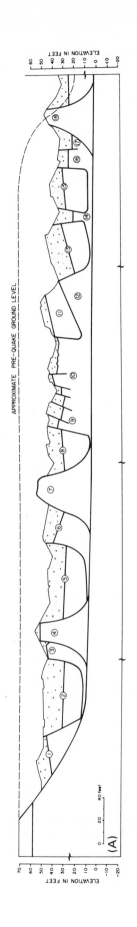
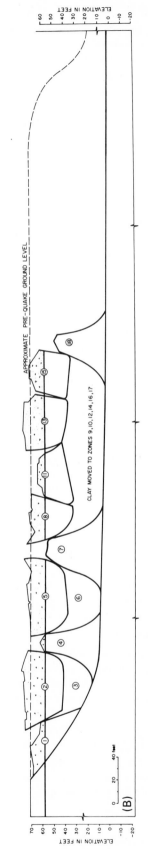

FIGURE 24 Reconstruction of soil displacement at east end of slide zone. (A) Soil profile after earthquake and (B) reconstructed soil profile.

142

istic ridges of clay, which translated with little change in elevation. The main surface of sliding was a weakened zone ranging in elevation from about 8-ft elevation at the east end of the slide area to about 20-ft elevation at the west end. The mechanics of soil movement above this zone were complex, involving the subsidence of large blocks of soil and the lateral displacement of clay in a layer of clay about 25 ft thick.

6. The material in the slide area following the earthquake varied widely—from relatively undisturbed material in some sections to extremely disturbed material in others. Reconsolidation of the remolded material under the new overburden pressures prevailing in the slide area would lead in time to considerable strengthening of the slide area and to marked differential settlements.

7. Assessment of the vulnerability of slopes to failures during earthquakes is a complex problem, involving considerations of the intensity and duration of ground shaking, the effect of the shaking on soil properties, the forces induced by the shaking, the nature of the soil deposits involved, and the magnitude of displacements that may occur. In many instances, the margin between severe destruction of an area of sliding and completely adequate performance may be very slight. As events developed, the Turnagain Heights landslide may now be cited as a classic case of a major slide disaster induced by an earthquake. If the duration of ground shaking in the Alaska earthquake had been appreciably shorter, or even comparable to that of many other large earthquakes—1 to 1.5 minutes perhaps—the slide would probably not have developed, and the area could have been cited as a classic case, illustrating the safety, even during major earthquakes, of slopes underlain by clay soils. In light of such possibilities, experiences of slope failures or nonfailures during earthquakes require careful appraisal before they can be translated to other areas and conditions.

ACKNOWLEDGMENTS

The field investigations described were directed by the authors and performed by Shannon & Wilson, Inc., for the U.S. Army Corps of Engineers, Alaska District. The model studies and the analyses of the slide mechanism were performed at the University of California as part of a research project, sponsored by the National Science Foundation, on "Soil Behavior during Earthquakes."

The authors extend their appreciation to the many engineers who aided in the investigations. Special acknowledgment is due to Warren George, Erwin Long, and J. Ireton of the U.S. Army Corps of Engineers; W. L. Shannon of Shannon & Wilson, Inc.; J. K. Mitchell, R. J. Woodward, Jr., H. Peacock, and I. M. Idriss, members of the staff of the University of California Soil Mechanics and Bituminous Materials Research Laboratory; L. Bjerrum, R. B. Peck, and T. Thomson, consultants to the U.S. Army Corps of Engineers; C. R. Allen, who provided the aerial view of the landslide in Figure 2; G. W. Housner, who provided the earthquake record in Figure 19; and the U.S. Geological Survey, which provided the photograph in Figure 21.

REFERENCES

Bjerrum, L., and B. Kjaernsli, 1957. Analysis of the stability of some Norwegian natural clay slopes. *Geotechnique*, 7 (No. 1), 1–16.

Bjerrum, L., and A. Landva, 1966. Direct simple shear tests on a Norwegian quick clay. *Geotechnique*, 16 (No. 1), 1–20.

Engineering Geology Evaluation Group, 1964. Geologic report 27 March 1964 earthquake in Greater Anchorage area. Alaska State Housing Authority and City of Anchorage, Alaska. 47 p.

Hansen, W. R., 1965. Effects of the earthquake of March 27, 1964 at Anchorage, Alaska. U.S. Geological Survey Professional Paper 542-A. Washington: Government Printing Office. 68 p.

Miller, R. D., and Ernest Dobrovolny, 1959. Surficial geology of Anchorage and vicinity, Alaska. U.S. Geological Survey Bulletin 1093. 128 p.

Seed, H. Bolton, and C. K. Chan, 1964. Pulsating load tests on samples of clay and silt from Anchorage, Alaska, Appendix D *in* Shannon & Wilson, Inc., 1964. Report on Anchorage area soil studies, Alaska. Seattle, Washington. p. D-1–D-18.

Seed, H. Bolton, and C. K. Chan, 1966. Clay strength under earthquake loading conditions. *Journal of the Soil Mechanics and Foundations Division* (American Society of Civil Engineers), 92 (March), 53–78.

Seed, H. Bolton, and I. M. Idriss, 1966. An analysis of soil liquefaction in the Niigata earthquake. Report Soil Mechanics and Bituminous Materials Laboratory, Institute of Transportation and Traffic Engineering, University of California, Berkeley, April.

Seed, H. Bolton, and Kenneth L. Lee, 1964. Pulsating load tests on samples of fine silty sand from Anchorage, Alaska, Appendix C *in* Shannon & Wilson, Inc., 1964. Report on Anchorage area soil studies, Alaska. Seattle, Washington. p. C-1–C-23.

Seed, H. Bolton, and Kenneth L. Lee, 1965. Studies of the liquefaction of sands under cyclic loading conditions. Soil Mechanics and Bituminous Materials Laboratory, Report TE 65-5, University of California, Berkeley, December.

Seed, H. Bolton, and Kenneth L. Lee, 1966. Liquefaction of saturated sands during cyclic loading. *Journal of the Soil Mechanics and Foundations Division* (American Society of Civil Engineers), 92 (November), 105–134.

Seed, H. Bolton, and Stanley D. Wilson, 1967. The Turnagain Heights landslide, Anchorage, Alaska. *Journal of the Soil Mechanics and Foundations Division* (American Society of Civil Engineers), 93 (SM4), Proceedings Paper 5320 (July), 325–353.

Shannon & Wilson, Inc., 1964. Report on Anchorage area soil studies, Alaska, to U.S. Army Engineer District, Anchorage, Alaska. Seattle, Washington. 300 p.

U.S. Army Engineer District, 1964. Eyewitness accounts. Anchorage: U.S. Army Engineer District, Alaska.

U.S. Army Engineer District, Anchorage, Alaska, 1966. Internal report on Turnagain earthquake slide studies. Anchorage: U.S. Army Engineer District, Alaska, April.

U.S. Coast and Geodetic Survey, 1964. Preliminary report—Prince William Sound, Alaskan earthquakes March–April 1964 (second printing). Seismology Division Report. Washington: U.S. Coast and Geodetic Survey. 101 p.

WILLIAM L. SHANNON
DAVID E. HILTS
SHANNON & WILSON, INC.

Submarine Landslide at Seward

The Alaska earthquake inflicted extensive damage on many cities, towns, villages, and small communities on the shores of the Gulf of Alaska. Seward, situated on the eastern side of the Kenai Peninsula at the head of Resurrection Bay (Figure 1), was one of the cities hardest hit by the earthquake. Ironically, damage caused by ground shaking was relatively minor compared to the devastation caused by submarine landsliding, tsunamis, and fire.

Seward is about 75 air miles south of Anchorage (inset, Figure 1). The Seward Highway and The Alaska Railroad provide access to the interior. Because of its ice-free harbor, Seward is one of the major ports of Alaska, with an economy closely related to its port facilities. These facilities, consisting of docks, warehouses, canneries, railroad staging yards, and a small-boat harbor were destroyed during the earthquake as a direct result of a massive submarine landslide that enveloped most of the Seward waterfront.

The U.S. government, recognizing that the successful rehabilitation of the community was contingent on the reconstruction of the port facilities, initiated, immediately after the earthquake through the Corps of Engineers, a subsurface investigation and engineering evaluation of the Seward waterfront and vicinity. This study was to determine the factors, apart from the earthquake, that might have contributed to the development of the massive submarine landslide, to evaluate the possible stability of the waterfront area in the event of another earthquake of similar magnitude, and to provide soils-engineering data necessary for the siting and design of new port facilities. The results are contained in a report by Shannon & Wilson, Inc. (1964) who performed the investigation and evaluation for the Corps of Engineers. Most of the information presented in this paper was obtained from that report.

AREA DESCRIPTION

SETTING

As shown in Figures 1 and 2, Seward lies in the northwest corner of Resurrection Bay, a deep fiord extending about

ABSTRACT: A massive submarine landslide destroyed a large portion of the Seward waterfront during the March 27, 1964, Alaska earthquake. An extensive subsurface investigation after the earthquake revealed that the presence of relatively deep deposits of loose alluvial sand and gravel interfingered with marine silts and fine sands, foreset bedding within the sand and gravel deposits, and artesian pressures in the vicinity probably were significant factors in the development of the landslide. Because the landslide was subaqueous, only limited evidence of the mechanism of sliding was available. The failure appears to have been progressive with successive slides continuing through the unusually long 4-minute duration of the earthquake. The slide terminated as a flow slide and large masses of materials were carried over great distances along the deep floor of Resurrection Bay.

The postearthquake studies indicated that the stability of the present Seward waterfront is unchanged and that subaqueous landsliding may occur again in the event of another large earthquake. Conventional methods for slope stabilization were considered impracticable at Seward because of the great depths involved.

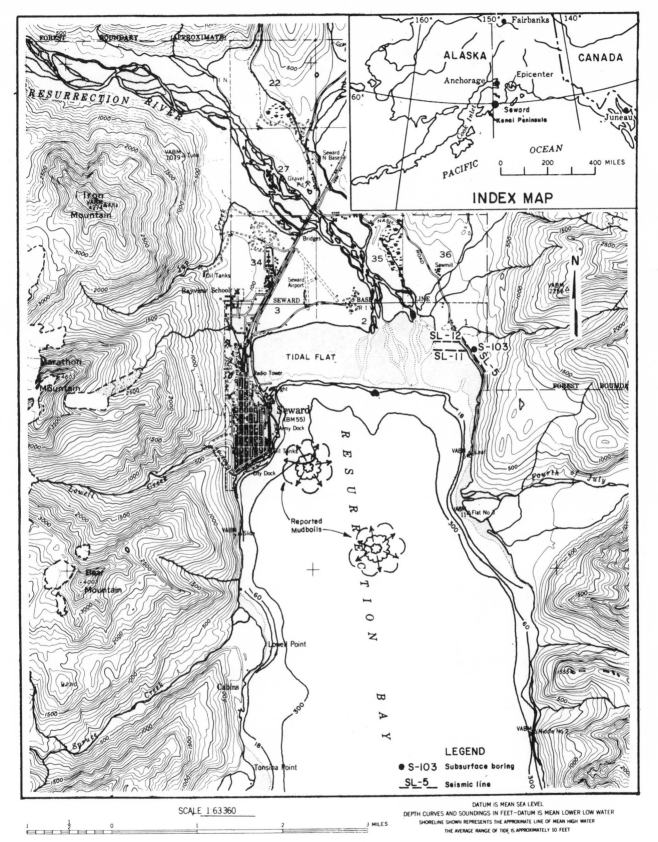

FIGURE 1   Map of Seward and surrounding area.

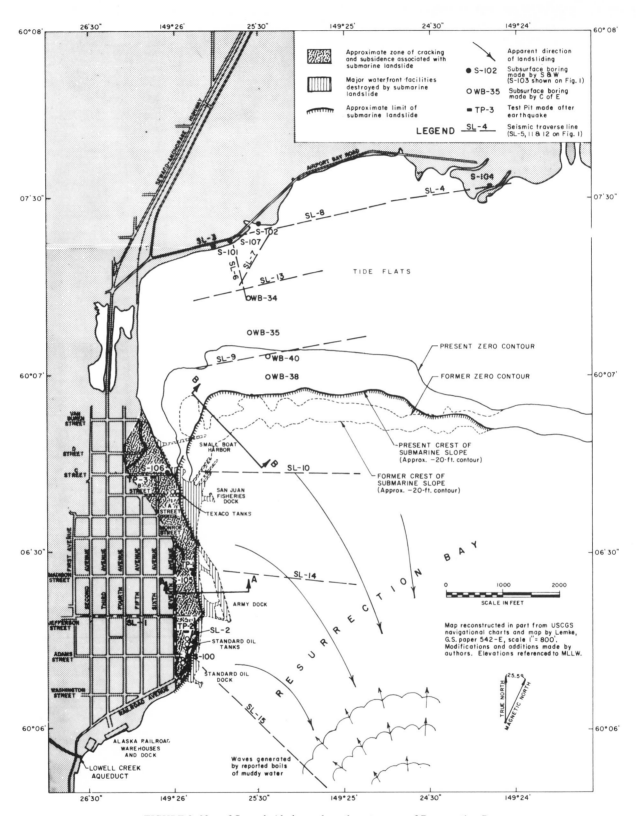

FIGURE 2 Map of Seward, Alaska, and northwest corner of Resurrection Bay.

25 mi inland from the Gulf of Alaska. The bay is approximately 2½ mi wide at Seward. Relatively steep submarine slopes are found near the coastline, with water as deep as 500 ft off Seward. A shallow tideflat, extending approximately 3,000 ft southward, has formed at the head of the bay. The Resurrection River, shown in Figure 1, is the major drainage course in the area. From its source in the glaciers and ice fields in the Chugach Mountains northwest of Seward, the river flows in a southeasterly direction to the head of the bay; north of the bay it flows through a broad braided floodplain over 1 mi wide.

The major residential and commercial areas of Seward, including the port facilities, are situated on an alluvial fan that has formed at the mouth of Lowell Creek (Figure 1). This creek is one of many major streams in the area that are tributary either to Resurrection Bay or to Resurrection River. Alluvial fans are present at the outlets of most of these streams. At one time, Lowell Creek flowed through the center of Seward on a course almost coincident with Jefferson Street, but, because of the hazards created by periodic flooding, it has since been diverted through a tunnel to its present outlet southwest of The Alaska Railroad dock (Figure 2).

Ground elevations within the city rise gradually from sea level along the shores to an altitude of 130 ft at the mouth of Lowell Creek canyon. At this point a steep mountain front rises abruptly to form the western boundary of the city. Steep rugged mountains also confine Resurrection Bay and the Resurrection River valley.

BEDROCK

Major geologic units in the area are related to two physiographic provinces: the mountain system, composed of structurally complex, highly deformed, and partly metamorphosed sedimentary rocks of Jurassic and late Cretaceous age; and the valley system, composed of Quaternary to Recent sediments that relate to the complex glacial, fluvial, and marine depositional history of the valley.

Alternating units of phyllite and graywacke constitute the predominant rock types in the mountains surrounding Seward. Phyllite is a low-grade metamorphic rock derived from shale and, characteristically, is thin bedded and locally fissile with a well-developed cleavage parallel to the bedding. Graywacke is a highly indurated, fine-grained felspathic sandstone and is commonly massive, often breaking into large blocks.

The structure within the phyllite–graywacke sequence is extremely complex, and beds dipping from 70° to 90° are common. Small-scale faults and zones of brecciation are common features in most outcrops. Although no major faults were observed in the area, the valley probably owes its primary origin to faulting. It has been suggested that

there was large-scale movement along existing faults beneath Resurrection Bay during the March 27, 1964, earthquake. Lemke (1967, and Geology volume) in his comprehensive postearthquake study of the Seward area, however, found no evidence to support this contention.

SOIL DEPOSITS

Soil deposits (including unconsolidated sediments and related deposits) within the Seward area are both glacial and nonglacial in origin and consist mainly of glacial till and associated compact glaciofluvial deposits of sand and gravel, alluvial fan and valley deposits of sand and gravel, marine deposits of organic fine sand and silt, and Recent alluvium composed of stream-deposited sand and gravel. Changes between these units are gradational, and the depositional processes appear to have occurred simultaneously. Subsurface profiles through the Seward waterfront showing the various soil deposits are contained in Figure 3. These profiles are based on eight borings made along the margin of the slide and at the head of Resurrection Bay and on 30,380 ft of seismic lines at locations shown in Figures 1 and 2. The borings were drilled by either rotary or churn drills and extended to depths of 83–481 ft.

Dense glacial till overlies bedrock at shallow depths in the northeast corner of Resurrection Bay. Glacial till and dense glaciofluvial deposits probably overlie bedrock beneath Seward, although here bedrock appears to be several hundred feet beneath the ground surface. The glacial till and dense glaciofluvial materials are composed of silt, sand, gravel, and occasional boulders; the relative proportions of each appear to vary from place to place. In some areas the stratum contains stringers of marine sand and silt. The unit is characterized by a seismic velocity of about 7,200–7,500 feet per second (fps). After the submarine slide, the surface of the dense silt, sand, and gravel beneath most of Seward is at a depth of about 50–100 ft but deepens along the distal edge of the fan.

The alluvial fan and valley material is typically a loose to medium-dense deposit of sand, gravel, cobbles, and boulders containing variable amounts of fine sand and silt. These deposits have a seismic velocity of 6,000 to 6,200 fps. Beneath Seward, stratification is common, and the particles, derived mainly from phyllite rock, are platy and subangular to subrounded. The particles are sometimes oriented in an imbricate or shingle-like pattern, forming a parallel-bedded structure that slopes toward the bay. Some of the samples recovered from subsurface borings exhibited foreset beds with slopes varying up to 27°.

The marine deposit is found beneath Resurrection Bay and is thickest beneath the tideflats. In the borings drilled in the tideflats at the head of the bay (Figures 1 and 2),

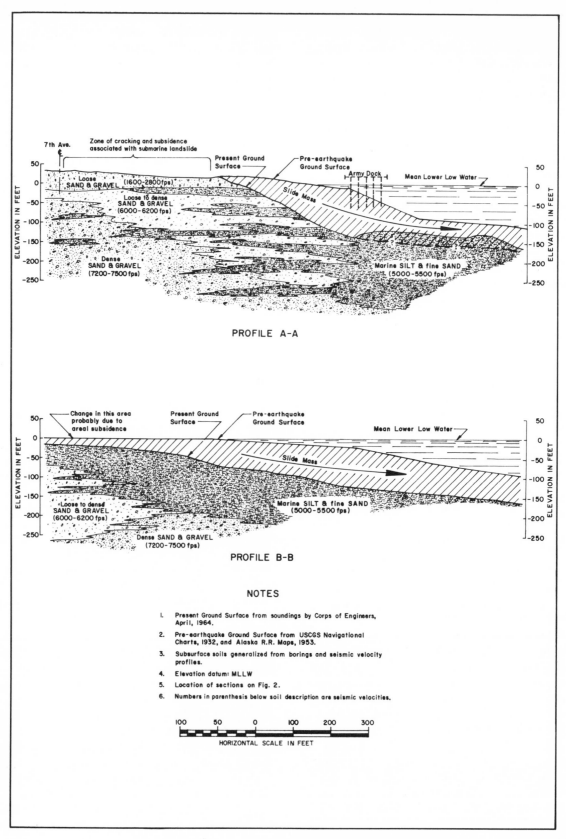

FIGURE 3 Subsurface profiles through submarine landslide.

the marine deposit extends from a depth of 35–45 ft to 120–160 ft. In boring S-106, near the former small-boat harbor, an extensive deposit of marine sediments was encountered from a depth of 80 ft to the bottom of the boring at 313 ft. Further south, in boring S-105, marine zones were present at depths of from 25 to 52 ft and from 298 to 312 ft, with occasional stringers of marine silt at various intermediate depths. In boring S-100, the southernmost boring, located in the vicinity of the Standard Oil Dock, only occasional stringers of marine sediments were encountered with one predominant marine zone from depth 292 to 306 ft; this indicates that beneath the Seward waterfront the marine deposit thins out toward the south.

The materials composing the marine sediments are black organic fine sand interlayered with organic clayey silt and layers of clean coarse sand. The seismic velocity ranges from 5,000 to 5,500 fps. The silt and sand are intricately interlaced with the alluvial fan and valley deposits along the Seward waterfront and in the area north of the bay.

The Recent alluvium is found mainly in the Resurrection River floodplain and consists of loose sands and gravels with a seismic velocity of 1,600–2,800 fps. In the tideflats, this material overlies the marine deposits to a depth of 40–50 ft.

LABORATORY TESTS

Disturbed split-spoon samples and relatively undisturbed 3-in.-steel-tube samples were both obtained from the subsurface borings. The laboratory tests included visual classification of the split-spoon samples and visual classification, triaxial-shear strength, consolidation, mechanical and hydrometer analyses, determination of Atterberg limits, and loss-on-ignition (organic-content) tests for the steel-tube samples. The tube samples were obtained from the marine sands and silts encountered in borings S-102, S-106, and S-107.

Triaxial tests performed on the tube samples were as follows: five consolidated undrained ($\bar{\text{R}}$-type) stage tests, five single-stage consolidated undrained tests, and seven unconsolidated undrained (Q-type) tests. Back pressures of 50 or 100 psi were employed on all $\bar{\text{R}}$-tests to ensure saturation and to permit the measurement of negative pore pressures.

Two consolidation tests were performed on the clayey silt materials. Mechanical and hydrometer analyses were run on selected Shelby-tube samples. Atterberg-limits tests were performed to determine the plasticity characteristics of the soils.

Different methods were tried to obtain the percentage of organic content. In one method, the sample was heated

in a crucible to 700°C, and the loss in weight from the previous oven-dry (105°C) condition was determined. In the other method, alcohol was poured over the sample and ignited. The loss in weight from the oven-dry condition was then determined. The results of these tests are summarized in Table 1.

Two types of soil—black organic sandy to slightly clayey silts (ML) and black uniform medium-to-fine sands (SP-SM)—were predominant in the steel-tube samples. The uniform medium-to-fine sand had an organic odor but hardly any organic content. It was composed primarily of black phyllite particles, which are generally more equidimensional than those found in the alluvial coarse sands. The soil is usually of medium density. Wet unit weights were approximately 130 pounds per cubic foot (pcf).

Triaxial tests on the samples showed that the soil has an effective (drained) angle of friction ϕ', of approximately 35°–39° and a total (undrained) ϕ ranging from 32° to 40°. Pore pressures at failure were low, ranging from slightly positive to slightly negative.

The organic sandy to slightly clayey silt had an organic content of less than 5 percent. The plasticity index varied from nonplastic to 13. Liquid limits ranged from 21 to 34. Natural water contents varied from 17 to 32 percent. Hydrometer analyses, summarized in Figure 4, showed that 10 to 30 percent of the material tested consisted of clay-sized particles.

The clayey silts at depths of 50–150 ft were usually of medium consistency. The wet unit weight of the silt was approximately 130 pcf.

The undrained triaxial tests performed on the silts showed positive pore pressures at failure. The effective (drained) ϕ' ranged from 35° to 38°. The undrained ϕ' was lower—about 21° for a consolidation pressure greater than the effective overburden pressure and averaging 26° for consolidation pressures equal to the effective overburden pressure.

GROUNDWATER

Borings made along the Seward waterfront showed very little evidence of artesian (or excess hydrostatic) pressures. Artesian pressures were, however, quite evident in the borings drilled at the head of the bay. There, artesian heads as high as 27 ft above mean lower low-tide level (or 16 ft above mean high tide) were measured in the sands and gravels underlying the marine deposit. Similarly, artesian heads about 20 ft above mean lower low-tide level were recorded in pervious zones of the marine sand and silt. The results of groundwater measurements in boring B-107 at the head of the bay are shown in Figure 5.

The reason for the apparent lack of artesian pressures along the waterfront may be twofold: First, there is a dif-

TABLE I
SUMMARY OF TEST DATA

BORING NO.	SAMPLE NO.	DEPTH FEET	USC*	CLASSIFICATION	NATURAL WATER CONTENT %	LL	PL	PI	ORGANIC CONTENT % (700°C)	WET DENSITY PCF	% PASSING 200	D_{60} MM	D_{10} MM	φ′ EFFECTIVE	φ TOTAL	Q TEST: $\sigma_1 - \sigma_3$, TSF
S-102	8	55.0-57.5	SP	Dark gray, medium fine SAND	24			NP†	0 (Alcohol)							
	9	65.0-67.5	ML	Black, organic, very fine sandy SILT	32	33	25	8	0.4 (Alcohol)	129	62.8	.06				
	12	89.9-91.9	ML	Black, organic, very fine sandy SILT	20	21	18	3	1.4 (Alcohol)	132	71.7	.05				
	14	97.0-98.5	ML	Dark gray, organic, very fine sandy SILT with occasional gravel	17											
	15	107.0-108.5	SM	Black, organic, silty fine to medium SAND	17					133	13.3	.20	.05	38°	39.5°	
	16	117.0-118.2	SM	Silty fine SAND	18						42.5	.10				
	17	127.0-128.8	SM	Organic, silty fine SAND	17	23	20	3			38.9	.14	.023			
S-106	12	116.3-119.1	ML	Black, organic, slightly clayey SILT	21	30	21	9	4.3		71.3	.055	<.001	35.5°	26°	3.20
	16	133.5-135.7	ML	Black, organic, slightly clayey SILT	24	34	21	13	4.4		97.3	.012	<.001	35.5°	31°	2.60
	22	212.0-214.5	ML	Medium, black, organic, slightly clayey SILT	26	27	25	2	4.4	133	88.5	.012	<.001	36°	25.5°	2.62
	23	221.0-223.5	ML	Stiff, black, organic, slightly clayey SILT, trace of gravel	26					147				38°	21.5°	0.44
S-107	5a	54.0-56.7	SM	Medium, black, silty fine to medium SAND	21				4.4	129				39°	32°	6.80
	5b	54.0-56.7	ML	Medium, black, slightly clayey, very fine sandy SILT	24			NP								
	6	63.7-65.8	SM	Medium, black, silty fine SAND	27	24	22	2	3.6	127				39°	36.5°	
	7a	73.0-75.5	SM	Loose, dark, silty fine SAND, some clayey and organic layers	33				4.6		69.5	.05	<.001			
	7b	73.0-75.5	ML	Medium, black, fine sandy SILT, some organics	27	33	22	11						39°	36.5°	8.60
	10	101.0-103.2	ML	Medium, black, very fine SAND and SILT	20			NP	3.9	125	45.9	.10	.0025			
	12	113.3-116.0	SM	Medium, black, silty fine SAND	20					126				38°	34.5°	7.90

*Unified Soil Classification (Casagrande)
†Non plastic

150

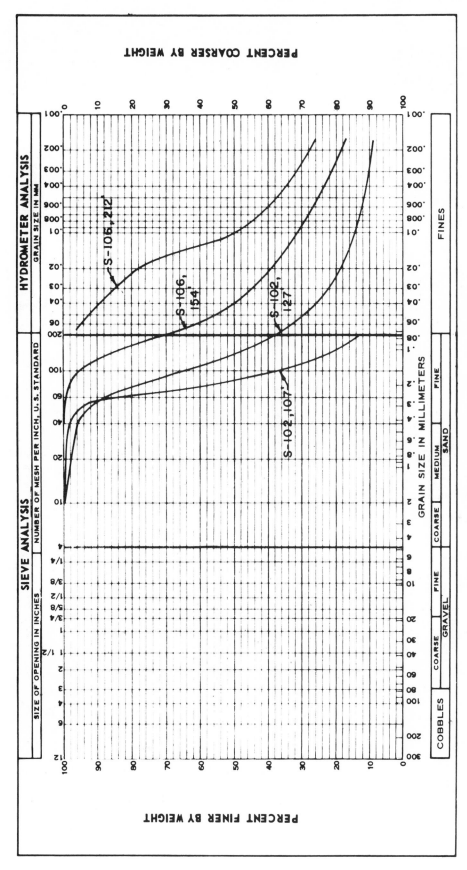

FIGURE 4 Representative grain-size gradations of marine deposits.

151

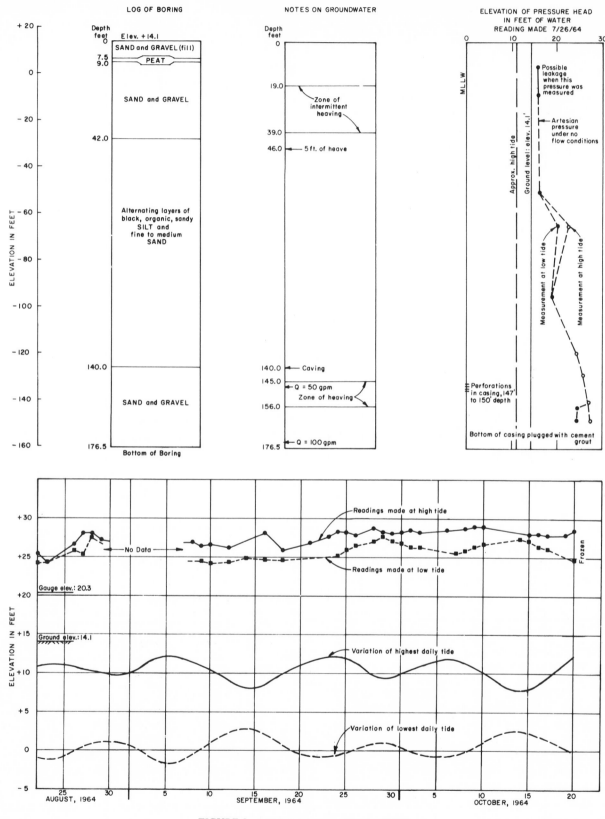

FIGURE 5   Artesian pressures at boring S-107.

ference in the amount of groundwater flowing in the two areas. Lowell Creek, which formerly flowed across the Lowell Creek fan, has now been diverted from the fan via a rock tunnel that empties the stream flow directly into the bay just south of the town, thus reducing the flow through the fan. On the other hand, Jap Creek, located approximately 1 mi northwest of the borings drilled at the head of the bay (Figure 1), enters its fan at an elevation of approximately 500 ft. This creek is at present flowing across its fan and probably feeds large quantities of groundwater at a high gradient to the region at the head of the bay.

Second, along the Seward waterfront the soil conditions after the earthquake are quite different from those at the head of the bay. There is a much thicker marine zone near the head of the bay, consisting of alternating layers of relatively permeable and impermeable soils. This stratification allows horizontal flow, but retards the vertical flow. Because the marine soils are less permeable than the sands and gravels, they are more effective as a barrier to the flow of groundwater. Artesian conditions could be expected to develop both within the marine deposit and in the lower sand and gravel unit, wherever impervious layers in the marine deposit retard the discharge of groundwater.

Present groundwater conditions along the Seward waterfront are not necessarily the same as those existing before the earthquake. The soil mass removed by submarine landsliding may have previously confined the groundwater and may have created higher artesian pressures than those observed after the earthquake.

DESCRIPTION OF THE EARTHQUAKE

The Good Friday earthquake, with a Richter magnitude of about 8.4, originated near the shores of Unakwik Inlet in northern Prince William Sound, lat. 61.1°N, long. 147.7°W (Grantz and others, 1964), an area about 75 mi northeast of Seward (inset, Figure 1). The first effects of this powerful earthquake were felt in Seward at 5:36 p.m. AST. The events that followed are well documented in the literature (Hansen and others, 1966; Lemke, 1967).

Strong ground motion reportedly traveling in a north–south direction lasted for at least 3–4 minutes. Shortly after the earthquake started, the water level, then approaching a −0.6-ft tide, receded an estimated 20–30 ft. The oil tanker *Alaska Standard*, berthed at the Standard Oil dock, where the water was 32 ft deep at MLLW, did not strike bottom at that time. At about the same time—and, according to some reports, about 30 seconds after the start of strong ground tremors—a large section of the Seward waterfront slid into Resurrection Bay, carrying with it oil tanks, docks, warehouses, and other harbor facilities.

During the latter stages of ground motion, a large mud boil was observed offshore; some people reported seeing two boils (Figures 1 and 2). Large waves radiated rapidly from the boil, striking the sides of Resurrection Bay and the Seward waterfront. The first wave, composed of debris-laden water and approximately 15 ft high, moved onshore spreading burning fuel from ruptured storage tanks along the waterfront. A series of tsunamis and recessions swept the waterfront at irregular intervals throughout the night, completing the devastation (Brown, 1964).

DESCRIPTION OF SUBMARINE LANDSLIDE

The major damage to Seward from the earthquake was the direct result of submarine landsliding, sea waves, and fire. Damage caused by strong ground motion, by contrast, was relatively minor; a few walls and foundations were cracked, chimneys were toppled, and windows were broken. Some buildings were extensively damaged, but few structures are reported to have collapsed.

Most significant from the standpoint of property damage was the effect of the submarine landslide, which completely destroyed most port and harbor facilities. A strip of waterfront, shown in Figure 2, about 50–400 ft wide and 4,000 ft long, disappeared into the bay. Immediately after the earthquake, sliding appeared to have been confined to the waterfront area. However, when the results of postearthquake soundings were made available and underwater contours were compared to contours made before the earthquake, it became immediately evident that the waterfront slide was only part of a much more massive landslide that included a portion of the tideflats at the head of the bay. The absence of a well-defined scarp made it difficult to define the extent of sliding at the head of the bay. In comparing the −20 ft contours that approximately define the crest of the underwater slope before and after the earthquake, it appears that a strip of tideflats, 500–600 ft wide and almost 1 mi long, disappeared into the bay. The extent of sliding can be seen in plan on Figure 2 and in perspective on the fence diagram of Figure 6. The shoreline at the head of the bay indicates that portions of the Airport Bay Road are at present inundated, reflecting a northward recession of the shoreline that resulted from areal tectonic subsidence of about 3.5 ft (Lemke 1967; Plafker, 1965) and is not associated with the landslide. Speaking of tectonic subsidence, Lemke (1967) states, "High tides now advance several hundred feet to nearly half a mile inland at the head of the bay. . . . The air strip must be reconstructed, the road around the head of the bay must be relocated, and other land has lost its private-use potential."

In Figure 3, typical subsurface profiles, one through the Seward waterfront and one through the tideflats, reveal the substantial quantity of material involved in the submarine

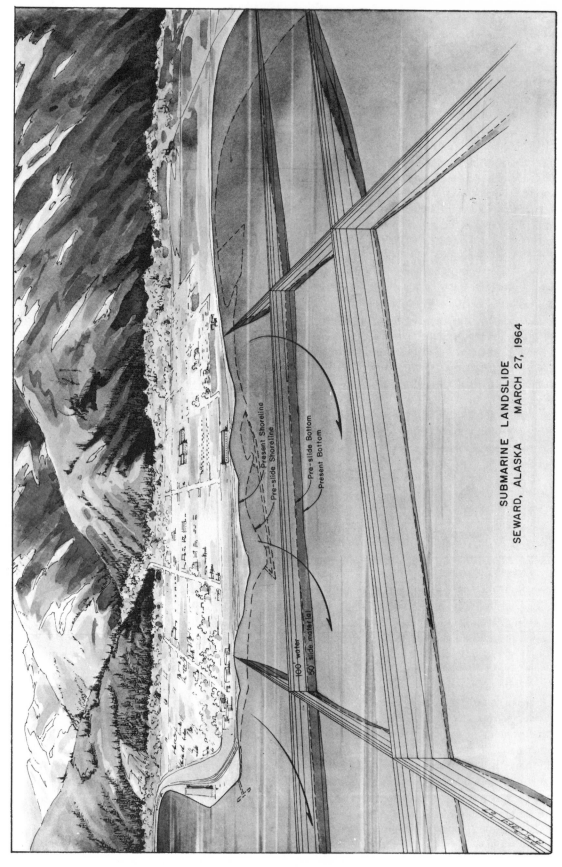

SUBMARINE LANDSLIDE
SEWARD, ALASKA   MARCH 27, 1964

FIGURE 6   Fence diagram of submarine landslide at Seward.

slide. Water originally 30–35 ft deep is now over 100 ft deep. Near the center of the bay, where water depth reaches 500 ft, data are insufficient to develop a good set of comparative contours, but the limited data that are available suggest that even here the present bottom of the bay may be deeper than before the earthquake, although the surface is probably mantled with slide debris.

Bathymetric data also reveal that no significant change in the geometry of the underwater slopes resulted from the landslide other than a slight steepening in the vicinity of the Standard Oil Dock. Underwater slopes vary in steepness, with a general flattening toward the north. At the southernmost limit of the slide (Standard Oil Dock), the average slope after the earthquake is 32°. At the Army dock (profile A-A, Figure 3), the average slope is 22°, and south of the San Juan dock it is about 16°. The slope at the edge of the tideflats (profile B-B) is about 10°–11°.

The Alaska Railroad warehouses and portions of the adjoining dock were destroyed as a result of the earthquake. These structures, on the south edge of the city, were supported on a fill retained by a long circular-cell sheet-pile bulkhead. Some cells reportedly extended up to 60 ft above the mudline. During the earthquake, or as the result of subsequent sea waves, most of the cells ruptured, destroying both structures. However, the collapse of the bulkhead was probably not the result of submarine landsliding. Lemke (1967) reports deepening of about 40 ft about 200–300 ft offshore and concludes that this sliding was local and probably confined to fine-grain marine sediments that blanketed the frontal slope of the fan.

Along the eastern edge of the Seward fan and contiguous to the head of the slides, a zone of cracking and subsidence was created that varied in width from 400 to 800 ft (Figure 2). A complex, irregular fracture system, including rotational blocks, was preserved in the frozen ground surface. Had the ground not been frozen at the time of movement, a fissure system closely paralleling that on the waterfront would probably have been produced. Most fissures showed a horizontal displacement of only a few inches, although some were as wide as 2–2½ ft. A few fissures had a vertical offset of several inches on the bayward side, indicating subsidence in the fractured area. The accumulative magnitude of rotational lateral offset, with downside movement on the seaward block, has been estimated to be about 2–3 ft. A fractured zone probably also existed behind the slide in the tideflats, but any evidence of this was quickly destroyed by the tidewaters that inundate the area. Slight subsidence was noted in the railroad embankment north of the city, and fissures were observed in local areas at the head of the bay. Divers working on salvage operations also reported extensive fissuring of the underwater slopes in the vicinity of the San Juan Dock and the presence of large blocks of undisturbed soil on the slope.

MECHANICS OF LANDSLIDE

Because the landslide was subaqueous for the most part, there were no eyewitnesses, and only limited information is available from which to determine the mechanism of sliding.

Limited evidence, such as the sudden drop, without striking bottom, of the *Alaska Standard*, berthed at the Standard Oil Dock, and the cracked and fissured ground remaining after the slide, suggests a progressive action of the slide. The first failure is believed to have been induced offshore and to have caused the observed recession of the water surface and the rapid drop of the *Alaska Standard* at her berth. The slide then extended rapidly onshore. Whether the slide started as a shear slide or as a liquefaction slide is not known, but without a doubt it terminated as a liquefaction or flow slide, with the mass of material carried for great distances and spread out over the floor of Resurrection Bay as a thin layer that is now undetectable in the great depth of water. The mud boils observed at the surface of Resurrection Bay and the subsequent large waves were evidence of the extent of water turbulence caused by the slide.

FACTORS CONTRIBUTING TO THE SUBMARINE SLIDE

It is obvious that the earthquake was the most important single cause of the submarine landslide. Sliding apparently began shortly after the start of strong ground motion and stopped when strong ground motion ceased. The earthquake was not only violent and enormous, but of extended duration (3-4 minutes). The subsurface investigation and engineering study made immediately after the earthquake, revealed several factors that indicated conditions conducive to a submarine landslide.

Beneath Seward, it was found that loose sands and gravels in alluvial fan deposits overlie dense glacial deposits, and the thickness of the overlying loose sands and gravels increases appreciably toward the distal edge of the fan. These materials were probably deposited at very nearly their natural angle of repose and were of marginal static stability to begin with, particularly near the south end of the slide where the slopes are steepest. When subjected to the additional dynamic forces provided by the earthquake, the slopes failed. The stability was decreased even further by the foreset bedding, which in some areas was almost parallel to the slopes. It is noteworthy that no submarine landsliding could be detected in the extreme northeast corner of the bay where bedrock overlain by dense glacial deposits is within 100–200 ft of the ground surface, and marine deposits and recent alluvium are generally less than 100 ft thick.

Associated with the flattening of the underwater slopes to the north is an increase in the thickness of the marine soils, consisting of alternating layers of sand and silt. Beneath the tide flats, the slopes are flattest where the sand and silt is thickest. The marine deposits are intersected with lenses or layers of sand, which are relatively pervious compared to the adjacent silt. Such layers are particularly susceptible to liquefaction when subjected to stress reversals. Moreover, it has been shown that liquefaction in such material is more likely to occur under flatter slopes than under steeper slopes (Seed, 1968), because the existing shear stresses on an element under the flatter slopes are relatively small and are more likely to undergo a complete reversal (i.e., total change in direction) than the higher existing shear stresses on an element of soil beneath a steep slope.

Groundwater measurements made during the subsurface investigation reveal artesian pressures beneath and within the marine deposits at the head of the bay (Figure 5). No artesian conditions were observed along the Seward waterfront after the earthquake.

The artesian pressures observed at the head of the bay were probably a significant factor in decreasing the stability of slopes in this area. Groundwater conditions beneath the Seward waterfront were probably different before the earthquake, and the failure to detect the presence of artesian pressures after the earthquake does not preclude their possible existence before the earthquake, particularly in areas interfingered with the marine silt. It is also possible that, in these areas, confining layers were removed by the landslide.

In summary, it seems that the magnitude and duration of the earthquake were the most significant factors responsible for the submarine landslide. The looseness, shape, and orientation of particles of the alluvial-fan deposits, together with the steepness of the slopes along the waterfront, the presence of the marine sand and silt, and the existence of artesian pressures also probably contributed to establish conditions conducive to such a disaster.

FUTURE STABILITY

As a result of the large submarine landslide, the stability of the present Seward waterfront is probably unchanged. Stat-

ically, the underwater slopes are reasonably stable; during another great earthquake, however, they could be expected to fail in much the same manner as they did during the Good Friday earthquake. The extent of new earthquake-triggered slides cannot be predicted; it is considered likely, however, that they could involve a strip of the Seward waterfront approximately equal in width to the Good Friday slide and that an area of local subsidence and fissuring similar to that indicated in Figure 2 would again develop behind the slide.

The stability of the waterfront could be improved by flattening underwater slopes and buttressing the toes of the slopes with fill, but these measures are deemed impracticable because of the great depths involved. Other methods of improving stability, such as drainage, are also considered impracticable.

REFERENCES

Brown, Delmer L., 1964. Tsunamic activity accompanying the Alaskan earthquake of 27 March 1964. Anchorage: U.S. Army Corps of Engineers, April 23. 31 p.

Grantz, Arthur, George Plafker, and Reuben Kachadoorian, 1964. Alaska's Good Friday earthquake, March 27, 1964: A preliminary geologic evaluation. U.S. Geological Survey Circular 491. Washington: U.S. Geological Survey. 35 p.

Hansen, Wallace R., Edwin B. Eckel, William E. Schaem, Robert E. Lyle, Warren George, and Genie Chance, 1966. The Alaska earthquake, March 27, 1964: Field investigations and reconstruction effort. U.S. Geological Survey Professional Paper 541. Washington: Government Printing Office. 111 p.

Lemke, Richard W., 1967. Effects of the earthquake of March 27, 1964, at Seward, Alaska. U.S. Geological Survey Professional Paper 542-E. Washington: Government Printing Office. 43 p. Also in The Great Alaska Earthquake of 1964: Geology. NAS Pub. 1601. Washington: National Academy of Sciences, 1971. p. 395–437.

Plafker, George, 1965. Tectonic deformation associated with the 1964 Alaska earthquake. Science, 148 (June 25), 1675–1687.

Seed, H. Bolton, 1968. Landslides during earthquakes due to soil liquefaction. Journal of the Soil Mechanics and Foundations Division (American Society of Civil Engineers), 94 (September), 1053–1122.

Shannon & Wilson, Inc., 1964. Report on subsurface investigation for city of Seward, Alaska, and vicinity, to U.S. Army Engineer District, Anchorage, Alaska. Seattle: Shannon & Wilson, Inc. 77 p.

JAMES K. MITCHELL
WILLIAM N. HOUSTON
UNIVERSITY OF CALIFORNIA, BERKELEY

GEORGE YAMANE
SHANNON & WILSON, INC.

Sensitivity and Geotechnical Properties of Bootlegger Cove Clay

The subsoil of the Greater Anchorage area consists of a sand-and-gravel outwash deposit (Naptowne outwash) overlying a thick stratum of blue-gray silty clay, known as the Bootlegger Cove Clay. The upper and lower zones of this clay are medium stiff to stiff, but the central portion is soft, weak, and sensitive. Lenses and layers of loose silt and sand are encountered frequently throughout the deposit, and compact gravels and tills underlie the Bootlegger Cove Clay.

Five major landslides accounted for a substantial portion of the damage that was caused in the Anchorage area by the March 27, 1964, earthquake. Although field investigations did not conclusively establish the failure surface at all locations (Shannon & Wilson, Inc., 1964), in most instances the failure zone was found to be near the top of the weak sensitive zone of the Bootlegger Cove Clay. The results of tests and analyses by Seed and Wilson (1967) provide evidence that slides may have been initiated during the earthquake as a result of liquefaction of the loose saturated silt and sand lenses. Because of the discontinuous character of these lenses, however, sliding also involved extensive shear zones in the clay. Remolding of the sensitive clay that accompanied the sliding motion led to substantial strength reductions that undoubtedly contributed significantly to the extent and severity of the failures.

The extensive failures that developed in the Bootlegger Cove Clay generated new interest in the factors responsible for the formation and properties of highly sensitive clays. The causes of clay sensitivity are examined in this study with particular reference to the Bootlegger Cove Clay, which has sensitivities that range from 6 to 50 in the central portion of the stratum. The general geotechnical properties of Bootlegger Cove Clay are interpreted in terms of relations between water content, effective stress, and liquidity index that have been found to apply to other sensitive clays. Some relations between sensitivity and behavior of the Bootlegger Cove Clay under cyclic loading are also examined.

ABSTRACT: The study of the causes of the sensitivity of the Bootlegger Cove Clay and of its general geotechnical properties and behavior under cyclic loading indicates that, like other highly sensitive clays, it demonstrates no specific correlation between its mineralogical composition and its sensitivity.

Of eight different mechanisms likely to cause the development of clay sensitivity, no predominant one may be singled out for the Bootlegger Cove Clay, although leaching of salt from the pore water and introduction of dispersing agents may be the most important. The geotechnical properties of the Bootlegger Cove Clay are generally similar to those of other highly sensitive glacial clays. We found a reasonable correlation between liquidity index and sensitivity that differed from that previously established for Norwegian sensitive clays because of different average effective stresses at the two locations.

For a given cyclic-stress level (ratio of cyclic-stress intensity to strength in a static test) the number of cycles to cause failure may be essentially independent of the sensitivity.

157

DEFINITIONS

Some of the terms and concepts used in this study are defined as follows:

Sensitivity refers to the loss that develops in the strength of an undrained clay as a result of disturbance of the structure. The quantitative measure of sensitivity, originally proposed by Terzaghi (1944), is the ratio of peak undisturbed strength to the remolded strength determined by using the unconfined-compression test. In very sensitive and quick clays, however, the remolded strength is so low that unconfined compression-test specimens cannot be formed. The vane-shear test has come into wide use for determining the strength of clays in the field and provides a rapid method of determining undisturbed and remolded soil strength. Quantitative expression of sensitivity in terms of vane shear strength is therefore common. The fall-cone test (Karlsson, 1961; Swedish State Railways, 1922) is used in Sweden to determine sensitivity. The term "quick clay" is often used to denote a clay of such high sensitivity that it behaves as a viscous fluid in the remolded state.

Several classifications of soil sensitivity have been proposed; care must be taken to specify the particular scale of reference when adjectival descriptions of sensitivity are given, or the association of these descriptions with quantitative sensitivity values may be misleading. Three such sensitivity classifications are given in Table 1. The Rosenqvist classification system is used in this paper, because the sensitivity–effective stress–liquidity index relation presented subsequently indicates a geometric increase in sensitivity with liquidity index or logarithm of effective stress.

Liquidity index (LI) is defined by the ratio of the following percentages:

$$\frac{\text{water content (W)} - \text{plastic limit (PL)}}{\text{plasticity index (PI)}}$$

The liquidity index is a normalized water content ratio that has been found useful for comparison of the properties of clays of different composition.

Thixotropy is defined as an isothermal, reversible, time-dependent process that occurs under conditions of constant composition and volume, whereby a material stiffens while at rest and softens or liquefies on remolding (Mitchell, 1961; Newland and Allely, 1961). The properties of a purely thixotropic material are illustrated in Figure 1 and those of a partly thixotropic material in Figure 2. Skempton and Northey (1952) have suggested that thixotropic hardening can account for low to medium sensitivities, but, at most, for only a part of the sensitivity of quick clays. The mechanism responsible for thixotropic hardening and the potential role of thixotropy in the development of high sensitivities in undisturbed clays in nature is discussed more fully later.

Fabric refers to the arrangement of soil particles, generally on a small scale, within a clay mass. Most sensitive clay deposits in nature contain platy clay particles and bulky silt and sand grains. The amount of clay present is generally sufficient to prevent direct interaction between granular particles, and the fabric of the clay particles may exert a dominating influence on behavior. Various modes of particle association have been classified by van Olphen (1963) (Figure 3).

With the possible exception of clays whose particles are strongly cemented by chemical means, the undisturbed fabric of sensitive clays is composed of flocculated assemblages of clay particles or aggregates (Mitchell, 1956; Pusch, 1962, 1966; Rosenqvist, 1959; Wu, 1958). Observations by Rosenqvist (1959) led to the conclusion that the undisturbed fabric of sensitive Norwegian marine clays corresponded closely to the schematic picture of a clay-mineral network, dominated by contacts between a corner of one mineral particle and the face of another, as suggested earlier by Tan (1957). Pusch (1962, 1966) concluded from electron

TABLE 1 Sensitivity Classifications Developed by Various Researchers from 1952 to 1964

Skempton and Northey (1952)		Rosenqvist (1953)		Shannon & Wilson (1964)	
$S_t =$ ~1.0	insensitive clays	$S_t =$ ~1.0	insensitive clays	$S_t =$ <3	low
1–2	clays of low sensitivity	1–2	slightly sensitive clays	3–5	low to medium
2–4	clays of medium sensitivity	2–4	medium sensitive clays	5–7	medium
4–8	sensitive clays	4–8	very sensitive clays	7–11	medium to high
8–16	extra sensitive clays	8–16	slightly quick clays	11–14	high
>16	quick clays	16–32	medium quick clays	14–20	high to very high
		32–64	very quick clays	20–40	very high
		>64	extra quick clays	>40	extremely high

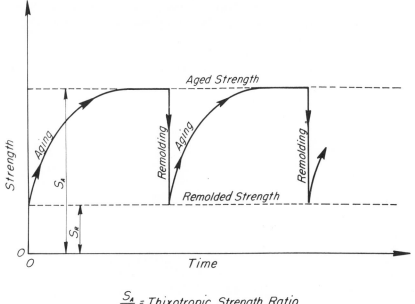

$$\frac{S_A}{S_R} = \text{Thixotropic Strength Ratio}$$

FIGURE 1 Properties of a purely thixo-tropic material.

micrographs of thin sections of 500 Å thickness that the microfabric is characterized by linkages of groups or chains of small particles in and between denser flocs or aggregates or between larger particles. No preferential orientation of small or large particles was observed. It appears, therefore, that each of the flocculated types of particle association shown in Figure 3 may be present to some extent in sensitive clays. It has been established, however, that in a given undisturbed clay, there may be no differences in fabric be-tween very sensitive or quick zones and zones that have only medium sensitivity.

Figure 3 demonstrates that any of the flocculated arrangements will be stronger and less compressible than any of the deflocculated arrangements for a clay at a given void ratio. Remolding a sensitive clay causes a change from one of the flocculated fabrics to a deflocculated state. Because remolding is carried out at constant water content, it is easy to understand why the remolded material is weaker and

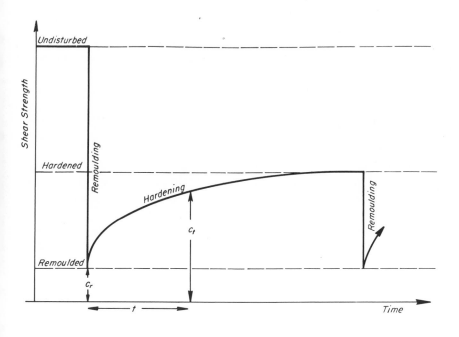

FIGURE 2 Characteristics of a partly thixotropic material.

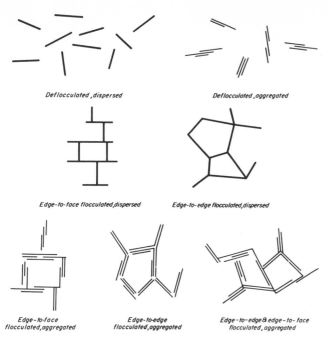

Defloculated ,dispersed

Defloculated ,aggregated

Edge-to-face flocculated,dispersed

Edge-to-edge flocculated,dispersed

Edge-to-face flocculated,aggregated

Edge-to-edge flocculated,aggregated

Edge-to-edge & edge-to-face flocculated,aggregated

FIGURE 3 Clay particle assemblages. After van Olphen (1963).

more compressible than the undisturbed clay. Two important questions, however, remain: Why is the undisturbed fabric flocculated in the first place? What has happened to the clay for the fabric to be easily changed by disturbance and in fact, to be, more stable after deflocculation?

COMPOSITION OF SENSITIVE CLAYS

Very high sensitivities may be observed in clays of greatly differing composition. Quick clays may not differ from clays of low sensitivity in mineralogical composition or grain-size distribution. The most important factors are that the grain size of clays is sufficiently small for the clay particles to behave as colloids and that clay particles have a platy or needle-like morphology. These characteristics permit the development of different fabric types under different physical and chemical conditions.

Most of the world's quick clays are postglacial clays. The mineralogy of the clay fraction from most glaciated areas is dominated by illite and chlorite, and the nonclay fraction is composed primarily of quartz and feldspar. Quick clays are usually characterized by a low colloidal activity (plasticity index/clay fraction), with values usually less than 0.5.

The composition of the pore fluid is of great importance, particularly the differences in composition that may develop between the time of formation of the clay deposit and the present. The type and amount of electrolyte, or-

ganic compounds, and small quantities of surface-active agents may control the development of high sensitivity.

CAUSES OF SENSITIVITY

At least eight different mechanisms that can account for various degrees of sensitivity are listed. Two of these mechanisms are essentially physical; the others involve chemical and physicochemical interactions of various types.

Physical mechanisms

1. Metastable particle arrangements
2. Silt skeleton-bond clay fabric

Chemical and physicochemical mechanisms

1. Leaching of salt from marine clays
2. Rupture of cemented interparticle bonds
3. Ion exchange
4. Weathering
5. Thixotropic hardening
6. Dispersing agent addition

Detailed descriptions, with examples cited from the literature, are given elsewhere (Mitchell and Houston, 1969).

Characteristics of these mechanisms are summarized in Table 2. Of those indicated, only three—leaching of salt water from marine clays, the introduction of dispersing chemicals (either through decomposition of material already present or by leaching into the clay), and the rupture of cemented bonds—appear adequate to account for extra-quick clays. Ion-exchange effects, thixotropic hardening, and metastable particle arrangements induced by physical factors only may lead to slightly quick clays, but the more usual contribution is probably much less. The remainder—the silt skeleton-bond clay structure and weathering—appear able to account only for medium sensitivities.

FORMATION OF THE BOOTLEGGER COVE CLAY

The geology of the Anchorage area is described in detail by Miller and Dobrovolny (1959) and is referred to herein only in connection with the formation of the Bootlegger Cove Clay and the properties of the clay.

Deposition of the blue-gray silty Bootlegger Cove Clay took place during the last stages of the Knik glaciation (the next-to-youngest ice advance). Although the origin and environmental conditions of the formation of the Bootlegger Cove Clay are somewhat uncertain, it is generally agreed that a delta was built in a lake during the ice recession. The

TABLE 2   Summary of the Causes of Sensitivity Development in Clays

Mechanism	Type of Reaction	Approximate Upper Limit of Sensitivity[a]	Predominant Soil Types Affected
Metastable particle arrangements	Physical	Slightly quick (8–16)	All clays
Silt skeleton–bond clay	Physical	Very sensitive (4–8)	Clay–silt–sand mixtures
Leaching of salt	Physicochemical	Extra quick (>64)	Glacial and postglacial marine clays
Cementation	Chemical	Extra quick (?) (>64)	All soils containing potential cementing components
Ion exchange	Physicochemical	Slightly quick (?) (8–16)	Leached and weathered clays
Weathering	Chemical	Medium sensitive (~4)	All soils—magnitude of effect depends on mineralogy
Thixotropic hardening	Physicochemical	Slightly quick[b] (<16)	Clays
Dispersing agent addition	Physicochemical	Extra quick (>64)	Clays—particularly, organic-bearing or organic deposit associated

[a] Adjectival descriptions according to Rosenqvist (1953). See Table 1.
[b] Pertains to samples hardened starting from present composition and water content. Role of thixotropy in causing sensitivity of clays *in situ* is indeterminate.

sediments for this delta are believed to have come from an ice lobe originating from the Alaska Range or from the Susitna Valley, a direction different from the known sources of ice. The eastern margin of the lake was bounded by ice, forming a depression of about 40 mi² that was filled with Bootlegger Cove Clay material.

The depositional environment for the Bootlegger Cove Clay, a very important consideration in the formation of high sensitivity, involved changes of base level and a salt-water invasion during an ice retreat.

A study of the foraminifera from the Bootlegger Cove Clay provides information on its formational environment (Smith, 1964). Samples from depths of 27–56 ft taken from Boring C110 in the Turnagain slide area were examined; soil data for this boring are given in Figure 4. This depth interval corresponds to the soft sensitive central portion of the Bootlegger Cove Clay formation. In this particular boring, sensitivities ranged from about 5 to 30. Foraminiferal fauna evidence throughout the 27–56 ft depth indicates a marine environment during formation, with apparent lessening of water depth and/or salinity toward the top. Samples from below a depth of 50 ft indicate a shallow marine environment (25 m) with near normal salinity.

Samples were also examined from Boring A120 in the Fourth Avenue slide area; the log of this boring and the pertinent soil data are given in Figure 5. The depth interval studied was 27–142 ft. Fauna from high in the section con-

sists mainly of the protozoa *Elphidium* similar to that found in present-day cold-water deltaic environments. Below a depth of 100 ft the variety of fauna is more indicative of a marine environment.

The clay is separated from overlying outwash by a silt contact representing an ice advance just before the maximum advance of the Naptowne ice. Iron staining along this contact indicates interglacial weathering before the last ice advance. The Naptowne glacial-drift sheet overlying this silt contact includes end-moraine deposits and outwash sand and gravel.

Several other materials that have been laid down since the last deposition of glacial drift include alluvial fans, sand and gravel on valley floors and in channels, and swamp or bog deposits. The relatively abundant swamp and bog deposits with peat up to 12 ft thick may be of considerable importance in the development of highly sensitive zones in the Bootlegger Cove Clay, because clays of high sensitivity frequently form in zones overlain by such materials.

COMPOSITION OF THE BOOTLEGGER COVE CLAY

Mineralogical and physicochemical analyses have been made of both sensitive and insensitive samples of Bootlegger Cove Clay (Shevlin, 1964; Mitchell, 1964). X-ray diffraction, dif-

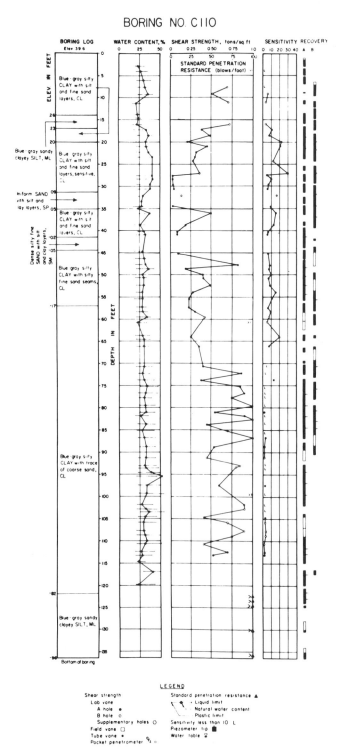

FIGURE 4   Boring log and soil-property data for Bootlegger Cove Clay in Turnagain slide area. See p. 121 for map of slide.

ferential thermal analysis, thermogravimetric analysis, and petrographic examinations were used for identification of minerals in four samples—two sensitive and two insensitive. All samples contained basically the same minerals, with the observed quantities relating primarily to the proportions of different particle-size fractions present. Finely divided quartz was found to be the most abundant mineral; feldspar (possibly highly weathered) was present in finely divided form; and the clay minerals kaolinite, illite, and chlorite were present in all samples. No apparent correlations were found to exist between the mineralogy and the sensitivity of the clay to disturbance.

The occurrence of significant quantities of kaolinite in the Bootlegger Cove Clay is somewhat surprising, because, generally, it is not found extensively in glacial environments where sensitive marine clay deposits are formed. Additional mineralogical analyses of samples from the Turnagain area also indicate the presence of some kaolinite, but only in small amounts (Higgs, 1966).

The results of the physicochemical analyses are given in Table 3, together with pertinent classification and engineering-property data. These data show that all specimens examined were quite basic (pH from 8.3 to 10.3). Few data are available concerning the pH of sensitive clays; the high values observed in the Bootlegger Cove Clay are, however, believed to be somewhat unusual. The physical behavior of the remolded clay is consistent with these high pH values, however, as evidenced most particularly by the very stable suspensions of the clay that could be made without the need for treatment with a dispersing agent.

The cation-exchange capacity of the clay is consistent with that of other silty clays with a clay fraction composed of illitic and chloritic clay minerals. The pore-water salt content varies from 2.7 to 5.8 g/liter as compared with 36 g/liter for normal seawater. From the limited data available, no apparent correlation exists between the present pore-water salt content and sensitivity such as that found for Norwegian marine clays by Bjerrum (1954). The present salt content is obviously much less than that of normal seawater, indicating that, for those zones of the Bootlegger Cove stratum laid down in a marine environment, considerable leaching of salt must have taken place.

The results of chemical analysis show that sodium, calcium, and magnesium make up the bulk of the cations in solution, the relative proportions of which are given in Table 3. Calcium is the most abundant ion, followed in order by sodium and magnesium. Because sodium predominates in a marine environment, the data indicate a substantial change in pore-water chemistry since the deposition of the clay.

Groundwater studies in the Anchorage area by the U.S. Geological Survey show the principal source of water to be from wells tapping an artesian system of confined sand and

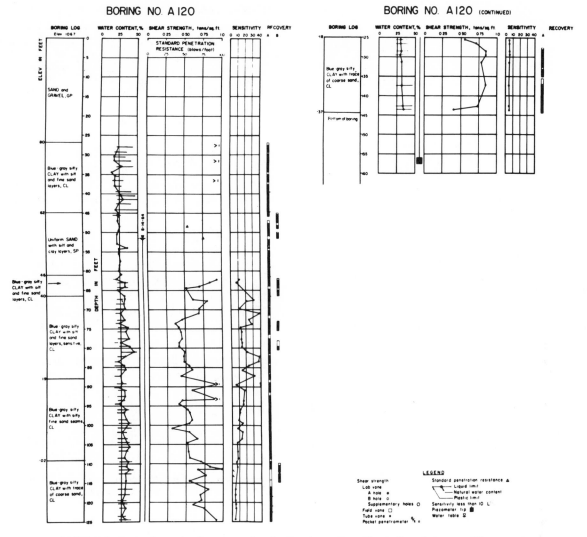

FIGURE 5   Boring log and soil-property data for Bootlegger Cove Clay in Fourth Avenue slide area.

gravel aquifers of outwash origin, interbedded with silt, clay, and glacial till. The water is of medium hardness and contains calcium–magnesium bicarbonate. Silt and fine sand lenses occur frequently throughout the Bootlegger Cove Clay, and some interconnection could be expected between the groundwater aquifers and these lenses that could account for the change in pore-water chemistry in the clay, because sodium is readily displaced by calcium and magnesium.

CAUSES OF BOOTLEGGER COVE CLAY SENSITIVITY

In an attempt to pinpoint the cause of sensitivity in the Bootlegger Cove Clay, the following points from the pre-

ceding discussion of the formation and composition of the clay should be considered:

1. The soft sensitive zone in the Bootlegger Cove Clay is sandwiched between layers of stiffer clay.

2. Geologic evidence indicates the soft zone was probably laid down in a marine environment, but a less saline environment may have existed during deposition of the overlying layer of stiff clay.

3. Some weathering of the clay may have taken place near the contact with subsequent glacial and postglacial deposits.

4. Silt and fine sand lenses are interspersed at close intervals throughout the clay stratum.

5. Present groundwater has a high calcium–magnesium content.

TABLE 3 Physicochemical Characteristics of Six Bootlegger Cove Clay Samples

Area	Boring[a]	Depth, ft	Consistency	Water Content, %	Liquid Limit, %	Plasticity Index, %	Undisturbed Shear Strength tons/ft^2	Sensitivity	pH[b]	Cation-Exchange Capacity, meq/100 g	Pore-Water[c] Salt Content, g/liter	Cations in Solution[d] $\dfrac{C_i}{\Sigma C_i} = \%$		
												Na$^+$	Ca^{2+}	Mg^{2+}
Fourth Avenue	A117AX	78	Sensitive	35	36	16	0.20	14	10.2	10.9	5.8	29	66	5
Fourth Avenue	A117AX	125	Stiff	29	40	18	>1.0	Low	10.2	10.6	2.8	36	61	3
L Street	B-120	24	Sensitive	38	–	–	0.35	>20	9.1	10.1	2.7	26	40	34
L Street	B-120	33	Stiff	29	–	–	0.65	11	8.3	9.6	4.2	29	67	4
Turnagain	C108B	73½	Sensitive	36	36	16	0.40	16	10.3	7.5	3.3	30	45	25
Turnagain	C117	117	Stiff	21	–	–	Stiff clay	Low	9.9	4.6	2.8	31	58	11

[a]Detailed boring logs are given in Bjerrum (1954).
[b]Determined on a suspension of 5 parts water to 1 part soil by weight.
[c]Equivalent NaCl content based on conductivity of clay suspension.
[d]C_i = concentration of given ion; $\Sigma C_i = C_{Na} + C_{Ca} + C_{Mg}$.

6. Swamp and bog deposits are abundant throughout the area.

7. The pH is relatively high.

Another significant observation is that the Bootlegger Cove Clay is not highly sensitive throughout. Of 2,100 samples tested, only 302, or about 14 percent, had sensitivities greater than 10 (Shannon & Wilson, Inc., 1964). Sensitivities in the range of 25–50 were measured in some of the soft zones, but the proportion of such zones of the total studied is low. In all zones of high sensitivity, silt and fine sand layers were found. Silt and fine sand layers were also found in most of the zones containing clay of low sensitivity, although a number of these zones apparently did not contain such layers. Thus the Bootlegger Cove Clay, although sensitive throughout to some degree, has not developed the extreme properties of the quick clays frequently encountered in Scandinavia and parts of Canada.

Each of the mechanisms listed in Table 2 may be considered in terms of its ability to account for the sensitivity of the Bootlegger Cove Clay.

METASTABLE PARTICLE ARRANGEMENTS

Metastable particle arrangements, which can be broken down by disturbance, seem to form in almost all types of fine-grained deposits when they are sedimented and consolidated from high water contents. How effective this mechanism could have been in the Bootlegger Cove Clay is unknown, but sensitivities as high as 12 that were developed in this manner have been observed in some clays.

Even after an undisturbed sample is thoroughly remolded and then reconsolidated under the same pressure as origi-nally acted on the soil in the ground, it will develop some sensitivity (Newland and Allely, 1957). Thiers (1965) subjected a sample of Bootlegger Cove Clay to this test and found that, after reconsolidation, the clay had a sensitivity of 1.6.

SILT SKELETON-BOND CLAY WITH CLAY MATRIX

Because the Bootlegger Cove Clay contains significant quantities of these coarser particles, a structure of this type is more than possible and probably accounts for a part of the sensitivity.

ION EXCHANGE

The ionic form of the clay at its time of deposition is not known. If it had been sedimented in a marine environment, the dominant cation after deposition would have been sodium; at present, calcium is the dominant cation. Because sodium clays are usually less flocculated and hence less sensitive than calcium clays, the exchange of calcium ion for sodium ion has probably not been a factor in developing high sensitivity, and it may even have limited the sensitivity.

WEATHERING

Because the main clay minerals in the Bootlegger Cove Clay are illitic and chloritic in nature and are nonexpansive, any weathering would be expected to lead to the release of potassium and to cause an increase in both undisturbed and remolded strength and a decrease in sensitivity (Moum and Rosenqvist, 1961). Weathering could account, in part, for the greater stiffness and lower sensitivity of the upper part of the Bootlegger Cove Clay, but additional chemical analyses would be required for confirmation of this theory.

THIXOTROPIC HARDENING

It has been demonstrated that if a clay remolded from its *in situ* undisturbed condition exhibits thixotropic hardening, thixotropy was not necessarily a significant factor in causing the original sensitivity. In the case of the Bootlegger Cove Clay, the results of thixotropy measurements made on remolded specimens indicated only whether the clay in its present state was thixotropic and its probable behavior in the field after disturbance.

Limited data on the thixotropic hardening characteristics of Bootlegger Cove Clay are available. Two samples of clay from the Turnagain area were studied, one with a liquid limit of 29.5 percent, plasticity index of 9 percent, and natural water content of 30.0 percent; the other had a liquid limit of 33.5 percent, plasticity index of 12.5 percent, and natural water content of 32.0 percent. Thoroughly remolded samples were allowed to age at constant water content, and the shear strength was determined at the end of various time intervals. Unfortunately, drying of the specimens was detected for periods longer than 30 days, and at this stage the tests were discontinued. The available data therefore cover an extremely short time period, compared to the geologic age of the clay.

Figure 6 shows that the Bootlegger Cove Clay does exhibit some thixotropic effects. Extrapolation of the data to 10,000 years, which represents an approximate geological age of the clay, gives values of acquired sensitivity of

about 5–9. The paucity of data and the tenuous nature of such an extrapolation make these values uncertain, but the thixotropic characteristics of the Bootlegger Cove Clay appear to be similar to those for other glacial clays.

Although they do not contribute directly to determination of the possible role of thixotropic hardening in development of the *in situ* sensitivity of the Bootlegger Cove Clay, the results do indicate that any zones that were thoroughly remolded by the slides induced by the 1964 earthquake are likely to be stronger today than they were immediately after the earthquake. If the extrapolations in Figure 6 are valid, because of thixotropic hardening alone and quite apart from the possible effect of reconsolidation of the remolded zones, the strength of these zones today (1969) may be up to five times greater than it was immediately after the earthquake.

CEMENTATION

The role of cementation in the Bootlegger Cove Clay is still unknown. Iron staining has been observed along the upper surface of the clay stratum, and iron compounds can act as cements in soils. Foraminifera commonly secrete a chambered shell of calcium carbonate; weak carbonate cements could be derived from these shells. Calcium and magnesium bicarbonates, found in the water in sand and silt lenses throughout the area, provide an additional source of cements. Silicates derived from the soil minerals themselves, or from the shells of Radiolaria inhabiting the clay, could also contribute to cementing action.

SALT LEACHING

Because there is strong evidence that the sensitive zone of the Bootlegger Cove Clay was deposited in seawater, and because the present salt content is relatively low (Table 3), leaching might possibly account for the high sensitivity. Problems arise, however, in ascribing all the high sensitivity to this source. The data in Table 3 show that the present salt content in the stiff clay below the sensitive layer is about the same as in the sensitive layer; in two instances, it is actually less than the sensitive layer. Geologic evidence indicates that the lower material was also formed in a marine environment. It is necessary to explain, therefore, why this underlying clay is not also highly sensitive. One possibility is that at the greater depths the clay has been consolidated to a point where sensitivities are low. Studies have shown that normally consolidated clays tend to become less sensitive as the water content is decreased, at least when the pressures become relatively high (Houston, 1967). This explanation is not very satisfactory, however, because reference to the detailed logs of borings indicates that there is in many cases very little consistent variation of water content

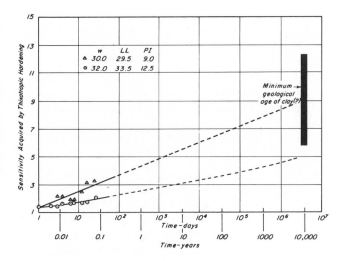

FIGURE 6   Thixotropic characteristics of Bootlegger Cove Clay from the Turnagain area showing percentages of water content (W), liquid limit (LL), and plasticity index (PI).

with depth in the Bootlegger Cove Clay (Shannon & Wilson, Inc., 1964).

The leaching mechanism might, therefore, possibly be the main cause of the sensitivity of the Bootlegger Cove Clay, but other factors must be taken into account in explaining the previously discussed anomalies.

DISPERSING AGENTS

Quick clays can develop as a result of the formation of dispersing agents within a clay, from decomposition of various constituents, or by leaching into a clay. Clays of high sensitivity are often found in proximity to organic deposits, and it has been established that the products of organic decomposition can act as powerful dispersants.

Organic deposits are abundant in the Anchorage area, and silt and fine sand lenses are interspersed frequently within the sensitive zones of the Bootlegger Cove Clay; thus, organically derived dispersants could find access to the clay through the groundwater. The Bootlegger Cove Clay has an abnormally high pH, a condition favorable for deflocculation and development of high sensitivity; the specific agent responsible for this high pH is as yet unknown. Conditions appear to be favorable in the Bootlegger Cove Clay for formation of sensitivity by the dispersing-agent mechanism.

CONCLUSIONS

It is impossible, on the basis of available data previously discussed, to specify which of the several mechanisms leading to the development of sensitivity is the most important cause of sensitivity in the Bootlegger Cove Clay. In the zones of highest sensitivity, leaching of salt from the pore water and the introduction of dispersing agents may be the most important factors.

Sensitivities of less than 10, which predominate in the Bootlegger Cove Clay, can be accounted for in terms of several mechanisms.

GEOTECHNICAL PROPERTIES OF BOOTLEGGER COVE CLAY

Some of the geotechnical properties of Bootlegger Cove Clay are summarized here, and their relations to other sensitive clays in terms of the general pattern of behavior established by Houston and Mitchell (1969) are examined. The results of thousands of tests are available (Shannon & Wilson, Inc., 1964, 1965, 1966). The range in which more than 80 percent of the test values fall for the sensitive central zone between the upper and lower stiff clays is given in Table 4. These values are typical of those for other marine glacial and postglacial sensitive clay deposits throughout the world.

TABLE 4 Summary of Properties of Hundreds of Bootlegger Cove Clay Sensitive Zone Samples

Property	Range[a]
Shear strength, tons/ft^2	0.4–1.0
Sensitivity	6–26
Moisture content (W), %	27–37
Liquid limit (LL), %	27–39
Plastic limit (PL), %	17–23
Plasticity index (PI)	7–15
Liquidity index (LI)	0.5–1.3
Percent finer than 2 μ	18–58
pH	7–10
Salt content, g/liter equivalent NaCl	2.7–4.2
Base exchange capacity, meq/100 g	5.0–10.0
Major clay constituents	illite and chlorite
Major nonclay constituents	quartz and feldspar

[a]Range in which 80 percent or more of the test values fall.

PLASTICITY CHARACTERISTICS

The plasticity characteristics of Bootlegger Cove Clay are indicated on the plasticity chart shown in the upper part of Figure 7; the great majority of points fall within the (CL) zone, thus indicating clays of low plasticity. The liquid-limit (LL) distribution curves, shown in the lower part of Figure 7, indicate that the clay from the sensitive middle zone has a slightly lower liquid limit than the lower stiff clay. This suggests that there may be some compositional differences between these two zones or that the extent of liquid-limit reduction by leaching is somewhat less in the lower zone. The distribution for the upper stiff zone shows a greater frequency of higher liquid-limit values but about the same average value as the sensitive zone. This may reflect essentially similar composition in the two zones, with perhaps somewhat less leaching in the upper zone. The data suggest desiccation or some other form of precompression as a more probable cause of the higher strength in the upper zone than compositional differences resulting from different source material or weathering.

Figure 8 shows some correlations between liquid limit and sensitivity. Frequency distributions are shown for samples with sensitivities greater than 10, 20, and 30. These distributions are based only on the data for those samples that had a sensitivity greater than 10 (about 14 percent of the total number of samples tested). From the distributions shown in Figure 8, it may be seen that as sensitivity increases, the highest liquid limit decreases. This result is consistent with observations of other clays, which show that greatest sensitivities are associated with the lowest liquid limits. The reduced liquid limit in such materials generally has resulted from leaching of salt from the pores or introduction of a dispersing agent.

An even stronger correlation exists between the liquidity

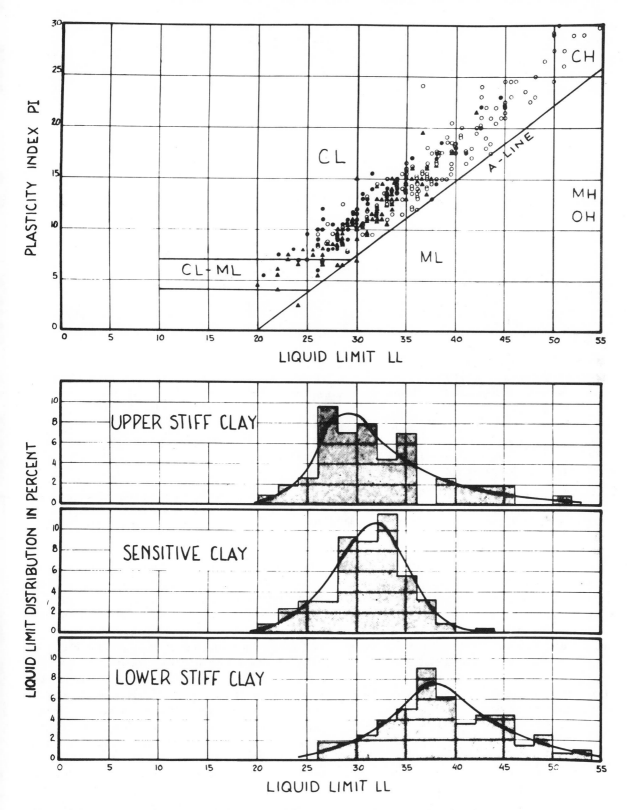

FIGURE 7   Plasticity index (PI) and liquid-limit (LL) distribution curves for Bootlegger Cove Clay from Turnagain area. (A-Line = Boundary separating CL and CH soils from OL, ML and OH, MH soils; CH = inorganic clays of high plasticity; CL = inorganic clays of low to medium plasticity; CL–ML = soil intermediate of CL and ML; MH = inorganic silts; ML = inorganic silts and very fine sands; OH = organic clays of medium to high plasticity.)

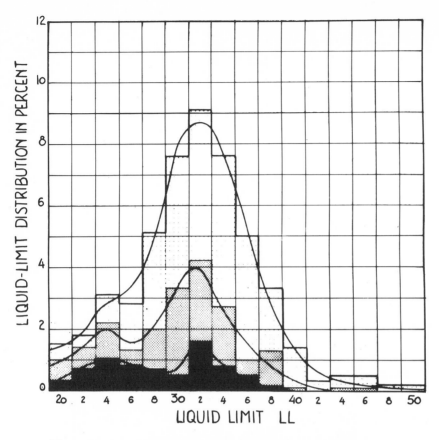

LIQUID-LIMIT DISTRIBUTION IN PERCENT

LIQUID LIMIT LL

☐ LIQUID-LIMIT DISTRIBUTION FOR SAMPLES WITH SENSITIVITY S > 10

▦ LIQUID-LIMIT DISTRIBUTION FOR SAMPLES WITH SENSITIVITY S > 20

■ LIQUID-LIMIT DISTRIBUTION FOR SAMPLES WITH SENSITIVITY S > 30

SUM OF ALL SAMPLES WITH SENSITIVITY S > 10 EQUALS 100 %

FIGURE 8 Liquid-limit–sensitivity distribution curves. The sum of all samples with sensitivity > 10 = 100 percent.

index and liquid limit, with the higher values of liquidity index being associated with lower values of liquid limit (Figure 9). This finding is consistent with observations for other glacial marine clays. Because of the relationships established by Figures 8 and 9, a correlation must exist between liquidity index and sensitivity (Figure 10). The data in Figure 10 exhibit a considerable amount of scatter, some of which may have resulted from sample disturbance. Also shown in Figure 10 is the correlation obtained by Bjerrum (1954) for Norwegian marine clays.

RELATIONS OF SENSITIVITY, LIQUIDITY INDEX, AND EFFECTIVE STRESS

The results of a recent study show that a unique relation between liquidity index and sensitivity can be expected to exist only if the effective stress does not vary widely (Houston and Mitchell, 1969). The general relation between sensitivity, liquidity index, and effective stress that

has been found to apply to a variety of clays is shown in Figure 11. Data for the Bootlegger Cove Clay have been examined with respect to this relation.

Estimates of vertical effective stresses were made for the samples shown on the boring logs given in Shannon & Wilson, Inc. (1966). Because of water-table fluctuations and limited information on densities, the estimates are subject to considerable error. In addition, at the time the borings were made, the clay was overconsolidated by the weight of 35 ft of material that was later removed during the earthquake. As shown in Houston and Mitchell (1969), the properties of an overconsolidated clay are more closely related to the preconsolidation pressure than to the existing effective stress. The variation of effective stress with depth that was assumed is consistent with the reported densities. Within the sensitive zone of the Bootlegger Cove Clay, the effective stress was found to vary within relatively narrow limits.

Sensitivity values, determined by using vane tests as given

in Shannon & Wilson, Inc. (1966) together with estimated effective stresses, have been plotted on the average sensitivity pattern shown in Figure 11. The results are shown in Figure 12.

Figure 12 shows that the effective stress does not vary widely for the test values examined; this small variation does not allow determination of the influence of effective stress variations on sensitivities within this one clay deposit. The influence of the effective stress can be seen more clearly when the results shown in Figure 12 are compared to the results reported by Bjerrum (1954) for Norwegian marine clays. The effective stress also varied within narrow limits for the clays that Bjerrum studied, but the average value of the effective stress for these clays was about 1 kg/cm² as opposed to about 3–4 kg/cm² for the Bootlegger Cove Clay. This difference in effective stress accounts for the fact that Bjerrum's correlation between sensitivity and liquidity index (see Figure 10) gives sensitivities at any given value of liquidity index that are about 25–45 percent smaller than the

values found for the Bootlegger Cove Clay.

The relation between sensitivity, liquidity index, and effective stress from Figure 11 can also be shown by plotting effective-stress contours on a sensitivity–liquidity-index plot. Such a plot is shown in Figure 13, with the Bootlegger Cove Clay data superimposed. Because it is very unlikely that the effective stress is anywhere less than 1 kg/cm², either the *in situ* sensitivities are somewhat greater than the measured values (i.e., the test procedures gave values that were too low), or the Bootlegger Cove Clay does not fit the pattern established for other sensitive clays.

The sensitivities for a number of the determinations, measured using vane shear tests, may have been too low for the following reasons:

1. The presence of many small silt lenses—some as thin as a fraction of an inch—will cause strength values to be somewhat erratic because, unavoidably, a vane test will occasionally be made partly or wholly in one of these lenses. The re-

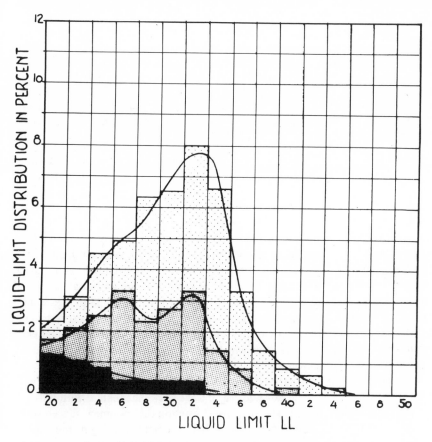

☐ LIQUID-LIMIT DISTRIBUTION FOR SAMPLES WITH LIQUIDITY INDEX LI > 1.00

▦ LIQUID-LIMIT DISTRIBUTION FOR SAMPLES WITH LIQUIDITY INDEX LI > 1.25

■ LIQUID-LIMIT DISTRIBUTION FOR SAMPLES WITH LIQUIDITY INDEX LI > 1.50

SUM OF ALL SAMPLES WITH LIQUIDITY INDEX LI > 1.00 EQUALS 100%

FIGURE 9 Liquid-limit–liquidity index distribution curves. Sum of all samples with liquidity index > 1.00 equals 100 percent. percent.

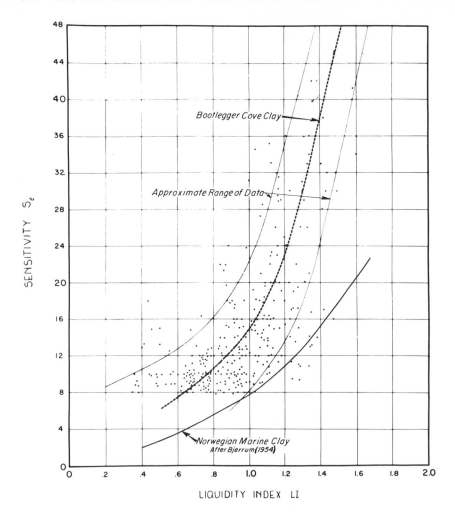

FIGURE 10 Relation between sensitivity and liquidity index. (Only test results of samples taken from borings in the Fourth Avenue slide area and Turnagain slide area, with a sensitivity of over 8 have been used.)

molded strengths are considered to have been more seriously affected than the undisturbed strengths, because they show much more erratic variation within small depth increments than do the undisturbed strengths. If a vane test is made partly in a silt lens, the remolded strength will be too high and will give sensitivities that are too low. In fact, any one value may not be representative of the true remolded strength, because the small amount of soil involved in the failure zone surrounding the vane may differ considerably from a sample taken from a thoroughly remolded larger mass of clay.

2. The presence of silt lenses made it difficult to obtain representative samples for moisture content and for Atterberg limits determinations. The proportion of the sample that is a silt lens will greatly affect the Atterberg limits, the moisture content, and therefore the liquidity index.

The scatter in remolded-strength values introduced by effects such as those mentioned can be seen in Figure 14. The open circles represent specimens taken from a large homogeneous mass of thoroughly remolded Bootlegger Cove Clay; these points define a relatively smooth curve.

The solid circles represent vane test results for different samples that were remolded by several revolutions of a small vane and reflect the influences of any local inhomogeneities that may have existed in the sample (Shannon & Wilson, Inc., 1966). These points show considerable scatter, with a predominance of values that are greater at any liquidity index than for the thoroughly remolded homogeneous specimens. A reasonable conclusion, therefore, seems to be that many of the sensitivity values determined in the field were too low, which accounts in part for the discrepancies shown in Figures 12 and 13.

A series of triaxial tests were performed on undisturbed samples of Bootlegger Cove Clay (Shannon & Wilson, Inc., 1964). The effective stresses on the specimens ranged from about 0.4 to 7 kg/cm². The remolded strengths were not determined, so it is not possible to assess directly the influence of effective stress on sensitivity over this wide range of effective stress. The data may be utilized, however, if we assume that the liquidity index versus remolded shear strength curve presented in Figure 14 is valid. With the aid of this curve and the known undisturbed strength, water content, and plasticity index values, sensitivity values could

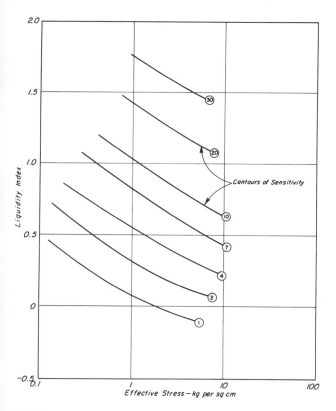

FIGURE 11 General relation between sensitivity, liquidity index, and effective stress for a variety of clays.

be calculated and plotted as shown in Figure 15. Although the sensitivities do not cover a very wide range, the influence of effective stress is obvious. The slope of the contours is very close to that of the average contours shown in Figure 11.

The overall sensitivity characteristics of the Bootlegger Cove Clay seem, therefore, to be in reasonable agreement with those of other sensitive clays in the world.

SHEAR STRENGTH–OVERBURDEN PRESSURE RELATIONS

Determination of the ratio of shear strength to overburden pressure (c/p) for the Bootlegger Cove Clay, based on shear strength defined as one-half the unconfined compressive strength, indicates for the zone of highly sensitive clay a range from 0.09 to 0.25, with an average value of about 0.17. Values in this range are typical of those for other sensitive clays.

With estimated values of vertical effective stress and an assumed linear variation with depth, it was possible to calculate c/p values for the vane shear strengths reported in Shannon & Wilson, Inc. (1966); these values are plotted against sensitivity in Figure 16. The very high values of c/p at low sensitivity are for samples from very shallow depths.

These samples may have been somewhat desiccated, and the estimated effective stresses may be too low. Figure 16 shows that, although the data scatter considerably, a definite decrease in c/p with increasing sensitivity is evident.

The lower stiff clay shows values of c/p in the range of 0.22–0.42, with an average of 0.29. This higher value of c/p for the stiff clay compared to the soft zone is compatible with both the somewhat higher plasticity and considerably lower sensitivity exhibited by the stiff clay. Correlation between c/p and plasticity index has been shown previously by Bjerrum (1954).

CONSOLIDATION CHARACTERISTICS

The results of a large number of consolidation tests on the Bootlegger Cove Clay indicate, on the basis of maximum past-pressure determinations, that the deposit is normally consolidated with the exception of the stiff upper crust, which overconsolidated by desiccation. Because of previous overburden, later removed by the earthquake, some areas of Bootlegger Cove Clay are now somewhat overconsolidated.

Compression-index values for the undisturbed clay range from 0.10 to 0.63, with an average value of about 0.33. The coefficient of consolidation was found to be of the order of 2 to 25×10^{-4} cm^2/sec. These values of coefficient of consolidation may be misleading in the field, however, because the presence of silt and fine sand lenses may serve to accelerate the rate of consolidation.

STRENGTH PARAMETERS

The effective-stress shear-strength parameters of Bootlegger Cove Clay were determined by using undrained triaxial-compression tests with pore-pressure measurements. The maximum effective principal-stress ratio σ'_1/σ'_3 was used as the failure criterion. For normally consolidated specimens, the effective cohesion $c' = 0$. The effective angle of shearing resistance ϕ' was found to vary with liquid limit as shown in Figure 17. This decrease of ϕ' with increase in liquid limit is consistent with results for other clays (Bjerrum, 1961).

The results of triaxial tests show an excellent correlation between the pore-pressure parameter $\overline{A}_f$ and c/p, with $\overline{A}_f$ decreasing significantly as c/p increases (Figure 18). This relation is consistent with that found for other clays (Houston and Mitchell, 1969).

BEHAVIOR OF BOOTLEGGER COVE CLAY UNDER CYCLIC LOADING

General aspects of the strength and deformation behavior of clays under the action of cyclic-stress conditions, such as those generated during an earthquake, have been studied by

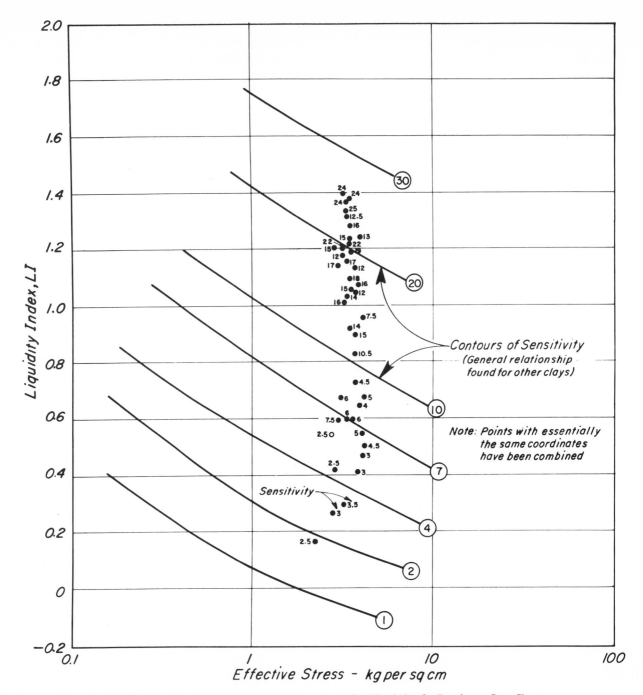

FIGURE 12   Relations of sensitivity, effective stress, liquidity-index for Bootlegger Cove Clay.

Seed and Chan (1966). Some specific response characteristics of the Bootlegger Cove Clay are reported by Thiers
and Seed (1969), Seed and Chan (1966), Seed and Lee
(1964), and Seed (1965). Tests on the Bootlegger Cove Clay
were mainly on the softer and more sensitive specimens (remolded shear strengths ranged from 0.003 to 0.05 kg/cm²).
Significant aspects of their findings as they relate to the

sensitivity and other geotechnical properties of this clay
are listed herewith:

1. The Bootlegger Cove Clay is susceptible to strength
losses under cyclic loading because failure may be induced
under repeated compressive and shear stresses of a magnitude considerably less than that needed to cause failure in

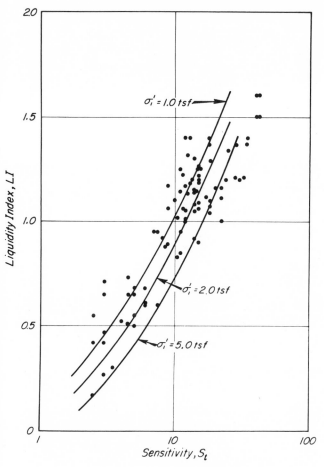

FIGURE 13 Sensitivity as a function of liquidity index.

static load tests. Figure 19 shows the relation between the pulsating deviator stress (expressed as a percentage of the static compressive strength) and the number of cycles to cause failure for soils from three Anchorage areas (Fourth Avenue, Area A; L Street, Area B; and Turnagain, Area C). The compressive strengths of the undisturbed specimens ranged from 0.34 to 3.20 kg/cm^2. Sensitivities of these specimens ranged from about 10 to 60, and little correlation appears to exist between the coordinates of any point and sensitivity.

2. If a rectangular pulse form is used, fewer repetitions of a given stress are required to cause failure than if a peaked stress pulse is used (Figure 19).

3. In stress-reversing tests, which involve a change in direction of major principal stress during each cycle, failure develops after fewer repetitions than when a nonreversing stress pulse is used.

4. Non-stress-reversing tests on sensitive specimens (sensitivities 10–15) from the Fourth Avenue area showed a progressive deformation with increasing numbers of stress cycles; there was no abrupt collapse or development of shear planes. When specimens were subjected to stress-reversing tests, however, no significant strain was observed until just before the failure cycle, when the sample collapsed abruptly into a fluid mass.

5. The lower the strain at failure in static tests, the greater is the reduction in modulus and in strength for specimens subjected to a given value of cyclic strain in strain-controlled cyclic-load tests. Figure 20 shows this behavior in terms of strength for specimens of Bootlegger

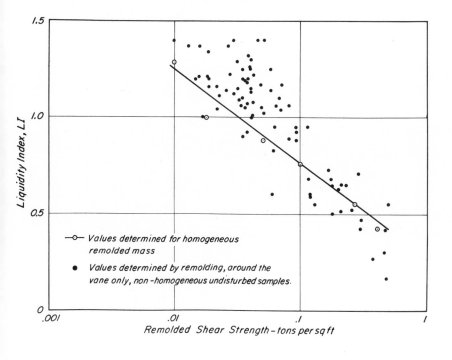

FIGURE 14 Liquidity index versus remolded shear strength for Bootlegger Cove Clay.

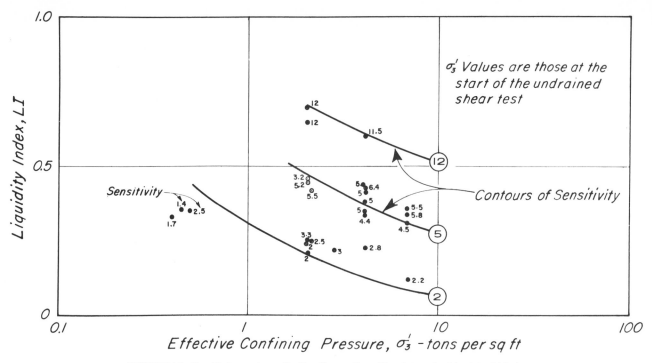

FIGURE 15   Sensitivity contours for Bootlegger Cove Clay determined by triaxial tests.

Cove Clay. In other words, the susceptibility to loss in strength and stiffness as a result of strain-controlled cyclic loading increases as strain required to cause failure decreases (Figure 21).

6. The behavior of the Bootlegger Cove Clay was the same for pulse frequencies of 1 and 2 cycles per second (cps). On the other hand, decreasing the frequency from 2 to 1 cps caused a 20 percent reduction in the cyclic stress required to cause failure in a given number of cycles in the case of San Francisco Bay mud.

7. Samples from the L Street area were thoroughly remolded and reconsolidated under the same pressure that acted on the clay *in situ*, and the susceptibility to strength loss under cyclic loading was determined. The results in Figure 22 show that the remolded, reconsolidated speci-

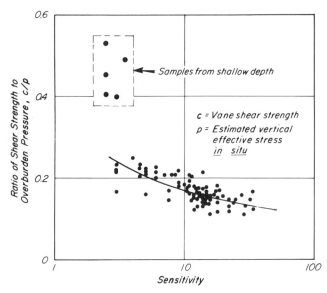

FIGURE 16   Shear strength to overburden pressure ratio (c/p) as a function of sensitivity for Bootlegger Cove Clay.

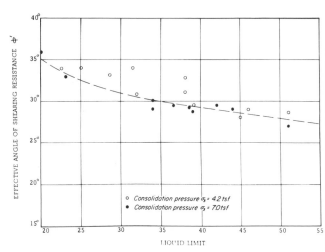

FIGURE 17   Relation between effective angle of shearing resistance and liquid limit.

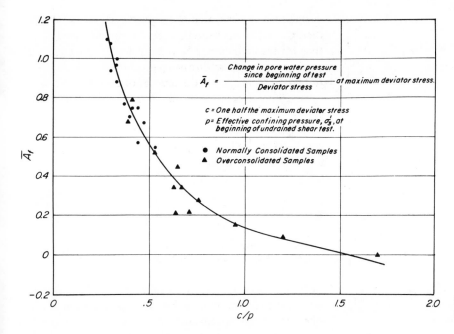

FIGURE 18   Ratio of $\bar{A}_f$ to c/p from triaxial tests on Bootlegger Cove Clay.

mens are, if anything, more susceptible than the undisturbed clay to failure under a given cyclic-stress level. The shear strength of the remolded reconsolidated specimens, however, was 0.27–0.36 kg/cm², whereas, that of the undisturbed clay was only 0.07–0.11 kg/cm². Furthermore, peak strength was mobilized at significantly lower strains (5–15 percent) for the undisturbed specimens than for the remolded reconsolidated clay (>20 percent).

The second finding in paragraph 7 is surprising, because we might reason that the more sensitive a soil, the more

easily could failure be induced under cyclic loading. An important part of this conclusion, however, is the cyclic-stress level, which is the ratio of the cyclic-stress intensity to the strength as determined in a static-strength test. Points in

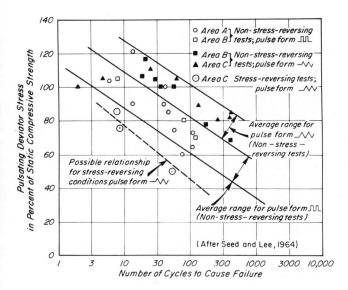

FIGURE 19   Summary of cyclic-loading data for Bootlegger Cove Clay. After H. B. Seed and K. L. Lee.

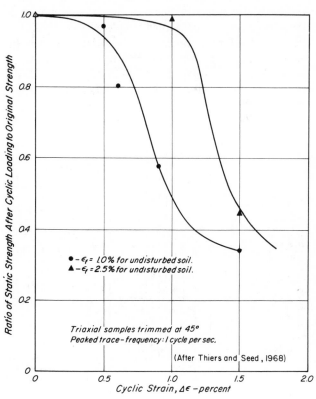

FIGURE 20   Effect of strain-controlled cyclic loading on static strength of Bootlegger Cove Clay. After G. R. Thiers and H. B. Seed.

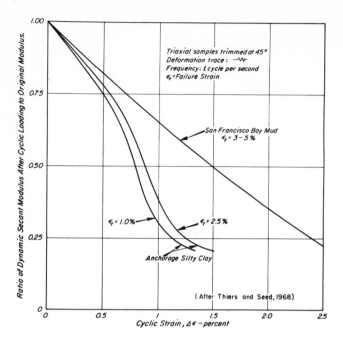

FIGURE 21 Effects of cyclic loading on dynamic modulus of undisturbed clays. After G. R. Thiers and H. B. Seed.

Figure 22 at any given stress level, therefore, refer to different values of stress intensity for undisturbed and remolded, reconsolidated specimens because, as previously indicated, the strength of the undisturbed samples was significantly less than that for the remolded reconsolidated samples. In addition, the more plastic nature of the remolded clay (> 20 percent strain to cause failure in static tests) relative to the undisturbed clay (5–15 percent strain to cause failure

in static tests) means that, for a given cyclic-stress level, there should be more cyclic strain for the remolded clay than for the undisturbed clay; more work is done per cycle on the remolded insensitive clay than on the the undisturbed sensitive clay. If the number of cycles required to cause failure depends on both the strain energy per cycle and the tendency for collapse of the soil structure as a result of deformation, then the undisturbed and remolded clay behavior under cyclic loading for tests at a given stress level would be as follows:

Clay State	Strain Energy per Cycle	Tendency for Collapse of Soil Structure
Undisturbed sensitive	Low	High
Remolded reconsolidated	High	Low

On this basis, it is reasonable that the number of cycles sufficient to cause failure is more or less independent of whether the clay is undisturbed or remolded. Such conclusions are highly speculative at this stage, and more research is needed to establish in more detail the factors responsible for failure of clays under cyclic loading.

For at least three important reasons, it cannot be inferred from results of the type shown in Figure 22 that highly sensitive clays are no more susceptible to failure during earthquakes than are insensitive clays: Highly sensitive clays in nature are invariably weaker in the undisturbed state than are insensitive clays at comparable depths; because the strain of failure is typically lower for a sensitive or quick clay than for an insensitive clay, a cyclic strain of some given amount is more likely to cause failure in the

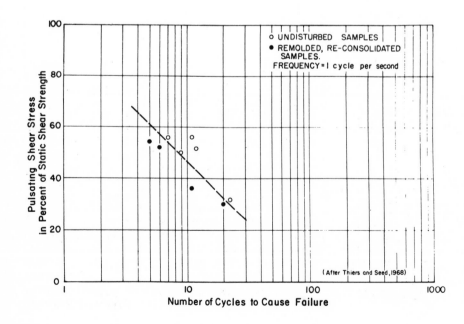

FIGURE 22 Effect of remolding and reconsolidation on failure conditions in pulsating loading simple shear tests. After G. R. Thiers and H. B. Seed.

sensitive clay than in the insensitive clay; and once the peak strength of a highly sensitive clay has been mobilized, the resistance to further deformation decreases appreciably with additional strain. Clays of low sensitivity, however, have an ultimate resistance to shear that may be nearly as great as the peak strength.

CONCLUSIONS

The purposes of this study have been to examine the causes of sensitivity in clays, with particular reference to the Bootlegger Cove Clay; to examine the similarities between the compositional and the geotechnical properties of Bootlegger Cove Clay and other sensitive clays; and to consider some aspects of the behavior of Bootlegger Cove Clay under cyclic loading.

Compositional analyses have shown that quartz is the most abundant mineral, feldspar (possibly highly weathered) is present in finely divided form, and illite, chlorite, and small amounts of kaolinite are present in finely divided form. No correlations seem to exist between the mineralogy and the sensitivity; this is consistent with findings for other highly sensitive clays throughout the world. Measurements of cation-exchange capacity, pore-water salt content, and solution cations gave values that are typical for leached marine clays. The pH of the Bootlegger Cove Clay, however, is in the range of 7.0–10.3. These values are believed to be unusually high and are consistent with the low remolded strength of the clay.

Eight mechanisms have been examined to determine their ability to account for the development of sensitivity (> 10 in 14 percent of the samples tested and 50 in some cases) in the Bootlegger Cove Clay. Because of lack of data, no predominant mechanism can be singled out. Leaching of salt from the pore water and the introduction of dispersing agents into the clay—either by formation *in situ* from decomposition of organic material, or other compounds, or by introduction from groundwater circulating through the many silt and sand lenses in the clay deposits—may be the most probable causes. Although remolded specimens of the Bootlegger Cove Clay exhibit some amount of thixotropic hardening, we cannot conclude that thixotropy was a significant contributor to the original sensitivity of the undisturbed clay.

The geotechnical properties of the Bootlegger Cove Clay are, in general, similar to those of other highly sensitive glacial clays. The great majority of samples fall within the (CL) zone of the plasticity chart. The average liquid limit of specimens from the sensitive middle zone of the clay deposit is less than that for the lower stiff clay. A reasonable correlation between liquidity index and sensitivity was found. This correlation differs from that found by Bjerrum

(1954) for Norwegian marine clays in that the sensitivity values at any given value of liquidity index are about 25–45 percent more for the Bootlegger Cove Clay than for the Norwegian clays. Analysis has shown that this difference arises mainly because the average effective stress in the Bootlegger Cove Clay is of the order of 3–4 kg/cm^2, whereas in the Norwegian clays it was only about 1 kg/cm^2. The overall sensitivity, liquidity index, and effective-stress relations for Bootlegger Cove Clay are similar to those for other sensitive clays.

The ratio of shear strength to overburden pressure (c/p) decreases with increasing sensitivity; values as low as 0.09 were measured for the most sensitive specimens. An average value for the soft sensitive zone is 0.17, whereas for the underlying stiff clay the average is about 0.29.

The susceptibility of the Bootlegger Cove Clay to failure under cyclic loading is strongly influenced by the form of the stress pulse and by whether the stress is reversing or nonreversing. Tests have shown that for a given cyclic-stress level (ratio of cyclic stress to strength in static test) the number of cycles required to cause failure is essentially independent of the sensitivity. Despite this observation, differences in strength and in stress versus strain characteristics between sensitive and insensitive clays may be expected to lead to very different responses under seismic loading.

ACKNOWLEDGMENTS

We are indebted to Professor H. Bolton Seed for his encouragement and helpful reviews during our preparation of this paper. The drawings were prepared by G. Dierking.

REFERENCES

Bjerrum, L., 1954. Geotechnical properties of Norwegian marine clays. *Geotechnique*, 4(2), 49.

Bjerrum, L., 1961. Effective stress strength parameters in a sensitive clay. Proceedings of the Fifth International Conference on Soil Mechanics and Foundation Engineering, Paris, France, Vol. 1. p. 23–28.

Higgs, N. B., 1966. Petrographic report, Appendix D, *in* Electro-osmosis field test section, preliminary stabilization studies for the Turnagain buttress. Seattle: Shannon & Wilson, Inc., June 30. 20 p.

Houston, W. N., 1967. Formation mechanisms and property interrelationships in sensitive clays (PhD dissertation). Berkeley: University of California, October.

Houston, W. N., and J. K. Mitchell, 1969. Property interrelationships in sensitive clays. *Journal of the Soil Mechanics and Foundations Division* (American Society of Civil Engineers), 95 (SM4), 1037–1062. Proceedings Paper 6666, July.

Karlsson, R., 1961. Suggested improvements in the liquid limit test, with reference to flow properties of remolded clays. Proceedings of the Fifth International Conference on Soil Mechanics and Foundation Engineering, Paris, France, Vol. 1. p. 171–184.

Miller, Robert D., and Ernest Dobrovolny, 1959. Surficial geology of Anchorage and vicinity, Alaska. U.S. Geological Survey Bulletin 1093. Washington: Government Printing Office. 128 p.

Mitchell, J. K., 1956. The fabric of natural clays and its relation to engineering properties. *Proceedings* (Highway Research Board), 35, 693.

Mitchell, J. K., 1961. Fundamental aspects of thixotropy in soils. *Transactions* (American Society of Civil Engineers), 126, Pt. I (No. SM3), 1586–1620.

Mitchell, J. K., 1964. Physico-chemical analyses, Appendix I, *in* Report on Anchorage area soil studies, Alaska. Seattle: Shannon & Wilson, Inc., August 28. 6 p.

Mitchell, J. K., and W. N. Houston, 1969. The causes of clay sensitivity. *Journal of the Soil Mechanics and Foundations Division* (American Society of Civil Engineers), 95 (SM3), Proceedings Paper 6568, May. p. 845–871.

Moum, J., and I. Th. Rosenqvist, 1961. The mechanical properties of montmorillonitic and illitic clays related to the electrolytes of the pore water. Proceedings of the Fifth International Conference on Soil Mechanics and Foundation Engineering, Paris, France, Vol. 1. p. 263–267.

Newland, P. L., and B. H. Allely, 1957. A study of sensitivity resulting from consolidation of a remolded clay. Proceedings of the Fourth International Conference on Soil Mechanics and Foundation Engineering, Vol. 1. p. 83.

Newland, P. L., and B. H. Allely, 1961. Discussion to fundamental aspects of thixotropy in soils, by J. K. Mitchell. *Transactions* (American Society of Civil Engineers), 126, Part I, 1621–1623.

Pusch, R., 1962. Clay particles. Handlingar Nr 40 *Transactions* (Statens Råd Byggforkning). 150 p.

Pusch, R., 1966. Quick clay microstructure. *Engineering Geology*, 1 (December), 433–443.

Rosenqvist, I. Th., 1953. Considerations on the sensitivity of Norwegian quick clays. *Geotechnique*, 3 (March), 195–200.

Rosenqvist, I. Th., 1959. Physico-chemical properties of soils: Soil-water systems. *Proceedings* (American Society of Civil Engineers), 85 (April), 31–53.

Seed, H. Bolton, 1965. Stress reversal tests, Appendix B *in* Remolding of Bootlegger Cove Clay with explosives, preliminary stabilization studies for the Turnagain buttress. Seattle: Shannon & Wilson, Inc., February 1. 7 p.

Seed, H. Bolton, and C. K. Chan, 1966. Clay strength under earthquake loading conditions. *Journal of the Soil Mechanics and Foundations Division* (American Society of Civil Engineers),

92 (SM2), 53–78. Proceedings Paper 4723, March.

Seed, H. Bolton, and K. L. Lee, 1964. Pulsating load tests on clays, Appendix D, *in* Report on Anchorage area soil studies, Alaska. Seattle: Shannon & Wilson, Inc., August 28. 18 p.

Seed, H. Bolton, and Stanley D. Wilson, 1967. The Turnagain Heights landslide, Anchorage, Alaska. *Journal of the Soil Mechanics and Foundations Division* (American Society of Civil Engineers), 93 (SM4), 325–353. Proceedings Paper 5320, July.

Shannon & Wilson, Inc., 1964. Report on Anchorage area soil studies, Alaska, to U.S. Army Engineer District, Anchorage, Alaska. Seattle: Shannon & Wilson, Inc., August 28. 300 p.

Shannon & Wilson, Inc., 1965. Remolding of Bootlegger Cove Clay with explosives. Preliminary stabilization studies for the Turnagain buttress. Seattle: Shannon & Wilson, Inc., February 1. 180 p.

Shannon & Wilson, Inc., 1966. Electro-osmosis field test section. Preliminary stabilization studies for the Turnagain buttress. Seattle: Shannon & Wilson, Inc., June 30. 153 p.

Shevlin, Thomas S., 1964. Mineralogical studies, Appendix H *in* Report on Anchorage area soil studies, Alaska. Seattle: Shannon & Wilson, Inc., August 28. 6 p.

Skempton, A. W., and R. D. Northey, 1952. The sensitivity of clays. *Geotechnique*, 3 (March), 30–53.

Smith, Patsy J., 1964. Foraminifera from the Bootlegger Cove Clay, Appendix J, *in* Report on Anchorage area soil studies, Alaska. Seattle: Shannon & Wilson, Inc., August 28. 4 p.

Swedish State Railways, 1922. Geotechnical Commission, 1914–22, Final report. Stockholm: Stat. Jarnvagar Medd. No. 2.

Tan, T. K., 1957. Report on soil properties and their measurement. Proceedings of the Fourth International Conference on Soil Mechanics and Foundation Engineering, Vol. 3.

Terzaghi, K., 1944. Ends and means in soil mechanics. *Engineers Journal* (Canada), V. 27, p. 608.

Thiers, G. R., 1965. The behavior of saturated clay under seismic loading conditions (PhD dissertation). Berkeley: University of California, September.

Thiers, G. R., and H. Bolton Seed, 1969. Strength of sensitive clays during seismic loading *in* Vibration effects of earthquakes on soils and foundations. American Society of Testing and Materials. Special Technical Publication No. 450. Philadelphia.

van Olphen, H., 1963. An introduction to clay colloid chemistry. New York: Interscience Publishers. 301 p.

Wu, T. H., 1958. Geotechnical properties of glacial lake clays. *Journal of the Soil Mechanics and Foundations Division* (American Society of Civil Engineers), 84 (SM3), 1732–1734. Proceedings Paper 1732, August.

RONALD F. SCOTT
KENNETH A. ZUCKERMAN
CALIFORNIA INSTITUTE OF TECHNOLOGY

Sandblows and Liquefaction

The occurrence of sandblows during an earthquake is an indication of a disturbance in the soil at some depth below the surface. During the Alaska earthquake there were many sandblows, indicating that the locations in which they developed were potentially hazardous to buildings. Similar events took place in the sandy soil of Niigata, Japan, during the earthquake of June 16, 1964, when the soil liquefied in built-up areas and damaged structures extensively.

Different mechanisms have been suggested to account for the behavior of sand spouts. Some geologists accept the explanation of Macelwane (1947): "The alternate tension and compression which is applied to the ground during the passage of earthquake waves opens fissures and sucks down the groundwater, then closes them, violently forcing out the water and with it large quantities of sand or mud that lay in its path." The same mechanism seems to have been in Coleridge's mind when he wrote

> And from this chasm, with ceaseless turmoil seething,
> As if this earth in fast thick pants were breathing,
> A mighty fountain momently was forced. . . .

Such a mechanism would apply to a fracture, rather than to a spout of circular symmetry, and would imply that the fracture drew water down and expelled it as the surface waves of the earthquake passed the crack. The accompanying fountain would pulse from zero to a maximum height, depending on the crack width and depth and the period of the surface waves. If we assume a crack of the order of 1 ft wide at its maximum at the surface and 15 ft deep, full of water, responding to surface waves of a period in the range of 1/2–1 second, a rough computation indicates that a sediment-laden water column would be ejected to a maximum height in the order of 3–15 ft. This ejection could only continue if enough flow of surface or groundwater were available to fill the crack during each opening phase of the cycle. The sand spout, even if fed continuously with water, would cease as soon as the strong ground motions ended.

ABSTRACT: Sandblows have occurred in many locations during earthquakes, including the Alaska earthquake. Their mechanism is not well understood, and several different theories have been advanced on the method of their formation.

It has been suggested that the liquefaction of loose soil layers below ground surface during an earthquake is related to the formation of sandblows at the surface. A series of laboratory experiments, designed to test this theory, indicates that the presence of a finer-grained layer of soil overlying the liquefiable zone is necessary for the formation of sandblows. It appears that the excess water produced by liquefaction makes its way to the surface by an unstable process of cavity formation and then of channel formation in the upper layer. If a coarse-grained denser upper layer is present that does not liquefy during the earthquake vibrations, it may liquefy after its suspension on underlying liquefied soil. The liquefaction may not always reach the surface. This process is termed "induced" or "secondary" liquefaction, and we present an analysis of this process and establish soil-property criteria to determine whether such liquefaction will reach ground surface.

The liquefaction of soil by an earthquake does not necessarily ensure that the soil profile is in a denser state after liquefaction. The soil may again be susceptible to vibration-caused liquefaction in a subsequent earthquake.

179

Although this explanation may account for some of the sand spouts observed in earthquakes, it has a number of deficiencies when compared to observations. It does not account for the presence of isolated spouts of circular symmetry unless they are assumed to be pumped from cracks below the surface. This is most unlikely, both from a mechanical point of view (the ground would crack to the surface) and because the volume of water collected in a crack and compelled to pass through a circular orifice would give spouts far higher than are actually observed. Although observed spouts attain heights of perhaps 6 ft and fluctuate in height, they do not appear to vanish altogether in what would correspond to the influx stage of the postulated cycle. Some spouts have been observed to continue for a number of minutes after strong ground motion ceases, a process that conflicts with the theory of a pumping mechanism associated with the presence of ground-surface waves. It is also difficult, in the case of spouts continuing for some time, to see how the explanation based on opening and closing of a crack can account for the amount of water supplied, except in flooded areas.

Another hypothesis is that sand spouts make manifest the presence of preearthquake artesian pressures in the underlying aquifers (Waller, 1966; Segerstrom and others, 1963). ". . . [T]hese extrusions indicate that high pressures must have existed in the water-table aquifer and thus a temporary confining layer must have been present." In the Alaska earthquake, the temporary confining layer is considered, in this hypothesis, to be the frozen surface soil. This explanation does not account for sand spouts observed in other earthquakes where no obvious confining layer such as frozen ground was present.

Housner (1958) suggested that an earthquake liquefies the underlying soil, which thereafter consolidates as does a compressible soil under an applied load. Analyzing the resulting process by the linear consolidation theory of soil mechanics, Housner calculated the quantity and rate of flow of water that would emerge at the ground surface. This theory was followed and elaborated on by Ambraseys and Sarma (1969). It seems likely that a process akin to this actually occurs, except that the mechanics of a fine-to-medium-grained sand settling out of suspension will not be those of a linearly consolidating medium. In the papers cited, the mechanism by which the expelled water arrives at the ground surface in the form of sandblows and mud fountains was not explained.

In a Japanese work, Kawakami (1965) says, "It is supposed that the sandblow occurs at first quite near the ground surface and propagates gradually to [the] depth." He observes that sandblows occur after a lapse of 2–3 minutes following the earthquake and do not appear during the main shocks. The blows may be as high as 1.2–1.5 m initially and diminish with the duration of spouting, which

may be as long as several minutes. The deposits around the spout contain materials from depths as great as 15–20 m.

These field observations are difficult to account for by Kawakami's mechanism. If the sandblow begins at ground surface by the flow of water supplied by the underlying liquefied soil into a surface cavity, one would expect the quantity of flow to increase with time, at least initially, as the cavity works its way down. The increasing volume and surface area of the opening would permit more water to enter from the surrounding soil in the later stages. The surficial deposits would also contain all the soils from the surface to the maximum depth; because of the diminution of the spout with time, the deepest soils would be expected to be only minimally represented. Substantial quantities of deeper layers, however, are often found to be present in the cone found after spouting ceases.

We consider that the most plausible basic mechanism underlying the development of sand spouts is that suggested by Housner (1958), which involves liquefaction of underlying loose saturated soil deposits. Before the earthquake, a hydrostatic condition exists in the water in the soil, and the soil at any level is subjected to effective stresses arising from the total unit weight of the soil above the water table in addition to the buoyant unit weight of the soil below the water table. If earthquake vibrations cause individual soil grains in a particular zone below the surface (and below the water table) to lose contact with one another (liquefaction), the effective stresses that were transmitted by the grain-to-grain contact are transferred to the pore water. The result is an increase in the pore-water pressure above the hydrostatic stress. In subsequent minutes, the soil grains settle to form a stable configuration once more, and the displaced water causes the suspension of overlying soil layers, however dense, that were not liquefied directly by the earthquake. What happens thereafter does not seem to have been examined in detail. Accordingly, we have studied the subsequent behavior of the indirectly liquefied soil.

QUALITATIVE ANALYSIS

This study describes a series of preliminary experiments on the mechanics of liquefaction and the generation of sandblows or sand spouts. Simple experiments show that a shock or vibration will cause a relatively loose saturated sand to become liquid for a short time, until the grains eventually settle to form a denser configuration. Immediately after liquefaction, some grains come to rest at the bottom of the container, while other grains continue to fall through the fluid until they strike the stationary grains. Thus at a given time after the shock, the system consists of a layer of stationary or solidified soil above which is a zone of soil in suspension in the fluid. The interface between the solid and fluid regions moves upward to the surface. When it reaches the surface, the process has ended.

If a loose sand layer is overlain by a dense layer of a relatively coarse grain size that is not liquefied by the initial vibration, a more complicated sequence of events occurs. Vibration liquefies the loose lower layer, and it begins to solidify at the base as it settles out. The upper denser and solid layer is now suspended directly on the underlying fluid. The dense soil proceeds to unravel at its lower surface in an inverse process to the solidification beginning at the base of the initially loose layer. We term this process "secondary" or "induced" liquefaction. Thus a solidification interface beginning at the base of the container moves upward through first the loose soil layer, then the dense soil layer, while a liquefaction interface begins at the underside of the dense soil layer and also moves upward. When all the soil is solidified, the loose soil is denser than formerly and the dense soil is looser. The rates of movement of the two interfaces depend on the initial and final porosities of the two materials and on their grain size. A quantitative description of this process is given later in this paper.

If the grain size of the dense layer is different from that of the loose layer, noticeable variations of the liquefaction-solidification process occur. In particular, if its grain size is smaller, then the settling velocity of the particles of the dense layer is lower than that of the particles in the loose layer, so that the surface of solidification may rise faster in the loose, coarse-grained material than the surface of liquefaction in the dense fine layer. A layer of fluid will develop containing few or no soil particles in the soil–water column.

Again, depending on the initial and final porosities at which the two soil layers can achieve a stable structure, the upper layer may not liquefy all the way to its upper surface; instead the solidification surface overtakes the liquefaction surface at some depth. The consequences of these different modes of behavior to a surface- or pile-supported structure can be inferred. In practice, the interference of the structure itself with the flow path of the emerging water will also cause variations in effect. For example, sandblows will tend to occur around the edges of buildings. Further, if the subsurface or surface flow conditions are different on two sides of a building (for example, the front of the building may face a paved street, the rear an unpaved parking lot) liquefaction will progress to the surface preferentially (the unpaved parking lot will liquefy first, for instance) and the soil support will diminish faster, or more on one side of the building, which may consequently tilt to that side, unless the position of the center of gravity of the structure favors motion in another direction.

In the cases discussed up to this point, liquefaction and solidification take place uniformly and continuously throughout the test soils. The question therefore arises as to the mechanism by which discontinuous liquefaction, manifested by sand boils and spouts, is generated. A number of preliminary laboratory tests indicated that, if the upper layer of soil was sufficiently fine, it did not in fact liquefy uniformly from its base; instead, boils appeared on its surface. This observation led to a more detailed investigation that showed that, when an upper layer of suitable properties was suspended on the underlying fluid, soil grains from the base of the upper layer would begin, after a short time, to fall in streams from a number of isolated spots, rather than uniformly over the base. Cavities therefore developed in the base of the upper layer. Conditions were apparently more suitable for unraveling to take place in these cavities than elsewhere, so that the cavities became tubes or pipes working toward the upper surface of the soil. When the water-filled cavity came sufficiently close to the free surface, the water under the excess pressure developed by the weight of the soil layer broke through the soil to form a jet or spout. Flow in the jet could become vigorous enough to carry entrained soil from both the lower and upper soil layers to the surface. This soil was deposited on the surface around the spout to form the typical sand or mud volcano observed after earthquakes.

It appeared, therefore, that a necessary condition for the generation of sandblows, rather than a uniform areal liquefaction, was the presence of a suitably fine-grained layer at the ground surface. The horizontal spacing between sandblows appears to depend on the thickness of this layer, which, with the other conditions (such as duration and intensity of ground motions and thickness of subsurface layer liquefied by the earthquake), plays a part in determining the height and duration of the sand spouts observed. If the finer-grained surface layer is brittle enough or subjected to large enough ground motions to crack, the underlying excess pressure will be relieved by the venting of water and sand through the cracks. This will produce elongated sandblows and the axially symmetric spouts will probably not develop in the same area.

The following experiments were designed to provide information on these mechanisms. The experiments were first suggested by Scott (1965) at a conference in 1965 following the Niigata earthquake.

RESULTS OF EXPERIMENTS

Because the generation of sandblows depends on suspending a layer of soil on a fluid (liquid in these experiments), it is not necessary for the suspension to be achieved by forming the soil layer over another looser layer that is vibrated as it would be in an earthquake. This and two other methods were used to generate excess hydrostatic pressures in soil samples:

1. A vibrational shock was given to a two-layered soil. This arrangement most nearly simulates the earthquake phenomenon.

2. A soil sample was prepared in a container whose base was connected with a water reservoir. Raising the reservoir level provided a step increase in excess hydrostatic pressure at the base of the sample.

3. A soil sample was prepared with glycerin as the pore fluid and enclosed in a filled, transparent airtight container. An excess pressure was created by inverting the sample container.

TWO-LAYER SOIL SUBJECTED TO VIBRATIONAL SHOCK

Soil samples were prepared in 4-in.-diameter glass beakers. The bottom layer consisted of 3 in. of loosely-placed, coarse Ottawa sand. Dry densities of approximately 1.5 g/cm³ were obtained. For the majority of these tests, the upper layer consisted of weakly cohesive gray silt, and varied in thickness from 1/4 to 1-1/8 in. Tests were also conducted using an upper layer of (a) fine Ottawa sand and (b) a mixture containing bentonite 5 percent by weight in water.

Applying a vibrational shock to a submerged two-layer sand-silt soil sample consistently resulted in the production of miniature sandblows, in which sand was carried up by the jet and deposited on the silt surface. In all instances a

FIGURE 2   Sandblow craters in silt after removal of supernatant water.

time delay between the shock, which resulted in immediate liquefaction of the bottom layer, and the bursting of the sandblow through the soil surface was observed. The length of this time delay varied with the thickness of the upper layer. Upper silt layers 1/4 in. thick produced sandblows within 5 seconds of the shock, whereas 1-in. layers caused time delays of approximately 30 seconds. The number of sandblow vents produced also varied with soil-layer thickness. It was found possible to generate the sandblows repeatedly by vibrating the specimen again some time after the previous response had ceased. After a few shocks, a 1/4-in. layer produced dozens of vents, whereas repeated shocking of a 1-in. layer produced no more than three sandblows. The duration of ejection was approximately 20 seconds for a 1-in. silt layer. When a sample was shocked a second or third time, previously formed sandblows would usually, but not always, resume ejecting water and soil within a few seconds. Any new vents that formed burst forth after longer time delays.

A typical test is illustrated in Figures 1, 2, and 3. To produce these photographs, the pore water was dyed red. In Figure 1, a sandblow is shown in operation. The three separate sandblows that formed can be seen in Figure 2, which was taken at the conclusion of the experiment after the supernatant fluid was siphoned off. After the experiment, the upper silt layer was dried out, carefully removed from the sand, and inverted. Figure 3 shows the bottom of the dried silt layer, which exhibits a distinct erosional pat-

FIGURE 1   Single sandblow in silt overlying sand. Water in sand was dyed red.

tern. The cause of this erosion could be observed when occasionally a sample developed a sandblow along the edge of the glass container.

Observations revealed that the interface between the two soil layers was the source of soil ejected onto the surface. Here, particles could be observed moving laterally along the interface toward the base of a vent and hence to the surface as illustrated in Figure 4. The formation of sandblows along the glass face also revealed that the disturbance that develops into a sandblow propagates from the base of the silt layer to the surface, and that the path of this disturbance to the surface is not necessarily a straight line; it appears to follow a path related to soil layering and stratification.

Although a sandblow in its fully developed form resembles in cross section the phenomenon of piping by subsurface erosion familiar to soil engineers, its mode of formation seems to be directionally opposite to that of piping. Terzaghi and Peck (1953) describe a pipe as typically propagating backward from its outlet to the source of pressure; the conventional analysis of the phenomenon is based on this mechanism. The sandblows we have observed in the laboratory propagate in the opposite direction, i.e., from the source of pressure to a point of outlet. This explains the explosive character of the sandblow when it finally breaks the surface. Careful observation of the soil surface revealed no disturbance of any surface soil particles before a vent's breakthrough, with the exception of a slight surface bulging at the point of breakthrough. The upper dark liq-

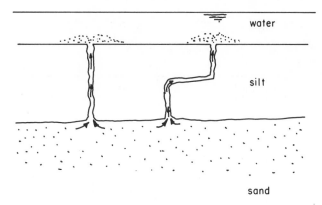

FIGURE 4   Paths followed by sandblow channels.

uid visible in Figure 1 is that ejected through the sandblow vent; no general seepage through the surface is occurring at a comparable flow rate.

The sandblows and boils formed behind levees and dams when water levels are high may also propagate from the base of a layer of low permeability to the surface. This would be more likely to happen when the levee is underlain by a zone of higher-permeability sand to conduct the high water pressures to the base of the lower-permeability material. It may be worthwhile to reexamine carefully the sequence of events by which the process known as piping develops in connection with dams and embankments.

Sandblows generated naturally by an earthquake would probably be similar in mechanism and morphology to those examined in this series of experiments.

When the identical experiment was performed with an upper layer composed of fine Ottawa sand, no sandblows developed. The expulsion of pore fluid from the soil was uniformly distributed over the soil surface. The source of ejected fluid was determined to be the pore water in the uppermost region of the fine-sand layer. Slow motion photography of the interface between the fine and coarse soil layers revealed a nearly instantaneous separation between these layers, caused by the settling of the coarse-grained layer after the shock. Immediately afterward the fine-grained layer began to settle onto the coarse-grained soil. This settling took the form of a liquefaction interface traveling upward in the fine-grained layer, and dying out as it moved toward the surface. The nature of this induced liquefaction process is more clearly revealed by another experiment, described later, in which glycerin was substituted for water as the soil pore fluid.

These observations may be interpreted as follows: Because of the relatively large particle size of the loose sand layer, this layer settled and solidified very rapidly on being given a slight shock. The upper layer, whose fine-grained particles have a slower settling velocity in water, was left suspended, and excess hydrostatic pressure equal to the

FIGURE 3   Underside of dried-out silt layer, showing erosion cavities where sandblows developed.

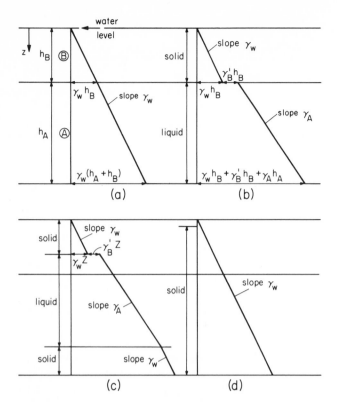

FIGURE 5 Pore-water pressure profiles during liquefaction process. (a) Before liquefaction of layer A; (b) just after liquefaction of layer A; (c) at an intermediate stage; (d) solidification complete.

buoyant weight of the soil was therefore created at the base of the upper soil layer. This condition is illustrated in Figure 5, in which γ_w is the unit weight of water, $\gamma_{A,B}$ the total unit weight, and $\gamma'_{A,B}$ the buoyant unit weight of the soil layers. The hydrostatic excess pressure can be relieved by flow of water to the surface and the rearrangement of soil grains into a looser configuration. If the flow of water were the only active mechanism and no soil-volume change occurred as, for example, would be the case if the upper layer consisted of a coarse porous stone, the surfaces of both soil layers would settle identical amounts. On the other hand, if the upper soil layer can expand sufficiently and remain solid at the higher void ratio, no water flow need reach the surface and no surface settling would occur. In reality, both these mechanisms are occurring simultaneously. In the experiment involving an upper layer of fine sand, both an expulsion of fluid and soil settling (which results in a looser grain structure) were observed. If the amount of soil expansion in the upper layer does not result in a stable solid state, a quicksand condition will develop all the way to the surface, to result in a complete breakdown of soil strength at the surface.

The employment of silt as an upper layer in the model

introduces two factors: reduced soil permeability and interparticle cohesion. Decreased permeability retards the flow of pore water to the surface. Interparticle cohesion holds the soil layer in a more coherent mass, restricting liquefaction both by vibration and by loosening from below in the manner characteristic of the fine-sand upper layer. The observed result is the upward erosion of channels through the silt layer, although the mechanism of their initiation and propagation is not yet entirely clear. There are similarities between the conditions in which sandblows occur during earthquakes and those under which "slug" or "plug" flow develops in fluidization processes (Leva, 1959).

EXTERNALLY INDUCED EXCESS PRESSURE

Using the apparatus shown in Figure 6, we subjected a soil sample consisting of sand with an upper layer of silt to a variable hydrostatic excess pressure from an external source. The underlying sand layer was not required for liquefaction purposes in this experiment, but we included it to smooth the upward water flow. The sample was not vibrated.

At excess heads of up to 1 in., small hairline cracks and pinholes were observed in the surface. As water flowed slowly through these openings, soil particles were not disturbed. The head was next raised to 1½ in., and two sandblows burst through the surface 1 minute 30 seconds later. Within another 30 seconds, four more vents developed. Ejection of subsurface material onto the upper surface lasted a total of 4 minutes, when the excess reservoir head stood at 7/8 in.

This experiment confirms the hypothesis that sandblows propagate from below to the surface of the soil. A minimum head seems to be necessary to produce a sandblow,

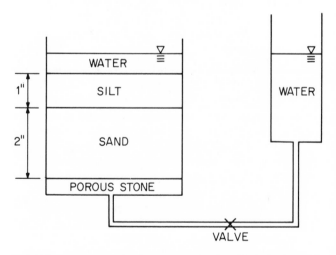

FIGURE 6 Apparatus for demonstrating induced liquefaction and sandblow generation under varying excess pressure.

but this minimum head may be less when liquefaction is initiated by vibration than in the case discussed here. A propagating disturbance would be helped by any loosening and settling of soil particles caused by a seismic shock. The head will also be dependent on the properties of the upper layer.

GLYCERIN AS PORE FLUID

The speed with which the liquefaction phenomena occurred made it difficult to observe some of the events clearly. We decided to substitute glycerin for water as the soil pore fluid, to slow down the process and to see if any qualitative changes in soil behavior resulted. Some early experiments showed that disturbing influences arose from the presence of air bubbles in the sand and glycerin mixture; to eliminate these bubbles, the mixture was placed under a partial vacuum for 24 hours before each experiment described.

Instead of employing vibration or head gradients, we found that we could conveniently induce liquefaction by inverting a sealed container filled with glycerin and soil. Different degrees of expansion could be produced by varying the amount of soil in the container. The inversion produced a uniform, slowly traveling displacement wave produced by settling soil grains when the soil consisted of a single layer of coarse Ottawa sand. A series of photographs (Figure 7) shows the nature of this traveling zone of settlement. The wave traveled through a soil sample that was initially 2 in. thick in 13 minutes. At the completion of the test the sand layer had expanded to a depth of 2–5/8 in. The width of the settling zone decreased as it traveled upward through the soil. Presumably, if the soil sample had been sufficiently thick, the width of the settling zone would have decreased to zero and the wave would never have reached the surface.

When the identical experiment was performed using fine instead of coarse Ottawa sand, a traveling zone of settling particles failed to develop. Instead, small regions along the base of the soil layer began to shed soil particles more rapidly than others. These irregularities began to work their way upward through the soil layer as shown in Figure 8a and formed cavities. The location of these features seemed to be a function of inhomogeneities in the soil.

When the development of the cavities was examined, it appeared that the cavity walls were shedding particles faster than the apex. The flux of soil grains from the walls was such that each cavity seemed to function as a convection cell, with fluid and some soil particles rising in the center and descending along the walls. It is possible that this is the cavity-advancement mechanism, in which the rising column erodes the head of the cavity as a low-velocity jet. it seemed obvious, however, that the circulation was driven by the particles falling along the walls. Figure 8 was made

with a 1-second exposure to indicate the movement of the soil particles.

When the channels that developed reached the surface, the effect was that of a slowed-down sandblow. As shown in Figure 8b, sand was ejected onto the surface of the soil.

When a channel reached the surface, the excess liquid pressure under the superincumbent mass of soil was discharged, and the soil consequently subsided. In the course of the subsidence, the bottom ends of the channels became confined, and the remaining excess liquid below the mass was forced through the constricted channels at relatively high, but diminishing, velocities. One such flow tube is shown in Figure 8c. The existence of the tubes persists because of the entrainment of particles from the walls in the high-velocity flow. Although the mechanism of the initiation of the cavities in the fairly uniform fine sand was not clear, it was found that they could be initiated by seeding the base of the sand layer with pebbles. In the natural state, they are probably triggered by inhomogeneities in the material, although they may develop as a consequence of the instability of the denser layer overlying the less dense liquid. The development of a channel by seeding is shown in Figure 9.

Similar results were obtained when silt was substituted for the fine-grained sand in this experiment, but the times involved were longer.

These observations indicate an apparent analogy between the behavior of fine sand in glycerin described here and the behavior of silt in water described in the section on two-layer soil subjected to vibrational shock. If this analogy does exist, it may indicate that cohesion of the upper layer is not in itself the necessary characteristic to cause the formation of sandblows.

QUANTITATIVE ANALYSIS OF UNIFORM SETTLING AND LIQUEFACTION

Consider a soil profile of two uniform materials as shown in Figure 10a. It consists of an underlying relatively loose, relatively coarse soil layer A with initial porosity n_i. In the mass (hindered settling), the settling velocity of its grains is a. Above it lies a relatively dense, relatively fine layer B of initial porosity n_d; the hindered settling velocity of its grains is b, which is smaller than a. An earthquake causes layer A to liquefy, but not layer B directly. As shown in Figure 10b, the suspended grains of layer A settle at velocity a to form a solidified soil at a new porosity n_f. Removal of the support of the soil grains in layer A from the bottom grains of layer B causes layer B to unravel from the bottom at such a rate that the falling grains form a suspension at porosity n_s.

Subsequently, in Figure 10c, the lower layer A has solidified entirely and the upper layer B partially, to leave an

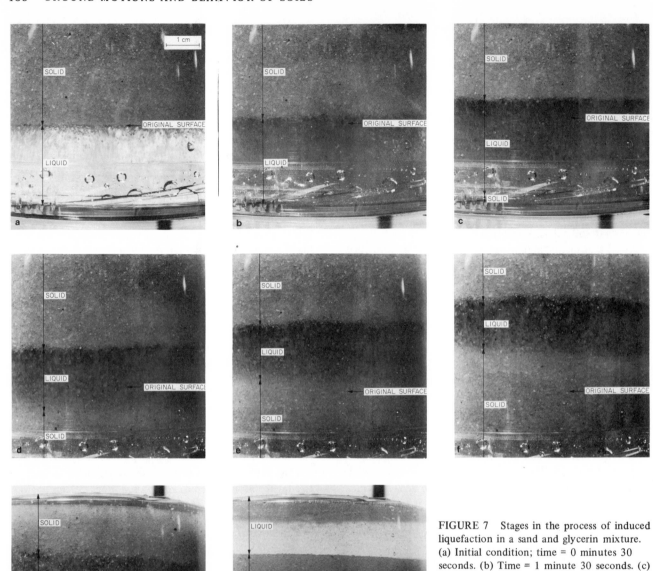

FIGURE 7   Stages in the process of induced liquefaction in a sand and glycerin mixture. (a) Initial condition; time = 0 minutes 30 seconds. (b) Time = 1 minute 30 seconds. (c) Time = 3 minutes 0 seconds. (d) Liquefaction is proceeding uniformly upward, with the three layers now well-developed; time = 5 minutes 0 seconds. (e) Time = 7 minutes 0 seconds. (f) Time = 8 minutes 30 seconds. (g) No apparent sign of a general settlement of the suspended layer; time = 10 minutes 0 seconds. (h) Process is complete; time = 13 minutes 0 seconds.

intermediate zone of liquefied soil B. No disturbance is as yet apparent at the surface. Finally, Figure 10d shows both materials solidified at their new porosities, in the case where liquefaction has reached ground surface. Because of the expansion of layer B and the contraction of A, the maximum subsidence occurs at the interface between the layers. If layer B is able to accommodate the porosity change induced by liquefaction entirely within its thickness, liquefaction does not reach ground surface (Figure 10e), and no surface

subsidence takes place, although subsidence does occur as before at depths below the surface.

The contraction in thickness of layer A can be obtained by considering that the volume of the soil solids remains constant; it is found to be equal to $(n_i - n_f)h_A/(1 - n_f)$. Similarly, if the entire layer B liquefies, its expansion in thickness is equal to $(n_e - n_d)h_B/(1 - n_e)$. If the stable porosities and layer thicknesses are such that the latter value for maximum expansion of layer B exceeds the amount of con-

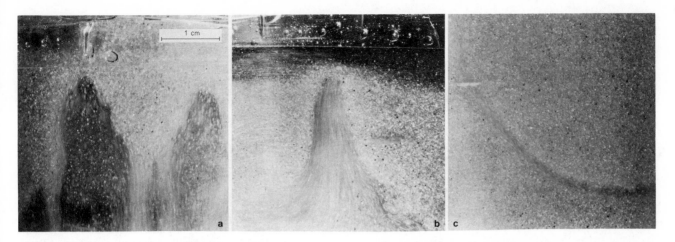

FIGURE 8 Stages in the progress of a cavity to the surface to form a sandblow in a sand and glycerin mixture. Exposure time, 1 second. (a) Two cavities are visible. The streaming of grains down the cavity walls is clearly apparent in contrast to the slow movement of grains in the center of the cavity. (b) Cavity is just about to break through the soil surface. Surface is bulging. (c) The final stage of cavity compression. The region below the tube settled out previously, whereas the region above settled as a solid mass as the excess liquid underlying it was expelled through the venting pipe.

traction of layer A, layer B will not liquefy all the way to ground surface. If the expansion is smaller, layer B will be entirely liquefied. Thus, the condition for complete lique-faction of layer B is

$$\frac{(n_e - n_d)}{(1 - n_e)} h_B \leqslant \frac{(n_i - n_f)}{(1 - n_f)} h_A \tag{1}$$

The same condition of solids volume constancy can be applied to determine the velocities of the two solid/liquid interfaces. Particles at the upper surface of bed A begin settling as soon as the soil becomes liquid at $t = 0$. They will continue to fall, until they strike the solidification interface. The distance they fall is the contraction in the thickness of layer A (previously calculated), and, if they have a settling velocity a (as they have in Figure 10a), the time t_f that they are in motion is

$$t_f = \frac{(n_i - n_f) h_A}{(1 - n_f) a} \tag{2}$$

Thus in time t_f, solidification of layer A progresses from the base of the layer to a height $[h_A - (n_i - n_f) h_A / (1 - n_f)] = (1 - n_i) h_A / (1 - n_f)$. The velocity of the solidification front v_{sA} is then given by dividing this latter distance by the time t_f, from (Eq. 2):

$$v_{sA} = \frac{(1 - n_i)}{(n_i - n_f)} a \tag{3}$$

By a similar calculation, the upward velocity $v_{\ell B}$ of the induced liquefaction interface in the upper soil layer is found to be

$$v_{\ell B} = \frac{(1 - n_d)}{(n_s - n_d)} b \tag{4}$$

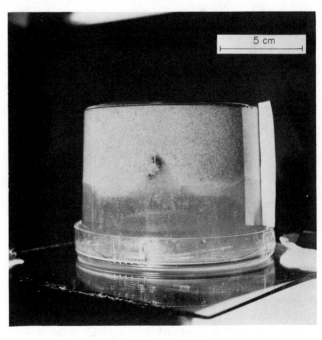

FIGURE 9 Illustration of progression of a pebble-seeded instability.

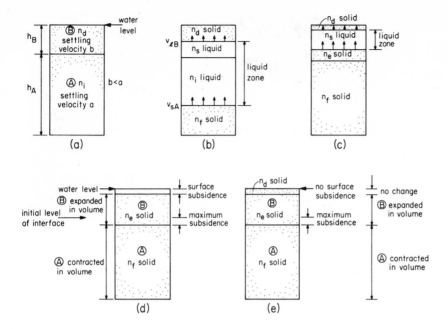

FIGURE 10   Stages in the process of stable induced liquefaction. (a) Initial condition. (b) Some time after direct liquefaction of layer A and induced liquefaction of layer B. (c) Liquefaction about to reach ground surface. (d) Condition where surface subsidence is encountered. (e) Condition where both kinds of liquefaction occur but process does not reach ground surface. See text for more complete discussion.

Because it is inherent in the mechanics of the process as outlined here that the settling velocity b is smaller than a, there will be a time lag t_L between the complete solidification of layer A at time t_f and the commencement of solidification of layer B. The time lag is the difference between the time it takes the bottom grains of layer B to fall the contraction distance of layer A, and t_f:

$$t_L = \left(\frac{1}{b} - \frac{1}{a} \right) \frac{(n_i - n_f)}{(1 - n_f)} \, h_A \qquad (5)$$

When layer B begins to solidify on top of layer A, the solidification interface in layer B will move upward at velocity v_{sB}, where

$$v_{sB} = \frac{(1 - n_s)}{(n_s - n_e)} \, b \qquad (6)$$

From these relations, it is possible to calculate, for a given soil profile, the time involved in liquefaction, whether liquefaction will reach ground surface and when, and the thickness of the liquefied zone as a function of time. It is not necessary that the soil in layer B be finer than that in A for the relations to hold; instead b may be greater than a. It is assumed, however, that layer B is dense enough not to liquefy by the vibrations imposed by an earthquake.

The pore-water pressure distributions while these processes are occurring are shown in idealized form in Figure 5.

CONCLUSIONS

When subjected to ground shaking or shock, a saturated loose-soil layer may become liquid and subsequently settle into a denser state. An overlying, relatively denser soil layer can be induced to liquefy from below by the behavior of the underlying layer. It may liquefy stably or unstably and develop sandblows. The parameters determining which of these phenomena will develop are principally soil density, soil grain size, pore-fluid viscosity, and soil inhomogeneities; in nature, the pore fluid is usually water, but may be air or other gases on occasion. The grain size and fluid viscosity are important in determining the settling velocity of the soil particles. Fast-settling velocities are associated with general liquefaction, whereas slow-settling velocities accompany the development of sandblows. Inhomogeneities can be the controlling factors in the location of sandblows, but they do not determine whether sandblows occur.

The cavities that lead to the production of sandblows begin at the base of the relatively fine-grained surface soil layer and propagate to the surface, where they emerge explosively some time after the vibratory disturbance that initiated the process. This mechanism, evidenced by the tests described in this report, explains all the features of sandblows that have been observed to occur in nature in the few minutes following an earthquake. Sand boils occurring behind levees or embankments at times of high water level may also develop by this mechanism rather than through the process of piping usually adduced.

Sandblows developed in fine sand when glycerin was the pore fluid. This sand itself is not a cohesive soil, so that cohesion may not be a primary factor in the presence or absence of sandblows. However, the low settling velocity associated with the development of sandblows in a water-saturated soil may correspond to a grain size that is small enough for the soil normally to exhibit some slight cohesion. If this is true, then only slightly cohesive water-saturated soils would develop sandblows in nature. It follows, therefore, that sandblows will not occur in moderate to highly cohesive soils overlying a liquefied layer, because the cohesion would inhibit the formation of cavities from below. If such soil profiles exist, the excess hydrostatic pressures generated in an earthquake probably dissipate through lateral water flow to adjacent aquifers or to topographical discontinuities. The ground surface would settle unevenly without evidences of immediately adjacent surface venting.

In a real soil profile of many layers with various states of relative density, liquefaction may be caused in more than one loose layer, and induced as a secondary phenomenon in more than one dense layer. It follows from this description of the phenomenon of induced liquefaction that the occurrence of an earthquake with accompanying liquefaction does not automatically ensure that the soil profile is in a denser and therefore safer state following liquefaction. The directly liquefied layers will be denser, but those layers in which liquefaction was induced will be looser after the process has ceased, and may well in turn be susceptible to direct vibration-caused liquefaction in a subsequent earthquake.

When a vessel containing granular material is placed in a vacuum chamber, and the air is removed too rapidly, sandblows can be observed at the soil surface. Thus, under the appropriate material-property conditions analogous to those discussed here, fine-grained material will liquefy and exhibit sand-spout phenomena when air or another gas is the pore fluid. On a larger scale, these conditions may be met in terrestrial or lunar volcanic-ash flows, so that some of the craters observed on the stationary surface of former flows may, in fact, be the products of sandblow phenomena.

REFERENCES

Ambraseys, N., and S. Sarma, 1969. Liquefaction of soils induced by earthquakes. *Bulletin of the Seismological Society of America*, 59 (April), 651–664.

Housner, George W., 1958. The mechanism of sandblows. *Bulletin of the Seismological Society of America*, 48 (April), 155–161.

Kawakami, F., 1965. Studies on the dynamic properties of soils in Japan. Paper presented at Japan–U.S. Cooperative Science Program, Soil Dynamics Conference, Tokyo, July.

Leva, M., 1959. Fluidization. New York: McGraw-Hill.

Macelwane, J. B., 1947. When the earth quakes. Milwaukee: Bruce Publishing Company. p. 17.

Scott, R. F., 1965. Conference on soil dynamics under Japan–U.S. Cooperative Science Program, Tokyo, July. Report to the National Science Foundation, August 1965. Washington: National Science Foundation.

Segerstrom, Kenneth, Lorenzo Casertano, and C. G. Galli, 1963. Eruptions of water and sand resulting from an earthquake near Concepción, Chile, *in* Short papers in geology and hydrology. U.S. Geological Survey Professional Paper 475-B. Washington: Government Printing Office. p. 131–134.

Terzaghi, Karl, and R. B. Peck, 1953. Soil mechanics in engineering practice. New York: John Wiley & Sons, Inc. 566 p.

Waller, Roger M., 1966. Effects of the March 1964 Alaska earthquake on the hydrology of south-central Alaska. U.S. Geological Survey Professional Paper 544-A. Washington: Government Printing Office. 28 p. Also *in* The Great Alaska Earthquake of 1964: Hydrology. NAS Pub. 1603. Washington: National Academy of Sciences, 1968. p. 12–39.

GRANT A. ROSS*
H. BOLTON SEED
UNIVERSITY OF CALIFORNIA, BERKELEY

RALPH R. MIGLIACCIO†
ALASKA DEPARTMENT OF HIGHWAYS

Expanded version from
Journal of the Soil Mechanics and Foundations Division,
(American Society of Civil Engineers), 95 (No. SM4),
"Bridge Foundation Behavior in Alaska Earthquake"

Performance of Highway Bridge Foundations

The Alaska earthquake of March 27, 1964, caused extensive damage to highway bridges. The region of general earthquake damage in south central Alaska and the main highway routes within the area are shown in Figure 1. The routes identified are the Glenn Highway, which runs from Anchorage northeast into the interior; the Richardson Highway, running from Valdez northward into the interior; the Seward Highway, which goes from Seward to Anchorage via the Kenai Peninsula and Turnagain Arm; the Sterling Highway, which joins Homer to the Seward Highway; and the Copper River Highway, which goes from Cordova up into the Copper River Valley toward the Richardson Highway.

Relatively little bridge damage occurred on the Glenn and the Richardson highways. Of approximately 21 bridges in service between Anchorage and Glennallen (Figure 1) on the Glenn Highway, none were destroyed and only 5 suffered minor damage. On the Richardson Highway, one single-span timber bridge was destroyed in longitudinal compression, apparently as a result of a large adjacent slope movement; otherwise, only 3 of approximately 19 bridges between Valdez and Glennallen sustained discernible damage.

Bridges along the Seward Highway, including a short section of the contiguous Sterling Highway, and along the Copper River Highway suffered the most damage, and this damage was concentrated in certain locations. On the Seward Highway the Resurrection River bridges, the Snow River bridges, one of the Kenai River bridges on the Sterling Highway near its junction with the Seward Highway, and the Turnagain Arm bridges were damaged. Along the Copper River Highway, the Scott Glacier stream bridges, the Sheridan Glacier stream bridges, and the lower Copper River bridges sustained damage.

These main bridge-damage locations are shown in Figure 1, together with the approximate position of the zone of major energy release. Approximate distances of the damage locations from this zone are listed in Table 1 and range

ABSTRACT: Extensive damage to highway bridges occurred during the Alaska earthquake of 1964. Data on foundation conditions, bridge and channel configurations, and foundation displacements have been collected and analyzed to assess the effects of foundation-support conditions on bridge performance during the earthquake.

*Now at the University of Calgary.
†Now with R&M Engineering and Geological Consultants, Fairbanks.

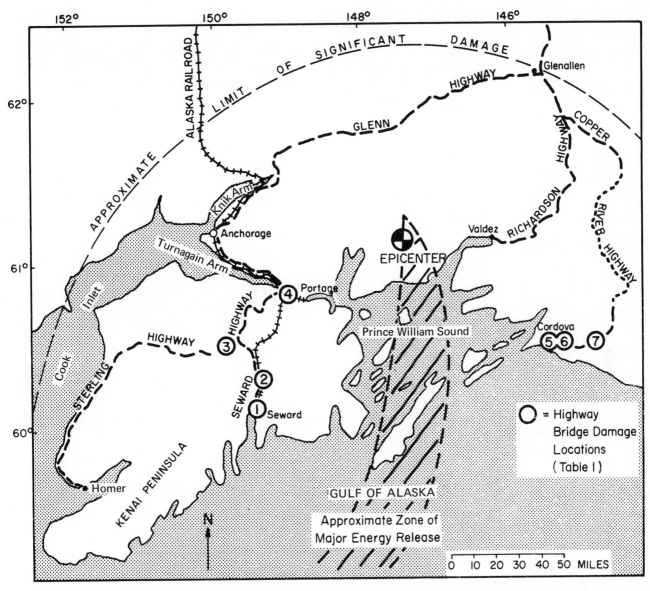

FIGURE 1   Highway routes of seven main bridge-damage locations in earthquake-damaged region, south central Alaska. Modified from Hansen and others (1966).

from 50 to 80 mi. The proximity of damage locations to the energy-release zone is therefore not likely to be a significant factor in determining the relative extent of damage at the various locations or in adjacent areas. Variations in bridge behavior are more likely to be due to differences in type of superstructure, type of foundation, foundation-soil conditions, and local topography.

The characteristics and performance of bridges along the Seward and Copper River highways will be discussed in relation to the prevailing foundation conditions. Each highway is shown on a small-scale map (Figures 2 and 43) that outline the areas shown on larger scale maps like Figure 3 showing the topographic settings of the various bridges.

Selected individual bridges are shown in simplified centerline sections, with additional figures containing foundation details where pertinent and available. The superstructures have been deleted on all bridge sections, but the foundation units in their respective locations, the average channel geometry before and after construction of the bridge, and test-boring information obtained by the Alaska Department of Highways either before or after the earthquake are presented. The selection of examples for detailed presentation was determined primarily by the extent of specific subsurface-boring information available. In the absence of such data in several regions, correlated field and airphoto observations by the authors and other investigators have

TABLE 1   Estimated Distances from Zone of Major Energy Release to Bridge-Damage Locations

Location (Figure 1)	Approximate Distance from Zone of Major Energy Release (mi)
Seward Highway	
① Resurrection River	60
② Snow River	60
③ Kenai River (on Sterling Highway near junction with Seward Highway)	80
④ Turnagain Arm (Portage area)	50
Copper River Highway	
⑤ Scott Glacier streams	50
⑥ Sheridan Glacier streams	55
⑦ Lower Copper River	70

been used to estimate foundation support conditions.

The types of bridge damage on the Seward, Sterling, and Copper River highways are later classified, and bridge behavior is correlated to the prevailing foundation conditions. Only general trends are reported on the Glenn and Richardson highways.

The following standard procedures have been followed in all the cross sections presented:

ELEVATIONS

Elevations are in feet to U.S. Geological Survey datum (preearthquake) mainly from Alaska Department of Highways drawings and reports.

PILE PENETRATIONS

Where they are shown staggered or by dashed lines, the pile depths represent the minimum and maximum depths that were determined or estimated for each foundation unit or bridge.

TEST BORINGS

Only borings that included soil sampling and classification data are shown. When a penetration test was made in conjunction with sampling, the results are plotted as follows:

N = The standard penetration-test blowcount—the number of blows of a 140-lb hammer falling through 30 in. required to drive the standard 2-in. outside diameter/1.4-in. inside diameter split-barrel sampler through 12 in. travel.

Blowcounts that were given numerically in the source reports are shown numerically; otherwise the general trend

of the blowcount versus depth profile is presented in simplified form.

Borings that were located off a bridge centerline have been projected onto the sections; in some cases the boring logs have been shifted slightly to facilitate presentation.

GRAIN-SIZE DISTRIBUTIONS

The grain-size curves presented are plotted from Alaska Department of Highways mechanical analysis tabulations for test-boring samples obtained at the selected bridge sites (maximum inside diameter of samplers used = 1.4 in.).

SOIL CLASSIFICATIONS

The soil-classification summaries shown represent the authors' interpretation of available data from the field logs, laboratory classifications, and foundation-investigation reports of the Alaska Department of Highways.

GROUND LEVEL

The solid ground line indicates the average profile across the channel according to bridge-design drawings and supplementary surveys. The dashed line represents average preconstruction grade where it differs from the foregoing.

STREAM LEVEL

The water levels shown were estimated from design drawings, boring reports, and postearthquake photographs. Where no water level is shown, the channel is believed to have been dry at the time of the earthquake.

SEWARD HIGHWAY

All major bridge damage on the Seward and Sterling highways was located within the area of Figure 2, which shows the Seward Highway from its southern terminus at Seward to a point on Turnagain Arm 18 mi. southeast of Anchorage, and the connecting Sterling Highway for a distance of 20 mi.

RESURRECTION RIVER BRIDGES

The first major crossings reached from the southern end of the Seward Highway are three channels of the Resurrection River, located as shown in Figure 3. The highway is built up across a broad gravelly flood plain only 1 mi from the mouth of the river on Resurrection Bay. Test borings have shown the granular sediments at the crossing to be at least 60 ft thick, but these fluvial and glaciofluvial materials may

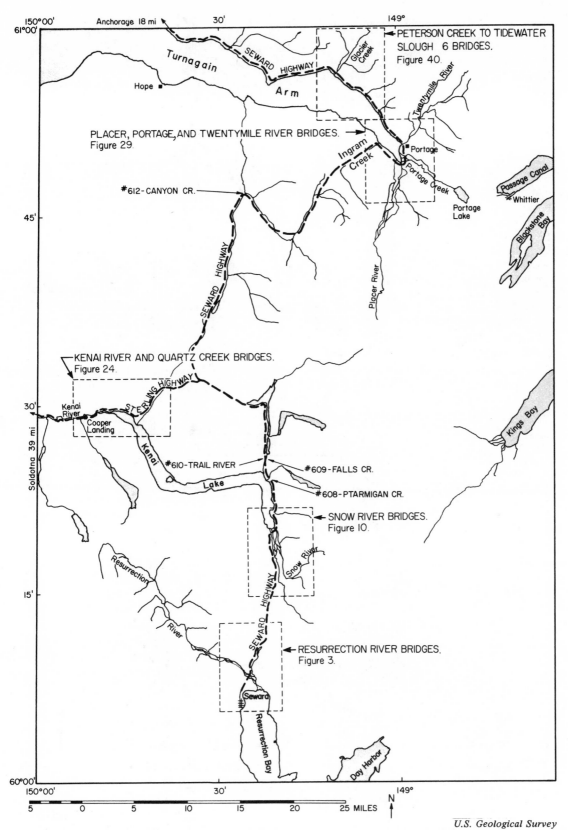

FIGURE 2   Location key for Seward and Sterling highway bridges. Outlined areas are covered by larger-scale maps. Base: USGS 1:250,000 series, Seward, Alaska, 1953.

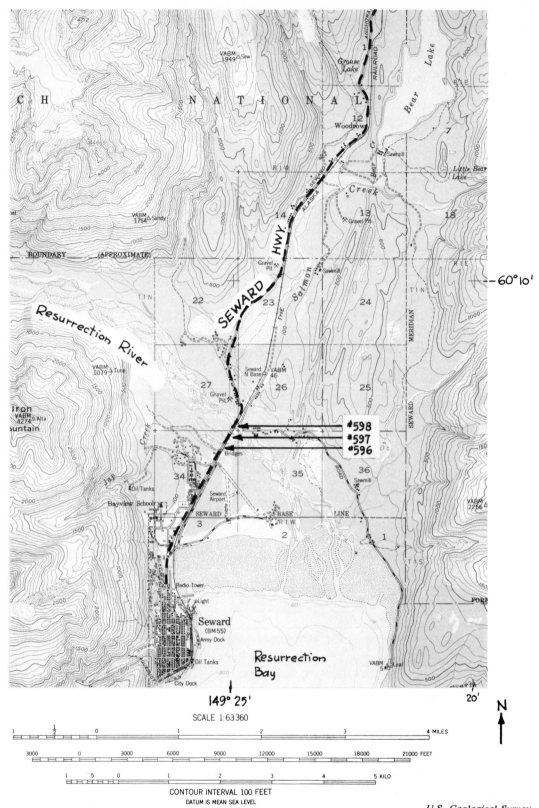

FIGURE 3   Location and topographic setting, Resurrection River bridges, Seward Highway. From USGS Seward (A-7), Alaska, 1951.

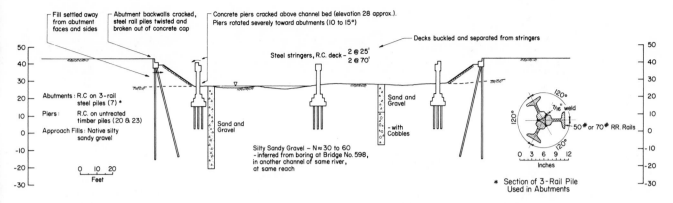

FIGURE 4 Bridge 596: Resurrection River 1. Centerline section looking upstream (natural scale).

extend to substantially greater depths and be underlain by tidal silts or clays.

Two bridges are shown in simplified section in Figures 4 and 5, the range of grain-size distributions for the soils sampled at one bridge is shown in Figure 6, and auxiliary foundation details for the bridges appear in Figure 7. The southern bridge (596) was seriously damaged, whereas the northern one (598) suffered moderate damage.

The two structures had very similar foundation units and the subsoil conditions appear to be essentially the same; the displacements suffered by the foundation units were also similar in nature but of different severities. Photographs of pier tilt and cracking in Bridge 596 are shown in Figure 8, and abutment deformations are shown in Figure 9.

One difference between the two bridges that might account for the difference in damage is the location of the piers in relation to the channel margins. In Bridge 596, the abutment fills extended almost to the piers, so that a movement of soil from beneath the abutment fills would exert high lateral loads on the pier footings and piers. This would

tend to cause rotation of the piers in the direction shown on the sections. In Bridge 598, a clearance of about 20 ft between the toes of the abutments and the piers provided space for displaced soil to accumulate and reduced the likelihood of high lateral loading of the pier foundations.

Figures 4 and 5 show that test borings resulted in classification of the foundation soil as a silty, sandy gravel with $N \simeq 30$–60 through the upper 50 or 60 ft. Such soil conditions would not generally be considered conducive to liquefaction, and a 20-ft-high embankment with 1½:1 slopes constructed of and on such material should prove relatively stable. However, the available boring data include only one standard penetration log, with samples taken at 10–15 ft intervals; the other borings shown provided only auger samples and field classifications. In addition, the presence of gravel sizes in a soil can yield high penetration resistance to small sampling tools even if the relative density of the soil mass is low. It is possible, therefore, that the shallow subsoil at this site may include lenses or layers of cohesionless soils that are less dense than indicated on Figures 4 and 5.

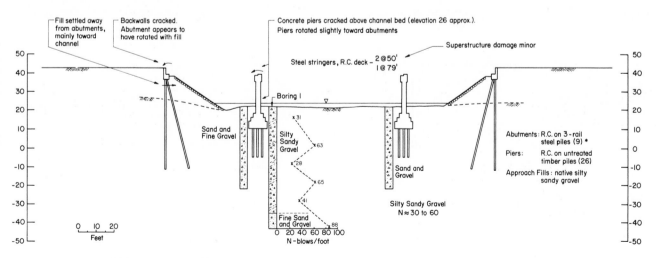

FIGURE 5 Bridge 598: Resurrection River 3. Centerline section looking upstream (natural scale).

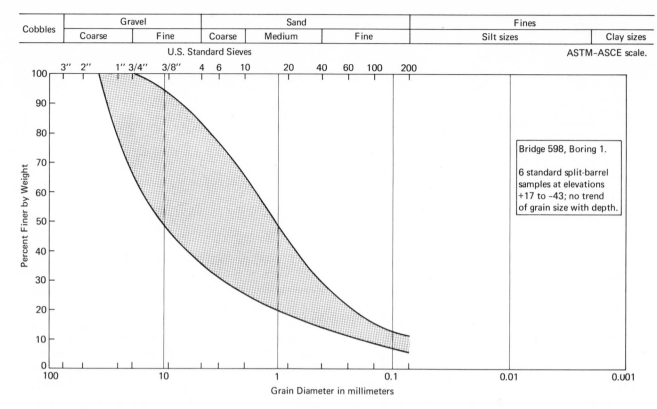

FIGURE 6   Grain-size distribution range for soils sampled at Bridge 598: Resurrection River 3 (less the fraction >1.4 in.).

BRIDGES BETWEEN RESURRECTION RIVER AND SNOW RIVER

Between the Resurrection River and the Snow River crossings there are five highway bridges of various designs. Damage to these structures was reported as ranging from minor to nil.

Except for one site on the Resurrection River alluvial plain near its northern margin, these bridges are located close to exposed bedrock slopes, or till-smeared bedrock slopes, of the Kenai Mountains. It is probable that their foundations extend to bedrock or into coarse glacial gravels close to bedrock.

SNOW RIVER BRIDGES

The Seward Highway crosses the valley of the Snow River where it forms a delta into the south end of Kenai Lake (Figure 10). An approximate cross section of the valley floor is shown in Figure 11. The river occupies an alluvium-

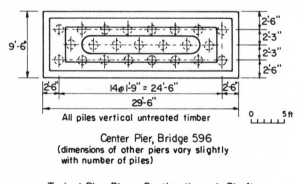

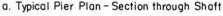

a. Typical Pier Plan – Section through Shaft

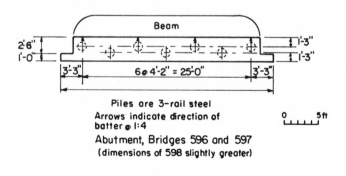

b. Abutment Plan

FIGURE 7   Bridges 596–598: Resurrection River. Typical foundation details.

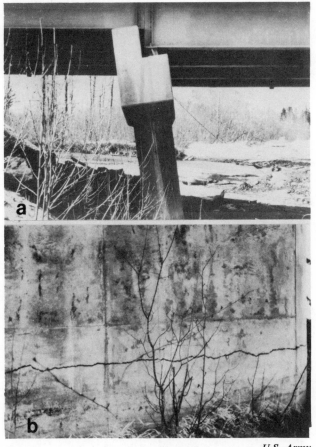

U.S. Army

FIGURE 8   Bridge 596: Resurrection River 1. (a) South pier looking upstream; note tilt. (b) Inner face of end pier, showing crack above channel bed.

U.S. Army

FIGURE 9   Bridges 596 and 598: Resurrection River. (a) Bridge 596: Three-rail piles broken out of abutment concrete. (b) Bridge 598: Fill settled away from abutment.

filled glaciated trough in bedrock that is approximately 4,500 ft wide at the highway crossing. This trough has been filled with glacial and fluvial sediments to form a virtually flat plain over which the braided stream meanders, although it was channelized by the highway embankment and bridges. Borings show that predominantly fine granular soils extend to at least 150 ft below the current valley floor, midway between the bedrock margins.

Four bridges were in service at the time of the earthquake. All were founded on timber bents and all were damaged, but to widely differing extents.

Bridge 603

The piling of Bridge 603, located at the western margin of the valley, appears to have penetrated the overburden sands to bedrock, at least on the western side. This is inferred from the borings for the replacement bridge located some 1,500 ft upstream (Figure 11). Substructure damage was minor, consisting of the settlement of one abutment (pre-

sumably the eastern one), and the bridge remained in service.

Bridge 605

Bridge 605 was located approximately midway across the valley. At the time of the earthquake, a replacement bridge was under construction immediately adjacent on the downstream side. Centerline sections of these two bridges are shown in Figures 12 and 13, with the new structure designated 605A. Grain-size distribution curves for soils sampled at this site are presented in Figure 14. Details of the timber bents are shown in Figure 15, and preearthquake and postearthquake photographs of Bridge 605 are shown in Figure 16. This bridge was destroyed by the earthquake, which caused the deck to collapse to the streambed over much of its length. Many of the timber bents settled, or were driven, about 10 ft downward. The abutments moved toward one another, compressing and buckling the superstructure.

The timber piling extended about 40–60 ft into crossbedded fluvial soil consisting mainly of sands and silts. The borings indicate that the upper 40–50 ft of soil has a stan-

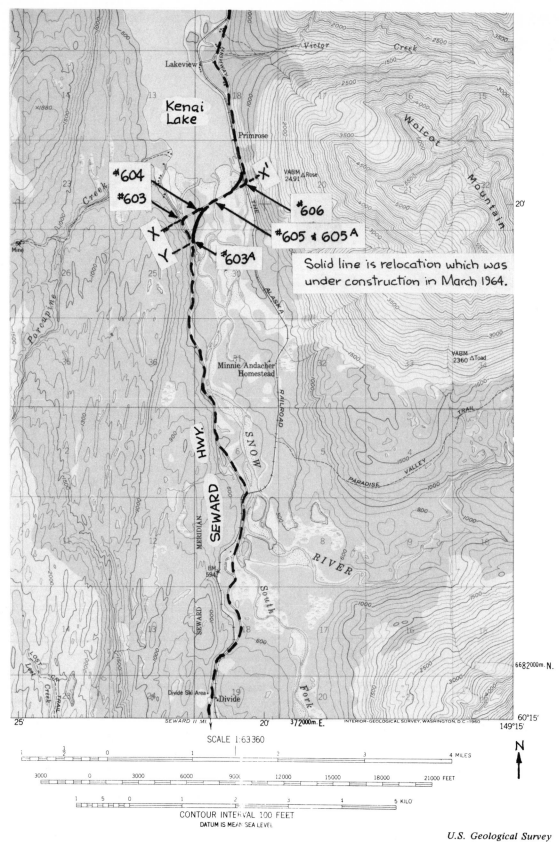

FIGURE 10   Location and topographic setting, Snow River bridges, Seward Highway. From USGS Seward (B-7), Alaska, 1951.

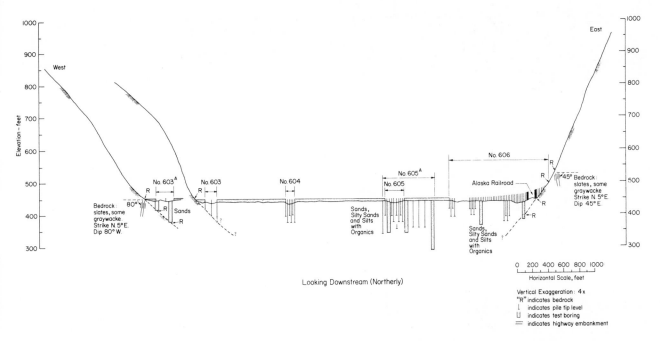

FIGURE 11   Composite section across Snow River Valley. Relative positions of Snow River bridges and foundation materials.

dard penetration resistance of 5–10, with some pile tips possibly extending into 30-blow material.

Bridge 604

Bridge 604 was of the same design as Bridge 605, but shorter. However, no borings are available for comparison of foundation conditions. Bridge 604 suffered much less severe damage than Bridge 605 and remained in service. Figure 17 is a postearthquake view showing the settlement of abutments and approach fills in relation to midstream piers and the resulting overall humped configuration.

Bridge 606

Bridge 606 was a long overpass structure of the same timber-bent design as bridges 604 and 605 (Figure 15), and extended approximately 1,500 ft into the valley from its eastern abutment on the bedrock valley wall. A single rigid-frame span of reinforced concrete was incorporated to overpass The Alaska Railroad. The timber bents were apparently founded on bedrock for a distance of about 400 ft from the eastern abutment (Figure 11), but it is not known whether the spread footings of the rigid concrete frame section were

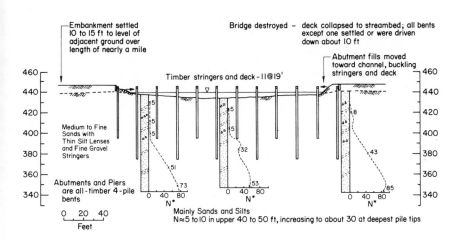

FIGURE 12   Bridge 605: Snow River 3. Centerline section looking downstream (natural scale).

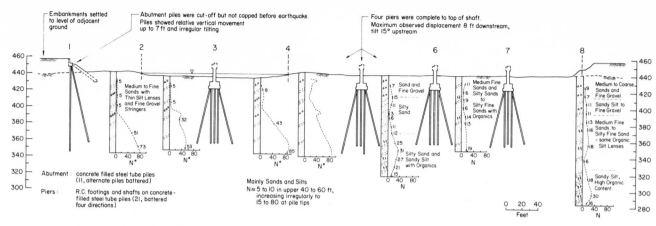

FIGURE 13   Bridge 605A: Snow River 3 (during construction). Centerline section looking downstream (natural scale).

on bedrock. The westerly two thirds of the timber trestle was founded in granular soils similar to those shown at bridges 605 and 605A (Figures 12 and 13). Postearthquake photographs (Figure 18) show that the trestle and rigid frame collapsed from the eastern abutment for a distance of about 600 ft, and the damage reports state that the westerly abutment settled as much as 2 ft.

Bridge 605A

The foundations for the new bridge, which was under construction beside Bridge 605, were also displaced during the earthquake. The centerline section of the new bridge, designated 605A, is shown in Figure 13 with auxiliary foundation details in Figure 19. The 11 steel-tube piles for one

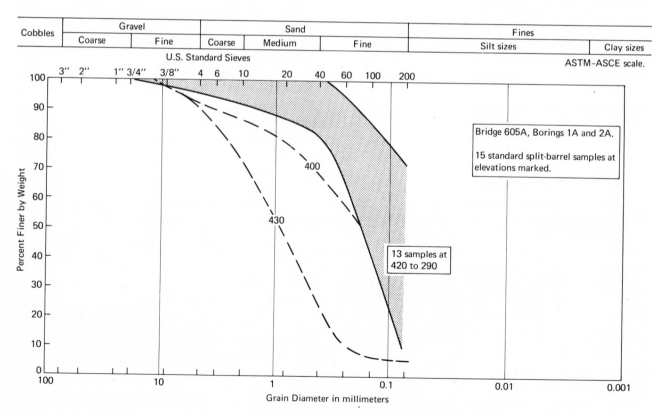

FIGURE 14   Grain-size distributions for soils at Bridge 605A: Snow River 3 (during construction).

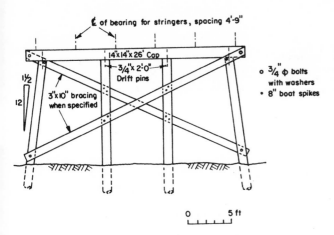

FIGURE 15   Typical treated-timber bridge bent. Common to many Seward and Sterling highway bridges.

D. S. McCulloch, USGS

FIGURE 17   Bridge 604: Snow River 2. Postearthquake view, looking east.

U.S. Army

FIGURE 16   Bridge 605: Snow River 3. (a) Preearthquake view, looking downstream. (b) Postearthquake view, looking downstream.

U.S. Army

FIGURE 18   Bridge 606: Snow River Overhead. (a) Looking west from east approach. (b) Looking toward east abutment.

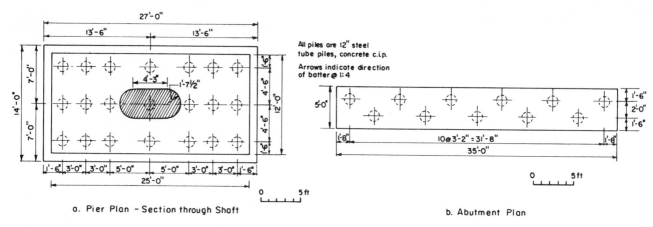

a. Pier Plan – Section through Shaft

b. Abutment Plan

FIGURE 19   Bridge 605A: Snow River 3 (during construction). Foundation details. (a) Pier plan section through shaft; (b) abutment plan.

abutment had been driven to a depth of approximately 100 ft, cut off to a common level, and filled with concrete. During the earthquake, these piles underwent relative vertical displacement and tilting (Figure 20a); observers estimated the maximum relative vertical displacement at 7 ft.

FIGURE 20   Bridge 605A: Snow River 3 (during construction). (a) Looking east from west approach. Abutment piles at left, temporary bridge over destroyed Bridge 605 at right. (b) Looking east from midspan. Note piers tilted upstream (to right).

Four of the heavy concrete piers had been completed to top of shaft (Figure 13). These piers—each supported on 21 concrete-filled steel-tube piles, extending an average of about 90 ft below adjacent streambed level—underwent tilting and lateral displacement during the earthquake (Figure 20b). Damage surveys revealed a maximum of 8 ft lateral displacement of the shaft tops downstream and up to 15° of tilt upstream, as shown in Figure 21. Longitudinal movements were less.

From the comments of first-hand observers and from the behavior of the bridge foundations, it is clear that liquefaction of cohesionless soils did occur in this region. Reports mentioned that "mud" oozed up in cracks and that the 10-ft-high road embankment was reduced to the level of the flood plain. The preferred downstream movement of the footings and upstream tilt of the pier shafts indicate liquefaction at a depth below footing level, possibly accompanied by a lakeward flow along a zone that was well below the ground surface.

A similar situation prevailed at the Knik River crossing on the Glenn Highway northeast of Anchorage (Bridge 1121), where four heavy concrete piers of a new bridge were in place at the time of the earthquake. These piers shifted a maximum of 2 ft, mainly longitudinally toward the channel centerline. They were supported on concrete-filled steel-tube piling driven into a deep body of cohesionless soil that ranged from gravels to silts.

BRIDGES BETWEEN SNOW RIVER AND TURNAGAIN ARM

Of the 16 highway bridges between the south end of Kenai Lake and Turnagain Arm, some sustained cracked abutment backwalls and piers and some suffered separation of superstructure members. However, several sizable structures on timber-bent or steel-rail pile foundations were notably free from damage. Examples are Ptarmigan Creek, Falls Creek,

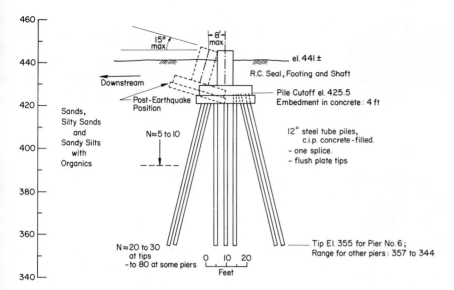

FIGURE 21   Bridge 605A: Snow River 3 (during construction). Lateral elevation of pier 6 as constructed at time of earthquake.

and Trail River bridges (608 to 610, Figures 2 and 22). These bridges are located along the east side of Kenai Lake and up the Trail River, with the crossings generally located near the heads of alluvial fans or fan deltas of steep-profile streams. These gravelly soils appear to overlie bedrock directly or via a veneer of glacial gravels, so that the bridge foundation piling probably extends to or near bedrock through gravels.

In addition, about ten bridges founded mainly on spread footings suffered little or no damage. These structures are located in narrow bedrock valleys between the Seward–Sterling highway junction and Ingram Creek at Turnagain Arm (Figure 2). The only surficial soils observed in this region are coarse gravels and gravel–sand mixtures. It is believed that at least six of the undamaged bridges are founded directly on bedrock. One example is Canyon Creek Bridge, a high steel trestle on spread footings believed to be cast on bedrock (Figures 2 and 23).

STERLING HIGHWAY BRIDGES

Bridge 675, located at the western end of Kenai Lake (Figures 2 and 24) collapsed on to the streambed as shown by the photographs in Figure 25. The centerline section is presented in Figure 26, indicating a subsoil of silt and fine sand into which the timber piles were driven an estimated 15 ft.

By contrast, Bridge 676 at Quartz Creek (Figure 24) suffered only minor damage. This bridge is shown in centerline section in Figure 27; the range of grain-size distributions of soils sampled at the site is given in Figure 28. The bridge materials and design were similar to Bridge 675, although the bridge was shorter and skewed to the channel. The foundation soil, however, was mainly gravel and the piling was estimated to penetrate about 20 ft.

FIGURE 22   Typical undamaged timber bridges on Seward Highway. (a) Bridge 608: Ptarmigan Creek, looking downstream. (b) Bridge 610: Trail River, looking north. The Alaska Railroad bridge in foreground.

FIGURE 23   Undamaged steel trestle. Bridge 612: Canyon Creek.

Damage to the other ten bridges of various types on the remainder of the Sterling Highway was minor to nil. Very little information is available on the foundation conditions at these sites, except one at which a box culvert appears to rest directly on bedrock.

TURNAGAIN ARM (PORTAGE AREA) BRIDGES

Where the Seward Highway descends from the mountains to Turnagain Arm at Ingram Creek (Figures 2 and 29), bridge damage became severe. Of the 15 structures located on tidal flats around the head of the arm from Ingram Creek to Twentymile River, at least 10 collapsed wholly or partly and all but three were severely damaged. The bridges that collapsed all consisted of concrete superstructures on timber-pile bents (the bent detail in Figure 15 is typical for all these structures) and ranged in length from 50 ft to over 800 ft.

Postearthquake photographs (Figures 30 to 33) show typical damage consisting of collapsed concrete decks pierced by the timber piling, timber bents that were twisted, splayed, and shifted, and channel banks and abutments that had moved toward the channel centerlines causing bowing of the superstructures.

Two bridges from this region, selected for their typical foundation conditions, are shown in centerline section in Figures 34 and 35; grain-size distribution curves for soils sampled at these sites are shown in Figures 36 to 39.

Turnagain Arm is a glaciated trough subject to a very

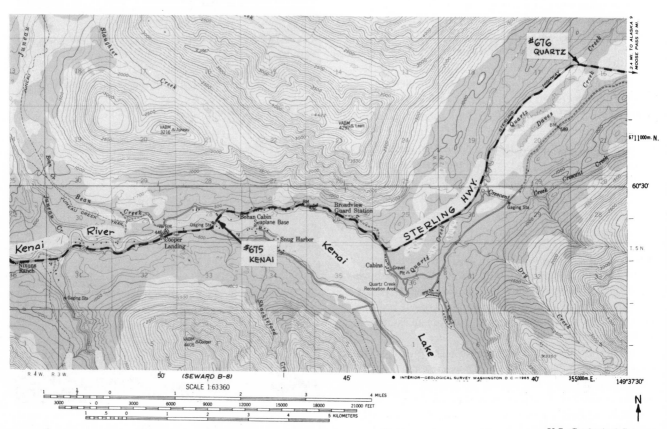

U.S. Geological Survey

FIGURE 24   Location and topographic setting of Kenai River and Quartz Creek bridges, Sterling Highway. From USGS Seward (C-8), Alaska, 1951.

U.S. Army

FIGURE 25   Bridge 675: Kenai River at Cooper's Landing, Sterling Highway. (a) Looking upstream; (b) longitudinal view.

vails over most of the piling length was relatively loose ($N \simeq 10$–15). However, the borings indicate that the pile tips may be embedded in stratified silts and sands of higher relative density (to $N \simeq 60$) although lower blowcounts were obtained at depths below elevation –20.

The soil profile at Twentymile River (Figure 35) is similar, but the standard penetration-test results were more erratic, with values as low as 10 recorded at depth.

The extensive longitudinal fissuring and spreading of the highway embankment observed in the Portage area is a typical result of foundation-soil liquefaction.

TURNAGAIN ARM (NORTHEAST SHORE) BRIDGES

The bridges along the northeast shore of Turnagain Arm between Twentymile River and Girdwood (Figure 40) sustained varying degrees of damage. Peterson and Kern Creek bridges (636 and 637), which span the mouths of relatively short, steep creeks, suffered only moderate damage. A timber-bent pier of Virgin Creek Bridge (638) failed (Figure 41), and a similar failure of the central spans occurred at Tidewater Slough 6, Bridge 640. The Glacier Creek Bridge (639) was damaged in much the same manner as the Resurrection River bridges, which have already been described (Figures 4 and 5); the tilted piers are shown in Figure 42. The latter three structures are located across the 1½ mi-wide mouth of a sediment-filled trough that is tributary to Turnagain Arm.

Between the Girdwood region and the end of the Seward Highway at Anchorage, damage to highway bridges ranged from moderate to nil.

COPPER RIVER HIGHWAY

The route of the Copper River Highway from its terminus at Cordova, along the shore of Eyak Lake, across the out-

high tidal range of about 40 ft. The soil conditions shown by borings are generally a surficial sandy gravel over interbedded sands and silts, underlain by an undetermined thickness of silt. At the site of Portage Creek Bridge 2 (Bridge 631, Figure 34), the surficial sandy gravel that pre-

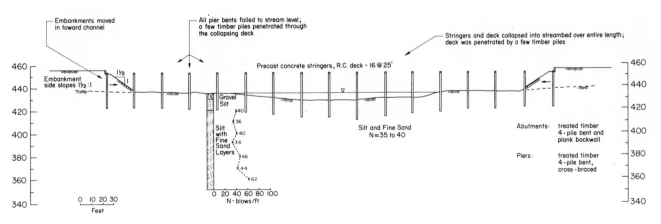

FIGURE 26   Bridge 675: Kenai River at Cooper's Landing. Centerline section, looking downstream (natural scale).

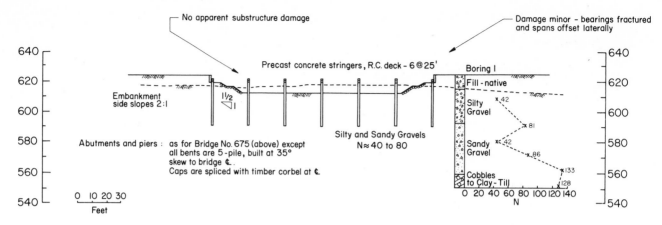

FIGURE 27   Bridge 676: Quartz Creek. Centerline section, looking downstream (natural scale).

wash fans of the Scott and Sheridan glaciers, and up the Copper River is shown in Figure 43.

At the time of the earthquake, this highway was in service for a distance of about 50 mi from Cordova. The distribution of damage to the 52 bridges involved has been outlined by Migliaccio (1965); specific cases will be examined in more detail later.

SCOTT GLACIER STREAM BRIDGES

The locations of 11 bridges spanning channels of the Scott Glacier outwash plain are shown in Figure 44. These bridges had a common superstructure design, but the western five were founded on timber bents with precast-concrete caps, and the remainder were on steel-rail bents with cast-in-place concrete caps (Figure 45).

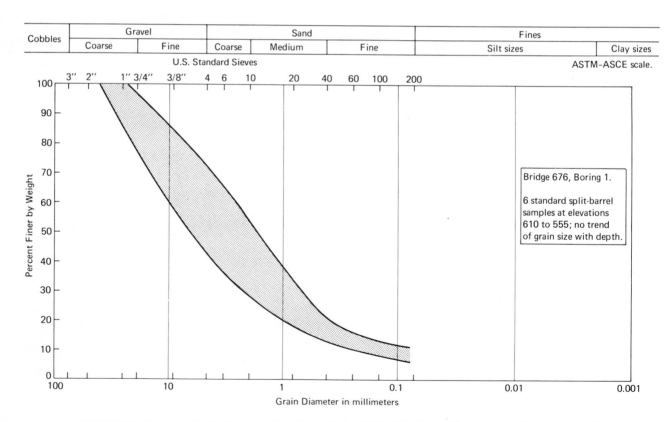

FIGURE 28   Grain-size distribution range for soils sampled at Bridge 676: Quartz Creek (less the fraction >1.4 in.).

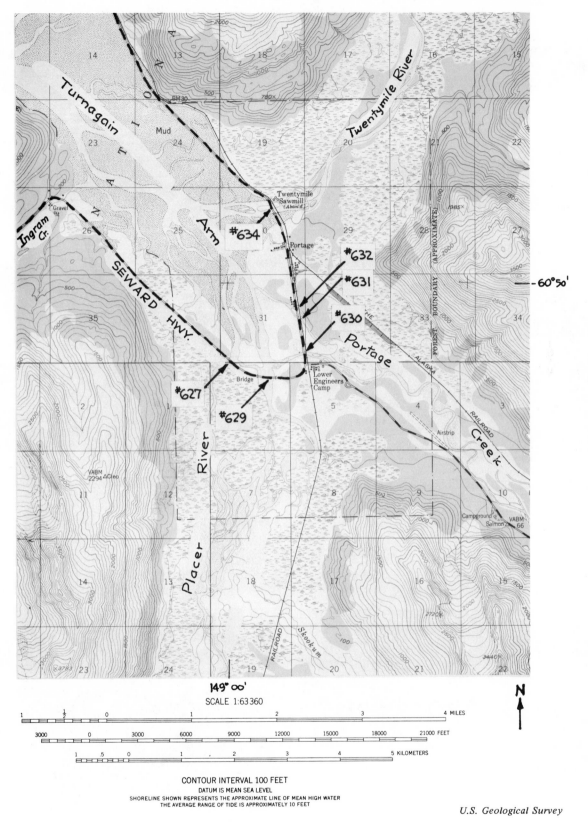

FIGURE 29   Location and topographic setting of Placer River, Portage Creek, and Twentymile River bridges, Turnagain Arm, Seward Highway. From USGS Seward (D-6), Alaska, 1952.

U.S. Army

FIGURE 30   Bridge 629: Placer River main crossing. (a) Looking north at bridge; stringers and deck have collapsed to stream-bed. (b) Lateral displacement of superstructure; concrete deck penetrated by timber piles.

U.S. Army

FIGURE 31   Bridge 630: Portage Creek 1. (a) Aerial view up-stream, showing banks displaced toward channel. Note humped Alaska Railroad bridge in background. (b) Longitudinal view, looking north.

U.S. Army

FIGURE 32   Bridge 631: Portage Creek 2. (a) Aerial view, looking upstream. (b) Longitudinal view, looking south.

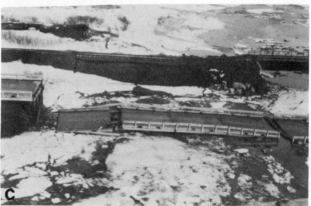

U.S. Army

FIGURE 33   Bridge 634: Twentymile River. (a) Looking upstream. Alaska Railroad bridge in background. (b) South abutment, looking upstream. (c) Looking upstream, near north abutment.

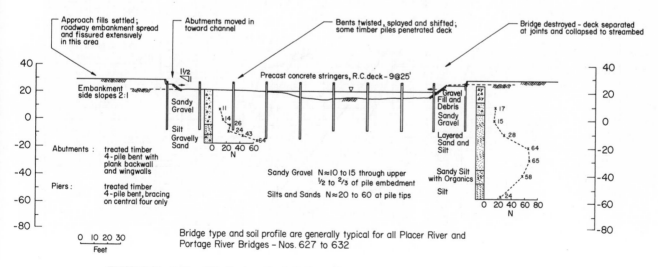

FIGURE 34   Bridge 631: Portage Creek 2. Centerline section looking downstream (natural scale).

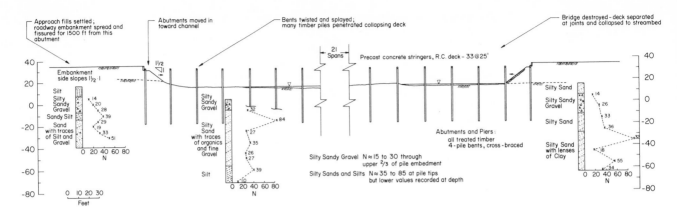

FIGURE 35   Bridge 634: Twentymile River. Centerline section looking downstream (natural scale).

The positions of the pile foundations in relation to the soil conditions indicated by the single borings made near 9 of the 11 channels after the earthquake are plotted in Figure 45. Bridges 348 and 411 are shown in centerline section in Figures 46 and 47; soil grain-size distributions for samples taken at these two sites are shown in Figure 48. The foundation soil, consisting of stratified sands and silts with organic components common in the silt, appears to be quite consistent across the outwash plain. Figure 45 shows that

the standard penetration test logs are irregular, but indicate that loose to medium-dense material, with N values ranging from about 10 to 20, extends well below the piling in most cases. These data have been combined into a single plot (Figure 45b) from which a blowcount range of $N \simeq 5-25$ with an average value of about $N = 15$ could be generalized over the pile-penetration depth of the Scott Glacier bridges.

The degree of damage reported by the Alaska Department of Highways, Bridge Division, ranged from severe to

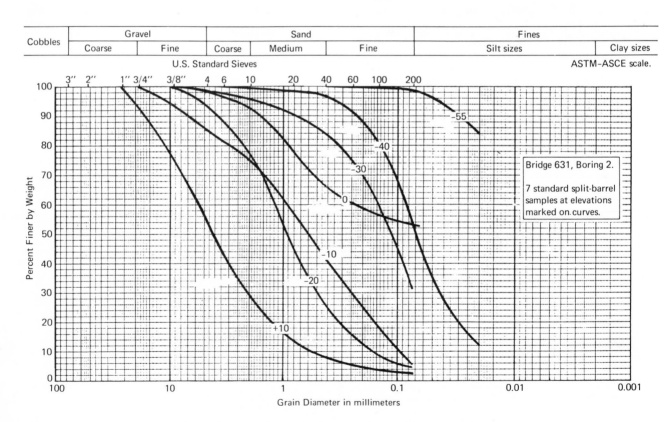

FIGURE 36   Grain-size distributions for soils at Bridge 631: Portage Creek 2.

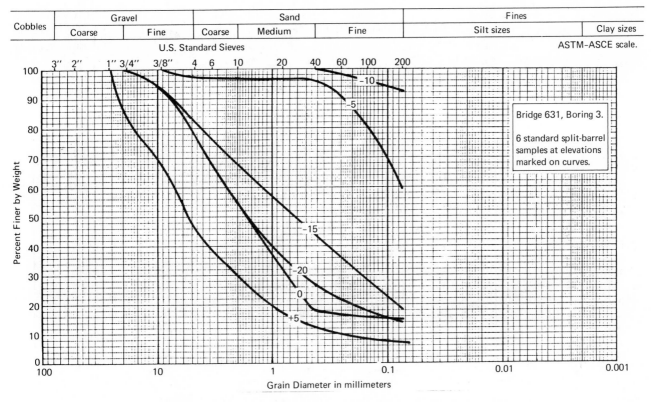

FIGURE 37   Grain-size distributions for soils at Bridge 631: Portage Creek 2.

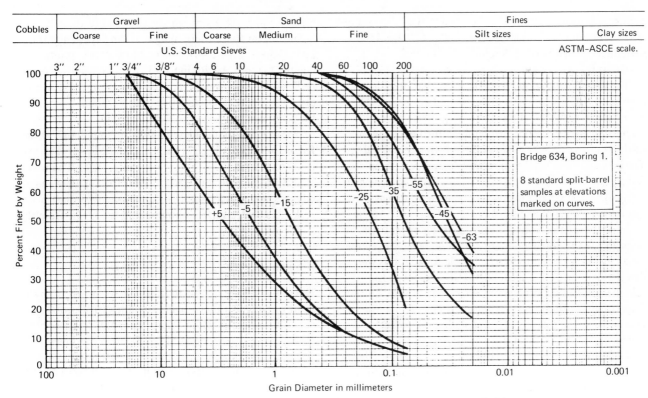

FIGURE 38   Grain-size distributions for soils at Bridge 634: Twentymile River.

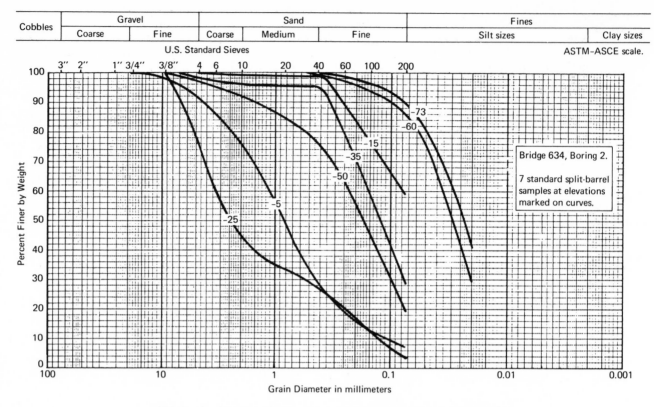

FIGURE 39   Grain-size distributions for soils at Bridge 634: Twentymile River.

minor, as shown in Figure 45a. The two bridges that did not have corresponding borings, Bridge 409 and Bridge 410, sustained damage rated as "minor" and "none," respectively.

The data presented in Figure 45 show that there is no apparent relation between the degree of damage and the penetration resistance of the underlying soils; similarly, there is no essential difference between the net behavior of the bridges on timber piles and those on steel-rail piles. The broken rail piling was immediately apparent to an observer, but the timber-supported bridges suffered damage of comparable extent and intensity. Examples of damage are shown in Figures 49 to 51.

In all these cases, it seems likely that the major cause of damage was the liquefaction, or partial liquefaction, of the sandy and silty soils into which the pile foundations were driven. These materials are difficult to compact and to retain in embankments and have been classed as spoil by the Department of Highways. Their loose to medium-dense condition would make them susceptible to liquefaction during severe and prolonged ground shaking.

Evidence that liquefaction did occur in the Scott Glacier outwash soils is provided by the behavior of a Department of Highways storehouse and shop building (Arlan Davis, personal communication, 1967). This single-story reinforced-concrete structure was located just north of the highway near the western margin of the Scott outwash plain (Mile 7, Figure 44). The building settled approximately 2 ft into the ground, and ground cracks up to several inches wide and several feet deep were observed near the building. Small mounds of fine sand were noted alongside the fissures.

Another bridge of the same substructure design as the five western Scott bridges spans the Eyak River at its effluence from Eyak Lake (Figure 44, Bridge 381). The west abutment is on bedrock and the piles for the piers and easterly abutment are probably driven either to or near bedrock. The bridge suffered no discernible damage from the earthquake.

SHERIDAN GLACIER STREAM BRIDGES

The outwash from Sheridan Glacier is separated from the Scott outwash by a low divide on which the Cordova airport is located. A total of 14 bridges were in service across the Sheridan Glacier flood plain (Figure 52, bridges 361–374 and 230). One of these bridges (230) was a modern concrete structure on concrete-filled steel-tube piles; the remainder were old 12-ft-wide all-timber trestles. An elevation sketch of a typical timber bent is included in Figure 53,

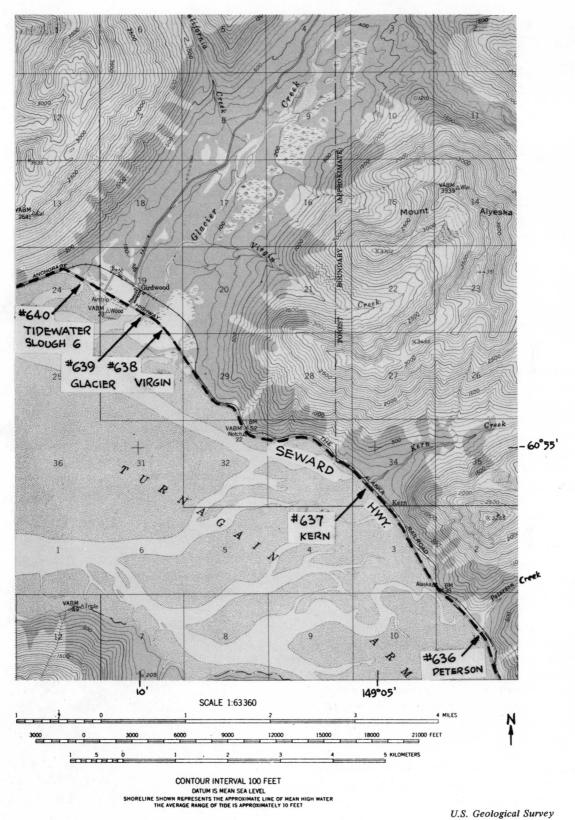

FIGURE 40   Location and topographic setting of Peterson Creek to Tidewater Slough 6 bridges, Turnagain Arm, Seward Highway. From USGS Seward (D-6), Alaska, 1952.

U.S. Army

FIGURE 41   Bridge 638: Virgin Creek.

and photographs of a typical section are given in Figure 54.

Test-boring information is available only for Bridge 367, which is located approximately midway across the outwash plain. There was no accurate information on the bridge and channel configuration at this crossing; therefore, it is only possible to compare the combined boring logs with the approximate elevation of the bridge piling (Figure 53) and present the grain-size curves for the samples recovered (Figure 55). The borings indicate coarser soils in the upper 60 ft than were encountered in the Scott Glacier outwash. The stratified sands and gravels appear to be loose ($N \simeq 5$–10) in the upper 20–25 ft, but considerably denser ($N \simeq 15$–50) lower in the stratum. At the test locations the gravels were underlain by silts with an N value of approximately 20.

Of the 13 light timber bridges, 6 showed no damage, 4 minor damage, and 3 would be classified as moderately damaged by the same scale as that used for the Scott Glacier stream bridges. The main damage consisted of movement of the abutments toward the channel (Figure 54b). Two of the three moderately damaged bridges (361 and 363) were located on the westerly half of the outwash plain; the undamaged bridges were all located on the easterly section closer to bedrock, which outcrops strongly on the eastern margin and forms an island in the outwash at the eastern third point. The single concrete bridge (Bridge 230), showed only slight damage: A backwall was cracked and a stringer spalled.

The earthquake ground motions caused settlement of the roadway embankment and of the approach fills for all bridges across the Sheridan Glacier outwash; a typical example of settlement of an approach fill is shown in Figure 54c. Although the fill material was from the same source, the extent of the settlement across the Sheridan Glacier outwash appeared to be much less than that which developed across the Scott Glacier outwash, presumably because of differences in characteristics of the foundation materials.

ALAGANIK SLOUGH BRIDGES

After crossing the Sheridan outwash, the highway skirts Alaganik Slough on a line characterized by numerous outcrops of igneous bedrock (Plafker, 1967) (Figure 52). Along this section of the road there are six timber bridges of the same type as those constructed across the Sheridan outwash

FIGURE 42   Bridge 639: Glacier Creek. (a) Looking upstream. (b) South pier, looking upstream.

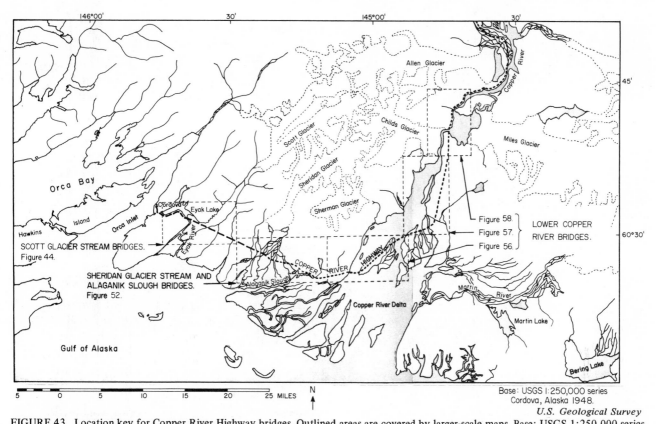

FIGURE 43   Location key for Copper River Highway bridges. Outlined areas are covered by larger-scale maps. Base: USGS 1:250,000 series, Cordova, Alaska, 1948.

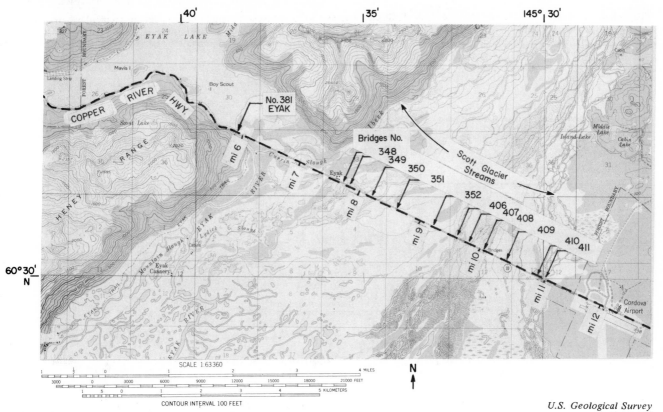

FIGURE 44   Location and topographic setting of Scott Glacier stream bridges, Copper River Highway. From USGS Cordova (B-4, B-5, C-4, and C-5), Alaska, 1951.

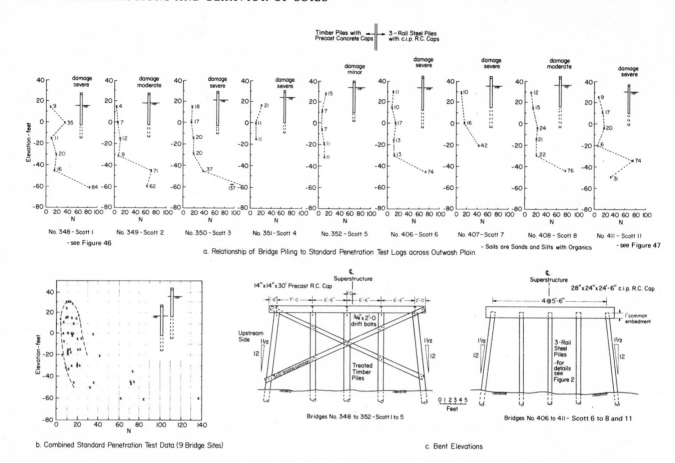

a. Relationship of Bridge Piling to Standard Penetration Test Logs across Outwash Plain

b. Combined Standard Penetration Test Data (9 Bridge Sites)

c. Bent Elevations

FIGURE 45   Bridges 348 to 352 and 406 to 411: Scott Glacier streams 1 to 11. (a) Relationship of bridge piling to standard penetration test logs across outwash plain. (b) Combined standard penetration test data (nine bridge sites). (c) Bent elevation.

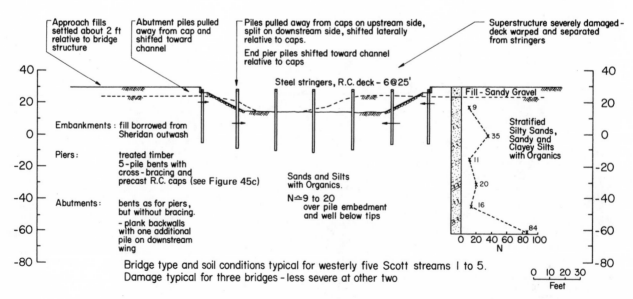

FIGURE 46   Bridge 348: Scott Glacier stream 1. Centerline section looking upstream (natural scale).

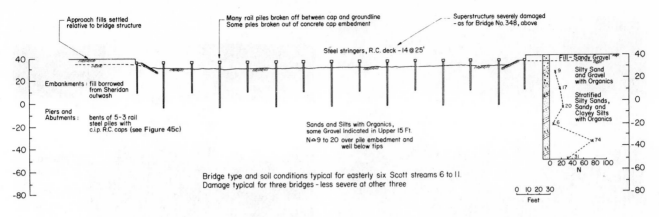

FIGURE 47   Bridge 411: Scott Glacier stream 11. Centerline section looking upstream (natural scale).

(Figures 53b and 54), but none of these showed any damage. One short single-span steel-and-concrete bridge at the eastern end of the Slough (Bridge 330, Figure 56) showed cracking and spalling of a concrete backwall and connected curbs.

No test-boring data are available on this section of the highway.

COPPER RIVER BRIDGES

At Mile 26, the highway reaches the Copper River Delta, which is over 10 mi wide at this point, and makes the first of many crossings of Copper River channels (Figures 56–58). In several cases, the highway utilizes steel-truss spans remaining from an abandoned railway that had been con-

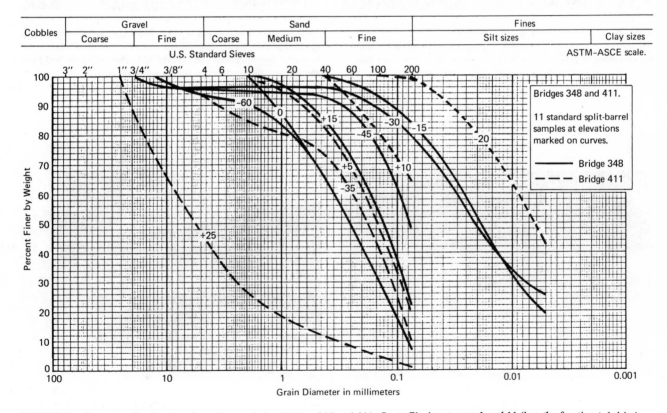

FIGURE 48   Grain-size distributions for soils sampled at Bridges 348 and 411: Scott Glacier streams 1 and 11 (less the fraction >1.4 in.).

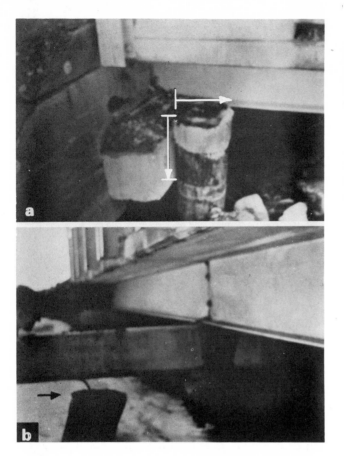

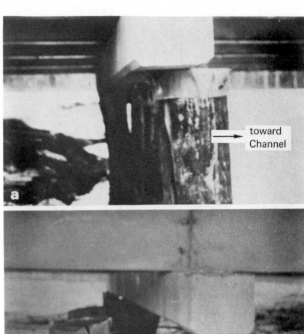

FIGURE 49   Bridges 348 to 352: Scott Glacier streams 1 to 5. (a) Bridge 351: Abutment piling displaced toward channel; abutment settled in relation to piling. (b) Bridge 348: upstream side; pier piling separated from cap and shifted downstream in relation to cap.

FIGURE 50   Bridges 348 to 352: Scott Glacier streams 1 to 5. (a) Bridge 348: Pier piling shifted toward channel in relation to caps and superstructure. (b) Bridge 351: Pier piling shifted toward channel in relation to caps and superstructure.

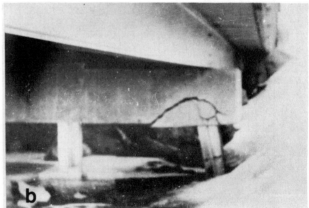

U.S. Army

FIGURE 51   Bridges 406 to 411: Scott Glacier streams 6 to 11. (a) Bridge 411: Three-rail piling broken between cap and streambed. (b) Bridge 408: Three-rail piling broken out of concrete cap embedment.

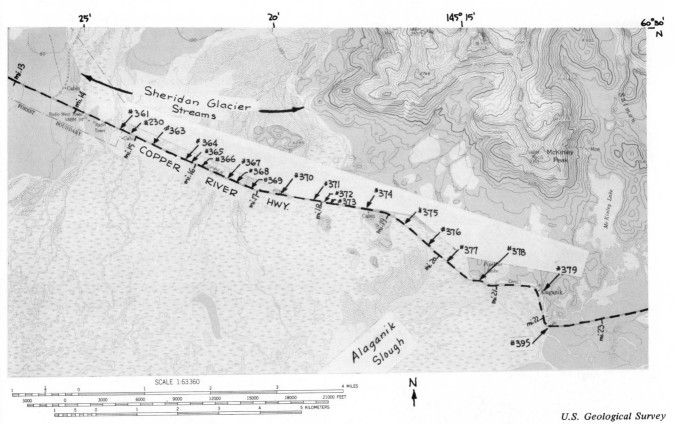

U.S. Geological Survey

FIGURE 52   Location and topographic setting of Sheridan Glacier stream and Alaganik Slough bridges, Copper River Highway.

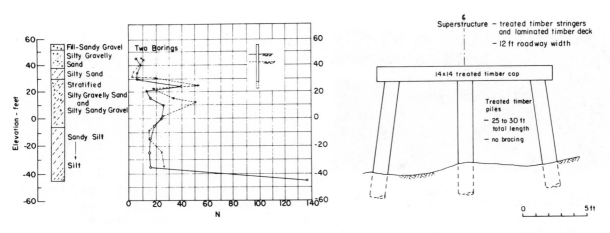

a. Bridge No. 367. Boring Logs and Approximate Relationship of Piling   b. Approximate Bent Configuration for 12 ft Timber Bridges 361 to 374

FIGURE 53   Bridges 361–374 and 230: Sheridan Glacier streams.

FIGURE 54   Bridges 361–374 and 230: Sheridan Glacier Streams. (a) Typical 12-ft timber bridge (Bridge 363). (b) Typical abutment displacement toward channel (Bridge 363). (c) Modern concrete structure, with no foundation failures; approach fill settled (Bridge 230).

structed in 1910. The extensive spans that have been built since that time consist of steel stringers and reinforced-concrete decks on bents made up of steel-rail piles with reinforced-concrete caps. The rail piles are built up from either three or four 50-lb or 70-lb rails welded together bulb to bulb (Figure 4); from four to seven of these piles are used in each bent. Most of the pier bents have reinforced-concrete webwalls extending from streambed level to the pile cap or to some intermediate level (Figures 59 and 61).

The 22-mi stretch of highway on the Copper River includes 19 bridges, all of which were damaged to some extent. Most of these bridges sustained moderate-to-severe deformations; spans collapsed in at least six crossings. Because Flag Point Bridge is one of those that collapsed (Bridge 331, Figures 56 and 59), the highway in 1968 ended at Mile 26. Prevalent types of failure in the Copper River region were severe abutment deformation and relative vertical displacement of foundation units (e.g., Figures 60–64).

The foundations of the Copper River bridges range from massive concrete caissons cast 50 ft below the streambed in gravel and boulder deposits, through timber-pile-supported concrete piers, to steel-rail pile bents. There is very little information available on the subsurface conditions in the lower Copper River region at this writing; extensive deposits of sand and gravel have been observed and probably predominate over the route from Mile 26 to Mile 50.

There was considerable evidence of liquefaction in the lower Copper River region in the form of fissures and subsidence craters with adjacent ejected soil.

SUMMARY OF HIGHWAY-BRIDGE-FOUNDATION MOVEMENTS

From a review of the performance of bridges along the Seward and Copper River highways, the following general observations concerning the main types of foundation movements can be made:

SPAN SHORTENING

The most prevalent effect of the 1964 earthquake on Alaska bridges was a shortening of the overall span between abutments, usually associated with settlement of the abutment fills. In cases where the superstructure did not collapse into the channel, the humping or buckling of the deck that resulted from compression between abutments was often the only effect observed (e.g., Figures 17 and 62). In many of the bridges that were considered to be only slightly damaged, partial closing of the expansion devices was noticed.

In some cases, the inward movement of abutments was due to a general streamward movement of natural channel

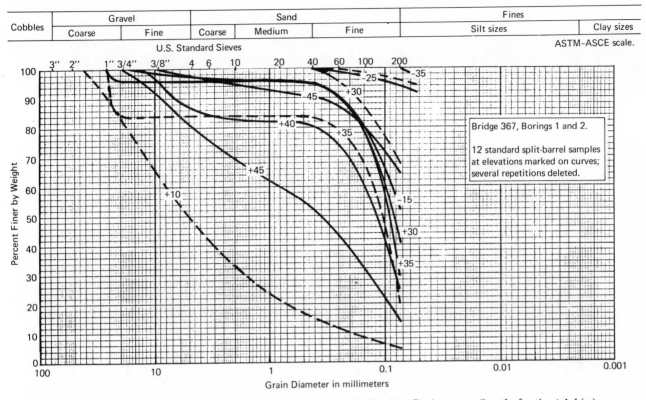

FIGURE 55 Grain-size distributions for soils sampled at Bridge 367: Sheridan Glacier stream (less the fraction >1.4 in.).

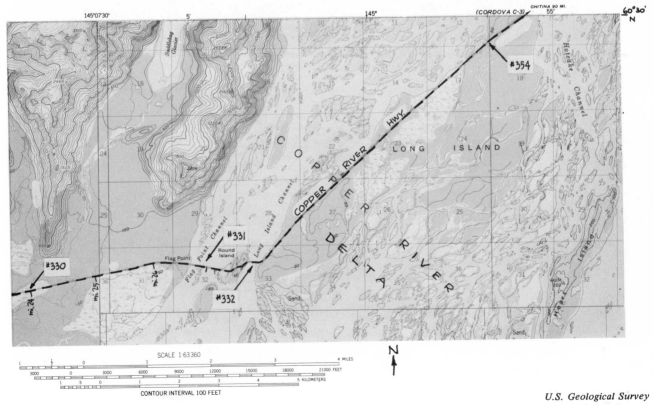

FIGURE 56 Location and topographic setting of lower Copper River bridges, Copper River Highway. Sheet 1 of 3. From USGS Cordova (B-3 and B-4), Alaska, 1951.

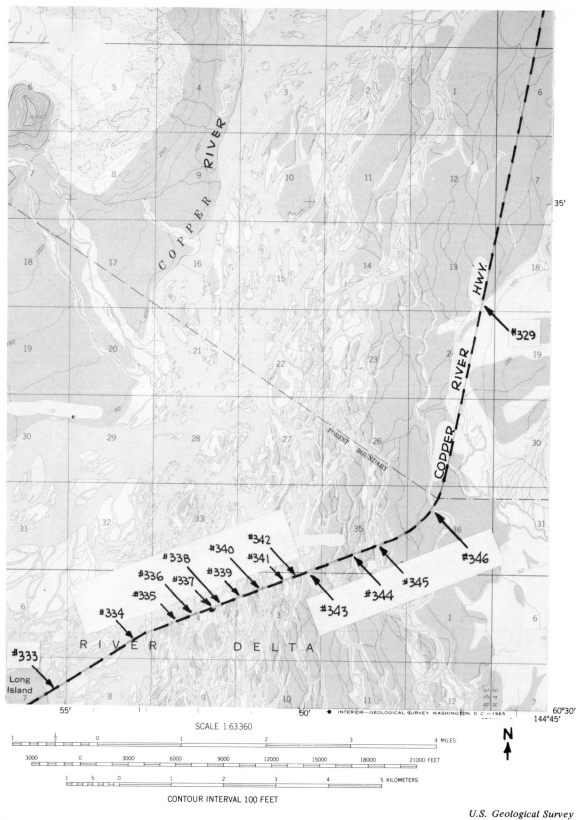

SCALE 1:63360

CONTOUR INTERVAL 100 FEET

U.S. Geological Survey

FIGURE 57   Location and topographic setting of lower Copper River bridges, Copper River Highway. Sheet 2 of 3. From USGS Cordova (C-3), Alaska, 1951.

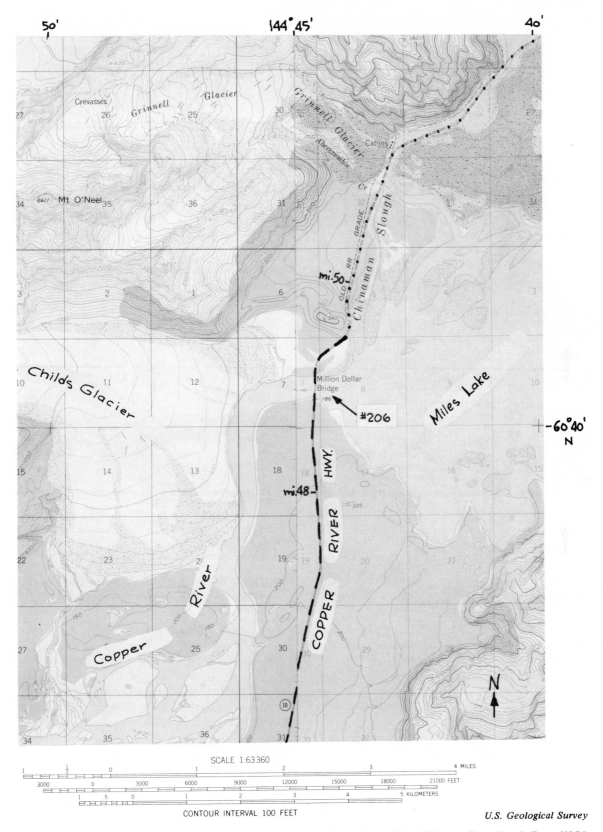

SCALE 1:63360

CONTOUR INTERVAL 100 FEET

U.S. Geological Survey

FIGURE 58   Location and topographic setting of lower Copper River bridges, Copper River Highway. Sheet 3 or 3. From USGS Cordova (C-2 and C-3), Alaska, 1951.

FIGURE 59   Bridge 331: Flag Point. Postearthquake end of
road. (a) Longitudinal view, looking south between truss spans.
(b) View upstream of old concrete pier and broken rail piles in
bent.

FIGURE 60   Bridge 332: Copper River 3. Midstream pier settled
below river level.

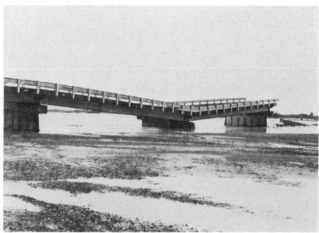

FIGURE 61   Bridge 334: Copper River 5. Note severe differential settlement of steel-rail-bent piers. Webwalls are reinforced
concrete.

banks that carried the abutments along with them. In other
cases where the streambanks were low and ill-defined, the
roadway embankment was the primary mass of soil displaced, spreading laterally as well as toward the channel
centerline. The former case is illustrated by the aerial
oblique view of Bridge 630 (Portage Creek 1, Figure 31a);
fissures are clearly visible paralleling the channel bank for
some distance on each side of the bridge. It can also be

noted that the superstructure of the bridge has ridden up
over both abutments. The resulting sway-backed longitudinal configuration might lead an observer to conclude that
the abutments settled less than the piers. Although this conclusion is undoubtedly correct in some cases, relative settlement should be distinguished from the overriding of
abutments by superstructure members as a result of span
compression, which can produce a similar effect. Figure
31a also shows the humping of the parallel Alaska Railroad
bridge. McCulloch (1966) and McCulloch and Bonilla
(1967) found this configuration prevalent along the railroad
route, together with lateral skewing and buckling of bridge
superstructures.

U.S. Army

FIGURE 62   Bridge 344: Copper River 15. Note humping of superstructure.

Many examples of abutment tilting and broken abutment backwalls are cited in the damage surveys (e.g., Figures 54b and 63); such failures would result from the movement of abutment foundations streamward, while the backwalls were restrained by the superstructures.

HORIZONTAL DISPLACEMENT OF PIERS

Damage surveys show that there were many cases of longitudinal displacement of bridge piers or of pier piles, especially of those located near the abutments. Such motion could be expected when piles in liquefied soil are subjected

U.S. Army

FIGURE 63   Bridge 345: Copper River 16. Superstructure driven through abutment backwall; total relative horizontal displacement $\simeq$ 5 ft.

U.S. Army

FIGURE 64   Bridge 206: Million Dollar. Preearthquake end of road. (a) Oblique view, looking upstream. (b) View upstream at north pier.

to lateral loading by the spreading stream banks or approach fills. Examples of displaced piles can be seen in Figure 50. Knik River Bridge (1121), which was under construction on the Glenn Highway at the time of the earthquake, provides an example of the movement of freestanding piers away from the stream banks.

There were also cases of lateral displacement of piers, i.e., movement upstream or downstream. In the examples provided by the bridges at the head of Turnagain Arm (e.g., Bridge 629, Figure 30b), there was some suggestion that the pile bents were pounded or dragged out of position by the superstructures. In the new Snow River Bridge 3, however, which was under construction at the time of the earthquake (Bridge 605A, Figures 20b and 21), several freestanding concrete piers on deep pile foundations moved primarily downstream.

The tilting of piers near stream margins toward the banks was exemplified by the Resurrection River bridges and Glacier Creek Bridge (e.g., Bridge 596, Figure 8a; Bridge 639, Figure 42). Such deformations will inevitably develop if the foundations move forward toward the streambed while the top of the pier is restrained by the bridge deck.

Lateral tilting of piers was also common, especially on the Copper River bridges (e.g., Figure 61).

RELATIVE VERTICAL DISPLACEMENT OF ABUTMENTS AND PIERS

Many bridges showed a final configuration in which the piers were higher than the abutments (Figures 17 and 62). This can be attributed to dragging down of abutments by the settling approach embankments and, possibly, in the case of light timber bents, to unloading of the piers as a result of buckling of the superstructure.

In other bridges, some or all of the piers were ultimately positioned lower than the abutments. In some of these cases, piers with broken caps and piling were found, possibly caused to some extent by pounding from the superstructure after the connections had been broken. Twentymile River Bridge (Bridge 634, Figure 33) provides an example of this type of damage. In other cases, the piers settled markedly into the streambed or even disappeared from view, whereas the abutments settled relatively little (e.g., Figures 60 and 61); these cases could be explained by differences in the resistance to liquefaction of the supporting soils.

EFFECTS OF FOUNDATION-SUPPORT CONDITIONS ON BRIDGE-FOUNDATION BEHAVIOR

Most of the major bridge damage and the bulk of the available information on foundation conditions are concentrated on the Seward, Sterling, and Copper River highways. Consequently, a comprehensive correlation between bridge behavior and foundation-support conditions has been attempted for these three routes.

Much less damage occurred and very little foundation data are available on the Glenn and Richardson highways, so that only the overall bridge-damage statistics and general relationships are discussed for these two routes. Even less information is available on the various spur roads located within the earthquake damage region, so that such routes are not considered herein.

SEWARD, STERLING, AND COPPER RIVER HIGHWAYS

A summary of information available on foundation conditions, foundation displacements, and the extent of damage to those bridges on the Seward, Sterling, and Copper River highways for which foundation-support conditions are reasonably well known is presented in Table 2. The information on bridge damage has been reduced from the reports of the Alaska Department of Highways and classified according to the following five degrees of severity:

Total collapse	All or most of the superstructure collapsed into the channel
Severe deformation and/ or partial collapse	Bridge impassable and beyond repair; total loss
Moderate deformation of components	Bridge may be repairable with replacement of some members
Minor	Bridge serviceable with minor repair work
None	No discernible damage

To distinguish foundation behavior from overall bridge performance, the foundation-displacement information obtained or deduced from damage reports, photographs, and first-hand observation was expressed by one of four single adjectives, as follows:

Severe	Abutments moved streamward and/or markedly subsided; piers shifted, tilted, or settle; substructure rendered unsalvable
Moderate	Distinct and measurable net displacements as in previous category, but to a lesser degree, so that the substructure could perhaps be repaired and used to support a new superstructure
Minor	Evidence of foundation movements (such as cracked backwalls, split piles, closed expansion devices), but net displacements small and substructure serviceable
Nil	No evidence of foundation displacements

This single-adjective classification required a considerable amount of interpretation in most cases. A report of "no damage" for a bridge was automatically taken to mean "no foundation displacement." However, a bridge that was reported to be severely damaged or even destroyed was, in some cases, not considered to have undergone severe foundation displacement. It appears to the authors that some bridges sustained sheared connections between superstructure and substructure, or between superstructure members, so that the superstructure was destroyed without the influence of large movements of the foundation units. In such cases, a reasonable degree of interpretive freedom was exercised.

A numerical summary of the foundation displacements

TABLE 2 Summary of Bridge Data for 63 Bridges of Known or Inferred Foundation Soil Conditions on Seward, Sterling, and Copper River Highways

Highway	Bridge Name	No.	Mile	Spans and Overall Length, ft	Foundation Type	Superstructure Type	Foundation Soil Conditions	Foundation Displacements	Bridge Damage
Seward (mileage starts at Seward)	Resurrection River 1	596	2.9	2 @ 25 2 @ 70/202	RC abuts.[a] on steel rail piles RC piers on timber piles	Steel stringers/RC deck	Piles embedded in sandy gravels; $N \simeq 30$–60	Severe/moderate	Severe deformation
	Resurrection River 2	597	2.9	2 @ 25 1 @ 79/152	RC abuts. on steel rail piles RC piers on timber piles	Steel stringers/RC deck	Piles embedded in sandy gravels; $N \simeq 30$–60	Moderate	Moderate deformation of components
	Resurrection River 3	598	3.0	2 @ 50 1 @ 79/182	RC abuts. on steel rail piles RC piers on timber piles	Steel stringers/RC deck	Piles embedded in sandy gravels; $N \simeq 30$–60	Moderate	Moderate deformation of components
	Grouse Creek 2	741	8.4	1 @ 23/24	RC spread footings	RC rigid frame	Bedrock (inferred)	Nil	None
	Snow River 1	603	17.3	2 @ 69/144	Timber pile bents	Steel stringers/ timber deck	One abutment on piles to bedrock through sands; remainder to or near bedrock	Minor	Minor
	Snow River 2	604	17.5	5 @ 19/97	Timber pile bents	Timber stringers and deck	Piles embedded in sands and silts; $N \simeq 5$ to 10 over pile lengths, 5 to 20 at tips (inferred)	Severe	Severe deformation
	Snow River 3	605	17.7	11 @ 19/211	Timber pile bents	Timber stringers and deck	Piles embedded in sands and silts; $N \simeq 5$ to 10 over pile lengths, 5 to 30 at tips	Severe	Total collapse
	Snow River 3 (during construction)	605A	17.7	—	RC abuts. & piers on concrete-filled steel tube piles	None in place	Piles embedded in sands and silts; $N \simeq 5$ to 10 over upper half of pile length, 12 to 50 over lower half, 15 to 80 at tips	Severe	—

227

TABLE 2 (Continued)

Highway	Bridge Name	No.	Mile	Spans and Overall Length, ft	Foundation Type	Superstructure Type	Foundation Soil Conditions	Foundation Displacements	Bridge Damage
Seward (cont.)	Snow River Overhead	606	18.0	73 @ 20/1460	Timber bents; RC spread footings for rigid frame	Timber stringers and deck, plus one RC rigid frame span	One abutment directly on bedrock, some bents on piles to bedrock through silts and sands (generally loose and containing organic lenses), remainder of piles embedded in sands and silts with organics (generally loose to medium-dense)	Severe	Total collapse
	Victory Creek	607	20.0	1 @ 18 1 @ 80 1 @ 70 1 @ 20/197	RC piers on steel rail piles	Steel stringers/RC deck	Piles to bedrock or into gravels close to bedrock (inferred)	Minor	Moderate deformation of components
	Ptarmigan Creek	608	23.5	6 @ 25/152	Timber pile bents	RC girders and deck	Piles to bedrock or into gravels close to bedrock (inferred)	Nil	None
	Falls Creek	609	25.0	5 @ 25/127	Timber pile bents	RC girders and deck	Piles to bedrock or into gravels close to bedrock (inferred)	Nil	None
	Trail River	610	25.5	14 @ 25/352	Timber pile bents except one pier and abut. RC on steel rail piles	RC girders and deck	Piles to bedrock through cohesionless soils at one abut., probably close to bedrock over remainder	Minor	Minor
	Quartz Creek	1137	42.0	1 @ 22/22	RC spread footings	RC rigid frame	Bedrock (inferred)	Nil	Minor

Name	No.		Spans	Substructure	Superstructure	Foundation conditions	Damage	
Canyon Creek	612	56.8	2 @ 50 2 @ 65 1 @ 59/302	High steel trestle on RC spread footings	Continuous steel stringers/RC deck	Abuts. directly on bedrock, piers on or close to bedrock	Nil	None
Dry Gulch Creek	613	57.1	2 @ 50 1 @ 20/120	RC spread footings	Steel stringers/RC deck	Bedrock (inferred)	Nil	None
Silvertip Creek	614	60.7	2 @ 20 1 @ 40/86	RC piers on spread footings, RC abuts. on steel H piles	Steel stringers/RC deck	Bedrock (inferred)	Nil	None
Placer River 1	627	77.9	18 @ 25/451	Timber pile bents	RC girders and deck	Piles embedded in sands and silts, through gravels and sands; $N \simeq 10$ to 15 over upper half of pile length, $N = 20$ to 60 at tips. Underlain by silts	Severe	Severe deformation, partial collapse
Placer River 2	628	78.2	5 @ 25/126	Timber pile bents	RC girders and deck	Piles embedded in sands and silts, through gravels and sands; $N \simeq 10$ to 15 over upper half of pile length, $N = 20$ to 60 at tips. Underlain by silts	Severe	Severe deformation, partial collapse
Placer River Main Crossing	629	78.4	22 @ 25/551	Timber pile bents	RC girders and deck	Piles embedded in sands and silts, through gravels and sands; $N \simeq 10$ to 15 over upper half of pile length, $N = 20$ to 60 at tips. Underlain by silts	Severe	Total collapse

TABLE 2 (Continued)

Highway	Bridge Name	No.	Mile	Spans and Overall Length, ft	Foundation Type	Superstructure Type	Foundation Soil Conditions	Foundation Displacements	Bridge Damage
Seward (cont.)	Portage Creek 1	630	79.1	7 @ 25/176	Timber pile bents	RC girders and deck	Piles embedded in sands and silts, through gravels and sands; $N \simeq 10$ to 15 over upper half of pile length, $N = 20$ to 60 at tips. Underlain by silts	Severe	Total collapse
	Portage Creek 2	631	79.6	9 @ 25/226	Timber pile bents	RC girders and deck	Piles embedded in sands and silts, through gravels and sands; $N \simeq 10$ to 15 over upper half of pile length, $N = 20$ to 60 at tips. Underlain by silts	Severe	Total collapse
	Portage Creek 3	632	79.7	5 @ 25/126	Timber pile bents	RC girders and deck	Piles embedded in sands and silts, through gravels and sands; $N \simeq 10$ to 15 over upper half of pile length, $N = 20$ to 60 at tips. Underlain by silts	Severe	Severe deformation, partial collapse
	Jim's Creek	633	80.3	2 @ 25/51	Timber pile bents	RC girders and deck	Piles embedded in sands and silts, through gravels and sands; $N \simeq 10$ to 15 over upper half of pile length, $N = 20$ to 60	Severe	Total collapse

230

						through sands and gravels; $N \simeq 15$ to 30 over upper half of pile length, to 35 to 85 at tips		
Peterson Creek	636	83.2	$2 @ 30$ $1 @ 60/126$	RC piers on steel rail piles	Steel stringers/RC deck	Piles embedded in sandy gravels; loose to medium dense over estimated pile length ($N \simeq 8$ to 30); at pile tips $N \simeq 30$ to 60. Underlain by silts	Moderate	Moderate deformation of components
Kern Creek	637	86.2	$2 @ 35$ $1 @ 79/155$	RC piers on steel rail piles	Steel stringers/RC deck	Piles to bedrock through gravel and silt at one abutment, embedded in gravels over remainder (inferred)	Moderate	Moderate deformation of components
Virgin Creek	638	89.6	$3 @ 25/76$	Timber pile bents	RC girders and deck	Piles embedded in silty sands and gravels with organics; N ranges 6 to 40 irregularly over estimated pile length	Severe	Severe deformation partial collapse
Glacier Creek	639	90.0	$2 @ 35$ $1 @ 79/155$	RC piers on steel rail piles	Steel stringers/RC deck	Piles embedded in sandy gravels and silty sand; N ranges 20 to 80 over estimated pile length	Moderate/ severe	Moderate deformation of components
Tidewater Slough 6	640	90.9	$4 @ 25/101$	Timber pile bents	RC girders and deck	Piles embedded in silty sand and silt; $N \simeq 8$ to 17 over estimated pile length	Severe	Severe deformation

TABLE 2 (Continued)

Highway	Bridge Name	No.	Mile	Spans and Overall Length, ft	Foundation Type	Superstructure Type	Foundation Soil Conditions	Foundation Displacements	Bridge Damage
Sterling (mileage from junction with Seward Highway)	Dave's Creek	680	1.4	2 @ 10/21	—	RC box culvert	Bedrock (inferred)	Nil	Minor
	Quartz Creek	676	2.8	6 @ 25/152	Timber pile bents	RC girders and deck	Piles embedded in gravels; $N \simeq 40$ to 80	Minor	Moderate deformation of components
	Kenai River at Cooper's Landing	675	9.5	16 @ 25/410	Timber pile bents	RC girders and deck	Piles embedded in silt and fine sand; $N \simeq 35$ to 40	Severe	Total collapse
Copper River (mileage starts at Cordova)	Eyak River	381	5.9	10 @ 25/255	Timber pile bents with precast concrete caps	Prestressed concrete	One abut. on bedrock; other abut. and piers on piles to or near bedrock	Nil	None
	Scott Glacier Stream 1	348	7.6	6 @ 25/150	Timber pile bents with precast concrete caps	Steel stringers/ RC deck	Piles embedded in sands and silts; $N \simeq 9$ to 20	Severe	Severe deformation
	Scott Glacier Stream 2	349	7.7	8 @ 25/200	Timber pile bents with precast concrete caps	Steel stringers/ RC deck	Piles embedded in sands and silts; $N \simeq 4$ to 10	Moderate	Moderate deformation of components
	Scott Glacier Stream 3	350	8.2	6 @ 25/150	Timber pile bents with precast concrete caps	Steel stringers/ RC deck	Piles embedded in sands and silts; $N \simeq 18$	Severe	Severe deformation
	Scott Glacier Stream 4	351	8.6	3 @ 25/75	Timber pile bents with precast concrete caps	Steel stringers/ RC deck	Piles embedded in sands and silts; $N \simeq 11$ to 21	Severe	Severe deformation
	Scott Glacier Stream 5	352	9.2	3 @ 25/75	Timber pile bents with precast concrete caps	Steel stringers/ RC deck	Piles embedded in sands and silts; $N \simeq 7$ to 15	Minor	Minor
	Scott Glacier Stream 6	406	9.5	12 @ 25 3 @ 34/403	Steel rail pile bents with RC caps	Steel stringers/ RC deck	Piles embedded in sands and silts; $N \simeq 10$ to 17	Severe	Severe deformation
	Scott Glacier Stream 7	407	9.8	7 @ 25/176	Steel rail pile bents with RC caps	Steel stringers/ RC deck	Piles embedded in sands and silts; $N \simeq 10$ to 16	Severe	Severe deformation
	Scott Glacier Stream 8	408	10.1	6 @ 25/151	Steel rail pile bents with RC caps	Steel stringers/ RC deck	Piles embedded in sands and silts; $N \simeq 12$ to 20	Minor	Moderate deformation of components
	Scott Glacier Stream 9	409	10.4	3 @ 25/75	Steel rail pile bents with RC	Steel stringers/ RC deck	Piles embedded in sands and silts;	Moderate	Minor

Location	No.			Structure	Deck	Foundation		Damage
				caps		no penetration resistance data		
Scott Glacier Stream 11	411	11.0	14 @ 25/352	Steel rail pile bents with RC caps	Steel stringers/RC deck	Piles embedded in sands and silts; $N \approx 9$ to 19	Severe	Severe deformation
Sheridan Glacier Stream 2	361	14.8	6 @ 25/152	Timber pile bents	Timber stringers and deck	Piles embedded in sand and gravel; no penetration resistance data	Moderate	Severe deformation
Sheridan Glacier Stream 3	230	14.9	5 @ 40/201	Concrete-filled steel tube pile bents	Prestressed concrete stringers/RC deck	Piles embedded in sand and gravel; no penetration resistance data	Minor	Minor
Sheridan Glacier Stream	363	15.8	8 @ 25/202	Timber pile bents	Timber stringers and deck	Piles embedded in sand and gravel; no penetration resistance data	Moderate	Severe deformation
Sheridan Glacier Stream	364	15.8	1 @ 25/27	Timber pile bents	Timber stringers and deck	Piles embedded in sand and gravel; no penetration resistance data	Minor	Moderate deformation of components
Sheridan Glacier Stream	365	15.9	2 @ 19/40	Timber pile bents	Timber stringers and deck	Piles embedded in sand and gravel; no penetration resistance data	Minor	Moderate deformation of components
Sheridan Glacier Stream	366	16.1	1 @ 25/28	Timber pile bents	Timber stringers and deck	Piles embedded in sand and gravel; no penetration resistance data	Minor	Moderate deformation of components
Sheridan Glacier Stream	367	16.5	4 @ 25/102	Timber pile bents	Timber stringers and deck	Piles embedded in sands and gravels; $N \approx 5$ to 10 over pile length to 15 to 50 at tips	Moderate	Severe deformation
Sheridan Glacier Stream	368	16.6	2 @ 25/52	Timber pile bents	Timber stringers and deck	Piles embedded in sand and gravel; no penetration resistance data. Bedrock outcrops nearby and may underlie site at relatively shallow depth	Nil	Minor

TABLE 2 (Continued)

Highway	Bridge Name	No.	Mile	Spans and Overall Length, ft	Foundation Type	Superstructure Type	Foundation Soil Conditions	Foundation Displacements	Bridge Damage
Copper River (cont.)	Sheridan Glacier Stream	369	16.9	4 @ 25/102	Timber pile bents	Timber stringers and deck	Piles embedded in sand and gravel; no penetration resistance data. Bedrock outcrops nearby and may underlie site at relatively shallow depth	Nil	None
	Sheridan Glacier Stream	370	17.4	4 @ 25/127	Timber pile bents	Timber stringers and deck	Piles embedded in sand and gravel; no penetration resistance data. Bedrock outcrops nearby and may underlie site at relatively shallow depth	Nil	None
	Sheridan Glacier Stream	371	17.9	2 @ 19/40	Timber pile bents	Timber stringers and deck	Piles embedded in sand and gravel; no penetration resistance data. Bedrock outcrops nearby and may underlie site at relatively shallow depth	Nil	None
	Sheridan Glacier Stream	372	18.2	2 @ 25/52	Timber pile bents	Timber stringers and deck	Piles embedded in sand and gravel; no penetration resistance data. Bedrock outcrops nearby and may underlie site at rela-	Minor	Minor

234

Stream								
					and deck	sand and gravel no penetration resistance data. Bedrock outcrops nearby and may underlie site at relatively shallow depth		None
Sheridan Glacier Stream	374	18.9	4 @ 25/102	Timber pile bents	Timber stringers and deck	Piles embedded in sand and gravel; no penetration resistance data; bedrock outcrops nearby	Nil	None
Million Dollar	206	49.0	2 @ 400 1 @ 300 1 @ 450/1550	Concrete piers on concrete caissons 35 to 50 ft below streambed	Steel thru truss	Sand and gravel; generally loose to 20 ft depth; sand, gravel, and boulders to 20 yd^3 encountered by caissons	Moderate	Severe deformation partial collapse
Allen River	248	59.7	—	Timber pile bents	Timber stringers and deck (temporary structure)	Stratified sands and gravels with some silt; N ranges 10 to 40 in upper 30 feet	Severe	Total collapse

[a]RC abuts. = reinforced-concrete abutments.

and overall bridge damage throughout the entire lengths of the Seward, Sterling, and Copper River highways is presented in Table 3. The table shows that approximately 50 percent of the bridges on these routes suffered severe to moderate foundation displacements and overall damage, 20 percent sustained minor damage, and 30 percent were undamaged. Distribution figures for the individual Seward and Copper River highways are similar to those for the combined routes.

The degree of severity of foundation displacements is correlated with the foundation-support conditions in Figure 65. The cases included are limited to those in which the bridge behavior is sufficiently clear to allow a reasonable estimate of foundation displacement severity and for which sufficient substructure information and subsurface data are available to allow reasonable interpretation of the foundation support conditions. Much of the available test-boring information was obtained by the Department of Highways for reconstruction design after the earthquake and is therefore concentrated on bridges that sustained heavy damage. Specific subsurface data are meager for bridges that suffered little or no damage, but at a number of sites it has been possible to infer the foundation soil conditions with reasonable confidence. These are mainly cases where bedrock is shallow or exposed, or where coarse glacial or fluvial gravels fill ravines in bedrock. These cases have been interpreted from aerial photography procured by government agencies either before or after the earthquake, supplemented in some instances by field observations by the authors or by geologists

of the U.S. Geological Survey. Indirect interpretations of this type have not been used in cases where bridge damage was severe.

Approximately half of the bridges on the Seward, Sterling, and Copper River highways are represented in Figure 65. Many undamaged bridges on the three highways are not included; some severely damaged structures on the Copper River Highway are missing. The information in Figure 65, nevertheless, provides a convenient summary of the correlation between foundation conditions and foundation displacements for 60 bridges. Because all the cases included in the figure are located within an estimated range of 50–80 mi from the zone of major energy release (Figure 1), it might reasonably be inferred that the intensity of ground movement at bedrock did not vary widely for the different locations. The structural types and materials of the bridges are not considered in this correlation.

A study of Figure 65 leads to the following observations:

1. No cases of evident foundation displacement were reported for bridges known to be founded wholly on bedrock. Of the nine bridges believed to be so founded, none showed evidence of appreciable movements. Of five other cases in which the bridges were founded on bedrock at one end, but piling over the remaining length may or may not have extended to bedrock, two showed no foundation displacement and three showed evidence of minor movements.

2. Two cases were reported of distinctly different support conditions along a bridge, with bedrock at one end and piling into cohesionless soils of varying thickness over the remaining bridge length; one long bridge sustained severe foundation displacements and collapsed in the transition zone from bedrock support to soil support, the other bridge showed evidence of moderate foundation displacements.

3. The greatest concentrations of bridges that sustained severe foundation movements were founded on piling driven through saturated sands and silts of low-to-medium relative density ($N<20$). The range of grain-size distributions for soils in this category is shown in Figure 66; the samples from which this range was derived were obtained from bridge sites at which severe foundation displacements occurred during the earthquake. Of approximately 60 test samples included in the range, two thirds were of uniform gradation, with uniformity coefficients of 2–4, most commonly in the fine sand and coarse silt size ranges. The remaining one third of the samples showed less uniform grading, with uniformity coefficients as high as 10 and greater. Typical examples of uniform and well-graded soil samples are shown in the figure.

4. Bridges founded on piles that were driven through loose to medium-dense sands and silts into denser sands and silts fared little better than those founded on piles that

TABLE 3 Summary of Foundation Displacements and Overall Bridge Damage on Combined Seward, Sterling, and Copper River Highways[a]

	Number of Bridges	Percentage Classified
Foundation displacements		
Severe	32	28
Moderate	25	22
Minor	21	18
Nil	36	32
Overall bridge damage		
Total collapse	9	8
Severe deformation and/or partial collapse	26	22
Moderate deformation of components	27	23
Minor	24	20
None	32	27

[a]Total number of bridges along highways ~120; number classified with regard to foundation displacements = 114; number classified with regard to overall bridge damage = 118.

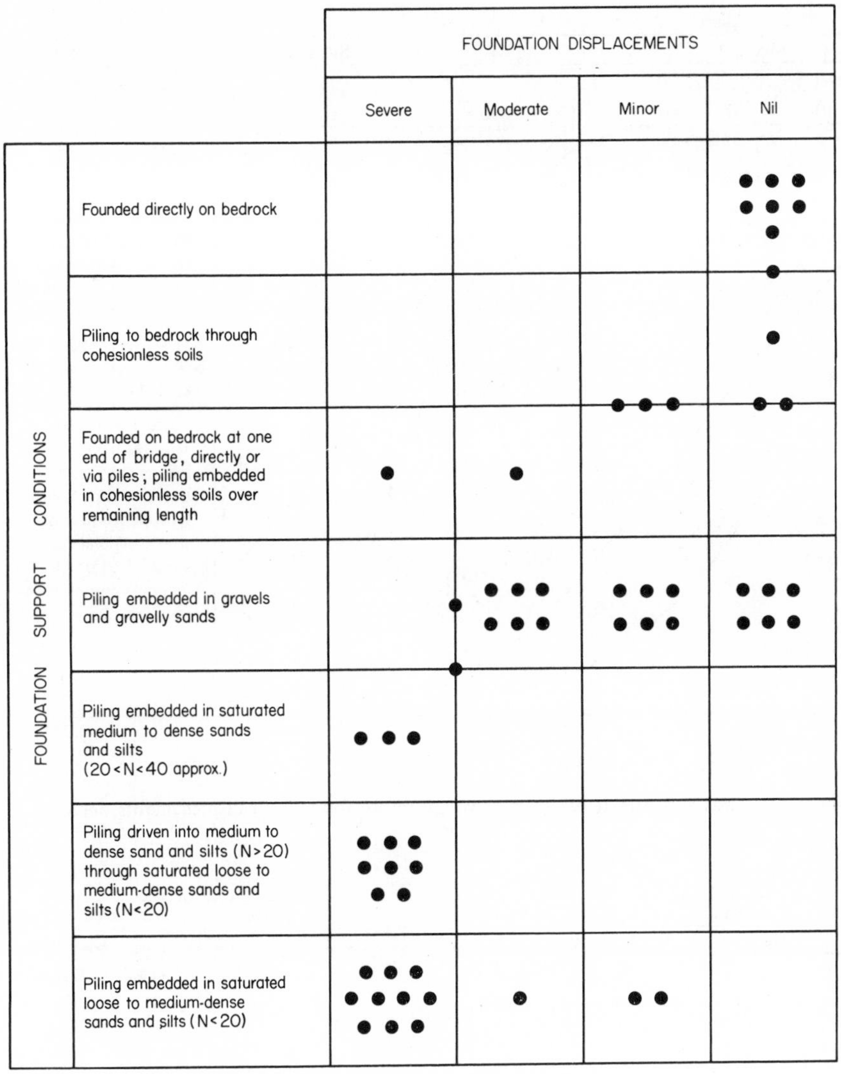

FIGURE 65   Correlation between foundation displacements sustained and foundation support conditions at bridges on the Seward, Sterling, and Copper River highways. Data was available from only 60 of a total of approximately 120 bridges on the three highways.

were embedded in loose to medium-dense sand and silt without reaching denser strata. The mode of failure may have been different in these two support conditions, but severe foundation displacements occurred in both.

5. Bridge foundations that were founded in gravels and gravelly sands (regardless of N values), rather than in sands and silts, behaved relatively well, with a generally even distribution between "nil" and "moderate" foundation displacement and one or two cases of moderate-to-severe displacement. The grain-size distribution range for samples obtained at two bridge sites where the subsoil consisted of gravels and gravelly sands, and where foundation displacements were minor to moderate, is shown in Figure 67. These samples were generally well graded, with uniformity coefficients of about 15–50, and contained relatively little fine

sand and silt sizes, compared to the soils in Figure 66. Some subsoils classified as gravels may have included strata or lenses of sands or silts, a condition that would probably have influenced the observed performance.

6. Although the structural types and materials of the bridge substructure are not indicated in Figure 65, the bridges that showed severe foundation displacements in sands and silts had foundations ranging from light flexible all-timber bents through steel-rail and concrete bents to heavy reinforced-concrete piers with four-way-battered concrete-filled steel-tube piles extending to a total depth of about 100 ft.

7. No failures of bridges founded in cohesive soils have been reported along the three highways. Similarly, no bridges in the region are known, at this writing, to be

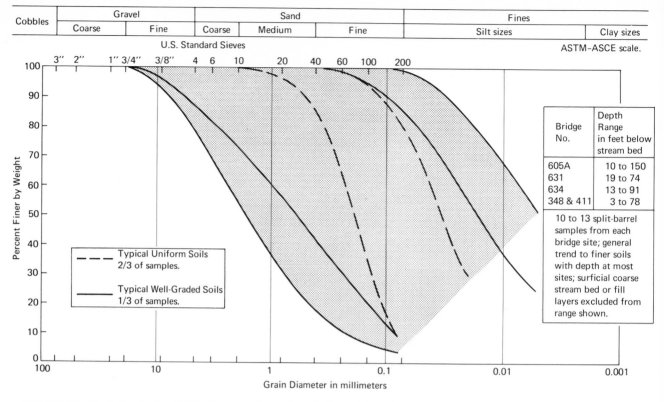

FIGURE 66 Typical grain-size distribution range for sands and silts at bridge sites where severe foundation displacements occurred.

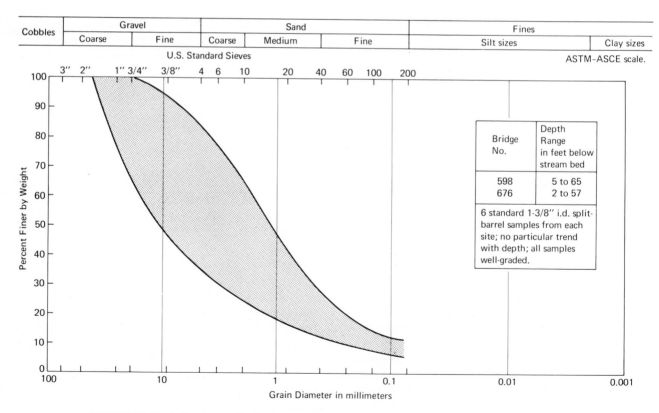

FIGURE 67 Typical grain-size distribution range for gravels and gravelly sands (less the 1.4 in. fraction only).

TABLE 4   Summary of Overall Bridge Damage on Combined Glenn and Richardson Highways[a]

	Number of Bridges	Percentage Classified
Overall Bridge Damage		
Total collapse	1	2½
Severe deformation and/or partial collapse	0	0
Moderate deformation of components	1	2½
Minor	8	20
None	30	75

[a]Total number of bridges along highways ~ 40; number classified = 40.

founded on piling driven to bearing on bedrock through cohesive soils.

GLENN AND RICHARDSON HIGHWAYS

The overall bridge-damage data on the combined Glenn and Richardson highways is summarized in Table 4, which shows that only 5 percent of the bridges on these two routes suffered moderate or severe deformations, 20 percent sustained minor damage, and 75 percent were undamaged.

A total of 10 bridges on these two highways are believed to have been founded on bedrock. Of these 10 cases, 7 showed no damage and the other 3 showed minor damage. The remaining 30 bridges were founded in various glacial and fluvial soils—predominantly gravels, sands, and silts.

Although insufficient data are available to estimate the foundation displacements and support conditions involved and to allow more comprehensive observations, there is no apparent contradiction of the data presented in Figure 65, which are based on the performance of bridge foundations along the Seward, Sterling, and Copper River highways.

CORRELATION BETWEEN FOUNDATION DISPLACEMENTS AND PENETRATION RESISTANCE OF FOUNDATION SOILS

In an attempt to ascertain whether the severity of foundation displacements was related to the density of the silts and sands in which the foundations were supported, Figure 68 was prepared to show the relation between foundation displacements and the average penetration resistance in the upper 30 ft of soil in which the foundation piles were embedded. Because almost all pile foundations known to be in sands suffered severe damage, it is not possible to determine the density of soil in which damaging displacements would not occur. Severe foundation displacements were, however,

common in sands and silty sands with average penetration-resistance values up to 25, and a single case of severe displacement occurred in a silt with an average penetration resistance value of about 35.

INFLUENCE OF SOIL LIQUEFACTION ON BRIDGE-FOUNDATION BEHAVIOR

During the Alaska earthquake of 1964 there were numerous cases of landslides resulting from liquefaction of soils with characteristics similar to those in which bridge-foundation displacements occurred. Such landslides occurred, for example, at Valdez and Seward because of liquefaction of saturated deltaic deposits ranging from silty sands to sandy gravels with standard penetration resistances ranging from 10 to 30 (Coulter and Migliaccio, 1966; Lemke, 1967; Seed, 1968); flow slides also occurred in similar types of material at seven or eight locations around Kenai Lake (McCulloch, 1966). Because the majority of bridge-foundation displacements occurred in these types of soils, it seems likely that liquefaction of the soil adjacent to the foundation units could have been a major factor in the performance of these bridges during an earthquake.

A review of bridge-foundation performance reveals much

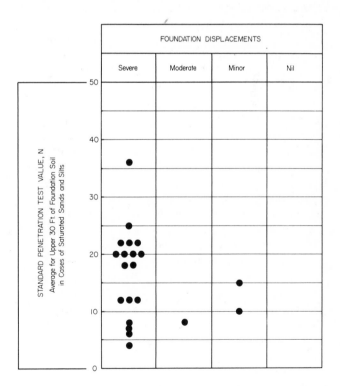

FIGURE 68   Correlation between foundation displacements sustained and penetration resistance of foundation soils at bridges on the Seward, Sterling, and Copper River highways.

evidence that liquefaction did develop in areas of major bridge damage. The following are typical examples:

1. Reported liquefaction at the Snow River crossings, on the Scott Glacier outwash, and in the lower Copper River region.

2. The movements of unloaded piers surrounded by level ground and well removed from stream banks through distances up to 8 ft, in spite of the provision of deep pile foundations to firm bearing strata, for example, Bridge 605A (Snow River Bridge 3, during construction) and Bridge 1121 (Knik River Bridge 1, during construction).

3. Extensive lateral spreading of the bases of embankment fills supported on the same foundation materials as the bridge structures; this type of movement has characteristically occurred where foundation materials have liquefied during other earthquakes.

In addition to the visual field evidence of soil liquefaction, the liquefaction of soil deposits in streambeds, accompanied possibly by partial liquefaction under stream banks and bridge approach fills, seems to provide the most likely explanation of the observed foundation behavior. The horizontal movements of piers in both lateral and longitudinal directions, the large settlements of piers and piles into the ground, and the tilting of piers located near adjacent stream banks or approach fills could only be explained by soil liquefaction; inward movement of bridge abutments would certainly be facilitated by this phenomenon. Furthermore, the displacements that occurred in sandy soils did not appear to be related to the type of foundation provided; this would also be a logical consequence of soil liquefaction. Experience in areas of liquefaction in the Niigata, Japan, earthquake has shown that pile foundations for bridges and buildings suffered lateral movements leading to severe structural damage (Seed and Idriss, 1967; Fukuoka, 1966). It would appear that similar events occurred during the Alaska earthquake in bridge foundations set in sandy materials. Apparently, none of the foundation types utilized had sufficient lateral resistance to withstand the lateral forces developed by the earthquake when the upper soil layers liquefied as a result of ground shaking. The deep and substantial pile foundations for Snow River Bridge 3 (Figures 13 and 21) were unable to withstand these lateral forces although the superstructure had not yet been built. This indicates that it is extremely difficult to provide sufficient lateral resistance in conventional pile foundations to prevent lateral movements and associated structural damage if liquefaction develops during earthquake ground movements of the intensity experienced in south central Alaska in 1964.

It seems reasonable to conclude that liquefaction of soils adjacent to bridge foundations played a major role in the development of bridge damage during the Alaska earthquake. The failure of conventional foundations to prevent damage under these conditions suggests that methods of improving foundation performance should be sought. Suitable alternatives might include the following courses of action:

1. The avoidance of routes where bridges must be constructed on deep deposits of sandy materials and the adoption of routes providing bridge sites where foundations can be constructed through shallow depths of cohesionless soils to rock formations.

2. The prevention of liquefaction during major earthquakes by stabilization techniques, such as densification or grouting, where deep deposits of sandy materials cannot be avoided.

In the absence of these or other appropriate measures, it seems likely that similar foundation and bridge damage would recur at sites underlain by saturated loose to medium-dense sandy soils (Figure 68) in the event of a similar earthquake in the future.

CONCLUSIONS

The results of a study of highway-bridge-foundation behavior during the 1964 Alaska earthquake have been presented and interpreted within the limits of the information at present available to the authors. The following conclusions can be drawn:

1. The 1964 Alaska earthquake caused extensive damage to a wide variety of bridge-foundation types located within a distance of approximately 80 mi of the zone of major energy release. The season in which the earthquake occurred should possibly be taken into account in evaluating the extent and intensity of bridge damage. The frozen ground and ice that prevailed in south central Alaska could, in general, be considered a stabilizing factor in foundation behavior under earthquake forces, because a frozen crust, obviously, could not liquefy. The presence of frozen zones may have been responsible for minor variations in the extent of foundation displacements, but they do not appear to have affected the general types of damage sustained.

2. Bridge-foundation damage included horizontal movement of abutment foundations toward the channels, spreading and settlement of abutment fills, horizontal displacement and tilting of piers, severe differential settlement of abutments and piers, and failure of foundation members.

3. The severity of damage to bridge foundations was dependent to a great extent on the foundation-support conditions.

4. No cases of evident foundation displacement were reported for bridges known to be founded wholly on bedrock; however, severe to moderate displacements were reported for bridges founded partly on bedrock and partly in soils.

5. The greatest concentrations of severe damage occurred in regions characterized by thick deposits of saturated cohesionless soils. Ample evidence exists of liquefaction of these materials during the earthquake; this phenomenon probably played a major role in the development of foundation displacements and bridge damage.

6. Bridges founded in saturated sands and silts sustained severe displacement of pile-supported foundations even where the average standard penetration resistance of the upper 30 ft of the soil was as high as 25 blows/ft. The degree of damage sustained by these bridges did not appear to be greatly influenced by an increase in density of the foundation soil at the pile tips and below.

7. Severely damaged foundations in loose to medium-dense saturated sands and silts included many structural types from light all-timber bents to heavy reinforced-concrete piers on long battered steel-and-concrete piles extending into denser sands. Any of these types of foundation for a conventional bridge constructed on such a subsurface profile would therefore appear to be inadequate to prevent severe damage from earthquake ground motions of the intensity experienced in south central Alaska in 1964.

8. In areas characterized by saturated loose to medium-dense sandy deposits, bridge-foundation displacements and associated structural damage during major earthquakes can best be prevented by avoiding routes where bridges must be constructed on deep deposits of these materials and adopting routes with sites at which bridge foundations can be constructed through shallow depths of cohesionless soil to rock. Where deep deposits of sandy materials cannot be avoided, structural damage can best be averted by preventing liquefaction of the upper zone of the deposit by soil stabilization techniques such as densification or grouting.

ACKNOWLEDGMENTS

This study was sponsored in part by the Alaska District, U.S. Army Corps of Engineers, and made possible by the extensive cooperation of the State of Alaska Department of Highways. The authors appreciate the encouragement provided by Warren George, U.S. Army Engineers, in the conduct of the investigations.

The study was initiated in the summer of 1967, over 3 years after the earthquake, and is therefore largely dependent on the first-hand observations of previous investigators. The main unpublished sources from which information was drawn are the reports, plans, and inventories of the State of Alaska Department of Highways and its predecessors. The authors are particularly indebted to Harvey Golub, Chief Bridge Engineer, for his generous cooperation in providing access to the files of the Bridge Division at its Douglas, Alaska, headquarters. He and his staff answered many queries on the design and construction details of the bridges affected by the earthquake and on the damage reports that they prepared immediately after the earthquake. Mr. Golub provided copies of drawings, reports, notes, and photographs for the authors' use. These materials have been used extensively in the preparation of this report, although in most cases without specific acknowledgment. Unless otherwise credited, all photographs used herein were provided by Alaska Department of Highways personnel.

The authors would also like to thank David S. McCulloch of the U.S. Geological Survey, Menlo Park, California, who, with his associate, M. G. Bonilla, spent several months immediately after the earthquake studying bridge deformation on The Alaska Railroad. Their field observations extended to the parallel highway structures on portions of the Seward and Glenn highways. Consequently, communications with Mr. McCulloch were of considerable assistance in the preparation of this report.

Arlan Davis, Project Engineer for the Alaska Department of Highways at Cordova, provided transportation and guided one of the authors over the first 27 mi of the Copper River Highway in July 1967. His first-hand knowledge of the region at the time of the earthquake and of the construction and reconstruction work on the highway was most helpful.

Reuben Kachadoorian of the U.S. Geological Survey, Menlo Park, California, kindly discussed with the authors some of the field observations that he made along the highways after the earthquake. This discussion was useful in estimating the probable foundation support conditions at several bridge sites for which test borings are not available, and which the authors did not have an opportunity to inspect for the purposes of this survey.

REFERENCES

Coulter, Henry W., and Ralph R. Migliaccio, 1966. Effects of the earthquake of March 27, 1964, at Valdez, Alaska. U.S. Geological Survey Professional Paper 542-C. Washington: Government Printing Office. 36 p. Also *in* The Great Alaska Earthquake of 1964: Geology. NAS Pub. 1601. Washington: National Academy of Sciences, 1971. p. 359–394.

Fukuoka, M., 1966. Damage to civil engineering structures. *Soil and Foundation*, 6 (March), 45–52.

Hansen, Wallace R., Edwin B. Eckel, William E. Schaem, Robert E. Lyle, Warren George, and Genie Chance, 1966. The Alaska earthquake, March 27, 1964: Field investigations and reconstruction effort. U.S. Geological Survey Professional Paper 541. Washington: Government Printing Office. 111 p.

Lemke, Richard W., 1967. Effects of the earthquake of March 27, 1964, at Seward, Alaska. U.S. Geological Survey Professional Paper 542-E. Washington: Government Printing Office. 43 p. Also *in* The Great Alaska Earthquake of 1964: Geology. NAS Pub. 1601. Washington: National Academy of Sciences, 1971. p. 395–437.

McCulloch, David S., 1966. Slide-induced waves, seiching, and ground fracturing caused by the earthquake of March 27, 1964, at Kenai Lake, Alaska. U.S. Geological Survey Professional Paper 543-A. Washington: Government Printing Office. 41 p. Abstract *in* The Great Alaska Earthquake of 1964: Geology. NAS Pub. 1601. Washington: National Academy of Sciences, 1971. p. 279.

McCulloch, David S., and M. G. Bonilla, 1967. Railroad damage in the Alaska earthquake. *Journal of the Soil Mechanics and Foundations Division* (American Society of Civil Engineers), 93 (September), 89–100.

Migliaccio, Ralph R., 1965. Earthquake damage to highways in the Valdez district, Alaska *in* Highway Research Record No. 91. NAS Pub. 1307. Washington: National Academy of Sciences. p. 64–72.

Plafker, George, 1967. Geologic map of the Gulf of Alaska Tertiary province, Alaska. U.S. Geological Survey Miscellaneous Geologic Investigations Map I-484. Washington: U.S. Geological Survey.

Ross, Grant A., H. Bolton Seed, and Ralph R. Migliaccio, 1969. Bridge foundation behavior in Alaska earthquake. *Journal of the Soil Mechanics and Foundations Division* (American Society of Civil Engineers), 95, No. SM4 (July), 1007–1036.

Seed, H. Bolton, 1968. Landslides during earthquakes due to soil liquefaction. *Journal of the Soil Mechanics and Foundations Division* (American Society of Civil Engineers), 94 (September), 1053–1122.

Seed, H. Bolton, and I. M. Idriss, 1967. Analysis of soil liquefaction: Niigata earthquake. *Journal of the Soil Mechanics and Foundations Division* (American Society of Civil Engineers), 93 (May), 83–108.

II
STRUCTURAL
ENGINEERING

Introduction

The area strongly shaken by the earthquake was sparsely inhabited; for this reason, the amount of data on damage to structures and facilities was not comparable to the data that could be provided, for example, by a destructive earthquake in California. Valuable engineering information, however, was obtained on the behavior of and damage to certain types of structures. In Anchorage, all seven buildings over five stories high were severely damaged, but no data were recorded on the ground shaking that caused the damage or on the motions of the buildings themselves. The damage indicated serious deficiencies in the building code and in structural design, and it motivated the city of Los Angeles to pass an ordinance requiring all new buildings 10 stories or more in height to be outfitted with three strong-motion accelerographs—one in the basement, one at the top, and one at mid-height. The purpose of these instruments is to record accurate information about earthquake ground motions and building motions for the improvement and verification of earthquake-resistant design. The papers in this section deal with those structures whose damage provides information especially helpful in improving earthquake analysis and design.

Glen V. Berg, presents a summary description of the response of buildings in Anchorage to the earthquake motions. Most of the buildings affected by the ground shaking were in Anchorage, and most were designed under the earthquake requirements of the *Uniform Building Code*. Many, in fact, were designed by structural engineers in California and Washington, making it probable that weaknesses exhibited by buildings in Anchorage will also be found in buildings in these two states.

K. Lee Benuska and Ray W. Clough describe the dynamic analysis of building failures. The time–history responses of several multistory Anchorage buildings were computed for base acceleration corresponding to a California earthquake. The results of these analyses are used to explain why damage occurred and to indicate the approximate magnitude of the forces that were actually produced by the Alaska earthquake. Information of practical importance for the improvement of the building code is presented.

The collapse of the Anchorage International Airport control tower killed one man and seriously hampered the operation of the airport. The analysis by Mete A. Sozen and N. Norby Nielsen discloses weaknesses in design that should be avoided in the future.

In his study, Paul C. Jennings analyzes the response of coupled shear-wall structures. Two of the tallest structures in Anchorage were 14-story reinforced-concrete apartment buildings; these suffered severe damage, which was the result of coupled shear-wall action. An analysis of the structural action explains why the damage occurred and suggests how an adequate design of such structures can be made.

Many liquid-storage tanks for petroleum products were damaged by the earthquake and some collapsed. Robert D. Hanson's paper reports some of the interesting damage to tanks, analyzes the nature of the forces caused by earthquake shaking, and explains why the tanks were damaged. Hanson explains how tanks should be designed to withstand earthquakes without posing a hazard.

Harold D. Hauf's paper was prepared to serve as a guide to architects. The earthquake resistance of a building can be strongly influenced by architectural design and by the decisions of architects. It is most important, therefore, that architects in seismic regions be aware of the importance of their profession in relation to earthquake resistance.

In their study, J. Marx Ayres, Tseng-yao Sun, and Frederick R. Brown describe nonstructural damage to buildings. For most buildings, only about one third of the total cost is for the structural elements that provide strength; two thirds of the cost is for architectural features, finish, and mechanical, electrical, and plumbing equipment. For this reason, the cost of repairing nonstructural damage usually exceeds the cost of repairing structural damage. The paper describes various kinds of nonstructural damage that occurred during the earthquake and explains why it occurred and how it could have been avoided. This is the first time that such a comprehensive description of non-structural damage has been published, and it should be especially helpful to architects.

A paper by George W. Housner and Paul C. Jennings describes the rehabilitation of the Eklutna Project. This project was a small hydroelectric power-generating station with an earth dam, not far from Anchorage. Damage was so serious that the dam had to be replaced by a new one. Because this is the first time that severe earthquake damage to an earth dam has been so well documented, the paper is of special interest.

GEORGE W. HOUSNER
PAUL C. JENNINGS
California Institute of Technology

GLEN V. BERG
THE UNIVERSITY OF MICHIGAN

Response of Buildings in Anchorage

ABSTRACT: The Alaska earthquake of 1964 destroyed many structures in Anchorage. Earthquake-induced landslides demolished some buildings, and, in areas unaffected by landslides, the strong ground vibration shook some buildings hard enough to damage them severely or even to cause collapse. Most of the structures in the city survived the earthquake, however, with minor or negligible structural damage.

In 1950, the city of Anchorage adopted the *Uniform Building Code*, which imposed requirements for earthquake resistance. It was intended to prevent excessive vibration damage by requiring that buildings be designed to resist specified lateral forces without exceeding specified limitations of stress and displacement. Most of the major buildings in Anchorage were designed and built after the *Uniform Building Code* was adopted. The 1964 Alaska earthquake thus provides an opportunity for engineers to study earthquake-induced structural damage to learn how failures occurred and what inadequacies of design or construction may have contributed to failure.

Our examination of the behavior of several buildings that were significantly damaged by vibration and that are not described elsewhere in this paper reveals that most, but by no means all, of the structural failures were associated with inadequate connections of structural members.

Several changes have been made in the *Uniform Building Code* since 1964, some of them to correct deficiencies that were exposed by the Alaska earthquake.

A check of the design of the West Anchorage High School classroom wing shows no apparent deficiency arising from the strength requirements of the code, yet the building was damaged so badly that the second story had to be removed. This case demonstrates that the code does not yet adequately ensure that structures will perform satisfactorily in earthquakes, and further improvements must be sought.

Because the Alaska earthquake is among the few that have struck a major city in which most of the buildings were constructed subject to the requirements of a modern seismic-zone building code, the effects of the earthquake on the structures in Anchorage are of particular interest to structural engineers.

An especially troublesome feature of earthquake engineering is that its theories are difficult, perhaps even impossible, to test adequately in the laboratory or in the field. We cannot construct true scale models that preserve dynamic similitude with a prototype structure, and, even if it were economically feasible to build full-scale structures to be tested under earthquake conditions, we could not generate the base accelerations needed to test them. In the Alaska earthquake, nature provided an uncontrolled experiment and an invaluable opportunity to engineers to study the effects in some detail and to learn the ways in which structures performed satisfactorily and the ways in which they failed.

We can classify building damage in two categories—damage caused by slides or large ground displacements and damage due to vibration. We shall only consider vibration damage here.

EXTENT OF THE DAMAGE

The report of the Panel on Engineering deals primarily with earthquake destruction, such as damage to structures, damage to transportation systems, damage to communication systems, landslides, and tsunami damage. This emphasis on damage, although proper in an engineering report, may leave an inaccurate picture in the mind of the reader.

An aerial view of the city of Anchorage, taken several days after the earthquake (Figure 1), shows the city was obviously neither flattened by the earthquake, nor did a majority of the buildings collapse (Berg and Stratta, 1964). Outside the landslide areas, only two major multistory

FIGURE 1 Anchorage after the earthquake.

buildings collapsed: the Four Seasons apartment building and the control tower at Anchorage Municipal Airport. Two more, the J.C. Penney Building and the Hillside apartment building, were damaged so badly they had to be completely demolished, and the top story of the classroom wing of West Anchorage High School had to be removed. Several large single-story structures outside the landslide areas collapsed or were damaged beyond economical repair. Included among these are the Gay Airways hangar, the Western Radio and Telegraph Building, a warehouse of The Alaska Railroad, and a cement bin of the Kaiser Permanente Cement Company. A small shop building of The Alaska Railroad collapsed partly and had to be removed. Partial collapses also occurred at the Alaska Sales and Service Building, at Fifth Avenue Chrysler Center, and at Warehouse 21–884 on Elmendorf Air Force Base, but these buildings were salvaged and rebuilt. An ash silo at the Knik Arm Power Plant of the Chugach Electric Association collapsed and was replaced. Other buildings that suffered vibration damage were repaired and restored to use. A far greater number of buildings throughout the city, including

most of the houses outside the slide areas, experienced negligible, or, at worst, minor structural damage. Among these were the Alaska Psychiatric Institute, the City Water Treatment Plant, the Public Safety Building, a city warehouse, the Merrill Field control tower, two fire stations, two telephone-exchange buildings, the Public Health Center, Central Junior High School, and East Anchorage High School, all of which are described in the reports contributed by the Corps of Engineers. Many others could be added to the list.

The earthquake caused great destruction in several landslide areas. Elsewhere it caused complete collapse of a few buildings, severe structural damage to many buildings, and minor or negligible structural damage to a majority of the buildings in the city.

DAMAGED BUILDINGS

Most of the major buildings that were severely damaged are described elsewhere in this volume (Benuska and Clough,

1973; George and others, 1973; Jennings, 1973; Sozen and Nielsen, 1973). Several buildings that are not discussed in other sections are described briefly in the following paragraphs. Their locations are shown in Figure 2.

THE ALASKA RAILROAD SHOPS

One of the car shops of The Alaska Railroad (the building farthest to the right in Figure 3) has a high bay on the north adjoined by a lower bay on the south. The framing consists of steel trusses supported on steel columns, wood purlins, and a wood roof deck. The inner ends of the roof trusses for the lower roof were supported on shelf-angle brackets on the middle line of columns. These shelf angles were welded along the sides, but not along the top. During the earthquake, the welds tore, and the shelf brackets pulled loose from the columns. The trusses dropped about a foot and came to rest with the ends of their top chords bearing on a steam line (Figures 4 and 5). Had the steam line not been there to act as an unplanned secondary support, damage to that part of the structure would have been much greater.

The remainder of the car shop was only slightly damaged. Some of the interior columns, built of two channels laced together with round bars, were distorted enough to cause the lacing bars to buckle (Figure 6). Some of the col-

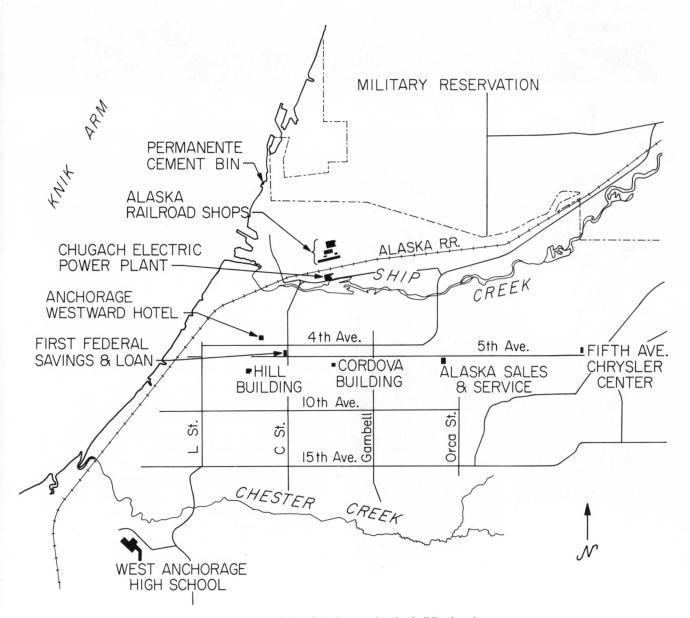

FIGURE 2   Map of city of Anchorage, showing building locations.

FIGURE 3   The Alaska Railroad shops.

FIGURE 4   Interior view of The Alaska Railroad smaller car shop.

umns in the north wall had rotated enough to stretch the anchor bolts about ¾ in. and to damage the concrete pedestals (Figure 7).

A small wheel shop (the skeleton building second from the right in Figure 3), was built of salvage material, with a steel frame and a concrete roof deck. It collapsed partly during the earthquake and had to be removed.

The larger car shop and the diesel-engine shop (the two buildings at the left of Figure 3), have braced steel frames with steel columns and steel roof trusses. In the large car shop, several of the connections between the bottom chords of the trusses and the columns were broken, some of the column lacing bars buckled, and the column anchor bolts were stretched about ½–¾ in. The diesel-engine shop was undamaged.

ALASKA SALES AND SERVICE BUILDING

The Alaska Sales and Service Building was a single-story shop and showroom building 200 ft square in plan. It was constructed of six rows of precast-concrete hammerhead-tee-column sections 20 ft high and 40 ft long, supporting precast prestressed-concrete roof tees. The roof tees were 10 ft wide and 40 ft long, placed side by side and spanning between adjacent lines of hammerhead columns. The general layout can be inferred from Figure 8.

The hammerhead-tee columns had 1¼-in. steel base plates anchored to the footings by four 1-in. anchor bolts. The tee heads were connected end to end by steel-plate connectors with shear keys, which were anchored to the

FIGURE 5   Truss detail in The Alaska Railroad car shop.

American Iron and Steel Institute

American Iron and Steel Institute

FIGURE 6   Column in The Alaska Railroad car shop. Note buckled lacing bars.

ends of the tees by six bar anchors. The connectors were bolted together with two field bolts. The roof tees were seated on neoprene pads on the column heads and were connected to the columns by means of bolts that extended down through the stem of the roof tee into the column head. These roof tees were connected side to side by welding together bar anchors that were embedded in the edges of the flanges; they were not connected end to end, except indirectly through their connections to the column heads.

The building was not yet complete at the time of the earthquake. Construction had been interrupted for the winter and had not yet been resumed. The precast structural members were all in place and connected, but peripheral bond beams that were to have been cast in place around the roof had not yet been cast. The roof was to be covered with a layer of foam concrete for insulation, overlain by a structural-concrete deck. Only part of the foam concrete and none of the structural slab had been placed. With the slab and the peripheral beams missing, the roof was unable to act as a diaphragm. There was, therefore, no effective mechanism for transmitting the inertia forces in the direction of the roof tees to the shear walls that were to provide lateral strength in that direction. No doubt this had a considerable effect on the response of the structure.

About half the structure collapsed during the earthquake, largely because of failures of the connections. Some of the anchor bolts holding the column base plates to the footings broke (Figure 9). Several connections between the ends of the column heads failed by fracture of the welds between the connection plates and their anchor bars (Figures 8 and 10). Many of the connections between adjacent roof tees failed, sometimes by fracture of the welds but more frequently by pulling the bar insert out of one of the flanges (Figures 10 and 11).

Most precast members remained sound; even some of those that fell to the ground were later salvaged.

The building has since been rebuilt using the same general construction but with stronger connections. Whether it would have escaped damage if the connections had been adequate is a matter for conjecture. Certainly the building failure emphasizes the need for careful attention to connection details in precast-concrete structures.

ANCHORAGE-WESTWARD HOTEL

The Anchorage-Westward Hotel has a 14-story tower on the east side, adjoined on the west by a three-story ballroom in the southwest part of the complex and a six-story hotel portion in the northwest part. The response of the tower portion to the earthquake is the most interesting. Figures 12 and 13 are general views of the tower; a plan of the tower is given in Figure 14.

The tower is about 52 × 139 ft in plan and about 133 ft high. It was built in two stages: The basement and lower eight stories were constructed in 1959, and the upper six stories were structurally complete and were being made ready for occupancy at the time of the earthquake. The 14-story tower is constructed of a partial steel frame with reinforced-concrete shear walls and cores. The columns that are contained in shear walls or core walls are reinforced-concrete structural columns built around light steel erection columns, usually 6-in. wide-flange shapes weighing 15.5 or 20 lb/ft. The columns that are not located

American Iron and Steel Institute

FIGURE 7   Column base in The Alaska Railroad car shop. The anchor bolts were stretched about ¾ in. as shown by the unpainted portions.

American Iron and Steel Institute

FIGURE 8   Alaska Sales and Service Building.

American Iron and Steel Institute

FIGURE 9 Tee-column base, Alaska Sales and Service Building.

in concrete walls are of structural steel. The beam-to-column connections in the top six stories are partial moment-resisting connections, with angles at the top and bottom flanges. The floors are one-way reinforced-concrete slabs on corrugated-steel forms.

There are two major shear walls in the east–west direction (Figure 14). One is in the south exterior wall, and the other is an interior wall one bay removed from the north end of the building. The interior shear wall has four door-way openings in each story. In the north–south direction, there are two principal shear walls. One consists of the north three bays of the west exterior wall. It has one opening, either a window or a door, in each story. The other is an interior wall, one bay removed from the east outside wall and extending over the northernmost bay of the building. It has no openings. Reinforced-concrete core walls house the stairs and elevators.

Typical hammering damage occurred where the tower adjoins the three-story ballroom portion (Figure 15). Such damage is frequently encountered where buildings of different height adjoin, because each will tend to oscillate independently at its own natural frequency unless the buildings are connected together firmly enough to force them to oscillate as a unit.

In the north–south shear walls, substantial damage occurred at two locations. Shear damage occurred in the west exterior shear wall at the top of the eighth story, which is the bottom of the six-story addition (Figure 16). There was also shear damage in the interior north–south shear wall at

Mac's Foto

FIGURE 10 Connection failures, Alaska Sales and Service Building.

FIGURE 11 Failed roof-tee connector, Alaska Sales and Service Building.

the second-story level (Figure 17). The north end of this wall contains a reinforced-concrete column with a 6-in. wide-flange-steel erection column encased in it. The fracture of the concrete column and severe local buckling of the wide-flange shape can be seen in Figure 17. Note that there were no shear connectors between the steel section and the

FIGURE 12 Anchorage-Westward Hotel, looking northwest.

concrete, so that the contact surface was a surface of zero shear strength in the reinforced concrete.

The principal failures in the east–west direction occurred in the interior shear wall near the north end of the building. This wall had four doorway openings in each story. At the east end of this wall is a concrete column with an encased steel erection column. In the second story, this column failed (Figure 18). The concrete fractured, the ties broke, and the steel bars and the erection column buckled. Observe in Figure 18 that the reinforcing bars are spliced in this story. Again the lack of shear connectors between the steel shape and the concrete made the contact surface a surface of zero shear strength. Directly above this, at the top of the eighth story, which is just below the six-story addition, the column was capped with a ¼-in. steel plate that was welded to the column and to the beam above. The plate fractured during the earthquake; the east half remained welded to the beam and climbed up over the west half, which remained welded to the column (Figure 19).

Failures in this east–west shear wall occurred in the lintels above all doors openings in every story. A typical failure is shown in Figure 20. Stirrups were used in the lintels in the lower eight stories, but not in the upper six stories. Lintels such as these are subjected to large vertical shears because the vertical forces in the wall to one side of the opening must be transmitted through the lintel as shear to reach the equilibrating vertical forces in the remainder of the wall. The west end of this shear wall adjacent to the exterior wall was also damaged. The worst damage occurred at the eighth floor (Figure 21).

Additional damage occurred to an outside column in the first story. This damage was similar to the other failures of reinforced-concrete columns containing steel erection col-

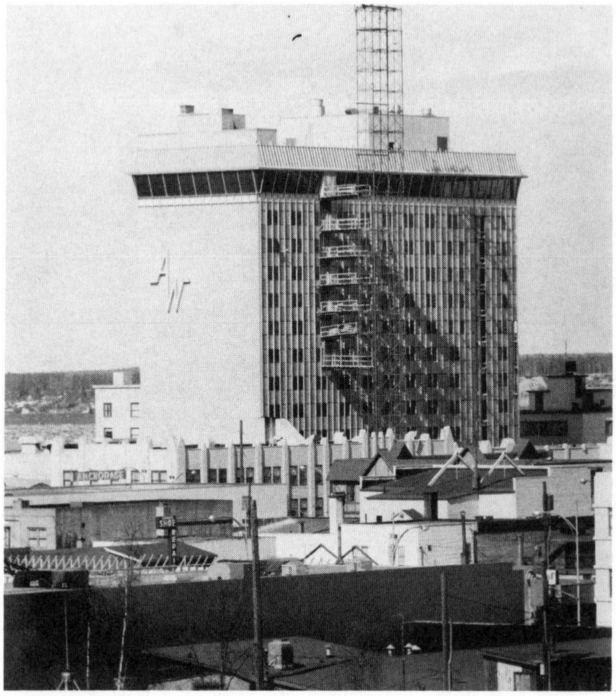

U.S. Army

FIGURE 13 Anchorage-Westward Hotel, looking east.

umns, but less severe; it also occurred at a location where the reinforcing bars were spliced.

CHUGACH ELECTRIC ASSOCIATION POWER PLANT

The Knik Arm Power Plant of the Chugach Electric Association is a steam-generating plant housed in a steel-frame building covered with corrugated-metal insulated panels. Construction was undertaken in three stages—in 1949, 1953, and 1957. The complete building is about 175 ft square in plan and is stepped, the maximum height being about 50 ft in the coal-bunker bay toward the north side of the building. X-bracing provides most of the lateral strength of the structure. Figures 22 and 23 show the west elevation and a schematic section of the building.

The turbine bay was undamaged, and the damage in the boiler bay was slight. Most of the structural damage occurred in the coal-bunker bay and was caused by oscillation of the bunkers, which were loaded to about 60 percent of their 500-ton capacity at the time of the earthquake. Some of the column-base connections were damaged and the anchor bolts were stretched. A few of the framing members were bent, and some of the columns were twisted at the framing connections because the bunker-bay framing collided with the adjacent boiler housing (Figure 24). Some of the diagonal bracing members were bent, and some of the horizontal struts in the adjacent bay buckled and their connections failed (Figures 25 and 26). A reinforced-concrete ash hopper, mounted on a platform over the railroad tracks at the north side of the building, shifted

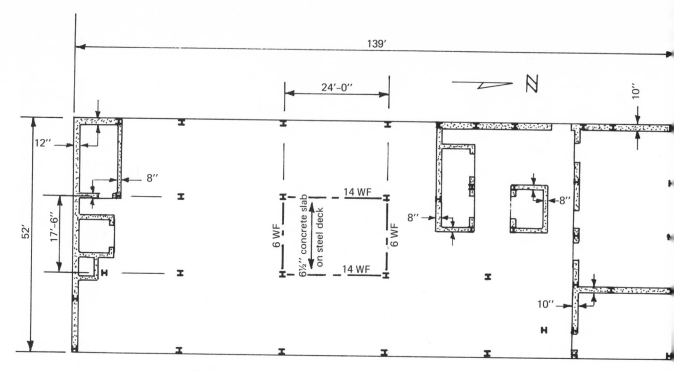

FIGURE 14   Plan of 14-story section, Anchorage-Westward Hotel.

northward and fell to the ground when its platform frame folded up like a pantograph (Figures 22 and 27).

The Knik Arm Plant was put out of operation by the earthquake. Within 24 hours, one of the boilers was fired again and on April 3, one week after the earthquake, a replacement ash-handling system was completed. The plant then began operating on three boilers and furnished large blocks of power to the Anchorage system. Five days later, the last of the boilers was put on line, and the plant was back in normal production although structural repair work was still in progress.

CORDOVA BUILDING

The Cordova Building (Figure 28) is a six-story office building 53 ft 8 in. × 129 ft 4 in. in plan. A typical floor plan is shown in Figure 29. The building has a full moment-resisting structural-steel frame in the east–west or narrow direction of the building, which is the strong direction of the columns. The connections are shop welded and field bolted with high-strength bolts. In the north–south or long direction of the building, partial moment-resisting connections were used. The floors are 2½-in. concrete slabs on corrugated-steel forms, supported by open-web steel joists. All the west face, nearly all the east face, and the west half of the south face of the building are covered with light-

weight insulated metal panels. The north face is a 4-in. reinforced-concrete curtain wall. The east half of the south face is also a 4-in. reinforced-concrete curtain wall that encloses a staircase. This wall continues around the corner and covers the south 9 ft of the east face of the building. All the exterior concrete curtain walls are supported on the basement walls.

The building has a reinforced-concrete service core with 8-in. reinforced-concrete walls enclosing an elevator shaft and stairwell toward the north end. A penthouse stands above the service core.

Earthquake damage occurred mainly in the first story of the Cordova Building. At the southeast corner the reinforced-concrete curtain walls sheared at the top of the basement walls, and the corner broke open in the first and second stories (Figure 30). The curtain walls had apparently not been anchored to the steel framing or to the floor system at the second- or third-floor levels. The north concrete curtain wall also shifted on the construction joint atop the basement wall, but to a lesser degree. The southeast corner column, a 14-in. wide-flange shape weighing 30 lb/ft (14 WF 30), buckled below the second floor beam (Figures 31 and 32). The local buckling was severe. Both flanges severed and tore away from the web, the web crimped, and the column shortened about 1½ in. The center column in the south wall, a 14 WF 61, buckled locally in the west flange at the bottom of the first story and in the east flange at the top of the first story (Figures 33 and 34). Local buckling also occurred in the southwest column, a 14 WF 30, in the east flange at the top of the first story and in both flanges and the web at the bottom of the first story. The bottom of this column is shown in Figure 35. The distortion was similar to that which occurred in the southeast corner column, but much less severe. The southeast column had a shorter effective length because of the stair framing at midheight of the story. The resulting increase in stiffness undoubtedly contributed to the greater degree of damage in that column.

The reinforced-concrete service core sheared at the base of the first story (Figure 36). The penthouse collapsed.

Except for the penthouse collapse and the first-story damage, structural damage to the Cordova Building was slight. The patches over the exterior metal panels seen in Figure 28 do not cover earthquake damage; the panels were knocked out to facilitate the removal of furniture and other contents after the earthquake.

The first story was repaired by removing the broken concrete, breaking out parts of the south wall to provide access to the columns, shoring up the south wall, replacing the damaged first-story columns, and replacing the concrete. Figures 37 and 38 show the repair work in progress.

FIFTH AVENUE CHRYSLER CENTER

The Fifth Avenue Chrysler Center is a single-story rectangular building about 70 × 157 ft in plan. The roof consists of 20 prestressed precast reinforced-concrete tees, 8-ft-wide placed side by side spanning the width of the building. Adjacent tees are connected flange to flange by welding to-

American Iron and Steel Institute

FIGURE 15 Hammering damage between two units of Anchorage-Westward Hotel.

American Iron and Steel Institute

FIGURE 16 Damage to west face of Anchorage-Westward Hotel.

FIGURE 17   Interior shear-wall damage at second-floor level, Anchorage-Westward Hotel.

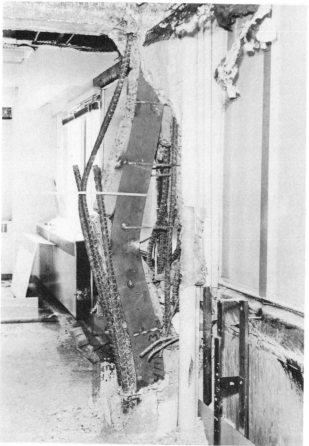

FIGURE 18   Column failure at second-story level, Anchorage-Westward Hotel.

gether bar anchors embedded in the edges of the flanges. This part of the construction is similar to that of the Alaska Sales and Service Building described earlier. Sixteen of the tees are supported on the 8-in. concrete-block sidewalls, the cores of which contain vertical reinforcing bars and are filled with concrete at the locations where the tee stems are supported. Short lengths of structural-steel split tees are embedded in the top of the block wall to provide a bearing surface. The ends of the roof tees have steel bearing plates anchored into the stem. These plates are field-welded to the steel bearing tees embedded in the walls.

The front (south) end of the building (Figure 39) is a showroom enclosed in glass exterior walls. The four front roof tees are supported on 12 X 24-in. concrete-block columns that contain vertical reinforcing steel and have the cores filled with concrete. Steel plates are anchored into the tops of the columns, and steel bearing-plates in the concrete roof-tee stems are field-welded to them. The four front roof tees are longer than the rest and overhang the columns at either end (Figure 39).

The concrete-block walls, which are reinforced horizontally as well as vertically, provide the resistance to lateral forces. The two sidewalls provide the strength in the north–south direction. The north end wall, a transverse wall running the full width of the building near the center, and two transverse stub walls, extending from the sides of the building just to the rear of the glass-walled showroom portion, strengthen it in the east–west direction. Essentially, the rear portion of the building is a closed rectangular box, and the front portion is a rectangular box with the front end missing.

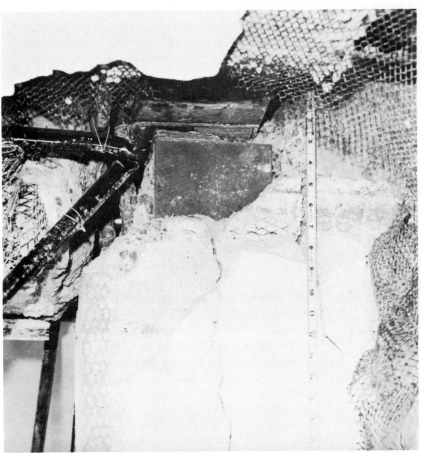

FIGURE 19   Overlapped column cap plate, Anchorage-Westward Hotel.

FIGURE 20   Shear-wall failure at eleventh story, Anchorage-Westward Hotel.

American Iron and Steel Institute

FIGURE 21   Shear-wall failure at eighth story, Anchorage-Westward Hotel.

The showroom part of the building collapsed in the earthquake. The four roof tees at the front of the building fell to the south (Figure 40). As far back as the middle transverse wall the tees fell and the walls—although they remained standing—were badly battered (Figure 41). From the middle wall to the rear wall the roof tees did not fall, but the walls were damaged. The ends of the middle wall (right part of Figure 41) and the north ends of the sidewalls (Figures 42 and 43) were damaged particularly severely.

A possible explanation of the behavior of this building lies in a consideration of the structural components resisting vibration of the roof in the transverse (east–west) direction. The most rigid elements were the 8-in. transverse walls at the middle and rear of the building. The middle wall was directly under the stem of a roof tee and was built up in contact with the stem, so that the connection between the wall and the tee was continuous. The north end wall was built up alongside the edge of the flange of the northernmost tee, and the connection was made by welding bar inserts in the edge of the tee flange to steel anchors embedded in the wall. Less rigid was the pair of stub walls just to the rear of the showroom portion—one of which extended beyond the end of the adjacent roof tee, with only a short section connected to the tee. The least rigid resisting elements were the block columns and wall piers that supported the ends of the tees in the showroom portion. The connections between the tee stems and the columns or walls were evidently not proportioned as moment-resisting connections.

If we consider the roof as a beam lying on its side and oscillating in the lateral direction, it would act—in its gross behavior—as a beam on three resilient supports, and its fundamental mode of oscillation would be approximately as

FIGURE 22   Chugach Electric Association Power Plant, looking east.

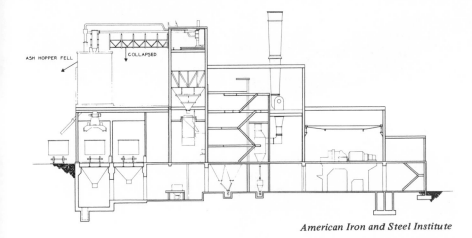

FIGURE 23 Schematic section of the Chugach Electric Association Power Plant.

American Iron and Steel Institute

shown in Figure 44. The left support (the stub walls) is less rigid than the other two supports (the full transverse walls). At the left support, both shear and bending moment in the beam would be high. Shear would tend to shear the connections between adjacent tee flanges, and bending moment would tend to pull apart the same connections. At the right support (rear wall) the shear would also be high, tending to shear the connections between the flange of the end roof tee and the rear wall; the tee-flange connections did indeed fail at these points. Once the connections between the fourth and fifth roof tees failed, there would be only nominal resistance to the southward collapse of the front part of the building. Because the left support was more flexible than the other two supports, the distortion in the left part of the beam would be greater than in the right part. The corresponding behavior in the building is greater lateral movement south of the middle wall than north of the middle wall, and it was the part south of the middle wall that collapsed.

Once the north end connections failed, lateral movement of the north part of the roof would cause lateral displacements of the top of the sidewalls. But at the north end of the building the restraint of the sidewalls by the end wall gives rise to severe local flexure in the sidewalls there. In this area the sidewalls do not contain vertical reinforcement or concrete-filled cells.

Although this rationale is only a rough approximation of the response of the total structure, it is believed to be a reasonable explanation for the failure of the structure.

FIRST FEDERAL SAVINGS AND LOAN BUILDING

The office building of the First Federal Savings and Loan Association (Figure 45), is a three-story steel-framed building, 50 × 130 ft in plan. The layout is shown in Figure 46. The floors are 3½-in. reinforced-concrete slabs on corrugated-metal longspan forms supported by wide-flange beams. Columns are 8-in. wide-flange shapes. Simple framing connections were used in both directions throughout the building. Resistance to lateral forces in the longitudinal (north–south) direction was to have been provided by a reinforced block wall in the west face, and apparently two brick panels in the east face and possibly also the stair-

American Iron and Steel Institute

FIGURE 24 Framing damage in the bunker bay, Chugach Electric Association Power Plant.

American Iron and Steel Institute

FIGURE 25   Bracing damage in the bunker bay, Chugach Electric Association Power Plant.

American Iron and Steel Institute

FIGURE 26   Framing damage in the boiler bay, Chugach Electric Association Power Plant.

well near the east face were to contribute to the resistance. A reinforced block wall at the north end and a brick panel and X-braced steel bent in the south face were to resist the transverse (east–west) lateral forces. The east and south faces of the building are mostly glass.

During the earthquake, the west wall of the building sheared through the second story (Figure 47). The north wall failed in a similar manner. One of the brick panels in the east face fell out and the other fractured vertically along the line of an embedded column (Figure 48). In the south wall, the brick panel was partly dislodged. Figure 49 shows the west and south faces after the masonry had been removed.

A substantial amount of damage was done to the interior partitions. Frame damage consisted of deformed anchor bolts, a weld failure in one of the X-bracing connections in the south wall at roof level, and a connection failure in a steel staircase. Little glass was broken.

This building illustrates the well-known principle that the most rigid elements encounter the greatest force when the building is deformed, because the flexible elements and the rigid elements will be equally displaced. In this case the masonry walls were much more rigid than the steel frame, and the walls suffered the distress. The lack of glass breakage may at first appear to be a contradiction of this principle, but although the glass panes are stiff, they are mounted in such a way that the surrounding frame can undergo substantial deformation without distorting the glass.

FIGURE 27   Ash silo, Chugach Electric Association Power Plant.

American Iron and Steel Institute

American Iron and Steel Institute

FIGURE 28   Cordova Building, looking west–northwest.

HILL BUILDING

The Hill Building is an eight-story office building 100 × 180 ft in plan. Figures 50 and 51 show an exterior view and a typical floor plan. The building has two reinforced-concrete cores enclosing stairwells, elevator shafts, and utility shafts. These cores are connected by reinforced-concrete beams at each floor. The framing system consists of steel beams and girders supported on the central cores, on four interior steel columns, and on 20 steel columns in the outside walls. The frame was designed to resist only vertical loads; the central cores were to resist all horizontal loads. The floors are one-way reinforced-concrete slabs 5 1/2 in. thick. Exterior faces of the building are lightweight curtain walls attached to the steel frame.

Exterior damage to the Hill Building was slight. The

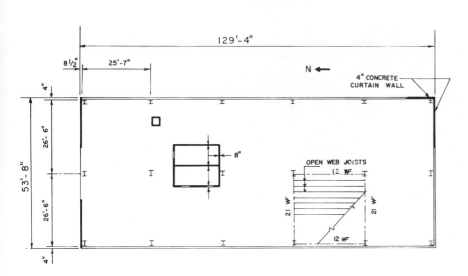

FIGURE 29   Typical floor plan, Cordova Building.

FIGURE 30   Southeast corner of Cordova Building.

FIGURE 32   Interior view of framing at southeast corner of Cordova Building.

FIGURE 31   Buckled column at southeast corner of Cordova Building.

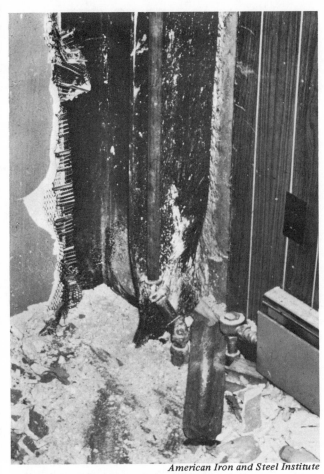

American Iron and Steel Institute

FIGURE 33   Center column of south wall bent at bottom of first story, Cordova Building.

FIGURE 34   Center column of south wall bent at top of first story, Cordova Building.

Bureau of Land Management

FIGURE 35   Southwest corner column at bottom of first story, Cordova Building.

American Iron and Steel Institute

FIGURE 36   Service core at first story, Cordova Building.

Bureau of Land Management

FIGURE 37 South wall of Cordova Building during repairs.

Bureau of Land Management

FIGURE 38 Southeast corner of Cordova Building during repairs.

lightweight curtain walls were undamaged. Some of the concrete blocks fell out of the south wall of the penthouse, which was not reinforced, and some tiles were damaged at the front entrance. A reinforced-concrete column (Figure 52) failed at its connection to a beam that supported a canopy roof over the service entrance.

There was no damage to the steel frame. Several of the beam-to-column connections were exposed for inspection and were found to be in good condition. They were simple connections, utilizing either ordinary or high-strength bolts; a number of bolts had sheared.

The lack of damage to the frame and exterior curtain walls is not surprising, because the frame members and connections are relatively flexible, and the wall panels are designed to accommodate frame distortion without deforming the panels. Lateral-force resistance was to be provided by the central cores, which were the most rigid components,

and it was in the central cores that the most severe structural damage was found. These had dropped about 5 in. at one corner and 3 in. at another, reportedly because the concrete core walls had pulverized just above footing level because of defective concrete. Some of the damage below grade can be seen in Figure 53. There was no discernible change in elevation of the footings. In addition to being damaged at footing level, the core walls were cracked, particularly in the lower stories, and the beams interconnecting the two central cores were sheared at all floors.

Mac's Foto

FIGURE 39 Fifth Avenue Chrysler Center before earthquake.

Bureau of Land Management

FIGURE 40 Collapsed south portion, Fifth Avenue Chrysler Center.

Figure 54 shows the resulting damage to the floors and to the adjacent core walls. This shear is due to the type of behavior discussed earlier in connection with the lintel damage in the transverse wall of the Anchorage-Westward Hotel. In repairing the building, it was necessary to jack up the core walls to their correct elevations, to remove and replace the concrete in the core walls up to second-floor level, and to remove and replace the concrete in the beams connecting the cores.

PERMANENTE CEMENT COMPANY BIN

A steel bin for cement storage at the storage facilities of the Permanente Cement Company collapsed and the top was torn open (Figures 55 and 56). The bin was cylindrical, about 30 ft in diameter and 30 ft high, with a bottom cone 15 ft high. The ring girder at the base of the cylinder was supported on eight wide-flange steel columns that were, in turn, supported by reinforced-concrete pedestals. Steel

U.S. Air Force

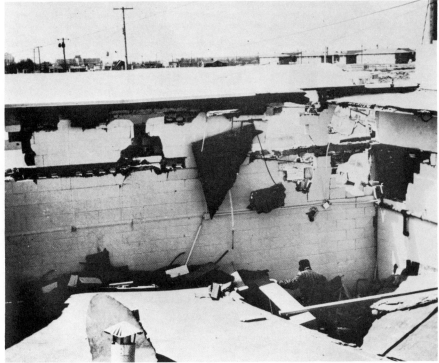

FIGURE 41 Collapsed roof section, Fifth Avenue Chrysler Center.

American Iron and Steel Institute

FIGURE 42   Northeast corner of Fifth
Avenue Chrysler Center, looking southwest.

American Iron and Steel Institute

FIGURE 43   Northwest corner of Fifth Avenue Chrysler Center,
looking east–southeast.

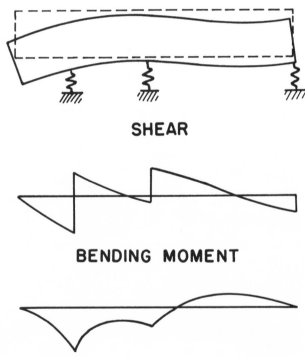

FIGURE 44   Fundamental mode of roof diaphragm, Fifth Avenue
Chrysler Center.

FIGURE 45   First Federal Savings and
Loan Building before earthquake.

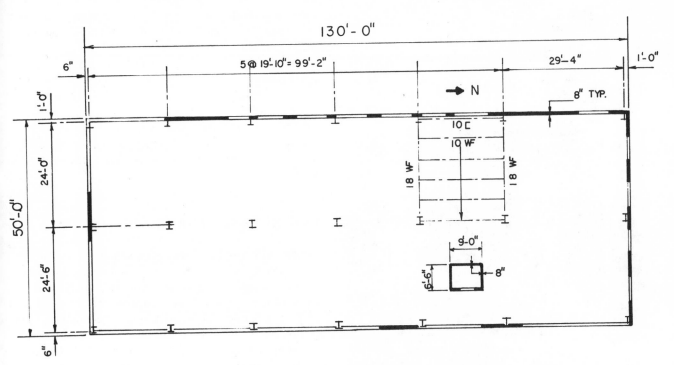

FIGURE 46   Framing plan, First Federal Savings and Loan Building.

Ward W. Wells

FIGURE 47   West wall, day after earthquake, First Federal Savings and Loan Building.

Stewart's Photo Shop

FIGURE 48   East wall of the First Federal Savings and Loan Building.

angle X-bracing was used for lateral stability. Figure 57 shows the remains of the assembly. The columns were 14-in. wide-flange sections welded to 1¼-in. base plates. Each base plate rested on a 1-in.-thick leveling plate and was anchored with four 2¼-in. anchor bolts.

During the earthquake the columns broke loose from the base plates and the bin fell. The welds connecting the columns to the base plates proved completely inadequate. On cleaning one of the base plates, we found that the weld was a 3/16-in. or smaller fillet over only part of the weldable length (Figure 58), and the red paint on the faying surface had not even been burned off by the heat of the welding process.

EARTHQUAKE BEHAVIOR

Residential structures in Anchorage sustained remarkably little damage, except where large ground displacements occurred. The small wood-frame dwelling predominates in Anchorage, and it is well endowed with earthquake-resistant properties. Because it has a roof structure consisting of wood rafters, wood sheathing, and shingles the inertia forces generated by earthquake motion are relatively small. Its exterior walls have 2 X 4-in. studs spaced at 16-in. centers, covered with ¾-in. wood or fiberboard sheathing and wood siding. The sizes and spacing of the components are set not by strength requirements, but by modular standards, stan-

American Iron and Steel Institute

FIGURE 49 West and south walls of First Federal Savings and Loan Building after removal of masonry.

dard lumber-cutting sizes, and convenience in shipping, handling, and erection. The nailed connections are strong and stiff, yet they can be deformed severely without fracture. Any deformation of the joints is accompanied by the dissipation of a considerable amount of energy through friction. The resulting wall units have transverse strength adequate to resist severe wind loads acting normal to them,

and they have shear strength far in excess of that required to resist the earthquake forces that load them in their planes. All these properties make the small frame dwelling remarkably resistant to earthquake-vibration damage. An extreme example of the ability of such a structure to withstand severe forces is shown in Figure 59.

The failures in steel and concrete structures were often

American Iron and Steel Institute

FIGURE 50 Hill Building, looking northeast.

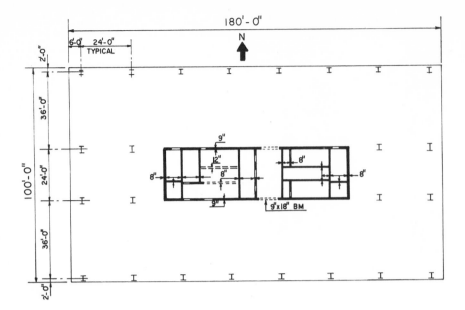

FIGURE 51   Typical floor plan of Hill Building.

American Iron and Steel Institute

FIGURE 52   Column damage at rear entrance of Hill Building.

American Iron and Steel Institute

FIGURE 53   Damage below grade at base of service core, Hill Building.

FIGURE 54   Floor damage between service cores, Hill Building.

associated with connection failures. The Alaska Railroad car shops, the Alaska Sales and Service Building, and the Permanente Cement Company bin are examples. Although connections are apt to be the most vulnerable parts of structures in earthquakes, they often receive less attention in the design than the structural members, and the details of their fabrication and assembly, in the shop or in the field, are sometimes left to a fabricator or contractor who may not be completely aware of the needs.

Ductility in the structural assembly is an important requirement. In steel structures, one can often gain adequate ductility by making the principal connections strong enough to develop the full strength of the members connected, so that the members will yield before the connections fail. If connections had been made stronger they would probably have saved the Permanente Cement Company bin and The Alaska Railroad car shops at very little added cost. In conventional cast-in-place reinforced-concrete construction, ductility may be more difficult to obtain, especially because erection methods often require reinforcing bars to be spliced at the joints. The failure of both the Four Seasons apartment building and the control tower at Anchorage Municipal Airport can be at least partly attributed to spliced reinforcing bars (Benuska and Clough, 1973; Sozen and Nielsen, 1973). Much of the damage to precast-concrete structures was attributable to connections. In the Alaska Sales and Service Building, connections between the ends of adjacent hammerhead-tee columns failed, as did connections between adjacent roof-tee flanges and connections of the roof tees to the hammerhead columns. The members generally remained sound, and many of them even withstood

FIGURE 55   Permanente Cement Company storage bin.

American Iron and Steel Institute

FIGURE 56   Top of collapsed Permanente Cement Company storage bin.

the fall to the ground without fracture. Connections were also troublesome at the Fifth Avenue Chrysler Center. Designing adequate strength and ductility into connections for precast-concrete members is difficult at best.

SEVERITY OF SHAKING

In appraising the effects of this earthquake, one must bear in mind that the severity of the shaking is not known. It is tempting to rationalize that this was an event of great magnitude, and that perhaps earthquake-resistant buildings should not really be expected to survive so great an earthquake. But the epicenter was 80 mi away from Anchorage, and a closer fault break was never found. There is no doubt that the ground shook for a long time, considerably longer than in other strong-motion earthquakes of record, but the maximum acceleration was evidently not great. An estimate of about 0.14 g maximum acceleration in Anchorage seems reasonable (Cloud, 1967), and accelerations several times as great have been recorded in other strong-motion earthquakes. A more significant factor is that the response spectrum can only be guessed. There is no reason to believe that the shaking in Anchorage was more severe than might be expected near a large earthquake anywhere else in the world.

THE ROLE OF A BUILDING CODE

The Uniform Building Code (*UBC*) of the International Conference of Building Officials (1967) states its purpose in Section 102:

The purpose of this Code is to provide minimum standards to safeguard life or limb, health, property, and public welfare by regulating and controlling the design, construction, quality of materials, use and occupancy, location and maintenance of all buildings and structures within the city and certain equipment specifically regulated herein.

In section 2314(a), at the beginning of its earthquake provisions, the *UBC* states:

Every building or structure and every portion thereof shall be designed and constructed to resist stresses produced by lateral forces

American Iron and Steel Institute

FIGURE 57   Columns and bracing of Permanente Cement Company storage bin.

American Iron and Steel Institute

FIGURE 58   Bearing plate detail,
Permanente Cement Company storage bin.

U.S. Air Force

FIGURE 59   Frame dwelling at L Street
slide graben.

as provided in this Section. Stresses shall be calculated as the effect of a force applied horizontally at each floor or roof level above the foundation. The force shall be assumed to come from any horizontal direction.

The *UBC*, in common with most existing building codes for earthquake-resistant construction, treats the lateral forces of an earthquake as equivalent static lateral forces. Although the code states that its purpose is to provide minimum standards, the designer infers logically that, if a structure can accommodate the specified lateral forces without exceeding the allowable design stresses, it should perform adequately in an earthquake. Adequate performance does not necessarily imply absence of structural damage, but damage beyond repair—even without total or partial collapse—would probably be considered by engineers to constitute inadequate performance.

The classroom wing of West Anchorage High School failed in the second story. The behavior of this building is discussed in detail elsewhere in this report (George and others, 1973, this volume). The exterior columns fractured at the top and bottom of the second story (Figure 60), apparently, primarily because of transverse oscillation, i.e., oscillation in the strong direction of the exterior columns. A check of the design of the second-story columns against the requirements of the *UBC*, 1964 edition, zone 3, which was in effect in Anchorage at the time of the earthquake, produces the following information. A plan of the second floor (Figure 61) shows that lateral strength is provided by shear walls at the ends of the classroom wing, by shear walls near the apex of the V, and by the columns. Because the structure has a 45° bend in it, the dynamic behavior would be more complex than a simple transverse oscillation. A check of the transverse strength of a typical module should, however, be adequate to disclose any likely weakness in the design. We shall check the lateral strength of a 32-ft module, ignoring the strength of the shear walls and treating the structure as though the frame were to resist the entire lateral force, unaided by the shear walls, in ac-

cordance with Section 2314(b), which gives the following instructions:

SPACE FRAME-MOMENT RESISTING is a vertical load-carrying space frame in which the members and joints are capable of resisting design lateral forces by bending moments. This system *may or may not be enclosed by or adjoined by more rigid elements* which would tend to prevent the space frame from resisting lateral forces.

The typical 32-ft module (Figure 62) has two exterior columns and four interior columns. The roof slab and floor slab act as transverse beams. In accordance with Section 2314(d) of the *UBC*, the total design lateral force *V* is computed from the formula

$$V = ZKCW,$$

in which $Z = 1$, as provided in Section 2314(c) for seismic zone 3; $K = 0.67$, in accordance with Table 23-H for "buildings with a moment-resisting space frame which *when assumed to act independently of any other more rigid elements* is capable of resisting 100 percent of the total required lateral force in the frame alone."

$C = 0.10$, as provided in Section 2314(d), Exception 1, for one- and two-story buildings; and $W =$ total dead load of the building, in accordance with Section 2314(c). Exception 1 of the paragraph on distribution of the lateral force over the height of the building, also in Section 2314(c), states that one-story and two-story buildings shall have uniform distribution. Hence, the design lateral forces for the module, indicated in Figure 63 are

$$F_1 = ZKCW_1$$

and

$$F_2 = ZKCW_2$$

in which *Z, K,* and *C* are as provided, and W_1 and W_2 are the dead loads assigned to the upper floor and the roof, re-

FIGURE 60 Damage to West Anchorage High School.

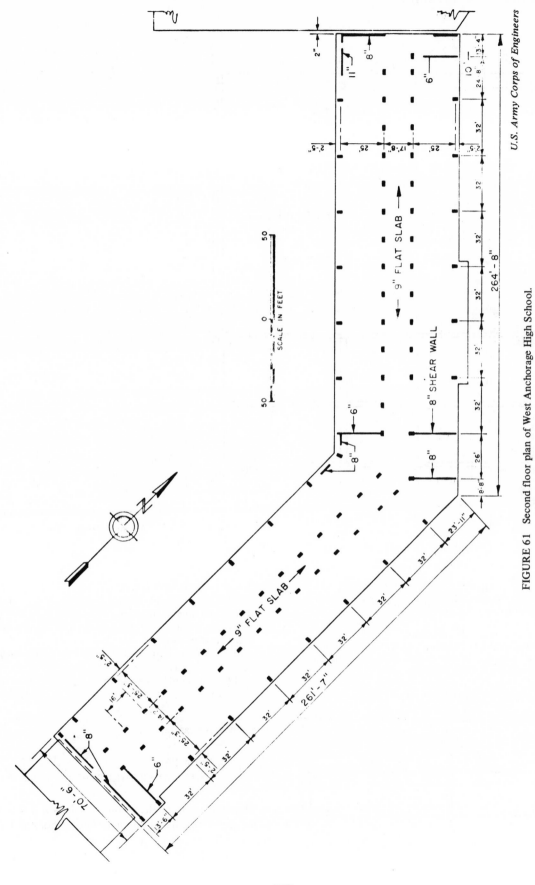

FIGURE 61 Second floor plan of West Anchorage High School.

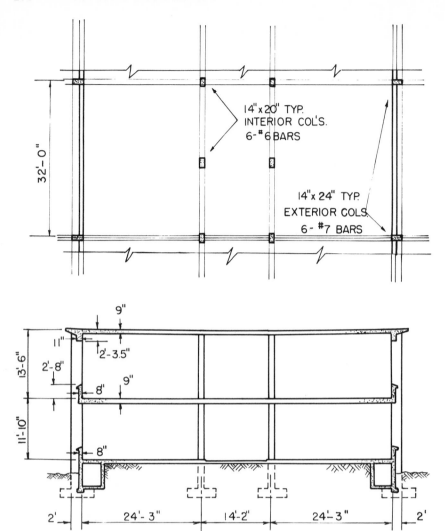

FIGURE 62   Basic 32-ft module, West Anchorage High School.

spectively. Only F_2 will be needed for this analysis. The dead load assigned to the roof is approximately

Roof slab, roofing, insulation, and ceiling,	
69.5 × 32 = 2,225 ft² at 130 psf	289,300 lb
Two spandrel beams	13,100 lb

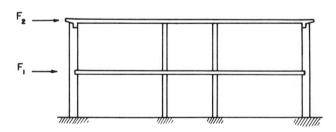

FIGURE 63   Design lateral forces, 32-ft module of West Anchorage High School.

Half of two exterior columns,	
14 in. × 24 in. × 12 ft 9 in.	4,500 lb
Half of four interior columns,	
14 in. × 20 in. × 12 ft 9 in.	7,400 lb
Half of two exterior walls,	
8 ft 6 in. × 30 ft 10 in. at 10 psf	2,600 lb
Half of two interior partitions,	
12 ft 9 in. × 30 ft 10 in. at 10 psf	3,900 lb
Total = W_2	320,800 lb

Therefore, the lateral force F_2 is

$$F_2 = Z K C W_2$$
$$= 1 \times 0.67 \times 0.10 \times 320,800 \text{ lb} = 21,500 \text{ lb}$$

The dimensions of the column sections and their computed properties, based on uncracked sections and an assumed cylinder strength of 2,500 psi, are shown in Figure 64. Section 2616(b)2 provides that the relative stiffnesses

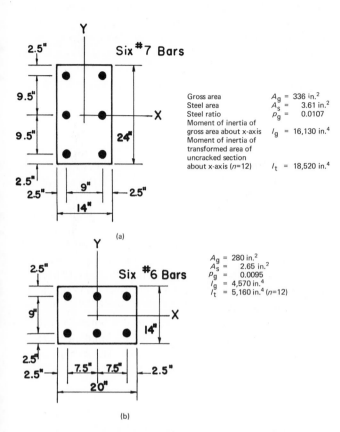

Gross area	A_g	$= 336$ in.^{2}
Steel area	A_s	$= 3.61$ in.^{2}
Steel ratio	ρ_g	$= 0.0107$
Moment of inertia of gross area about x-axis	I_g	$= 16,130$ in.^{4}
Moment of inertia of transformed area of uncracked section about x-axis (n=12)	I_t	$= 18,520$ in.^{4}

(a)

A_g	$= 280$ in.^{2}
A_s	$= 2.65$ in.^{2}
ρ_g	$= 0.0095$
I_g	$= 4,570$ in.^{4}
I_t	$= 5,160$ in.^{4} (n=12)

(b)

FIGURE 64 Exterior (a) and interior (b) column section properties.

of slabs, beams, and columns may be computed on the basis of gross concrete area, neglecting the reinforcement. On this basis, the shear in each column may be computed thus:

Two exterior columns at 16,130 in.^{4}	$=$	32,260 in.^{4}
Four interior columns at 4,570 in.^{4}	$=$	18,280 in.^{4}
Total moment of inertia		50,540 in.^{4}

The design lateral force is allocated to each column according to its relative stiffness.

$$\text{Exterior column } S = \frac{16,130}{50,540} \times 21,500 = 6,850 \text{ lb}$$

$$\text{Interior column } S = \frac{4,570}{50,540} \times 21,500 = 1,950 \text{ lb}$$

The axial loads on the columns are

Exterior

Roof slab, roofing, insulation, ceiling	
32 ft × 15 ft = 480 ft^2 at 130 psf	62,400 lb

Spandrel beam	6,550 lb
Overturning (portal assumptions)	
$\dfrac{6.75 \text{ ft}}{64.67 \text{ ft}} \times 21,500$ lb	2,250 lb
Total axial load N	71,200 lb

Interior

Roof slab, roofing, insulation, ceiling	
16 ft × 19.7 ft = 315 ft^2 at 130 psf	41,000 lb
Overturning (portal assumptions)	0
Total axial load N	41,000 lb

Because the roof and floor slabs are much more rigid than the columns, we may treat them as being infinitely rigid. The exterior columns have an effective load eccentricity less than two thirds of the depth, so we may use uncracked-section theory, as provided in Section 2622(i)1 of the code. The requirement then becomes

$$\frac{f_a}{F_a} + \frac{f_b}{F_b} \leq 1.33,$$

in which f_a and F_a are the computed and allowable stresses due to axial load alone, and f_b and F_b are the computed and allowable stresses in the concrete caused by flexure alone. The foregoing formula comes from Section 2622(i)1, with the right-hand side increased to 1.33 instead of 1.00 to account for the one-third increase in allowable stress permitted by Section 2303 for the condition of earthquake forces acting in combination with vertical loads.

For the external column the computed axial stress is

$$f_a = N/A = \frac{71,200 \text{ lb}}{336 \text{ sq in}} = 212 \text{ psi.}$$

In accordance with Section 2622(d)1 and 2622(c)1 of the code, the allowable axial stress, assuming 2,500 psi concrete and intermediate grade steel, is

$$\begin{aligned}
F_a &= 0.80 \times (0.225 f'_c + f_s \rho_g) \\
&= 0.80 \times (0.225 \times 2,500 \text{ psi} + 16,000 \text{ psi} \times 0.0107) \\
&= 587 \text{ psi}
\end{aligned}$$

The computed flexural stress is

$$f_b = \frac{Mc}{I_t}$$

$$= \frac{(6,850 \text{ lb} \times 81 \text{ in.}) \times 12 \text{ in.}}{18,520 \text{ in.}^4} = 360 \text{ psi}$$

and the allowable flexural stress, according to Table 26-B, Section 2616, for 2,500 psi concrete, is $F_b = 1,125$ psi.

Combining these values, we get

$$\frac{f_a}{F_a} + \frac{f_b}{F_b} = \frac{212}{587} + \frac{360}{1125} = 0.361 + 0.320 = 0.681,$$

which is just slightly more than half the limiting value of 1.33.

Similar computations for the interior column give the following:

$$f_a = 146 \text{ psi}$$
$$F_a = 580 \text{ psi}$$
$$f_b = 214 \text{ psi}$$
$$F_b = 1,125 \text{ psi}$$

$$\frac{f_a}{F_a} + \frac{f_b}{F_b} = 0.252 + 0.190 = 0.442$$

Again, all are well within the code limits.

A similar set of computations for earthquake forces in a direction normal to the module, i.e., in a direction parallel to the exterior walls, leads to a lower stress index in the exterior columns and a slightly higher stress index in the interior columns.

The actual design of West Anchorage High School was for the zone 2 requirements of the 1949 *UBC*, for which the earthquake-force stipulations are different from those of the code used above. The principal differences are the absence of a factor *K* in the equation for lateral force and a different equation for the seismic coefficient *C*. In this particular case, the lateral force F_2 in Figure 62, which is the lateral force that governs the design of the columns in the second story, is the same for zone 2, 1949 *UBC*, as it is for zone 3, 1964 *UBC*.

Different designers would doubtless use other assumptions about the behavior of the columns than were made in this investigation. Some designers might take into account the flexibility of the roof slab, and some might use transformed areas instead of gross concrete areas for evaluating relative stiffnesses. Any of the assumptions ordinarily employed would lead to results not very different from those obtained above. The designer could justifiably infer that this structure should survive an earthquake without great distress.

The quality of the construction of West Anchorage High School appears to have been reasonably good. No glaring deficiencies have been mentioned. The design was conventional, utilizing no new concepts, unfamiliar materials, or unusual devices. The heavy roof slab and the 45° break in the direction of the wing are uncommon, but neither of these features is contrary to any provision or suggestion in the code. The 45° break might give rise to some concern over possible torsional response, but the shear walls at the ends of the classroom wing were well placed to resist torsional deformation, and there does not appear to have been any torsional distress.

The fundamental mode of vibration of this building would involve not only translation of the roof slab as a rigid body, but also bending of the roof slab in the horizontal plane. The stresses due to this in-plane flexure would be greatest in the vicinity of the reentrant corner, where the bending moments would be greatest, and the reentrant corner would give rise to stress concentrations. It seems likely that these stresses are associated with the fracture of the roof slab near the 45° break. The amount of reinforcement in the roof slab was nominal in the longitudinal direction. The existence of shear walls at the ends and near the middle of this building would have increased the in-plane bending moments in the roof slab beyond those that would have existed if there had been no shear walls. Neglecting the shear walls would be unconservative with regard to this behavior.

The unsatisfactory behavior of West Anchorage High School suggests that continuing study of building codes and structural behavior in earthquakes is needed and that current provisions are not yet adequate to assure structural safety in earthquakes.

BUILDING-CODE DEVELOPMENT

In reviewing the development of building-code provisions for earthquake-resistant construction, the reader should bear in mind the significance of the equivalent-lateral-load concept. The static lateral forces prescribed in a code are not intended to be equal to the dynamic forces that might be expected in an earthquake; rather, they are intended to be equivalent in the sense that a structure that can accept the static forces prescribed by the code without exceeding the prescribed limitations on stress or deflection should reasonably be expected to survive an earthquake without destruction or severe damage and without endangering human life.

The *Uniform Building Code* (International Conference of Building Officials, 1967) has evolved over nearly 40 years, during which time the provisions pertaining to lateral forces and earthquake resistance have undergone several changes. The basic concept of representing the earthquake as equivalent static lateral forces has been retained, but the amount and distribution of the lateral forces have been modified from time to time.

The 1930 edition of *UBC* specifies that the total horizontal design shear in any story is $F = CW$, in which W is the total dead load plus design live load above that story, and the seismic coefficient C is either 0.075 or 0.100, depending on the design strength of the foundation material. Stresses are permitted to exceed the normal working stresses by half for structural steel and by one third for other materials when earthquake forces are being considered.

The 1935 edition alters the definition of W to be the dead load plus half the design live load. Seismic zoning is introduced in this edition; for zone 3, the seismic coefficient C is 0.08 or 0.16, depending on the foundation material. The permissible overstress is made one third for all materials. These basic provisions are the same in the 1937, 1940, 1943, and 1946 editions.

In the 1949 edition, a major change is introduced. The coefficient C for zone 3 is redefined to be $0.60/(N + 4.5)$, in which N is the number of stories above the one being considered. W is redefined to be the total dead load above the story. This revised definition of C brings about two significant changes: First, C increases with height above the foundation, bringing the distribution of lateral forces into closer agreement with the dynamic forces distribution that would be encountered in the first few modes of vibration of a building. Second, C for the bottom story is less for a tall building than for a low building, which indirectly accounts for the inverse relation between base shear coefficient and natural period of oscillation. The permissible overstress remains one third. These provisions are retained in the editions of 1952, 1955, and 1958.

The 1961 edition modifies the lateral force provisions to specify a base shear V for zone 3 to be $V = KCW$, in which W is the total dead load above the base, C is a seismic coefficient, and K is a coefficient determined by the type of framing. K takes a value ranging from 0.67 to 1.33 for buildings and is smaller for structural arrangements that can exhibit ductile behavior when overstressed and greater for structural arrangements that would have a tendency to be brittle. The factor K does not imply that the earthquake forces are really smaller for ductile systems than for brittle systems, but it acknowledges that a ductile system can tolerate a greater overstress without disaster than a brittle system can. Hence, for equal probabilities of survival, the design strength of the ductile system need not be as great. The seismic coefficient C is specified as $C = 0.05/\sqrt[3]{T}$, where T is the fundamental period of vibration in seconds. Because T cannot readily be established before the design is complete, an empirical expression is given to relate it to the building dimensions, i.e., $T = 0.05 H/\sqrt{D}$, in which H and D are the height and depth of the building in feet. These provisions for base shear are retained in the 1964 and 1967 editions of the code.

The 1961 and 1964 editions provide that, if H/D exceeds five, one tenth of the base shear is treated as a lateral force at roof level. The remainder of the base shear is distributed to the various floors, including the roof, according to the formula

$$F_i = \frac{w_i h_i}{\sum w_i h_i} V,$$

in which F_i is the lateral force at the ith level above the base, w_i is the weight at the ith level, and h_i is the height of the ith level above the base.

The 1967 edition retains the same basic distribution except that the force at roof level is taken to be $0.004 (H/D)^2 V$ for all buildings for which $H/D > 3$. For $H/D = 5$, this gives the same result as the 1961 formula. For any other value of H/D, the 1967 formula gives a greater force at roof level than did the 1961 formula.

Field studies of structures that have been subjected to an earthquake sometimes furnish useful information that is reflected in building-code changes, especially in the provisions pertaining to details of construction. The 1967 edition of *UBC* contains several changes from the 1964 edition that are at least partly based on field experience in the Alaska earthquake.

In the section on masonry-wall anchors, a sentence has been added: "Required anchors in masonry walls of hollow units or cavity walls shall enter a reinforced grouted structural element of the wall."

The table of horizontal forces on parts of structures has been augmented to provide a lateral force of 0.30 times the weight of prefabricated structural elements, applied in any horizontal direction at the center of gravity of the assembly.

The section on reinforced-masonry design has been altered to include that "in computing flexural stresses for masonry where reinforcement occurs the effective width 'b' shall not be greater than six times the wall thickness in running bond, nor more than three times the wall thickness in stacked bond." Another change in this section specifies that "reinforcing perpendicular to the principal wall steel shall be limited to a maximum spacing of four feet (4') on center."

The section on flat slabs now stipulates that "in lift slab construction, steel reinforcement shall be secured or held by the collar to support the slab in the event of loading in excess of the ultimate load and shall be capable of supporting the design live load plus dead load without exceeding the ultimate strength of the reinforcement in tension."

As new knowledge and new experience are gained, the articles contained in building codes are modified to reflect them. The process is continuous, and we can never expect code provision to become completely fixed.

SUMMARY

The Alaska earthquake of 1964 performed an uncontrolled natural experiment on the man-made structures of Anchorage. Most of the major structures in Anchorage had been designed and built while a modern building code for earthquake-resistant construction was in force. Most of them withstood the shaking well, although many were damaged and a few collapsed. Although the severity of the shaking is not known, we believe that equally severe shaking might be expected in the vicinity of a great earthquake anywhere else in the world.

Structural failures were initiated most frequently in connections. In several cases the inadequacies were obvious after the disaster; to have located them before would have been more difficult. Not all structural failures could be attributed to shortcomings of design or construction as measured by code requirements; the failure in West Anchorage High School is one example.

Engineers have profited from the experience provided by this earthquake to improve the requirements of building codes for earthquake-resistant construction. This natural experiment has shown that codes are not yet adequate to ensure structural safety in earthquakes, and the search for further improvements must continue.

ACKNOWLEDGMENT

The field observations reported in this paper are based on a site inspection made by a team of six engineers, including the author, who were sent to Alaska by the American Iron and Steel Institute (AISI) shortly after the earthquake. This paper has drawn much of its information and many of its photographic illustrations from the AISI report.

REFERENCES

Benuska, K. L., and R. W. Clough, 1973. Dynamic analyses of building failures *in* The Great Alaska Earthquake of 1964: Engineering. NAS Pub. 1606. Washington: National Academy of Sciences.

Berg, Glen V., and James L. Stratta, 1964. Anchorage and the Alaska earthquake of March 27, 1964. Report of the American Iron and Steel Institute. New York: American Iron and Steel Institute. 63 p.

Cloud, William K., 1967. Strong-motion and building-period measurements *in* Volume II-A: The Prince William Sound, Alaska, earthquake of 1964 and aftershocks. Environmental Science Services Administration, U.S. Coast and Geodetic Survey. Washington: Government Printing Office. p. 319–331.

George, Warren, Paul Knowles, John K. Allender, James F. Sizemore, and Duane E. Carson, 1973. Structures in Anchorage *in* The Great Alaska Earthquake of 1964: Engineering. NAS Pub. 1606. Washington: National Academy of Sciences.

International Conference of Building Officials, 1967. Uniform Building Code, 1967 edition. Pasadena: International Conference of Building Officials. 595 p.

Jennings, Paul C., 1973. Response of coupled shear-wall structures *in* The Great Alaska Earthquake of 1964: Engineering. NAS Pub. 1606. Washington: National Academy of Sciences.

Sozen, Mete A., and N. Norby Nielsen, 1973. Analysis of failure of the International Airport Control Tower at Anchorage *in* The Great Alaska Earthquake of 1964: Engineering. NAS Pub. 1606. Washington: National Academy of Sciences.

K. LEE BENUSKA*
T. Y. LIN AND ASSOCIATES

RAY W. CLOUGH
UNIVERSITY OF CALIFORNIA, BERKELEY

Extracted and revised from
Clough, Ray W., and K. Lee Benuska, HUD TD-3, 1966
"FHA Study of Seismic Design Criteria for High-Rise Buildings"

Dynamic Analyses of Building Failures

ABSTRACT: Three Anchorage buildings, damaged during the March 27, 1964, earthquake, were analyzed by digital computer to correlate effects predicted by dynamic-response theory with observed damages.

Comparison of observed damage to the 1200 L Street apartment building, the Cordova Building, and the Four Seasons apartment building with the results of dynamic analysis indicates that the ground shaking at Anchorage had an intensity in the range of (1 ± 0.4) times that recorded at Taft, California, on July 21, 1952.

All three buildings were designed according to the *Uniform Building Code*. The 1200 L Street building was checked in 1951 for zone 2 requirements, the Cordova Building and the Four Seasons building were designed for zone 3 requirements in 1956 and 1963, respectively. The analyses show that the observed damage would be expected even if there were no construction deficiencies. Further, ground motion appreciably less intense than that which occurred would have produced significant damage in the Cordova and Four Seasons buildings.

---

*Now with Kinemetrics, San Gabriel, California.

From the point of view of the earthquake engineer, the Alaska earthquake of 1964 served as a gigantic dynamic-test mechanism that subjected hundreds of full-scale structures to severe dynamic loadings and displacements. The evaluation of the structural effects of these loadings, particularly the correlation of observed damages with effects that might be predicted from dynamic-response theory, is an important aspect of earthquake engineering. Only by such comparison of theory with experience is it possible to determine the validity of basic assumptions regarding material behavior and ground-motion characteristics and to test analytical procedures.

The Alaska earthquake, in common with all other major earthquake disasters, had many deficiencies as a structural-mechanics experiment. None of the controls typical of laboratory testing were present, and more important, no measurements had been made of the excitation or of the dynamic response. The only evidence available for detailed study was the end result—the damaged condition of the buildings that were subjected to the earthquake. Consequently, it was difficult to evaluate current knowledge of material properties or of analytical techniques on the basis of this evidence. In spite of these difficulties, however, it was considered advisable to make a limited number of dynamic analyses, estimating the necessary earthquake ground motion on the basis of past experience and estimating the structural properties on the basis of existing knowledge.

Analyses of three buildings located in Anchorage are described in this report. Comparison of the results of the analyses with observed damages is thought to give considerable support to the theoretical dynamic-analysis procedures.

METHOD OF ANALYSIS

Analysis of the response of a structure to specific earthquake motion is a standard problem of structural dynamics. If the properties of the structure can be defined correctly and if the exact ground-motion history is known, the analysis can be carried out with any desired degree of accuracy. The only difficulties encountered in practice are in the definition of the structural properties and of the ground motion.

Two different but closely related digital-computer programs were available for analyzing the dynamic behavior of the Anchorage buildings (Clough and Benuska, 1966). In the first of these programs, the building is assumed to remain ideally elastic during the entire earthquake, i.e., the stiffness characteristics of the structure remain constant. In the analysis of the stiffness, the building is assumed to consist of a series of parallel rectangular frames, either with or without shear walls, interconnected by the floor slabs. The floors are assumed to be ideal diaphragms, rigid in their own plane, but perfectly flexible normal to that plane. The building is also assumed to be symmetrical, or at least the centers of the mass and rigidity are assumed to be located so that the earthquake excitation produces no torsional response. Axial, shear, and flexural deformations are considered in all columns and shear walls, but only shear and flexural deformations are permitted in the girders; girder axial distortions are excluded in conformity with the rigid-floor-diaphragm assumption.

The analysis of the building-frame stiffness is carried out by matrix operations based on a determination of the stiffness of each story segment and an assembly of the story segments to obtain the complete building stiffness. The building stiffness is ultimately reduced to the form of a matrix whose coefficients represent the forces at the various floor levels that result from displacements applied at the floor levels. The inertial properties of the building are expressed by a mass matrix that is merely a diagonal listing of the mass associated with each floor level.

When the mass and stiffness matrices have been defined, the computer determines the vibration-mode shapes and frequencies for the structure. The dynamic response to any given earthquake is then computed numerically by the mode-superposition method. Generally, five or six modes of vibration are considered, and the total-response time history is obtained by the direct superposition of the modal-response histories. Damping is assumed to be of the viscous type and is applied to each mode separately.

The second computer program is similar in many respects to the first, but it is designed to account for the response of nonlinear structure, which are structures for which the stresses exceed the elastic limit and thus develop yielding. Mass and stiffness matrices similar to those used in the linear analysis are defined, but because the response is nonlinear the mode-superposition procedures cannot be used. Instead, the response of the entire system is evaluated by direct step-by-step integration. Within each short time increment, the structure is assumed to behave in a linear elastic manner. The elastic properties are changed as required, however, from one interval to the next; thus the nonlinear response is obtained as a sequence of linear responses of successively differing systems.

The procedure involves the application of the following steps for each successive time interval:

1. The stiffness of the structure appropriate to the time interval is evaluated on the basis of the moments existing in the members at the beginning of the time interval.

2. Changes in displacements of the elastic structure are computed, with the accelerations assumed to vary linearly during the interval.

3. These incremental displacements are added to the deformation state existing at the beginning of the interval to obtain total member deformations.

4. Based on these member deformations, member forces are computed from which stiffness coefficients appropriate to the next time interval may be determined.

The nonlinear property of each frame member (columns as well as beams) was assumed to be of bilinear form in which the moment at each end increased linearly with curvature until the yield moment was reached. For curvatures greater than the yield level, the moment increased at a reduced rate, which was only 5 percent of the initial stiffness in this study. The response of each member was expressed in terms of a ductility factor, which was defined in this case as the total rotation at the end of a member (yield plus elastic) to the rotation developed at the yield limit.

GENERAL CHARACTERISTICS OF THE ANCHORAGE GROUND MOTION

No record is available of the actual ground motion, because no strong-motion recording instrument was in operation in Alaska when the earthquake occurred. Consequently, the ground motion used in the vibration analyses must be based on that recorded for strong-motion earthquakes in the past.

The great Alaska earthquake occurred at 5:36 p.m. AST on Good Friday, March 27, 1964. According to the seismogram recorded at Pasadena, California, the Richter magnitude of this earthquake was 8.4, making it one of the strongest on record. The epicenter was at lat. 61.05°N and long. 147.05°W (Grantz, Plafker, and Kachadoorian, 1964), the northern shore of Prince William Sound. The focus has been estimated to be about 12.5 mi below the surface, a typical depth for shallow-focus earthquakes. The seismic waves generated during this great earthquake are now thought to have been released by successive shocks whose faulting progressed in a southwesterly direction.

Figure 1 illustrates the region of aftershock epicenters and indicates the direction and extent of faulting during the earthquake. The city of Anchorage is located about 80 mi west of the main-shock epicenter.

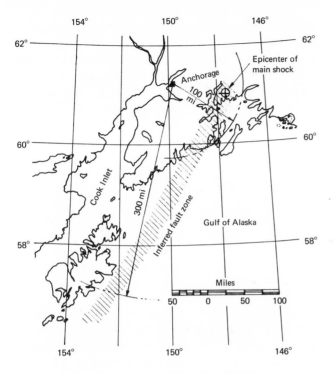

FIGURE 1   Probable direction of faulting.

DURATION OF THE GROUND MOTION

The epicenters of the shock and subsequent aftershocks lie within a well-defined belt that extends from the north of Prince William Sound and sweeps southwest past Kodiak Island. The indicated slipped length of fault during the main shock is approximately 450 mi.

Strong shaking at Anchorage could be expected from waves originating 80 mi (the epicentral distance) to 100 mi distant. It is significant that the southwesterly sweep of the fault break would expose Anchorage to about 130 mi of slipped fault, all within 100 mi. If we assume that the propagation velocity of the slip along the fault was about 2 mi/sec and that the same value applies to the velocity of subsequent shear waves, the strong shaking at Anchorage could be expected to have a duration of a little more than 1 minute. A less intense and diminishing motion would continue for a time, as energy is released at increasingly greater distances. The distance from which waves could cause perceptible motion is difficult to estimate. However, the limit of perceptible motion northward into the interior of Alaska has been estimated as 300 mi, based on the reported experience of persons living inland. If about 200 mi of subsequent slipping is added to 300 mi of shear-wave propagation back to Anchorage, an additional 4 minutes of shaking is indicated, making a total of 5 minutes total shaking.

The ground motion was reported by Anchorage residents to have lasted from about 1½ to 4 minutes. This bears out the foregoing calculated estimates if it is assumed that the

strong shaking lasted 1½ minutes and that the duration of perceptible motion was 4 minutes.

INTENSITY OF GROUND MOTION

In Anchorage, the observed damage was greater to multistory long-period buildings than to one- and two-story short-period buildings, indicating a greater attenuation with distance of short-period components of ground motion. This is consistent with past experience, which indicates that components with periods of less than about 0.5 seconds are strongly attenuated at a distance of 80 mi. Past recordings of earthquake ground accelerations indicate that at 80 mi from the causative fault of a magnitude 8.4 earthquake, the maximum ground acceleration should normally be between 10 and 25 percent of gravity. Because there are no recordings of the ground motion of earthquakes of this magnitude at this distance, it is necessary to use other recorded ground motion to represent that at Anchorage.

A more detailed study of the ground motion at Anchorage has been made by Hudson and Cloud (1967). An independent estimate of the maximum ground acceleration has been given by Shannon & Wilson, Inc. (1964), who state that earth slope-stability considerations indicate a peak ground acceleration of somewhat less than 0.14 to 0.18 g.

The accelerogram recorded at Taft, California, during the earthquake of July 21, 1952 (south 21° west component), was selected as input for the dynamic analyses of the buildings. This accelerogram was recorded on sedimentary rock at a distance of approximately 30 mi from the causative fault (dip slip) of a magnitude 7.7 earthquake, whereas the Anchorage buildings were on several hundred feet of relatively soft sands and clays at a distance of approximately 80 mi from the causative fault. For purposes of analysis, the intensity of the Taft accelerogram was varied by multiplying the ground-acceleration values by appropriate scale factors. Relative effects of stronger or weaker earthquake ground motions could thus be investigated. The duration of strong shaking of the Taft record was less than that estimated for Anchorage—only one half to one third as long. Once damage has been initiated, its severity increases with increasing duration of strong shaking. Consequently, the use of the Taft ground acceleration, although suitable for investigating the initiation of damage, will tend to underestimate the severity of damage if the analysis is extended into the nonlinear range.

THE 1200 L STREET APARTMENT BUILDING

STRUCTURE

The 1200 L Street apartment building is a 14-story reinforced concrete structure, 52 ft 4 in. × 129 ft 8 in. in plan,

FIGURE 2   1200 L Street apartment building. Photograph taken from southeastward viewpoint.

oriented with its long dimension in the north–south direction, and facing westward (Figures 2 and 3).

The exterior walls between window and entrance openings are designed as columns. Exterior column (wall) thicknesses are 8 in. from the roof down to the eighth floor, 10 in. from the eighth to second floor, and 12 in. below the second floor. Because the spandrels function as beams, although not particularly designed for this purpose, the peripheral columns and spandrels constitute two-dimensional space frames. For architectural reasons the exterior spandrel faces are set back approximately 1½ in. from the column face in the transverse end walls and in the two north and two south

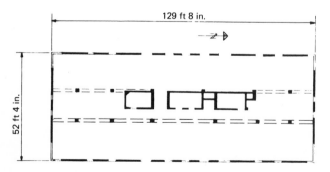

FIGURE 3   Typical floor plan of 1200 L Street apartment building.

bays of the longitudinal sidewalls of the building (Figure 2).

The core (Figure 3) consists substantially of two elements—one a composite of the elevator shaft, stack stairwell, and (apparently) a heating or ventilating duct and the other a detached stairwell. Twelve-inch wall sections of the core are designed as columns, two square columns are integrated with the core, and the filleted southwest corner of the detached stairwell is designed as a column. The exterior wall frames and the core constitute the lateral force-resisting elements of the structure.

EARTHQUAKE DAMAGE

Shear failure of the spandrels in the transverse end walls was evidenced by pronounced X-cracking from the third to the eleventh floors inclusive (Figure 2). A relatively fine but plainly discernible X-crack occurred in one second-floor spandrel. X-cracking was more pronounced in the eastward bays of the end walls.

In the south end wall, the westward column failed completely in flexure in the second story (Figure 2). Similar partial failures occurred in the eastward column at the third-floor level, and there is evidence of compression failure in the center column. The absence of comparable column failures in the north end wall is attributed to the northward eccentricity of the center of rigidity of the central core with respect to the center of mass of the building.

Shear failures occurred in approximately one third of the spandrels in each of the two side walls, although almost all spandrels had some sign of distress. Substantially, all the cantilevered corner spandrels failed. They were subject to the combinations of forces induced by the east–west and north–south motion.

In the west sidewall, pronounced X-cracking occurred in four columns in the second story over the main entrance to the building. Similar failures did not occur in the east sidewall.

EVALUATION OF ULTIMATE STRENGTHS OF SECTIONS UNDER COMBINED SHEAR AND AXIAL LOAD

There is known to be considerable variance in the frequency distribution of results of shear-failure tests of beams of fairly uniform cylinder strength concrete. In using test results to generate the formulas in Chapter 17, "Shear and Diagonal Tension—Ultimate Strength Design," *ACI Building Code*, the American Concrete Institute Committee justifiably used the conservative side of the distribution. The derivation of the formulas in Chapter 17 has been presented in an explanatory document written by Carl O. Knop, Structural Engineer, Atlas Organization, Inc., Oklahoma City, in connection with the review of the *ACI Code*.

By a transformation of the equation for principal stress

at a point, based on the traditional working-stress relationships coupled with the assumption that the maximum principal stress could be approximated as a function of the square root of the cylinder strength, the committee derived the general form of an expression for shear stress at the incipience of diagonal-tension cracking in members without web reinforcement. The expression contained constants to be evaluated empirically from test data. These were evaluated on the low side of the distribution of results of 194 beam tests in the generation of formulas in the code. By reevaluation on the high side of the distribution, the governing value of ultimate shear in combination with axial load is adjudged to be

$$v_u = 4.75 \sqrt{f'_c (1 + 0.002 \, N/A_g)} \qquad (1)$$

where

f'_c = cylinder strength, psi; (pounds per square inch)
N = total axial force in pounds; and
A_g = gross area of section, in^2.

Equation (1) is used to estimate the earthquake intensity at shear failure.

ULTIMATE SHEAR STRENGTH OF SPANDRELS

Spandrel lengths in the building are 3 ft 4½ in. and 6 ft 10½ in. All spandrels have a gross depth of 4 ft 0 in. In the short spandrels, the point furthest removed from the face of a column is at a distance of 20¼ in. Most design specifications, including the *ACI Code*, limit the position of a section at which shear is computed for diagonal-tension analysis, to a distance equal to the effective depth from the face of the support. This is consistent with the concept of a 45° shear plane. The explanation of Chapter 17, *ACI Code*, contains a plot of shear strengths of uniformly loaded beams with no web reinforcement, which presents shear at the ultimate in addition to the diagonal-cracking load. The upper bound of ultimate shear strength reaches 400 psi at a cylinder strength of 3,000 psi. This value was used in determining the shear resistance of the short spandrels. The ultimate resisting moment in the short spandrels was found to be 1,420 in.-kips at a concrete cylinder strength of 3,000 psi and concurrent steel stress of 51,000 psi.

The ultimate shear stress in the 6-ft 10½-in. spandrels was calculated to be 260 psi by means of Eq. (1), with N set equal to zero and an assumed cylinder strength of 3,000 psi.

ULTIMATE SHEAR STRENGTH OF COLUMNS

In considering the shear strength of columns that are subjected to large reversals of moment, cognizance must be taken of concrete's dependence on compressive force for high shear strength and of the fact that the compression area shifts from side to side during each vibration cycle. It is apparent that reduction in shear resistance is associated with the relief of compressive internal stress in one side of the column as the resultant axial force shifts to the other side under a reversal of bending moment. It was decided that a reasonable approximation could be made by using Eq. (1), modified by a sign change within the term under the radical; thus the ultimate shear strength can be expressed as,

$$v_u = 4.75 \sqrt{f'_c (1 - 0.002 \, N/A_g)} \qquad (2)$$

where

N = axial force in the column produced by vertical loads.

Equation (2) yields the following ultimate shear-stress capability for exterior columns: 212 psi for columns over the entrance at the sidewall and 256 psi for the wide endwall columns.

ELASTIC DYNAMIC ANALYSIS OF THE 1200 L STREET BUILDING

The building was analyzed for its elastic response to the Taft, California, earthquake of 1952 (S21°W component). This accelerogram was assumed to represent the Anchorage earthquake.

The normal modes of vibration and their associated frequencies were calculated by the standard Jacobi Diagonalization procedure. The mode shapes were normalized so that the generalized mass for each mode was equal to unity. The building's structural stiffness and weight properties were taken from microfilm copies of the structural plans.

Time-dependent response analyses were carried out separately for both the transverse and longitudinal axes of the building. For this purpose, the mode-superposition computer analysis described earlier was used; the first six modes of vibration were considered and each mode was assured to be 10 percent critically damped ($\lambda = 0.1$). The program automatically computed the maximum forces developed in each column, spandrel, and core element, as well as the maximum story displacements, shears, and overturning moments for the entire structure.

By comparing the maximum element moments and shears with the yield moment and ultimate shear computed for each element, the relative overstressing of the building that would be produced by the assumed earthquake could easily be determined or, conversely, the reduction in earthquake intensity required to avoid overstress could be determined.

The computer program used in the dynamic analysis

takes into consideration the relative vertical displacement of the ends of the spandrels produced by the rotation of wide columns. The nature of this deformation is shown in Figure 4.

ANALYSIS OF RESPONSE IN EAST–WEST DIRECTION

The mode shapes and periods of vibration are presented in Figure 5 for the first, second, and third modes of transverse vibration. A 1.07-second period of vibration was computed for the fundamental mode. The concrete modulus of elasticity was assumed to be 3,000 ksi (kips per in.^{2}).

A maximum relative roof displacement of 2.2 in. was computed from the ground-motion excitation. Maximum relative displacements through the height of the building are plotted and listed in Figure 6.

The distribution of maximum strong shear in the end-wall frames and to the central core is shown in Figure 7. The percentage of story shear carried by the end walls increases through the height of the building. About 60 percent of the base shear is in the end walls and this increases to 80 percent in levels 3–11. At the roof, the end-wall frames are restraining the core in addition to resisting the total story shear.

The major portion of lateral stiffness is contributed by the end-wall frames. Within the frames, the spandrels are highly stressed in relation to their capacity. Shearing forces across the spandrels in the south end wall are listed in Table 1, together with their shear capabilities. The lowest ratio of ultimate shear force to applied shear force is 0.60 at the fifth story. Thus 60 percent of the Taft ground-motion intensity represents the level of incipient shear failure.

Table 1 also compares the computed and actual failures for the full earthquake intensity. The agreement between actual and computed failures in the east-bay spandrels of the south wall is better than might have been expected in view of the possible inaccuracies in the analysis. The maximum disagreement, in the west bay of the eighth story,

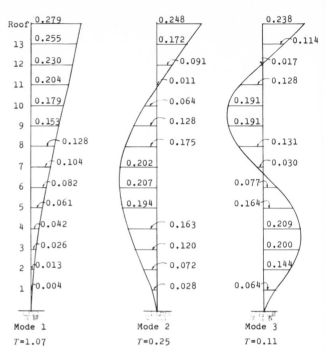

FIGURE 5   Mode shapes and periods of transverse vibration, 1200 L Street building. T = vibration period in seconds.

amounts to a 58 percent overstress based on the computed ultimate shear resistance of the spandrel. Plausible explanations for the fewer failed spandrels in the west bay than in the east bay might be that the failures in the wall columns permitted some very small relieving distortions in the frame geometry. The widespread distribution of failed sections must have introduced frictional damping, which is an effective energy dissipator if it remains substantially constant throughout the vibration cycle. Frictional damping from early failures undoubtedly protected some sections that otherwise would have failed. Also, after significant damage has occurred, the dynamic properties of the structure may be so altered as to make the computational results inapplicable.

The large column section that failed at the second floor in the south wall (Figure 2) had a shear stress of 245 psi at the second floor under the ground-motion excitation. The calculated shear capacity of this section was 256 psi. Field examination of the failure led to the opinion that it was due to concrete crushing under repeated reversals of moment combined with increased axial force, rather than to excessive shear. Reinforcing consisted of number 5 bars at 18-in. centers in each face. The Taft accelerogram induced extreme fiber-bending stresses of ±1,700 psi. The resultant axial force at the second story, representing the vertical dead load and overturning moment, was located 2 in. beyond the middle third of the cross section, so that the com-

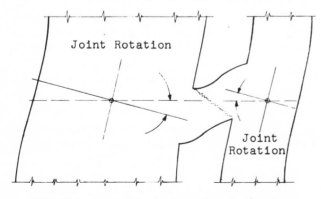

FIGURE 4   Spandrel shearing by rotation of wide columns.

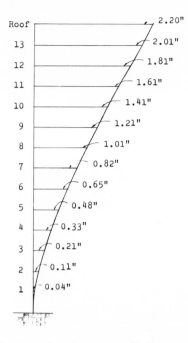

FIGURE 6 Envelope of maximum story displacements in the transverse direction, 1200 L Street building (Taft accelerogram, λ = 0.1).

TABLE 1 Shears across Spandrels in the South End Wall, 1200 L Street Building (Taft Accelerogram, λ = 0.1)

Story	Applied Shear Forces (kips)	Ultimate Shear Resistance (kips)	Occurrence of Failure		
			Actual[a]		
			East Bay	West Bay	Computed
14	42	92	no	no	no
13	70	92	no	no	no
12	90	92	no	no	no
11	108	92	yes	no	yes
10	125	92	yes	no	yes
9	140	92	yes	no	yes
8	145	92	yes	no	yes
7	180	117	yes	yes	yes
6	185	117	yes	yes	yes
5	190	117	yes	yes	yes
4	195	117	yes	yes	yes
3	180	117	yes	yes	yes
2	176	117	yes	yes	yes
1	136	144	yes	no	no

[a]Actual occurrences were determined by examination of the photograph shown in Figure 2.

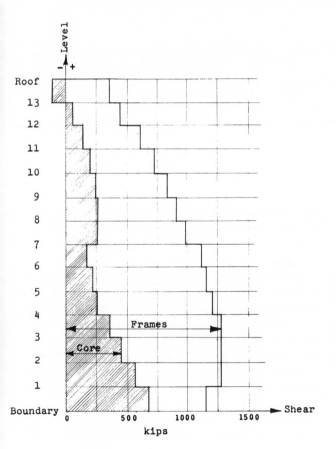

FIGURE 7 Distribution of story shears in transverse direction, 1200 L Street building (Taft accelerogram, λ = 0.1).

bined maximum compressive stress (bending plus axial) was approximately 3,600 psi.

Yielding of the end-wall spandrels tends to shift the overturning resistance due to axial force in the large columns into increased bending at the column base. Spandrel yielding also has a tendency to redistribute a portion of the total lateral shear into the core area. The aggregate effect of spandrel failure was to increase the column moment and decrease its shear response from that calculated by an elastic dynamic analysis. It is therefore reasonable to conclude that the column failure was a moment failure.

ANALYSIS OF RESPONSE IN NORTH-SOUTH DIRECTION

The mode shapes and periods of the first, second, and third modes of longitudinal vibration are presented in Figure 8. A 0.41-second period of vibration was computed for the fundamental mode. The concrete modulus of elasticity was assumed to be 3,000 ksi. The building was considerably stiffer in the longitudinal direction than in the transverse direction. A maximum relative displacement of 0.6 in. due to the ground motion excitation was computed at the roof. Figure 9 illustrates the distribution of maximum relative displacement through the height of the building.

The distribution of story shears to the combined shafts and to the sidewall frame (shown graphically in Figure 10) reveals that the building's longitudinal rigidity is supplied

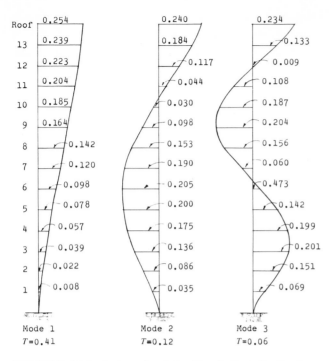

FIGURE 8   Mode shapes and periods of longitudinal vibration in the first three modes, 1200 L Street building. T = period of vibration in seconds.

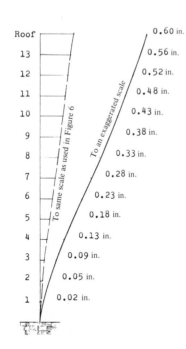

FIGURE 9   Envelope of maximum story displacements in the longitudinal direction, 1200 L Street building (Taft accelerogram, $\lambda = 0.1$).

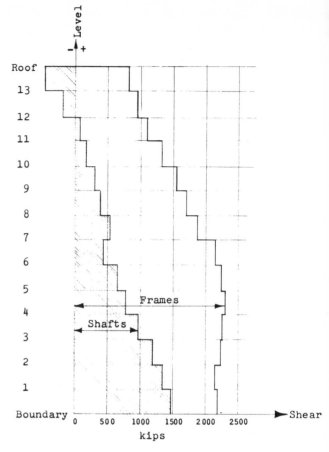

FIGURE 10   Distribution of story shears in long direction, 1200 L Street building (Taft accelerogram, $\lambda = 0.1$).

largely by the sidewall frames, composed of wall columns and spandrels. The percentage of story shear carried by the sidewalls increases from about 60 percent at the base to over 80 percent at the eleventh story. At the roof the sidewall frames are restraining the core in addition to resisting the total story shear. This distribution of story shear with height is similar to that which occurs in the transverse direction.

Shearing forces across the spandrels in the sidewall are listed in Table 2, together with their shear capabilities. The lowest ratio of ultimate shear force to applied shear force is 1.0 at the eighth story, bay 3. Thus, the Taft ground-motion intensity represents the level of incipient shear failure in the spandrels for the longitudinal response of the building.

Figure 2 reveals some degree of failure in nearly every story of the five central bays of the east sidewall (bays 3, 4, and 5 of Table 2); however, the failures outside the bounded area in Table 2 are clearly indicative of longitudinal slip at the construction joints. Failure to remove laitance is mentioned in reports of damage assessment of several buildings in Anchorage. In view of this, apparent construction-joint

TABLE 2 Shears across Spandrels in the East Sidewall, 1200 L Street Building (Taft Accelerogram λ = 0.1)

Story	Applied Shear Force (kips)[a, b]					Ultimate Shear Resistance (kips)	
	Bay 1	Bay 2	Bay 3	Bay 4	Bay 5		
14	12	12	29	30	21	bays 1 and 2:	90
13	15	25	45	49	51	bays 3 and 4:	70
12	24	35	50	53	53	bay 5:	108
11	32	46	56	57	57		
10	45	56	62	60	60		
9	54	65	66	63	62		
8	59	73	69	64	65		
7	76	90	81	73	68	bays 1 and 2:	114
6	84	98	85	76	74	bays 3 and 4:	86
5	90	103	83	73	73	bay 5:	134
4	95	106	80	69	69		
3	91	106	75	63	65		
2	95	99	64	53	58		
1	88	87	51	41	52	bays 1, 2 and 5:	156
						bays 3 and 4:	103

[a] Bays numbered from end to centerline; building is symmetrical about centerline.
[b] Spandrel failures were revealed within the enclosed area by a photograph of the east sidewall.

slippage has not been included as a failure where there is no evidence of diagonal-tension failure. The failures adjacent to the boundary in Table 2 are listed in Table 3 to determine the Taft accelerogram scale factor necessary to produce them.

It will be recalled that the ultimate resisting moment in the short spandrels was found to be 1,420 in.-kips at a concrete cylinder strength of 3,000 psi and concurrent steel stress (top and bottom bars) of 51,000 psi. In view of computed end moments ranging from 1,600 to 6,100 in.-kips,

TABLE 3 Taft Accelerogram Scale Factors Necessary To Produce Borderline Failures Indicated in Table 2

Story	Bay	Applied Shear Force (kips)	Ultimate Resistance (kips)	Necessary Scale Factor[a]
8	1	59	90	1.53
9	2	65	90	1.38
7	3	81	86	1.06
10	4	60	70	1.17
3	1	91	114	1.25
1	2	87	156	1.80
3	3	75	86	1.14
5	4	73	86	1.17

[a] Mean value of necessary scale factors = 1.31.

one naturally questions the absence of evidence of flexural failure. Because of the very steep moment gradient and lack of mechanical anchorage of the steel, bond failure probably occurred promptly and precluded mobilization of the computed tensile stress in the steel. The overpowering strength and rigidity of the columns, compared to the spandrels, probably kept the spandrel concrete confined and acted on it in the manner of a powerful shear-loading mechanism.

The results of the analysis of diagonal-tension cracking in columns of the west sidewall over the entrance in the second story are given in Table 4.

CONCLUSIONS ABOUT THE 1200 L STREET BUILDING

The pattern of shear failures in the spandrels of the south end wall is strongly indicative of east–west ground-motion intensity equivalent to the Taft accelerogram (S21°W component). The indication is well supported by the crushing failure in the southwest column near the base in the second story. With regard to probable north–south motions, there is not the same agreement among the spandrels in the sidewalls that there is among those in the end walls, because they call for scale factors from 1.06 to 1.80. The mean of the necessary scale factors is 1.31. The diagonal tension failures in the second story of columns over the entrance indicate scale factors of 1.41 and 1.38.

The foregoing calculations indicate an intensity of ground motion in the range of 1.0–1.4 times the Taft, California, ground motion. These calculations were made for a damping of 10 percent of critical for each mode, which might be excessive. Had the computations been made for 5 percent damping, they would have indicated an intensity of ground motion in the range of 0.6–1.0 times the Taft ground motion. The effective damping in the building is estimated to have been in the range of 5–10 percent and it is therefore concluded that the observed damage to the 1200 L Street building is consistent with an intensity of ground motion in the range of 1 ± 0.4 times the Taft ground motion. In general the digital-computer analysis indicated stress distribu-

TABLE 4 Taft Accelerogram Scale Factors Necessary To Produce Diagonal Tension Failures in Second Story in Columns over Entrance, 1200 L Street Building (λ = 0.1)

Column[a]	Applied Shear Force (kips)	Ultimate Shear Force (kips)	Necessary Scale Factor
4	65.7	93	1.41
5	58.7	81	1.38

[a] Column numbering progresses toward centerline of symmetrical building.

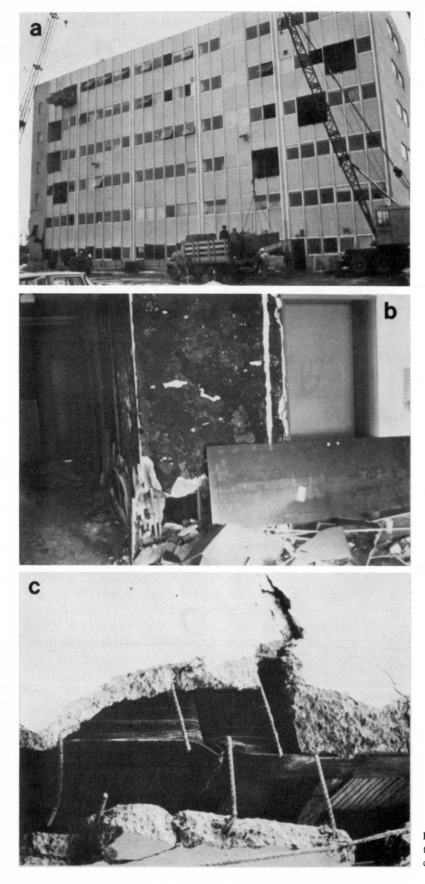

FIGURE 11   The Cordova Building. (a) East elevation; (b) shaft failure facing southeast; (c) southeast corner column.

tions through the structural elements that were consistent with the observed earthquake damage.

THE CORDOVA BUILDING

STRUCTURE

The Cordova Building is a six-story office building, 53 ft 8 in. × 129 ft 4 in. in plan, oriented with its long dimension in the north–south direction, and facing westward (Figure 11a). The structural plan and transverse sections are shown in Figures 12 and 13, respectively. It has a full moment-resisting structural-steel frame in the narrow direction, which is the strong direction of all the columns. In the long direction of the building, partial moment-resisting beam-to-column connections were used. The peripheral columns are seated just below the ground-floor girders on 2 ft 6 in. square piers in the line of the basement wall. Square spread footings supporting these piers are founded from 3 to 6 ft below the basement floor. Interior columns are seated near the basement-floor level on stub piers with similar footings.

The north face of the building is a 4-in. concrete curtain wall and the south face is a 4-in. concrete curtain wall on the east 18 ft that extends around the southeast corner and continues 9 ft northward along the east face. Curtain walls are supported on the basement wall. There was evidence after the earthquake that the southeast curtain wall had not been anchored to the framing or to the floor system at the second and third story levels.

The building has a reinforced-concrete core enclosing the stairwell and elevator shaft. The center of the core is located 22 ft 8 in. north and 4 ft 6 in. east of the center of the building. Walls are 8 in. thick, reinforced vertically with number 9 bars at 12-in. centers in the north and south walls, number 7 bars at 12-in. centers in the east and west walls, and number 4 bars at 12-in. centers in the interior wall. The horizontal steel in all walls consists of number 4 bars at 12-in. centers.

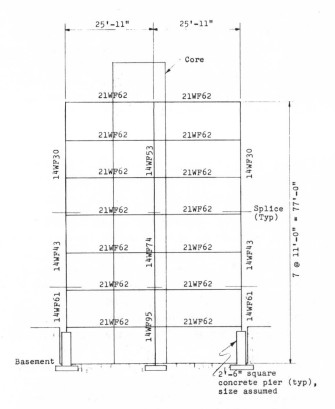

FIGURE 13 Cross section at an interior frame, Cordova Building.
  Note: All steel columns and girders are wide-flange sections, designated by WF. Thus, 21WF62 describes a 21-in. deep wide-flange member that weighs 62 lb/ft of length.

EARTHQUAKE DAMAGE

Earthquake damage occurred mainly in the first story. The core enclosing the elevator shaft and stairwell failed at the base of the first story. Failure of the core at this level was complete along the north wall and at the northwest corner (Figure 11b). The southeast curtain walls sheared at the top of the basement walls, and the corner broke open in the first and second stories where the walls apparently were not anchored to the framing or to the floor system. The north curtain wall shifted on the construction joint atop the basement wall, but to a lesser degree. The southeast-corner column (Figure 11c) buckled severely below the second-floor beam and shortened about 1½ in. The midstory stair landing was anchored to this column, making it much stiffer than the rest of the columns in the first story. The penthouse collapsed. Only slight damage occurred in stories other than the first.

The interior reinforced-concrete core appears to have initially resisted the major portion of lateral earthquake forces. Lateral displacement was accompanied by some torsional rotation due to the location of the core northward of the building's center of mass (Figure 12). The steel frame at

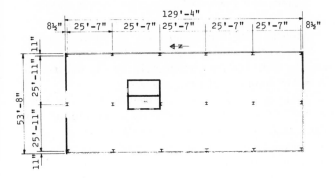

FIGURE 12 Structural plan of the Cordova Building.

the south wall sustained more damage than any other frame because of the stiffening effect of the stair construction and because of its greater distance from the center of rigidity.

Following the failure of the core (Figure 11b) the building was subjected to larger lateral displacements, and the steel frames furnished the lateral resistance to subsequent ground motions.

EVALUATION OF ULTIMATE STRENGTH IN THE CORE IN THE FIRST STORY

Bending-Moment Capacity

Resisting moments in the core were calculated in combination with the axial force of dead load (650 kips) at the first-floor level. Dividing the area of potential tension flange steel by the gross plan dimensions of the core gives a reinforcement percentage of less than 0.05 percent for both east-west and north-south bending. Thus, yielding of the vertical-tension reinforcement would control the maximum overturning resistance if the core acts as a single cantilevered element.

Under east-west bending, the center portion of the west wall tends to be isolated from the main structural core. Because of a shear lag across the lintels at the door openings, this portion of wall will not contribute effectively to resisting eastward deflection until large deformations have taken place in the vertical tension steel at the corners of the core.

The calculated yield moment with eastward deflection is 120,000 in.-kips, providing the wall segment between doorways is omitted and a tension-yield stress of 45 ksi in the reinforcing steel is assumed.

Shear Capacity

In the evaluation of probable shear strength, it was recognized that the conservative side of shear tests was used in generating ultimate strength-design codes. This concept is discussed in the section dealing with the 1200 L Street apartment building.

The complete shattering of the base of the Cordova Building core suggests failure and disintegration under sudden application of overturning and shear forces considerably in excess of the core's resistance, whereas the clearly defined X's in the columns at the 1200 L Street building entrance are indicative of a progressive failure under side-to-side motion. Equation (1) was therefore, used to evaluate the ultimate shear-stress capacity of the core, taking into account the confining effect of the dead-load force of 650 kips, and yielded an ultimate shear stress of 315 psi to be applied to the shear area. If the quality of concrete at this point were poor, the ultimate stress would be much less than 715 psi.

The *ACI Code* (Section 1701) specifies that the nominal ultimate shear stress as a measure of diagonal tension in reinforced concrete members shall be computed by

$$v_u = V_u/bd,$$

where

v_u = shear stress
V_u = shear force
b = breadth of section
d = distance from extreme-compression fiber to centroid of tension reinforcement.

The code further specifies that for beams of I or T section, the width of web shall be used as the breadth-resisting shear. Inasmuch as the horizontal-wall steel was composed only of unanchored nominal tie-bars, it was deemed advisable to use only the wall thickness (8 in.) as the breadth of section.

The ultimate shear resistance of the shaft accordingly was found to be 516 kips in the east-west direction and 652 kips in the north-south direction.

ELASTIC DYNAMIC ANALYSIS OF THE CORDOVA BUILDING

Dynamic analyses were made of the building's elastic lateral response to the Taft earthquake of 1952 (south 21° west component) by the same method used for the analysis of the 1200 L Street building. Each floor level was assumed to translate without rotation, thus subjecting each frame and the core to the same lateral displacement at any given floor level.

Time-dependent responses were computed separately for both the transverse and longitudinal axes of the building. The first three modes of vibration were considered in the analyses, and each mode was assumed to be 10 percent critically damped ($\lambda = 0.1$).

ANALYSIS OF RESPONSE IN EAST-WEST DIRECTION

The first three mode shapes and periods of vibration for the building's transverse elastic lateral response are illustrated in Figure 14.

A fundamental period of transverse vibration of 0.53 seconds was computed. The modulus of elasticity of the core concrete was taken as 3,000 ksi. The effective width of core walls acting as flanges, parallel to the axis of core bending, was limited to a projection of six times its thickness beyond the width of wall acting as a web.

A maximum relative roof displacement of 0.95 in. was computed for the assumed Anchorage ground motion. This figure assumes that the core remains elastic and does not fail. Figure 15 shows the maximum displacements through the height of the building. The deflected shape is controlled strongly by the cantilever deflection characteristics of the core.

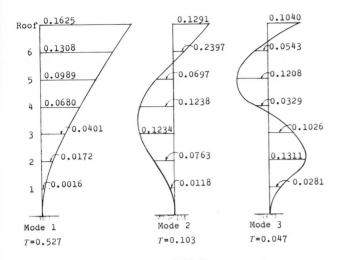

FIGURE 14 Mode shapes and periods of transverse vibration in the first three modes. Cordova Building. *T* = period of vibration in seconds.

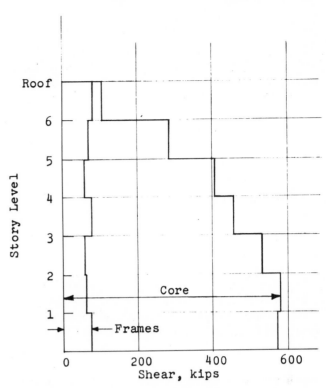

FIGURE 16 Distribution of elastic story shears in transverse direction, Cordova Building (Taft accelerogram, λ = 0.1).

Figure 16 illustrates the distribution of dynamic story shear between the core and frames. Eighty to 90 percent of the story shear is carried by the core throughout the height of the building, with the exception of the roof level.

Table 5 lists the force response associated with the above distribution of dynamic shear for typical structural elements. The ratios of structural capacity to structural response also are listed.

The lowest ratio of element capacity to applied force is 0.41, the bending-moment response of the core at level 1. Thus about 40 percent of the Taft ground motion intensity represents the limit of elastic action for the core. This ratio, or comparison, points out the relatively high stress concen-

tration in the core at its base. As long as the core retains its structural capacity, the frame elements are stressed to a low level.

ANALYSIS OF RESPONSE IN THE NORTH–SOUTH DIRECTION

The mode shapes and periods of the first three modes of longitudinal vibration are presented in Figure 17. The central core predominates in the elastic-vibration characteristics of the building. Because its stiffness is higher in the north–south direction than in the east–west direction, the building's fundamental period of longitudinal vibration is only 0.49 seconds. This period shift, however, between 0.53 and 0.49 second is not significantly large.

The computed longitudinal elastic displacement shown in Figure 18 is very similar to the corresponding elastic transverse response (Figure 15).

There is much less participation of the frames in the longitudinal direction in resisting dynamic story shear (compare Figure 19 with Figure 16). This results from the weak axis orientation of the steel columns within the frames. Thus, as long as the core retains its elastic structural capacity, it is the only structural element of the building with significant stress levels caused by longitudinal excitation.

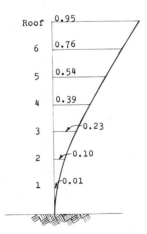

FIGURE 15 Envelope of maximum transverse displacements, Cordova Building (Taft accelerogram, λ = 0.1).

TABLE 5   Internal Force Responses and Capacities of Members: East–West Vibration, Cordova Building (Taft Accelerogram $\lambda = 0.1$)

Member Force	Yield Capacity (in.-kips)	Ultimate Capacity (kips)	Response (in.-kips)	Response (kips)	Capacity-to-Response Ratio
Core shear	–	516	–	581	0.89
Core moment	120,000	–	296,000	–	0.41
Typical frame girder, moment	5,650	–	492	–	11.45
Frame interior column, moment	2,670	–	418	–	6.40
Frame exterior column, moment	1,830	–	201	–	9.10

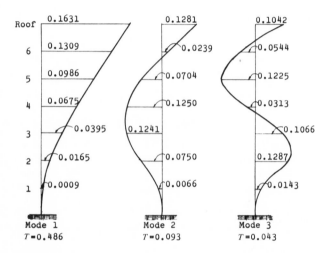

FIGURE 17   Mode shapes and periods of longitudinal vibration in the first three modes, Cordova Building. T = period of vibration in seconds.

The elastic bending moment and shear response of the core at level 1 is tabulated in Table 6. Comparison of the response of the core to the Taft accelerogram with its ultimate strength capacity reveals that it may be expected to fail in bending response. The limit of longitudinal elastic action for the core is an excitation of about 40 percent of the Taft ground motion.

NONLINEAR DYNAMIC ANALYSIS OF THE CORDOVA BUILDING

The central core was very lightly reinforced for bending with a reinforcement of less than 0.05 percent of the core's plan area. About 10 times this area of tension steel is gen-

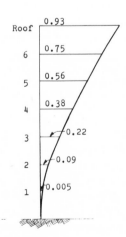

FIGURE 18   Envelope of maximum longitudinal displacements, Cordova Building (Taft accelerogram, $\lambda = 0.1$).

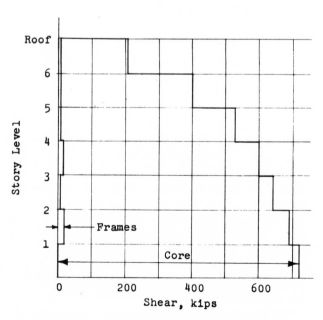

FIGURE 19   Distribution of elastic story shears in longitudinal direction, Cordova Building (Taft accelerogram, $\lambda = 0.1$).

TABLE 6 Internal-Force Capacities and Responses of the Shaft at the First-Floor Level: North–South Vibration, Cordova Building (Taft Accelerogram, $\lambda = 0.1$)

Force	Capacity	Response	Capacity-to-Response Ratio
Shear	(Ultimate) 652 kips	689 kips	0.95
Moment	(Yield) 150,000 in.-kips	393,000 in.-kips	0.38

erally recommended as minimum for ductile performance of flexural members. The north wall of the core (Figure 11b) appears to have had a tension failure caused by southward overturning and further aggravated by the east–west shear acting along the wall. Subsequently, lateral story shear was transferred to the steel frames, the building became considerably more flexible, and lateral displacements increased.

A dynamic nonlinear analysis was carried out for the purpose of determining the probable distribution and magnitude of yield deformation required of the steel frame in order to furnish lateral stability after core failure.

The principal objective of the nonlinear-analysis program is the evaluation of the maximum inelastic flexural deformations produced in each member of the frame during the course of the earthquake. This deformation is represented by the plastic hinge angle (β), which is evaluated for each end of each member at the end of each time increment.

The maximum value of β, which is stored in the computer for each member and printed at the end of the analysis, represents the ductility requirement imposed on the member by the earthquake. In order that this ductility requirement may be interpreted easily, the angle β is compared with the maximum elastic-rotation angle (Φ_e) that the member may develop. This elastic-limit rotation angle is the angle developed when the member is subjected to its yield moment. The ductility factor (μ) then represents the ductility requirement, which is defined as

$$\mu = 1 + \frac{\beta_{max}}{\Phi_e}.$$

The ductility factor is the ratio of elastic yield rotation plus plastic hinge rotation to the elastic-yield rotation. An equivalent measure of the response in members that remain elastic is provided by the ratio of maximum moment developed in the member to the member yield moment, a number less than 1.0.

Because of the brittle nature of the core failure, the computation of nonlinear response was programmed so that, at the end of the response cycle during which the shaft reached its yield moment in the first story, the value of its bending moment of inertia in the first story was changed to

zero. Thereafter, the six-story shaft segment above the first floor was assumed to move freely with the space frame.

RESPONSE IN THE EAST–WEST DIRECTION AFTER CORE FAILURE

The maximum nonlinear-displacement response of the building is shown in Figure 20. The core was assumed to fracture at an overturning moment of 120,000 in.-kips. The elastic displacement response is shown also for comparison. As expected, the nonlinear displacement was considerably larger with four times the maximum elastic displacement at the roof.

To show the change in deflection characteristic that occurred after failure of the core, the elastic displacements have been multiplied by four and replotted as the dashed line of Figure 20. It is apparent that the maximum elastic-deflection response is controlled strongly by the cantilever-deflection characteristic of the core. After failure, the six-story core segment above the first floor acts as a rigid spine so that the deflection increases linearly with height.

Table 7 lists the estimated yield-moment capacities for

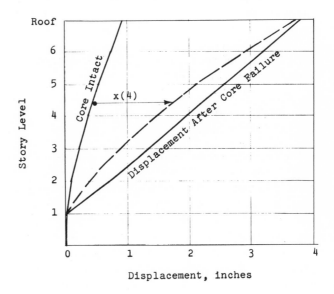

FIGURE 20 Comparison of nonlinear and elastic transverse displacements, Cordova Building (Taft accelerogram, $\lambda = 0.1$).

TABLE 7 Yield-Moment Capacity of Steel-Frame Members, Cordova Building, Transverse Direction

Member	Yield Moment (in.-kips)
Girders	
16WF45	2710
21WF62	4770
Columns	
14WF30 (P^a = 84 kips)	1240
14WF43 (P = 118 kips)	1830
14WF53 (P = 180 kips)	2100
14WF61 (P = 170 kips)	2700
14WF74 (P = 304 kips)	2670
14WF95 (P = 366 kips)	3820

[a]P = calculated gravity load.

the girder and column elements of a typical frame that were used in the nonlinear analysis.

Computed girder and column ductility requirements are shown in Figure 21. With only lateral forces considered, the maximum girder stress was about 50 percent of its yield capacity. The largest column deformation took place between the ground-floor and second-floor levels, the elevation of core failure. The interior columns of a typical frame show a maximum ductility requirement of 2.3.

A major change in the fundamental period of vibration occurred on failure of the core. The period was 0.53 second with the core intact and increased to 1.36 seconds, with the core fractured at level 1.

The spectacular damage to the southeast corner column (Figure 11c) occurred just below the second-level girder and was due largely to the intermediate bracing effect of the adjacent stair construction. Reduction of the effective height of this column resulted in very large deformation requirements to accommodate the increased relative first-story displacement after failure of the core.

RESPONSE IN THE NORTH–SOUTH DIRECTION AFTER CORE FAILURE

In the longitudinal direction of the building, girder-to-column connections could develop only a portion of the girder yield capacity. Also, the longitudinal frames resisted lateral motion by weak-axis bending of columns. Because of the weak-axis orientation of the steel columns, a very large increase in fundamental period of vibration occurred as a result of core failure. The calculated period was 0.49 second with the core intact and increased to 3.3 seconds after failure. Because of the increased flexibility, however, larger deflections and lower dynamic shears were developed in the steel frames after core failure.

A dynamic nonlinear analysis was not made for the longitudinal direction. The steel frames were able to accommodate the subsequent ground motions within the elastic capacity of the partial moment-resisting connections. Inspection of average earthquake-displacement spectra, however, indicates that longitudinal displacements of two to three times the calculated transverse deflections could have occurred. It is likely that the Cordova Building underwent a maximum relative roof displacement of 8–12 in. in the longitudinal direction after core failure.

CONCLUSIONS ABOUT THE CORDOVA BUILDING

The initial core failure occurred at a ground-motion intensity of about 40 percent of the Taft earthquake of 1952 and was caused by the yielding of tension steel under overturning moment.

The steel frames were able to withstand the ground motion after failure of the core. No doubt the original design intended the steel frames to resist the earthquake forces and the core was supposed to contribute nothing to the resistance.

The response of the Cordova Building provides an enlightening example of the differing responses of brittle and ductile members. If a concrete core element with large rel-

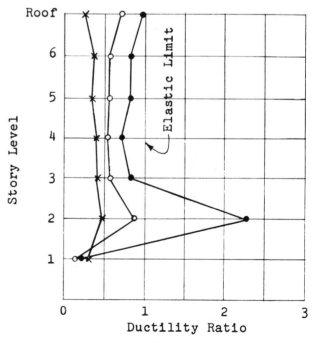

FIGURE 21 Ductility requirement for steel frame after core failure, transverse direction, Cordova Building (Taft accelerogram, λ = 0.1).

ative rigidity is to function effectively throughout a strong-motion earthquake, it must be reinforced to function as a ductile member even if its strength is not needed. If the design concept is to transfer lateral structural resistance to ductile frames and to provide lightly reinforced walls for limiting deflection under low-intensity earthquakes, care must be exercised to ensure that the fractured wall does not endanger personnel within the building and that it does not lead to damage that is costly to repair.

THE FOUR SEASONS APARTMENT BUILDING

STRUCTURE

The 3-bay × 6-bay structural system of the six-story Four Seasons apartment building was composed of 8-in. post-tensioned concrete flat slabs supported in 10-in. wide-flange steel columns, with resistance to lateral loads provided by the two elevator and stairwell shafts (Figures 22 and 23). The slabs were cast on the ground and lifted into position and the two shafts were then poured. The structure rested on spread footings. A basement extended under part of the building. The 34 ft × 34 ft footing under the north shaft was founded 12 ft 8 in. below the basement floor slab (Figure 23). The footing under the south shaft was the same size but was founded at an elevation 5 ft higher, outside the basement area. The central part of the lobby slab was depressed 3 ft below the basic first-story level with the elevation change occurring at the north face of shaft A.

EARTHQUAKE DAMAGE

At the time of the earthquake, the building was structurally completed and was to be readied for occupancy in about 2 weeks. The photographs in Figure 24 show that the shafts were severed near their bases (level 1, Figure 23) and overturned to the north, carrying the slabs with them. Figure 24(b) shows the corner of the roof overhang (see column line 6, Figure 25) displaced northward about 30 ft. If the slabs had followed the shafts to the ground, describing an arc with the shaft's base as center, this displacement would have been 52 ft. However, the large angular displacement of the shafts completely shattered the adjacent slab areas so that the slabs could drop down. Figure 24(d) shows how the shaft rotation caused the slabs on either side to twist, forming a yield line behind the shaft that was observable in the rubble.

All vertical reinforcing bars in the shafts were spliced at level 1 with a 20-bar diameter lap. Large number 8 and junior number 11 bars had failures in the splice, whereas number 4 bars were broken with a ductile rupture.

A spectacular secondary effect was the release of many prestressed cables (½ in. greased and wrapped tendons) as the structure collapsed. Figure 24(d) shows the severe twisting imparted to the slabs as the shafts rotated toward the north. Figure 25 shows how this twisting would deform

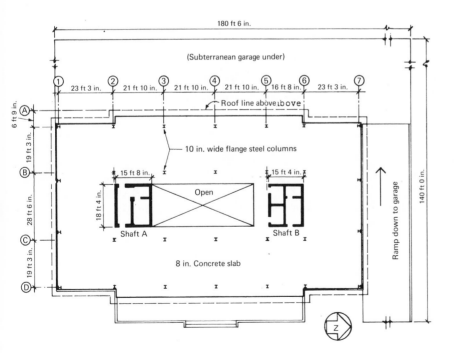

FIGURE 22 Plan of typical floor, Four Seasons apartment building.

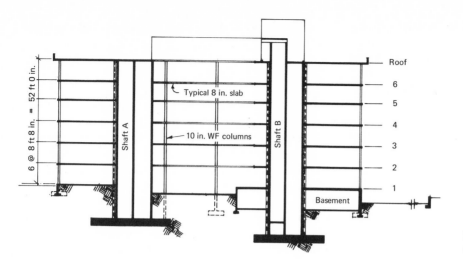

FIGURE 23   Longitudinal section, Four Seasons apartment building.

the concrete around the anchorages located at the slab junction with the shaft outer wall. Wedge-type anchorages, located in an area of maximum slab distortion, released the cables as soon as they were broken loose from the concrete.

During the descent of the slabs, severe distortion at the column connection resulted in the shear-head connection punching through the slab. The slab concrete had varying degrees of prestress due to the progressive release of prestressed cables as the shafts rotated northward. Figure 24(f) shows a typical steel column in a buckled configuration with shear heads in place.

The Four Seasons structure was located about 100 ft to the south of the graben that formed at the head of the L Street slide (Shannon & Wilson, Inc., 1964, Plate 9.2). The adjacent graben had a width of about 150 ft and subsidences of 7–10 ft. Relatively few major ground cracks occurred outside the graben. However, small surface cracks, oriented in a general transverse direction, were observed at the Four Seasons site.

The cumulative width of surface cracks along the longitudinal dimension of the building was about 2 in. This surface cracking might indicate that the shafts moved apart, but this could not be established by examination of the collapsed structure. The slabs, however, were functioning as horizontal diaphragms at the time of shaft failure, because they were able to enforce compatible northward displacement of both shafts. In subsequent analysis, possible soil movement has not been considered; if it did occur, it would have increased the bending moments at the bases of the shafts and would have led to earlier failure.

It appears likely that the location of the shaft bases made shaft B stiffer than shaft A (Figure 23). The first-floor slab and the basement slab in conjunction with the basement walls form a fairly rigid shear box enclosing shaft B. The reactions of the two slabs form a couple that restrains the base of the shaft. The condition in the comparable region of

shaft A obviously offers less restraint and suggests that shaft B provided more resistance to lateral loads until it failed; the consequently overloaded shaft A then failed. Because it is difficult to determine the difference in base stiffness with any degree of accuracy, the possible detrimental effect of this condition is merely mentioned.

STRENGTH EVALUATION OF THE SHAFTS

Bending-Moment Capacity

Resisting moments in the shafts were calculated for the reinforcement shown on the structural plans at level 1. It is assumed that the shaft weight of 560 kips was acting as a vertical load.

Figure 26 gives the moment capacity for northward overturning of shafts A and B, assuming the reinforcing bars to yield at 45 ksi. The moment capacities are 19,500 ft-kips and 24,600 ft-kips, respectively. The potential tension-flange steel shown in Figure 26 represents a reinforcement for bending of less than 0.02 percent of the core's plan area; yielding of the vertical tension reinforcement would thus control the yield-moment capacity of the shafts.

To mobilize the calculated yield-moment capacity, each shaft had to transmit relatively large shears across door openings to the isolated portion of the tension flange. Because the door lintels showed almost no sign of distress, it is doubtful that the gross yield-moment capacities were mobilized during the Alaska earthquake.

Shear Capacity

In evaluating the probable ultimate shear strength at level 1, it has been taken into account that conservative values of ultimate shear tests were used to generate ultimate-strength design codes. This is discussed in the section dealing with the 1200 L Street apartment building.

Equation (1) was used to evaluate the probable shear re-

FIGURE 24   Four Seasons apartment building after March 27, 1964, earthquake. (a) General view. (b) Shaft B and roof slab displaced to the north. (c) West side of shaft A. (d) West edge of roof slab. (c) North side of shaft B base after cleanup. (f) Typical steel column.

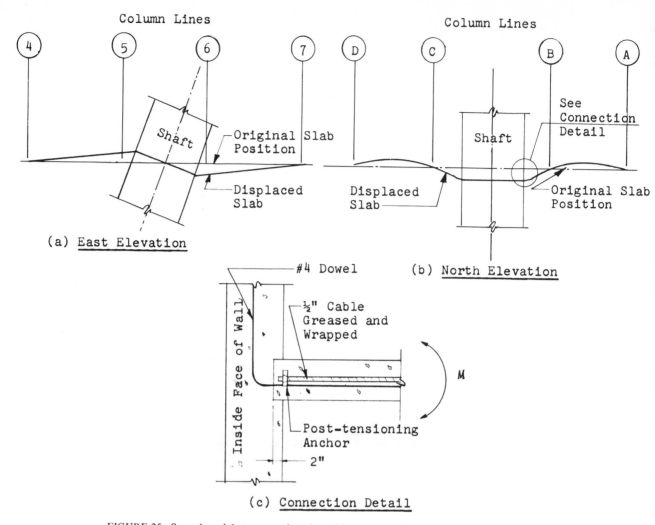

FIGURE 25 Secondary slab stresses at junction with shaft wall, Four Seasons apartment building.

sistance of the shafts, taking into account its dead-load weight of 560 kips. Assuming a concrete cylinder strength of 3,000 psi, Eq. (1) yields an ultimate shear stress of 315 psi to be applied to the shear area. The ultimate resistance for northward shear was found to be 990 kips for each shaft.

Evaluation of Ultimate Bond Strength

The ultimate bond stress between reinforcing bars and concrete was evaluated according to Section 1801(c)(1), *ACI Standard Building Code Requirements for Reinforced Concrete*, for "bars other than top bars." A concrete cylinder strength of 3,000 psi was assumed for use in the ACI formula, which indicated an ultimate bond stress of 400 psi.

Table 8 lists the bond stress required to develop the overturning-tension reinforcement shown in Figure 26. The bond stress calculations assume a 20-bar diameter overlap, as noted on the structural plans. Because of the high bond

stresses, only a portion of the calculated gross overturning resistance of the shafts could be mobilized at ground level.

ELASTIC DYNAMIC ANALYSIS OF THE FOUR SEASONS APARTMENT BUILDING

The building's structural stiffness and weight properties were taken from microfilm copies of the structural plans. Dynamic analyses were carried out for the building's north–south response to the Taft earthquake of 1952 (S21°W component). Time-dependent responses were computed for two methods of representing shaft stiffness. First, the shafts were treated as integral units, with flexural stresses distributed over the total cross section and plane sections assumed to remain plane. Second, each shaft was divided into a series of walls and frames to account for distortion of the lintels. The lateral stiffness of the vertical load-carrying frame was found to be so small that its stiffness contribution

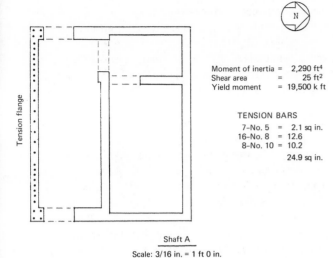

Moment of inertia = 2,290 ft⁴
Shear area   =   25 ft²
Yield moment   = 19,500 k ft

TENSION BARS

7–No. 5 = 2.1 sq in.
16–No. 8 = 12.6
8–No. 10 = 10.2

24.9 sq in.

Shaft A
Scale: 3/16 in. = 1 ft 0 in.

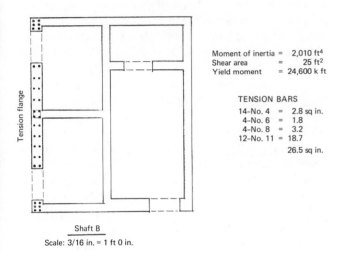

Moment of inertia = 2,010 ft⁴
Shear area   =   25 ft²
Yield moment   = 24,600 k ft

TENSION BARS

14–No. 4 = 2.8 sq in.
4–No. 6 = 1.8
4–No. 8 = 3.2
12–No. 11 = 18.7

26.5 sq in.

Shaft B
Scale: 3/16 in. = 1 ft 0 in.

FIGURE 26   Shaft properties at level 1, Four Seasons apartment building.

was neglected. The method of analysis was the same as that previously described; again, the first three modes of vibration were considered, with each mode assumed to be 10 percent critically damped ($\lambda = 0.1$). This damping is probably too large for the structure so the computed displacements and forces are correspondingly too small.

RESPONSE OF SHAFTS ASSUMED TO ACT AS INTEGRAL UNITS

Figure 27 illustrates the first three mode shapes and lists their associated periods of vibration. The mode shapes were normalized so that the generalized mass for each mode was equal to unity. The fundamental period of vibration was computed as 0.37 second, with the entire shaft cross section assumed to be effective as an integral unit (Figure 26), with a modulus of elasticity of 3,000 ksi.

TABLE 8   Ultimate Bond Stress Required To Develop Overturning Tension Reinforcement in a Deformed Bar Assuming a 20-bar-diameter Overlap, Four Seasons Apartment Building

Bar Size Number	P_y f_y = 45 ksi, kips	20 diameters, in. (minimum)	Bond Stress, psi
4	9	12	475
5	14	13	560
6	19.8	15	560
8	35.5	20	560
10	57	25	560
11	70	28	560

The maximum lateral displacements relative to ground (shown in Figure 28) exhibit the cantilever deflection characteristics of the shafts. The maximum relative roof displacement was 0.55 in. This analysis assumes that the shafts remain elastic and do not fail.

Table 9 lists the dynamic overturning moment and shear force response for the two shafts. The ratios of structural capacity to response are also presented.

The lowest ratio of applied stress to stress capacity is 0.49; this is the bond stress in shaft A that occurs at the lap splice located at level 1. Developing the tensile capacity of a reinforcing bar at a lap splice depends on the transfer of bar force into the concrete at the lap by means of bond stresses as shown in Figure 29. At all points along a lap splice the accumulations of strain in the two bars differ significantly; consequently, there must be relative displace-

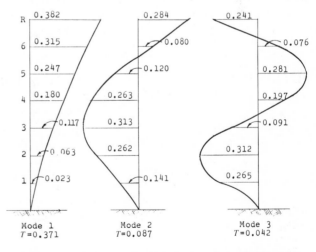

FIGURE 27   Mode shapes and periods of north–south vibration in the first three modes, Four Seasons apartment building. T = the period of vibration in seconds. The shafts were assumed to be fixed at 8.67 ft below level 1 (Figure 23); similarly the shafts were assumed to act as integral units.

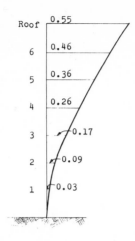

Roof	0.55
6	0.46
5	0.36
4	0.26
3	0.17
2	0.09
1	0.03

FIGURE 28 Envelope of maximum north–south displacements, Four Seasons apartment building (Taft accelerogram, λ = 0.1). Shafts were assumed fixed at 8.67 ft below level 1 (Figure 23) and were assumed to act as integral units.

ment between the two bars. A highly stressed lap, therefore, is subject to shakedown under repeated loading. Less than 50 percent of the Taft ground-motion intensity represents the initiation of bond failure near the base of shaft A, if it is assumed that the door lintels could fully mobilize the tension flange.

RESPONSE OF SHAFTS ASSUMED TO ACT AS A SERIES OF SHEAR WALLS AND FRAMES

When the gross-overturning capabilities of the shafts were calculated, the south walls were assumed to act as tension flanges. However, because of the door openings, relative deformations took place within the lintels and wall seg-

ments. These deformations were not accounted for by assuming that the shafts acted as integral units under flexure.

In general, slight local yielding of tension reinforcement will accommodate relative deformation across the lintels until the full tension flange is mobilized. If the yield capacity of the reinforcement cannot be realized because of bond failure at a lap, these tension readjustments cannot take place. It is therefore probable that local bond failures would be initiated at an earthquake intensity less than that predicted by an integral cross-section analysis.

It was found possible to idealize the placement of door openings in each story by segmenting the shafts into systems of walls and one-bay frames. One-bay frames were idealized with walls as columns and with the 20-in.-deep lintels over the openings as beams. Because several of the sections performing as columns were in the wide-column category, the effect of relative displacement of lintel ends due to joint rotation was taken into account (Figure 4). The segmentation of the shafts into walls acting as flanges parallel to the axis of bending was limited to a projection of six times its thickness beyond the width of wall acting as a web.

The first three mode shapes and associated frequencies are given in Figure 31. Each shaft segment (Figure 30) displaces equally at each floor level. The increase in fundamental period of vibration was from 0.37 second for the integral shaft to 0.57 second for the segmented shaft. The idealized segmented shaft is therefore over twice as flexible as the integral shaft. It is probable that the actual shaft flexibility was somewhere between these two idealizations.

The calculated maximum elastic roof displacement was 1.0 in. (Figure 32) for the Taft ground motion.

On the basis of the computed distribution of dynamic overturning moments to the various wall and frame segments, the critical bond stresses under northward displacement were found to occur within the west wall of shaft B

TABLE 9 Shaft Shear Force, Overturning Yield Moment, and Bond Stress Capacities and Responses at Level 1 of the Four Seasons Apartment Building (Taft Accelerogram, λ = 0.1)

Stress at Level 1	Shear	Moment		Applied Stress Response	Capacity: Response Ratio
	Ultimate Capacity, kips	Yield Capacity, ft.-kips	Bond Capacity, psi		
Shaft A					
Shear	990			790 kips	1.25
Moment		19,500		28,600 ft-kips	0.68
Bond			400	820 psi	0.49
Shaft B					
Shear	990			730 kips	1.36
Moment		24,600		25,600 ft-kips	0.96
Bond			400	590 psi	0.68

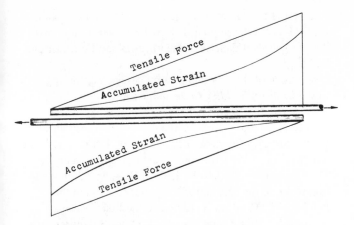

FIGURE 29 Idealized force transfer in a rebar lap splice.

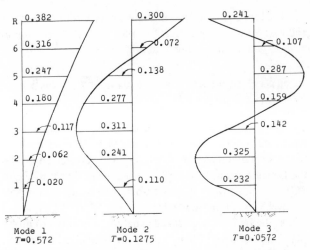

Mode 1
T=0.572

Mode 2
T=0.1275

Mode 3
T=0.0572

FIGURE 31 Mode shapes and periods of north–south vibration in the first three modes, Four Seasons apartment building. T = the period of vibration in seconds. Shafts were assumed fixed at 8.67 ft below level 1 (Figure 23); shafts were segmented according to Figure 30.

(Wall 1, Figure 30) and the south corners of shaft A (frames 3 and 5). Ultimate bond stress of 400 psi was reached at 47 percent and 36 percent, respectively, of a Taft intensity ground motion.

The analysis indicates that failure of the reinforcing-bar splices near the bases of the shafts occurred first. After this the shafts were free to rock on their bases, but were restrained by the connections to the floor slabs. When these connections failed, the shafts were able to overturn.

Thus an earthquake ground motion of about 35 percent of the intensity of the Taft ground motion would initiate

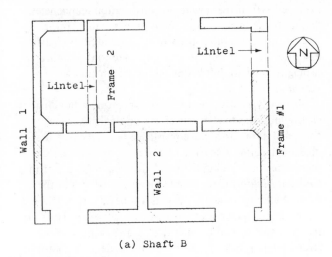

(a) Shaft B

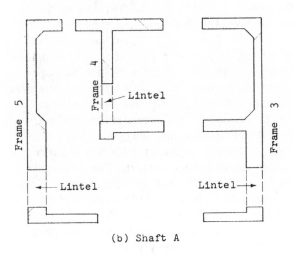

(b) Shaft A

FIGURE 30 Segmentation of shafts into frames and walls.

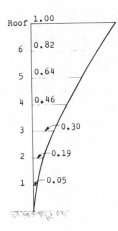

FIGURE 32 Envelope of maximum north–south displacements, Four Seasons apartment building (Taft accelerogram, $\lambda = 0.1$). Shafts were assumed fixed at 8.67 ft below level 1 (Figure 23) and were segmented according to Figure 30.

bond failure at the splices. Actually, since both north–south and east–west motions stress the same bars, even less intense motion would initiate bond failure.

LATERAL RESPONSE OF THE VERTICAL LOAD-CARRYING FRAME

The gravity loads were carried primarily by the 8-in. post-tensioned concrete flat slabs supported on 10-in.-deep wide-flange steel columns. The slab-to-column connection utilized the typical vertical load-carrying shear head shown in Figure 24(f). No positive method of transferring bending moments from slab to column was provided.

On the basis of the dynamic analysis, a northward displacement of about 35 percent of the fully elastic response to the Taft ground motion would initiate bond failure in the shafts. Since the fully elastic response resulted in a 1.0 in. roof displacement (see Figure 32), bond failure would initiate at about 0.35 in. The story-to-story displacements would be about 0.07 in. in the upper two thirds of the building.

The flexible vertical load-carrying frame consisting of columns and floor slabs would not experience significant lateral load stresses under story-to-story displacements of 0.07 in. This bears out the previous observation that the slabs were functioning as horizontal diaphragms at the time of shaft failure. Because about 86 percent of the building's elevated mass was supported by the vertical load frame, an early diaphragm failure would have reduced the lateral load on the shafts to well below their overturning moment capacity.

CONCLUSIONS ABOUT THE FOUR SEASONS APARTMENT BUILDING

Collapse of the building was the direct result of bond failure in the lap splices of the main vertical reinforcement in the shafts immediately above the first floor. Bond failure would be initiated at a ground-motion intensity less than 35 percent of the Taft 1952 ground motion. This is a surprisingly low intensity of ground shaking, and it indicates the need for entirely different earthquake design requirements for structures like the Four Seasons apartment building.

GENERAL CONCLUSIONS

The results of the dynamic analyses, when compared to observed damage to the 1200 L Street apartment building, the Cordova Building, and the Four Seasons apartment building, indicate that the ground shaking at Anchorage had an intensity in the range of 1 ± 0.4 times that recorded

at Taft, California, on July 21, 1952. Ground motion appreciably less intense than this would, however, have produced significant damage in the Cordova and Four Seasons buildings.

All three of these buildings were designed according to the *Uniform Building Code* and, except for the Four Seasons building, were checked by the International Conference of Building Officials, the organization responsible for the *Uniform Building Code*. The 1200 L Street building was checked in 1951 for zone 2 requirements and unconfirmed reports state that the Federal Housing Administration required the contractor to further strengthen the building. The Cordova Building and the Four Seasons apartment building were designed for zone 3 requirements in 1956 and 1963, respectively.

It is possible, of course, that errors in construction could lead to weaknesses in the buildings that would make them especially susceptible to damage. The analysis shows, however, that damage approximating that observed would be expected even if there were no construction deficiencies. Similar buildings when subjected to reasonably strong ground motion in other parts of the United States, such as California, may therefore be expected to experience damage similar to that sustained by the Anchorage buildings.

The analysis of the Four Seasons apartment building clearly indicates that to rely solely on slender vertical concrete shafts for earthquake resistance requires more thorough engineering analysis and more conservative design than were employed in that case. The requirements of the *Uniform Building Code* should be revised so that in the future buildings of similar design will be able to withstand stronger earthquake motions without collapsing. The *Code* requirements should be such that, in the event of very strong ground shaking, there will be an adequate factor of safety against collapse.

The analysis of the Cordova Building indicates that there would have been little damage if there had been no concrete elevator shaft in the building and no concrete wall sections and if the stairway had not improperly restrained the corner column. This conclusion indicates that stiff elements that are not intended to resist earthquake forces can be the sources of costly damage. Such damage can be avoided by appropriate architectural and engineering design.

The extensive damage sustained by the 1200 L Street building is noteworthy because this is a type of building frequently constructed in other parts of the United States. The analysis indicates that such buildings, because of the proportions of the beam and column elements of the exterior walls, are particularly subject to high stresses that can lead to extensive damage. Buildings of this type can be designed to resist earthquakes with little damage, but to accomplish this requires much more thorough structural analysis than has been customary. Certain changes in proportions of the wall elements would probably improve the earthquake-resisting ability of this type of structure.

The objectives of the building code are supposed to be to enable buildings to survive moderate earthquake ground shaking with little or no damage and to survive strong shaking with damage but no injury and loss of life. The Four Seasons building did not meet this criterion, but the 1200 L Street and Cordova buildings did. There was no injury or loss of life in the 1200 L Street building or in the Mt. McKinley building; both buildings have been repaired and are again occupied. However, each of these buildings cost approximately $1.2 million initially, and it is estimated that the cost was about $0.5 million each to restore them to the approximate preearthquake condition. The damage to the Cordova Building cost about $0.2 million, nearly one fifth of the total building cost to repair. These figures represent costly damage and indicate the desirability of analyzing the building-code requirements with the purpose of optimizing the cost-benefit ratio.

ACKNOWLEDGMENT

This investigation was carried out under the sponsorship of the U.S. Department of Housing and Urban Development, Federal Housing Administration (Clough and Benuska, 1966).

REFERENCES

Clough, Ray W., and K. Lee Benuska, 1966. FHA study of seismic design criteria for high-rise buildings. A Report for Federal Housing Administration, Technical Studies Program (HUD TS-3). Los Angeles: T. Y. Lin and Associates. 347 p.

Grantz, Arthur, George Plafker, and Reuben Kachadoorian, 1964. Alaska's Good Friday earthquake, March 27, 1964: A preliminary geologic evaluation. U.S. Geological Survey Circular 491. Washington: U.S. Geological Survey. 35 p.

Hudson, Donald E., and William K. Cloud, 1973. Seismological background for engineering studies of the earthquake *in* The Great Alaska Earthquake of 1964: Engineering. NAS Pub. 1606. Washington: National Academy of Sciences.

Shannon & Wilson, Inc., 1964. Report on Anchorage area soil studies, Alaska, to U.S. Army Engineer District, Anchorage, Alaska, August 28. Seattle: Shannon & Wilson, Inc. 300 p.

METE A. SOZEN
N. NORBY NIELSEN*
UNIVERSITY OF ILLINOIS

Analysis of the Failure of the Anchorage International Airport Control Tower

The role of ductility in the success of structural frames in resisting earthquakes has been explicitly discussed in the professional literature. It has also been acknowledged that the lateral-load coefficients for structural frames are depressed because of the energy absorption made possible by the ductility of framed systems.

In contrast to the fundamental requirement related to deformation, the orthodox design process is preoccupied primarily with lateral loads and corresponding stresses. Deformation requirements are expressed indirectly and inadequately, and it appears to be tacitly assumed that, if the frame is designed to resist the stresses, ductility follows automatically.

The ductility of a reinforced-concrete frame depends primarily on the rotation capacity of its connections. The factors that control the rotation capacity of the connections, although well recognized in the research community, are almost entirely ignored in the design process, possibly because they revoke some of the fundamental oversimplifications of the "ultimate-strength theory."

This paper attempts to indicate and emphasize the sources of ductility in reinforced-concrete connections. The observed behavior of the Anchorage International Airport Control Tower—a very simple reinforced-concrete structure in Anchorage, Alaska, during the earthquake of March 27, 1964—is used to illustrate some of the fundamental concepts related to ductility.

SOURCES OF DUCTILITY IN REINFORCED-CONCRETE CONNECTIONS

CONNECTIONS WITHOUT REINFORCEMENT SPLICES

To simplify the discussion of the sources of ductility in a reinforced-concrete frame, it is desirable to consider only that portion of a frame member between the point of contraflexure and the point where the member is connected to a node of the frame. Such a portion is shown by

ABSTRACT: The phenomena associated with this collapse of a reinforced-concrete structure in Anchorage, Alaska, illustrate the weakness of a structural design system for earthquake resistance that is based only on forces. If energy absorption by yielding of the structural elements is a design criterion, the designer should be required to demonstrate explicitly that the movements of the structural system related to yielding can take place, and that the axial loads, bending moments, and shears associated with the expected mode of yielding can be resisted successfully by the structural elements. Designing the structure simply by relating assumed external loads to internal stresses can be misleading and unsafe.

*Now with the University of Hawaii.

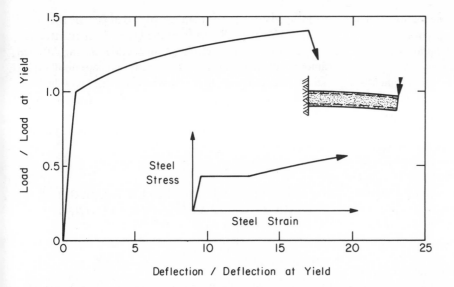

FIGURE 1   Ductility of a connection.

the inset in the upper right-hand corner of Figure 1. It is, in effect, a cantilever beam subjected to a transverse load (shear) applied at the end (point of contraflexure). The axial load will be ignored to further simplify the discussion. A good measure of the ductility of this system is provided by the relation between the load and the deflection measured at the loading point.

The dimensionless load-deflection curve shown in Figure 1 was obtained from a test specimen simulating the cantilever beam shown in the figure [for quantitative data, see Burns and Siess (1962, beam J4), or Blume and others (1961, p. 125)]. Over and above the manifest ductility of the joint, the load-deflection curve has a noteworthy but seldom-noted characteristic: Despite the well-defined break

at yielding of the reinforcement, there is no "flat top" or plastic portion.

The stress-strain curve for the reinforcement used in this specimen did have a plastic portion, as illustrated by the stress-strain curve inset in Figure 1. Accordingly, the moment-curvature relation for the section would also exhibit a plastic range as reflected in the load-deflection curve for the specimen with the 40-in. splice and the constant-moment span in Figure 2.

In the system having a varying moment along the span (Figure 1), the plastic portion of the moment-curvature relation is not reflected in the load-deflection curve because the curvature that occurs at constant or nearly constant moment between yielding and strain hardening of the steel is

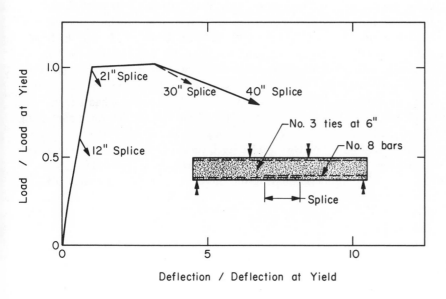

FIGURE 2   Effect of reinforcement splices on ductility.

limited to an extremely small distance at the section of maximum moment. Consequently, the plastic portion of the moment–curvature relation generates only an imperceptibly small amount of deflection.

The moment must increase beyond the yield moment for the "plastic-hinging zone" at the connection to spread into the span, a condition that is achieved by strain hardening of the reinforcement. That this phenomenon occurred for the system shown in Figure 1 becomes quite evident when it is considered that the break in the curve refers to yielding of the steel. As the moment increased beyond yield, the plastic-hinging zone extended out from the face of the connection and provided greater and greater rotational ductility. It has also been observed (Thomas and Sozen, 1965) that if the steel does not have a significant strain-hardening characteristic, the plastic zone does not spread.

It can be concluded, therefore, that a substantial portion of the ductility of a reinforced-concrete connection depends on the strain hardening of the reinforcement. To ensure ductility, steel stresses well above yielding must be developed.

CONNECTIONS WITH REINFORCEMENT SPLICES

Because of construction needs, it is often necessary to splice the reinforcement at the column connection, a point where the splice is least desirable. Figure 2 shows the effect of spliced reinforcement on the load–deflection curve, which is directly related to the moment–curvature relationship for the type of loading involved. The details of the test specimens to which the curves shown in Figure 2 refer are reported by Colaco (1965).

Consider the specimen with the 21-in. (or 21-diameter) splice. The concrete strength was 4,670 psi. If ACI 318-63 (American Concrete Institute, 1963) is taken as the voice of current professional opinion and the strength reduction factor ϕ is taken as unity (because the actual concrete strength in the specimen is measured by control tests), the limiting bond stress would be $9.5 \sqrt{f'_c} = 650$ psi. In accordance with the ordinary design assumption that $f_y = 40,000$ psi, the development length is 16 in., which is considerably short of the 21 in. provided. On the basis of these quantities, the designer would not question the ductility of this beam, which had no ductility at all. Coupon tests indicated a steel yield stress of 47,600 psi. Even if this information had been available to the designer (and it usually is not), he would have been satisfied with the splice, which evidently was barely sufficient to develop the yield stress.

Figure 3 provides information pertinent to the problem of frame ductility: the response of a 40-in. splice of number 8 bars at a connection. For this type of loading, the splicing problems are aggravated because steel stresses well in excess of yield must be developed. Furthermore, the anchorage distance is reduced because of the development

of inclined cracks: The nominal 40-in. lap may be shortened by approximately the depth of the beam. A comparison of the behavior of the two spliced connections having different amounts of transverse reinforcement points out another factor: The bursting stresses developed at the last splice have to be restrained by transverse reinforcement. It can be concluded that if ductility is required at a joint, the splice must develop more than the nominal yield stress of the reinforcing bar.

DESCRIPTION OF OBSERVED DAMAGE TO THE ANCHORAGE INTERNATIONAL AIRPORT CONTROL TOWER

THE STRUCTURE

The control tower at the Anchorage International Airport, designed in 1951, was a simple reinforced-concrete frame rising six stories above its footings and consisting of a single bay in each direction. The tower was approximately 4 mi southwest of downtown Anchorage. The terrain is Bootlegger Cove Clay overlain by silt deposits (Miller and Dobrovolny, 1959). The orientation of the building in plan is shown in Figure 4.

The north elevation is given in Figure 5. The four columns rested on $11 \times 11 \times 2.5$-ft isolated footings. The ground level was 12 ft 6 in. above the top of the footings. Up to level 1, the tower was surrounded on three sides (Figure 4) by a single-story steel building. The plan dimensions were 31 ft 6 in. (east–west) $\times$ 28 ft 8 in. (north–south) out-to-out of the frame columns.

The sizes and the reinforcement for the beams are given in Table 1. Hooks were prescribed at the ends of the reinforcing bars. Each floor contained an intermediate beam running north–south. The thickness of the reinforced-concrete floor slab varied from 6 in. to 5 in. The equipment and cab levels had steel floors. At all levels the floor systems were stiff enough to limit distortion in the horizontal plane. The columns were 18×18 in. throughout the building; the reinforcement for the columns is shown in Table 2. It is assumed that the concrete had a compressive strength of 3,000 psi and that the deformed reinforcing bars were of intermediate grade (40,000 psi).

Above ground level, cladding was composed of insulated-metal wall panels, which would have provided little resistance to the distortions of the frame in the vertical plane.

THE DAMAGE

The damage was total: The structure collapsed. A sketch of the north elevation (Figure 6) shows approximately the spill of the structural members. The top floors fell toward

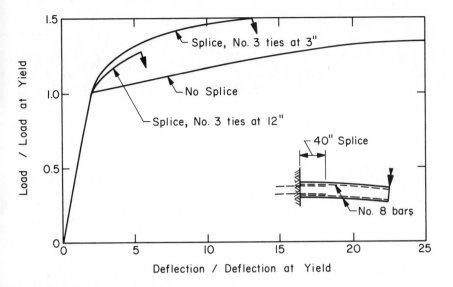

FIGURE 3 Effect of reinforcement splices on the ductility of a connection.

the west, almost perpendicular to the north–south axis of the structure, with a slight bias toward the south.

Figures 7–11 show the debris from various angles as indicated in Figure 4. The girders showed little damage that could be ascribed to causes other than impact with the ground. It was evident that the cause of the collapse was the failure of the column connections. Detail of a splice (column at equipment floor) is shown in Figure 11. The same connection can be seen in the upper right-hand corner of Figure 9 along with other broken connections. How

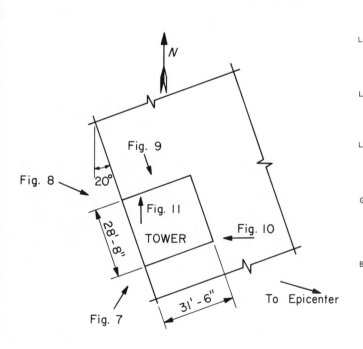

FIGURE 4 Orientation of control tower.

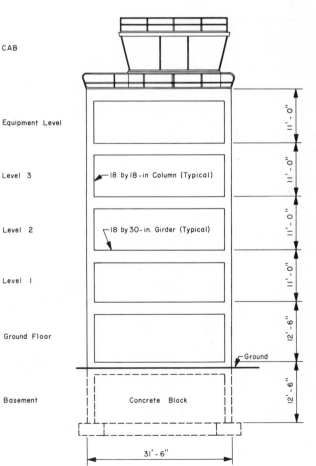

FIGURE 5 North elevation of control tower.

TABLE 1 Beam Reinforcement

Level	Elevation	Longitudinal Reinforcement[a] Straight	Bent	Transverse Reinforcement[b]	
Cab	N, S	2 No. 11	3 No. 10	No. 4:	3 at 8 in. W; 9 at 12 in. E
	E, W	2 No. 10	2 No. 10	None	
Equipment	N, S	3 No. 10	2 No. 11	No. 3:	2 at 12 in. W; 9 at 12 in. E
	E, W	2 No. 10	2 No. 10	None	
Third	N, S	3 No. 11	2 No. 11	No. 4:	4 at 12 in. W; 9 at 12 in. E
	E, W	2 No. 10	2 No. 10	None	
Second	N, S	2 No. 11	2 No. 11	No. 3:	2 at 12 in. W; 9 at 12 in. E
	E, W	2 No. 10	2 No. 10	None	
First	N, S	2 No. 11	2 No. 11	No. 3:	2 at 12 in. W; 9 at 12 in. E
	E, W	2 No. 10	2 No. 10	None	
Ground	N, S	3 No. 11	2 No. 11	No. 4:	4 at 12 in. W; 9 at 12 in. E
	E[c]	2 No. 9	2 No. 9	None	
Basement	W	2 No. 10	2 No. 10	None	

[a] The straight bars extend along the bottom face of the beam. The bent bars are bent so that they provide a flexural reinforcement at midspan and at the faces of the columns.

[b] Transverse (web) reinforcement provided by U-stirrups. First numeral indicates size of bar. Spaces between stirrups are given for both west and east ends of the beam.

[c] 18 × 22-in. beam. All other beams 18 × 30 in.

the column bars tore out of the top girder is seen in the middle foreground of Figure 7.

SPECULATIONS ON STRUCTURAL DESIGN

Reportedly, the control tower was not designed to resist earthquake effects because it was outside the city limits of Anchorage, which, at the time of construction of the tower, was considered to be in earthquake-risk zone 2. Consequently, the failure of the structure does not consititute evidence that bears on the success or failure of any building code. However, it is pertinent to speculate, with the help of hindsight, about what might have been foreseen, had the building been designed to resist earthquakes.

TABLE 2 Column Reinforcement

Level	Vertical	Transverse
Equipment	4 No. 9	No. 2 ties at 12 in.
Third	4 No. 9	No. 2 ties at 12 in.
Second	4 No. 11	No. 2 ties at 12 in.
First	4 No. 11	No. 2 ties at 12 in.
Ground	8 No. 10	No. 2 ties at 12 in.
Basement	8 No. 11	No. 2 ties at 12 in.

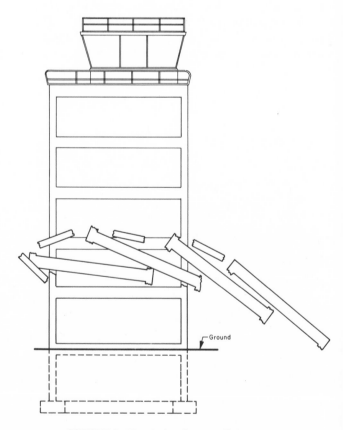

FIGURE 6 Sketch showing overall damage.

FIGURE 7   Southwest view.

FIGURE 8   Northwest view.

FIGURE 9 North view.

FIGURE 10 East view.

FIGURE 11   A reinforcement splice.

The following discussion refers to phenomena in the east–west direction of the frame, the direction in which the collapse occurred. It is assumed that the basement and the ground floor were inert. A masonry wall filled the frame at the basement. The ground floor was stiffened by the surrounding steel building (Figure 4).

The fundamental period of vibration for the frame, calculated on the basis of flexurally rigid floors and uncracked columns with the concrete modulus of deformation taken as 3 million psi, is 0.46 second (top four floors). The calculated period compares well with the period of 0.42 second based on the *Uniform Building Code* expression $T = 0.05H/\sqrt{D}$, where H is the height above the level considered and D is the width. Because the metal cladding would have provided little stiffness to the frame and because the columns would have cracked after a few oscillations of large magnitude, the period of the building would have been lengthened during the initial seconds of the strong ground motion. It follows that the structure was quite susceptible to the earthquake of March 1964, which had reportedly dominant periods greater than one-half second.

According to the *Uniform Building Code* (1949), the total design shear at the first floor would be 39,000 lb, or 6.6 percent of the weight of the structure above. This shear is based on the expression

$$F = \frac{0.6W}{(N + 4.5)},$$

where W is the weight and N is the number of stories above the level considered. At the time of the earthquake, buildings in the city of Anchorage were presumably being designed in accordance with this expression. The current *Uniform Building Code* (1964) (International Conference of Building Officials, 1964) expression results in an identical lateral-force coefficient. A total shear of 39,000 lb would correspond to a maximum moment of approximately 560,000 lb-in. at each one of the first-story columns. The interaction of axial-load and bending-moment capacities for a first-story column is shown in Figure 12a. The column capacity is obviously adequate, even if the design moment is boosted by a load factor and combined with a moment caused by motion in the transverse direction. If the design had been based on a zone 3 rating, which would double the moment, the designer still would have seen little cause for alarm in the column capacity.

The splicing of the column bars, however, is another matter. Once the necessity of a plastic hinge at the column is admitted, it follows that the column reinforcement must be stressed to more than its yield stress. On the basis of the orthodox (and incorrect) view that only the yield stress of 40,000 psi need be developed, it appears that the length of

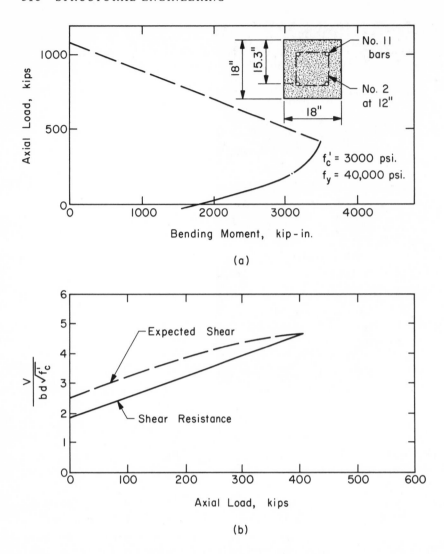

(a)

(b)

FIGURE 12   Resistance of columns at level 1. See text for discussion of graphs (a) and (b). f'_i = compressive strength of concrete in psi; f_y = yield stress of reinforcing steel in psi.

embedment for a No. 11 bar should be 45 in. or about 30 diameters (based on ACI 318–63, American Concrete Institute, 1963). The splices in the damaged structure were 20 diameters as recommended for compression splices in general. To have ductility, it is essential to develop more than the *actual* yield stress and it is certainly desirable to develop the full tensile strength of the bar; therefore, the required splice would be approximately 7 ft, ridiculously long but necessary in a column of 8 ft 6 in. clear height. If the structure had been designed to resist earthquakes, and if the ductility requirement of the prevailing code had been explicit, the designer might have extended the splices to 30 bar diameters, but this length of splice might still have not been adequate.

Another aspect of the design problem not evident from the design method is illustrated in Figure 12b. The column shear corresponding to the formation of plastic hinges (ignoring strain hardening) at the top and bottom connec-

tions of level 1 columns is shown in Figure 12b by the broken curve. The solid line represents the estimate of the shear resistance of the column given by the expression $V_c = (1 + P/16A_{tr} \sqrt{f'_c})\, 1.9\, bd \sqrt{f'_c}$ (Blume and others, 1961). Again, the potential trouble is not evident from the design method. The calculations imply shear stress in each column of about $0.6 \sqrt{f'_c}$. Such a value, even if tripled, would not concern the designer.

The critical question is whether the structure would have survived the earthquake if the splices had developed the strength of the bars and if adequate web reinforcement had been used in the columns. A categorical answer to this question is not possible because of the speculation involved, but some insight is provided by the strength of the structure that could have been built. Under ideal conditions of detailing, the shear in each column corresponding to a mechanism at level 1 would have been at least 37,000 lb. The total shear capacity in the four columns would correspond to 25 percent of the weight of the structure above level 1. This shear capacity, coupled with a ductility potential that might never have been called upon, would have been sufficient to prevent failure at level 1.

If the ground motion at Anchorage is assumed to have been like California earthquakes and to have had a maximum acceleration of 20 percent of gravity (g) the corresponding lateral, base shear force can be determined by means of typical spectrum curves. If we assume 3 percent of critical damping for the tower, the maximum base shear would be approximately 25 percent of the total weight. This is large enough to account for the failure of the tower with its inadequate splices.

CONCLUSIONS

Barring problems with the deformational capacity of the concrete itself, the critical factor affecting the plastic rotation capacity of reinforced concrete connections is the strain hardening of the reinforcement. Consequently, if lap splices must be used at column connections, the laps should be long enough to develop considerably more than the yield stress of the reinforcement, and adequate transverse reinforcement must be provided to restrain the bursting stresses caused by the bond stresses.

If ductility is a criterion in the design of earthquake-resistant frames, it must be explicit in the design process. The designer must be asked to recognize and show by what mechanism he will obtain the ductility in the frame and how the structure will resist the moments and shears compatible with the mechanism. Designing for forces alone is inadequate and can be misleading.

Ground motion like that recorded at Taft, California, in 1952 and having 20 percent g maximum acceleration is sufficient to account for the failure of the tower as designed. It is, of course, possible that there were also defects in construction. If these existed, they would have reduced an already inadequate structure.

ACKNOWLEDGMENTS

The inspection of earthquake damage in Anchorage, Alaska, was made possible through a grant of the National Science Foundation and the cooperation of the U.S. Naval Civil Engineering Laboratory, Port Hueneme, California.

REFERENCES

American Concrete Institute, 1963. ACI standard building code requirements for reinforced concrete (ACI 318–63). Detroit: American Concrete Institute.

Burns, N. H., and C. P. Siess, 1962. Load-deformation characteristics of beam-column connections in reinforced concrete. Civil Engineering Studies, Structural Research Series No. 234. Urbana: University of Illinois.

Blume, J. A., N. M. Newmark, and L. H. Corning, 1961. Design of multistory reinforced concrete buildings for earthquake motions. Chicago: Portland Cement Association.

Colaco, J. P., 1965. Prediction of steel force distribution in reinforced concrete members from bond-slip characteristics, PhD dissertation. Urbana: University of Illinois.

International Conference of Building Officials, 1964. Uniform Building Code, 1964 edition, Vol. 1. Pasadena: International Conference of Building Officials.

Miller, Robert D., and Ernest Dobrovolny, 1959. Surficial geology of Anchorage and vicinity, Alaska. U.S. Geological Survey Bulletin 1093. Washington: Government Printing Office. 128 p.

Thomas, K., and M. A. Sozen, 1965. A study of the inelastic rotation mechanism of reinforced concrete connections. Civil Engineering Studies Structural Research Series No. 301. Urbana: University of Illinois.

PAUL C. JENNINGS
CALIFORNIA INSTITUTE OF TECHNOLOGY

Response of Coupled Shear-Wall Structures

ABSTRACT: Analysis of coupled shear-wall idealizations of the Mt. McKinley and 1200 L Street apartment buildings in Anchorage shows that the distribution of failures in the spandrel beams and the fracturing of the shear-walls in the two buildings are logical consequences of vibration of the structures in their fundamental modes. Comparisons of the analytically determined fundamental modes and spandrel shear distributions to similar results from a computer-aided study of one of the buildings and with a postearthquake vibration test of the Mt. McKinley building, all show good agreement. The agreement indicates that many of the essential features of the response of the two buildings are exhibited by the simple shear-wall idealizations. The agreement also shows the difficulty of interpreting postearthquake vibration tests in the absence of preearthquake data.

A common type of earthquake damage is a characteristic formation of X-shaped cracks in the spandrels of buildings. These cracks result from an overstress in shear. If the spandrel is considered as a horizontal beam built-in at both ends, the shear force in this beam would depend on the lateral forces developed by the earthquake-induced vibrations of the building, as well as on the physical proportions of the beams and columns. When the spandrels are part of a frame in which the individual beams and columns are relatively slender, standard methods of structural analysis can be used to determine the shear forces, axial forces, and bending moments in the members. However, as the slenderness ratio of the members decreases, that is, as the length-to-width ratio approaches unity or less, standard methods of structural analysis are not applicable, and the distribution of forces and moments is much different from that in a corresponding frame of slender members. This fact has, apparently, not been widely recognized in the engineering profession, and analysis appropriate for design in earthquake-prone areas has not usually been done. During the Alaska earthquake, the extensive cracking of spandrels in several buildings in Anchorage made the existence of the problem more obvious. The objective of this paper is to show that the major features of the response of two of these buildings can be described by the vibration of a simple system of coupled shear walls, indicating that the forces and moments in the spandrels and columns of such structures can be determined by a simplified and practical method of analysis.

The Mt. McKinley building and the 1200 L Street building, two nearly identical 14-story apartment buildings, were damaged severely during the Alaska earthquake. Some of the significant features of the damage can be seen on the north side of the Mt. McKinley building. Here the failure of interior spandrel beams and also the failure of one of the shear walls of the building are clearly visible (Figure 1). We shall show later that the normal forces developed in the shear walls during the vibration of the building could have contributed significantly to the failure of this shear wall.

Flores, 1963). In that earthquake, the failure pattern was called "vertical shear failure," a term which is adopted here.

Because of its distance from the causative fault, its situation on a deep bed of rather poorly consolidated alluvium, and also because of the observed structural damage in the city of Anchorage, it is generally agreed that the ground motion at Anchorage consisted primarily of waves having periods greater than one-half second. Because of the absence of short-period components in the ground motion, the response of tall buildings would consist primarily of oscillations in the first mode of vibration. A vibration test performed after the earthquake showed that the Mt. McKinley building (Cloud, 1967) had a fundamental period of vibration in the short direction of about 1.16 seconds. Although the earthquake undoubtedly destroyed some stiffness, the period of the undamaged structure was probably not less than 1 second. (A change from 1.0 to 1.15 seconds would

George W. Housner

FIGURE 1   Mt. McKinley building, looking south.

An end view of the 1200 L Street building is shown in Figure 2; the similarity in the damage pattern of the two buildings is remarkable, although the 1200 L Street building was damaged less extensively. The two buildings are about 1 mi apart and are oriented 180° to each other. A general view of the Mt. McKinley building (Figure 3) shows that a damage pattern similar to but more complex than that on the north side occurred also on the long east face of this building. The corresponding sides of the 1200 L Street building showed a similar but milder damage pattern. The interior spandrels on the narrow south side of the Mt. McKinley building (Figure 3) were not damaged as much as those on the opposite end (Figure 1), but X-cracking was present from the second to the seventh floors.

This type of spandrel-beam failure is not unique to the Alaska earthquake; it also was reported in damaged buildings in the Chilean earthquake of 1960 (Steinbrugge and

Mac's Foto

FIGURE 2   1200 L Street building, looking north.

American Iron and Steel Institute

FIGURE 3   Mt. McKinley building, looking northwest.

of the shear walls are denoted by I_1, A_1 and d_1, respectively; I_2, A_2, and d_2 are the corresponding constants for the spandrel beams. The distance between the neutral axes of the shear walls is a_1, the centerline distance between spandrels is given by a_2, the height of the shear walls is l_1 and the length of the spandrel beam is l_2. The vertical coordinate is x, and y denotes the lateral displacement of the neutral axis of a shear wall with respect to the base of the structure. For this analysis the dimensions and properties are considered uniform over the height of the structure.

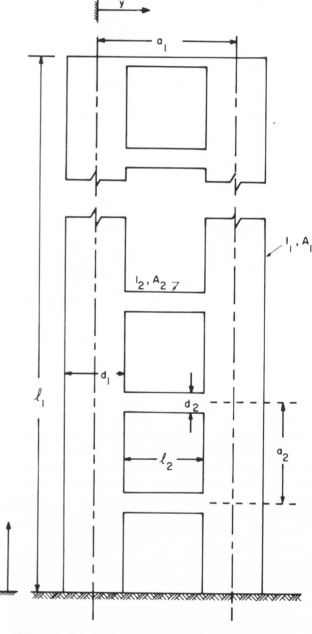

FIGURE 4   Coupled shear-wall and spandrel-beam notation.

correspond to about 25 percent loss of stiffness.) It therefore appears reasonable to assume that the observed failure pattern of the spandrel beams of the 1200 L Street and Mt. McKinley buildings can be explained by an analysis of the fundamental mode of vibration.

Because the intensity of the ground motion at Anchorage is unknown, the equations developed later are expressed in terms of y_0, the maximum deflection at the top of the building relative to the ground. (All symbols used are defined where they first appear and are also listed alphabetically and defined in the Appendix.)

COUPLED SHEAR WALLS

Many of the important features of the response of the apartment buildings can be understood by studying the response of a simple system of coupled shear walls, as shown in Figure 4. In this figure, the moment of inertia, area, and depth

The deformation of a coupled shear-wall system under lateral loading is illustrated in Figure 5. In general, it has been found that analysis of deflection requires consideration of the effect of axial deformation of the shear walls (see, for example, the spandrel deformation in Figure 7). Each of the spandrels in Figure 5 is deformed in such a way as to elongate the left shear wall and compress the right wall. Although the forces contributed by any one spandrel might be neglected, their effects accumulate to give an appreciable strain in the shear walls. The magnitude of the effect of axial deformation of the shear walls is illustrated in the 14-story example presented below: The deflection at the roof, if axial deformation is permitted, is more than six times the deflection obtained if the shear walls are considered inextensible.

In the analysis of coupled shear walls, it has proved useful to replace the spandrel beams by a continuous system that has the same bending and shear resistance per length of shear wall as the spandrel beams. This continuous system can be visualized as small, independently acting laminae of thickness dx, moment of inertia $I_2 dx/a_2$, and area $A_2 dx/a_2$. The shear at the point of contraflexure of the spandrels thereby becomes a continuous function of x. The shear in a given spandrel beam is approximated by integrating the shear force from $x - a_2/2$ to $x + a_2/2$, where x is the height to the spandrel beam being considered.

The above method of analysis was first applied to coupled shear walls by Chitty (1947). Beck (1962) has presented a detailed solution, including graphs applicable to design, for constant beam and wall properties and uniform lateral loading. Results also have been published for a concentrated load acting at the top of the wall (Rosman, 1964); this analysis includes a treatment of systems having more than two walls and also a discussion of the effects of different foundation conditions and of different top and bottom spandrel beams. Burns (1965) has studied a triangularly distributed lateral load, such as those specified in many seismic codes; his results also include the effects of parabolically varying wall and beam stiffnesses, a treatment of symmetrical two-bay frames, and a comparison of results to those of conventional methods of analysis performed on a digital computer. Burns found that the results obtained by using the equivalent system compared closely to those from the computer. Burns' work also can be used to show that the effects of small variations in shear-wall properties are minor for shear-wall systems of the dimensions considered herein.

DYNAMIC RESPONSE

Because the analysis of dynamic response of coupled shear walls is, in general, substantially more difficult than analysis of static response, it is convenient to begin the analysis by looking at two special, simplified examples. As we have stated, the study is limited to the fundamental mode of vibration.

If a coupled shear wall is not more than a few stories tall and if the spandrel beams are very flexible with respect to the shear wall, the shear-wall deformation will be that of a simple cantilever beam (Figure 6). Under these conditions, the axial deformation of the shear walls may be neglected; the forces in the spandrel beams will depend only on the deflection of the shear walls. The problem is therefore reduced to an analysis of the geometry of vibration of the fundamental mode.

Figure 7 shows that the deformation, δ, introduced into the spandrel beams by the lateral deformation of the shear walls is given by

$$\delta = a_1 \frac{dy}{dx} \qquad (1)$$

in which dy/dx is the slope of the shear wall at the spandrel height. The shear in the spandrel beam is related to the shear-wall slope by

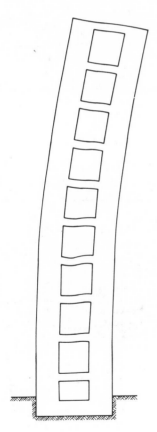

FIGURE 5   The general pattern of deformation of a coupled shear wall.

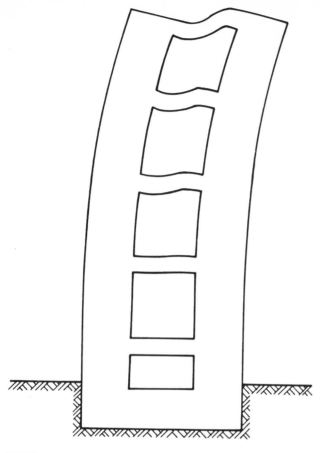

FIGURE 6 Coupled shear-wall system deforming as cantilever beams.

$$V = \left(\frac{12EI_2 a_1}{l_2^3 \beta^2} \right) \left(\frac{dy}{dx} \right) \qquad (2)$$

in which

$$\beta^2 = \left[1 + \frac{12EI_2}{l_2^2 A_2^* G} \right]. \qquad (3)$$

In Eq. (2) and (3), E and G are the elastic and rigidity moduli, respectively, of the spandrels, A_2^* is the spandrel composite cross section for shear deformation, V is the spandrel shearing force, and β^2 is a measure of the relative flexural and shearing stiffnesses of the spandrel beams. Taking β^2 as unity is equivalent to neglecting the shearing resistance of the spandrels.

The maximum value of the spandrel shear will occur in the spandrel nearest the point where dy/dx in Eq. (2) is greatest. For the cantilever response, this maximum occurs at the end of the beam. The maximum slope of a cantilever

beam vibrating in the first mode is $1.376\, y_0/l_1$, where y_0 is the maximum deflection of the beam (Bishop and Johnson, 1960). Assuming that a spandrel beam is centered about the point of maximum slope, this value yields the maximum spandrel shear as shown:

$$V_{\max} = 16.52 y_0 \left(\frac{EI_2 a_1}{l_1 l_2^3 \beta^2} \right). \qquad (4)$$

Therefore, where the shear walls deflect as cantilever beams, the maximum spandrel shear induced by vibration in the first mode occurs at $x = l_1$ and is given by Eq. (4).

The fundamental mode of a cantilever beam is approximated closely by the deflection under a uniform lateral load, and it is relevant for this study to examine this approximation.

The deflection of a cantilever beam for uniform loading is given by

$$y = \frac{y_0}{3} \left(\xi^4 + 6\xi^2 - 4\xi^3 \right). \qquad (5)$$

If we proceed as stated, this static approximation yields

$$V_{\max} = 16 y_0 \left(\frac{EI_2 a_1}{l_1 l_2^3 \beta^2} \right) \qquad (6)$$

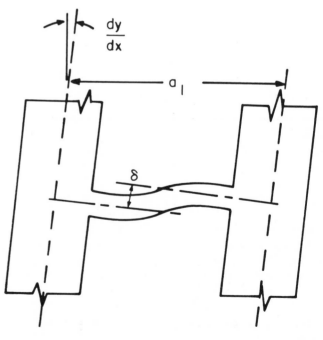

FIGURE 7 Deformation of a spandrel beam in a coupled shear wall.

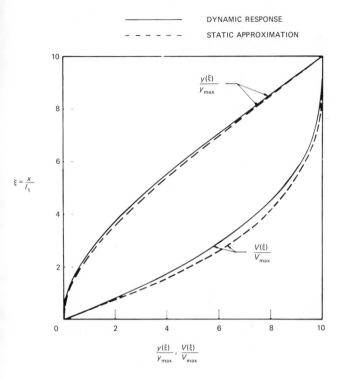

FIGURE 8   Relative deflection and spandrel-shear distribution for a cantilever type of shear-wall system.

Dynamic response:

$$y = \frac{y_0}{1.616} [(\sin 2.365\,\xi - \sinh 2.365\,\xi + 1.0178)\,(\cosh 2.365\,\xi - \cos 2.365\,\xi)] \qquad (7)$$

$$V_{max} = 18.49 y_0 \left(\frac{EI_2 a_1}{l_1 l_2{}^3 \beta^2} \right) \text{ at } x = 0.448\,l_1 \qquad (8)$$

Static approximation:

$$y = y_0\,(\xi^4 + 4\xi^2 - 4\xi^3) \qquad (9)$$

$$V_{max} = 18.47\,y_0 \left(\frac{EI_2 a_1}{l_1 l_2{}^3 \beta^2} \right) \text{ at } x = 0.423\,l_1 \qquad (10)$$

The maximum deflection y_0 again occurs at $x = l_1$.

in which, as for the dynamic response, the maximum values occur at $x = l_1$. Comparison of Eq. (4) and (6) shows that the static approximation gives a value within 3 percent of that from the fundamental mode of vibration.

The results for shear walls deflecting as cantilever beams in the first mode are summarized in Figure 8, in which the relative shear-wall deflection and spandrel shear are plotted as functions of height. Figure 8 shows that the static approximations to the shear-wall deflection and spandrel shear present in the dynamic response are satisfactory and also that a failure of the spandrel beams in this cantilever system would begin at the topmost level.

Another deformation pattern of interest is that of a beam clamped at the base and guided at the upper end (Figure 9). This deformation may occur where the top spandrel is deep and the intermediate spandrels are so flexible that the axial deformation of the shear-walls is negligible. This model may apply also for systems of multiple shear walls capped by a heavy spandrel beam, where axial deformation of the walls is prevented. The latter situation is achieved approximately in the long sides of the Mt. McKinley and 1200 L Street buildings.

Equation (2) is applicable for the clamped-guided deformation pattern also. An analysis similar to that described yields the following results:

FIGURE 9   Coupled shear-wall system deforming as clamped-guided beams.

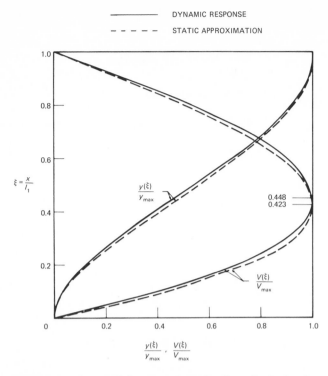

FIGURE 10 Relative deflection and spandrel-shear distribution for a clamped-guided type of shear-wall system.

The relative shear-wall deflection and spandrel shear for the clamped-guided beam are shown in Figure 10. Equations (7)–(10) and Figure 10 show that the approximate values given by the static analysis are in close agreement with those occurring in vibration in the fundamental mode.

Figure 10 shows that, if the deformation of the shear walls can be modeled by the deflection of a clamped-guided beam, then the larger spandrel shears will be concentrated near the midheight of the wall; failure of the spandrels would therefore be expected first near this point. This deformation pattern correlates well with the damage pattern exhibited by the long sides of the Mt. McKinley and 1200 L Street apartment buildings.

GENERAL SHEAR-WALL ANALYSIS

The dynamic response of coupled shear walls can be modeled by that of a cantilever or clamped-guided beam only under special circumstances. In the general case, where axial deformation and spandrel stiffness are not negligible, the dynamic response of coupled shear walls is rather complicated. However, the analysis of the cantilever and clamped-guided deformations indicates that a satisfactory approximation to the response in the fundamental mode of vibration probably can be obtained from the static deforma-

tion under uniform load. From the results of Beck (1962) with $\xi = x/l_1$, the deflection under uniform load can be written as

$$y(\xi) = y_0 g(\xi)/g(1) \qquad (11)$$

in which the maximum deflection, y_0, occurs at $\xi = 1$, and $g(\xi)$ is given by

$$g(\xi) = \frac{1}{12\gamma^2} \left[\frac{(\gamma^2 - 1)\bar{\alpha}^2}{24} (6\xi^2 - 4\xi^3 + \xi^4) + \frac{1}{2}(2\xi - \xi^2) \right.$$
$$\left. - \frac{\tanh\bar{\alpha}}{\bar{\alpha}} + \frac{\cosh\bar{\alpha}\xi}{\bar{\alpha}}(\tanh\bar{\alpha} - \tanh\bar{\alpha}\xi) + \frac{\cosh\bar{\alpha}\xi - 1}{\bar{\alpha}^2 \cosh\bar{\alpha}} \right], \qquad (12)$$

in which

$$\gamma^2 = 1 + \frac{4I_1}{a_1^2 A_1}, \alpha^2 = \frac{6a_1^2 l_1^2 I_2}{a_2 l_2^3 I_1}, \bar{\alpha} = \frac{\alpha\gamma}{\beta}. \qquad (13)$$

By using Eq. (12), the spandrel shear found by Beck (1962) for the kth elevation can be written as

$$V(\xi_k) = \left[y_0 \left(\frac{EI_2 a_1}{l_1 l_2^3 \beta^2} \right) \left(\frac{1}{g(1)} \right) \right] [1 - \xi_k$$
$$\qquad (14)$$
$$- C_1^* \cosh\bar{\alpha}\xi_k + C_2^* \sinh\bar{\alpha}\xi_k]$$

with

$$C_1^* = \left(\frac{2l_1}{a_2\bar{\alpha}} \right) \left(\sinh\frac{a_2\bar{\alpha}}{2l_1} \right),$$
$$\qquad (15)$$
$$C_2^* = C_1^* \left(\tanh\bar{\alpha} + \frac{1}{\bar{\alpha}\cosh\bar{\alpha}} \right).$$

The constant γ^2 is unity if axial deformation of the shear walls is neglected; its significance is seen in the first term of the right side of Eq. (12).

The following values, chosen from the plans of the Mt. McKinley and 1200 L Street apartment buildings, represent a simple coupled shear wall having the general dimensions of the buildings.

$$a_1 = 18 \text{ ft} \quad l_1 = 14\, a_2 \quad d_1 = 12 \text{ ft} \quad t_w = t$$
$$a_2 = 8.5 \text{ ft} \quad l_2 = 6 \text{ ft} \quad d_2 = 4 \text{ ft} \quad t_s = t/2 \qquad (16)$$

in which t_w is the uniform thickness of the shear wall, and t_s is the uniform spandrel thickness.

The numbers of Eq. (16) lead to $\bar{\alpha} = 11.8$. The magnitude of $\bar{\alpha}$ indicates that the coupled shear-wall system is responding nearly as a single cantilever beam. Also, for this value of $\bar{\alpha}$, the largest contribution to the deflection comes from the first term inside the brackets in Eq. (12).

Equations (11)–(15) were used to plot the relative deflection and spandrel-shear distribution shown by the solid lines in Figure 11. Figure 11 shows that the maximum spandrel shear occurs at $x = 0.21 l_1$. Using this value in Eq. (14)—in which $g(1) = 0.219$—produces the maximum spandrel shear:

$$V_{\max} = 3.22 y_0 \left(\frac{EI_2 a_1}{l_1 l_2{}^3 \beta^2} \right) \qquad (17)$$

Comparison of Figure 11 with Figures 8 and 10 shows that the deflected shape of this coupled shear wall is similar to that of the cantilever beam, whereas the spandrel-shear distribution is qualitatively similar to that for the clamped-guided beam. Because the static response to uniform load is a close approximation to the response in the fundamental mode of vibration in both of these simpler examples, the assumption that the first modal response of a coupled shear wall is adequately given by Figure 11 is reinforced.

The response of the three types of shear wall to the same uniformly distributed lateral load can be compared under the condition that the overall dimensions of the different systems are given by Eq. (16). A lateral force W, uniformly distributed over each of the three coupled systems, produces maximum deflections of the cantilever, clamped-guided, and coupled shear-wall systems in the ratio of $6.7 : 2.2 : 1.0$; these ratios show the flexibility of the cantilever system and the stiffness of the coupled shear walls. Comparisons of the maximum shear forces in the spandrel beam by using the appropriate values of y_0 in Eq. (6), (10), and (17) gives the ratio of $33 : 13 : 1.0$ for the maximum spandrel shears of the three systems. These ratios show that the cantilever or clamped-guided deformation patterns are inappropriate models for coupled shear walls of the dimensions of the apartment building end walls.

The values of the maximum deflection and spandrel shear for a lateral load W are summarized in Table 1.

The results in Table 1 hold in general for the cantilever and clamped-guided systems, but for the coupled shear wall they apply only for the constants of Eq. (16). For the cantilever and clamped-guided shear walls, the deflections and spandrel shears were calculated by using shear-wall bending stiffness only, and neglecting spandrel stiffness and shear-wall elongation. The results show clearly that these two latter factors should be considered for shear walls of the dimensions of the end walls of the Mt. McKinley and 1200 L Street apartment buildings.

The coupled shear-wall analysis includes the effects of both spandrel stiffness and shear-wall elongation, and both these effects are significant for structures of the dimensions considered here. In the example defined by Eq. (16), neglecting the effect of axial deformation results in the underestimation of the maximum deflection by more than 500 percent. The maximum spandrel shear is less sensitive to the axial deformation of the shear walls; neglecting this effect gives a spandrel shear only 11 percent higher than that from the more general analysis.

VERTICAL SHEAR FAILURE OF THE APARTMENT BUILDINGS

The end walls of the Mt. McKinley and 1200 L Street apartment buildings can be modeled more closely than was done in the example discussed above. If the exterior spandrels of the shear walls of the buildings are ignored (see Figure 1), the shear walls can be treated as a symmetric

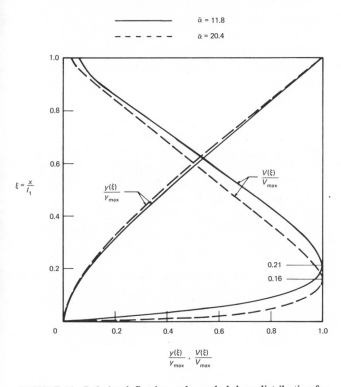

FIGURE 11 Relative deflection and spandrel-shear distribution for coupled shear-wall models of the Mt. McKinley and 1200 L Street apartment buildings.

TABLE 1   Response of Shear-Wall Systems to Uniform Lateral Load

Shear-Wall System	Maximum Deflection	Maximum Spandrel Shear	Location of Maximum Spandrel Shear
Cantilever	$y_0 = 0.0625 \dfrac{Wl_1^3}{EI_1}$	$V_{max} = 1.00 \dfrac{Wl_1^2 a_1 I_2}{l_2^3 \beta^2 I_1}$	$x = l_1$
Clamped-guided	$y_0 = 0.0208 \dfrac{Wl_1^3}{EI_1}$	$V_{max} = 0.384 \dfrac{Wl_1^2 a_1 I_2}{l_2^3 \beta^2 I_1}$	$x = 0.423 l_1$
Coupled shear wall[a]	$y_0 = 0.00939 \dfrac{Wl_1^3}{EI_1}$	$V_{max} = 0.0302 \dfrac{Wl_1^2 a_1 I_2}{l_2^3 \beta^2 I_1}$	$x = 0.21 l_1$

[a] Resulting values apply only to constants of Eq. (16).

two-bay frame. One half of this two-bay frame then can be considered as an unequal coupled shear wall (Burns, 1965) and the analysis proceeds much as before, except that the area of the center wall is taken to be infinite in order to meet the condition that this wall does not undergo axial deformation. Figure 12 illustrates the two-bay frame and the equivalent coupled shear wall. The shear walls actually vary from 12 in. at the base to 8 in. at the top, and the spandrels are approximately 1½ in. shallower than the shear walls.

From the dimensions given in Figure 12, the following values are obtained:

$$\alpha^2 = 1920, \beta^2 = 5.05, \gamma^2 = 1.0937, \bar{\alpha} = 20.4 \qquad (18)$$

The fact that β^2 is considerably greater than unity indicates that the spandrels derive their stiffness primarily from shearing resistance. The resulting shear distribution and relative deflection for this example are given by the dashed lines in Figure 11, which show that the deformation pattern is substantially the same as that of the simpler example of the same general dimensions presented above.

The maximum deflection and the maximum spandrel shear for this shear wall in response to a uniformly distributed static load W are

$$y_0 = 0.00585 \left(\frac{Wl_1^3}{EI_1} \right) \qquad (19)$$

$$V_{max} = 0.0115 \left(\frac{Wl_1^2 a_1 I_2}{l_2^3 \beta^2 I_1} \right), \text{ at } x = 0.16 l_1. \qquad (20)$$

These values show that the shear-wall model for the apartment end walls is stiffer, by nearly twice, but induces signi-

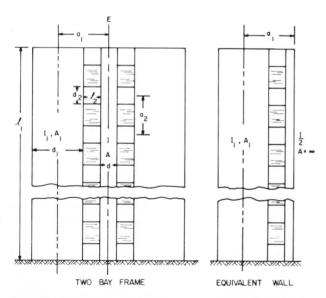

FIGURE 12   The equivalent coupled shear wall for the two-bay end walls of the Mt. McKinley and 1200 L Street apartment buildings. Representative dimensions follow:

$a_1 = 141.5$ in.	$d_1 = 148$ in.
$a_2 = 102$ in.	$d_2 = 48$ in.
$l_1 = 1428$ in.	$d = 54$ in.
$l_2 = 40.5$ in.	$t_w = 10$ in.
	$t_s = 8$ in.

ficantly less spandrel shear than that associated with the simpler shear wall of Table 1.

Figure 11 indicates that the maximum spandrel shear for the two buildings would be developed near $0.16l_1$, that is, just above the top of the second story. The damage pattern shown in Figures 1 and 2 seems to be heaviest at the top of the third story. This pattern probably reflects the influence of the substantially sturdier first stories of the buildings, seen most clearly in Figure 3. The greater rigidity of the lower parts of the structures has a tendency to make the buildings respond as 13-story rather than as 14-story buildings and thereby shifts upward the location of large spandrel shears. Comparison of Figures 1 and 2 to Figure 11 shows that the distribution of distress in the spandrel beams along the height of the building correlates closely with the shear forces expected from the analysis of elastic response.

The deformation shown in Figure 5 helps illustrate one possible failure mechanism of coupled shear walls. If the most heavily stressed spandrels should fail, the deflection of the shear-wall system implies that the neighboring spandrels will receive an increased load, which in turn may lead to their failure. This failure progression is schematically shown in Figure 13. As the middle spandrels lose more and more strength, the shear walls tend to approach the deformation of cantilever beams; larger spandrel shears are thereby induced near the top of the walls. Thus, the failure zone tends to move up the buildings, and the shear walls might even become "unzipped" if the excitation were to continue long enough.

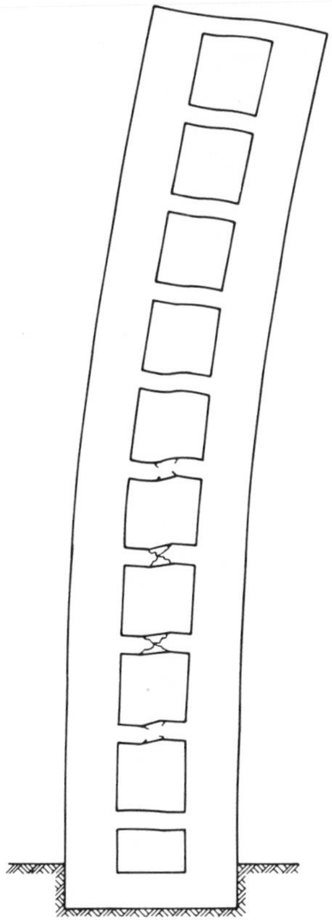

Another failure mechanism is illustrated by the shear-wall fractures visible in Figures 1 and 2. The lesser damage in the left inner spandrels shows that the failure of the shear wall has relieved the spandrels of the shearing deformation that they would otherwise undergo.

The magnitude of the spandrel shearing stresses and the shear-wall normal stresses near the failure zones can be estimated using the constants of Figure 12. These constants are first used in Eq. (14) to give the maximum shear in the spandrels as a function of y_0. The average shearing stress can then be approximated by dividing by A_2^*, which is taken as $A_2/1.2$. Similarly, the bending stress in the shear wall and the normal stress associated with the axial deflection of the shear wall can be found from the results of Beck (1962). The resulting stresses, evaluated at the point of maximum spandrel shear ($x = 0.16l_1$), are:

$$\tau_s = 400\,y_0, \quad \sigma_n = 740\,y_0, \quad \sigma_b = 280\,y_0, \qquad (21)$$

in which τ_s is the maximum average shearing stress in a spandrel beam for elastic response, σ_n is the normal stress in the shear wall from the effects of axial deformation, and σ_b is the maximum bending stress on the shear wall at $x = 0.16l_1$. The bending stress σ_b varies considerably with height; its value at the base is $790\,y_0$, whereas at the base σ_n is almost the same as given in Eq. (21).

Equations (14) and (21) show that a deflection of a few inches would be sufficient to cause the spandrels to fail in shear and to introduce significant normal stresses in the shear walls. The normal stresses induced by the vibration apparently also could have contributed substantially to the failure of the shear walls of the two buildings. Clough and Benuska (1966) have estimated that the maximum deflection of the 1200 L Street building in the transverse direction was 2.2 in. during the earthquake. Using this deflection in Eq. (21) gives an indication of the magnitude of the stresses in the shear walls and spandrel beams.

EARTHQUAKE LOADING

An earthquake-resistant design using a uniform lateral load may be satisfactory under special circumstances, but the design of tall buildings generally requires consideration of other loadings. Many building code specifications include a triangularly distributed lateral load, varying from zero at the base to a maximum at the top of the building. The static

FIGURE 13   Sketch of the failure pattern of the spandrel beams in a coupled shear wall.

response of coupled shear walls to triangular loading has been studied by Burns (1965). His presentation includes results for buildings with nonuniform properties and charts applicable to design.

To illustrate the difference in spandrel shear produced by uniform and by triangular loading, the spandrel shear resulting from a force W uniformly distributed along a coupled shear wall and the results for the same force distributed triangularly are shown in Figure 14. This figure shows that the triangular loading does not greatly affect the location of the maximum spandrel shear, but that it does significantly increase the value of the maximum shear throughout the shear wall. This increase reflects the greater leverage of the forces in the triangular distribution. Figure 14 also illustrates the type of changes that are expected in the spandrel shear if higher modes are included in the response.

COMPARISON OF ANALYSES WITH TEST RESULTS

Certain portions of the results given in the preceding paragraphs can be compared to the results of the shaking test performed on the Mt. McKinley building shortly after the earthquake (Cloud, 1967). In addition, the comparison can include some of the results of a digital computer study of the earthquake response of the 1200 L Street building (Clough and Benuska, 1966). The results of the computer study are also given in this volume by K. L. Benuska and R. W. Clough (1973).

The first-mode shapes of the apartment buildings in the transverse direction as calculated from the coupled shear-wall theory ($\bar{\alpha} = 20.4$) and as calculated from the digital

computer study of the 1200 L Street building by Clough and Benuska are compared in Figure 15. These two results, which are virtually identical, can be compared to Cloud's experimentally determined mode shape of the Mt. McKinley building. In Figure 15 the experimental mode shape was normalized at $\xi = 0.8$, rather than at 1.0, because more consistent results between different tests were obtained this way. There was considerable torsion of the top floor during the tests, and the value plotted for $\xi = 1.0$ is the average of two readings made at opposite ends of the building. With the possible exception of the roof point, the agreement between the theoretical mode shapes and the experimental values is considered to be good.

Also shown in Figure 15 is a comparison of the spandrel-shear distribution predicted by the shear-wall theory and by the computer study. Clough and Benuska's (1966) digital results, which give the maximum shear in response to earthquake excitation, include the effects of the core walls of the structure, of higher modes of vibration, and of the variations of stiffness and mass that occur in the structure. These effects are not considered in the shear-wall theory; therefore, it is expected that the two approaches would produce differences in the spandrel-shear distributions. Nevertheless, the two patterns are quite similar. Figure 15 compares only the distributions of spandrel shears, not the maximum values. The maxima cannot be compared precisely, but for equal roof deflections, the shear-wall theory gives spandrel shear about 40 percent higher than the computer results. This difference is consistent with the effects of the core, which, if included in the analysis, would reduce the spandrel shears in the lower stories.

Similar comparisons of results for vibration in the longitudinal direction are shown in Figure 16, in which the mode

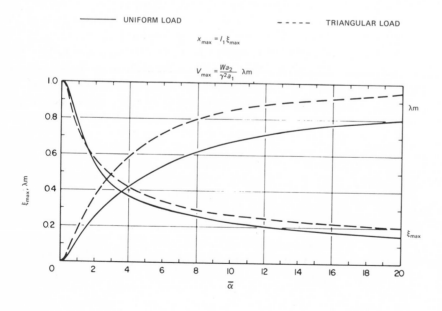

FIGURE 14   Comparison of the location and magnitude of the maximum spandrel shear for uniformly and triangularly distributed lateral loads.

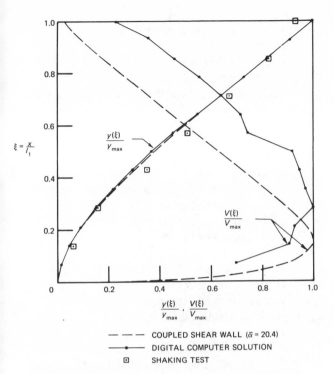

$\xi = \dfrac{x}{l_1}$

$\dfrac{y(\xi)}{y_{max}}$

$\dfrac{V(\xi)}{V_{max}}$

$\dfrac{y(\xi)}{y_{max}}$, $\dfrac{V(\xi)}{V_{max}}$

--- --- COUPLED SHEAR WALL ($\bar{\alpha}$ = 20.4)
———•——— DIGITAL COMPUTER SOLUTION
    ▣   SHAKING TEST

FIGURE 15 Comparison of theoretical and experimental deflections and spandrel-shear distributions, transverse direction. Digital computer solution from Clough and Benuska (1966); shaking test from Cloud (1967).

Street building before the earthquake and the maximum spandrel shears for linear response to a particular earthquake excitation; the earthquake response includes all the modes, hence the somewhat irregular appearance of the results. Next, the coupled shear-wall and clamped-guided beam results are from the first-mode responses of highly idealized continuous models of the buildings that neglect, for example, the core-walls and variations of stiffness with height. Finally, the experimental results are first-mode responses from a postearthquake vibration test of the Mt. McKinley building, the more severely damaged of the two apartment buildings. Despite all these differences, the agreement between the three sets of results is close.

The closeness of the agreement points out the difficulty in interpreting postearthquake vibration tests in the absence of preearthquake data. If it is possible for the fundamental-mode shapes of a severely damaged structure to agree closely with elastic analyses of the undamaged structure, then the value of finding postearthquake mode shapes (and frequencies) is questionable when preearthquake data or other comparable results are not available. Studies are needed to determine what dynamic experiments would be most informative in postearthquake building tests.

shape and spandrel-shear distribution of a clamped-guided beam are compared to the digital results by Clough and Benuska (1966) and to the experimental mode shape found by Cloud (1967). Figure 16 shows that the results of the computer study are not too dissimilar to those for a clamped-guided beam and that the data points are not inconsistent with either result, although there is more tendency toward the clamped-guided beam mode shape in the lower and middle stories.

Figure 16 shows also that the distribution of spandrel shears found in the digital computer study is similar to that expected if the building deformed as a clamped-guided beam. The discrepancy is largest near the top of the building where the clamped-guided approximation indicates spandrel shears consistently smaller than those from the computer analysis. In general, however, the agreement between the spandrel-shear distributions in Figure 16 is closer than it is in Figure 15. This closer agreement probably reflects the relatively greater contribution of the core walls to the building stiffness in the transverse direction; in the longitudinal direction the resistance was supplied primarily by the sidewall frames (Clough and Benuska, 1966).

The nature of the comparison shown in Figures 15 and 16 should be made clear: The computer results give the first-mode shape from a finite-element model of the 1200 L

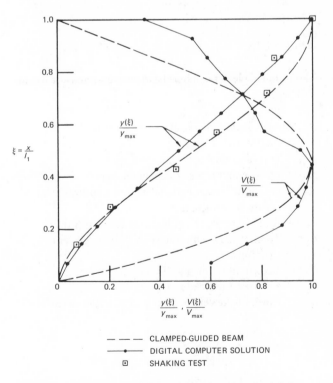

$\xi = \dfrac{x}{l_1}$

$\dfrac{y(\xi)}{y_{max}}$

$\dfrac{V(\xi)}{V_{max}}$

$\dfrac{y(\xi)}{y_{max}}$, $\dfrac{V(\xi)}{V_{max}}$

--- --- CLAMPED-GUIDED BEAM
———•——— DIGITAL COMPUTER SOLUTION
    ▣   SHAKING TEST

FIGURE 16 Comparison of theoretical and experimental deflections and spandrel-shear distributions, longitudinal direction. Digital computer solution from Clough and Benuska (1966); shaking test from Cloud (1967).

CONCLUSIONS

From comparisons of the first-mode shapes and the spandrel-shear distributions obtained from coupled shear-wall models of the two apartment buildings with those from a digital computer study of the 1200 L Street building (Clough and Benuska, 1966) and with the experimentally determined mode shapes (Cloud, 1967), we conclude that a coupled shear-wall vibrating in the fundamental mode describes the major features of the response of the two 14-story Anchorage structures to the earthquake motion. A general shear wall was used to model the response in the transverse directions, and a shear wall deforming like a clamped-guided beam was used to model the longitudinal responses. The comparisons indicate that the coupled shear-wall theory is a useful one for earthquake-resistant design. In particular, it should prove a valuable guide for determining the strength requirements of spandrel beams.

Comparison of test results with analytical results for the undamaged building and examination of the test results themselves indicate further that it is very difficult to deduce damage from postearthquake vibration tests. In general, it appears possible to make meaningful statements about damage from postearthquake vibration tests only where preearthquake tests are available, or for structures in which the damage is especially severe.

APPENDIX

The following letter symbols have been adopted for use in this paper:

A = cross-sectional area of center shear wall of a symmetric two-bay frame
A_1 = cross-sectional area of a shear wall
A_2 = cross-sectional area of spandrel beam
A_2^* = composite cross-sectional area of a spandrel beam for shear deformation
a_1 = distance between neutral axes of shear walls
a_2 = distance between centerlines of two adjacent spandrels
C_1^* = a constant defined in Eq. (15)
C_2^* = a constant defined in Eq. (15)
d = width of the center shear wall of a symmetric two-bay frame
d_1 = depth of a shear wall
d_2 = depth of a spandrel beam
E = modulus of elasticity
G = modulus of rigidity
$g(\xi)$ = algebraic expression defined in Eq. (12)
I = moment of inertia of the center shear wall of a symmetric two-bay frame
I_1 = moment of inertia of a shear wall

I_2 = moment of inertia of a spandrel beam
k = integer denoting story
l_1 = height of a shear wall
l_2 = length of a spandrel beam
t_s = thickness of a spandrel beam
t_w = thickness of a shear wall
V = shear force in a spandrel beam
W = a laterally applied force
x = vertical coordinate
y = lateral displacement of the neutral axis of a shear wall
y_o = maximum lateral displacement of a shear wall
α^2 = a constant defined in Eq. (13)
$\bar{\alpha}$ = a constant defined in Eq. (13)
β^2 = a constant defined in Eq. (3)
γ^2 = a constant defined in Eq. (13)
δ = vertical deflection of one end of a spandrel with respect to the other end
τ_s = shearing stress in a spandrel beam
σ_b = bending stress in a shear wall
σ_n = axial stress in a shear wall
ξ = x/l_1, a dimensionless vertical coordinate
ξ_k = the value of ξ at the kth spandrel, numbered from the bottom of the shear wall

REFERENCES

Beck, Hubert, 1962. Contribution to the analysis of coupled shear walls. *Journal of the American Concrete Institute*, 59 (August), 1055–1070.

Benuska, K. L., and R. W. Clough, 1973. Dynamic analyses of building failures, *in* The Great Alaska Earthquake of 1964: Engineering. NAS Pub. 1606. Washington: National Academy of Sciences.

Bishop, R. E. D., and D. C. Johnson, 1960. The mechanics of vibration. New York: Cambridge University Press. p. 282–352.

Burns, R. J., 1965. An approximate method of analyzing coupled shear walls subject to triangular loading. Proceedings of the Third World Conference on Earthquake Engineering, Auckland–Wellington, New Zealand, January. p. 123–143.

Chitty, Letitia, 1947. On the cantilever composed of a series of parallel beams interconnected by cross members. *Philosophical Magazine* (London), 38 (October), 685–694.

Cloud, William K., 1967. Forced vibration of the Mt. McKinley Building (field measurements), *in* Volume II-A: The Prince William Sound, Alaska, earthquake of 1964 and aftershocks. Environmental Science Services Administration, U.S. Coast and Geodetic Survey. Washington: Government Printing Office. p. 333–355.

Clough, Ray W., and K. Lee Benuska, 1966. FHA study of seismic design criteria for high-rise buildings. A report for Federal Housing Administration, Technical Studies Program (HUD TS-3). Washington: T. Y. Lin and Associates (Consulting Engineers). 347 p.

Rosman, Riko, 1964. Approximate analysis of shear walls subject to lateral loads. *Journal of the American Concrete Institute*, 61 (June), 717–733.

Steinbrugge, Karl V., and Rodrigo Flores A., 1963. The Chilean earthquakes of May, 1960: A structural engineering viewpoint. *Bulletin of the Seismological Society of America*, 53 (February), 225–307.

ROBERT D. HANSON
THE UNIVERSITY OF MICHIGAN

Behavior of Liquid-Storage Tanks

ABSTRACT: Although much of the widespread damage to storage tanks was caused by earth settlement or tsunamis, a significant portion of this damage was the result of direct structural action of the tank and its contents. The cylindrical, flat-bottomed tanks that were nearly full sustained damage such as collapse, buckling of the roof or wall, or roof-column failure, whereas similar tanks that were partly filled were not damaged. A review of the theoretical analysis of these tanks shows that the earthquake-generated forces can cause uplift of the tank edge, and this uplift increases the possibility of tank damage and subsequent loss of its contents. We recommend either that liquid-storage tanks be designed and constructed to resist realistic earthquake forces without significant uplift, or that provisions be made to contain the contents of the tank after its collapse.

The behavior of large liquid-storage tanks during earthquakes has an importance far beyond the mere economic value of the tanks and contents. If, for instance, a water tank collapses, as it did during the 1933 Long Beach, California, earthquake, the loss of the public water supply can have serious consequences. Similarly, the failure of tanks storing combustible materials, such as gasoline and other petroleum products, may lead to extensive, uncontrolled fires, as it did during the 1964 Niigata, Japan, earthquake. During the Alaska earthquake of March 27, 1964, damage to Union Oil Company tanks in the small community of Whittier resulted in the release of combustible liquids and a fire that burned for 3 days. In Anchorage, seven tanks containing combustible fluids collapsed and released their contents; three Standard Oil of California tanks released 750,000 gallons of aviation fuel. Fortunately, there was no fire in Anchorage; however, under different circumstances, there well might have been a conflagration.

Considerable damage to storage tanks occurred over a wide area of Alaska during the earthquake. Much of this damage was caused by tsunamis, earth settlement, and liquefaction of the subsoil resulting from the earthquake. These sources of damage must be considered in future designs of liquid-storage tanks; however, in this paper only the damage caused by direct structural action generated by the earthquake ground shaking will be discussed. The types of damage to liquid-storage tanks are described and illustrated, and the dynamic behavior of the tanks is reviewed so that this theoretical tank action can be used in describing the possible failure mechanisms and in indicating the earthquake forces that should be considered in the design of tanks.

This analysis indicates that the present design of these tanks does not take into account the actual forces generated by earthquake ground motion. The tanks are extremely simple in design, consisting essentially of a cylindrical steel wall that resists the outward fluid pressure, a thin flat bottom plate that rests on the ground and prevents the fluid from leaking out, and a thin roof plate that protects the contents from the atmosphere. In the future, such tanks should be designed to resist, with an adequate factor of safety, the forces likely to be imposed by earthquakes. If such tanks are not designed to resist the earthquake forces, the possibility of failure during an earthquake should be taken into account in designing the system to which the tanks belong. For example, a water-supply system that includes a water-storage tank should be designed to provide the needed water if the tank is inoperable; tanks storing combustible fluids, such as gasoline and crude oil, should be surrounded by dikes that can contain the entire contents of the tanks. These precautions were not in effect for most tanks in Alaska. The damage to numerous tanks and the collapse of some indicates that the design was not quite adequate for the ground motion actually experienced and would have been grossly inadequate for stronger ground motion.

In this paper, the descriptions of the damage to tanks, the properties of the tanks, and the tank conditions im-

TABLE 1   Tank Properties and Damage[a]

Tank	Diameter, (D) ft	Height, (H) ft	Capacity, bbls	Condition at time of Earthquake	Damage Observed
A	30	48	–	Full of water	Collapsed
B	100	32	44,700	Full of oil	Damage to roof, top wall, and roof columns
C[b]	45	32	9,000	Full of turbine fuel	Damage to roof, top wall, and roof rafters and the bottom wall buckled
D[c]	120	32	64,500	Full of oil	Damage to roof, top wall, and roof columns
E	120	32	64,500	Almost empty	No damage
F	120	32	64,500	Almost empty	No damage
G	110	32	54,000	Almost empty	No damage
H	90	32	36,100	2/3 full	No damage, except to the swing joint in the floating section
I	55	23	10,171	Full of fuel oil	Damage to roof rafters and top wall
J	30	40	5,000	Full	Extensive buckling of the bottom wall
K	30	40	5,000	Full	
L	30	40	5,000	Full	
M[d]	28	40	4,388	Full	Collapsed
N	42	40	10,123	–	Buckled bottom wall
O	20	40	2,233	–	Bottom wall buckled and broke the wall-to-bottom-plate weld
P	144	56	–	–	Floating roof buckled; indications of large waves
Q	112	56	–	–	Floating roof pontoon damaged
R	49	48	–	–	Bottom wall buckled; indications of 10–12 in. uplift of the tank
S	90	48	–	Over 3/4 full	Roof-top wall connection and roof structural steel damaged
T	160	56	200,000	–	Support columns twisted and rafters damaged
U	160	56	200,000	–	No damage

a Based on personal communications from Standard Oil Company of California and from Shell Oil Co., Seattle Division.
b See Figures 1, 2, and 3.
c See Figures 4 and 5.
d See Figures 6 and 7.

mediately preceding the earthquake are derived largely from Rinne (1967) and from personal communications from O. N. Miller and from the Seattle Division of the Shell Oil Co. Tanks that exhibited no visible damage are described if they have properties similar to, but storage conditions different from, corresponding damaged tanks. Table 1 lists important tank properties, capacity in barrels (bbls), the condition of the tank at the time of the earthquake, and the type of damage sustained. The types of damage discussed are total collapse, roof buckling, roof-column damage, roof-to-shell connection damage, and shell buckling.

TOTAL COLLAPSE

The wall of tank A, which was full of water at the time of the earthquake, buckled 6–24 in. from the bottom, and the tank fell over. The bottom of the tank ripped loose from the tank wall on the side opposite the buckle, and the cone roof was ripped off completely, presumably as the tank fell over. The roof was propelled 75 yd in the direction of the collapse.

ROOF BUCKLING

Buckling of roof-plates and structural steel occurred in a number of column-supported cone-roof tanks (Figures 1–3).

George W. Housner

FIGURE 2   Closeup view of the tank shown in Figure 1. The buckle at the bottom of the wall extends completely around the tank.

An example of such roof buckling is shown in Figure 3. Figures 4 and 5 show the progressive failure of tank D, caused by the combination of heavy snowfall, water ponding, and earthquake aftershocks.

ROOF COLUMNS

Figures 4 and 5 illustrate a roof collapse where the major contributing factor was the failure of the interior columns that support the roof. In normal design, the columns are

George W. Housner

FIGURE 1   Shell Oil Company tanks at Anchorage airport. The wall of the large tank in the foreground buckled completely around the bottom (Figure 2), and the tank also had a badly buckled top plate (Figure 3).

George W. Housner

FIGURE 3   Buckled roof plate of the tank shown in Figure 1.

FIGURE 4 A tank with buckled roof and wall near the port of Anchorage. The buckling was less severe immediately after the earthquake. The tank continued to deform until it collapsed (Figure 5).

guided but not rigidly attached to the bottom plates of the tank. This design is intended to prevent tearing of the bottom plate and subsequent loss of the tank contents.

ROOF-TO-SHELL CONNECTION

The roof-to-shell connection is normally designed as a weak connection so that if the tank is overfilled, the connection will fail before the tension in the shell can cause a failure of the shell-to-bottom-plate connection.

SHELL BUCKLING

Shell buckling occurred around the bottom of many tanks. All the tanks with this type of failure were nearly full at the time of the earthquake. The nature of this buckle is shown in Figure 2. A similar buckle occurred in a tank that collapsed (Figures 6 and 7). Some of these buckles were localized, but others extended completely around the tank and gave the impression that the tank had buckled as a cylindrical column under a large vertical compressive force. Actually, this type of buckle is attributed to a tendency of the tank to rock during the earthquake and thus to develop a relatively large compressive force at the toe. This rocking is caused by the action of the sloshing and accelerating liquid, which exerts forces in varying directions. The rocking toe moves to different locations around the tank wall and in time spreads the buckle around the tank. It was reported that some tanks in Whittier, which were surrounded by snow at the time of the earthquake, displayed at their

perimeter, after the snow had melted, a thin layer of ice under the bottom plate. Presumably, during the earthquake the tanks rocked and snow moved underneath where it was consolidated.

The damage illustrated in Figures 1–7 is representative of the types of damage that occurred in Alaska, but it is not meant to portray the total damage.

DYNAMIC RESPONSE OF STORAGE TANKS

Theoretical analyses of the dynamic response of liquids in storage tanks have been developed by both exact and approximate methods. The approximate methods give results within a few percent of the exact methods and have the advantage of presenting the results in an easily used form; their theoretical development is given in U.S. Atomic Energy Commission Report TID-7024 (1963). That development is the result of work reported by Housner (1957), Jacobsen (1949), and others. The present discussion is restricted to cylindrical tanks, built on the ground, which have a free liquid surface, although the theoretical developments are more general.

The contents of a liquid-storage tank on the ground will be excited into a sloshing motion by an earthquake, and the amplitude of the sloshing is a measure of the ground-motion intensity. The fluid pressures generated by the horizontal

FIGURE 5 This tank was only moderately buckled by the earthquake, but progressive deformation led to its collapse.

George W. Housner

FIGURE 6   Standard Oil of California tank at Anchorage airport. A buckled plate at the bottom of the wall has been replaced by a new, unpainted plate. The remains of collapsed tanks visible in foreground are being cut up and removed.

acceleration of the ground are conveniently divided into those associated with the inertia of the liquid accelerating with the ground (impulsive pressures) and those associated with the liquid accelerating with the sloshing motion (convective pressures). These dynamic pressures act both on the walls and the bottom of the tank. In addition to causing

George W. Housner

FIGURE 7   Bottom of a collapsed tank, showing a tight buckle that is also visible in Figure 6.

forces and moments on the shell wall of the tank, the wall pressures combine with the bottom pressures to cause a net overturning moment on the tank as a whole. The following general discussion of the dynamic response of liquid-storage tanks is given to provide background for utilization of the appropriate theoretical results.

The impulsive pressures associated with the inertia forces in the liquid are directly related in time to the ground accelerations and are primarily of high frequency in the range of 2–5 cycles per second (cps). By contrast, the convective pressures associated with the sloshing motion of the liquid are directly related in time to the oscillatory response of the liquid generated by the earthquake accelerations and are primarily of low-frequency close to the natural frequency of the sloshing fluid. The maximum ground acceleration and the maximum liquid sloshing motion probably will not occur at the same time; however, it is possible for a combination of impulsive and convective pressures at a given time to exceed the maximum impulsive or convective pressures considered separately. Thus, engineering judgment must be used in selecting the maximum dynamic-load condition for which the liquid-storage tank is to be designed.

The effect of the impulsive and convective pressures on the tank is similar and, therefore, the convective pressure will be used in discussing the tank action, because the origin of these pressures and the way they vary are more easily visualized. The nature of the sloshing motion of the liquid and the corresponding pressure distribution on the walls and bottom of a tank (Figure 8) make clear the origin of the overturning moment acting on the tank structure. If the tank were rigid, the effect of this new pressure distribution in the liquid would be to redistribute pressure in the supporting foundation that must satisfy force and moment equilibrium. However, because in practice the bottom of such a tank is a thin, flexible steel plate, the soil pressure on the tank bottom cannot contribute resistance to the overturning effect of the fluid moments. For this type of tank the overturning resistance must be supplied directly to the shell wall from the foundation. The tension force cannot be

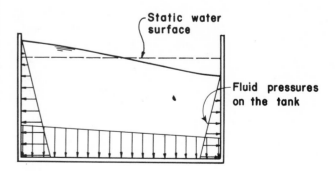

FIGURE 8   A section through a tank, showing the sloshing fluid and the corresponding fluid pressures.

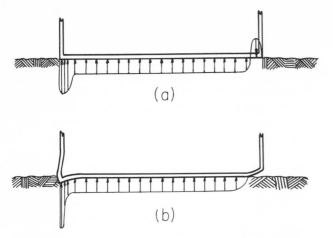

FIGURE 9   The footing pressures produced by the overturning moment of the sloshing fluid are shown (a) where the foundation can exert tension on the bottom of the tank and (b) where the foundation cannot exert tension and the bottom lifts off of the ground.

transmitted to the foundation because, in the usual practice, the tank is not bolted to it. Therefore, the tank wall must rise in this tension zone until a large enough portion of the bottom fluid pressure is available to overcome the tensile force. This action is illustrated in Figure 9a, which shows that the tank could be in equilibrium without uplift if both tension and compression forces could be developed at the bottom of the wall. Figure 9b shows that when the tension side of the tank rises, a large compressive load is applied to the shell at the opposite side of the tank. The portion of the shell between the compression zone and the tension zone carries the stress as the web of a beam. The large compressive force in the thin shell of the tank can cause the plate to buckle. Because the internal fluid pressure at this point is outward, the natural tendency is for the shell to buckle outward. Even without uplift, the shell may buckle, but it is less likely to do so. The maximum compressive stress is greatly increased when uplift occurs, and prevention of uplift will therefore reduce the possibility of shell buckling. Probably one of the most acceptable methods of prevention is to stiffen the bottom plate around the edge so that the tank wall cannot rise a significant amount without also raising several feet of the bottom plate. This stiffening could be accomplished by increasing the thickness of the bottom plate around the edge or by using either structural shapes or gusset plates. In addition to buckling the wall, the uplift of a tank could also break pipe connections and release the contents, which might then be ignited—another important reason for preventing significant uplift.

So far, only damage to the tank bottom and lower shell has been considered. As previously mentioned, the roof and roof-shell connection were also damaged. This damage had

two possible causes. If the amplitude of the sloshing motion of the liquid is greater than the freeboard provided, the direct contact of the liquid with the roof may damage the roof-shell connection or buckle the shell at the roof support member-shell connection. Such damage can best be prevented by providing freeboard equal to the maximum expected sloshing amplitude. The other possible source of roof damage is the same as that which causes buckling of the shell at the bottom; that is, the uplift of one side of the tank requires the roof to act as a structural diaphragm to hold the top of the shell circular. This diaphragm action tends to make the roof buckle unless it has been designed as a structural element.

Thus, the observed tank damage can be attributed to the combined action of the liquid sloshing motion and the impulsive inertia pressures. Vertical ground accelerations probably do not play a significant role. The magnitudes of the overturning moment and of the horizontal shear force and the amplitude of the sloshing motion can be determined from the velocity response-spectrum values for the earthquake being considered. The overturning moment caused by pressures on the walls is the significant item.

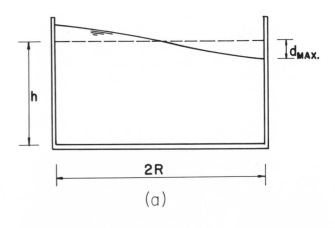

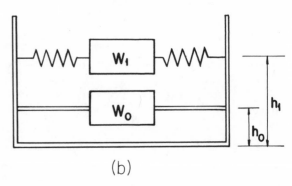

FIGURE 10   Equivalent dynamic model for a cylindrical tank with oscillating fluid. The zeroth and first modes of vibration are modeled.

TABLE 2   Formulas for Cylindrical Tanks Supported on the Ground

---

$$\frac{W_0}{W} = \frac{\tanh\left(\sqrt{3}\frac{R}{h}\right)}{\sqrt{3}\frac{R}{h}} \tag{1}$$

$$h_0 = \frac{3}{8} h \tag{2}$$

$$P_0 = \frac{\dot{u}_0}{g} W_0 \tag{3}$$

$$\frac{W_1}{W} = 0.46 \frac{R}{h} \tanh\left(1.84\frac{h}{R}\right) \tag{4}$$

$$h_1 = h\left[1 - \frac{\cosh\left(1.84\frac{h}{R}\right) - 1}{1.84\frac{h}{R}\sinh\left(1.84\frac{h}{R}\right)}\right] \tag{5}$$

$$\omega_1{}^2 = 1.84\frac{g}{R}\tanh\left(1.84\frac{h}{R}\right) \tag{6}$$

$$\theta_h = 1.534\frac{A_1}{R}\tanh\left(1.84\frac{h}{R}\right) \tag{7}$$

$$P_1 = W_1\theta_h\sin\omega_1 t \tag{8}$$

$$d_{max} = \left[\frac{0.408 R\coth\left(1.84\frac{h}{R}\right)}{\dfrac{g}{\omega^2{}_1\theta_h R} - 1}\right] \tag{9}$$

THE ANALYSIS OF FORCES AND MOMENTS

The nomenclature and equations presented here are from U.S. Atomic Energy Commission Report TID-7024, Article 6.3 (1963) for cases of $h < 1.5R$. Similar equations for $h > 1.5R$ are given in Article 6.5 of this reference. The equivalent dynamic model for the cylindrical liquid-storage tank is illustrated in Figure 10b and the resulting equations are summarized in Table 2. Nomenclature is defined in Table 3.

The procedure for calculating the overturning moments, shear force, and free liquid-surface displacement generated by an earthquake is as follows:

1. Calculate W_o and h_o, excluding the liquid pressure on the bottom plate.

2. From the weight of the tank and the values determined in (1), compute the gross equivalent weight $W_o{}''$ and the associated $h_o{}''$ value.

3. Obtain the impulsive force $P_o{}''$ from $W_o{}''$ using the maximum horizontal acceleration of the earthquake, $\dot{u}_o$.

Table 3   Nomenclature Defined for Equations Summarized in Table 2 and Those Used To Determine the Equivalent Earthquake Forces

Term	Definition
A_1	Maximum displacement of W_1
d_{max}	Maximum liquid-surface displacement
g	Acceleration of gravity
h	Height of liquid surface above the bottom of the tank
$h_0, h_0{}'', h_1$	Vertical distance from the tank bottom to W_0, $W_0{}''$, and W_1, respectively
M_0, M_1	Moment on a horizontal section of the tank just above the bottom, due to P_0 and P_1, respectively
$M_0{}''$	Modified M_0 value corresponding to equivalent weight $W_0{}''$
P_0, P_1	Impulsive and convective forces, respectively, on tank wall
$P_0{}''$	Modified P_0 value corresponding to equivalent weight $W_0{}''$
R	Radius of cylindrical tank
S_v	Ordinate of velocity spectrum
T	Period of vibration
t	Time for which seismic deflection is evaluated
$\dot{u}_0$	Maximum horizontal acceleration of the ground during an earthquake
W	Total weight of fluid in a cylindrical tank
W_0	Equivalent weight of fluid to produce the impulsive force P_0 on the tank wall (W_0 is assumed to be fastened rigidly to the tank walls at height h_0 above the tank bottom)
$W_o{}''$	Gross equivalent weight to produce the impulsive force $P_0{}''$ on the tank wall (W_0 plus tank weight and tributary weight of the support structure). In the case of a slender tank with $h > 1.5R$, $W_0{}''$ also includes the weight of constrained fluid. (The corresponding forces, heights, and moments are designated $P_0{}''$, $h_0{}''$, and $M_0{}''$, respectively)
W_1	Equivalent oscillating weight to produce the convective force P_1 on tank wall (W_1 is assumed to be fastened to the tank walls by springs at height h_1 above the tank bottom)
θ_h	Angular amplitude of free oscillations at the fluid surface, based on the assumption of a plane liquid surface
ρ	Mass density of fluid
ω_n	Circular frequency of free vibration for the nth mode

4. Determine the impulsive overturning moment, $P_o"h_o"$.

5. Calculate W_1 and h_1, excluding the dynamic liquid pressure on the bottom.

6. Calculate the natural frequency ω_1 and the period of vibration T from which S_v may be obtained from the appropriate velocity response-spectrum curve.

7. Using S_v, compute the maximum amplitude of the displacement A_1, the angle of free oscillation at the free liquid surface θ_h, and the convective force P_1.

8. Determine the convective overturning moment P_1h_1, the base shear, and the maximum amplitude of the sloshing motion of the liquid d_{max}.

The foregoing steps determine the equivalent earthquake forces acting on the tank. With these forces, the performance of the tank in question may be evaluated, or a tank may be designed. Application of the above steps is to tank C (Table 1), whose shell was buckled at the bottom. This tank has the following properties: 45 ft diameter; H (height of tank) = 32 ft; h (height of liquid surface above bottom of tank) = 28.3 ft; h/R = 1.26; R/h = 0.795; 9,000 barrels capacity; turbine fuel at 42 lb/ft^3.

ANALYSIS OF IMPULSIVE FORCES

From Eq. (1) (Table 2), it is found that W_o = 1,200,000 lb and the effective height h_o is 10.6 ft, excluding bottom pressure. If the wall and roof of the tank are taken to weigh 60,000 lb with the center of gravity at h = 20 ft, then $W_o"$ = 1,260,000 lb and $h_o"$ = 11.0 ft. Assuming a ground acceleration of 0.20 g to represent the maximum ground acceleration at Anchorage, then $P_o"$ = 250,000 lb, and the overturning moment $M_o"$ = 2,750,000 ft-lb.

ANALYSIS OF CONVECTIVE FORCES

From Eq. (4) (Table 2), it is determined that the effective weight W_1 is 675,000 lb. The effective height, excluding bottom pressure, is h_1 = 18.2 ft. Equation (6) gives ω_1 = 1.61 radians/sec, which corresponds to a natural period of vibration of T = 3.9 seconds. By using a velocity response spectrum value S_v = 2.0 fps at 3.9 seconds period to represent the Anchorage ground motion, the amplitude of motion is found to be $A_1 = S_v/\omega_1$ = 1.24 ft. The angular amplitude of motion is θ_h = 0.083, and the force P_1 is given by (675,000)0.083 = 56,000 lb. The overturning moment, excluding bottom pressure, is M_1 = 1,030,000 ft-lb. The corresponding amplitude of the wave at the wall of the tank is d_{max} = 1.64 ft. These values are for one-directional motion; during an earthquake, however, the ground motion is approximately the same for both horizontal components of motion. In the fluid, the two components combine into a

single wave whose energy is the sum of the energies of the two components; hence, the amplitude, force, and moment must be multiplied by $\sqrt{2}$. The resultant values are P_1 = 80,000 lb, M_1 = 1,450,000 ft-lb, and d_{max} = 2.3 ft.

EFFECTS OF OVERTURNING MOMENT

As shown in the preceding analysis, the convective and impulsive pressures exert maximum moments of 1,450,000 ft-lb and 2,750,000 ft-lb, respectively, or a total of 4,200,000 ft-lb on tank C during the earthquake. The 60,000 lb estimated weight of tank wall and roof provides a stabilizing moment of 1,300,000 ft-lb and leaves a net overturning moment of 2,900,000 ft-lb, which must be provided by the bottom edge of the tank wall. This moment corresponds to a vertical force applied around the wall at the bottom plate equal to 1,830 $\sin\phi$ lb/ft. The weight of the fluid and bottom plate is 1,200 lb/ft^2; therefore, the uplift must progress inward a maximum of 1.5 ft to provide the required 1,830 $\sin\phi$ lb/ft weight. In the uplifted position, the tank is standing on its toe with approximately 130,000-lb force. If distributed over a length of 20 ft, this force produces 6,500 lb/ft vertical compression. It is estimated that a compressive force in the range of 1,000–3,000 lb/ft would cause buckling; the computed earthquake forces are consequently more than sufficient to account for the observed damage. The tank is also subjected to a horizontal shear force of 80,000 lb (convective) and 250,000 lb (impulsive), or a total of 330,000 lb.

When the tank is in the static equilibrium position, its cylindrical shape and flat bottom are well suited to resist the fluid pressures by membrane shell stresses. Furthermore, a shell anchored so that it cannot rise is better suited to resist the overturning pressures and horizontal shear force by membrane shell stresses than a shell in the uplifted position. Apparently, the first evidence of distress in an uplifted condition is buckling; if the uplift is too great, the roof of the tank may buckle and then the tank may collapse. The true stresses under these conditions and the precise progress of failure would be very difficult to analyze, and any reasonable estimate of the factor of safety against collapse would be difficult to make. It seems advisable, therefore, to design tanks so that significant uplift will not develop and so that the vertical force in the wall will be kept below the buckling load during an earthquake.

CONCLUSIONS

An assumed ground motion that has 20 percent g maximum acceleration and a lightly damped spectral velocity S_v = 2.0 fps is sufficiently intense to cause a typical tank to uplift and to account for the observed damage. Most of the tanks affected by the earthquake belong to oil companies; these have apparently been constructed according to standard designs that do not take into account the true forces developed by earthquake ground motions. An analysis of the forces for which a tank must be designed if it is to be earthquake resistant indicates that future tanks should be designed to resist these forces without significant uplift; recorded ground motions and spectra representative of expected ground shaking should be utilized in such design. It is recommended that existing tanks that are in danger of collapse if strong ground motion occurs be strengthened to a satisfactory degree of earthquake resistance or that provisions be made in anticipation of collapse during an earthquake. In particular, such tanks containing combustible liquids should be surrounded by dikes that can contain all of the liquid if collapse occurs. Such safety precautions were not uniformly in effect in Alaska and are not in effect for all tanks in other seismic areas of the country. In view of the extensive fires that have resulted during past earth-

quakes from the release of combustible fluids from tanks, it seems highly desirable to minimize the possibility of such disastrous conflagrations in the future.

REFERENCES

Housner, G. W., 1957. Dynamic pressures on accelerated fluid containers. *Bulletin of the Seismological Society of America*, 47 (January), 15–35.

Jacobsen, Lydik S., 1949. Impulsive hydrodynamics of fluid inside a cylindrical tank and of fluid surrounding a cylindrical pier. *Bulletin of the Seismological Society of America*, 39 (July), 189–204.

Rinne, John E., 1967. Oil storage tanks *in* Volume II-A: The Prince William Sound, Alaska, earthquake of 1964 and aftershocks. Environmental Science Services Administration, U.S. Coast and Geodetic Survey. Washington: Government Printing Office. p. 245–252.

U.S. Atomic Energy Commission, 1963. Nuclear reactors and earthquakes. Report TID-7024, August. Washington: U.S. Atomic Energy Commission. p. 367–390.

HAROLD D. HAUF*

UNIVERSITY OF SOUTHERN CALIFORNIA

Architectural Factors in Earthquake Resistance

This paper was written primarily for architects who design structures in seismic regions. Study of building damage caused by the Alaska earthquake of March 27, 1964, emphasizes the influence of architectural decisions on building behavior. Because building height, bulk, and form are factors in the structural response to seismic forces, architectural planning and design can be highly significant factors in earthquake resistance. Although the design team of architect and structural engineer is best assembled at the inception of a project, the engineer is often presented with an architectural scheme and asked to handle the seismic requirements within the proposed functional solution. Consequently, planning and design decisions may already have been made without full consideration to alternative schemes that might lend themselves more readily to effective resistance to earthquake forces.

Although buildings are constructed to house specific functions, and it is necessary that elements of the structural system not obstruct or inhibit performance of these functions, there is normally more than one functional scheme that will satisfy the occupancy requirements for a given project. There are also several possibilities for the structural solution. Imaginative cooperative effort between architect and engineer during the development of preliminary studies therefore can produce effective solutions to the problems of the building program, without resorting to unduly complicated and extravagant structural arrangements. The movement of water-storage tanks and pieces of heavy mechanical equipment observed on the upper floors of some buildings in Anchorage is a reminder that mechanical systems also contain elements whose behavior under seismic forces warrants early consideration of their strategic placement within the building in relation to occupancy functions.

This brief discussion of the few but significant factors largely under the architect's control does not, of course, equate effective earthquake resistance with avoidance of all damage. An attempt to achieve the latter, except in moderate earthquakes that might occur during the life of a

ABSTRACT: Because building height, bulk, and form are factors in the structural response of buildings to seismic forces, many decisions taken by architects in the early design stage can either facilitate or obstruct measures intended to control earthquake damage. Of particular significance is the ability of the plan to provide for a reasonably symmetrical location of shear walls, thereby reducing built-in eccentricity inimical to torsional resistance. Although the shape of a building is always determined primarily by its functional requirements, the provision for separations between dissimilar units or wings will provide pounding room to accommodate oscillations of the structure. Choice of materials can have a significant effect on the length of time required to restore normal functioning of portions of a building after earthquake damage has occurred; this is of major importance in facilities such as hospitals whose need to operate may be at a maximum immediately after a disastrous shock. The falling-missiles hazard presented by the breaking loose of heavy nonstructural curtain-wall elements, dramatically demonstrated in Anchorage, suggests that this type of construction should not be specified in earthquake-prone areas. Close cooperation between architect and structural engineer at an early stage in design can minimize damage. Such professional collaboration need not generate architectural constraints, but can assure that all factors controlling response to earthquake forces are examined and provided for.

---

*Now an Architectural Consultant, Sun City, Arizona.

building, would not be justified economically. Current design objectives therefore seek to limit the type and extent of damage that might cause bodily injury or loss of life when a building is exposed to a severe earthquake. Because the infrequent severe earthquake may cause considerable costly property damage, an element of calculated risk is involved when potential repair costs are balanced against the additional initial cost of preventive measures designed to eliminate the damage entirely or against the cost of earthquake-damage insurance. A few basic design considerations, however, make it possible to reduce potential damage without a significant increase in initial cost. Some of these considerations are examined in the following discussion.

THE PLAN AND TORSIONAL RESISTANCE

With respect to the torsional resistance of a planned structure, the objective is to prevent torsional movement that may occur in a building subjected to earthquake forces when there is an eccentricity between the center of mass and the center of rigidity (Figure 1). Whenever possible, buildings should be designed to avoid any substantial built-in eccentricity. Theoretically, this condition can be achieved when the architectural planning symmetrically disposes shear-resisting elements and the dead load of the structure in relation to the principal axes of the plan. Such an arrangement is not always easy to accomplish since the exigencies of space layout and utilization do not necessarily coincide with ideal shear-wall locations. A great deal may, nevertheless, be accomplished if this objective is borne in mind during development of the building plan. Robert L. Alexander (1964), one proponent of this approach, maintains:

As an experienced architect conceives the spatial and esthetic requirements for a multistory building in a seismic area, he thinks in terms of structure intuitively. From his rough sketches . . . to his preliminary drawings, he has determined the structural form, column and story spacings, shear-wall locations and surface openings.

Where such an attitude prevails, the possibility of developing compatible functional and structural schemes is obviously increased.

The effect of large torsional motion, attributed to a relatively large eccentricity between center of rigidity of resisting elements and center of mass of the structure, was dramatized by the failure of the J. C. Penney Building in Anchorage (Figure 2) (Berg and Stratta, 1964). This was a five-story approximately square building constructed of reinforced concrete. The column bays were 22 × 26 ft and the floors were 10-in. thick flat plates constituting relatively rigid diaphragms. The arrangement of effective shear-resisting elements, however, was quite asymmetrical (roughly similar

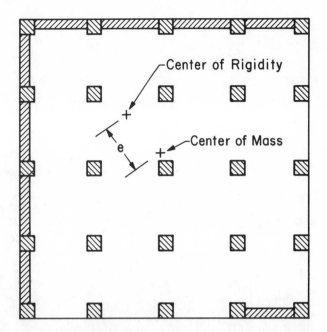

FIGURE 1   Diagrammatic plan of building subject to torsion due to unsymmetrical positioning of shear walls. Center of mass is offset from center of rigidity because of mass of the shear walls. Distance between these two points represents the eccentricity.

to Figure 1), consisting principally of the south and west walls that were constructed of poured concrete for the full building height. There was no shear wall in the north facade, which was covered with 4-in. thick precast nonstructural reinforced-concrete panels. The east wall, also covered with the precast panels, had poured-concrete shear walls between columns in the two northerly bays, and in the bottom three stories of the two southerly bays. The two central bays of the east wall were open. The rotational displacement induced by the earthquake apparently caused failure of this east-wall shear-resistant element, thereby rendering the remainder of the shear-wall pattern even more eccentric in relation to the center of mass. As a consequence, the building became more susceptible to rotational distortion, and this caused progressive failure in the principal south and west shear walls.

Torsional phenomena may be of greater significance in the resistance to earthquakes of tall frame buildings than has been generally recognized. This applies particularly to modern curtain-wall buildings because of their lack of peripheral resistance, whether the curtain wall consists of precast-concrete panels or metal-and-glass panels. The architectural scheme can have significant influence here, depending on the extent to which it permits provision of lateral resistance in the outermost periphery of structural support either by symmetrical moment-resisting frames or by shear walls. The problem is more difficult to handle architecturally in buildings where the service core is unsymmetrically

FIGURE 2   Damage to north wall of J. C. Penney Building, attributable in large measure to torsional displacement of floors.

placed in the entire building envelope. Since the walls surrounding the core are usually available for structural purposes, symmetrical core location is obviously advantageous but not always feasible. The ingenuity of both architect and structural engineer may be taxed to minimize potential torsional displacement in buildings with asymmetrical plans. In earthquake-prone areas, however, this factor should be weighed thoroughly and the architectural scheme developed so as to accommodate structural elements required to prevent undue eccentricity between the center of mass and the center of rigidity of lateral force-resisting elements. Imaginative design thinking can produce compatible solutions to this highly significant problem if the problem is recognized during the early stages of a project.

POUNDING ROOM

Recognition of the importance of building separations early in the planning and design stage may make it possible to eliminate hammering of adjacent structures during an earthquake, with the attendant local damage and potential hazard to people in the streets. Although the amount of separation required to avoid contact under seismic oscillation is not known with any high degree of precision, planning for spaces between individual buildings on a site will obviously minimize this hazard. Connections between buildings of any one project can be made by lightly constructed and fairly flexible corridor links. Separations are also necessary between units of a single building when the units have greatly different vibration characteristics and cannot be designed to act as an integral unit. This situation frequently may be critical where low wings adjoin a higher tower-like unit, or where wings of widely different mass and extent intersect. Damage due to hammering or pounding under these conditions was observed in several buildings in Anchorage, for example at the Anchorage-Westward Hotel where the six-story block adjoined the 14-story tower portion and at the West Anchorage High School where gymnasium and classroom sections joined. A similar condition exists in very long buildings that require joints to accommodate movement caused by temperature change. It is important that the separation be great enough to provide for earthquake deflection as well as for thermal considerations. Construction of such joints must be watched carefully by field-inspection forces because the best-designed separation will not function if the joint accumulates construction debris.

The problem of providing adequate separation of buildings erected by different owners on adjacent sites also must be considered. The application of measures to ensure such separation in congested city business districts is often very difficult. High land values have encouraged the tendency to construct buildings flush with the lot lines, except for alley or courtyard requirements dictated by other considerations. It is here that the architect's ingenuity in planning the building to release space to provide property-line clearance without serious economic penalty furthers the principles of good earthquake engineering.

BUILDINGS WITH WINGS

Buildings with irregular plan forms that induce parts of the structure to vibrate independently of each other are, in general, more subject to cracking and overstressing than are buildings of simpler shape. A building whose plan form is as shown in Figure 3a is more likely to sustain earthquake damage than is a rectangular building such as that in Figure 3b, even when they are both designed according to the same building-code requirements. Damage at the reentrant corner C can result from the tendency during an earthquake for the wings to "flap" and thus produce relatively high stresses around this corner. This is not to say that such a shape should be prohibited when the requirements of plan and site indicate its desirability, but special precautions must be taken in detailing the articulation of the wings, or in providing additional structural strength at the junction.

CHOICE OF MATERIALS

Observation of damage in the Alaska earthquake refocuses attention on the desirability of avoiding unnecessary dead load when designing buildings for earthquake-prone areas. Large loads aloft, such as the heavy roof of the classroom section of the West Anchorage High School, generate large inertial forces under the accelerations produced by earthquake motion. Although these forces may be contained by proper design of supporting elements, the selection of lighter-weight construction will reduce their magnitude and make the problem of restraining them less difficult. The construction of shear walls in multistory buildings usually requires the use of relatively heavy materials, but there is considerable latitude in selecting the materials for nonstructural exterior walls and interior partitions.

Rigid walls and partitions may contribute to resistance

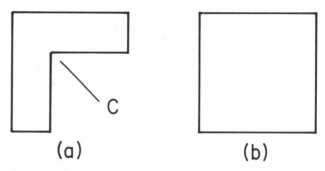

FIGURE 3 Diagrammatic plan of a building subject to damage at reentrant corner. See text for further discussions of plans (a) and (b).

against seismic forces, even though they are not designed to do so. For example, a partition of block masonry running between two columns and from floor to overhead beam may be intended only as a filler wall. Whether this wall assists the frame elements in resisting lateral force depends on several factors, especially on the manner in which it is connected to the beams and columns. Clearance on one or more edges of the panel requires the frame to resist lateral force by itself until its deflection brings the wall resistance into play. On the other hand, if the masonry wall is fitted tightly to the frame on all sides, there will be composite action of frame and wall until the wall fails. After this failure, the frame will resist lateral force alone or with only partial assistance from the wall. Obviously, the intended interaction between frame and walls or partitions needs resolution in the early stage of the design. Where composite action is envisaged, specifications must require that partitions be reinforced and tied to framing members so as not to create a hazard to occupants. Where such action is not desired, the use of lighter-weight, more-flexible partitions with panel faces consisting of plastic laminates, plywood, and similar materials should be considered. It was observed in Anchorage that, although solid plaster partitions developed large cracks and in many instances had to be completely rebuilt, partitions consisting of plaster on metal or gypsum over steel or wood studs were less costly to repair.

Another occurrence in Anchorage emphasizes the importance of giving careful thought to the interior finish of facilities that may be needed desperately during an earthquake's aftermath. In one of the hospitals, although there was little damage, the dust generated by cracked plaster in the operating room made the room unusable until it had been thoroughly washed. In this case, the inability to use the room was of much greater significance than the cost of repairing the modest damage.

STAIRS AS STRUCTURAL ELEMENTS

Stairs are usually relatively rigid elements and can resist earthquake forces even when not intentionally designed to do so, particularly when the structural elements of the building are less rigid than the stairs. This may lead to failure of the stairs because they pick up most of the earthquake force but are not designed with sufficient strength to do so. Stairs may damage the main structure of a building in other ways; for example, in the Cordova Building, steel stairs fastened to a main column at midheight caused the column to fail. Although locations of stairways are usually determined by occupancy and legal egress requirements, they should be designed and detailed to avoid an unfavorable interaction between the stairs and the structure of the building.

THE FALLING-MISSILES HAZARD

The breaking loose of precast-concrete nonstructural panels on the north and east walls of the J. C. Penney Building

cited earlier generates a doubt as to the wisdom of using such heavy units for nonstructural curtain walls in seismic areas. In addition to raising the center of gravity of the structure by increasing the weight aloft, such panels become truly lethal missiles when they fall into the street below, as is dramatically illustrated by Figure 4. These same considerations also seem pertinent to the design of exterior sun-shading devices on multistory buildings. Further development of fastenings for heavy nonstructural elements may lessen this potential hazard, but the observed generally satisfactory behavior of insulated metal-and-glass curtain walls during the Alaska earthquake (Hixon, 1965) can no doubt be attributed to their inherent flexibility, which permits a considerable measure of distortion without complete and sudden collapse.

As the number of high-rise buildings increases in metropolitan centers located in seismic zones, the matter of keeping damaged components on or in the building where

Anchorage Daily Times

FIGURE 4 Heavy nonstructural exterior-wall panels constitute a major hazard to people in the streets when connections fail.

damage occurs becomes increasingly important. The problem is the same for low-rise structures, of course, but the potential volume of falling wall panels, sunshades, and veneers increases with the height. Because the elements discussed here contribute to a building's architectural character, the architect is obviously in a position to exert considerable influence on this potential hazard by his design decisions.

OTHER EXTERIOR-WALL CONSIDERATIONS

The relation between architectural character of a building's facades and its susceptibility to earthquake damage was clearly demonstrated by the behavior of the two 14-story apartment buildings in Anchorage. These had reinforced-concrete exterior walls with short, deep spandrel beams framing into relatively husky vertical members. The extensive damage sustained by these walls is attributed to the large shear forces generated in the spandrels under the strong shaking, which caused them to shatter. It is thus possible for architectural design decisions to invite, albeit inadvertently, potential damage. Situations of this nature can be avoided by collaboration between architect and structural engineer at an early stage in the design, when all factors controlling a building's response to earthquake forces can be examined.

Because windows compose such a large proportion of the area of exterior walls in modern buildings, glazing details are worthy of special consideration. During an earthquake, the vibrations of a building produce relative horizontal displacements between adjacent floors. In a steel-frame building, where the relative displacement in a strong earthquake may be as much as ½ in., provision for adequate play in the details may prevent widespread breaking of windows.

SITE CONSIDERATIONS

The degree to which the architect can influence the selection of the site for a proposed building varies widely with the type of project and with its sponsor. When all the factors relating to functional aspects of location for the proposed enterprise have been considered, and when alternative sites are available, the relative seismic hazards should be investigated so that purchase price can be balanced against the estimated cost of anticipated special-foundation problems. For many buildings in metropolitan areas, however, there will be no opportunity for choice. The sponsor of a project will already have acquired his site, after availing himself, it is hoped, of soils-engineering and geologic counsel, on the basis of market analysis or other economic considerations. In such cases, the architect will have to accept the geology and seismicity as they exist. If sufficient money is available to cover the cost of marshaling competent engineering-design talent and to provide quality control of both materials and construction techniques, there are relatively few sites that cannot be built on with reasonable assurance of achieving effective earthquake resistance.

Presumably, man is going to continue to build and carry on his social, economic, and political activities in areas where earthquakes occur; hence, ways must be found to limit an earthquake's destructiveness. Attention to the few but significant architectural-design decisions that have been identified here should contribute to this end.

REFERENCES

Alexander, Robert L., 1964. Where the architect stands on the team: An introduction to aseismic design. *A.I.A.* [American Institute of Architects] *Journal*, 42 (December), 39–42.
Berg, Glen V., and James L. Stratta, 1964. Anchorage and the Alaska earthquake of March 27, 1964. American Iron and Steel Institute, New York. 63 p.
Hixon, Lloyd E., 1965. How to design against earthquakes. *A.I.A.* [American Institute of Architects] *Journal*, 42 (October), 78–84.

J. MARX AYRES
TSENG-YAO SUN
FREDERICK R. BROWN*
AYRES & HAYAKAWA
Consulting Mechanical and Electrical Engineers

Based on report to U.S. Army Corps of Engineers,
"Non-Structural Damage to Buildings Due to the
March 27, 1964, Alaska Earthquake"

Nonstructural Damage to Buildings

In the past, earthquake-resistant design has been concerned primarily with the structural integrity of buildings, and very little attention has been given to the performance of the nonstructural elements of buildings. This procedure has been based on the philosophy that to design a building to avoid all damage during an earthquake is not economically justifiable; the structural system of the building is intended to be deformed by the seismic forces, and damage to some of the nonstructural elements is expected. The extent of this damage, however, and its effect on the safety of the building's occupants have never been fully evaluated, although the nonstructural elements often constitute more than two thirds of the total cost of a building. Greater knowledge and understanding is needed of the damage sustained by nonstructural building elements during an earthquake.

By definition, the nonstructural elements of a building are those materials that are not a part of the structural system. The structural system, or building frame, must be designed to withstand the live and dead loads of the building, in addition to wind and earthquake forces, without the assistance of the nonstructural elements. These elements are actually added to the frame in the last stages of the construction of the building and include facades, ceilings, partitions, elevators, lights, electrical systems, plumbing, ventilation and air-conditioning systems, heating systems, fire-protection systems, telephone and communications systems, storage racks, and even large pieces of furniture or portable equipment.

The final measure of a well-constructed building is the safety and comfort that it affords its occupants. If, during an earthquake, they must exit through a shower of falling light fixtures and ceilings, maneuver through shifting and toppling furniture, stumble down dark corridors and stairs, and then be met at the street by falling glass, veneers, or facade elements, then the building cannot be described as a safe structure.

Aside from the loss of life caused by tsunamis, the number of people killed or injured because of vibrational damage

ABSTRACT: The Alaska earthquake caused extensive damage to nonstructural elements of buildings such as facades, ceilings, partitions, elevators, lights, electrical systems, plumbing, ventilation and air-conditioning systems, heating systems, fire-protection systems, telephone and other communications systems, and furniture. In most cases the cost of repairing nonstructural damage was appreciably greater than the cost of repairing structural damage. Most of the nonstructural damage could have been avoided at little or no extra cost in the original design of the building. A study of typical nonstructural damage suggests recommendations for methods of avoiding such damage during future earthquakes.

*Now with Frederick Russell Brown & Associates.

to buildings during the March 27, 1964, Alaska earthquake was surprisingly small. Had more of the buildings been occupied at the time of the earthquake (5:36 p.m.), a great many more people would have been killed or injured because of failure of the structural and nonstructural building elements. The disaster would have been compounded if the earthquake had been followed by fires. In Anchorage, the fire potential was greatly reduced after landslides ruptured the gas mains and the electric power system failed. Even so, at least three deaths, numerous injuries, and considerable panic were caused by the failure of nonstructural elements.

The earthquake provided a rare opportunity to evaluate the performance of modern building construction under severe earthquake conditions. Anchorage, Alaska's largest city, is about 80 mi west–northwest of the epicenter of the earthquake; because of its size, it bore the burden of the majority of property damage caused by the earthquake. Anchorage is a young and growing city with new modern buildings, some as high as 14 stories. Most of these buildings were built under a code that required earthquake-resistant design and were constructed using up-to-date building techniques. Detailed studies of these earthquake-tested structures are essential as a basis for future evaluations of current design practices.

OBJECTIVES AND SCOPE

Our purpose is to document the nonstructural damage to buildings caused by the earthquake, to analyze this information, to establish what lessons can be learned from the failures, and where possible to recommend design improvements that could minimize nonstructural damage in future earthquakes.

One of our main objectives was to compile a record of information on nonstructural damage, so that it would be available for future studies. Wherever possible, photographs and drawings have been used to illustrate and describe the damage. No effort was made to analyze the actual stress patterns that brought about the failures of the nonstructural elements or to make rigorous correlations with the performance of the surrounding structural systems. We hope that these data will serve as a basis for future evaluations of current design and construction practices and for building codes.

Structural engineers have conducted most of the detailed studies of building damage caused by this earthquake. Our objective was to supplement such studies by examining the earthquake damage through the eyes of mechanical and electrical engineers and architects. This type of interdisciplinary study was expected to uncover useful information about the earthquake damage that might have been overlooked by other investigators.

The scope of the study was limited to damage of buildings, and it specifically excludes exterior utility systems such as electrical power, telephone, water, gas, sewerage, or storm-drainage systems. No effort was made to analyze the nonstructural damage in buildings that housed power plants, water-supply systems, and other facilities serving utility systems. Information on damage to this type of structure was included only if the type of damage was also applicable to other buildings.

The amount and type of damage sustained by nonstructural elements in a building are almost totally dependent on the performance of the surrounding building frame. For this reason, no studies were made of buildings that lost their foundations in slide areas, or that completely collapsed because of severe structural failures. The building location, its size and shape, the type of structural system, the materials used, and the foundation soil conditions all affect the damage to nonstructural elements.

According to Hansen (1965), the seismic motions in Anchorage lasted 3–4 minutes, and, because of the distance from the epicenter, the seismic vibrations were characterized by long periods. The predominantly long-period characteristic of the ground motion induced greater lateral forces in tall flexible buildings than in short rigid buildings. The magnitude of the damage is attributed to the duration of the earthquake and the resulting accumulation of failures of structural and nonstructural elements.

This study has been restricted to military and commercial buildings in the Anchorage area because the other cities, such as Seward, Valdez, and Cordova, have no large modern structures. A few buildings in Whittier, including the 14-story Hodge Building, the adjacent school, the Buckner Building, and warehouses, are exceptions to this rule and are included in this work.

PROCEDURES

Because this study of earthquake damage was started almost 2 years after the disaster, the investigators were faced with the problems of hazy memories, lost files, repaired buildings, destroyed photographs, and countless other difficulties. It would have been much more logical to have studied the damage immediately after the earthquake and to have drawn from first-hand information and knowledge. When we started this study, very little "raw" earthquake damage was available for analysis; however, the delay in starting had one advantage—access to the photographs and studies of other investigators. In many cases a photograph taken to illustrate a structural failure showed significant information about adjacent nonstructural failures.

The team of investigators consisted of three licensed professional engineers: one mechanical, one electrical, and one mechanical with additional specialized training in structural engineering. This group was assisted by consulting architects in Anchorage and Los Angeles and by an elevator consultant.

We also requested specific information from manufacturers of elevators, electrical equipment, emergency generator sets, ceiling systems, and lighting fixtures and endeavored to obtain photographs or reports of the performance of their products during the earthquake. We inquired, too, whether they were currently working on designs to make their products more resistant to damage by earthquakes. Most of the manufacturers who responded indicated that earthquake resistance was not one of their design criteria; a few of the lighting-fixture manufacturers displayed an awareness of the earthquake problem and offered some worthwhile suggestions.

An association was established with a firm of Anchorage architects to provide the necessary liaison with Anchorage residents, to assist in the collection of data, and to provide first-hand information on the damage and repairs to specific buildings. The Anchorage newspapers announced that the study was taking place and emphasized the need for detailed information and photographs.

We examined the files of the Alaska District Corps of Engineers, Elmendorf AFB, Fort Richardson, *The Anchorage Daily Times*, and all commercial photography shops in Anchorage, in addition to numerous files of investigators and private citizens, in search of photographs that showed nonstructural damage; these pictures were then filed for detailed analysis later.

Despite the time that had elapsed since the earthquake, the investigating team was able to make field studies of several buildings that had not been repaired or fully occupied since the earthquake. These were the 14-story Hodge Building, the school, and the 5-story Buckner Building in Whittier, and the 14-story Mt. McKinley apartment building in Anchorage. The buildings in Whittier were examined in August 1966, when they were still boarded up and unoccupied. By detailed questioning of the former occupants and maintenance personnel who were present during and immediately after the earthquake, it was possible to establish what little repair and cleanup work had been done and what portions of the observed damage were actually caused by the earthquake. The Mt. McKinley building was examined first in January 1965 and again in May and August 1966, and in April 1967. By questioning the building operating engineer who was in the building during the earthquake, the contractors who conducted emergency repairs immediately after the earthquake, and the engineers and contractors who rehabilitated the structure, it was possible to establish what parts of the damage observed were actually caused by the earthquake.

Apart from the actual examination of "raw" earthquake damage, the greatest source of information was the damage reports at Elmendorf AFB and Fort Richardson and the many files and drawings at the Alaska District Office of the Corps of Engineers.

DESIGN PRACTICES AND BUILDING CODES

It is impractical to discuss why buildings suffered nonstructural damage during the earthquake, without examining the effectiveness of the building codes in use at the time as well as the correctness of current design practices and construction techniques.

The development of plans and specifications for a modern building is a team effort. An architect acts as a coordinator and general manager of the project as it moves from concept to design and into the field and is finally erected. The primary outside consultants on the design team are the structural, mechanical, and electrical engineers. This group often controls the design of 75 percent of the total construction cost of a building. The structural engineer and the architect require the services of foundation and soils engineers, and continual liaison with material manufacturers and governmental agencies in the development of the design is necessary.

The first concepts of the size and shape of a building are developed by the architect from his knowledge of the client's needs. In most instances, these fundamental decisions are rendered before the structural engineer is called to develop a structural frame to meet an architectural design and before mechanical and electrical engineers are called in to design their systems. It is during the preparation of the working drawings and specifications that the final decisions are made regarding the detailing—or lack of detailing—of the nonstructural elements.

Because the drawings are prepared for competitive bidding, alternative equipment and materials must be accepted if they are equal in quality and performance to those specified in the contract documents. Shop drawings prepared by the successful contractors or materials manufacturers must be submitted to the design team for approval before installation. These shop drawings contain the actual installation details and become the final guide to the execution of the design. This shift from the plans prepared by the design team to the shop drawings and then to the work of the installer at the building requires careful supervision if the intent of the design is to be executed properly.

Many details of nonstructural elements are omitted from drawings because of trade practices in the construction industry. These details, such as how to hang light fixtures or ceilings, how to install elevators or mechanical equipment, and how to anchor heavy veneers or facades, have often been left to the manufacturers and installers. Architects and engineers must give more attention to these details, see that they are clearly shown on the drawings or are described in the specifications, and demand that they be properly executed by the contractors.

Very little knowledge exists regarding the performance of nonstructural elements subjected to earthquake forces. Usually, the structural engineer is the only member of the design team to analyze the dynamic forces induced by earthquakes. He directs his attention primarily to the structural system and leaves the detailing of the nonstructural elements to the other members of the team. This generally results in no analysis at all. The structural engineer must lead the design team in the analysis and solution of this problem and establish the forces to which the nonstructural elements will be subjected. These forces vary throughout the building and are almost totally dependent on the performance of the building frame. All members of the design team, however, must inform themselves of the nature of earthquake-induced forces in buildings and of the manner in which the stress paths occur between the structural and nonstructural elements of a building.

The architect and his consultants are responsible for developing plans and specifications for a building that meets the client's requirements and all applicable building codes. The purpose of a building code is to set only minimum standards for earthquake-resistant design to safeguard life, limb, health, property, and public welfare; it does not regulate for minimum property damage. The design team and the building owner make the economic decisions regarding the advisability of increasing the first cost of a building to reduce repair costs following an earthquake. Decisions of this nature are made on all the building components and systems, based on the experience and judgment of the design team. It is hoped that the lessons learned from the Alaska earthquake will serve as a basis for broad reevaluation of these judgments.

The following codes were in effect in the City of Anchorage at the time of the earthquake (the city had no elevator code): *Uniform Building Code* (*UBC*), 1961 edition, published by the International Conference of Building Officials; *Uniform Housing Code*, 1961 edition, published by the International Conference of Building Officials; *Uniform Plumbing Code*, 1961 edition, published by the Western Plumbing Officials Association; *National Electrical Code*, 1962 edition, published by the National Fire Protection Association; and *American Standard Installation of Gas Appliances and Gas Piping Code*, 1959 edition, published by the American Gas Association.

All these codes are modern and are constantly revised to keep abreast of current knowledge including developments in earthquake-resistant design. The existence of a good building code, however, does not in itself ensure that its provisions will be properly applied by the design team or installed by the contractors. Serious construction deficien-

cies showed up in the Alaska earthquake, indicating a need for code modifications and considerable strengthening of enforcement procedures.

Legislative controls over building-safety standards for the design and construction of public school buildings in California came into effect immediately after the 1933 Long Beach, California, earthquake. This legislation not only required that the specifications be prepared by licensed architects and engineers, but established strong legal controls over their work, the methods of plan checking and approval, and the procedures for construction supervision and inspection. These code provisions have led to design changes and construction practices that have improved the safety of California schools and should be extended and enlarged to include other critical high occupant-density buildings.

The development and enforcement of building-code requirements for earthquake-resistant design varies in different cities and in the federal and state agencies. For example, immediately after the 1952 earthquake in Kern County, California, the City of Los Angeles established criteria for the design and construction of pendant-mounted light-fixture supports and developed test requirements on a machine that simulated earthquake conditions. As far as we know, no other governmental agency requires such a test program on light fixtures, yet one of the major findings of this study was that thousands of pendant-mounted light fixtures in the Anchorage area collapsed and fell during the earthquake. It is hard to understand why this important code requirement was not adopted by the other governmental agencies when it was first enforced in Los Angeles.

The amount of damage sustained by nonstructural building elements could have been greatly reduced by relatively inexpensive corrective measures. The lessons learned from the Alaska earthquake must be widely disseminated among practicing architects and engineers, governmental agencies, and all members of the construction industry. Increased instruction is needed on the importance of avoiding nonstructural earthquake damage in buildings, not only to reduce damage costs, but also to improve the safety of buildings.

ELEVATORS

Elevator systems in the Anchorage area were significantly damaged by the Alaska earthquake, but no one was injured in any of the elevators, and those people who were trapped were quickly released by alert elevator repairmen. At the time of the earthquake, there were just over 100 elevators in Anchorage; about half of these were hydraulic, and the rest were operated by traction. The only other elevators of engineering interest in the earthquake-affected area were in the Hodge and Buckner buildings in Whittier. The greatest damage was sustained by the traction-type elevator systems; the hydraulic-type received only minor damage, and the few escalators in Anchorage survived the earthquake with almost no damage.

In the past, very little attention has been given to the performance of elevators during earthquakes. Anchorage, like most cities and most federal and state agencies, had no elevator code and depended completely on the manufacturer's adherence to the requirements of the *American Standard Safety Code for Elevators, Dumbwaiters, Escalators, and Moving Walks* and on the integrity of the elevator installers to protect the health and safety of the public. It was not until 1962 that the City of Los Angeles completely rewrote its elevator code to meet the need for closer regulation of vertical transportation as the city moved into the era of high-rise construction, but even this new code failed to consider earthquake-resistant design.

One of the major manufacturers of elevators told the authors that "earthquake survival, as such, is not a consideration in the design of our equipment or system. We depend upon the design of the building structure to withstand outside forces. Since elevators' load, impact, etc., are transmitted to the building, there is little we can do when buildings collapse." This statement is partly true for buildings such as the International Airport control tower and the Four Seasons apartment building, where the buildings did, in fact, collapse. It is not true, however, in the case of the J. C. Penney Building, the Cordova and Hill buildings, the L Street and Mt. McKinley apartment buildings, and the Elmendorf AFB Hospital, where various structural failures occurred, but the entire buildings did not collapse. The elevators in these buildings and in other buildings that did not suffer structural failures required extensive repair work. This type of damage must be carefully evaluated to design elevator systems that are capable of withstanding earthquake forces.

In many respects an elevator is a safe place to be during an earthquake. The car is enclosed, affording protection from falling debris, and it is supported on cables with large factors of safety. Any excessive downward movement of the car is detected by a governor that is mechanically linked to braking shoes on the car. In addition, the elevator is usually located within a structurally sound building core constructed of reinforced concrete. This situation is dramatically illustrated in Figure 1, which shows the collapsed Four Seasons apartment building where the only recognizable elements remaining after the earthquake were the stair shafts and the elevator hoistways. No one was in the building during the earthquake, but it is obvious that the only place where anyone could possibly have survived would have been in the elevator car.

Elevator repairmen working in Alaska and Washington State considered it inevitable that earthquakes would always "knock out" the elevator systems. Interviews with elevator

U.S. Army

FIGURE 1 Collapsed six-story Four Seasons apartment building. The only identifiable elements remaining were the stair shafts and the elevator hoistway.

repairmen immediately after the relatively small April 29, 1965, Seattle earthquake revealed elevator damage very similar to that caused in Anchorage by the much larger Alaska earthquake. In both earthquakes, the traction elevators sustained damage from motor generator sets that "walked around" the machine rooms, counterweights that "jumped" out of their guide rails, and broken guides.

Loose counterweights, for example, were reported in both earthquakes as follows:

L Street apartment building in Anchorage (Don St. Louis, *Elevator World*, May 1964, p. 20):

In order to get an elevator running in the 1200 L-Street Building, I had to climb up the rails to the 4th floor, where I put a 4 × 4 behind the counterweights and 2 × 10's to the hatch opening. The counterweights had made three half turns, but we easily put them back because they were hanging on about 100 feet of cable.

Lowell apartment building in Seattle (Len Winslow, *Elevator World*, January 1966, p. 18):

Actually the car was stopped at the 6th floor and had collided with the counterweight which had come completely out of the rails. The weight had crushed in the car top. We found the counterweight rails bowed out at the 11th floor.

The only reason the loose counterweights did not collide with the cars in Anchorage was because the power failure stopped the drives. The power did not fail in the Seattle earthquake. Although the speeds of the counterweights and cars are relatively low (from 2 to 12 mph), the potential collisions and the swinging counterweights constitute a serious hazard that should be eliminated.

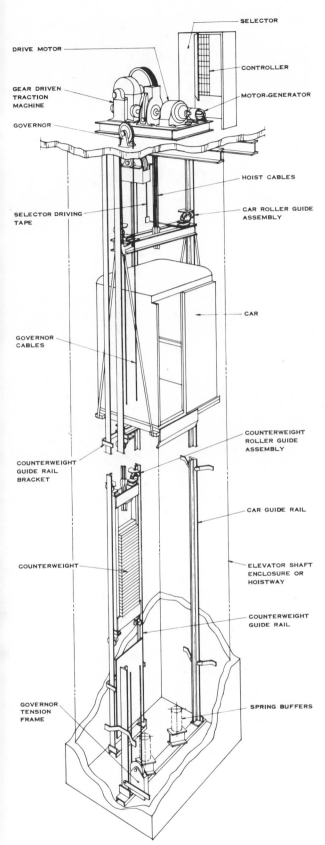

SELECTOR

DRIVE MOTOR

CONTROLLER

GEAR DRIVEN
TRACTION
MACHINE

MOTOR-GENERATOR

GOVERNOR

HOIST CABLES

SELECTOR DRIVING
TAPE

CAR ROLLER GUIDE
ASSEMBLY

CAR

GOVERNOR
CABLES

COUNTERWEIGHT
ROLLER GUIDE
ASSEMBLY

COUNTERWEIGHT
GUIDE RAIL
BRACKET

CAR GUIDE RAIL

COUNTERWEIGHT

ELEVATOR SHAFT
ENCLOSURE OR
HOISTWAY

COUNTERWEIGHT
GUIDE RAIL

GOVERNOR
TENSION
FRAME

SPRING BUFFERS

FIGURE 2   Traction-type passenger elevator, showing major components only.

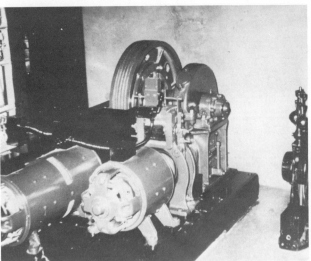

Don St. Louis

FIGURE 3   L Street apartment building elevator equipment before the earthquake. The motor-generator set is on the left, the motor and drive are in the center, and the governor is on the far right.

TRACTION-TYPE ELEVATORS

An illustrative drawing of a traction-type passenger elevator is shown in Figure 2. Figure 3 is a preearthquake photograph of the L Street apartment building elevator equipment.

Damage to Machinery and Panels

At least 80 percent of the earthquake damage to elevator machinery was caused by motor-generator sets being thrown from their vibration-isolation mounts. These high-speed units are usually isolated from the structure to provide vibration control and this makes them vulnerable to earthquake vibrations. Typical failures are illustrated in Figures 4 and 5 in the Alaska Native Hospital and in Figures 6 and 7 in the L Street apartment building. Stephenson (1964) reported a situation, subsequently confirmed by interviews with the repairman, in which the five motor-generator sets in the Elmendorf AFB Hospital were scattered about the penthouse by the earthquake; some walked up to 8 ft from their original position. Some of the motor generators would have moved further had they not been constrained by connecting wires and conduits. In the Four Seasons apartment building (Figure 1), the generator set was actually thrown through the wall of the penthouse as the building collapsed.

The vibration-isolation mounts failed because they were not tied to the floor and to the legs of the motor generator. Figure 8 is a closeup view of a typical mounting in the Mt. McKinley apartment building. The center pin in the steel plate extends down into the rubber isolator with a press fit and also up into the bolt holes in the leg of the motor-generator set. When motor generators are subjected to a lateral force, they rock on the rubber isolators until

Don St. Louis

FIGURE 4   Motor generator in Alaska Native Hospital that was thrown off its vibration-isolation mounts by the earthquake.

Don St. Louis

FIGURE 6   L Street apartment building, showing the motor generator before the earthquake (left).

Don St. Louis

FIGURE 5   Another view of the motor generator in Alaska Native Hospital. Note the vibration isolator lying on the floor and the partly torn wires.

they tip over (Figure 5). When the earthquake damage was repaired, most of these installations were remounted in the original manner, and they will surely topple over again during the next severe earthquake.

Some of the corrective measures taken after the earthquake will be effective during future earthquakes. In the new Captain Cook Hotel, the vibration isolators under the legs of the motor generators were bolted to the legs and to the floor (Figure 9). An equally successful corrective effort was made at the Elmendorf AFB Hospital (Figure 10). The heavy base of the motor generator was set on neoprene pads and constrained on all sides by sections of angle iron padded with neoprene strips and bolted to the floor.

The driving motors and gear-driven traction machines are usually mounted on a steel base, which is then bolted to the floor (Figure 3) to ensure good alignment between the motor, drive, and the cables in the shaft. These units operate at very slow speeds and usually do not require vibration-isolation mounts. In the Hodge Building in Whittier, how-

Don St. Louis

FIGURE 7 L Street apartment building after the earthquake. The motor-generator set shown in Figure 6 has shifted, and the selector driving tape and conduit have been broken.

ever, the mounting frame was set on rubber-in-shear vibration isolators in order to minimize transmission of vibration to the structure. These isolators were bolted to the steel frame and to the floor as shown in Figure 11 and survived the earthquake without damage.

FIGURE 8 Typical unsecured vibration isolators under motor-generator legs, Mt. McKinley apartment building.

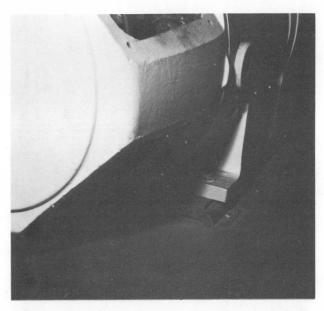

FIGURE 9 Motor-generator mounting in the Captain Cook Hotel. This postearthquake vibration isolator was bolted to the leg of the motor generator and also to the floor.

Selector and controller panels sustained very little earthquake damage where they were tied securely to the floor and/or penthouse walls. The maintenance engineers at the Elmendorf AFB Hospital reported that one control panel fell over because it was not bolted to the floor. In the L Street apartment building, the relays in the selector panel shown in Figure 12 were seriously damaged by the earth-

FIGURE 10 Postearthquake corrective measures taken at Elmendorf AFB Hospital. The motor generator was set on neoprene pads and constrained by neoprene-padded angle irons bolted to the floor.

FIGURE 11   Gear-driven traction machine and driving motor on steel frame mounted on multiple rubber-in-shear vibration isolators. Postearthquake photographs of Hodge Building in Whittier.

Don St. Louis

FIGURE 12   Damaged relays in selector panel in the L Street apartment building.

quake. These relays were mounted on a hinged door that was thrown open by the seismic forces and smashed into the adjacent cable drum. No other damage to the control equipment in the selector and control panels was reported.

The Mt. McKinley and L Street apartment buildings are almost identical and it is interesting to compare the damage in the two buildings. A photograph of the Mt. McKinley penthouse taken after the earthquake is shown in Figure 13. The elevators had been repaired to allow the occupants to move out, but no other repairs had been made in the building. The building operating engineer, who entered the room shortly after the earthquake, reported that both motor-generator sets were found leaning against the lower left corner of the control panels. The motor-generator sets in the L Street apartment building moved in the same manner (Figure 7). It was reported that the selector panel relays in the Mt. McKinley apartment building were not damaged by the earthquake, although Figure 13 shows the hinged door open at the right-hand end of the panel. The identical hinged door in the L Street apartment building was thrown open by the earthquake causing the damage shown in Figure 12.

Elevator machinery and control panels in the penthouses of tall buildings were subjected to greater lateral forces during the earthquake than was similar equipment located in basements. In the three-story Alaska Psychiatric Institute the traction-type elevator was underslung to save space for a future fourth floor, and all the machinery and control panels in the basement were undamaged by the earthquake.

Damage to the Guiding Systems

Elevator counterweight guiding systems were badly damaged by the earthquake. According to the elevator-maintenance

FIGURE 13   Penthouse of Mt. McKinley apartment building in January 1965. The motor generator was remounted without vibration isolators, and the hinged door on the right-hand end of the selector panel is standing open.

personnel, almost all the counterweights on traction elevators in Anchorage popped out of their guide rails during the earthquake. Figure 14 illustrates the manner in which the counterweights were tossed about within the elevator hoistway. The swinging counterweights often struck and deformed the spreader beams, but most of the damage consisted of bent counterweight guide rails and brackets, broken roller-guide assemblies, and twisted cables.

In the Hill Building, all three elevators were damaged by swinging counterweights. Figure 15 shows a collapsed counterweight guide rail in the foreground and broken or missing top roller-guide assemblies in the upper right corner. Figure 16 shows the lower half of the loosened counterweight shown in Figure 15, which tore the right-hand guide rail loose and completely deformed the counterweight bracket. The same picture shows a bent spreader beam and electrical conduit, both damaged by the swinging counterweight in the adjacent hoistway. Figure 17 shows similar damage to counterweight guide rails in the Anchorage-Westward Hotel; the deformation started at the fishplate that ties the rail sections together. New counterweight guide rails were required in the upper half of the eight-story Elmendorf AFB Hospital, and bent rails had to be repaired in the Providence Hospital.

To avoid the damage caused by derailed counterweights,

Fred Hosel

FIGURE 15   Damaged counterweight and guide rail in the Hill Building. Collapsed right guide rail is in foreground. The roller-guide assembly on upper-left corner of counterweight is missing.

we suggest certain design improvements. We believe that the counterweight guide rails installed in seismically active areas should be heavier than the 8-lb rail normally used. The guide-rail brackets should be installed at more frequent intervals, or should be sufficiently reinforced to withstand the earthquake-induced forces on the counterweights. Figure 18A shows various types of counterweight guide-rail brackets that are commonly used. If the steel plates are not

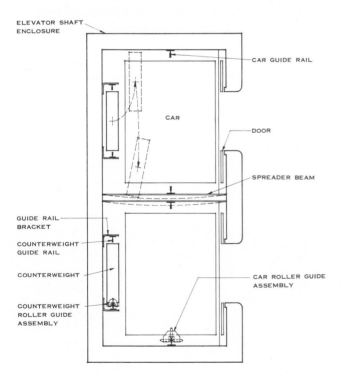

FIGURE 14   Typical two-car elevator shaft, showing guide rails for car and counterweights. Dotted lines indicate motion of counterweights when freed from their guide rails by the earthquake and a deformed spreader beam.

Fred Hosel

FIGURE 16   Lower half of counterweight shown in Figure 15. Spreader beam on the left was bent by the swinging counterweight in the adjacent hoistway.

Fred Hosel

FIGURE 17   Bent counterweight guide rail in the Anchorage-Westward Hotel.

thick enough, they will yield and deform when subjected to the inertial forces of the counterweights. Figure 18B shows suggested design improvements for these brackets; designs are numbered in sequence with increasing degrees of rigidity. The relatively simple types 1 and 2 are based on the theory of having two cantilevered brackets working together. By tying the two brackets together, the rigidity of each is more or less doubled. If a tie between the brackets is not practical, type 3 or 4 can be used. Type 4 is an improvement over type 3 because the distance between brackets is preset and the required bolt sizes are smaller. Gussets welded to the brackets greatly increase the strength of the assembly. Types 5 and 6 may be used in situations where the availability of the elevator in emergency situations is mandatory.

Roller guides were found to be the weak links between the counterweights and their guide rails. The rollers are spring-loaded (Figure 19) and, during the earthquake, they were twisted and hammered against the guide rails by the counterweights. Typical damage to these assemblies is shown in Figure 20 in the Hill Building.

A safety shoe, bolted to the counterweight frame (Figure 21), could protect the roller-guide assembly during an earthquake. The shoe could be similar to the type now used on hydraulic and freight elevators, where rollers are not required. It would be provided with sufficient bearing area to withstand the earthquake forces, and, under normal operation, it would ride free of the guide rails. During an earthquake, the roller spring would give way to allow the safety

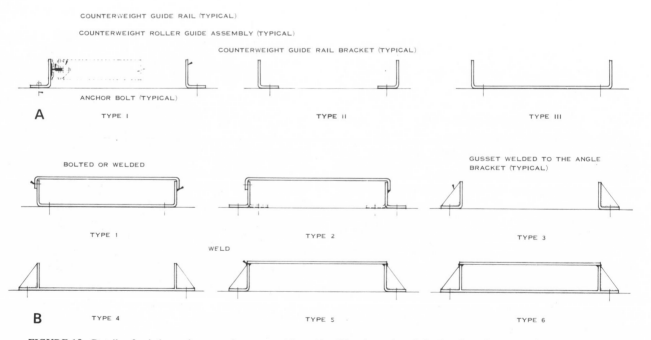

FIGURE 18   Details of existing and proposed counterweight guiderail brackets. A, existing brackets; B, proposed improved brackets.

FIGURE 19 Closeup view of a typical counterweight roller-guide assembly.

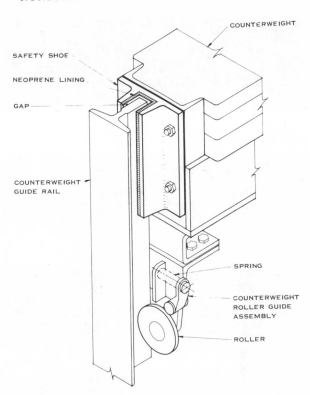

FIGURE 21 Proposed safety-shoe design to prevent damage to counterweight roller-guide assembly.

shoe to contact the guide rail and carry the lateral forces from the counterweights.

The guide-rail systems for the elevator cars sustained very little earthquake damage, primarily because these guide rails are stronger than the counterweight guide rails. They are

Don St. Louis

FIGURE 20 Damaged counterweight roller-guide assemblies in the Sharilyn Arms apartment building. The assembly on the right side was broken off by the earthquake and fell to the bottom of the hoistway.

designed to withstand eccentric live loads being added to the car during loading and unloading, in addition to braking forces from the car safety brakes. These guide rails are fastened to the building structure (Figure 14), either to the walls of the elevator hoistway or to heavy wide-flange spreader beams. The car guide rails and their supports, however, should be analyzed for earthquake-induced forces, even if they are not badly damaged during the earthquake. One effort to strengthen the car guide rails is shown in Figure 22. At the new Captain Cook Hotel, the elevator contractor installed spacers between the back-to-back rails at all midpoints between all spreader beams to increase the rigidity of both rails.

Another type of earthquake-induced damage to the elevator guiding systems was caused by falling debris and concrete-masonry units. Figures 23 and 24 illustrate damage in the Sharilyn Arms apartment building, where unreinforced-concrete-masonry units in the elevator-hoistway walls were displaced by the earthquake and fell into the shaft. This type of secondary damage indicates a need for adequate reinforcement in walls made from concrete-masonry units, or suggests the use of other materials, such as stud-and-plaster or poured-in-place reinforced concrete.

Damage to elevator door frames is a potential hazard

FIGURE 22   Strengthened car-guide rails in the Captain Cook Hotel. Note the spacer clamped between the two back-to-back car guide rails, just above the control switches. The counterweights are on the left.

Don St. Louis

FIGURE 23   Damaged elevator hoistway wall in Sharilyn Arms apartment building.

that is closely related to the structural integrity of the building and of the elevator hoistway. If the door frames are shifted or distorted during an earthquake, the doors could be prevented from opening. Although no damage of this type in Anchorage came to our attention, it was reported in the smaller 1965 Seattle earthquake. The soundness of the structural frame around the door openings to elevator hoistways is essential to the successful operation of the doors.

HYDRAULIC ELEVATORS AND ESCALATORS

There were approximately 50 hydraulic elevators in the Anchorage area, all of which survived the earthquake with very little damage. These elevators are essentially hydraulic jacks, consisting of a fixed cylinder and a movable plunger that is attached to the elevator car. The elevator is activated

Don St. Louis

FIGURE 24   Closeup of Figure 23, showing unreinforced-masonry units that damaged the counterweight roller-guide assembly.

by pumping fluid into the base of the cylinder, and the car moves up and down in guide rails mounted on the walls of the hoistways. Lubricated guide shoes are used to maintain the alignment of the plunger. The application of hydraulic elevators is limited to low buildings and their inherent simplicity of design makes them less susceptible to earthquake damage than the traction elevators.

At the time of the earthquake, the largest hydraulic elevator in Anchorage was in the six-story Presbyterian Hospital. The photograph of the base of the cylinder on this elevator, taken immediately after the earthquake (Figure 25), shows that the unit sustained no damage; it resumed operation as soon as emergency power was restored to the hospital by portable motor-generator sets brought into Anchorage by the U.S. Army.

A hydraulic elevator in the First Federal Savings and Loan Building was slightly damaged when concrete-masonry units from the walls of the elevator hoistway fell and blocked the movement of the car. In the Loussac Sogn Building, a ground crack passed through the elevator pit, causing the cylinder to shift out of plumb when a section of the building settled. The cylinder did not break or settle, and the system was put back into service after the section of the building that settled was pressure-grouted and brought back to a level position. This type of elevator-repair work is minor when compared to the damage sustained by the traction elevators.

There were only a few escalators in Anchorage, and all survived the earthquake with little or no damage, probably because they consisted essentially of two welded steel trusses between floors that supported the tracks, sprockets, machine drives, and other apparatus. The most dramatic illustration of the ability of escalators to survive an earthquake was in the seriously damaged J. C. Penney Building, where the four escalators provided a way out of the building for the occupants during the earthquake. According to the elevator maintenance personnel, after these escalators were cleared of debris that had jammed the moving treads, they could have resumed operation. The same minimum amount of damage was reported on the escalators in the Caribou department store, where only one tread was damaged.

EMERGENCY POWER FOR ELEVATORS

During power blackouts and other disasters, people have frequently been trapped in stalled elevator cars, often without benefit of light, ventilation, or communication with rescue workers. In Anchorage, all elevator cars were stalled by the power outage. Even if the power had not failed, most of the cars would have been stopped by failures in the guiding systems and elevator machinery. In light of this experience, it is desirable to review the hazards of and solutions to freeing occupants from stalled elevator cars.

The elevator repairmen, building operating engineers, and other officials in Anchorage generally agreed that occupants trapped in elevator cars should remain there until rescued and not try to get out of the car through the roof hatch. The top of an elevator car is dark and unfamiliar to the layman, the hoistway is subject to falling debris, the opening of the doors is not simple, and one can easily slip from the car roof and fall into the hoistway. Efforts should be made to eliminate the coffin-like atmosphere in a stalled elevator car, instead of developing more elaborate escape procedures from within the car.

Some federal agencies, but very few state and municipal authorities, recognize the need to reduce panic in a stalled elevator car and require emergency battery-powered light units in elevators. These lights are usually designed to turn on automatically when the power fails, and the battery is maintained under continuous trickle charge. This rather minimum requirement should be expanded to include the operation of a ventilation fan in the car and the availability of an emergency communication system connected to some central location such as the building lobby.

The power outage in Anchorage reduced the potential damage to the elevator equipment, but if the guiding systems were usable, it also prevented the movement of the stalled elevator car to the nearest landing. In Great Britain, government agencies require that elevators be equipped with manually operated drives designed to slowly raise or lower the car in case of a power outage. A more practical solution is to provide emergency power in the building, capable of operating at least one elevator and all the emergency lights in the building. In buildings with several elevators, controls can be added to lower each of the elevators to a predetermined level to release trapped passengers and then to transfer

Don St. Louis

FIGURE 25   Undamaged hydraulic elevator in the Presbyterian Hospital. Hydraulic plunger is in center and buffer springs are on each side.

the emergency power to one elevator for the evacuation of the building occupants, or for the use of firemen and other rescue crews. If emergency power is provided for the elevator drives, this power can then be used to operate the elevator-car fans, communication system, and lights. To protect the elevator equipment from damage and fires caused by electrical short circuits during an earthquake, installation of a manually reset earthquake-sensitive switch in the normal power supply to the elevator machinery should be considered. This safety switch, located at some central location such as the building lobby, together with emergency standby power for at least one elevator, should provide adequate earthquake protection to the elevator electrical systems.

DAMAGE SUMMARY

Traction-Type Elevators

1. Almost all motor-generator sets were thrown off their unanchored vibration-isolation mounts.

2. Control panels fell over when they were not anchored to the floor or walls.

3. Control relays were damaged when unlatched hinged panels were thrown open.

4. Counterweight guiding systems were badly damaged and counterweights were derailed. Spreader beams were damaged by swinging counterweights and supporting cables were twisted.

5. Car-guiding systems sustained very little damage, and driving motors and gear-driven traction machines were undamaged.

6. Falling concrete masonry units from the hoistway walls and other debris jammed some guiding systems.

Hydraulic Elevators and Escalators

1. The cylinder of one hydraulic elevator was shifted out of plumb by a minor landslide. All other hydraulic elevators were undamaged.

2. One hydraulic elevator was blocked by concrete-masonry units that fell from the hoistway walls.

3. Escalators were undamaged except where treads were jammed by falling debris.

RECOMMENDATIONS

Earthquake-resistant design for elevators should take into consideration the following:

1. Vibration isolators under the motor generators should be bolted to the floor and to the legs of the motor generators. The isolators should have sufficient strength to withstand the earthquake forces.

2. Selector and controller panels should be bolted to the floor and if possible provided with sway braces at the top.

All electrical components within the panels should be secured to the panel frame and all doors and hinged panels fitted with positive locking latches.

3. Counterweight guide rails serving buildings of five-stories or more should be 15 lb/ft, or heavier, and their supports should be designed to withstand earthquake forces.

4. An arrangement of the type shown in Figure 18B should be used for counterweight guide-rail bracket design; the type of bracket used should depend on the building height and location in the hoistway.

5. Properly designed safety shoes for roller guides should be provided to protect the roller assemblies from being damaged by the counterweights.

6. Ventilation, communication, and lighting systems in the cars should be connected to an emergency power system and should be designed to operate when the normal power system fails.

7. In high-rise buildings with multiple elevators and in other buildings with critical occupancies, at least one elevator should be connected to an emergency power system.

8. A manually reset earthquake-sensitive switch in the power supply to the elevator should be developed.

9. The elevator hoistway and the surrounding structural system should be adequately reinforced and braced to prevent distortion at the doors and to prevent debris from falling into the shaft.

MECHANICAL SYSTEMS

For the purposes of this study, the mechanical systems include boilers; furnaces; flues; chimneys; plumbing; piping; fans; ducts; refrigeration compressors; heating, ventilating, and air-conditioning systems; tanks; fire sprinklers; and gas systems. With a few significant exceptions, these systems were not badly damaged by the earthquake, mainly because of the strength and resiliency of the piping systems; some failures, however, occurred at fittings and connections to equipment and to tanks that shifted or toppled during the earthquake. To a lesser degree, the same situation existed for the duct systems and their connections to fans and air-handling units.

Because of the cold climate, only a few buildings in the Anchorage area were provided with air-conditioning systems, but all buildings were heated. Because the air-conditioning systems were small, they all used direct-expansion refrigeration compressors, and, in most instances, city water for condensing purposes. In some installations, city water was used directly for cooling. At the time of the earthquake, no centrifugal water-chilling units or large cooling-tower installations were in use in Anchorage. Most of the large commercial and public buildings were heated by means of gas-fired steam or hot-water boilers, with oil or coal as standby fuels. Residential and small commercial buildings were generally heated by gas or oil direct-fired furnaces or small boilers, although a few used electric-resistance heating. Most of the military buildings were heated by low-pressure steam, supplied from central coal-fired high-pressure steam plants and underground distribution systems.

The plumbing and fire-sprinkler systems in Anchorage were all of conventional design. The plumbing and interior wet and dry standpipe systems all followed the *Uniform Building Code*, and the fire-sprinkler systems were installed in accordance with the requirements of the National Board of Fire Underwriters (NBFU) and the Pacific Fire Rating Bureau (PFRB) currently known as the National Fire Protection Association (NFPA). Street water pressures were adequate to serve most of the buildings, but a few of the taller buildings were provided with constantly running house pumps to develop enough pressure to serve the upper floors.

Except for the requirements established by the NFPA (Appendix A) to protect fire-sprinkler systems, very little thought has been given to earthquake resistant design of mechanical systems in buildings. Normal practice has been to design for forces created by thermal expansion, for the dynamics of moving fluids, for reciprocating or rotating equipment, and for the weight of piping and equipment, but lateral forces caused by earthquakes have been almost totally ignored. Most design engineers consider the earthquake-bracing requirements of the NFPA as expensive additions that cannot be justified on all piping systems. Because little is known of the performance of mechanical systems during earthquakes, the design engineer is unable to decide where earthquake-resistant design is mandatory, where it is desirable, and where it is unnecessary.

To ignore earthquake forces in the design of mechanical systems can lead to significant design errors. For example, large pieces of mechanical equipment, such as water chillers, pumps, boilers, engine generators, and cooling towers, have been customarily installed on the roofs or upper floors of tall buildings. Although the equipment and interconnecting piping have been mounted on springs to provide the necessary acoustical control and vibration isolation from the building, no one has tried to analyze the performance of these large floating masses when subjected to earthquake-induced forces. Additional research is necessary to establish the forces acting on equipment and to develop alternate supporting methods. It is hoped that the information contained in this study will stimulate further work in this area.

PIPING SYSTEMS

The overall damage to piping systems was surprisingly low. Many instances were reported where piping systems remained intact, despite the significant structural and nonstructural damage suffered by the building. For example, the plumb-

ing pipes in the Enlisted Men's Service Club at Fort Richardson remained standing after the earthquake (Figure 26) although the walls around them collapsed. Contractors also reported that most systems were put back into service when pressure-testing revealed no leaks.

Where damage occurred, it was caused by excessive pipe movements and differential deflections between piping systems and the connected equipment. Whether a piping system failed or not depended to a great extent on the type of fittings used and the way the pipe was supported. Except in areas where there was a complete structural failure, very few pipes were actually broken; most failures in piping systems occurred at fittings.

In general, fittings in welded-steel pipe and soldered or brazed copper lines survived the earthquake with very little damage. Screwed fittings, however, were the source of several failures, and a few caulked joints in horizontal cast-iron lines were damaged by the earthquake. Brittle nonmetallic dielectric couplings, used to isolate ferrous and nonferrous pipes, collapsed when the pipes were deflected. There were only a few installations where mechanical-joint pipe connections were used above grade, and these were not damaged by the earthquake.

The contractors reported that many of the failures in screwed fittings could not be detected by visual inspections. The joints were not pulled apart during the earthquake, but the threads on the pipe and in the fittings were completely broken up by the repeated deflections of the pipes. The damaged joints would always show up under pressure tests,

U.S. Army

FIGURE 26 In the Enlisted Men's Service Club at Fort Richardson, plumbing vents and water piping remained standing after the earthquake, although the surrounding walls collapsed.

and when the workmen tried to stop the leak by tightening the fitting, it usually fell apart.

To avoid pipe damage, greater attention must be given to differential deflections of pipe segments and the equipment that they serve. At Fort Richardson Power Plant, for example, large steam mains were suspended from the structure on hanger rods that allowed the pipe to swing with very little restraint, whereas small condensate lines connected to drip legs on the steam line were clamped tightly to the structure. During the earthquake, the large pipes moved and the small pipes were torn from the main. Many unit heaters suffered similar damage where, although both the unit heater and the piping were freely suspended, they had different natural frequencies and responded to the earthquake with different movements. Invariably, the failure occurred at a fitting on the condensate-return line. This type of failure is shown in Figure 27, where the pipe pulled out of a screwed elbow. The suspension system on the unit heater was not provided with lateral bracing, and the larger-diameter steam line did not fail. This type of failure was repeated throughout most of the large warehouses at Fort Richardson and at Elmendorf AFB.

Some of the failures at screwed elbows occurred where long suspended pipelines turned into shorter segments. This type of failure is believed to have been caused by the excessive swaying of the long pipe run and the inability of the

FIGURE 28 Split elbow in fire-sprinkler line at Elmendorf AFB warehouse.

short run to cope with the movement. The repeated stressing of the threads resulted in their total failure, or if the joint was very tight, the elbow itself was cracked or split. These types of failure are illustrated in Figures 28–30. These post-earthquake photographs of damaged sprinkler lines in the

FIGURE 27 Unit heater in Elmendorf AFB warehouse, showing broken condensate-return line at screwed fitting. Note damaged insulation on suspended storm-drain line at right.

FIGURE 29 Pipe pulled away from the elbow at Elmendorf AFB warehouse.

FIGURE 30 Closeup of Figure 29, showing damaged pipe threads.

FIGURE 31 Hanger rods, supported from beam clamps in Elmendorf AFB warehouse, were shifted by the earthquake.

collapsed and unrepaired warehouses 21-885 to 21-889 at Elmendorf AFB were taken in May 1966. They are presented here only to illustrate the type of failure sustained by screwed fittings. They do not represent typical failures in fire-sprinkler lines. Unfortunately, failures in other piping systems must be illustrated by examples of damaged fire-sprinkler systems, although these were the only piping systems that were actually provided with earthquake bracing.

Long runs of heavy cast-iron pipe, suspended from the roofs of warehouses, were damaged by excessive movement. Similar damage was sustained by the cast-iron soot line in the Fort Richardson Power Plant, where three sections fell, causing secondary damage. Without lateral bracing, these heavy sections of pipe were easily set in motion by the earthquake, and the flexible joints pulled apart. Typical damage to storm-drain lines in the warehouses at Elmendorf AFB is illustrated in Figures 31–34.

Most of the pipe damage was reported in low, large structures such as warehouses and large shops. These buildings required long horizontal runs of pipe and, except for fire-sprinkler systems, the piping had usually been installed without any earthquake bracing. In the design of the mechanical systems for high-rise buildings, a concerted effort is made to localize the vertical pipe shafts and stack the plumbing fixtures. Most of the long horizontal pipe runs are then limited to the lower levels, where the earthquake forces are less severe. The vertical plumbing and heating stacks in the 14-story Anchorage-Westward Hotel, the L Street and Mt. McKinley apartment buildings, or the

Hodge Building in Whittier were practically undamaged, although all these buildings, except the Hodge Building, sustained severe structural failures.

Some damage was reported in the utility connections to buildings, where differential settlement caused pipe joints to pull apart. The use of flexible connections with several

FIGURE 32 Twisted and damaged insulated storm-drain line in Elmendorf AFB warehouse.

FIGURE 33   Torn storm-drain connection at roof drain in Elmendorf AFB warehouse.

offsets at these points will protect against some minor earth movements if the soil is soft, but no design will resist major ground movements. All pipes that pass through basement or foundation walls should go through sleeved openings to avoid excessive strains on the pipe. After installation, the space between the pipe wall and the sleeve should be caulked or otherwise made watertight. No damage to gas lines within buildings or at the service point came to our attention, but broken underground fuel lines to emergency generators were reported.

SEISMIC JOINTS AND EXPANSION LOOPS

Structural separations, or seismic joints, are often provided in buildings to allow for movement between different structural units during an earthquake. Where piping systems cross these joints, they must be designed to absorb the maximum anticipated movement at that point. There were buildings in Anchorage where this movement was ignored, and small-diameter pipes were crushed during the earthquake, or, if the pipes were large, the walls surrounding the pipes were broken. In the Elmendorf AFB Hospital, flexible connections were provided in the pipes where they crossed seismic joints, but many of these were badly damaged by the earthquake.

In the Hodge Building in Whittier, an expansion loop was installed at the seismic joint on the fourteenth floor (Figure 35). The 28 × 6-in. opening in the concrete shear wall and the 7-ft-long expansion loop were designed to take the anticipated lateral movement, and the 21-ft run parallel to the joint was used to dissipate the longitudinal movement. This installation survived the earthquake without damage, although occupants of the building stated that the two structures slapped together during the earthquake (Figures 36 and 37). The damage inflicted on the concrete wall at the seismic joint was possibly caused by poorly placed reinforcing bars and the failures in the adjacent corridor walls.

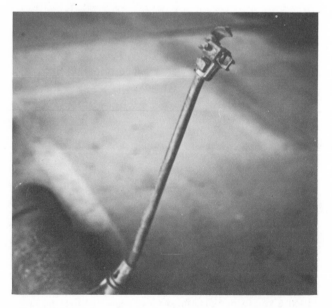

FIGURE 34   Typical broken beam clamp on pipe hanger.

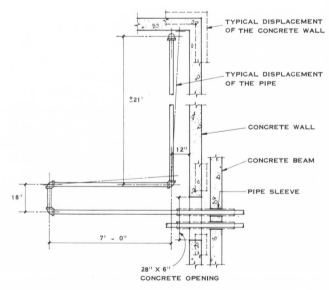

FIGURE 35   Plan view of pipe crossing seismic joint in the fourteenth floor of the Hodge Building in Whittier.

FIGURE 36   The heating-hot-water pipes shown in Figure 35; structural damage is visible above the corridor ceiling.

In tall structures, the seismic separations between structural units can often exceed 12 in., and design engineers should try to avoid all pipe crossings on the upper floors. In installations where space does not permit the use of pipe loops, the anticipated movement can be absorbed by offsets with ball joints at elbows, or by flexible connections in the arms of the loop as shown in Figure 38. The pipe sections within the offset must be properly supported to prevent sagging.

FIGURE 37   Closeup view of pipes passing through 28 × 6-in. opening in shear wall shown in Figure 36. Insulation at the bottom of the pipes was not damaged by the earthquake, but was cut out during the original installation.

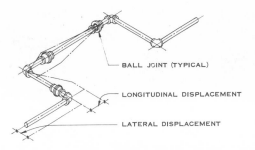

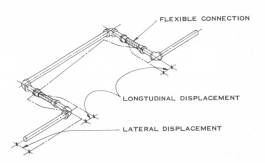

FIGURE 38   Proposed piping arrangements for crossing seismic joints in buildings where space limitations prevent the use of pipe loops shown in Figure 35.

The performance criteria of flexible connections on piping systems must be carefully evaluated, because such connections tend to stiffen under high pressure and to lose their flexibility. This must be done whether the connection is intended to absorb movement in a seismic joint, provide vibration isolation at a piece of machinery, or absorb movements caused by thermal expansion. If the connection loses its flexibility, the pipe movements will overstress the flexible portion and cause it to fail. Many of the bellows-type flexible pipe connections used for thermal expansion in heating lines failed during the earthquake, possibly because of loss of flexibility, but more probably because of a lack of pipe guides. In one instance, a free-swinging pipe actually tore the flexible pipe at its point of connection.

Large expansion loops in steam or hot-water lines were also damaged by the earthquake because they lacked earthquake bracing. The repeated oscillations of the long pipes set up excessive stresses at the elbows of the expansion loops that first caused failures at the joints and then collapse of the pipes. This type of pipe failure occurred in the condensate return in the intransit storage and port office building in Whittier (Figures 39–40). When the pipe broke, the adjacent hangers were suddenly overloaded and yielded, starting a chain reaction that ultimately caused the entire pipe run to collapse. The large-diameter steam line remained in place, although some of its hangers were broken because of excessive swaying.

U.S. Army

FIGURE 39   Broken thermal-expansion loop in condensate-return line in intransit storage and port office, Whittier. The steam line lost some hangers but remained in place.

FIRE SPRINKLERS

The NBFU (1964) reported that there was very little earthquake damage to the fire-sprinkler systems in Anchorage. Discussions with sprinkler contractors in Seattle who made the repairs in Anchorage, and interviews with plumbing and heating contractors in Anchorage confirmed this report. Except for pipe damage in the collapsed warehouse at

Elmendorf AFB, the only damage to fire sprinklers that came to our attention was a few broken sprinkler heads and some torn ceiling tile in the Central Junior High School and the Providence Hospital.

In the gymnasium of the Central Junior High School, a sprinkler head was improperly located directly under the cross bracing of the roof. According to the maintenance engineer at the school, when the building started to vibrate during the earthquake, the cross bracing struck the head and activated it. When the repairs were made, the head was merely put back in its original position (Figure 41).

In the multipurpose room of the same school, many surface-mounted sprinkler heads in the acoustic-tile ceiling cut the tiles because of the differential movement between the sprinkler system and the ceiling system. The maintenance engineer said that some cuts in the tile were more than 1-ft long. No economical method of avoiding this type of damage is available unless the ceiling system is as well braced against earthquakes as the sprinkler system. Figure 42 shows the difference between the two suspension systems in the new Sears department store in Anchorage in 1967. The sprinkler systems are well braced to the roof structure, whereas the ceiling is suspended on flexible wires.

The excellent performance of fire-sprinkler piping suggests that the direction for the proper protection of all piping systems against damage by earthquakes might be found in sections 3150–3169 of the NFPA Standard 13, which deal with the bracing of fire-sprinkler piping (see Appendix A). The basic procedures suggested by these standards are to brace the horizontal pipes to the floor slabs or

U.S. Army

FIGURE 40   Collapsed condensate-return line in adjacent bay to that shown in Figure 39.

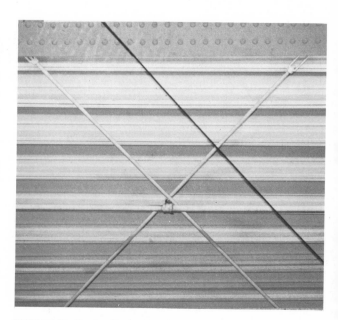

FIGURE 41   During the earthquake, the movement of the roof cross bracing set off this sprinkler head at Central Junior High School gymnasium.

FIGURE 42 New Sears department store in Anchorage in 1967, showing the difference in rigidity between the ceiling suspension system and the laterally braced fire-sprinkler pipes.

U.S. Army

FIGURE 43 Damaged sand filters in Fort Richardson Power Plant. Note the sockets for supporting legs in the bottom of the center tank.

roof to prevent excessive pipe oscillations and to make them move with these structural elements. If the risers pass through floor slabs, they are provided with flexible couplings above and below slab to ensure freedom of movement between the different floor slabs without damaging the riser. All pipes passing through walls and slabs are provided with clearance or flexible couplings to avoid concentrated loads. The lateral bracing is designed to withstand a force equal to 50 percent of the weight of the piping, attached valves, and water. At seismic-joint crossings, flexible couplings are provided on pipes 3½ in. in diameter or larger.

TANKS

The importance of anchoring heavy tanks to the structural systems of buildings was repeatedly illustrated in all damage reports. Most of these tanks, including domestic water tanks, heating-hot-water expansion tanks, sand filters, water softeners, and other vessels containing fluids, were inadequately supported and either toppled over when legs failed or walked across the floor during the earthquake. This movement of the tanks also caused the pipes connected to them to shear or pull apart and inflicted other damage on the surrounding piping system.

Figure 43 is a good illustration of the performance during the earthquake of tank legs that were designed for static

loads only. Each of these sand filters in the Fort Richardson power plant were supported by four cast-iron legs, standing free on the floor and fitting into sockets that were welded to the tank bottom. Evidently, the heavy tanks were tilted by the earthquake, and the legs failed from overloading (Figure 44). When the legs collapsed, the tanks fell against the wall causing extensive secondary damage to the connect-

FIGURE 44 One of the broken cast-iron legs used to support the tanks shown in Figure 43.

FIGURE 45   Water softener in Fort Richardson Power Plant re-mounted on old cast-iron legs after the earthquake and paralleled with new legs welded to the tanks and anchored to the floor.

FIGURE 46   Repaired sand-filter tanks in Fort Richardson Power Plant. The new legs were welded to the tank and then bolted to the floor.

ing pipes. The original mounting can be seen in Figure 45, where the water-softener tank in the same building was supported in an identical manner. During the emergency repairs immediately after the earthquake, this tank was remounted on salvaged cast-iron legs from the sand-filter tanks, and the new permanent legs were added at a later date. The new legs were welded to the tank and bolted to the floor, and the same details were later used in restoring the sand filters (Figures 46 and 47). Similar failures were reported on the sand filters that served the swimming pool in the field house at Elmendorf AFB.

The importance of anchoring down the legs under vertical tanks is illustrated in Figures 48 and 49. The domestic hot-water generators in Elmendorf AFB Hospital, shown in Figure 48, were firmly bolted to the basement floor and were undamaged by the earthquake. A similarly sized domestic hot-water generator in the Central Junior High School, shown in Figure 49, was not bolted to the floor and, according to the operating engineer, it was found leaning against a nearby gas line after the earthquake.

Figure 50 has been prepared to assist the reader in a comparison between the forces acting on free-standing and on anchored tanks. The force resulting from the gravitational and inertial forces creates an overturning moment around the point of support. Anchor bolts are needed to counteract this moment and inhibit the resulting rocking movement of

FIGURE 47   Closeup view of new tank legs for the sand filters shown in Figure 46.

FIGURE 48   Domestic hot-water generators in Elmendorf AFB Hospital were not damaged by the earthquake, because their legs were anchored to the floor.

FIGURE 49   The legs of this domestic hot-water generator in Central Junior High School were not anchored to the floor; after the earthquake, the generator was found tilted against the gas line shown in the foreground.

the fluid in the tank. The starting point for the analysis is to determine the earthquake force that the supports must be designed to withstand. This force depends on many variables, including the contents of the tank, the tank location within the building, and the anticipated performance of the surrounding structural system during an earthquake.

At Fort Richardson and at Elmendorf AFB, most of the domestic hot water was generated from steam immersion coils in large horizontal hot-water storage tanks. A typical tank, located in the basement of a 200-man barracks building at Elmendorf AFB, is shown in Figure 51. These tanks were not anchored to the floor during the earthquake; the maintenance foremen at both military bases stated that many of these hot-water tanks rolled off their supports. Although there were several barracks buildings with identical installation details, not all the tanks fell from their supports.

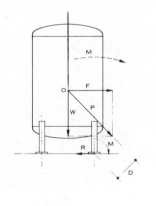

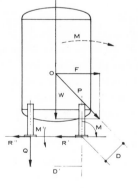

W	WEIGHT OF THE TANK PLUS THE CONTENT
F	EARTHQUAKE FORCE
P	RESULTANT FORCE OF W AND F
M	OVERTURNING MOMENT EQUAL TO P X D
Q	SUM OF THE TENSILE FORCES ON THE ANCHOR BOLTS
M'	RESTRAINING MOMENT EQUAL TO Q X D'
R	FRICTIONAL FORCE
R' R''	SUM OF THE FRICTIONAL FORCE AND THE SHEARING FORCES ON THE ANCHOR BOLTS
NOTE	VERTICAL REACTIONS DUE TO THE WEIGHT W ARE NOT SHOWN IN EITHER CASE

TANK WITH FREE STANDING LEGS

TANK WITH BOLTED LEGS

FIGURE 50   Earthquake forces acting on a bolted and a freestanding tank.

FIGURE 51 This unanchored domestic hot-water storage tank in a 200-man barracks building at Elmendorf AFB rolled over during the earthquake and has been reinstalled in the same way as before the earthquake.

FIGURE 52 The torn insulation at the pipe saddle of 2,100-gallon hydropneumatic tank on top of the Hodge Building in Whittier indicates that this tank was shifted 5 in. by the earthquake.

MT. McKINLEY BUILDING MECHANICAL SYSTEMS

We examined the Mt. McKinley apartment building on several occasions after the earthquake: in January 1965, when the building was unoccupied except for the ground-floor television station; in May 1966, when the building was com-

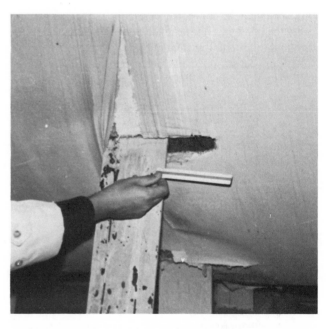

FIGURE 53 Closeup view of torn insulation at pipe saddle shown in Figure 52.

The direction of the ground motion and the tank orientation probably influenced these failures. If the direction of the ground motion was perpendicular to the tank axis, the tank was likely to roll over, but if the ground motion was parallel to the tank axis, the tank would be much more stable. Unfortunately, most of these tanks were reinstalled in the same way as before the earthquake.

All stress paths must be analyzed when developing anchors for tanks. The 2,100-gallon hydropneumatic tank on top of the 14-story Hodge Building in Whittier was shifted 5 in. by the earthquake. The tank saddles were bolted securely to concrete piers, but the saddle was not welded to the tank. This movement (Figures 52 and 53) sheared the connecting water lines and effectively interrupted domestic water service to the upper floors of the building. Similar shifting of tanks in their supports was reported in the Providence Hospital and at the First Federal Savings and Loan Building, where heating-hot-water expansion tanks slipped away from their supports and fell, breaking loose all the connecting pipes. A similar, but much smaller shift of a heating-expansion tank in the penthouse of the Hodge Building is shown in Figure 54. The tank should have been strapped to the angles and the entire assembly tied to the wall or braced to the slab above.

FIGURE 54 View of heating-hot-water expansion tank in pent-house of the Hodge Building in Whittier shows where the tank shifted on its supports during the earthquake.

pletely abandoned; in August 1966, when the structure was being repaired; and in April 1967, when many of the apartments were occupied by new tenants.

The building was heated by two hot-water boilers located in the basement, each provided with forced-draft burners and vented to the roof by a masonry stack. Heating hot water was pumped to the roof where it was vented in an open expansion tank, manifolded, and fed down to base-board convectors on each floor.

Boiler water was used to generate domestic hot water in a basement storage tank, and domestic hot and cold water was distributed to the plumbing fixtures; booster pumps were used to maintain pressures on the upper floors. The toilets and kitchens in each apartment were exhausted through vertical shafts and the attic plenum to one large fan in the penthouse (Figure 55). A masonry trash chute connected all floors to the basement trash room that contained an incinerator.

Damage to the mechanical systems was primarily limited to the movement of the unanchored heating-hot-water expansion tank (Figures 56 and 57) in the elevator-machinery-room penthouse, a few broken joints in the copper branch lines serving convectors near structural failures, and a few water connections to plumbing fixtures that pulled loose from their wall valves. The basement plumbing and heating equipment was undamaged except for a water line that froze when the building was closed. The contractor who rehabilitated the building reported that the sanitary drainage system was undamaged and all that was required to put it back in service was to rod out a few lines that were blocked by debris.

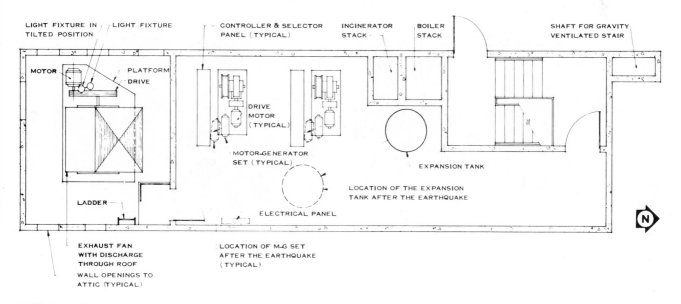

FIGURE 55 Penthouse plan, Mt. McKinley apartment building. Dotted lines indicate the final location of the equipment after the earthquake.

FIGURE 56   In the Mt. McKinley apartment building penthouse, this 390-gallon heating-hot-water expansion tank was moved 10 ft by the earthquake. Torn pipe is visible on the top of the tank.

Don DeWoody, the building operating engineer, was in his apartment on the thirteenth floor when the earthquake struck. After escorting his family to safety, he returned to the building to shut off the gas and water and to investigate the cause of the water damage in the ceiling of the ground-floor lobby. Less than 1 hour after the earthquake, he entered the elevator-machinery room to find that the 390-gallon heating-hot-water expansion tank had moved approximately 10 ft south–southeast (Figures 55 and 56). The tank was full of water at the time of the earthquake, and when it was shifted the connecting pipes were broken. The water drained from the pipe connection at the bottom of the tank and spilled down the pipe shafts to the ground floor. The closeup view of the tank leg (Figure 57) shows that the tank was not bolted to the floor. When the building was rehabilitated in 1967, the expansion tank was returned to its original position (Figure 58), but again it was not anchored to the floor.

The large exhaust fan in an adjacent room 8 ft 6 in. below the elevator-machinery-room level, was undamaged by the earthquake. The fan and motor were mounted on rubber-in-shear vibration-isolation rails (Figure 59) that were bolted to a base made of several layers of wood planks. The wall opening behind the fan motor was one of several holes that connected the attic with the fan room. Figure 60 is a closeup view of the northeast corner of the fan base; apparently, the bolt was pulled up by the fan as it tipped away from this corner. All the other bolts in the fan base were undamaged.

The manner in which the penthouse equipment was dislocated by the earthquake (Figure 55) suggests that most of the damage occurred during the first part of the earthquake. The tank, the motor generators, and a pendant-mounted

FIGURE 57   Closeup view of the tank leg shown in Figure 56. There were no provisions for anchoring the leg to the floor.

FIGURE 58   Heating-hot-water expansion tank in Mt. McKinley apartment building, restored to its original location after the earthquake. The legs are not anchored to the floor, and this tank will probably shift again in the next earthquake.

FIGURE 59 Motor and drives on exhaust fan in Mt. McKinley apartment building penthouse were undamaged by the earthquake.

FIGURE 60 Closeup of the fan base shown in Figure 59. Note that the rubber-in-shear vibration isolators were undamaged, but an anchor bolt was loosened by the earthquake.

light fixture over the fan were all moved in the same direction. The motor generators would have been thrown across the room if the control panels had not stopped them. We were unable to find any skid marks on the floor from the tank legs; the tank and the motor generators may have been moved by the first high-intensity short-duration oscillations, and then may have stayed more or less in that location throughout the rest of the earthquake.

MECHANICAL EQUIPMENT AND DUCTWORK

Damage to air-handling equipment was limited to torn flexible-duct connections and broken or bent supports and hangers. The fans, motors, and drives were essentially undamaged by the earthquake as was true for the many convectors and baseboard radiators. A great many unit heaters fell because of inadequate supports, and ductwork was damaged when hangers failed, joints were torn open, or other equipment fell against it.

According to the damage reports and interviews with the maintenance foremen, the large heating and ventilating units in the Elmendorf AFB field house swung back and forth during the earthquake, tearing loose pipe connections and crushing the connected ductwork. Figure 61 shows one of

FIGURE 61 Restored heating and ventilating unit in Elmendorf AFB fieldhouse. During the earthquake, the unit swung back and forth, tearing loose all the connected piping and ductwork.

these units as it was restored after the earthquake, still suspended from hanger rods without any bracing to restrict lateral movements.

The many convectors in the Anchorage area sustained little or no damage although they were adjacent to major structural failures. Figure 62 shows a badly damaged column on the second floor of the Anchorage-Westward Hotel with the adjacent convector practically undamaged.

Inadequate bracing also caused damage to the unit heater (Figure 63) in the composite shop in Whittier. In Hangar 32-060 at Elmendorf AFB a large unit heater was torn loose from its hangers by the earthquake and fell 30 ft to the floor. Numerous failures of unit-heater supports and connected piping were reported throughout the large warehouses and shops on both military bases.

U.S. Army

FIGURE 63 Damaged unit heater in composite shop, Whittier, with broken steam line to the right of the heater. The condensate-return line was completely torn loose by the earthquake and fell to the floor.

The operating engineer at the Alaska Psychiatric Institute reported that during the earthquake the vital air-conditioning unit serving the surgical area was shifted more than 2 ft, causing secondary damage to the connected pipes and ducts. The unit was mounted on steel legs that were anchored to the floor, but the small bolts were sheared off. In the same building, the suspended cabinet-type kitchen-exhaust fan collapsed because two ¾-in.-diameter hanger rods failed at threaded joints.

The performance during the earthquake of almost identical air supply systems in two different penthouses on top of the Hodge Building in Whittier is shown in Figures 64 and 65. Both systems consisted of two down-blast single-inlet fans that pulled air through a heating coil to supply the interior areas of the building. The angle-iron base under the supply fan shown in Figure 64 was not damaged by the earthquake.

Except for the exhaust fans in the penthouse of the Elmendorf AFB Hospital, most large floor-mounted fans and air-handling units survived the earthquake undamaged. They were either anchored directly to floor slabs or were mounted on well-anchored rubber-in-shear vibration-isolation rails. According to the mechanical contractors in Anchorage and the maintenance crews on the military bases, most of the flexible connections between fans and ducts were torn apart by the earthquake. The connections were installed to provide enough movement to isolate the

Walter Brugger

FIGURE 62 Convector on the second floor of the Anchorage-Westward Hotel. The column was badly damaged, but the convector was practically unscathed.

fans from the ducts, but evidently not enough folds were provided to take the excessive differential movements that were developed during the earthquake.

All the main exhaust fans at the Elmendorf AFB Hospital were located in the penthouse over the eighth floor. According to the operating engineer at the hospital and the contractors who made the repairs, the six large exhaust fans shifted around during the earthquake, tore up their bases, and crushed the adjacent ducts. One large fan and its motor were twisted about 30° and were left tilting off their concrete housekeeping pad. The rubber-in-shear vibration-isolation rails were bolted to the fans, but they were only loosely pinned to the floor. When the fans were subjected to the earthquake-induced forces, the bottom plate of the rail and pins were lifted out of their 1-in.-deep holes in the floor. The repair work included replacing the pins with heavy expansion bolts firmly anchored to the floor. Some of the rubber vibration isolators and most of the ductwork in the penthouse had to be replaced.

The large vertical ducts connected to the exhaust fans in the hospital penthouse were also severely damaged by the earthquake. The duct joints in the original installation were made up with government locks crimped on only three sides without any fastening screws or outside support to carry part of the weight. The earthquake caused these partly completed joints to be repeatedly opened and closed, and all the joints had to be remade. Repair work included reinforcing joints and adding angle-iron brackets and supports.

Most of the horizontal ducts above the corridor ceilings

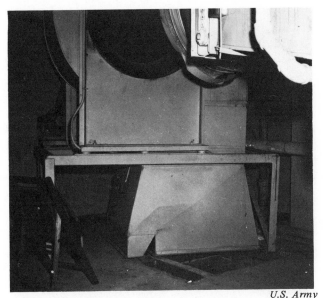

U.S. Army

FIGURE 64 Supply fan in one penthouse of Hodge Building, Whittier, shifted away from the duct shaft because it was not anchored to the floor. Note the torn flexible connector at the fan intake.

FIGURE 65 Supply fan in the other penthouse of the Hodge Building, Whittier, was not damaged because the legs were anchored to the floor.

on the upper floors of the hospital were found resting in the ceilings after the earthquake. The ducts almost filled the space above the corridor ceiling, and light fixtures, and ceilings were improperly attached to the ducts. The excessive loads caused the duct hanger supports to pull out of the slab above. The contractor corrected the installation by supporting ducts on 2-in. angle irons hung from 3/8-in. hanger rods secured to the slab with Phillips shields.

In contrast to the damage in the penthouse, the main air-conditioning supply systems on the second and third floors and the other air-handling systems in the hospital were undamaged by the earthquake. The 8-in.-diameter asbestos-cement exhaust ducts for the laboratory-fume hood were damaged when the long horizontal runs were subjected to repeated oscillations that opened the cemented joints and broke a few couplings. Repair work consisted of remaking the joints and adding more hangers and braces to restrict the lateral movement.

Most of the sheet-metal ductwork survived the earthquake with very little damage. In the J. C. Penney Building, although severe structural failures occurred and the building had to be demolished, most of the ductwork was undamaged (Figure 66). Damage to some of the ductwork, however, was similar to that sustained by piping systems. Long duct runs on flexible hangers swung back and forth, breaking open joints (Figure 67); hangers shifted where they were not tied to the ducts, and improperly sized and

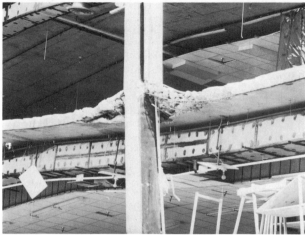

John L. Cerutti

FIGURE 66 Insulated ductwork in J. C. Penney Building adjacent to severe structural failure. The ductwork and the fire-sprinkler piping were distorted but undamaged.

secured hangers broke or were pulled out of concrete slabs (Figure 68).

Many of the round duct elbows in the Alaska Mutual Savings Building were damaged by the earthquake. These elbows were made of four mitered sections locked together with pressed grooves. Although round ducts are inherently stronger than rectangular ducts, the locks in these elbows were very weak, and they popped open when subjected to small forces. The damage would have been greatly reduced if the joints had been welded.

U.S. Air Force

FIGURE 67 Torn joints in ductwork at Elmendorf AFB. This failure was caused by excessive swaying of the duct and not enough supports.

U.S. Air Force

FIGURE 68 Shifted duct hangers at Elmendorf AFB. Note that hanger on right has almost slipped off the end of the duct.

Structural engineers too often concentrate their efforts on reinforcing large openings in walls—such as doors and windows—and pay scant attention to many smaller openings for ducts and pipes. These openings weaken the structure, especially when they are near other larger openings, and cause stress concentrations when the wall is subjected to lateral forces. This type of failure occurred in a 500-man barracks building at Fort Richardson (Figure 69). Many of the unreinforced-concrete-masonry walls collapsed at duct

U.S. Army

FIGURE 69 Concrete shear wall in 500-man barracks building at Fort Richardson was weakened by duct opening.

U.S. Army

FIGURE 70 Concrete-masonry-unit wall in the Ordnance Vehicle Repair Shop at Fort Richardson was weakened by pipes and ducts and collapsed during the earthquake.

openings and severely damaged the ductwork. Figure 70 shows a wall in the Ordnance Vehicle Repair Shop at Fort Richardson that collapsed because of oscillating pipes and ducts that passed through it. All wall openings for pipes and ducts should be adequately reinforced and have sufficient clearance to avoid this type of damage.

At the time of the earthquake, only one "air ceiling" was in use in Anchorage. It was installed in the Petroleum Club on the fourteenth floor of the Anchorage-Westward Hotel. In this system, supply air was introduced into the occupied space through perforated ceiling tiles. The space above the ceiling was supposed to be made airtight and then to act as a supply plenum served from conventional low-velocity supply ducts. The earthquake did not damage the ceilings, but serious air leaks were created in the ceiling supply plenums. The repair contractor found it almost impossible to find and seal all the leaks after the earthquake, which indicates that this type of system is not advisable in seismically active areas.

BOILERS, VENTS, STACKS, AND CHIMNEYS

Most of the heating boilers were in the basements of buildings, and they sustained only minor damage from the earthquake. Some packaged boilers shifted a few inches, and a few cracks developed in the fire boxes; in general, however, they were ready for use when the gas service was restored in

Anchorage. This was not true, however, for their masonry stacks.

Heavy masonry stacks are often damaged in earthquakes, especially if they are not properly reinforced. Figure 71 shows the cracked base of the stack in the Elmendorf AFB bowling-alley boiler room. According to the operating engineers, the top part of this stack broke at the roof line during the earthquake, fell through the roof, and destroyed the boiler. The stacks in the Military Air Transport Service terminal building on the same air base failed in the same way (Figures 72 and 73). The upper part of the stack fell into the waiting room, which fortunately was unoccupied at that time. Nonreinforcing steel was at the roof line where the earthquake developed maximum bending and shearing stresses in the stack.

Chimneys are classic victims of earthquakes, especially in residential or low-rise construction where, for aesthetic reasons, stonework is used. A typical collapsed unreinforced chimney at the golf clubhouse at Fort Richardson is shown in Figure 74.

Lightweight double-wall vents and boiler stacks, where properly installed and guyed, survived the earthquake with very little damage. The only damage that was reported was

FIGURE 71 Bowling alley boiler room at Elmendorf AFB. The top part of this masonry stack broke at the roof line during the earthquake and fell into the boiler room, destroying the boiler. Note the crack at the base of the stack just below the cleanout door.

FIGURE 72 Masonry stack failed at roof of the Military Air Transport Service terminal building at Elmendorf AFB. Note the lack of reinforcing steel at the break.

FIGURE 74 Collapsed chimney at golf-course club house, Fort Richardson.

at the vent connectors to boilers, furnaces, or domestic water heaters, where the movement of the appliance damaged the vent connector. The outstanding performance of lightweight sheet-metal vents during earthquakes is illustrated in Figures 75 and 76.

The heating contractors reported that many of the prefabricated stacks with heavy refractory insulated liners collapsed during the earthquake. The heavy mass of the sections overstressed the connection joints, which broke and caused

the total collapse of the stack. A stack of this type collapsed on the roof of the Cordova Building (Figures 77 and 78). A 4-ft section of 24-in.-diameter stack with refractory lining weighs 800 lb, whereas a double-wall sheet-metal stack of similar size weighs only 40 lb. Obviously, the lighter stack is a better selection in seismically active areas.

PLUMBING

The damage to plumbing fixtures was limited to breakage caused by falling debris such as that shown in Figure 79, where an adjacent wall fell on a water closet in a 500-man barracks building at Fort Richardson. Some water damage

FIGURE 73 Interior view where masonry stack, shown in Figure 72, fell through the roof.

FIGURE 75 J. C. Penney Building was severely damaged by the earthquake, but the four lightweight double-wall vents on the roof were undamaged.

U.S. Army

FIGURE 76 Undamaged lightweight vent on the outside of a severely damaged building in downtown Anchorage.

Walter Brugger

FIGURE 78 Another view of collapsed boiler stack shown in Figure 77. Note heavy refractory lining in stack sections on the right.

U.S. Army

FIGURE 77 Collapsed penthouse and boiler stack on roof of Cordova Building.

U.S. Army

FIGURE 79 Water closet in 500-man barracks building at Fort Richardson that was broken when the adjacent wall collapsed.

was reported in tall buildings where water slopped out of toilet bowls, but the loss of electrical power resulted in reduced water pressures and minimized damage caused by pipe leaks. In the Anchorage-Westward Hotel, the seals on all the wall-hung water closets in the new building were replaced after the earthquake to correct minor leaks.

According to the reports from the Anchorage Natural Gas Company, 700–800 domestic gas-fired water heaters had to be repaired after the earthquake. Most of the damage occurred because gas-fired water heaters, not bolted to the floor, toppled over and their legs collapsed. The same thing happened with free-standing electric water heaters. The maintenance foremen at Elmendorf AFB stated that 80 percent of the 80-gallon electric water heaters in the Miami quarters fell over during the earthquake. The legs for domestic water heaters should be designed to withstand earthquake forces and must be anchored to the floor or strapped to a wall if damage by falling is to be avoided.

Leaks in the natural-gas lines can be extremely dangerous during an earthquake and could be a major cause of fires. These hazards were avoided in Anchorage largely because of the foresight of the local gas company. The system was installed in 1960, and the newly formed corporation enforced the use of new safety devices throughout the system, establishing rigid regulations governing the installation of gas-fired appliances. Pilot safety valves were mandatory on all appliances, and pressure-test certificates had to be signed by the city inspector or by a gas-company representative before the service could be turned on. In addition, gas-pressure regulating valves, which closed when a large pressure drop occurred on either side of the valve, were installed on almost all service connections. During the earthquake, the valves closed when the street mains or any of the interior gas lines were broken; when the gas service was resumed, the valves were all in the closed position and could only be opened or reset by a gas-company representative. These valves are effective only if there is a ruptured line; a more complete protection against all gas leaks would have been an earthquake-sensitive valve located downstream from the pressure regulators. Earthquake valves of this type were not used anywhere in the Anchorage area.

MACHINERY MOUNTS AND VIBRATION ISOLATION

A serious conflict exists between the need to anchor heavy machinery to the structure to avoid earthquake damage and the requirement that vibrating equipment be isolated from the structure for acoustical control. This conflict is intensified when entire air-conditioning systems, including boilers, water chillers, pumps, fans, cooling towers, and other equipment such as emergency power generators are located on the top of 30- and 40-story office and apartment buildings. This equipment must be carefully isolated from the struc-

ture to avoid noise transmission to the high-rental spaces immediately below; the result is a free-floating mass of equipment and water-filled pipes that could be seriously damaged by an earthquake.

At the time of the earthquake, there were very few steel-spring vibration-isolation mounts or hangers in use in the Anchorage area, and most isolators used rubber-in-shear elements. In the basement of the Elmendorf AFB Hospital the three 100-kW (kilowatt) emergency power generators, the three 100-ton direct-expansion air-conditioning compressors, a small air compressor, and a vacuum pump were all mounted on springs. The three refrigeration compressors were bolted to a single-rigid steel base and then mounted on a series of open-spring isolators (Figure 80). The emergency power generators in the next room were each bolted to a rigid steel frame and then mounted on spring isolators (Figure 81). The refrigeration compressors, the vacuum pump, and the air compressor installations were undamaged by the earthquake, but two flexible connectors in the cooling water system and one piece of flexible exhaust pipe were damaged on the emergency power generators.

The lack of damage to the refrigeration, compressed air, and vacuum systems probably resulted from the light mass of the piping systems, the lack of flexible connectors, and the ductility of the small-diameter pipes. The authors be-

FIGURE 80   Two of the three 100-ton direct-expansion refrigeration machines in the basement of the Elmendorf AFB Hospital. This installation was not damaged by the earthquake. Note the spring mounts attached to the base between the two compressors.

FIGURE 81 Three 100-kW emergency power generators in the basement of the Elmendorf AFB Hospital. Each unit was mounted on six sets of spring vibration-isolation mounts and had flexible pipe connections.

when excessive motions take place. Suggested details for these constraints are shown in Figure 82.

When water is circulated in a piping system, the pump vibrations are transferred to the pipe walls and the water and are transmitted to the building through pipe anchors and supports. This vibration is often avoided by the use of vibration-isolation hangers and supports to break the contact with the structure; this installation then permits a mass of water and piping to sway about during an earthquake, making constraints necessary. When these lines are mounted in vertical shafts, or pass through sleeved floor openings, the weight can be supported at the bottom, on the floors, or from a single support at or near the top. The last suggestion would offer the most stable installation, and, with guides or sleeves on each floor and properly designed supports, this arrangement probably would withstand the earthquake forces.

DAMAGE SUMMARY

Piping Systems and Tanks

1. Most pipe failures occurred at fittings. Most welded, brazed, or soldered joints were undamaged, many screwed joints failed, and a few caulked joints were pulled apart or twisted.

2. Failures in screwed joints often occurred where long unbraced horizontal runs of pipe joined short vertical risers

lieve that the flexible connectors in the pipes serving the emergency power engine generators failed because the unbraced hanger system allowed the pipes to sway excessively during the earthquake. The increased inertial forces ruptured the pipelines at their weakest link—the flexible connectors.

When a machine is mounted on a set of vibration isolators, the isolators become the weak link between the machine and the structural slab. Because of the flexibility of the isolators, the machine is allowed to shift, rock, and twist when subjected to earthquake forces. This added flexibility lowers the natural frequency of the machine for each of the three vibration modes. When the lowered frequency of one particular mode approaches the natural frequency of the building, this particular movement of the machine becomes very sensitive, and it can develop large amplitudes relative to the structural slab. If the movement is horizontal or torsional, it could shear the isolator, and a rocking motion could rupture the isolator.

To constrain this motion and at the same time inhibit a transmission path around the vibration isolators, we suggest that braces be installed that during normal operation would not touch the machine base or pipe but become effective

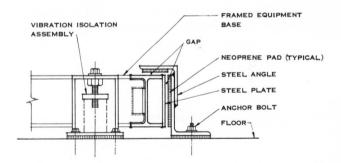

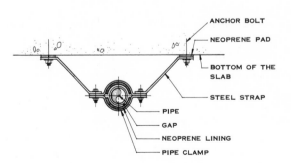

FIGURE 82 Corrective measures suggested to constrain the movement during an earthquake of vibration-isolated equipment and piping.

or were connected to equipment. Small branch lines that were clamped tightly to the building were torn from large horizontal mains if these were unbraced and allowed to sway.

3. Joints were loosened or pulled apart in long horizontal runs of unbraced cast-iron pipe, and hanger rods were bent, shifted, or broken.

4. Pipes crossing seismic joints were damaged if provisions were not made for the relative movements between structural units of buildings.

5. Thermal expansion loops and joints were damaged when the pipes were not properly guided.

6. Fire-sprinkler piping was practically undamaged, because it was provided with lateral bracing.

7. Sand filter, water softener, domestic hot water, heating-hot-water expansion and cold-water-storage tanks shifted, toppled, or rolled over when they were not firmly anchored to buildings.

Mechanical Equipment and Ductwork

1. Most flexible duct connectors at fans were torn apart.

2. Many of the suspended unit heaters fell down when the supports were inadequate.

3. Large suspended heating and ventilating units without lateral bracing broke loose pipe connections and crushed the adjacent ductwork.

4. Some floor-mounted fans and air-handling units were shifted where they were not anchored to the floor.

5. Joints were loosened or pulled apart in long horizontal runs of unbraced sheet-metal ducts and asbestos-cement fume-hood exhaust pipe. Some large vertical sheet-metal ducts were damaged when they were improperly supported and braced. Press-grooved mitered elbows in round sheet-metal ducts were badly damaged.

6. An air-ceiling system developed serious leaks in the ceiling supply plenum.

Boilers, Vents, Stacks, and Chimneys

1. A few packaged boilers were shifted, and some vent connectors were damaged.

2. Several unreinforced-masonry stacks and a few stone chimneys collapsed.

3. Many prefabricated metal stacks with heavy refractory liners collapsed in sections.

4. Lightweight double-wall sheet-metal vents and stacks were practically undamaged.

Plumbing

1. Hundreds of small gas-fired and electric domestic water heaters fell over. Many of the legs on which heaters stood collapsed, and vent connectors were damaged.

2. Some plumbing fixtures were damaged by falling debris.

3. Vertical plumbing stacks in tall buildings were practically undamaged.

RECOMMENDATIONS

Earthquake-resistant design for mechanical systems should take into consideration the following:

1. Pipelines should be tied to only one structural system. Where structural systems change, and relative deflections are anticipated, movable joints should be installed in the piping to allow for the same amount of movement.

2. Suspended piping systems should have consistent freedom throughout; for example, branch lines should not be anchored to structural elements if the main line is allowed to sway.

3. If the piping system is allowed to sway, movable joints should be installed at equipment connections.

4. Pipelines leading to thermal expansion loops or flexible pipe connections should be guided to confine the degree of pipe movement.

5. Whenever possible, pipes should not cross seismic joints. Where they must cross seismic joints, arrangements such as those shown in Figures 35 and 38, or other designs that achieve the same purpose, should be used. The crossing should be made at the lowest floor possible, and all pipe deflections and stresses induced by the deflections should be carefully evaluated.

6. Standards of the National Fire Protection Association for earthquake protection to fire-sprinkler systems should be referred to for successful, field-tested, installation details that are applicable to any piping system.

7. Supports for tanks and heavy equipment should be designed to withstand earthquake forces and should be anchored to the floor or otherwise secured.

8. Suspended tanks should be strapped to their hanger system and provided with lateral bracing.

9. All suspended equipment should have lateral bracing. If the equipment must be allowed to move, damping elements or restraints should be built into the hanger system to restrict the amount of movement.

10. Long hangers and supports for ductwork should be provided with lateral bracing.

11. Flexible duct connections should be installed in a semifolded condition with enough material to allow for the expected differential deflection between the fans and the ductwork.

12. Pipe sleeves or duct openings through walls or floors should be large enough to allow for the anticipated movement of the pipes and ducts.

13. All chimneys and masonry stacks should be subjected to earthquake-resistant design.

14. Lightweight double-wall sheet-metal flues should be used where possible. Prefabricated stacks or chimneys with heavy refractory liners should be avoided or used with great care.

15. Domestic hot-water heaters should be provided with

legs that can withstand earthquake forces, and they should be anchored to the floor and/or strapped to a structurally sound wall.

16. Earthquake-sensitive shutoff valves on gas-service lines should be provided where maximum protection from gas leaks is required.

17. Vibration isolation

Vibrating and noisy equipment should, if possible, be located far from critical occupancies, so that the equipment can be anchored to the structure, and vibration isolation is not required.

Avoid mounting heavy mechanical equipment on the top or upper floors of tall buildings unless all vibration-isolation mounts and supports are carefully analyzed for earthquake-resistant design.

When equipment and the attached piping must be isolated from the structure by vibration isolators, constraints of the type shown in Figure 82 should be used.

To reduce inertial forces, the use of heavy bases under equipment mounted on vibration isolators should be avoided where possible.

All vibration isolators for equipment should be anchored to the floor and to the equipment.

LIGHTING FIXTURES

The widespread collapse of suspended lighting fixtures was one of the most serious items of nonstructural earthquake damage. The U.S. Air Force Alaskan Air Command building at Elmendorf AFB was effectively crippled by falling fluorescent-lighting fixtures, and many active-duty airplanes in hangars were damaged by falling high-bay mercury-lighting fixtures. Similar damage in other buildings, both military and civilian, resulted in property damage and seriously endangered the building occupants.

The damage to lighting fixtures was closely related to the method of installation. Surface-mounted and recessed fixtures survived the earthquake with little or no damage, although some of the buildings in which they were mounted sustained serious structural failures. Suspended fixture installations were badly damaged by the earthquake; in some instances they failed because of weak stems and in others because of inadequate supports at the ceiling. Chain-hung fixtures fell because of failures in the chain or in the attachments to the supporting hooks at the ceiling. Plastic diffusers and side panels dropped from fluorescent fixtures during the earthquake, and grilles and globes fell from incandescent fixtures, mainly because of insufficient retaining clips and poor design.

The need for earthquake-resistant support systems for pendant-hung lighting fixtures has been recognized for several years. Lighting fixtures in several tall buildings in Los Angeles and Long Beach collapsed during the 1952

Kern County, California, earthquake. The epicenter of that earthquake was about 80 mi from these buildings, and the long-period characteristics of the ground motion excited the tall buildings, inducing damage to the pendant-mounted lighting fixtures. The City of Los Angeles therefore modified its building code to require laboratory tests simulating earthquake conditions for most pendant-hung lighting fixtures. Evidently, this information was not widely disseminated, and today the City of Los Angeles continues to be the only government entity requiring earthquake testing of lighting fixtures.

PENDANT-HUNG FLUORESCENT FIXTURES

Pendant-hung fluorescent-lighting-fixture installations were severely damaged by the earthquake. Long continuous rows of fixtures mounted end-to-end were damaged more frequently than were individually suspended fixtures. A comparison of the performance of these two types of installation was possible in the Fort Richardson commissary building. Over the sales area were 87 individually hung 8-ft fixtures, only two of which were damaged by the earth-

U.S. Army

FIGURE 83 Collapsed row of pendant-hung end-to-end fixtures in commissary building at Fort Richardson. Stems are intact, indicating failure was at ceiling bracket.

FIGURE 84   View from rear of commissary building at Fort Richardson, taken in 1966. The second fixture in the center row is of a different type from the others; it replaced one damaged during the earthquake.

quake—one fell to the floor, and the other pulled away from the ceiling at one stem. A long continuous row of pendant fixtures hung end-to-end over the check stands, however, collapsed during the earthquake (Figure 83).

We were able to reconstruct the earthquake damage by interviewing the Fort Richardson electrical maintenance crew that repaired the installation, and by inspecting the existing and the replaced fixtures. Figure 84 shows the individually hung 8-ft fixtures over the sales area in the commissary. The second fixture, different from the others, was a replacement for the one damaged during the earthquake. The continuous row of fixtures that collapsed during the earthquake can be seen in the background extending to the left.

The stem of each fixture was hung from a surface bracket at the ceiling (Figure 85) and was rigidly connected to the fixture (Figure 86). The individually hung 8-ft fixtures were supported by two stems, whereas each 8-ft fixture in the continuous row was supported by a single stem, which consequently carried twice the weight of a similar stem in the individually hung fixture. At one end of the individually hung fixtures, the surface brackets were attached to a fixture-mounting stud on an electric-outlet box; at the other end, they were tied to the ceiling with two toggle bolts. All the surface brackets supporting the continuous

FIGURE 85   Surface bracket and supporting stem at ceiling of commissary building at Fort Richardson.

row of fixtures were attached to outlet boxes, which were supported by the suspended metal lath and plaster ceiling (Figure 87).

By examining Figures 83 and 85, we surmised that, during the earthquake, either the stem jumped out of the support bracket at the ceiling, or the lip of the stem and the bracket were deformed by the repeated swaying of the fix-

FIGURE 86   Top of light fixture in commissary building at Fort Richardson, showing rigid connection at supporting stem.

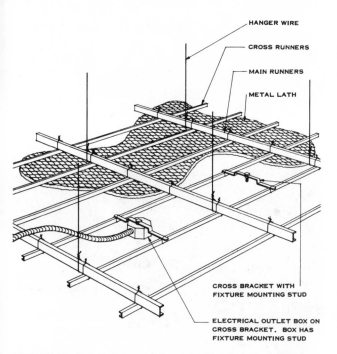

FIGURE 87   Detail of suspended metal-lath and plaster ceiling in commissary building at Fort Richardson. Note the outlet box and cross brackets for mounting the suspended fixtures.

FIGURE 88   Restored row of end-to-end fixtures over check stands in commissary building at Fort Richardson.

ture until the stem was able to fall through the bracket. The restored row of end-to-end fixtures over the check stands is shown in Figure 88.

One of the more dramatic failures of lighting-fixture installations occurred in the Caribou department store, in Spenard. Damaged fixtures are shown in Figure 89 stacked outside the store as debris during the rehabilitation. The lighting installation consisted of fluorescent fixtures, mounted end-to-end in rows about 120-ft long on the underside of a suspended steel wireway (Figures 90 and 91). These pictures, although taken in 1966, also represent the installation as it was before the earthquake. The steel wireway was supported from the ceiling by a standard fixture-suspension system (Figure 92), with stems about 24 in. long on the ground floor and about 12 in. long on the second floor, spaced 12–16 ft apart.

The continuous rows of fixtures collapsed during the earthquake, because most of the fixture stems failed at the point of connection to the steel support wireway. As shown in Figure 92, the stems were rigidly connected, and the lay-in hanger did not allow any longitudinal movement. The contractor restored the lighting system, using the preearthquake design and construction methods, although the store manager told us that additional stems had been used to reduce the maximum spacing to 12 ft. The electrical contractor who installed the original system and repaired the earthquake damage found that the ceiling support brackets

were practically undamaged by the earthquake. He restored the lighting system using new fixtures and stems, but reused the ceiling-support brackets, canopies, and steel channels.

The type of damage sustained by continuous rows of pendant-hung end-to-end fixtures was also illustrated by the failures in the single-story school adjacent to the Hodge Building in Whittier. Damage to the lighting installation in a typical classroom (Figure 93) was caused by the method of

Walter Brugger

FIGURE 89   Debris of lighting fixtures stacked in front of Caribou department store in Spenard after the earthquake.

FIGURE 90   Restored lighting installation in Caribou department store, 1966.

FIGURE 91   Closeup of fixture-suspension system shown in Figure 90.

installation and not by the connections of the stems to the light fixtures or the ceiling brackets. Each bracket was fastened by two screws to wooden boards above the ceiling runners (Figure 94); several support brackets were torn away from the ceiling during the earthquake. The damage at this school indicates the need for more rigorous control of

installation procedures. The fixture and the factory-manufactured support system appear to have withstood the earthquake, but the field-installed ties to the ceiling did not.

The lighting installation in the Supplies Office, Building 21-882, at Elmendorf AFB was essentially undamaged by

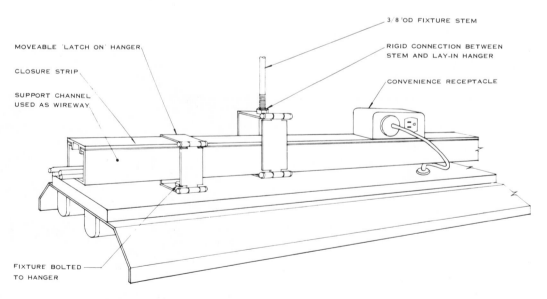

FIGURE 92   Detail of fixture-suspension system in Caribou department store.

FIGURE 93 Damaged fixture installation in Whittier school classroom. Many ceiling-support brackets, screwed to wooden boards above the ceiling runners, were torn loose during the earthquake.

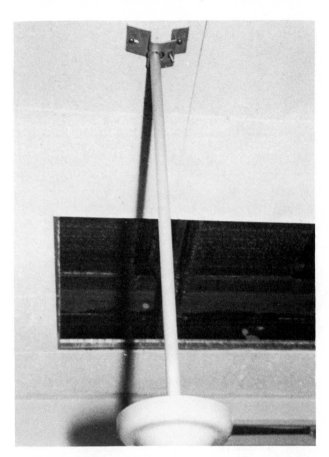

FIGURE 94 Closeup of loosened and bent ceiling-support bracket shown in Figure 93.

the earthquake. This building was a large warehouse partly converted to offices (Figure 95). The fixtures were mounted on the underside of steel wireways that were suspended on stems of 3/8-in.-diameter steel rod, about 12 ft long, rigidly tied to the underside of the roof (Figure 96). The supporting stems were approximately 10 ft on center along the channel, and the continuous rows of wireway occurred approximately 6 ft on center. The rows were about 150 ft long, and except for the length of the stem, the installation was very similar to that used in the Caribou department store. The suspended fixture wireway in this large warehouse, however, did not collapse during the earthquake, and although some side panels and louvers fell, only 28 fixtures had to be replaced.

Several factors affected the damage sustained by pendant-hung fixtures: The behavior during the earthquake of the structural element or ceiling to which the fixture-suspension system was attached, the method of suspension, the length of the stem, and the spacing between stems. The effect of the length of the stem can be seen in Figure 97. If the ceiling support moves distance d, the angular deflection and

FIGURE 95 Suspended lighting-fixture installation in the Supplies Office, Building 21-882, Elmendorf AFB.

FIGURE 96 Stem support at ceiling of installation shown in
Figure 95.

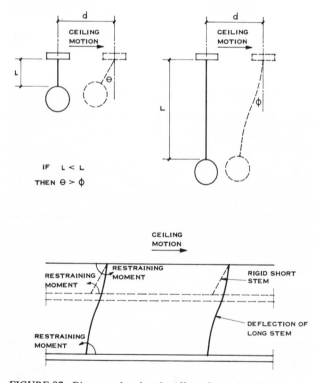

d
CEILING
MOTION

d
CEILING
MOTION

L

L

θ

φ

IF L < L
THEN θ > φ

CEILING
MOTION

RESTRAINING
MOMENT

RESTRAINING
MOMENT

RESTRAINING
MOMENT

RESTRAINING
MOMENT

RIGID SHORT
STEM

DEFLECTION OF
LONG STEM

FIGURE 97 Diagrams showing the effect of stem length on
pendant-hung lighting fixtures. If the ceiling support moves distance
d, the angular deflection and the restraining moment will be greater
with short rigid stems than with long flexible stems.

the restraining moment will be greater with short rigid stems
than with long flexible stems. This may, in part, explain the
lack of damage to the fixtures in the Supplies Office, Building 21-882 at Elmendorf AFB, and the failures in the commissary building at Fort Richardson and in the Caribou
department store, where the installations that collapsed
were suspended on relatively short stems.

Fluorescent fixtures suspended on dual stems from one
ceiling bracket were badly damaged by the earthquake.
A typical mounting detail for this kind of installation is
shown in Figure 98. During the earthquake, the heavy light
fixture acted as a pendulum, and the stems twisted the support brackets at the ceiling. This type of damage occurred
in the corridor of the five-story Buckner Building in Whittier
(Figure 99) and in the garage of the Eklutna Power Plant,
where one stem on each fixture was torn from the ceiling-
support brackets (Figure 100). In the District Engineer's
building at Elmendorf AFB, hundreds of dual-stem 4-ft fixtures fell over desks and work areas. In the Alaskan Air
Command building at Elmendorf AFB almost all of the fixtures had dual stems, and according to Floyd Huttslander,
the Chief Electrical Engineer for the base, 600 ft of 4/40
fluorescent fixtures had to be replaced after the earthquake
(Figure 101).

The damage to suspended fluorescent fixtures described
in this study represents only a fraction of the many failures
that were documented by inspection teams. The magnitude
of this type of damage indicates that greater effort must be
directed toward improving the design of suspension systems
for pendant-hung fixtures. When a fixture is supported on a
single stem, flexibility is required only at the ceiling support;

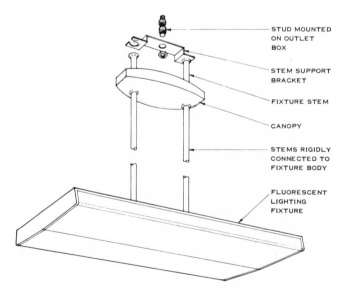

STUD MOUNTED
ON OUTLET
BOX

STEM SUPPORT
BRACKET

FIXTURE STEM

CANOPY

STEMS RIGIDLY
CONNECTED TO
FIXTURE BODY

FLUORESCENT
LIGHTING
FIXTURE

FIGURE 98 Detail of typical dual-stem fixture supported from one
ceiling bracket.

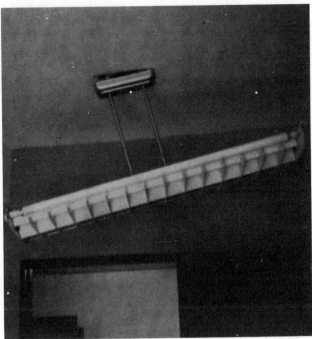

U.S. Army

FIGURE 99   Typical damage to dual-stem fixture supported from one ceiling bracket in corridor of Buckner Building, Whittier.

U.S. Air Force

FIGURE 101   Collapsed dual-stem fixtures in corridor of Alaska Air Command building, Elmendorf AFB, showing twisted stems.

U.S. Bureau of Reclamation

FIGURE 100   Damaged dual-stem fixtures in garage at Eklutna Power Plant. Note that one stem has been torn from the ceiling-support bracket.

if it is supported by two stems, however, then flexibility is required at the ceiling and at the point where the stems connect to the fixture body. Most fixture supports are manufactured without lower swivel joints and are unable to withstand large longitudinal displacements. One manufacturer's effort to provide flexibility and at the same time dampen the fixture oscillations during an earthquake is shown in Figure 102. Most fixtures can take some movement without immediate failure because of the thin metal used in the fixture bodies, the slack in most stem connections, and the flexibility of stem materials.

The City of Los Angeles requires that most light-fixture supports be submitted to their Electrical Testing Laboratory for testing on an earthquake simulating machine (Appendix B) tests in this machine have shown that swivel suspensions generally fail when the design restricts the pendant swing to less than 45° from the vertical.

Current practice assumes that the prevention of earthquake damage to pendant-hung fixtures necessarily requires a flexible swivel-type ceiling support. This belief may be too limiting in concept; it may be within the ability of the lighting-fixture designer to provide rigid pendant supports that will adequately withstand the later accelerations during an earthquake. Ball-aligner-type hangers, incidentally, were not originated to resist earthquakes but for vertical alignment.

To date, the trial-and-error method has been used to design suspension systems, with earthquakes and the City of Los Angeles' earthquake-simulating machine as the only

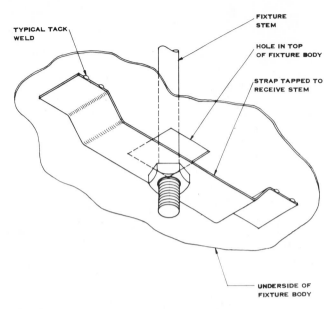

FIGURE 102 Detail of bottom support for pendant-hung fluorescent fixture, designed to provide flexibility at the connection and dampen the fixture oscillations during an earthquake.

U.S. Air Force

FIGURE 103 Chain-hung fixtures that collapsed in Alaskan Air Command building, Elmendorf AFB. Note the supporting chain at the ceiling in the upper-right corner and the one remaining eyebolt on the third fixture from the left.

known arbitrators. Design criteria similar to those used in structural design must be developed for use by the lighting-fixture industry. The stresses anticipated at every point in the suspension system during an earthquake, including the ties of the support brackets to the ceilings, should be calculated so that the components can be designed to withstand these forces. The failures in the Whittier school classrooms indicate that an engineering evaluation of the support requirements should be made by the fixture manufacturer and given to the contractor; they should not be left to the ingenuity of the installer.

CHAIN-HUNG FLUORESCENT FIXTURES

Chain-hung fluorescent-lighting-fixture installations sustained considerable damage during the earthquake. Many of these failures occurred in the large aircraft hangars at Elmendorf AFB. In the maintenance shops of Building 11-470, where the lighting-fixture installation consisted of four-lamp, 96-in.-long fixtures, hung from the ceiling by chains, most of these fixtures fell during the earthquake because the bottom link of the chains opened. In Building 11-570, another aircraft hangar with ancillary offices and shops, similar failures occurred in 50 percent of the chain-hung fixtures in the offices and shops.

Continuous rows of chain-hung fixtures collapsed in the Alaskan Air Command building, Elmendorf AFB (Figure 103). Damage to chain-hung single fixtures in the large loading area in the intransit storage and port office at Whittier is shown in Figure 104. No segments of the sup-

porting chain remained on the fixtures, indicating that the chain links probably failed at the connection to the fixtures. This is also true for the collapsed fixtures shown in Figure 103.

During the earthquake, hundreds of the heavy dual-stem 4-ft fixtures collapsed in the District Engineer's building at

U.S. Army

FIGURE 104 Collapsed chain-hung fixtures in the intransit storage and port office at Whittier.

FIGURE 105   Chain-hung fixtures installed after the earthquake in the District Engineer's building, Elmendorf AFB.

Elmendorf AFB. After the earthquake, they were replaced by new lightweight fixtures and supported from heavy chains (Figure 105). The support hooks were screwed into the ceiling and closed to prevent the chains from jumping out.

SURFACE-MOUNTED FLUORESCENT FIXTURES

Surface-mounted fluorescent-lighting-fixture installations were generally undamaged by the earthquake, probably because the typical mounting details tied the fixtures tightly to the ceiling system (Figures 106 and 107). During the

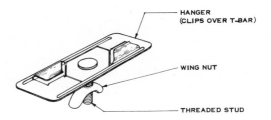

FIGURE 107   Closeup of typical tee-bar hanger shown in Figure 106.

earthquake, the fixtures moved with the ceiling and were not subjected to the pendulum action that damaged so many of the pendant- and chain-hung fixtures.

The outstanding performance during the earthquake of surface-mounted light fixtures was illustrated in the badly damaged J. C. Penney Building. The original surface-mounted fixtures were used to provide light for demolition work as shown in Figure 108. The electrical contractor who handled the demolition stated that wherever the ceiling had not collapsed, the lighting fixtures were generally undamaged and operable. In the First Federal Savings and Loan Building (Figure 109) the surface-mounted fixtures were still in place on the partly collapsed exposed-tee-grid ceiling.

Serious column failures and damage to the concrete core occurred in the six-story Cordova Building, but the ceiling and the surface-mounted light fixtures were almost undamaged. The ceiling consisted of acoustic tile glued to plaster-

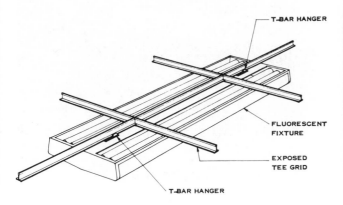

FIGURE 106   Detail of surface-mounted fixtures on an exposed-tee-grid ceiling-suspension system.

Anchorage Daily Times

FIGURE 108   J. C. Penney Building during demolition; undamaged surface-mounted fixtures provided illumination on the top floor. Note that undamaged wiring and conduit served these fixtures.

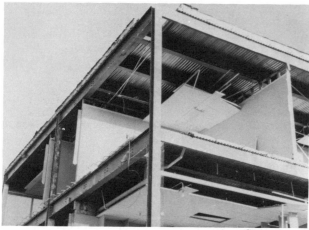

John L. Cerutti

FIGURE 109   First Federal Savings and Loan Building during rehabilitation. Surface-mounted fixtures were still in place on the partly collapsed third-floor exposed-tee-grid ceiling.

board panels, which, in turn, were nailed to wood runner strips. Surface-mounted fixtures were supported by toggle bolts through the plasterboard. The building engineer reported that only four or five light fixtures fell during the earthquake, and repairs consisted mainly of tightening loosened toggle bolts.

RECESSED FLUORESCENT FIXTURES

Recessed fluorescent-fixture installations were damaged by the earthquake where the ceiling-suspension systems sup-

porting the fixtures failed. Damaged recessed fixtures in a typical classroom at the Kenai High School are shown in Figure 110. The ceiling consisted of exposed-tee-grid with 2 × 4-ft lay-in tiles, and the fixtures were supported by the flanges of the ceiling tees. The ceiling-suspension system collapsed at the perimeter above the blackboard, and the lighting fixtures—each weighing approximately 60 lb—were left dangling on flexible-conduit extensions. This kind of damage was reported elsewhere in Anchorage and indicates a need for independent safety supports on the light fixtures or ceiling-suspension systems designed to carry the weight of the light fixtures during an earthquake.

The recessed-fixture installation in the 2 × 4-ft exposed-tee-grid ceiling-suspension system in the six-story Hill Building was undamaged by the earthquake, although the building sustained severe structural failures at its cores. These fixtures were mounted on the ceiling tees (Figures 111 and 112), and the fixtures were each supported by four clips that rested on the top of the suspended ceiling tees. A more conventional recessed-fixture installation in an exposed-tee-grid ceiling-suspension system is shown in Figure 113. The fixture rests on the flange of the ceiling tee and is only guided at the top by the tee. The contractor who rehabilitated the Hill Building reported that some of the recessed fixtures shifted on top of the ceiling tees during the earthquake, but the movement was not enough to cause any damage.

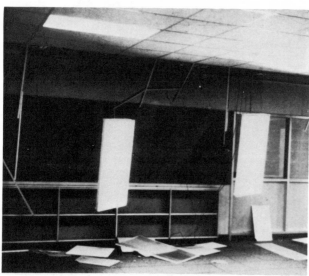

U.S. Army

FIGURE 110   Damaged recessed fixtures in classroom at Kenai High School. The ceiling-suspension system collapsed at the perimeter wall.

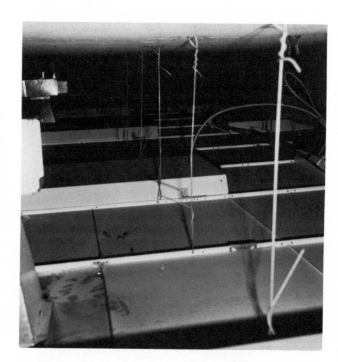

FIGURE 111   Recessed-fixture installation in Hill Building. The supporting clips near the end of the light fixtures rest on the top of the suspended ceiling tees.

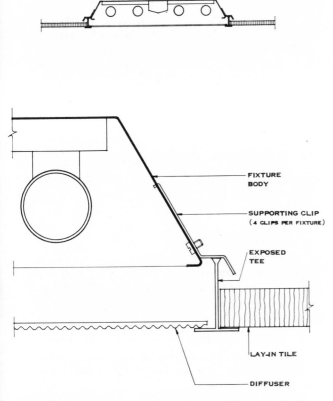

FIGURE 112   Detail of recessed-fixture installation shown in Figure 111.

HIGH-BAY MERCURY-LAMP FIXTURES

Many of the high-bay mercury-lamp-fixture installations were badly damaged by the earthquake. Most of these failures occurred in the large aircraft hangars at Elmendorf AFB, where the heavy fixtures jumped out of their supporting hooks or collided with nearby structural elements. The fixtures often fell on parked aircraft inflicting costly secondary damage.

The main floor area of a typical aircraft hangar was illuminated by high-bay mercury-lamp fixtures (Figure 114). A mechanism attached to the top support bracket was usually provided to allow the fixture to be lowered to the floor for relamping, and the heavy ballast and lamps were supported by a single hook and eye. During the earthquake, these fixtures acted as free-swinging pendulums.

In the Birchwood Hangar 32-217 at Elmendorf AFB, 103 of the 132 high-bay mercury-lamp fixtures fell to the floor. A detail of the actual installation is shown in Figure 115. The 150-lb fixture was supported at the top by an open hook and was installed too close to the wood truss to avoid collision at the bottom during the earthquake. In Hangar 11-570, the maintenance foreman reported that 21 fixtures fell to the floor, and many other fixtures jumped off the

open hooks, but were held up by the flexible power cables. Similar damage was reported in many other aircraft hangers and in the National Guard Armory.

Almost all the high-bay mercury-lamp lighting fixtures in the fieldhouse at Elmendorf AFB were undamaged by the earthquake. These fixtures were supported on long pendants hanging from hooks and damage was probably avoided because the fixtures were free to move without colliding with other building elements.

Most of the damage to the high-bay mercury-lamp lighting-fixture installations could have been avoided if the design engineers had used greater discretion in locating the fixtures and in selecting the suspension components. For example, the manufacturer of the support systems used in most of the installations offered support hooks with safety latches as a standard catalog item at practically the same price as the open hook.

INCANDESCENT FIXTURES

Incandescent-fixture installations survived the earthquake with very little damage compared to that sustained by fluorescent fixtures. Pendant-hung dome-type fixtures in

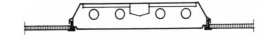

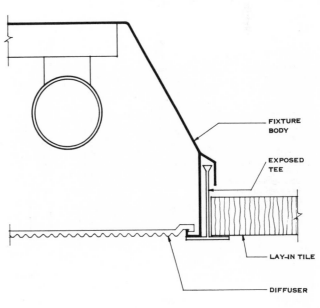

FIGURE 113   Detail of conventional recessed-fixture installation in exposed-tee-grid ceiling-suspension system.

U.S. Air Force

FIGURE 114   High-bay mercury-lamp-fixture installation in typical hangar at Elmendorf AFB.

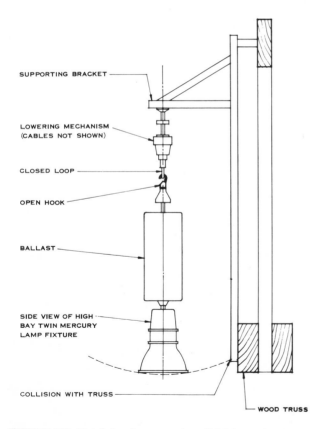

SUPPORTING BRACKET

LOWERING MECHANISM
(CABLES NOT SHOWN)

CLOSED LOOP

OPEN HOOK

BALLAST

SIDE VIEW OF HIGH
BAY TWIN MERCURY
LAMP FIXTURE

COLLISION WITH TRUSS

WOOD TRUSS

FIGURE 115   Detail showing suspension of high-bay twin-mercury-lamp fixture in birchwood Hangar 32-217 at Elmendorf AFB. Note open hook support at top and ease of collision with truss at bottom.

the penthouses of the 14-story Hodge Building, Whittier, and the Mt. McKinley apartment building, Anchorage, were both unharmed by the earthquake, despite extensive damage to other building components. In the fan room of the Mt. McKinley apartment building penthouse, one fixture suspended on rigid conduit with a ball aligner at the outlet box in the ceiling was left hanging obliquely (Figure 116). The fixture was thrown in the same direction as the elevator-motor generators and a water tank in the same penthouse.

Pendant-hung incandescent fixtures with concentric-ring grilles were badly damaged by the earthquake. A typical installation in a classroom in the West Anchorage High School is shown in Figure 117. In other rooms at this school and in other installations, grilles dropped onto the desks during the earthquake although the actual fixtures and lamps remained intact and in place at the ceiling (National Board of Fire Underwriters and Pacific Fire Rating Bureau, 1964). In some instances the fixtures were left hanging from the ceiling outlet boxes on their connecting wires. Manufacturers of this type of fixture claim that, if properly installed, the grille diffuser cannot fall off accidentally. The evidence indicates that a further safety feature, possibly a safety chain, should be a mandatory requirement for all loose grilles.

Surface-mounted incandescent fixtures, like surface-mounted fluorescent fixtures, were generally undamaged by

FIGURE 116   Pendant-hung dome-type incandescent fixture in penthouse of Mt. McKinley apartment building after the earthquake.

U.S. Army

FIGURE 117   Damaged concentric-ring grilles on pendant-hung incandescent fixtures in West Anchorage High School.

FIGURE 118   Undamaged plaster ceiling and surface-mounted lighting fixtures and damaged solid-plaster partitions in corridor in Mt. McKinley apartment building.

the earthquake. In the 14-story Mt. McKinley apartment building the surface-mounted fixtures in the corridor were undamaged, although the corridor walls were badly damaged (Figure 118). Surface-mounted fixtures were undamaged in many buildings where severe structural failures occurred, or where the building was torn apart by landslides.

Recessed incandescent fixtures were generally undamaged by the earthquake except where they were mounted in ceilings that collapsed. The 24-in. square recessed incandescent fixtures in the corridors in Elmendorf AFB Hospital were undamaged, although some of the adjacent ceiling tiles fell (Figure 119).

Cord-hung incandescent fixtures of the type commonly used in residential construction were often damaged by collisions with other building elements. One electrical engineer reported that the dining-room fixture in his house was hung on a cord about 3 ft long and that, during the earthquake, the swinging fixture left a visible trace where it hit the ceiling. In the First Federal Savings and Loan Building, several pieces of glass on the cord-hung decorative fixture in the main lobby were broken by collisions. An installation of this type should never be used in public areas where the free-swinging fixture can collide with its surroundings during an earthquake.

Pendant-hung incandescent fixtures in the entrance of the Whittier school were damaged during the earthquake (Figure 120). The pendants had swivel-type ceiling brackets, and the glass globes might have been shaken loose when the length of the swing of the fixture was restricted at the ceiling supports. An installation of this type should never be used in a public area, especially not near an exit.

U.S. Air Force

FIGURE 119   Undamaged recessed incandescent fixtures in corridor ceiling in Elmendorf AFB Hospital.

FIGURE 120 Pendant-hung incandescent fixtures in damaged main entrance of Whittier school. Note the damaged ceiling and the missing glass globes.

DAMAGE SUMMARY

1. More pendant-hung fluorescent-fixture installations collapsed than any other type of fixture installation.

2. Chain-hung fluorescent-fixture installations frequently collapsed because of weak chains.

3. Surface-mounted fluorescent and incandescent fixtures were practically undamaged except when ceilings collapsed.

4. Recessed fluorescent-fixture installations were damaged where the supporting ceiling-suspension systems collapsed. Some diffusers fell out even when the fixture remained in place.

5. High-bay mercury-lamp fixtures were damaged when they jumped out of open support hooks or collided with adjacent structural elements.

6. Pendant-hung incandescent fixtures sustained little damage except for loss of glass bowls and diffusers.

7. Recessed incandescent-fixture installations were undamaged unless the ceiling collapsed.

A tabular summary of damage sustained by typical fluorescent-lighting-fixture installations is shown in Figure 121.

RECOMMENDATIONS

Earthquake-resistant design for lighting fixtures should consider the following recommendations:

1. Support systems for all lighting fixtures—including attachments to the overhead mounting surface, the number and type of stems or hangers, and the bottom connections to the fixtures—should be subjected to engineering analysis and laboratory tests for earthquake-resistant design. Tests should simulate conditions that might develop in the actual installations, and the criteria of the test should be varied, if possible, to account for different accelerations, periods of oscillation, and lengths of travel. Test data on one or two fixtures should not be applied to long rows of fixtures mounted end to end or in other configurations.

2. Pendant-hung fluorescent fixtures, especially where mounted end to end in long rows, should be provided with lateral bracing or flexibility at both the ceiling supports and the bottom connections to the fixtures.

3. All hooks used to hang lighting fixtures should have safety latches.

4. Lighting fixtures supported by flexible hangers should be located so that they will not collide with other building elements. Extreme flexibility in hangers is less desirable than damped flexibility.

5. Support systems designed for pendant mounting from a horizontal surface should not be used on a sloping surface, because some of the freedom of movement is used up in vertical alignment.

6. Grilles, diffusers, and lenses should not be made of glass or metal and should be permanently fastened to the fixture or provided with safety chains.

7. Recessed lighting fixtures should be secured to, and supported by, a ceiling-suspension system designed to carry the weight of the lighting fixture, or the fixtures should be provided with independent safety supports.

ELECTRICAL SYSTEMS

Electrical systems in buildings survived the earthquake with very little damage. In general, conduit systems were unharmed, even in buildings that sustained severe structural failures, and in many instances, conduits remained standing although the surrounding walls collapsed. Some conduit

TYPE OF MOUNTING	BUILDING	DAMAGE
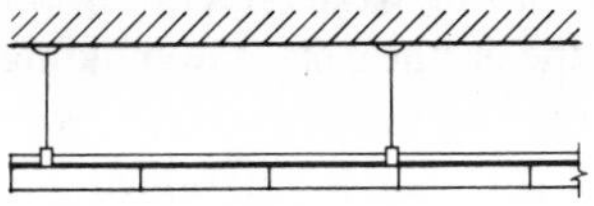 CONTINUOUS ROWS BOLTED TO UNDERSIDE OF SUSPENDED STEEL CHANNEL	CARIBOU DEPARTMENT STORE (SHORT STEMS)	COLLAPSE OF COMPLETE SYSTEM GENERALLY DUE TO STEM YIELDING AT RIGID CONNECTION TO SUPPORT CHANNEL
	SUPPLIES OFFICE, BUILDING 21-882, ELMENDORF AFB (LONG STEMS)	INSTALLATION UNDAMAGED EXCEPT FOR MINOR LOSS OF DIFFUSERS
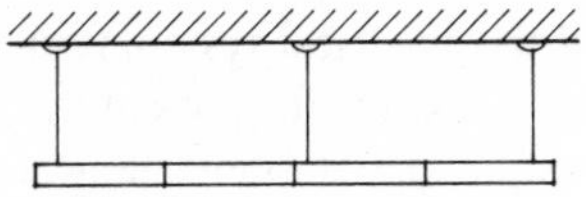 CONTINUOUS ROWS SUSPENDED ON FIXTURE STEMS WITH TOP SWIVEL BRACKETS	COMMISARY BUILDING, FORT RICHARDSON AP	COLLAPSE OF ONE ENTIRE ROW DUE TO STEMS LEAVING CEILING BRACKETS
	WHITTIER SCHOOL	CEILING SUPPORT BRACKETS PULLED AWAY FROM CEILING
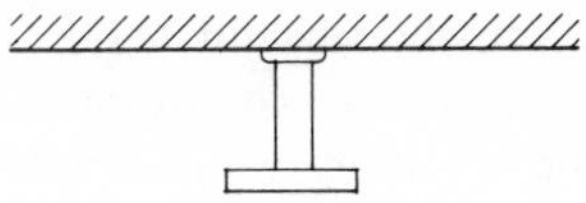 SINGLE FIXTURE ON DUAL STEMS AND ONE CEILING BRACKET	EKLUTNA POWER PLANT GARAGE	CANTILEVER ACTION DISTORTED SUPPORT BRACKET ALLOWING STEM TO DROP OUT
	BUCKNER BUILDING WHITTIER	CANTILEVER ACTION DISTORTED SUPPORT BRACKET
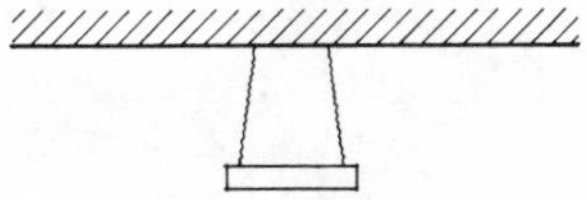 SINGLE FIXTURE CHAIN HUNG	INTRANSIT STORAGE AND PORT OFFICE, WHITTIER	FIXTURES FELL DUE TO OPENING OF CHAIN LINKS
	ALASKA AIR COMMAND BUILDING, ELMENDORF AFB	FIXTURES FELL DUE TO OPENING OF CHAIN LINKS
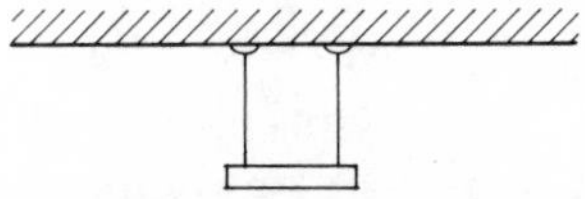 SINGLE FIXTURE WITH TWO STEMS HAVING INDIVIDUAL CEILING BRACKETS	COMMISARY BUILDING, FORT RICHARDSON AP	ONLY 2 OUT OF AN INSTALLATION OF 81 WERE DAMAGED
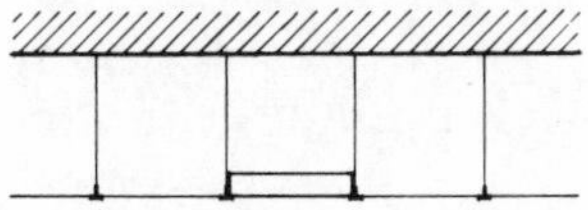 RECESSED FIXTURE IN SUSPENDED EXPOSED GRID TEE BAR CEILING	KENAI HIGH SCHOOL	FIXTURES DROPPED OUT OF CEILING & WERE LEFT HANGING ON FLEXIBLE CONDUIT LEADS
	HILL BUILDING	FIXTURES SHIFTED ON TOP OF CEILING GRID SOME DIFFUSERS FELL
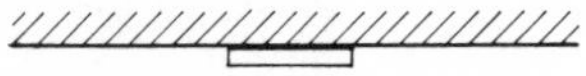 SURFACE MOUNTED FIXTURE	J. C. PENNY BUILDING	NO DAMAGE WHERE CEILING DID NOT COLLAPSE
	CORDOVA BUILDING	2 OR 3 FIXTURES FELL FROM GYPBOARD CEILING ALL SUPPORTING TOGGLE BOLTS REQUIRED TIGHTENING

FIGURE 121   Summary of damage sustained by typical fluorescent-lighting-fixture installations.

runs through seismic joints failed, and a few long horizontal runs pulled apart at their couplings. Switchboards, substations, bus ducts, and panelboards survived the earthquake with practically no damage.

At the time of the earthquake, there were only a few large electrical distribution systems in buildings in the Anchorage area. The majority of the buildings had conventional overhead or underground services with 120/240-V single-phase or 240-V or 480-V three-phase distribution systems. The high-rise buildings, such as the 14-story L Street and Mt. McKinley apartment buildings and the Anchorage-Westward Hotel, had vertical-conduit distribution systems; the only vertical bus-duct systems were in the 14-story Hodge and the five-story Buckner buildings in Whittier. Most of the buildings had standard rigid and thin-wall conduit systems, but some of the small commercial buildings, and most of the residential buildings, were wired with flexible nonmetallic sheath cable. Electrical construction methods, and official inspections were comparable to those found in any small city that followed the requirement of the *National Electric Code* and the *Uniform Building Code*.

During the earthquake, commercial power service was disrupted in Anchorage and in an area roughly bounded by Homer in the south and Valdez in the east. Electrical crews immediately set to work to restore power service; Scott (1964) reported that limited power was available in Anchorage within 3 hours after the main shock. Many of the buildings, however, could not be served because of broken distribution lines and other damage to the electric utility system. Immediately after the earthquake, teams of inspectors checked individual buildings for electrical safety, and work crews repaired or replaced damaged electrical services, service equipment, and feeders. Within 5 days after the main shock, all services in the Anchorage area that could safely receive electrical power were reconnected and in use.

ELECTRICAL-SERVICE EQUIPMENT AND PANELBOARDS

Electrical-service equipment and panelboards were essentially undamaged by the earthquake. In Whittier, for example, electrical service to all buildings failed soon after the main shock, but it was restored to the Hodge and Buckner buildings as soon as the service became available from the power plant. The undamaged main switchboard in the Buckner Building is shown in Figure 122.

Power service was supplied to the Hill Building at 480 V, three-phase, underground from a high-voltage-transformer vault under the loading dock. The 2,000-ampere (A) main switchboard and 120/208-V dry-type transformers in the ground-floor electric room were not bolted to the floor, but rested on raised concrete pads. Distribution throughout the building consisted of standard rigid-conduit and circuit-breaker panels, with flexible conduit runs above the ceiling to light fixtures. According to the operating engineer, who was present during the earthquake, the building electrical system was undamaged by the earthquake. When power service was restored, the system functioned normally without any short circuits or grounding faults.

The First Federal Savings and Loan Building sustained considerable damage during the earthquake, and the entire facade had to be removed during rehabilitation. The contractor who repaired the electrical system found it undamaged by the earthquake, except for broken light fixtures and branch circuits where the main lobby ceiling collapsed. The electrical service equipment was located at grade at the rear of the building (Figure 123).

The Mt. McKinley apartment building sustained severe structural failures, but the building operating engineer and the electrical contractor who rehabilitated the building stated that the electrical service and distribution system were in good working condition—without faults or short circuits. Similar reports were received of the absence of

FIGURE 122   Main switchboard in Buckner Building, Whittier, was undamaged by the earthquake.

U.S. Army

FIGURE 123 First Federal Savings and Loan Building during rehabilitation. Note that electrical-service equipment in lower-left corner was undamaged by the earthquake.

electrical damage in the L Street apartment building, the Anchorage-Westward Hotel, and other buildings.

The Birchwood hangars at Elmendorf AFB consisted of a high-bay hangar with low offices on each side (Figure 124). Electrical service was provided for these hangars from overhead lines, with a service drop to a substation mounted on the flat roof over the offices. In Hangar 32-217, the substation toppled off its platform and broke the service con-

ductors. The maintenance crews reported that the transformer was not bolted to the platform but was held in position only by its own weight and conduit connections.

A unit substation failed in one of the 200-man barracks buildings at Fort Richardson. The substation consisted of a high-voltage compartment, dry-type transformer, and end-mounted low-voltage circuit-breaker panel, rated at 150 kilovolt amperes (kVA), 7,200 120/208-V, three-phase, four-wire. In the primary switch section, the connection between the switch mounted in the top part of the section and the fuses in the lower part was made with short lengths of rigid copper bus. During the earthquake, several copper-bronze connection bolts sheared and repairs were made by substituting a braided-copper flexible connection for the rigid bus and by replacing one of the two copper–bronze bolts with two cadmium-plated steel bolts (Figure 125). The secondary circuit-breaker panel burned out when the substation was reenergized—probably because of a high-impedance low-current arc to ground, because the bus and main circuit breaker were completely destroyed without the high-voltage fuse blowing. Repeated questioning of Anchorage electrical engineers, contractors, and maintenance men failed to uncover other faults of this type.

Switchboards were practically undamaged by the earthquake, because they were usually located against a wall,

FIGURE 125 High-voltage switch and fuse section of unit substation at Fort Richardson. Braided-copper flexible connector was a replacement for a solid-bus connection that failed during the earthquake when the bolts sheared.

U.S. Air Force

FIGURE 124 Typical birchwood hangar at Elmendorf AFB. Note the substation on the low roof at the center.

anchored to the floor, and stabilized by rigid conduits that were attached to them at the top. Some control panels, however, toppled over during the earthquake because they were not anchored to the floor or provided with lateral bracing. Control panels are less stable than switchboards because of their high height-to-depth ratios; they are usually free-standing, and are not connected to heavy overhead conduits. An instrument panel in the Whittier Power Plant was undamaged by the earthquake, but it must have moved enough to damage the concrete supporting base (Figure 126). An unanchored pneumatic-electric control panel in the power plant at Elmendorf AFB fell over, causing serious secondary damage. Unanchored switchboards shifted, and a control panel fell over in the City of Anchorage Power Plant.

DISTRIBUTION SYSTEMS

Bus-duct distribution systems in the Hodge and Buckner buildings in Whittier were undamaged by the earthquake. The vertical bus duct and panels in the electrical closet on the fourteenth floor of the Hodge Building are shown in Figure 127, and a closeup view of the duct support on the thirteenth floor is shown in Figure 128. The support brackets were not resting on the floor slab, suggesting that the duct and the bracket might have been raised slightly by the earthquake.

Support brackets for a vertical bus duct are designed to

FIGURE 127   Electrical closet on fourteenth floor of the Hodge Building, Whittier. Bus duct and panel at left and lighting panel at right were undamaged.

U.S. Army

FIGURE 126   Instrument board in Whittier Power Plant. Note damage to corners of concrete supporting base.

FIGURE 128   Bus-duct support on the thirteenth floor of the Hodge Building, Whittier.

carry the weight of the vertical duct with a uniform distribution of the load at each floor. If this is accomplished in the field, the lateral movement of the duct would be constrained during an earthquake by the frictional drag of the support brackets on the floor. To ensure uniform load distribution at each floor, one bus-duct manufacturer provides spring mounts under the support brackets. With this type of installation, the floor opening should be small enough to inhibit excessive horizontal movement during an earthquake, and flexible connections should be provided in any taps to fixed panels or equipment.

A wall was damaged by a horizontal run of bus duct in the Buckner Building in Whittier (Figure 129). The damage in Figure 129 is almost identical to that caused by horizontal runs of pipes and ventilation ducts in mechanical systems and was probably caused by the excessive swaying of the suspended duct system. It could have been avoided by lateral bracing of the suspension system and greater clearances between the wall and the bus duct.

Conduit systems survived the earthquake with very little damage. Many instances were reported where conduit systems were found standing alone in the middle of a collapsed wall. In the Hodge Building in Whittier, many of the unreinforced-concrete-masonry-unit partitions on the upper floors collapsed during the earthquake, leaving the wall outlet boxes and conduit exposed (Figure 130).

Surprisingly, little damage was done to the conduit system in the heavily damaged J. C. Penney Building. The electrical contractor who assisted in the demolition work reported that the main feeder risers were destroyed in the structural collapse of a portion of the building, but that temporary power feeders were connected to the existing lighting panels, and the permanent lighting system was used

FIGURE 130   Kitchen on fourteenth floor of Hodge Building, Whittier. The partition around the exposed electric conduits and outlet boxes in the foreground collapsed during the earthquake.

to provide illumination (Figure 108). He stated that, because of broken and shorted circuits, a few branch circuit breakers tripped when they were energized, but that the majority of the branch circuit systems were undamaged.

There were a few reports of conduit couplings that were pulled loose because of excessive swaying during the earthquake, or because the system was placed under strain by structural deformations. The electrical maintenance engineer at the power plant at Fort Richardson reported that several long conduit runs across the roof were ruptured at the couplings during the earthquake, and a few conductors were broken because of tensioning. An electrical engineer, who inspected the plant immediately after the earthquake, found that two 3-in. conduit feeders were torn loose from their hangers and that the circuit to the overhead conveyor drive was grounded on one phase. An inspection team at the west heat and power plant at Elmendorf AFB reported that at least four conduits pulled apart in the ash-blower room. Stephenson (1964) reported that some thin-wall conduit runs were damaged in the interior partitions. This type of damage could have occurred because the connectors in these systems are usually of the compression or indent type and are more susceptible to separation than threaded rigid-conduit connectors.

Some conduit systems were damaged where they crossed structural separations or seismic joints because they were not designed to absorb the maximum amount of differential movement between the two structural units of the building. The failures in the flexible conduit jumpers at the 8-in.-wide seismic joint on the fourteenth floor of the Hodge Building in Whittier are shown in Figure 131. The conduit was cast in

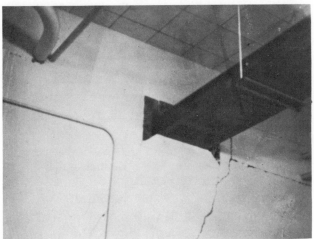

U.S. Army

FIGURE 129   Bus duct passing through wall in Buckner Building, Whittier. Note plaster spalling and cracks at duct opening.

FIGURE 131 Damaged flexible conduit jumpers in 8-in. seismic joint on fourteenth floor of the Hodge Building.

the slab on each side of the joint, and a little less than 2 in. of movement was provided for in the flexible conduit. The seismic separation was 8 in., and the deformed floor plates in the corridor indicated that the lateral movement of the joint was 7 in. Occupants of the building stated that the two structural units on each side of the joint slapped together. With this type of movement, the destruction of the flexible conduit jumpers was inevitable.

In tall buildings, the seismic separations between structural units can often exceed 12 in.; design engineers should try to avoid all conduit crossings in the upper floors. If the electrical distribution system must cross a seismic joint, special designs are required that allow for the maximum amount of movement anticipated at that point. A suggested corrective measure for the damaged conduit crossing in the Hodge Building is shown in Figure 132. The conduit is kept out of the slab, and because one side is fixed by the shear wall, a hole is provided in the wall in the other side to

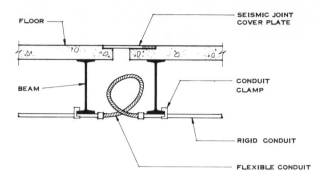

FIGURE 133 Suggested detail for conduit crossing seismic joint.

allow for differential movements. Suggested details for conduit and bus-duct crossings at seismic joints where there are no shear walls and there is space above the ceiling and below the slab are shown in Figures 133 and 134. The bus duct is terminated on either side of the seismic joint by end-cable tap boxes and is provided with flexible conduit and wire jumpers to absorb the anticipated movement. The horizontal bus duct and cable boxes should be connected to the floor slab above and provided with bracing to inhibit excessive lateral movement.

ELECTRICAL APPLIANCES AND MOTORS

Other minor failures occurred in the electrical systems. In the power plant at Fort Richardson, a fan-motor starter and two small motors burned out, and a circuit breaker on a combination motor starter was damaged. Motor burnouts were also reported in other buildings where motors were damaged by falling debris, but most burnouts were probably caused by motors starting under low-voltage conditions when power was restored after the earthquake. For example, the officer in charge of Anchorage Fire Station No. 4 re-

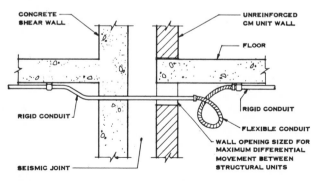

FIGURE 132 Suggested corrective measure for conduit crossing seismic joint as shown in Figure 131.

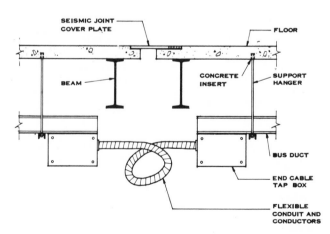

FIGURE 134 Suggested detail for bus duct crossing seismic joint.

ported that the motor of the refrigerator and both elements of the hot-water heater burned out when the power was restored, and the operating engineer at the Alaska Psychiatric Institute reported that a glycol pump motor burned out when the power was restored.

Signal and communication systems in buildings were practically undamaged by the earthquake. No repair work was required on the nurses' call, fire alarm, and doctors' call systems at the Elmendorf AFB Hospital, the Providence Hospital, or the Alaska Psychiatric Institute. Damage to telephone equipment and systems during the earthquake was limited to relay racks that tilted or fell because of inadequate anchors and bracing, damaged batteries that shifted, and broken users' equipment. Cotton (1965) reported that the damage to telephone equipment in the Anchorage district included 1115 instruments including key equipment, five PABXS boards, and one PBXS board.

Little or no damage was done to electrical grounding systems. Basic fault protection in building electrical-distribution systems, which normally have solidly grounded neutral conductors, requires that all non-current-carrying metallic raceways, enclosures, and boxes be solidly and continuously grounded to the building main service ground. The purpose of the grounding system is to equalize the potential of the occupants of the building and all exposed non-current-carrying metal parts of the electrical system with that of earth. A well-grounded raceway serves as a low-impedance return path in case a phase line contacts the metallic raceway, and the resulting high current will trip the protective device. If the raceway were not grounded, it could have a potential close to that of the system and become a hazard to personnel. Such high-impedance faults usually cause arcing (as they did in the substation in the 200-man barracks building at Fort Richardson) without necessarily tripping protective devices. The use of separate grounding jumpers should be considered across every point in the system where there is a possibility that the continuous metallic return path for fault current could be broken by the earthquake.

DAMAGE SUMMARY

1. Almost all electrical service equipment and panelboards were undamaged.

2. Some free-standing unanchored control panels fell over.

3. Distribution systems were essentially undamaged except in the vicinity of structural failures and at seismic-joint crossings.

4. A few electrical appliances and motors were damaged by falling debris. Some motors were burned out when they were started under low-voltage conditions.

5. Signal and communication systems were practically undamaged.

RECOMMENDATIONS

Earthquake-resistant design for electrical systems should take into consideration the following:

1. All electrical equipment such as transformers, switchboards and control panels should be anchored to the building.

2. Flexible braided connections should be used in place of rigid copper bus whenever relative movements may occur between switchboard components.

3. Avoid crossing seismic joints with conduits and bus ducts. Where seismic joints must be crossed, arrangements of the type shown in Figures 132, 133, and 134, or other designs that achieve the same purpose, should be used. The crossing should be made at the lowest floor possible.

4. Separate ground conductors should be provided in all conduit runs that cross seismic joints and elsewhere in the electrical system where grounding systems could be broken.

5. Additional pull boxes with slack conductor should be provided in long conduit runs to avoid tensioning of conductors.

6. Starters for motors subject to damage by low-service voltages after an earthquake should be provided with under-voltage relays.

EMERGENCY POWER AND LIGHTING SYSTEMS

The earthquake caused immediate and, in some cases, major damage to electrical power plants and distribution systems serving the City of Anchorage, Elmendorf AFB, Fort Richardson, and the surrounding area. The resulting power outage affected all buildings and pointed out the importance of emergency power and lighting systems during disasters. Only a few buildings in Anchorage had emergency power engine generators, and several of these were unable to get started immediately after the earthquake. As soon as the extent of the earthquake damage became known, the military authorities at Elmendorf AFB and Fort Richardson trucked in portable engine generators to provide additional power to hospitals and other public buildings. The presence of a large pool of military equipment and resources minimized many of the postearthquake problems in Anchorage.

Some buildings were equipped with battery-powered lighting units located to facilitate egress. These included the J. C. Penney Building, the Caribou department store, and many of the military facilities. Where they operated, these emergency lighting units were very effective, but in many instances they were not properly mounted and the first shock of the earthquake caused them to fall.

During the earthquake, people in the tall buildings in

Anchorage were repeatedly thrown to the floor and struck by moving furniture and other loose objects; then, to get out of the building, they had to walk down corridors and stairways in total darkness. A few people in the new Petroleum Club, on the top of the Anchorage-Westward Hotel, managed to escape down 14 flights of stairs, led by a bellboy with a flashlight. The people in the 14-story Mt. McKinley and L Street apartment buildings found themselves in a similar predicament, and eyewitnesses reported panic-stricken occupants blindly feeling their way downstairs.

In Alaska, there were many small portable engine generators and an unusually large supply of flashlights—a characteristic of this frontier state. We are unable to comment on the performance, or lack of performance, of all of these small engine generators, but we examined the emergency power plants in most of the major buildings, and these are evaluated in this study. In general, most of the engine generators started up and performed satisfactorily; when failures occurred, they were caused by faulty installation techniques rather than by malfunction of machinery.

The need for emergency power and lighting systems in buildings can be evaluated from the experiences of this earthquake. There is a difference between emergency power for egress illumination and emergency power for the operation of facilities such as hospitals or other disaster centers. Emergency power for egress illumination is usually required for less than 30 minutes, assuming that all occupants can easily depart in that time. Hospitals, however, must continue to operate and may even reach peak occupancy after a disaster. It is vital that the standby source of power be available for illumination and power loads such as medical refrigerators, operating rooms, communication systems, vital air-conditioning and ventilating systems, vertical transportation facilities, and other loads essential to patient welfare. Minimum design criteria for hospital electric service are outlined by the standards of the National Fire Protection Association and in the codes and regulations of other governmental agencies. Most of these codes do not require emergency power and lighting systems in occupancies other than hospitals, and only in areas of buildings that contain heavy concentrations of people. It is the authors' opinion that emergency lighting should be provided whenever the extinguishing of light could lead to loss of life or imperil human safety.

EMERGENCY POWER ENGINE GENERATORS

At the time of the earthquake, emergency power engine generators were installed in the Anchorage Public Safety Building and in all the major hospitals, including Providence, Alaska Psychiatric Institute, Alaska Native, and Elmendorf AFB. Engine generators were also located in the Anchorage Telephone Utility Headquarters and in four exchange buildings, the Anchorage Natural Gas Headquarters Building, and the Alaska Communications System (ACS) Toll Building on Government Hill. The radio station over the Fourth Avenue Theatre was served by an engine generator in an adjacent building.

Generally, the earthquake damage to the engine generators was minor, but in a few instances it was enough to prevent their continued use. Some were undamaged by the earthquake, but failed to start because of poor checkup and maintenance routines. It is paradoxical that this type of error should have occurred in the Public Safety Building, the headquarters of the Civil Defense, Police, and Fire Departments, where an empty fuel tank created a major problem precisely when the facility required total effort.

When the power service to the Public Safety Building failed, the 50-kW air-cooled gasoline-engine generator in the basement automatically started up and operated normally for a period of from 5 to 30 minutes; conflicting reports on the duration of operation were received. All the fire trucks were away from the building at the time, but when communications with headquarters ceased, one truck returned to investigate. A crew of firemen were unable to restart the engine, and they concluded that the problem was a malfunctioning cranking overload safety device. While a mechanic was being located, a small portable engine generator from the fire truck was temporarily hooked up to the emergency power distribution panel to supply some of the lighting and communication equipment. At about 8 p.m., approximately 2 hours after the engine generator had shut down, a mechanic found that the gasoline tank was empty, although the fuel gage in the basement indicated that it contained about 300 gallons.

The engine generator in the Public Safety Building is shown in Figure 135. The entire unit was mounted on studs and bolted to the floor through vibration-isolation pads. The engine exhaust was connected to the muffler through a flexible pipe connection (Figure 136); the fuel line in the room was one long piece of flexible hose. The fuel tank was buried a few feet outside the engine-room wall and was undamaged by the earthquake. The black-iron fuel line and a small copper gage line were installed in, and protected by, a larger black-iron pipe, which extended from the tank to the inside face of the engine-room wall (Figure 136).

The largest installation of emergency power engine generators in the Anchorage area was located in the basement of the Elmendorf AFB Hospital. The installation (Figure 137) consisted of three 100-kW water-cooled diesel-engine generators, with remote air-cooled heat exchangers on the roof of an adjacent two-story wing. Diesel fuel was stored in a 2,500-gallon tank buried just outside the basement wall and pumped to three 50-gallon day tanks mounted on the wall adjacent to the three engines. Exhaust gases were carried to the outside through pipes mounted in an adjacent utility tunnel. The rigid steel base that supported each engine generator was mounted on six spring vibration-isolation units, and the cooling water, fuel oil, exhaust, and electrical lines were attached to the unit through flexible connections. All overhead piping was suspended by hanger rods with no lateral bracing. During the earthquake, two of the engine generators failed. The third unit remained on the line, but it had to be augmented by portable engine generators until the two damaged units were repaired.

Evidently, the earthquake caused the overhead piping and the emergency generator sets to swing and rock excessively, placing heavy strains on the flexible connectors in the cooling-water and exhaust pipes. The rubber-hose connectors in the cooling-water lines on two of the engines broke loose during the earthquake, and the loss of water caused overheating, which made the engines automatically shut down because of high temperatures. A flexible connector in the exhaust line serving one of these engines also developed cracks in the metal bellows that had to be repaired before the engine could be put back into service. The rubber-hose connectors in the top of the engines were restored (Figure 137), and the flexible connector in the exhaust line was repaired by brazing and reinstalled (Figure 138).

The failures in the cooling-water and exhaust-piping systems in the engine generators at Elmendorf AFB Hospital

FIGURE 135   Engine generator in the Public Safety Building was undamaged by the earthquake.

FIGURE 136   Exhaust pipe and muffler from engine generators shown in Figure 135. Note the pipe sleeve through the wall, the flexible gasoline-fuel line, and the tank gage on the right.

FIGURE 137   Rubber-hose connections in cooling-water lines on two of these engine generators at Elmendorf AFB Hospital broke loose during the earthquake.

FIGURE 138   Repaired flexible connector in engine generator exhaust pipe at Elmendorf AFB Hospital. Note where cracks in metal bellows have been closed by brazing.

emphasize the need for seismic analysis of the effects of vibration isolation on mechanical equipment.

At the time of the earthquake, each of the four buildings in the Anchorage Telephone Utility had standby battery power and three had standby diesel-engine generators. The engine generators were easily started in the Broad and Federal exchanges, but the unit in the Fairfax exchange failed because a fuel-oil line ruptured owing to earth movement. Although it is impossible to protect emergency fuel systems in a landslide, they should be able to absorb minor earth settlements; this failure points out the need for stronger buried fuel-oil lines and conduit protection for the smaller lines.

The Anchorage Natural Gas Company in Spenard was equipped with a small 3-kW gasoline-engine generator as shown in Figure 139. This generator provided power for an emergency lighting system, communications equipment, and a gasoline pump. When outside power service failed, the engine generator operated automatically without problems. The gasoline tank and fuel line serving this unit were mounted on an exterior wall (Figure 140); fortunately, the exposed tank and fuel line were not damaged during the earthquake by falling debris.

The Providence Hospital and the Alaska Psychiatric Institute were equipped with 75-kW diesel-engine generators supplied from buried 1,500-gallon oil tanks. The engine generators and fuel-oil systems were undamaged by the

FIGURE 139   Emergency generator at Anchorage Natural Gas Company, Spenard.

FIGURE 140   Gasoline-storage tank with unprotected fuel line to engine generator shown in Figure 139.

earthquake and started up properly when the outside power-service failed. The Presbyterian Hospital was not equipped with any emergency power facilities, except for one battery-powered light in the operating room. Earthquake victims were given emergency first aid in this hospital by the light of flashlights. As a direct result of the earthquake, the Providence Hospital, the Alaska Psychiatric Institute, and the older Presbyterian Hospital have all enlarged, or are planning to enlarge their emergency power systems so that they can operate at least one elevator, all emergency lighting and communication systems, and a few other critical loads during a power outage.

The J. C. Penney Building sustained severe structural failures during the earthquake and had to be demolished. It was equipped with a 25-kW natural-gas engine generator that served a few night lights on each floor and the heating and ventilating system. In addition, four battery-powered lighting units were installed on each of three sales floors and at the foot of each stairwell. When the outside power service failed, the engine generator started up automatically, but shut down when the gas service to the building failed. There was no secondary fuel supply to the engine. The battery-powered lighting units operated satisfactorily during and after the earthquake and provided the only illumination for egress from the badly damaged structure.

Long-distance telephone calls between Alaska and the outside world were routed through the ACS Toll Building on Government Hill in Anchorage. Although a major landslide occurred at Government Hill, the ACS Toll Building stood on firm ground and sustained only minor structural damage during the earthquake. The 300-kW diesel-engine generator in this building was undamaged by the earthquake and played a key role in maintaining civilian communication. The engine was supplied with oil from a buried tank and cooled by water from air-to-water heat exchangers in the same room. The unit was mounted on spring vibration isolators with horizontal constraints, and all-electrical conduit and piping connections were made with flexible connectors (Figure 141). The outside exhaust pipe from the engine rested on grade and was securely strapped to the building (Figure 142).

BATTERIES AND BATTERY-POWERED LIGHTS

Direct-current power for relaying equipment in the ACS Toll Building was obtained by rectifying commercial power with a large bank of batteries floating on the line to provide stability and continuity in the event of power failures. The main 130-V battery bank consisted of 72 large batteries, stacked on a three-tier rack. The total weight on the rack was approximately 22,000 lb, which collapsed during the earthquake (Figures 143 and 144). Within minutes of the earthquake, operating personnel started the engine generator

FIGURE 141   300-kW emergency power diesel-engine generator at ACS Toll Building was undamaged by the earthquake.

FIGURE 142   Engine generator exhaust pipe on exterior of ACS Toll Building. Pipe was supported from grade and strapped securely to the structure.

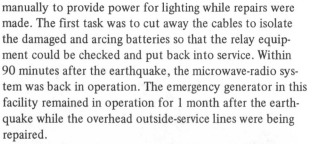

U.S. Army

FIGURE 143 Collapsed battery racks in ACS Toll Building on Government Hill.

U.S. Army

FIGURE 144 Another view of the collapsed battery racks shown in Figure 143.

manually to provide power for lighting while repairs were made. The first task was to cut away the cables to isolate the damaged and arcing batteries so that the relay equipment could be checked and put back into service. Within 90 minutes after the earthquake, the microwave-radio system was back in operation. The emergency generator in this facility remained in operation for 1 month after the earthquake while the overhead outside-service lines were being repaired.

Nonstructural damage to the ACS Toll Building consisted of collapsed battery racks, fallen fluorescent-lighting fixtures in the administration area, and shifting of several toll-dialing relay racks by the earthquake. Corrective measures included building a stronger rack for the main battery bank (Figure 145), bracing the 48-V control battery rack with gusset plates (Figure 146), and additional cross bracing at the ceiling for all relay and equipment racks.

Storage batteries invariably provided the first source of emergency power to crank and provide ignition for an engine generator, to provide a floating source of power for telephone systems, or to supply power for emergency lighting. Most mounting details for groups of batteries considered only gravitational forces and resulted in the inadequate constraints to earthquake forces illustrated in the reactions

FIGURE 145 New battery rack that replaced the collapsed rack shown in Figures 143 and 144. Note the gusset plates at the frame connections.

FIGURE 146 Strengthened 48-V battery rack in ACS Toll Building. Gusset plates were added at frame connections after the earthquake.

FIGURE 147 In this battery installation in the Hill Building that survived the earthquake, the batteries were not secured to the rack.

of the ACS Toll Building. According to the operating engineer, the battery installation for the Federal Aviation Agency equipment in the Hill Building (Figure 147) was undamaged by the earthquake. The batteries were not secured to the rack; after the earthquake, a battery rack was installed in the Hill Building with many more earthquake-resistant features (Figure 148). The batteries for the engine generators in the Elmendorf AFB Hospital were undamaged by the earthquake. They were set in low wooden boxes with deep sides that prevented the batteries from slipping out.

At the time of the earthquake, only a few buildings in the Anchorage area were equipped with individual battery-powered emergency light units; many such units have since been added to buildings in the area. A typical unit contains not only a battery and lamp, but also a trickle charger and a relay. The unit is connected to a convenience receptacle; during normal service, the light is off and the trickle charger keeps the battery fully charged. When the power to the receptacle fails, the relay closes to connect the battery to the lamp circuit.

Individual battery-powered emergency light units were invaluable in the Caribou department store in Spenard. The earthquake caused long rows of fluorescent-lighting fixtures to fall, adding to the danger from falling merchandise and debris. Panic, and possibly loss of life, was averted when a single recessed battery-powered emergency lighting unit,

FIGURE 148 In this new battery rack in the Hill Building, the base was well braced and bolted to the wall; wood plank prevented any horizontal movement of batteries.

located at the head of the escalators, illuminated the only major exit from the second floor.

The earthquake damaged many of the battery-powered emergency lighting units because they were not tied securely to the building. In hangar Building 11-470 at Elmendorf AFB, 11 out of 24 units fell from unprotected shelves. Battery-powered emergency lighting units were installed in the Elmendorf AFB Hospital exit stairways after the earthquake (Figure 149). The hospital maintenance staff added the safety chain because the wall bracket furnished by the manufacturers would not prevent the unit from falling out during an earthquake. New emergency lighting units were also installed in the exit stairways in the Anchorage-Westward Hotel (Figure 150). The units were supported on all sides and, if securely fastened to the ceiling, will survive the next earthquake.

DAMAGE SUMMARY

1. Engine generator set failure resulted from faulty maintenance on fuel-tank gage, broken underground fuel line, broken rubber-hose connectors in cooling-water lines and damaged flexible connector in exhaust pipe, and loss of natural-gas supply to engine.

2. Some battery racks collapsed.

3. Many unsecured battery-powered emergency lighting units fell.

FIGURE 149   Battery-powered emergency light unit, installed in Elmendorf AFB Hospital exit stairway after the earthquake. Wall bracket was furnished by the manufacturer; the chain was added by the hospital.

FIGURE 150   Battery-powered emergency light unit installed in Anchorage-Westward Hotel after the earthquake.

RECOMMENDATIONS

Earthquake-resistant design for emergency power and lighting systems should include the following features:

1. Emergency lighting systems in all buildings that are over one story high other than single-family dwellings.

2. Emergency power systems in all hospitals and high-rise buildings that include power for operating at least one elevator.

3. Emergency power engine generators should be located in a building where they can be exercised regularly without creating vibrational and acoustical disturbances in adjacent spaces. Where vibration isolation must be provided, the floor mounts and the connecting piping should be provided with horizontal constraints.

Self-contained engine generators should be used wherever possible to reduce potential damage to fuel, cooling-water, and exhaust lines. Lines should be kept as short as possible.

Fuel tanks should be located as close as possible to the engine generator. When they must be remote, then day tanks should be provided on the engine generator or on an adjacent wall. The day tanks should be large enough to provide fuel to operate the generator for several hours and should be equipped with alarm devices to indicate loss of line pressure and low level. Powered fuel-oil pumps should be backed up with hand pumps.

Small copper fuel-gage lines from the tank to the engine

room should be protected from damage by a second pipe or conduit; larger lines with thick walls may not require this protection. Where they pass through walls, all fuel lines should be protected by sleeves.

In selecting the fuel for an engine generator, the use of dual carburetors that operate on natural gas, but that can switch to diesel oil or another fuel in the event of low gas pressure, should be considered.

Regular maintenance schedules should be set up to check all elements of emergency power engine generator systems, including weekly off-load exercising for a minimum of 30 minutes.

Critical building loads that are provided with emergency power should be on separate circuits and not connected to any other general building loads.

4. Battery-powered emergency lighting units should be securely tied to the building.

5. All batteries in racks should be securely strapped or otherwise constrained to prevent movement, and the racks should be designed to withstand earthquake forces.

EXITS

Requirements for safe exiting include space for egress and emergency lighting, and freedom from falling debris, jammed doors, and floor obstructions. According to the 1967 edition of the *Uniform Building Code*, an exit is defined as follows:

A continuous and unobstructed means of egress to a public way, and shall include intervening doors, doorways, corridors, exterior exit balconies, ramps, stairways, smokeproof enclosures, horizontal exits, exit passageways, exit courts and yards.

We shall attempt to record the type of damage sustained by exits and, when possible, to indicate how these failures might have been avoided.

Unreinforced-concrete-masonry-unit walls and partitions failed extensively during the earthquake. When these walls constituted part of a corridor or a stairway, the falling debris was extremely dangerous. In the Enlisted Men's Service Club at Fort Richardson, a man was killed by falling concrete-masonry units at the foot of the exit stairway (Figure 151). The entire stairway was covered with debris and escape was impossible. A portion of the concrete-masonry unit wall also collapsed in another exit stairway (Figure 152). When the wall fell, it carried with it a piece of wall insulation. In the Alaska Air Command building at Elmendorf AFB, the concrete-masonry wall over an exit door collapsed, but a portion of the wall was held up by electric cables (Figure 153).

The failures of the unreinforced-concrete-masonry-unit exit walls were in sharp contrast to the excellent perform-

U.S. Army

FIGURE 151 Exit stairway in the Enlisted Men's Service Club at Fort Richardson where a man was killed by falling concrete-masonry units during the earthquake.

ance of the lath-and-plaster stair shafts in the Cordova Building and in Providence Hospital, where the plaster was extensively cracked, but the exits were usable. This was also true in the plastered corridors of the Mt. McKinley apartment building (Figure 154).

Meehan (1967) reported that fireproofing concrete in

U.S. Air Force

FIGURE 152 Exit stair littered with concrete-masonry units and piece of wall insulation.

U.S. Army

FIGURE 153   Damaged corridor wall over exit door in Alaskan Air Command building, Elmendorf AFB. A portion of the concrete-masonry-unit wall was held up by electric cables.

U.S. Army

FIGURE 155   Damaged finish tile on wall of stairway in the West Anchorage High School.

the bottom of a stair landing in the West Anchorage High School broke loose and littered the exit. In the same school a structural failure caused the finish tile on the wall of a stairway to break loose (Figure 155). This type of damage suggests that brittle finish materials should not be used in

FIGURE 154   Plaster walls in corridors of Mt. McKinley apartment building were badly cracked by the earthquake, but the exit was usable.

exits, unless all mounting details are of earthquake-resistant design.

Seismic joints separating structural units in a building usually cross exit corridors. The material used to cover the joints must be such that the exits remain clear and usable at all times. Most seismic-joint covers for corridors were designed to allow for longitudinal movements between structural units, but ignored lateral movements. Damage to the seismic-joint cover plates in the corridor on the thirteenth floor of the Hodge Building in Whittier is shown in Figure 156. The two structural units of the building were 8 in. apart, and eyewitnesses reported that the units struck each other during the earthquake. By measuring the deformation at the floor plates and the scratch marks on the floor, the lateral movement at this point was estimated to be 7 in. The magnitude of the lateral movement at a seismic joint also was indicated by the damage to cover plates in the corridor of Building 600, a 500-man barracks building at Fort Richardson (Figure 157).

The seismic-joint floor cover plates in the corridors of the Hodge Building were made of light-gage metal, and the deformations were localized at the corridor walls. In the Elmendorf AFB Hospital, however, the floor plates were approximately 1/4 in. thick, and all the deformation was in the center of the corridor (Figure 158). This extremely dangerous condition could have been avoided by using thinner material for the entire cover plate, or at least at the edges of the corridor. Most commercially available seismic-joint covers have the same deficiency; they make provisions for vertical and longitudinal relative movements, but ignore lateral movements. For this reason, the design and applica-

FIGURE 156 Seismic-joint floor plate in corridor on thirteenth floor of Hodge Building in Whittier. Lateral movement at joint was 7 in.

U.S. Air Force

FIGURE 158 Deformed seismic-joint floor cover plate in corridor of Elmendorf AFB Hospital. For view from opposite side, see Figure 163.

tion of seismic-joint covers should be reevaluated. Light-gage metal should be used throughout, or the corridor walls should be designed to receive the lateral movement of the heavy-gage cover plates.

Exit doors were jammed during the earthquake by structural failures around the doors, as in the Anchorage-Westward Hotel (Figure 159), or by deformed frames, as in the West Anchorage High School auditorium (Figure 160). In many instances exit doors were blocked by heavy pieces of furniture or equipment that fell or shifted in front of doors. A doorway in the Elmendorf AFB Hospital was effectively blocked by a refrigerator (Figure 161). In the

Presbyterian Hospital a heavy safe was reported to have been thrown against a door, blocking an exit.

Many exits in stores were blocked or rendered hazardous by falling merchandise and glass, especially where standing or recessed glass-front showcases or glass lay-in shelves were located near exits. In the ACS Toll Building on Government Hill the maintenance engineer reported that all the lockers in the hallway leading to the fire exit toppled over during the earthquake and effectively blocked the door. The lockers were set back in place without the addition of any hold-down bolts or wall clips (Figure 162) and will probably block the exit again during the next earthquake.

U.S. Army

FIGURE 157 Seismic-joint wall and ceiling cover in corridor of Building 600, a 500-man barracks at Fort Richardson.

Walter Brugger

FIGURE 159 Jammed exit door in the Anchorage-Westward Hotel. Deformed frame was caused by structural failure.

FIGURE 160   Jammed exit door in West Anchorage High School auditorium. Note the bent door frame and plaster cracks. Glued-on tile fell from the gypsum-board ceiling in the corridor.

Many exits became extremely hazardous during the earthquake when light fixtures and ceiling tiles fell, or plaster and other debris littered corridors and stairways. Pendant-mounted light fixtures fell in the corridors in the Alaska Air Command building at Elmendorf AFB (Figure 101). Ceiling tiles fell in the corridors at the Elmendorf AFB Hospital (Figure 163), and spalled plaster fell in the corridors and stairways of the Anchorage-Westward Hotel (Figure 164).

FIGURE 162   Fire exit in the ACS Toll Building, where the storage lockers on the right fell into the passageways during the earthquake.

In the main lobby of the Elmendorf AFB Hospital, marble veneer near the elevator exit broke loose and collapsed during the earthquake (Figure 165); according to the maintenance engineer the 48 in. × 42 in. × 1 in. marble panels were secured to the concrete wall by 10-gage copper

FIGURE 161   Blocked exit door at Elmendorf AFB Hospital. The refrigerator shifted to the left during the earthquake, and sterilizer toppled over.

FIGURE 163   Collapsed ceiling tile in corridor of Elmendorf AFB Hospital. See Figure 158 for closeup view of deformed floor cover plate at seismic joint.

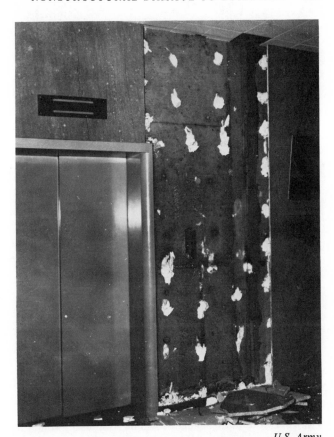

U.S. Army

FIGURE 165   Collapsed marble veneer in main lobby of Elmendorf AFB Hospital. Slabs broke loose where they were attached to a concrete wall, but they remained in place on the right-hand side where they were mounted on a metal-lath and plaster wall.

Richard Peterson

FIGURE 164   Exit stairway in Anchorage-Westward Hotel littered with plaster.

wires that were tied to the panels and embedded in patches of white cement. The cement patches probably lost their bond when subjected to shearing forces between the rigid concrete wall and the marble slabs. The marble slabs remained in place on the right-hand side where they were mounted on a more flexible metal lath and plaster wall. All the heavy marble veneer was removed after the earthquake, and the lobby was refinished with paneling and plaster (Figure 166).

DAMAGE SUMMARY

1. Many stairways and corridors were blocked when their unreinforced-concrete-masonry-unit walls collapsed.

2. Some seismic-joint floor covers in corridors were raised approximately 12 in. in the center of the corridors because of lateral movements between structural units of the building.

FIGURE 166   Main lobby of Elmendorf AFB Hospital after the earthquake. Marble veneer was replaced by plaster.

3. Many exit doors were jammed by deformed door frames. Some doors were blocked by heavy furniture or equipment that was shifted by the earthquake.

4. Many store exits were blocked by falling merchandise and were rendered hazardous by broken glass from showcases.

5. Many corridors were littered with collapsed light fixtures, ceiling tiles, and broken plaster.

6. Marble ornamentation collapsed in one building lobby, and some finish tiles on exit walls were broken loose.

RECOMMENDATIONS

Earthquake-resistant design for exits should take into consideration the following:

1. Unreinforced-concrete-masonry units should not be used in any walls, especially not in exit walls.

2. Brittle veneers, such as tiles, should not be applied directly to the inside of concrete stairways. If they must be used, they should be mounted on separate stud walls or furrings.

3. Floor covers for seismic joints in corridors should be designed to take three-dimensional movements. Special attention should be given to movement parallel to the joint.

4. All exit-door openings should be structurally sound to prevent jamming of the doors.

5. Free-standing showcases or glass lay-in shelves should not be placed in public areas, especially not near exit doors. Displays in wall-mounted or recessed showcases should be tied down so that they cannot come loose and break the glass front during an earthquake. Where this is impractical, tempered glass should be used for greater strength.

6. Pendant-mounted light fixtures should not be placed in exits. Recessed or surface-mounted lights are preferable.

7. Heavy ornamentation, such as marble veneers, should be avoided in exit lobbies. If a marble veneer must be used, it should be securely fastened to structural elements with dovetails and clip angles, or it should be mounted on furring walls.

8. Additional recommendations affecting exits appear in sections on emergency power and lighting systems, light fixtures, ceiling systems, storage racks, and furniture and loose objects.

FACADES AND GLAZING

The damage to building facades was of considerable significance to engineers. Lightweight metal-and-glass curtain walls survived the earthquake well, whereas heavy masonry facades and walls with face brick were severely damaged. Glass damage was moderate; where failures occurred, they were generally caused by rigid mounts or falling debris.

During an earthquake, the most rigid building element will take the initial forces, regardless of the designer's classification of the building element. The structural and nonstructural elements are all parts of a building system and must be analyzed together. For example, when a flexible building frame is deflected, part of the lateral load will be transferred to the attached facade. If the facade is rigid, it will try to resist these lateral forces, and the transfer of stresses will take place at the point where the facade is tied to the structural system. These forces can easily exceed many times the static load of the facade, and the supports will fail. This type of failure would not take place if the rigid facade were properly attached to a rigid frame, or if a relatively flexible facade were properly attached to a flexible frame.

In several instances, the structural frames of buildings were damaged by facade elements that were supposed to be nonstructural. This damage occurred where the structural frame was filled with rigid concrete-masonry units to make up an exterior wall. During the earthquake, the interaction between the frame and the wall resulted not only in X-cracking of the filler panels but also in tension cracks in the structural members at the corner of the frame.

The damage sustained by all nonstructural elements was directly related to the response of the building structural system or frame to the earthquake forces. This relation was clearly demonstrated in the performance of the nonstructural facades in Anchorage, and it is for this reason that the discussion of damage to facades must be presented on a building-by-building basis.

J. C. PENNEY BUILDING

The five-story reinforced-concrete J. C. Penney Building sustained catastrophic failures during the earthquake. The torsional failures occurred because the heavy facade, made of precast concrete panels, shifted the center of gravity away from the center of rigidity of the building. Evidently, the heavy precast-concrete panels on the north and east facades assisted in the development of the rotational forces, and then as the structural system failed and became more flexible, the rigidity of the panels themselves contributed to the complete failure of their supporting clips.

The heavy precast-concrete panels fell to the street during the earthquake as shown in Figures 167 and 168. (These photographs were taken immediately after the earthquake when the dust from the falling debris was still in the air.) Two people were killed when the panels fell onto parked cars.

Structural failures contributed to the collapse of the precast-concrete panels. A closeup view of a damaged slab at a column is shown in Figure 169. A shear wall failed at the second floor during the earthquake and was shifted out-

Anchorage Daily Times

FIGURE 167   J. C. Penney Building immediately after earthquake. Note the dislocated column and falling precast-concrete facade panels.

Anchorage Daily Times

FIGURE 168   J. C. Penney Building immediately after the earthquake. Two people were killed by the falling precast-concrete facade panels.

ward from the wall below (Figure 170). The wall was weakened at the floor line by small openings that held the support brackets on the precast panels. The precast-concrete panels were mounted on a ledge at the line of the marquee and were tied to the building on each floor by two brackets on each panel in addition to anchoring inserts at 4 ft on center both ways for panels attached to shear walls. Many of these brackets were torn out of the floor slab during the earthquake and ended up in the street, still attached to the back of the precast-concrete panels (Figure 170).

Accurate information is difficult to obtain in the investigation of earthquake damage, especially when the damage results in human casualties. Lawsuits may be instituted against all parties involved in the construction of the building, including the contractors, architects, and engineers. Until the case is settled, no one wishes to discuss the construction details that failed and eventually led to the fatalities. The installation detail of the precast-concrete panel shown in Figure 171 was therefore reconstructed by the

John L. Cerutti

FIGURE 169   Closeup view of damaged slab at column in J. C. Penney Building. Structural failures led to the collapse of facade panels.

U.S. Army

FIGURE 170   Shear-wall failure in J. C. Penney Building caused precast-concrete panels to fall into street. Note that support brackets were still attached to the panels.

authors from information shown on the architect's original contract drawings, from evaluations of damage photographs, and from discussions with several architects and engineers in Anchorage. The installation did not follow the architect's drawings because a note on the drawings allowed the contractors to submit for approval an alternate installation detail. The actual shop drawing showing this detail was not available to the authors at the time of this study.

The damage sustained by the J. C. Penney Building indicates that a rigid facade, when attached to a relatively flexible structural system, can contribute to structural failures. If a heavy rigid facade must be used, it should be tied into and made a part of the structural system. The designers for the new J. C. Penney Building decided to avoid the problems of heavy rigid facade elements. The aesthetic effects on the street fronts were achieved by the use of lightweight metal siding (Figure 172).

ELMENDORF AFB HOSPITAL

According to an unpublished report prepared 1½ years after the earthquake by K. J. Huseby (1965), Supervising Structural Engineer for the U.S. Army Corps of Engineers in Anchorage, repair of earthquake damage to the Elmendorf AFB Hospital cost $2.4 million. Approximately $1 million were spent in repairing the structural frame; the remaining

sum was for repairs to the concrete-masonry-unit facade, interior partitions and finishes, mechanical work, and so forth. He said that "approximately 70 percent of the exterior block filler walls were removed down to the sill line of the windows. In a few cases, the entire wall was removed ... the first five floors required nearly total replacement of the block walls." The damage to these nonstructural walls was not particularly dangerous to the occupants of the building, but it was very expensive to repair.

The reinforced-concrete frame of the hospital was damaged by the earthquake; numerous cracks developed in the shear walls around the elevator and stair cores and in column-to-beam connections. During rehabilitation, the cracks were repaired with epoxy grout, which made them stand out as black lines (Figure 173). X-cracks occurred between the windows in the concrete-masonry-unit filler walls that made up the facade. These diagonal tension

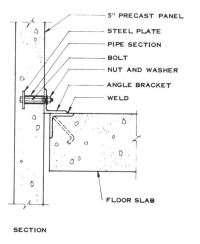

SECTION

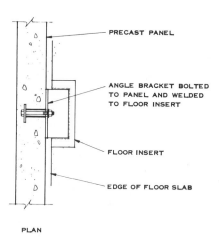

PLAN

FIGURE 171   Anchoring detail of J. C. Penney Building facade, as reconstructed by the authors.

FIGURE 172 Facade of new J. C. Penney Building, constructed of lightweight metal siding.

U.S. Army

FIGURE 173 Elmendorf AFB Hospital during rehabilitation. X-cracks can be seen between the windows in concrete-masonry-unit filler walls and tension cracks in beams and columns. Dark lines are cracks filled with epoxy grout.

cracks indicate that, when the structural frame racked during the earthquake, the design did not prevent the transfer of this movement to the nonstructural filler wall. The filler wall resisted the lateral forces and failed at its weakest points—i.e., between the windows.

The interaction between the frame of the building and the filler wall produced local cracking at the corners of the frame (Figure 173). This kind of failure was analyzed by Esteva (1966) in experimental studies on framed diaphragms subjected to alternating loads; he reported cracking in the frame as shown in Figure 174. In this building, the flexible structural frame was damaged by the nonstructural filler wall because there were no provisions in the design for movement between the two elements. The cracking of the frame in this building is a good illustration of how a structural system can be damaged during an earthquake by its nonstructural elements.

Very little glass was damaged in the hospital, although the facade walls were cracked at the windows, because the double-hung steel-sash windows had enough space between their frames and slides to absorb movement without placing any force on the glass. Some of the large sheets of glass on the ground floor, however, were cracked by the earthquake and had to be replaced.

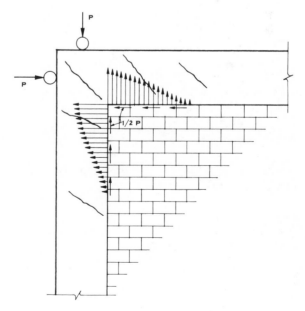

FIGURE 174 Corner interaction between reinforced-concrete frame and concrete-masonry-unit diaphragm. After Esteva (1966).

MT. MCKINLEY AND L STREET APARTMENT BUILDINGS

The facade damage to the 14-story Mt. McKinley (Figure 175) and L Street apartment buildings was almost identical. All the spandrels in these two buildings were a part of the structural system, making their failure beyond the scope of this study. It should be noted, however, that they failed in diagonal tension, showing the characteristic X-cracking seen in the failures in the filler walls in the facade of the Elmendorf AFB Hospital.

These buildings had windows of similar type to those at the hospital, but glass breakage was more extensive because the failures in the spandrels caused excessive deformation that could not be absorbed by the sash and the glass panel. A close examination of Figure 175 shows that the glass was undamaged when the spandrels were only cracked. The large store-front windows on the ground floor were broken mainly because of failures in adjacent structural elements (Figure 176).

FIRST FEDERAL SAVINGS AND LOAN BUILDING

The facade and glazing damage to the three-story First Federal Savings and Loan Building is of special interest be-

FIGURE 176   Damaged facade on lower floors of Mt. McKinley apartment building.

cause of the variety of exterior-wall materials. A view of the building before the earthquake is shown in Figure 177. The east, south, and a portion of the west facades were glass-spandrel curtain walls, and the major portion of the west wall was constructed of reinforced-concrete-masonry units with a series of window openings.

The steel frame behind the brick panel in the south wall was cross braced (Figure 178), but there was no lateral bracing in the frame behind the two panels in the east facade. During the earthquake, the west and north walls of the building sheared at the second floor, one brick panel on the

FIGURE 175   Damaged facade of Mt. McKinley apartment building.

FIGURE 177   First Federal Savings and Loan Building before the earthquake, looking northwest.

U.S. Army

FIGURE 178 Southwest corner of the First Federal Savings and Loan Building after the earthquake. Note the cross bracing in the steel frame behind the damaged brick panel.

east facade collapsed, and the remaining brick panels on the east and south were badly damaged (Figures 178 and 179). The facade of the entire building was removed during rehabilitation (Figure 123).

The curtain wall suffered only minor damage during the earthquake, because its flexibility was compatible with the

U.S. Army

FIGURE 179 Collapsed facade at First Federal Savings and Loan Building. Falling brick panel pulled down a section of window wall. Center cracking on remaining brick panel on right was caused by hammering action against the steel column behind.

flexible steel frame of the building. The exact details of this curtain wall and its ties to the structural frame are shown in Figures 180 and 181. The construction joints were built with vinyl gaskets, and all connections to glass or wall panels were made with vinyl glazing beads. These construction details made the curtain wall flexible enough to respond to movements of the building frame during the earthquake without being damaged. The glazing beads that held the insulated panels or window glass acted as a cushion to prevent metal-to-glass contact, and the space at the end of the glass inside the mullion allowed the glass to move without striking the metal frame.

Only a few panels of glass were broken during the main earthquake, but several more were damaged by aftershocks. Some of the vinyl glazing beads around the glass panels worked out of their seats as a result of the earthquake. These beads can be seen as black lines at the edge of the windows in Figures 178 and 179. Without the glazing beads, the glass was left unprotected, and any additional vibratory movement of the curtain wall made the glass panel rattle against the mullions, causing it to break.

The only curtain-wall section that collapsed during the earthquake was anchored to the collapsed brick panel on the east facade. This section can be seen lying across the hood of the car in Figure 179. When it came down, evidently it split the mullion on the left, leaving the remainder of the curtain wall undamaged.

The conflict between the flexible structural frame and the rigid nonstructural brick facade was quite evident in this building. The panel in the south facade could not cope with

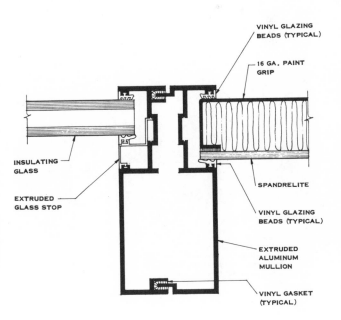

FIGURE 180 Curtain-wall detail at First Federal Savings and Loan Building.

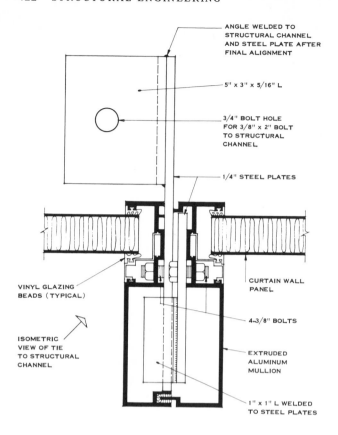

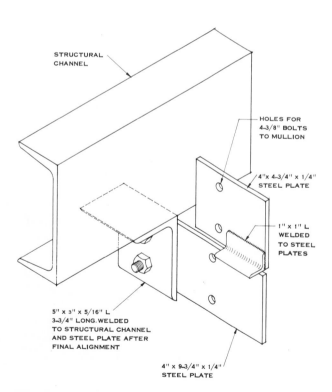

FIGURE 181   Curtain-wall anchor detail at First Federal Savings and Loan Building.

the movements of the steel frame and, as shown in Figure 178, it broke into sections; the lower piece collapsed, and the middle section slipped down several inches. The surviving panel on the east facade was damaged in the center (Figure 179), where it was battered from the rear by a steel column. If the brick panels had been tied to a metal lath and stud wall that was not in contact with the structural frame, their chances of survival could have been greatly improved.

ANCHORAGE-WESTWARD HOTEL

Although the Anchorage-Westward Hotel sustained significant structural failures during the earthquake, the facades and glazing survived with only minor damage. The hotel consisted of a 14-story tower and two adjacent structures, six stories and three stories high, respectively. An aerial view of the hotel, looking east, is shown in Figure 182. Considerable battering damage occurred where the three-story portion of the hotel joined the tower (Figure 183). An interior

U.S. Army

FIGURE 182   Aerial view of Anchorage-Westward Hotel, looking east, showing damaged shear wall on left.

John L. Cerutti

FIGURE 183   Facade damage at Anchorage-Westward Hotel, where three-story and fourteen-story structural units pounded together during the earthquake.

John L. Cerutti

FIGURE 184   Closeup view of damage to west exterior shear wall shown in Figures 182 and 186. Openings in wall were temporarily closed with plywood at the time of the earthquake.

Richard Peterson

FIGURE 185   View of damaged west exterior shear wall at Anchorage-Westward Hotel, showing curtain-wall mullion damage near the center.

shear wall was extensively damaged, and the west exterior shear wall was badly cracked at the eighth floor (Figures 184 and 185). At the time of the earthquake, the wall openings had been temporarily closed with plywood; after the earthquake, all these openings were filled in with reinforced concrete.

Figure 186 shows the excellent performance of the curtain wall and of the large sloping picture windows on the fourteenth floor. The only damage sustained by the curtain wall occurred next to structural failures on the eighth and ninth floors, as shown on the right side of Figure 184 and near the center of Figure 185. A closeup view of the damaged curtain-wall mullion (Figure 187) shows that it came apart at the slip joint but did not fall. Another curtain-wall

Anchorage Daily Times

FIGURE 186   Curtain wall and windows at Anchorage-Westward Hotel were practically undamaged by the earthquake.

mullion was slightly damaged next to a structural failure at the northeast corner on the ninth floor (Figure 188). We were unable to determine whether this window was opened by workmen or whether it fell open during the earthquake; a damaged seismic-joint cover is also visible (Figure 186) between the tower and the six-story building.

The curtain wall was supported on brackets at each floor and tied to concrete inserts in the slab. The inserts were 6 in. long, 3-in. × 3-in. × 1/4-in. angles, with 3/8-in. × 4-in. U-shaped rebar welded in two places at 45° to the angle. The architect who examined the hotel for the owners on the Monday after the earthquake found that the curtain wall had pulled away from the edge of the floor slab in a few places. The facade on the top of the tower was tied to the fourteenth-floor slab with the same type of concrete inserts that were used to support the curtain wall. During the earthquake, this part of the facade was subjected to heavy racking, and the concrete slab cracked around the inserts. As a corrective measure after the earthquake two 3-in. × 1/4-in. plates were welded to each side of the loosened inserts and bolted to the floor (Figure 189).

CORDOVA BUILDING

The curtain-wall facade on the Cordova Building was almost undamaged by the earthquake, although the penthouse collapsed and portions of the structural system were badly damaged. Figure 190 shows an aerial view of the building, looking southwest. A closeup view of the damaged southeast corner (Figure 191) shows that some of the aluminum mullions failed on the first floor next to the damaged 4-in. concrete wall and allowed the curtain wall to sag. This movement probably caused the second-floor windows to break.

According to Berg and Stratta (1964), the damaged 4-in. concrete walls at the southeast corner rested on the basement wall and were not anchored to the framing at the second or third floors. Because all the steel frames in the

Richard Peterson

FIGURE 187   A closeup view of damaged curtain-wall mullion shown in lower left of Figure 186.

Richard Peterson

FIGURE 188 Damaged curtain-wall mullion on the ninth floor at the northeast corner of the Anchorage-Westward Hotel.

Richard Peterson

FIGURE 189 Corrective measures necessary to strengthen facade supports on the top floor of Anchorage-Westward Hotel. Steel plates were bolted to the floor slab and welded to weakened inserts. Cracks are visible in slab around inserts.

east–west direction had moment-resisting connections, it appears that the damaged south wall was designed as a non-structural element. During an earthquake the most rigid elements in a building, whether structural or nonstructural, resist the lateral forces. Evidently, this rigid nonstructural wall resisted the lateral forces until it failed, and then the southeast corner column buckled (Figure 192).

OTHER BUILDINGS WITH CURTAIN-WALL FACADES

The eight-story Hill Building (Figure 193) sustained practically no facade damage from the earthquake except for some broken glass on the ground-floor store fronts. The reinforced-concrete center core, which was designed to take all the lateral force, failed at its base and settled approxi-

U.S. Army

FIGURE 190 Aerial view of Cordova Building. Although the penthouse collapsed and the concrete wall at the southeast corner on the first floor failed, the curtain wall was practically undamaged.

Walter Brugger

FIGURE 191   Damage to 4-in. concrete wall at the southeast corner of Cordova Building. The large opening in the curtain wall on third floor was not caused by the earthquake; portions of the facade were dismantled after the earthquake for removal of furniture.

mately 5 in. The settling of the core probably caused the failure of the unreinforced-concrete-masonry-unit wall of the penthouse (Figure 194). Although mounted in vinyl gaskets, a few large panels of glass on the first floor were damaged. We were unable to determine the actual cause of this glass failure.

Anchorage Daily Times

FIGURE 192   Buckled column at the southeast corner of the Cordova Building.

Walter Brugger

FIGURE 193   The facades of the eight-story Hill Building (in background) and the two-story Simpson Building (in foreground) were practically undamaged by the earthquake.

The Alaska Psychiatric Institute, 3 mi from downtown Anchorage, sustained only minor structural damage, and the poured-in-place-concrete and curtain-wall facade was practically undamaged (Figure 195). Many of the gaskets around the glass and spandrel panels worked loose during the earthquake, and three lights of glass were broken. One window fell out during the earthquake because it was not properly locked in place.

The facade on the two-story 700 Building consisted of curtain walls with concrete-masonry-unit filler panels simi-

Walter Brugger

FIGURE 194   Damaged concrete-masonry-unit penthouse wall of Hill Building.

U.S. Army

FIGURE 195   Undamaged curtain-wall facade in Alaska Psychiatric Institute.

lar to those used on the First Federal Savings and Loan Building. Because of inadequate supports, one section of the curtain wall on the second floor collapsed during the earthquake. The curtain wall was hung from the roof frame and was merely attached to the adjacent masonry-unit wall and to the second-floor frame. The removal of the masonry-unit wall during rehabilitation is shown in Figure 196.

The performance during the earthquake of the two-story building shown in Figure 197 illustrated the close relationship between the curtain-wall damage and the overall design

U.S. Army

FIGURE 197   Damaged curtain wall on two-story building in Anchorage. Rigid porcelain-tile facade on the second floor was undamaged, but the flexible curtain wall on the first floor broke out most of the glass.

concept of the building. The porcelain-tile facade made the second floor heavier and more rigid than the light glass-and-metal-panel facade used in the first floor. During the earthquake, the building evidently vibrated like an inverted pendulum; the more flexible curtain wall broke most of the glass on the first floor and dislodged the stone veneer.

BUILDINGS WITH BRICK VENEER AND GLASS BLOCKS

The exterior walls of several school buildings and single-story commercial buildings in the Anchorage area were constructed of reinforced-concrete-masonry units with attached face-brick or stone veneers. The face brick was supported from the foundation and held to the insulated concrete wall by wire inserts or tie rods. During the earthquake, many of these brick veneers pulled away from their supporting walls and collapsed for lack of bond. This type of facade failure occurred at the East Anchorage High School and Eagle River School (Figures 198 and 199). This damage could have been avoided if the facades had been tied to the concrete wall by one of the standard methods shown in Figure 200. At the East Anchorage High School, all the stone veneer was removed after the earthquake and replaced with lightweight metal siding.

The glass block in the facade at the Denali Elementary School (Figure 201) apparently survived the earthquake with no damage. This view of the front of the school was

John L. Cerutti

FIGURE 196   Removal of the masonry-unit facade on the 700 Building during rehabilitation. The curtain-wall section on the left side of the brick wall collapsed during the earthquake because of poor supports.

R. A. McCann

FIGURE 198   Collapsed stone veneer at East Anchorage High School. During rehabilitation, veneer was replaced with lightweight metal siding.

taken while the building was being repaired. The glass-block panel in the exterior wall of the Ordnance Vehicle Repair Shop at Fort Richardson was undamaged (Figure 202), but the roof was displaced slightly where it joined the wall.

STOREFRONTS AND WINDOW GLASS

During the earthquake, the behavior of the large glass panels in storefronts varied from building to building. The type

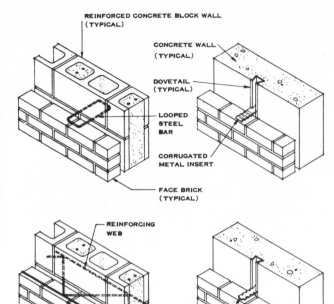

FIGURE 200   Suggested anchoring details for face brick.

and strength of glass, its weight and size, the mounting details, and the behavior of the adjacent structural elements all affected the performance of the glass panels. One kind of failure is illustrated by the damaged storefront of the Book Cache (Figure 203). The glass panels were broken and the corner mullion damaged because the mounts were rigid and the mullion was weak. The identical corner mullion on the

John L. Cerutti

FIGURE 199   Collapsed face brick on east wall of multipurpose room at Eagle River School. Exposed 8-in. concrete-masonry-unit wall is partly covered with pieces of 1½-in. styrofoam insulation.

U.S. Army

FIGURE 201   Denali Elementary School during rehabilitation. The glass block in facade was undamaged by the earthquake.

U.S. Army

FIGURE 202   Undamaged glass-block panel in exterior wall of Ordnance Vehicle Repair Shop, Fort Richardson. The roof was displaced slightly where it joins the wall.

Anchorage Daily Times

FIGURE 203   Storefront of Book Cache. Note that the lightweight mullion at the store entrance failed at the ceiling.

other side of the entrance, however, was undamaged. Similar contradictory evidence of this kind of damage was found throughout Anchorage.

The damage to glass installations in storefronts did not follow a consistent pattern. For example, many large glass panels were broken during the earthquake although they were set in resilient mounts. This situation might suggest that the failures were caused by structural weakness in the glass, or that inertial forces induced by the glass caused movements that could not be absorbed by the mounts. The inertial forces could be minimized if the weight of the glass could be reduced without sacrificing its strength. The use of a tempered glass, which has greater strength and does not shatter when it fails, should be considered for storefronts or for large glass windows that are installed near public exits or sidewalks.

More research is needed on earthquake-resistant design for large glass panels in storefronts and for window glass. Osawa and others (1965) analyzed failures of window glass in reinforced-concrete buildings in Shizuoka Prefecture, Japan, and came to the following conclusion:

... the glass with high percentage of failure has something in common with "steel sash," "fixed" and "hardened putty." This means that because of "fixed" the deformation of structure was directly transmitted to the sash, and because of "steel sash" glass could not encroach into the sash, and because of "hardened putty" there was no clearance between glass and sash.

Bouwkamp and Meehan (1960) analyzed the behavior of window panels under in-plane forces and came to the following conclusion:

This investigation has shown that where care is taken to insure clearance for movement of the glass in the sash, a considerable amount of drift can be tolerated before the glass breakage will occur. However, where movement is impaired such as by a hardened mastic or the sash frame, a hazard exists for both the building occupants and the public outside the building. When the glass fails, fragments of glass are thrown outward from both sides of the sash. Upon failure of the 2 × 4 ft. panels under static loading, glass fragments were found as far as five feet out from both sides. On the 8 ft. high × 4 ft. wide panels, the lateral travel of the glass was as far as 25 ft. from the sash.

Our investigations of glass damage in Anchorage confirms the need for resilient mounts and adequate space for movement in the supporting frame.

DAMAGE SUMMARY

1. Heavy precast-concrete panels that were attached to the building frame by clip angles and inserts collapsed.

2. Concrete-masonry-unit filler walls were badly cracked and in some instances they damaged the surrounding structural frame.

3. Brick veneers, attached to flexible steel frames without

backing or with insufficient backing, cracked and in some instances collapsed. Some stone and brick veneers collapsed where they were improperly tied to concrete walls.

4. Curtain walls sustained very little damage, except in the vicinity of structural failures. Some mounting brackets broke or pulled loose their concrete inserts at the floor slabs.

5. Glass-block panels were practically undamaged.

6. Window glass was damaged where adjacent structural elements failed or sustained excessive deflections. Where mounts were rigid and mullions were weak, large panels of glass in storefronts were broken. Some glass panels in curtain walls were damaged when flexible mountings worked loose.

RECOMMENDATIONS

Earthquake resistant design for facades and glazing should take into consideration the following:

1. Both the architect and structural engineer should understand that the nonstructural facade selected for a building affects the dynamic, as well as the static loading of the building frame.

2. Heavy rigid facades should be used only on rigid structural systems; they should never be attached to relatively flexible building frames.

3. Concrete-masonry-unit filler walls should not be installed in a manner that will restrain the lateral deflection of the building frame. A gap with an adequately sized resilient filler should separate the structural frame from the nonstructural filler wall.

4. Brick-veneer facades on steel-frame buildings should be avoided. If brick veneers must be used, the brick should be securely tied to a separate wall that is independent of the steel frame.

5. Curtain walls should be securely attached to the building frame. Flexible gaskets in curtain walls should be designed and installed so that they do not come loose when the wall is subjected to repeated racking.

6. Wire or straight-rod ties should not be used to anchor face brick or stone to a wall, especially where a layer of insulation or an air gap separates the two elements. One of the anchoring methods shown in Figure 200 should be used.

7. Large masonry facades should be designed as a part of the structural system. They should not be considered as nonstructural ornamentations unless they are properly attached to a structural wall.

8. All glass panels should be set in resilient mounts with sufficient space for in-plane motion and should be supported by mullions designed to withstand earthquake forces.

9. Tempered glass should be used for store fronts in exits or facing public sidewalks.

CEILINGS

Ceiling installations in Anchorage were similar to those found throughout the United States. Most ceilings were constructed of suspended metal lath and plaster, or of tile glued onto gypsum board. In many of the newer buildings, the ceilings consisted of exposed-tee-grid or concealed-spline suspension systems carrying acoustic tile. Only one or two buildings had small luminous-ceiling installations, and to our knowledge, only one building had suspended perforated ceiling tiles through which ventilation air was introduced into the occupied area.

The plaster and gypsum-board ceilings survived the earthquake with practically no damage, but many of the suspended-ceiling systems with lay-in tile were badly damaged, especially at their perimeters. The economical, and therefore more popular, exposed-tee-grid suspended ceilings sustained the greatest damage. The differential movement between the walls or partitions and the suspended ceilings evidently damaged the suspension systems; as the earthquake progressed, the ceilings started to sway and were battered against the surrounding walls. This type of action was aggravated when the ceilings also supported lighting fixtures, and in many instances the suspension systems were so badly damaged that the lighting fixtures fell out of the ceiling.

SUSPENDED TILE CEILINGS

The construction details of an exposed tee-grid ceiling-suspension system with lay-in tile are shown in Figure 204. The cross tees merely rest on the wall molding and are held in place by the weight of the tile. The tees are usually installed tightly enough to resist movement by hand, but they can slide away from the molding if laterally displaced. The

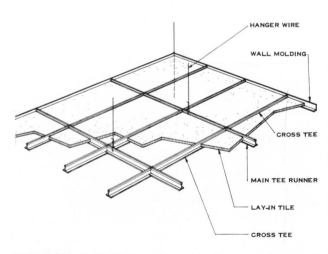

FIGURE 204 Details of exposed-tee-grid ceiling-suspension system with lay-in tile. Cross tees are not fastened to the wall molding.

main tee runners are usually installed in 10-ft lengths, with rigid connections at the joints. In most instances they are installed parallel to the long side of the recessed lights, and depending on the module, they are spaced on 2-ft centers. The cross tees are interlocked to the main tee runners (Figure 205).

The exposed-tee-grid suspended ceilings in the classrooms at the Kenai High School were badly damaged by the earthquake (Figure 111). The 2 × 4 ft 60-lb lighting fixtures were mounted directly on the ceiling-suspension system without independent supports. During the earthquake, there was probably differential displacement between the walls and the ceiling, and the inertial forces developed by the ceiling mass caused the suspension system to sway. This movement was enough to pull the cross tees off of the wall molding and to allow the ceiling tiles and lighting fixtures to fall. Another classroom sustained the same kind of damage, but the lighting fixtures were held in place by the main tee runners (Figure 206). The ceilings in the corridor were damaged in the same manner, even though the total mass of the relatively narrow surface-mounted ceiling lights was less than that of a classroom. The cross tees were dislodged from the wall molding, but the connection to the main tee runner stayed in place (Figure 207). Probably the localized damage along the long corridor wall was related more to the movements of the wall than to the swaying of the ceiling.

The exposed-tee-grid suspended ceiling in the multipurpose room in Central Junior High School was also badly damaged by the earthquake. The type of damage was similar to that in the Kenai High School, although the lights were in concentrated groups. A view of the restored ceiling is shown in Figure 208. Most of the damage occurred at the perimeter. According to the operating engineer at the school, the exposed sprinkler heads tore holes over 12 in.

U.S. Army

FIGURE 206   Damaged exposed-tee-grid suspended ceiling in Kenai High School. Recessed lighting fixtures supported on two main tee runners stayed in place.

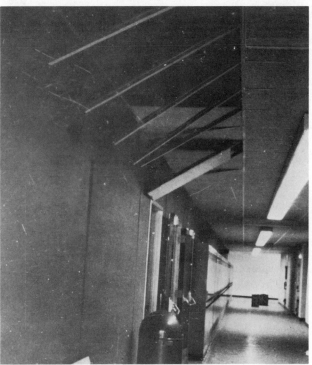

U.S. Army

FIGURE 207   Damaged ceiling in corridor in Kenai High School, showing cross tees pulled off of wall molding.

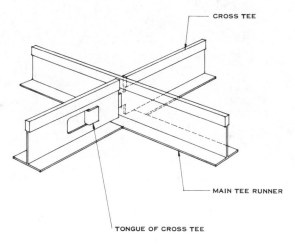

CROSS TEE

MAIN TEE RUNNER

TONGUE OF CROSS TEE

FIGURE 205   Detail of tee interlock for ceiling shown in Figure 204.

FIGURE 208   Restored exposed-tee-grid ceiling in multipurpose room in Central Junior High School. Light-colored ceiling tiles are replacements for those damaged by the earthquake. Tiles were dislodged at the perimeter and torn at the sprinkler heads.

long in the ceiling tile, indicating the magnitude of the relative displacement between rigidly braced sprinkler pipes and the flexible unbraced suspended ceiling.

The West Anchorage High School sustained severe structural failures during the earthquake. The exterior wall of a typical classroom collapsed, as shown in Figure 209, but most of the exposed-tee-grid suspended ceiling stayed in place. The pendant-mounted incandescent-lighting fixtures made the suspended-ceiling system in this school much lighter than the systems in Kenai High School and Central Junior High School. Also, the ceiling was installed close to the roof, so that the suspension hangers were short, and the amount of ceiling movement was restricted. These two factors probably explain the relatively good performance of this installation.

The exposed-tee-grid suspended ceilings in the six-story Hill Building survived the earthquake practically undamaged. The ceiling was constructed in a 2 × 4-ft module, and recessed lighting fixtures occupied about 25 percent of the ceiling area. The fixtures were supported on the main tee runners by clips (Figure 210). The hanger wires were short, and the light fixtures on the right were in contact with the fireproofed beam. The top guides for the movable metal partitions were attached to the ceiling grid system by sheet-metal screws. The outstanding performance of this ceiling

FIGURE 209   Exterior wall in classroom in West Anchorage High School collapsed, but most of the exposed-tee-grid suspended ceiling stayed in place.

must be attributed to the physical ties to the partitions, the lighting-fixture contact with the structural system, which inhibited lateral movement, and the 2-ft spacing of the main tee runners. Despite serious structural damage to the building core on the ground floor, only a few ceiling tiles were displaced by the earthquake.

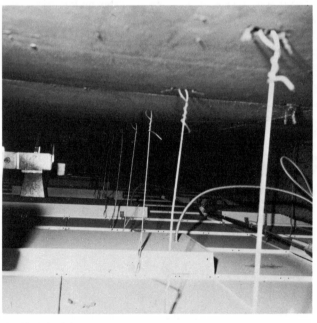

FIGURE 210   Attic side of exposed-tee-grid ceiling-suspension system in Hill Building. The hanger wires were short, and the light fixtures on the right were in contact with the fireproofed steel beam.

The construction details of a concealed-zee-spline ceiling-suspension system are shown in Figure 211. Concealed-tee-spline ceilings are similar, except for the slope of the spline; wall moldings of the type shown in Figure 204 are also often used. The system is stronger and more rigid than the exposed-tee-grid system because of the main support channels, and splines lock the tiles into the kerfs on all four sides. Because no ties are provided between the splines and the wall molding, differential movements between the wall and the ceiling can cause the tile and splines to pull away and fall. The concealed-tee-spline suspended ceilings in the Elmendorf AFB Hospital were damaged in the corridors near the seismic joints (Figure 212). Damage was limited to the area at the corridor walls, where the tiles and splines pulled away from the wall molding.

The Whittier school, shown in the lower left corner of Figure 213, survived the earthquake with very little damage except to masonry walls, lighting fixtures, and ceilings. The concealed-spline suspended ceilings in a classroom were damaged (Figure 93). The racking of the lighting fixtures during the earthquake contributed to the ceiling failures. The stems of the fixtures were screwed to the wood strips above the ceiling and enlarged the kerfs in the tiles until they lost their supports and fell. Evidently, the wall movement in this room was enough to dislodge the blackboard and to cause battering damage to the ceiling tile at the perimeter. Similar ceiling damage was sustained in the other classrooms and corridors of this school building.

In the new Sears department store in Anchorage, erected after the earthquake, the architect specified that the ceiling-suspension system include lateral bracing, and that the surface-mounted fluorescent-lighting fixtures be provided with an independent safety suspension system. An attic view of the 2 × 2-ft module exposed-tee-grid suspended

U.S. Army

FIGURE 212   Damaged concealed-spline suspended ceiling near seismic joint in corridor in Elmendorf AFB Hospital.

ceiling is shown in Figure 214. Note that the separate channel above the surface-mounted fluorescent-light fixtures has been independently supported and provided with extra wires for lateral bracing. Figure 215 gives a closeup view of the extra support channel, the lateral bracing, and the safety chain for the lighting fixtures.

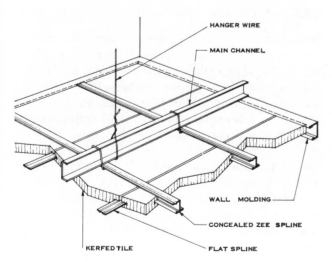

FIGURE 211   Details of concealed-zee-spline ceiling-suspension system.

FIGURE 213   Aerial view of Whittier. Fourteen-story Hodge Building and one-story school are in lower left corner, and five-story Buckner Building is in upper right corner.

FIGURE 214   Attic view of exposed-tee-grid suspended ceiling in new Sears department store, erected after the earthquake, showing the lateral bracing and independent suspension for the light fixtures.

FIGURE 215   Closeup view of ceiling-suspension system shown in Figure 214. Note the separate supports and lateral bracing for extra support channel and safety chain for the lighting fixtures.

Meehan (1967) suggested that tile in exposed-tee-grid suspended ceilings should be held down against the runner tees to provide lateral support and that the tees should be continuous and anchored to the structure. Clips to hold down the tile would add rigidity to the ceiling plane, but we found no evidence that the tiles were lifted out of their tees by the earthquake, except where the cross tees were deformed by battering action or were displaced and fell out of the wall molding. The problem of battering action at the ceiling perimeter is most acute in large rooms with high ceilings and deep attics, where the lateral movement of the ceiling and lighting fixtures and the flexing of the tall walls is at a maximum. Under these conditions, lateral bracing of the ceiling, and the necessary strengthening of the suspension system to make this effective, is needed to reduce the differential movement between the ceiling and the walls. A small physical separation between the ceiling and walls could be provided to accommodate any minor differential movements, and, if necessary, this separation could be covered by a closure strip with slip joints.

The need for independent support and lateral bracing of the lighting fixtures mounted in, or attached to suspended ceilings requires further study. The City of Los Angeles has adopted an ordinance that stipulates minimum requirements for ceiling-suspension systems supporting acoustic-tile ceilings and lighting fixtures (see Appendix C). The ordinance requires that ceiling-suspension systems be designed to support a minimum load of 2½ lb/ft^2 of ceiling area; if the suspension system also supports lighting fixtures, this requirement is increased to 4 lb/ft^2. It also stipulates that the lighting fixtures shall not exceed 50 percent of the ceiling area and that they be fastened to the web of the load-carrying member. It does not, however, require independent support of the lighting fixtures or any lateral bracing.

TILE AND GYPSUM-BOARD CEILINGS

In installations in Anchorage, gypsum-board ceilings were installed on wood runner strips and finished with glued-on mineral tile. These ceilings generally sustained very little damage, except where pieces of tile broke loose, although Meehan (1967) reported that some gypsum-board ceilings in schools fell down. He indicated that the nailheads were only 1/4 in. diameter, and the bowing and buckling of the board probably caused spalling at the nails. The same type of movement would have caused the tile to fall at the West Anchorage High School (Figure 160).

The tile and gypsum-board ceilings of the six-story Cordova Building were nailed to wood runner strips fastened to the bottom of open bar joists that supported the floor slabs. The wall studs were nailed to the floor and nailed to the wood runner strips in the ceiling. The building operating engineer reported that the ceiling damage from the earthquake was limited to the falling of a few tiles and to some minor spalling in the gypsum board where toggle bolts supporting lighting fixtures worked loose.

A somewhat similar ceiling installation was used in the ticket lobby of the Anchorage International Airport. Mineral tiles were glued directly to wood lath and runner strips attached to the bottom of steel trusses. This ceiling was undamaged by the earthquake and was removed during rehabilitation (Figure 216) only because of age and a need to inspect the steel trusses.

PLASTER CEILINGS

The construction details of a suspended metal-lath and plaster ceiling are shown in Figure 87 and include support details for lighting fixtures. Heavier support channels and the rigidity of the metal lath and plaster make this type of ceiling stronger than the exposed-grid or concealed-spline suspended ceiling. Plastered ceilings generally survived the

Richard Peterson

FIGURE 217   Undamaged suspended metal-lath and plaster ceiling in corridor of Anchorage-Westward Hotel. Note the badly damaged plaster walls of corridor partition and similarity to damage shown in Figure 118.

earthquake with only minor damage. Cracking and spalling occurred where the adjoining walls or partitions were racked and twisted, or where structural failures imposed deformation on the suspension systems.

In general, where plaster damage occurred in buildings, the walls sustained much greater damage than the ceilings, which were usually damaged only at connections to walls. This happened because the walls were subjected to repeated in-plane deformations as the building rocked back and forth, whereas the ceilings were not. If the buildings had been twisted during the earthquakes, the ceilings would have been subject to similar in-plane forces. The suspended metal lath and plaster ceilings in the corridors of the Anchorage-Westward Hotel were practically unharmed by the earthquake, but the walls were badly damaged (Figure 217).

The 14-story Mt. McKinley and L-Street apartment buildings and the Hodge Building in Whittier did not have suspended ceilings. The underside of the floor slabs served as ceilings, finished with a coat of plaster to improve their appearance. All these ceilings were undamaged by the earthquake, unless there were structural failures in the slab. For example, damage to the only ceiling of this type in the

Anchorage Daily Times

FIGURE 216   Mineral tile, glued directly to wood lath, in lobby of Anchorage International Airport was undamaged by the earthquake. It was removed during rehabilitation for inspection of the steel trusses and because it was old.

Mt. McKinley apartment building occurred when a portion of the penthouse wall pounded a hole in the roof slab. An undamaged plaster corridor ceiling in the same building is shown in Figure 118.

SPECIAL CEILINGS

The few small luminous-ceiling installations in Anchorage were practically undamaged by the earthquake. They are mentioned here, however, because they are used extensively in other seismically active regions of the country. The light diffusers or lenses should be properly secured to the ceiling-suspension system to keep them from falling out during an earthquake.

In the penthouse of the Anchorage-Westward Hotel, a ventilated ceiling was installed as part of the air-supply system. It was essentially a concealed-spline suspended ceiling with perforated tile and the space behind the ceiling was used as a supply plenum. During the earthquake, a plaster partition in the plenum collapsed, damaging part of the ceiling. All the joints where the ceiling tied into the perimeter walls had to be resealed and made airtight when the building was repaired.

DAMAGE SUMMARY

1. Exposed-tee-grid suspended ceilings with lay-in tile were badly damaged, especially where they carried heavy light fixtures.

2. Concealed-spline suspended ceilings sustained only minor damage.

3. Gypsum-board ceilings with pasted tile were slightly damaged when tiles fell or pieces of gypsum board were loosened.

4. Metal-lath and plaster suspended ceilings and plaster-on-concrete ceilings were practically undamaged.

RECOMMENDATIONS

Earthquake-resistant design for ceilings should take into consideration the following:

1. Fluorescent-lighting fixtures should not be installed in or on exposed-tee-grid or concealed-spline suspended ceilings, unless the ceiling-suspension system is designed to carry the added weight of the fixtures during an earthquake, or unless the fixtures are independently supported and laterally braced.

2. Exposed-tee-grid or concealed-spline suspended ceilings should be laterally braced and provided with a physical separation at the walls especially in large rooms with high ceilings and deep attic spaces.

3. Nails with large heads should be used to install gypsum-board ceilings. Further study is required on materials and methods for fastening mineral tile to gypsum-board ceilings.

PARTITIONS

Many interior partitions were badly damaged by the earthquake. The extent of the damage varied with the type of material used and the method of installation. Masonry units suffered catastrophic failures, whereas prefabricated metal partitions were undamaged. Plaster partitions were badly cracked and spalled, but studs and drywall construction sustained only minor damage.

The design and installation of interior partitions were similar to those found in most parts of the United States, and the widespread damage to masonry-unit nonbearing walls indicated that the construction industry in Anchorage had not recognized the importance of good mortar and proper reinforcing. In numerous instances, reinforcing was completely omitted, and, in others, masonry was installed with inadequate bonding and ties. Several lessons can be learned from this damage, and considerable improvement is needed in the earthquake-resistant design of these partitions.

The usual practice of tying interior partitions to the building frame should be reevaluated. When a flexible building frame was deflected by the earthquake, the lateral forces were resisted by the most rigid elements in the building. If these rigid elements were nonstructural filler walls, they were quickly overstressed and failed. (Filler-wall failures of this type occurred in the facade of the Elmendorf AFB Hospital.)

MASONRY-UNIT PARTITIONS

The collapse of unreinforced-masonry-unit partitions was probably the most obvious evidence of nonstructural damage in this earthquake. Examination of the damage indicated that most of the 4-in. concrete-masonry-unit (CM unit) partitions were installed without reinforcing and that those with 6-in. and 8-in. units had only partial reinforcing. Most of the CM units were not cracked or split by the earthquake, indicating that the failures occurred at the mortar joints. In many instances the reinforcing was detailed on the plans and in the specifications, but was not installed by the contractors.

The only reported death at Fort Richardson was caused by falling CM units in the stairway of the Enlisted Men's Service Club (Figure 151). The extreme hazard of falling CM units is also shown in Figure 218, taken immediately after the earthquake in the same building; the lack of reinforcing in the 4-in. CM units is apparent. The collapse of the CM-unit partitions in toilet rooms often left the pipes and electrical conduit undamaged and the sheet-metal

U.S. Army

FIGURE 218 Collapsed CM-unit partition in Enlisted Men's Service Club at Fort Richardson.

toilet partitions only slightly bent. The collapse of these partitions could have been aggravated by the plumbing pipes, which moved in different modes and amplitudes. Where the CM-unit partitions were installed in high-bay military structures, the collapse was dramatic. Figure 219 shows the remains of a tall screening wall in Building 976, Quartermaster Maintenance Shop, Fort Richardson, after the earthquake.

The 14-story Hodge Building in Whittier sustained only minor structural damage, but many of the CM-unit parti-

tions on the top floors were severely damaged. After the earthquake, the building was cleared of debris, partially occupied in the lower floors for a short period, and then vacated and boarded up. No repairs were made on the upper floors. When the authors examined the building in August 1966, it was in the same condition as it had been immediately after the earthquake. Many of the CM-unit partitions on the upper floors collapsed at the seismic joints (Figure 220); the partition lacked reinforcement, and the failures occurred at the mortar joints. The slot in the overhead beam was a recessed keyway that received masonry clips attached to the CM unit (Figure 221); the same detail was used to tie the partitions to the columns. A corridor partition on the fourteenth floor with the same seismic joint failed at the top of the door frame as shown in Figure 222. Similar views of identical bathrooms on the eighth and the thirteenth floors, respectively, are shown in Figures 223 and 224. The ceramic-tile-finished unreinforced-CM-unit partition on the thirteenth floor collapsed, whereas the identical partition on the eighth floor was cracked but did not collapse. The ceramic-tile finish probably strengthened these partitions, but not enough to prevent the failures in the thirteenth floor, where the lateral forces were greater.

Similar damage to CM partitions was found in other buildings in Whittier. A collapsed partition in the five-story Buckner Building is shown in Figure 225; the partition was tied to the structural frame on all sides and was only partly

U.S. Army

FIGURE 219 Collapsed CM-unit partitions in Building 976, Quartermaster Maintenance Shop, Fort Richardson.

FIGURE 220 Collapsed CM-unit partition on one side of seismic joint in Hodge Building, Whittier.

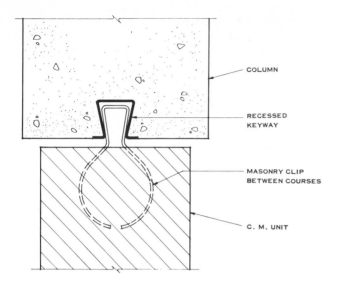

FIGURE 221 Detail of method used to tie CM-unit partitions to concrete columns and beams in Hodge Building, Whittier.

reinforced. Differential movements of the door frame and ventilation duct, in addition to the deflections of the surrounding structural elements, all contributed to the failure of this partly reinforced CM-unit partition. All openings in partitions for electrical and ventilation ducts, pipes, or conduits should be designed to withstand seismic forces and made large enough to preclude direct contact with the fixtures.

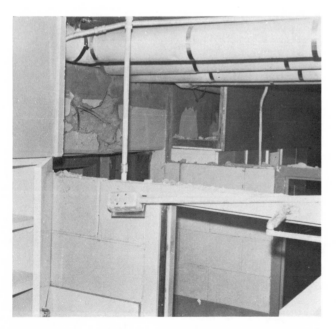

FIGURE 222 Damaged corridor partitions on fourteenth floor of Hodge Building, Whittier. CM units collapsed above the door frame on each side of the corridor.

FIGURE 223 Bathroom on the eighth floor of the Hodge Building, Whittier, shows cracks in the partition above the medicine cabinet. The ceramic-tile finish probably strengthened the CM-unit partition.

At Anchorage International Airport, the restaurant dining area was separated from the kitchen by a partition constructed of 4-in.-thick glazed tile. During the earthquake this unreinforced partition collapsed into the kitchen (Figure 226). The CM-unit exterior wall on the left remained standing.

Rosenblueth and Esteva (1962) suggested that nonstructural partitions in structurally flexible buildings should be anchored to only one structural element and separated by a gap from all other structural elements. In Mexico, where walls and partitions are commonly constructed of CM units, details have been developed that isolate the partitions from all structural elements other than the floor. A typical partition detail taken from construction drawings for a condominium in Acapulco is shown in Figure 227; the masonry units were held in a reinforced-concrete frame that was anchored to the floor. The gaps at the columns and ceilings slabs were covered with a molding or some other flexible architectural feature.

If a CM-unit filler wall or partition is tied to structural elements, it becomes part of the structural system and requires seismic analysis to determine the extent of deformation that it will sustain and the consequent damage to plaster or other finishes. Partitions constructed with 4-in. CM units cannot be reinforced with conventional procedures, and further study is required to determine if practical methods

FIGURE 224 Bathroom on thirteenth floor of the Hodge Building, Whittier, corresponds to the bathroom on the eighth floor in Figure 223. The CM-unit wall collapsed just above the washbasin where the ceramic tile stopped.

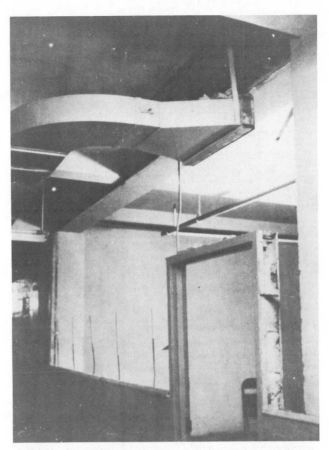

FIGURE 225 Collapsed CM-unit partition in the Buckner Building, Whittier. Vertical reinforcing bars had been installed only in the lower half of the partition.

of using these units can be developed to construct partitions in seismic zones. Since the earthquake, the U.S. Army Corps of Engineers, Alaska District, have abandoned the use of 4-in. CM-unit partitions in their designs for new buildings and, in repairing existing partitions, they have installed angles at the ceiling on either side of the partition to inhibit lateral movements.

PLASTER PARTITIONS

Metal-lath and plaster partitions were badly cracked and spalled in tall buildings with flexible frames. The plaster walls did not collapse and people were not injured, but repair costs were extremely high. The costs included not only the repair of the plaster but repainting of the entire room and repair of tile veneers or other surface treatments. Dam-

Anchorage Daily Times

FIGURE 226 Anchorage International Airport kitchen immediately after the earthquake; 4-in. thick glazed-tile partitions between the kitchen and dining areas collapsed.

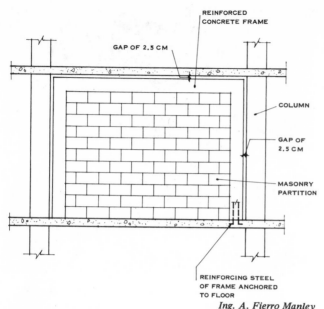

Ing. A. Fierro Manley

FIGURE 227   Construction method used in a condominium in Acapulco to isolate nonstructural CM-unit partition from structural frame.

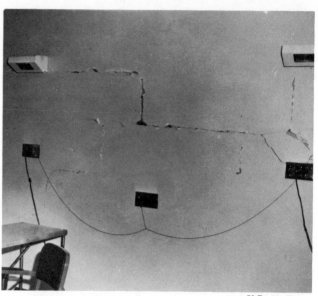

U.S. Air Force

FIGURE 228   Damaged metal-lath and plaster partition in patient room at Elmendorf AFB Hospital.

age occurred to plaster partitions because the studs were tied either to two different slabs or to columns. When the building frame was deflected during the earthquake, the partitions were subjected to repeated deformation, and the brittle, rigid plaster cracked and spalled.

After the earthquake, almost all the patient rooms at the Elmendorf AFB Hospital had badly cracked metal-lath and plaster partitions; in some rooms, entire sections of metal-lath and plaster were loosened from their backing; a few partitions were left slightly tilted, with cracks between the partition and the floor. Damage to a plaster partition in a typical patient room is shown in Figure 228; the cracks run from one electric outlet box to another. The boxes were probably tied to one of the slabs by rigid conduit and resisted any relative movement of the plaster partition with respect to the slab.

Plaster was also damaged in the elevator lobbies at the Elmendorf AFB Hospital (Figure 229). The metal-lath and plaster was applied directly to structural concrete walls. When the walls were deflected during the earthquake, the brittle plaster broke loose. This type of damage could possibly have been avoided if the plaster had been applied to a separate partition or furring that was not in contact with the structural wall but was tied to the floor slab and only guided at the ceiling slab.

The plaster damage at the Anchorage-Westward Hotel was, in many respects, similar to that described at the Elmendorf AFB Hospital. Both buildings sustained structural failures and their flexible frames were heavily racked

by the earthquake. Metal-lath and plaster partitions in the corridor of the Anchorage-Westward Hotel were damaged (Figure 217), and plaster covering a damaged concrete shear wall was broken loose (Figure 230).

The plaster partitions in the 14-story Mt. McKinley apartment building were constructed of 2 in. of solid plaster,

U.S. Air Force

FIGURE 229   Damage to plaster on concrete elevator shaft in Elmendorf AFB Hospital.

Walter Brugger

FIGURE 230   Damage to plaster on concrete shear wall in Anchorage-Westward Hotel.

FIGURE 232   Damaged solid-plaster partitions in corridor in Mt. McKinley apartment building.

with an embedded metal lath extending from floor slab to floor slab (Figure 231). Most of the plaster partitions were damaged by cracking. The solid plaster partitions in the corridors were also damaged (Figures 232 and 118).

Suggestions for avoiding plaster damage to partitions must be evaluated by comparing the added initial cost of effecting protection to the estimated repair bills after an earthquake. For example, the damage to the 2-in. plaster partitions in the Mt. McKinley apartment building could

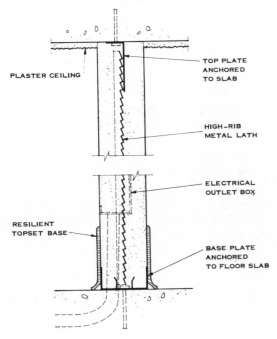

FIGURE 231   Detail of 2-in. solid-plaster partitions in Mt. McKinley apartment building.

possibly have been avoided if the partitions had been isolated from the slab above and from shear walls and columns. This could have been done by anchoring the partition to the floor slab and guiding it in lubricated channels fixed to the ceiling slab on the top and to columns or shear walls on the ends.

In the 43-story Latino Americano Tower in Mexico City, the designers paid special attention to details of the earthquake-resistant features in the design of nonstructural components, and very little damage was observed after the 1957 Mexico City earthquake. Partitions were effectively isolated from all components other than the floor, as described by Zeevaert (1957):

The partition walls are of different materials—light concrete, steel, wood, glass, and so on, but the design of the partition walls follows these rules:

1. They do not run to the columns. They stay on the side.

2. They are firmly tied to the floor by means of a 3-inch channel and bolts.

3. They are loose on the top, but tied to the ceiling so that a movement between the ceiling and the next concrete floor can be taken without having any damage or cracking of the plaster. On the corners of the partition walls, we have a very rigid joint between them.

In three places in the building the tenants forced their project to have the partition walls running to the columns. In these cases we observed a small crack between column and partition walls. This was the only damage after the earthquake of the 28th day of July, 1957.

WOOD-STUD AND DRYWALL PARTITIONS

Wood-stud partitions faced with gypsum board, or drywall, survived the earthquake with very little damage. In a few cases, the racking of the partitions caused the drywall to splay a little at the nails, and some drywall panels fell loose. The drywall partitions at the First Federal Savings and Loan Building were only slightly damaged. In the third floor, the wall section was shifted slightly at the base plate. The returning contractor found that several anchoring nails for the stud-wall plate had sheared, but that the plates themselves had not split. Repair work consisted of moving the partitions back into place and reanchoring them to the floor slab.

The wood-stud and drywall partitions in the Cordova Building were undamaged by the earthquake. Figures 233 and 234 illustrate their construction details. The partitions consisted of panels about 3 ft wide, fitted into guides along the floor, ceiling, and end walls and held in position by spacer clips. The head guides were screwed into the tees of the suspended-ceiling grid, and the other guides were rigidly screwed or bolted to the building structure. The partitions were clamped into position and appeared to be very rigid, but in reality they were flexible when deflecting against the curtain wall and the exposed-tee-grid suspended ceiling.

DAMAGE SUMMARY

1. Unreinforced masonry-unit partitions collapsed and sustained more damage than any other partitions.
2. Metal-lath and plaster partitions were badly cracked and spalled, particularly in tall buildings with flexible building frames.

FIGURE 233 Metal partitions in Hill Building with top cover plate removed, showing clips between panels and between panel and top guide. These partitions were undamaged by the earthquake.

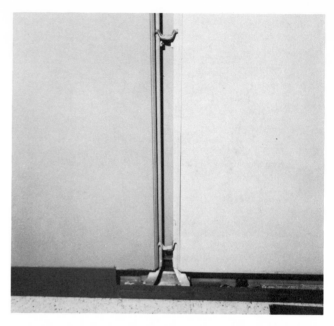

FIGURE 234 Metal partition in Hill Building, with bottom and joint cover plates opened.

3. Wood-stud and drywall partitions sustained negligible damage.
4. Metal partitions were undamaged.

RECOMMENDATIONS

Earthquake-resistant design for partitions should take into consideration the following:

1. Partitions in buildings with flexible structural frames should be anchored to only one structural element, such as a floor slab, and separated by a physical gap from all other structural elements.
2. Reinforced-concrete-masonry-unit partitions tied to more than one structural element should be considered as part of the structural system.
3. Unreinforced-concrete-masonry units should never be used for partitions or filler walls.
4. Conduits and piping in partitions should be tied to the structural element to which the partition is anchored.
5. Openings in partitions for pipes, conduits, and ducts should be properly reinforced and made large enough to preclude direct contact with the fixtures.

STORAGE RACKS, FURNITURE, AND LOOSE OBJECTS

It is surprising that more people were not injured by falling objects during the earthquake. The intensity and duration of the vibrations caused many large storage racks to collapse or fall over; if they remained standing, most of their contents were spilled out onto the floor. Heavy furniture was tossed about and tipped over, and drawers in heavy steel cabinets were often thrown out of their supporting frames. A serious need exists to develop practical designs that can protect storage elements and their contents from damage during an earthquake and also prevent pieces of furniture and other heavy objects from injuring people. This need is emphasized in emergency facilities, such as hospitals, which must operate at peak efficiency during a disaster, and in warehouses, where damage to food and mechanical supplies can impair the health and safety of an entire community.

During the earthquake, loose objects were subjected to accelerations in various directions and intensities. The complex ground movements of the earthquake were illustrated by the horizontal trace of a dresser leg in a single-story residence (Figure 235). This piece of furniture would have reacted quite differently if it had been on the top floor of one of the 14-story buildings in Anchorage. The acceleration to which an object was subjected varied with the type of structure and the position of the object in the structures. The predominantly long-period characteristic of the ground motion caused more damage to tall buildings than to low buildings such as residences. In general, loose objects remained on shelves in low rigid structures but were violently tossed about in tall flexible structures.

STORAGE RACKS

The extensive damage to storage racks indicates that most of these miniature structures were designed and built without concern for earthquake forces. Some storage racks collapsed during the earthquake, and others fell over because they were not anchored to the floor or tied to the structure of the building.

The storage racks carrying the heavy batteries in the ACS Toll Building on Government Hill collapsed during the earthquake (Figure 143). A storage mezzanine in warehouse Building 800 at Fort Richardson failed (Figure 236) because of lack of supports. Similar failures of storage racks in other warehouses were also reported.

At Elmendorf AFB, where there were serious structural failures in warehouses, numerous failures of storage racks also occurred. In warehouse Building 21-883, for example, almost all the long continuous rows of 12-ft-high storage racks collapsed during the earthquake. These racks were oriented in the north–south direction; identical racks in the adjacent warehouse Building 21-882, which were oriented in the east–west direction, were undamaged by the earthquake. Most of the damaged racks were replaced after the earthquake, but a few were reused. The old and the new

racks are shown in Figure 237. The old racks on the right consisted of stamped-steel sections, bolted together with no lateral bracing except for the sheet-metal panel at the ends; the new racks on the left were of substantial construction and had lateral bracing. Neither rack was anchored to the floor or braced to the roof structure.

In warehouse Building 21-882 at Elmendorf AFB, a large section of storage bins was damaged by the earthquake. The bins, or storage racks, were set in 130-ft-long rows running north to south and were tied together with a mezzanine about 7 ft above the floor slab. The mezzanine acted as a horizontal diaphragm that helped to stabilize the installation, but during the earthquake the entire assembly was shifted 4 in. to the west and left tilting against the structural wall. After the earthquake, the racks were straightened up and put back into use. The movement of the racks can be seen in Figures 238 and 239.

In warehouse Building 21-883 at Elmendorf AFB, racks for flat storage of sheet metal were shifted by the earthquake (Figure 240), but the drawers were not thrown open. The trace on the floor of a corner of one of the bins (Figure 241) showed that the total movement was approximately 8 in.

In warehouse Building 11-420 at Elmendorf AFB, rows of free-standing storage racks toppled over during the earthquake (Figures 242 and 243). The material stored on the shelves gave the racks a high center of gravity and created a large overturning moment during the earthquake. Without anchors at the floor or overhead ties to the structure to restrain them, the racks fell over like a row of dominoes. Open storage racks in the Hill Building, some of which had no lateral bracing, sustained similar damage (Figure 244).

Book shelving for libraries sustained only minor damage during the earthquake, although it served the same purpose as storage racks. One leading manufacturer of steel library shelving made a written survey of his customers in Alaska soon after the earthquake. Twelve out of the 23 libraries that replied said that the books fell from shelves running from north to south in the first shock of the earthquake, whereas the books on shelves extending from east to west remained on their shelves. Library shelves in one section of the library at the West Anchorage High School were undamaged (Figure 245). Evidently, the bookshelves were unloaded in the first shock of the earthquake; without the weight of the books, the lateral forces were small, and the shelving was left undamaged. In another part of the same library, the shelving collapsed (Figure 246), and the contents of the adjacent filing cabinets were emptied and scattered on the floor. If the bookshelves had been anchored to the floor, the filing cabinet fastened to the wall, and the drawers provided with catch latches, this damage could probably have been avoided.

We were unable to find any codes or regulations for the

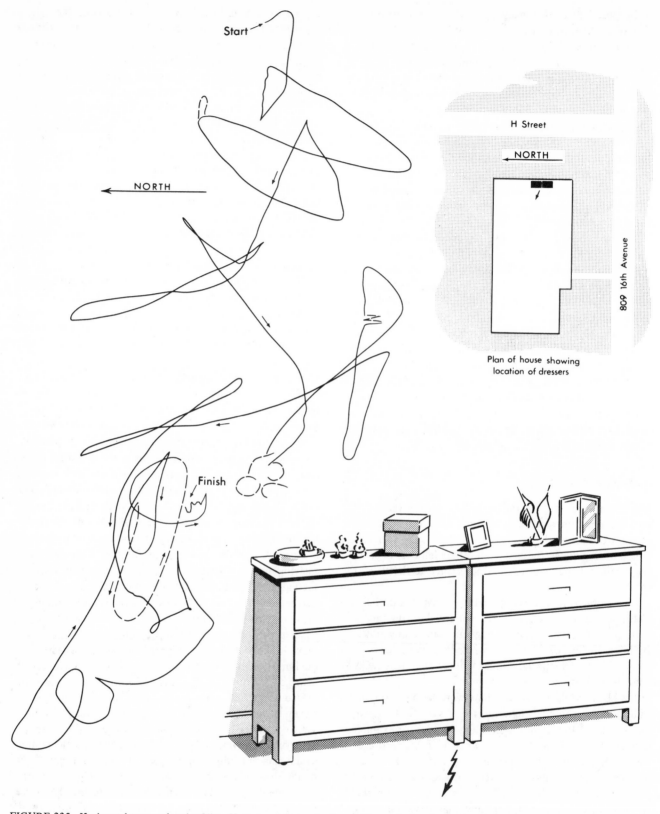

FIGURE 235   Horizontal trace, taken by Oliver V. Kola, of dresser leg in a residence during the earthquake. Scale of trace, half-size. After Hansen (1965).

U.S. Army

FIGURE 236   Collapsed storage mezzanine in warehouse Building 800 at Fort Richardson.

FIGURE 238   Foot of steel stair in warehouse Building 21-882 at Elmendorf AFB; the anchor bolt was sheared, and the stair moved 4 in.

FIGURE 237   Restored storage racks in warehouse Building 21-883 at Elmendorf AFB. The new racks are at left and the reused racks at right.

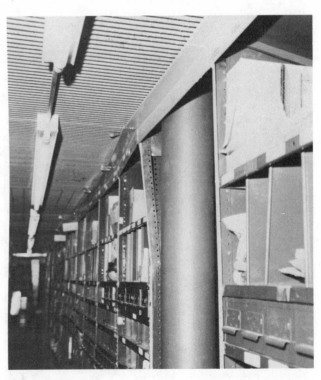

FIGURE 239   Inside view of storage racks in warehouse Building 21-882, showing the movement of the rack at the structural column just below the mezzanine decking.

FIGURE 240   Sheet-metal storage racks in warehouse Building 21-883, Elmendorf AFB, were shifted out of alignment by the earthquake.

U.S. Air Force

FIGURE 242   Toppled storage racks in warehouse Building 11-420, Elmendorf AFB.

FIGURE 241   Closeup view of storage rack shown in Figure 240. The skid mark on the floor showed that the corner moved about 8 in.

U.S. Air Force

FIGURE 243   Another view of collapsed storage racks at Elmendorf AFB shown in Figure 242.

Walter Brugger

FIGURE 244 Damaged storage racks in Hill Building. The open-ended frames on the left lacked lateral bracing.

support of storage racks and bookshelves other than Title 21 of the *California Administrative Code*, which requires that all bookshelves in California schools be anchored to the floor or laterally braced at the top of the rack. Bolts and bracing members must be designed to resist predetermined overturning forces equal to 20 percent of the weight of the

Anchorage Daily Times

FIGURE 245 Undamaged bookshelves in a section of the West Anchorage High School library.

Anchorage Daily Times

FIGURE 246 Collapsed bookshelves and displaced filing cabinets in another section of the West Anchorage High School library.

shelves when fully loaded. This type of regulation seems to be also needed in other building codes and regulations.

FURNITURE AND LOOSE OBJECTS

During earthquakes, flying objects and toppling or shifting pieces of heavy furniture are serious hazards that have received little attention from governmental agencies responsible for public health and safety. Almost every building in the earthquake area experienced damage of some description from these hazards.

A typical office in the Alaskan Air Command building, Elmendorf AFB, is shown immediately after the earthquake in Figure 247. The overturned furniture was not only a hazard to the occupants but also blocked the exit. This was also true in the Hill Building, where unlatched drawers were thrown out of filing cabinets into exits (Figure 248). Because the cabinet shown was not anchored to the wall, the drawers came out, and the cabinet tipped and spilled the top drawers onto the floor.

In the Headquarters Building of the District Engineer at Elmendorf AFB, large map files, stacked to heights of 8 ft or more, were tilted and shifted by the earthquake. Their drawers were thrown open and in some cases the cabinets fell over. Fortunately, no one was working in the room at the time of the earthquake, or he would have been seriously injured. Since the earthquake, these files have been braced to the structure, but latches were not added to the drawers.

At the Elmendorf AFB Hospital, medical records were spilled onto the floor by the earthquake (Figure 249), and medical instruments and supplies were thrown from their cabinets (Figures 250 and 251). The sliding doors on these cabinets were either standing open at the time of the earthquake or were thrown open by the earthquake. A free-standing medical cabinet fell over because it was not anchored to the floor or wall (Figure 252), and a sterilizer was damaged for the same reason (Figure 161). Unsecured oxygen bottles were tossed about by the earthquake (Figure 253).

Almost everyone in the Anchorage area reported that the contents of their kitchen cabinets had spilled onto the floor during the earthquake (Figure 254). Most of the people interviewed, however, showed very little enthusiasm for the inconvenience of sliding and latched doors to avoid the damage. The damage to loose furniture in single-story residences is well documented in other studies, but only a few photographs are available of damage to furniture in the 14-story apartment buildings (Figure 255).

Numerous reports were received of damage from loose objects in store buildings. For example, canned goods and other merchandise in most of the supermarkets fell into the aisles, often piling up 2–3 ft deep and obstructing the normal exit. Merchandise also was spilled into aisles in de-

U.S. Air Force

FIGURE 247　An office in the Alaskan Air Command building, Elmendorf AFB.

John A. Blume

FIGURE 248　Unlatched drawers in unanchored filing cabinets were spilled onto the floor of the Hill Building.

U.S. Air Force

FIGURE 249　Damaged and scattered medical records in Elmendorf AFB Hospital.

U.S. Air Force

FIGURE 250   Medical instruments spilled on the floor of a storage room in Elmendorf AFB Hospital.

U.S. Air Force

FIGURE 251   Medical supplies thrown from their cabinets in Elmendorf AFB Hospital.

U.S. Air Force

FIGURE 252   Overturned medical cabinet in Elmendorf AFB Hospital.

partment stores. The manager of the Caribou department store in Spenard stated that a seamstress in the alteration room on the second floor was unable to leave the building because her escape route led through a storeroom that was completely blocked by fallen merchandise. The manager also related that most of the heavy cash registers in his store were thrown to the floor by the earthquake.

U.S. Air Force

FIGURE 253   Oxygen bottles in an examining room were toppled by the earthquake.

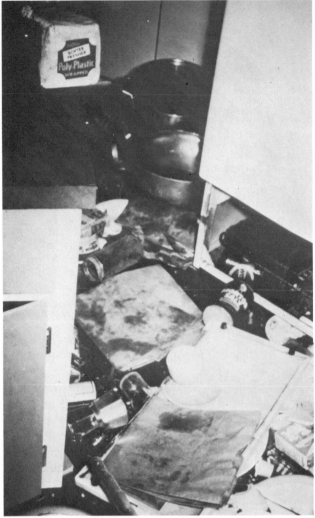

Walter Brugger

FIGURE 254   A typical kitchen scene after the earthquake.

SUMMARY OF DAMAGE

1. Large storage racks, carrying heavy objects, collapsed or were tipped over.

2. Free-standing rows of tall storage cabinets fell over like rows of dominoes.

3. Library books were thrown from their shelves, and in some instances the shelving collapsed.

4. Unlatched drawers of filing and drawing cabinets were thrown out of their frames.

5. Medical records, instruments, and supplies were thrown from their shelves, and free-standing cabinets and oxygen bottles in hospitals were tipped over.

6. Merchandise and cash registers in supermarkets and department stores fell into the exit aisles.

RECOMMENDATIONS

Earthquake-resistant design for storage racks, furniture, and loose objects should take into consideration the following:

1. All storage racks should be designed to withstand earthquake forces and should be anchored to the floor or laterally braced from the top to the structural elements.

2. Medical supplies should be kept in cabinets that are anchored to the floor or walls and fitted with latched doors.

3. Filing cabinets and map or plan drawers should be anchored to the floor or wall, and all drawers should be fitted with positive locking safety latches.

4. Merchandise in stores should not be stacked near exits.

5. Vital furniture and equipment should be anchored to the floor or wall. Vital records should not be stored in open shelving.

6. Loose materials stored on high shelves should be held in place by face bars.

Don St. Louis

FIGURE 255   Living room of apartment on the eleventh floor of the L Street apartment building, taken immediately after the earthquake.

ACKNOWLEDGMENTS

This report is based on the results of a study performed under contract for the Alaska District, U.S. Army Corps of Engineers.

We are grateful for the assistance and cooperation of Warren George, Chief, Engineering Division, and Robert E. Lyle, Chief, Design Review Section Alaska District, U.S. Army Corps of Engineers, Department of the Army. We thank them and their staff for arranging meetings with military personnel and for obtaining copies of numerous photographs, damage reports, and other data.

We appreciate, too, the cooperation of the military authorities, including Colonel C. Farley, District Engineer, Department of the Army, Alaska District, Corps of Engineers; Colonel Sochacki, U.S. Army, Base Civil Engineer, Fort Richardson; Lieutenant W. R. Herring, USAF, 21st C. E. Squadron Engineer; and their staffs.

The assistance and guidance of the members of the Panel on Engineering, Committee on the Alaska Earthquake, National Academy of Sciences—particularly of panel chairman George W. Housner and panel members Paul C. Jennings, D. E. Hudson, Harold Hauf, and E. F. Rice—were greatly appreciated.

We also acknowledge the contributions of Emelio Rosenblueth and Luis Esteva, National University of Mexico City, and A. Fierro Manley, Structural Engineer, in gathering information on construction techniques in Mexico.

We were assisted in our endeavors by the contributions of individuals and firms too numerous to list. A few, however, deserve particular mention. In Anchorage: E. Crittenden, Architect; R. Jacobs, Structural Engineer; John L. Cerutti, Structural Engineer; John Manning, University of Alaska; Don L. St. Louis, Western Elevator Company; and R. Jacobson, Otis Elevator Company. In Seattle: H. Pittelko, Structural Engineer; Richard Peterson, Architect. In San Francisco: E. H. Hesselberg, Elevator Consultant. In Los Angeles: Walter Brugger, Chief, Engineering Research and Development Bureau, City of Los Angeles; Dean Bell, draftsman and artist.

We are particularly grateful to the elevator-maintenance personnel whose photography has been very valuable in this study.

Finally, we acknowledge the help of Lawrence Schultz and Kenneth Maynard, Anchorage architects, in arranging meetings, gathering photographs and other documents, and generally representing the authors in Anchorage for the duration of the study.

APPENDIX A

NATIONAL FIRE PROTECTION ASSOCIATION, NFPA No. 13-1965. STANDARD FOR INSTALLATION OF SPRINKLER SYSTEMS. SECTIONS 3150-3169.

3150. *Protection of Piping Against Damage Due to Earthquakes.*

3151. Flexibility.

3152. Breakage of sprinkler piping caused by building movement can be greatly lessened and in many cases prevented by increasing the flexibility between major parts of the sprinkler system. One part of the piping should never be held rigidly and another be free to move without provisions for relieving the strain. Flexibility can be provided by the

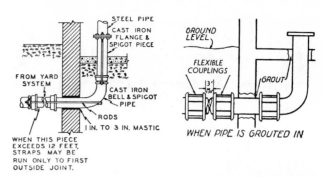

FIGURE 3151   Arrangement of supply piping entering building.

use of flexible couplings at critical points and allowing clearances at walls and floors. If too freely hung, however, sections of the sprinkler system will oscillate excessively or shift out of line. This action can be prevented by anchors or hangers which will damp oscillations or check movement, but not rigidly hold piping.

3153. The top and bottom of risers are critical points where the installation of approved flexible couplings is advisable. In a multi-story building a flexible coupling may be advisable also at the floor and another at the ceiling line in an intermediate story if structural weakness or unusual flexibility is present. A pair of couplings should usually be provided on a monitor riser. A pair of approved flexible couplings with a length of pipe between, readily permits a considerable horizontal offset in any direction. Piping crossing the joint between two buildings usually needs a pair of flexible couplings as the buildings will vibrate differently unless identical in all respects. Flexible couplings may be omitted at pipes less than 3½-inch diameter.

3154. One- to two-inch clearance should be provided around pipes at all floors. In one-story buildings the space at the ground floor can be filled with asphalt mastic. In multi-story buildings a sleeve should be cast in concrete floors, extending three to six inches above the top of the wearing surface and capped with a pipe collar, to prevent passage of water, smoke or fire. Tight metal collars are advisable about pipes to cover such holes through wooden floors in multi-story buildings.

3155. Riser drains, fire department connections and auxiliary piping should not be cemented into nearby walls or floors, if they can throw a strain on riser piping. Similarly, pipes which pass horizontally through walls should not be cemented solidly in them, or strains will accumulate at this point. Holes through fire walls should be packed with mineral wool or other suitable material held in place with pipe collars on each side. Pipes passing through foundation

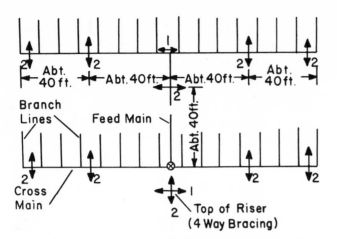

Branch
Lines

Feed Main

Cross
Main

Top of Riser
(4 Way Bracing)

Indicates suitable location of hangers to oppose
the movement of feed and cross mains in the
direction along the main. One hanger will be
sufficient for each main unless it is of exceptional
length or contains offsets or changes in direction.
Two-inch and smaller pipes do not require this
type of bracing.

Indicates suitable location of hangers to oppose
transverse (perpendicular to pipe) movement of
feed and cross mains. They should be located
at intervals of 30 to 40 feet. The end hanger of
this type should be on the last piece of cross or
feed main.

FIGURE 3164   Typical locations of sway bracing hangers.

walls or pit walls in soft ground should have clearance with
these walls but holes should be made watertight.

3156.   Tank risers or discharge pipes should be treated
the same as sprinkler risers for their portion within a building. The discharge pipe of tanks on buildings shall have a
control valve above the roof line so any pipe-break within
the building can be controlled.

3160. Sway Bracing.

3161.   Feed and cross mains must be braced to prevent
excessive oscillation. The tops of risers shall be secured
against drifting in any direction. Branch lines will not require bracing.

3162.   It is the intent to laterally brace the piping so that
it will withstand a force equal to 50 per cent of the weight
of the piping, valve attachments and water. It is felt that if
the lateral bracing is designed to withstand this force without breaking or permanently deforming, the system will be
reasonably safe from earthquake forces.

3163.   All piping outside of buildings which is not buried
shall be securely anchored to prevent swaying.

3164.   Where a system is hung with U-type hangers they
may satisfy most of the requirements for sway bracing except, in general, the longitudinal hangers as numbered "1"
in Figure 3164 will be necessary in addition. U-type hangers
are better lateral braces when the legs are bent out 10°.

3165.   Where a system is hung with single rods it will
generally be necessary to provide all sway bracing by the
installation of special hangers. (Very short rods, less than
6 inches, are fairly satisfactory.)

3166.   Large piping should not be held by small branches.
The piping should not be fastened to two dissimilar parts of
the building such as a wall and a roof which will move differently.

3167.   Transverse braces may also act as longitudinal
braces if they are within 24 inches of the center line of the
pipe being braced longitudinally, except that branch lines
cannot hold cross mains. In general, the last piece of pipe at
the end of a feeder or cross main will require a transverse
brace suitable for the loads involved. Earthquake braces
should not be connected to a pair of companion flanges.

3168.   In most cases specially placed U-type hangers, or
pipe clamps with rods or angle braces, will satisfy bracing

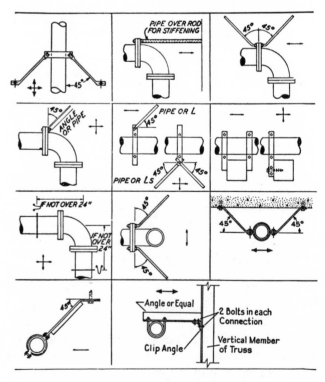

FIGURE 3168   Acceptable types of sway bracing.

TABLE 3169

Item	Max. Length l/r = 200	Item	Max. Length l/r = 200
Angles		Flats	
1½ × 1½ × ¼ in.	4 ft. 10 in.	1½ × ¼ in.	1 ft. 2 in.
2 × 2 × ¼ in.	6 ft. 6 in.	2 × ¼ in.	1 ft. 2 in.
2½ × 2 × ¼ in.	7 ft. 0 in.	2 × 3/8 in.	1 ft. 9 in.
2½ × 2½ × ¼ in.	8 ft. 2 in.	Pipe	
3 × 2½ × ¼ in.	8 ft. 10 in.	1 in.	7 ft. 0 in.
3 × 3 × ¼ in.	9 ft. 10 in.	1¼ in.	9 ft. 0 in.
Rods		1½ in.	10 ft. 4 in.
3/4 in.	3 ft. 1 in.	2 in.	13 ft. 1 in.
7/8 in.	3 ft. 7 in.		

requirements. Any properly detailed design will be acceptable. Fig. 3168 illustrates some acceptable arrangements of sway bracing.

3169. In the design of sway braces, the slenderness ratio l/r should not exceed 200 where "l" is the distance between the center lines of supports and "r" is the least radius of gyration, both in inches. For example, a flat bar 2 inches × 3/8 inch should not be over 1 foot 9 inches between fastenings. The maximum length of shapes used for sway bracing is shown in Table 3169.

APPENDIX B

CITY OF LOS ANGELES, DEPARTMENT OF BUILDING AND SAFETY ELECTRICAL DIVISION. STANDARD FOR LIGHTING FIXTURE SUPPORTS. BOARD FILE NO. 61.302-RR 5025

Scope

1. These requirements cover stems, canopies, swivels, and accessory fittings for the support of lighting fixtures.
2. These requirements do not apply to supports for:
   a. Individually hung fixtures weighing 18 pounds or less; or
   b. Fixtures which are rigidly supported by suitable means to the ceiling and separated therefrom by not more than two inches by suitable spacers; or
   c. Industrial type fixtures in industrial occupancies which are suspended by suitable chains or cables or by suitable rods not less than three feet in length.

General

3. Fixture supports shall employ materials which are suitable for the purpose. Cast metal parts of other than malleable iron or threads shall be subject to special investigation. Cast or rolled threads shall be subject to special investigation.

Design and Construction

4. Canopies shall be constructed of sheet steel of not less than #26 M.S.G. (0.016") or of sheet copper, brass or aluminum of not less than #24 A.W.G. (0.020").
5. Stems shall have a wall thickness of not less than 0.050 inches.
6. A supporting assembly which is intended to mount on an outlet box shall be designed to accommodate mounting on four-inch boxes, three-inch plaster rings and fixture studs.
7. A canopy and stem assembly which is intended to enclose fixture supply conductors shall be free of burrs and sharp edges. The motion of swivels or hinged joints shall not cause sharp bends in conductors or damage insulation.

NOTE: There are no specific requirements as to the use of swivels at the ceiling canopy or at the fixture. It has been found, however, that swivels which restrict the swing to much less than 45° from the vertical generally fail during testing.

Test Equipment

8. The earthquake machine consists of a carriage suspended on rollers from an overhead track. A gear motor and crank assembly is linked to the carriage to provide an oscillatory motion of approximately one cycle per second. The underside of the carriage is used as a mounting surface for the fixtures and supports to be tested.
9. The crank arm is adjustable to provide various stroke lengths for special tests. The normal crank arm is two inches resulting in a four-inch stroke. This produces an acceleration of approximately 0.2 of gravity when operated at one revolution per second.
10. The mounting surface is ten feet long and will accommodate one eight-foot fixture or two four-foot fixtures connected end-to-end.
11. The mounting surface may be rotated in a horizontal plane and locked in various positions from parallel to the line of traverse up to 90° to the line of traverse.

Test Requirements

12. The earthquake machine shall be set for a frequency of one cycle per second and a stroke (total travel) of four-inches.
13. Two fixtures, coupled together in the intended manner, shall be attached to the mounting surface of the machine with the supports to be tested.

EXCEPTION: Supports intended only for individually hung fixtures may be tested with a single fixture.

14. Supports intended for fixtures which exceed four feet in length and intended for end-to-end connection shall be tested with four-foot fixtures of equivalent weight.

15. All tests are to be conducted with the shortest stems and maximum weight for which approval is desired.

16. The machine shall be operated for one minute with the mounting surface in line with the line of traverse, one minute at 45° to the line of traverse and one minute at 90° to the line of traverse.

17. After the three one-minute test periods, the fixtures shall still be reliably secured in place. There shall be no undue damage to the fixture or supports.

18. In addition, a sample of the complete stem assembly from the above tests shall be subjected to a tensile strength test. The sample shall withstand a force of not less than four times the weight it is intended to support without failure.

Samples Required for Test

19. Two fixtures and two complete sets of hangers shall be provided for the test. This would normally consist of six complete supports including all components necessary for securing the fixture to the mounting surface.

20. The fixtures supplied for the test shall provide the maximum load on the supports for which approval is desired. Additional ballasts or weights may be added to obtain desired loading.

21. No components will be accepted by themselves nor will approval be granted on an individual component. The fixture support shall be complete to bear approval.

Marking

22. Each fixture support shall be plainly and permanently marked with the following information:
    (a) The name of the manufacturer.
    (b) A distinctive model or catalog designation.
    (c) The maximum weight to be supported by each stem.
    (d) The minimum stem length to be used.

23. Where proper assembly of the approved fixture supports is not readily apparent, a printed brochure showing the proper assembly shall be included with each support. A copy of this brochure shall be submitted to be included with the test report.

DWN: cc – 1/23/61
Board File No. 61.302 – RR 5025

APPENDIX C

CITY OF LOS ANGELES, DEPARTMENT OF BUILDING AND SAFETY. MINIMUM REQUIREMENTS FOR CEILING SUSPENSION SYSTEMS SUPPORTING ACOUSTICAL TILE CEILINGS AND LIGHTING FIXTURES.

City of Los Angeles Board of Building and Safety Commissioners Resolution No. 664

Subject: Minimum Requirements for Ceiling Suspension Systems Supporting Luminous Ceilings and Acoustical Tile Ceilings With or Without Lighting Fixtures—RR 23209

BE IT RESOLVED, that the following minimum requirements for ceiling suspension systems supporting acoustical tile ceilings and lighting fixtures be adopted:

I. General

Approvals of ceiling suspension systems will be based upon calculations according to Code provisions or shall be based on load tests by an approved testing laboratory. Where the testing procedure is used, the allowable load on the suspension system shall be 1/3 of the load applied but not more than 1/3 of the minimum load which caused the system to fail.

The load carrying members of all ceiling suspension systems shall be designed to support loads as set forth in Section II below. Cross members shall not support lighting fixtures unless they are identical to the main supporting members in size and span or have equal load capacity as evidenced by identification (see VI).

Lighting fixtures shall be attached to the suspension system members in a positive manner that does not tend to rotate the suspension member. All such connectors must be specifically approved by the Superintendent of Building.

II. Criteria for Approval

A. All ceiling suspension members and their connections not supporting lighting fixtures shall be designed to support a total load of not less than 2½ lbs. per sq. ft. of ceiling area.

B. All ceiling suspension members and their connections supporting lighting fixtures shall be designed to support a total load of not less than 4 lbs. per sq. ft. of ceiling area.

C. Recessed lighting fixtures shall not weigh more than 7 lbs. per sq. ft. unless fixtures are independently supported or a special system is designed for heavier loads.

Lighting fixtures which are supported by a Standard System (see III) shall not occupy more than 50% of any 4′ 0″ by 4′ 0″ area.

D. The weight of tile or other covering material shall not exceed 1.6 lbs. per sq. ft. in a Standard System (see III).

III. Types of Systems

Approvals of ceiling suspension systems shall be either by individual job approval or by general approval. For individual jobs, plans and calculations shall be filed in conformance with Code provisions. The minimum total load is 2½ lbs. per sq. ft.

General approvals shall comply with one of the following systems:

A. Standard System. Load carrying members shall be designed for a span of 4′ 0″ and a spacing of members of 4′ 0″.

The maximum load from fixtures which can be placed on Standard System members between points of support shall not exceed 56 lbs. for recessed fixtures or 20 lbs. for surface mounted or pendant hung fixtures. Recessed fixtures shall be supported at each corner. If more than one load is applied, the total of the loads shall not exceed the aforementioned amounts.

EXCEPTION: If surface mounted or pendant hung fixtures are supported within 8″ of a support, the load on the member may be 36 lbs. maximum.

B. Special Systems. Load carrying members which are spaced or supported other than 4′ 0″ apart, or are intended to support lighting fixtures heavier than those permitted on Standard Systems shall be designed for the intended conditions of use.

IV. Materials

Materials shall be aluminum or steel.

A. Aluminum shall be an approved structural alloy. Bending stresses shall be based on the ultimate strength of the alloy as specified in "Standards for Wrought Aluminum Mill Products–Aluminum Association–March 1960" divided by a safety factor of 3.

B. Steel shall be one of the following:

1) A steel listed in the Code with allowable stresses as specified.

2) Commercial Strip Steel
    a. An allowable bending stress of 10,000 psi.
    b. An allowable maximum bending stress of 16,000 psi, where approved by the Department based on tests and quality control by an approved testing laboratory.

Buckling of the compression portion of members shall be investigated. See Alcoa Structural Handbook, 1960 Edition, page 118 and the Light Gage Cold-Formed Steel Design Manual, 1961 Edition. Section 3.3.

V. Wire Supports

Wire shall be 12 gage or heavier soft annealed wire. The maximum allowable load on a wire shall be 1/3 of the ultimate load as determined by test. The test shall include the attachment at each end of the wire. The maximum load on a 12 gage wire shall not exceed 80 lbs.

VI. Identification

All suspended ceiling systems covered by a general approval shall be identified. Indentification shall be by non-removable decals, paint, or by indention into members.

Identification shall be on main members and shall occur at least every 12′ and shall include the following:

A. Standard System
    1) Company name or symbol
    2) Approval identification
    3) Load capacity (2.5 or 4.0) designating 2.5 or 4.0 lbs. per sq. ft.

B. Special System
    1) Company name or symbol
    2) Approval identification
    3) Load capacity
    4) Maximum spacing of members
    5) Allowable fixture weight

BE IT FURTHER RESOLVED, that effective March 1, 1967, all general approvals of ceiling suspension systems not meeting the minimum requirements set forth herein shall be cancelled.

I hereby certify that the foregoing Resolution No. 664 was adopted by the Board of Building and Safety Commissioners at its meeting of July 25, 1966.

BY ORDER OF THE BOARD,
S. S. NAIMARK, Secretary,
Building & Safety Commission.
    (D43978) Aug. 1

REFERENCES

Berg, Glen V., and James L. Stratta, 1964. Anchorage and the Alaska earthquake of March 27, 1964. Report of the American Iron and Steel Institute. New York: American Iron and Steel Institute. 63 p.

Bouwkamp, J. G., and J. F. Meehan, 1960. Drift limitations imposed by glass. Proceedings of the Second World Conference on Earthquake Engineering, Tokyo, Japan, July. p. 1763.

Cotton, J. J., 1965. A telephone story from Anchorage, Alaska. *Telephony* (April 17), 40–44, 51.

Esteva, Luis, 1966. Behavior under alternating loads of masonry diaphragms framed by reinforced concrete members. Paper presented at International Symposium on Effects of Repeated Loading of Materials and Structural Elements, Mexico City, September. 36 p.

Hansen, Wallace R., 1965. Effects of the earthquake of March 27, 1964, at Anchorage, Alaska, U.S. Geological Survey Professional Paper 542-A. Washington: Government Printing Office. 68 p. Also in The Great Alaska Earthquake of 1964: Geology. NAS Pub. 1601. Washington: National Academy of Sciences, 1971. p. 289–356.

Huseby, K. J. [1965]. Report, repair of earthquake damage to 5040th Air Force Hospital at Elmendorf A.F.B. Unpublished report by the Supervisory Structural Engineer, U.S. Army Corps of Engineers. Anchorage: U.S. Army Engineer District, Alaska. 16 p.

Meehan, John F., 1967. The response of several public school buildings in Anchorage, Alaska, to the March 27, 1964, earthquake *in* Volume II-A: The Prince William Sound, Alaska, earthquake of 1964 and aftershocks. Environmental Science Services Administration, U.S. Coast and Geodetic Survey. Washington: Government Printing Office. p. 219–243.

National Board of Fire Underwriters and Pacific Fire Rating Bureau, 1964. The Alaska earthquake, March 27, 1964. San Francisco: The National Board of Fire Underwriters. 35 p.

Osawa, Yutaka, Toshizo Morishita, and Masaya Murakami, 1965. On the damage to window glass in reinforced concrete building during the earthquake of April 20, 1965. *Bulletin of the Earthquake Research Institute* (University of Tokyo), 43 (December), 819–827.

Rosenblueth, Emelio, and Luis Esteva, 1962. Folleto complementario diseno sismico de edificios. Ediciones Ingenieria, Mexico. Division De Estudios Superiores De La Facultad De Ingeneria. p. 76–78.

Scott, Hugh P., 1964. Electrical damage and restoration in Alaska. *Electrical Construction and Maintenance* (June), 75–82.

St. Louis, Don, 1964. L-Street apartment building in Anchorage. *Elevator World* (May), 20.

Stephenson, J. M., 1964. Earthquake damage to Anchorage area utilities—March 1964. Technical Note N-607. Port Hueneme, California: U.S. Naval Civil Engineering Laboratory. 47 p.

Winslow, Len, 1968. Lowell apartment building in Seattle. *Elevator World* (January), 18.

Zeevaert, Adolpho, 1957. Address to convention printed in Proceedings of the Twenty-sixth Annual Convention Structural Engineers Association of California, Coronado, California, October 31 to November 2. p. 57–69.

GEORGE W. HOUSNER
PAUL C. JENNINGS
CALIFORNIA INSTITUTE OF TECHNOLOGY

Abridged from U.S. Bureau of Reclamation Report, 1967,
"Rehabilitation of the Eklutna Project Features
Following 1964 Earthquake"

Rehabilitation of the Eklutna Project

The severe consequences of the failure during an earthquake of any of the numerous dams and hydraulic structures in seismic areas throughout the world make a thorough understanding of the response of these structures to earthquake motions of the utmost importance. The dynamic behavior of earth and rock-fill dams is not yet completely understood, and earthquake-resistant design techniques for these structures are still being developed. For these reasons, as much as possible should be learned from the experience of the Eklutna project, which included the largest earth dam in the strongly shaken area of the earthquake. Very little information has been published on earth dams that have been damaged by earthquakes. Although the Sheffield Dam failed during the 1925 Santa Barbara earthquake, the Dry Canyon Dam was seriously damaged during the 1952 Tehachapi earthquake, and the Hebgen Dam was damaged to the point of incipient failure during the 1959 Montana earthquake, there is very little technical information about these dams in the available literature. This study of the Eklutna Dam—the first to contain an engineering description of the dam, of the damage sustained by the dam, and of the repair and rehabilitation measures carried out—should be of great value to those concerned with the resistance to earthquakes of earth dams. A significant aspect of the earthquake damage was the fact that immediately after the shock, superficial inspection indicated only minor damage to the dam and to its appurtenances. After some time had elapsed and after more careful investigations had been made, however, it became apparent that the damage was so pervasive that building a new dam would be more economical than repairing the old one.

The dam is approximately 60 mi northwest of the epicenter of the earthquake. There were no instruments in Alaska to record the destructive ground shaking, but it is estimated that, in the vicinity of the dam, the maximum ground acceleration was in the range of 10–15 percent of gravity and that the strong shaking had a duration of about 1 minute. The components of ground acceleration with fre-

ABSTRACT: The Eklutna earth dam and power plant, located approximately 60 mi from the epicenter of the Alaska earthquake, were shaken by ground motion of 10–15 percent g maximum acceleration. During the 3 months after the earthquake, it became apparent that the damage to the dam and its appurtenances was more extensive and severe than had been supposed immediately after the shock. Consequently, a decision was made to build a new earth dam. Because it was impracticable to design the new dam to materially increase the capacity of Eklutna Lake, the spillway crest of the replacement dam was built only 3.5 ft higher than the existing spillway. The active storage capacity was thus raised from 160,000 to 175,000 acre-feet. The crest of the new dam itself was raised 16 ft, which greatly increased the surcharge storage capacity in the event of flood. The total repair and replacement costs for the dam and spillway were $2,877,301.

This is the first well-documented account of severe earthquake damage to an earth dam.

quencies greater than 2 cycles per second (cps) were, no doubt, relatively attenuated at this distance from the fault.

HISTORY AND DESCRIPTION

The considerable damage sustained by the Eklutna Power Plant and appurtenant works was one of the lesser effects of the Alaska earthquake. As soon as possible after the earthquake, the Bureau of Reclamation (1966) undertook a program of temporary repair and rehabilitation to restore the power plant and pressure tunnel to normal operation and to ensure, as far as possible, an adequate dependable water supply for the Eklutna Power Plant for the indefinite future.

LOCATION AND PURPOSE OF EKLUTNA PROJECT

To familiarize the reader with the general nature and purpose of the Eklutna project, and to promote a better under-

standing of the operation of each segment of the project, this article includes selected maps, schematic diagrams, and explanatory material that were contained in the original publication (U.S. Bureau of Reclamation, 1958).

The Eklutna project (Figure 1) is a 30,000-kilowatt (kW) hydroelectric-power development designed and constructed by the Bureau of Reclamation to bring urgently needed electric power to the rapidly expanding area of Anchorage. The project, the first major development by the Bureau of Reclamation outside the conterminous United States, was constructed between 1951 and 1955.

The Eklutna Power Plant (Figure 2) is on the Glenn Highway, between Anchorage and Palmer, Alaska, about 35 mi northeast of Anchorage. The Eklutna project area includes the Willow Creek mining district on the north, the Matanuska Valley on the east, and the city of Anchorage and environs to Turnagain Arm on the south. Cook Inlet, a branch of the Gulf of Alaska, lies to the west. The area is a northern reach of the Pacific Mountain system, the parallel ranges of which enter Alaska through British Columbia, and

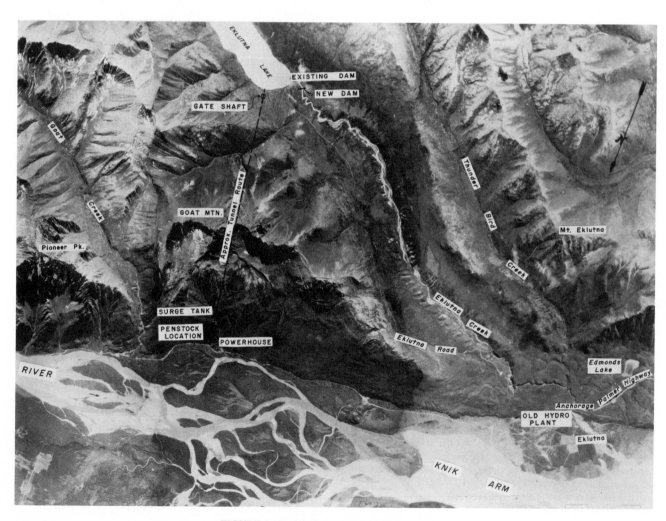

FIGURE 1   Aerial photograph of Eklutna project.

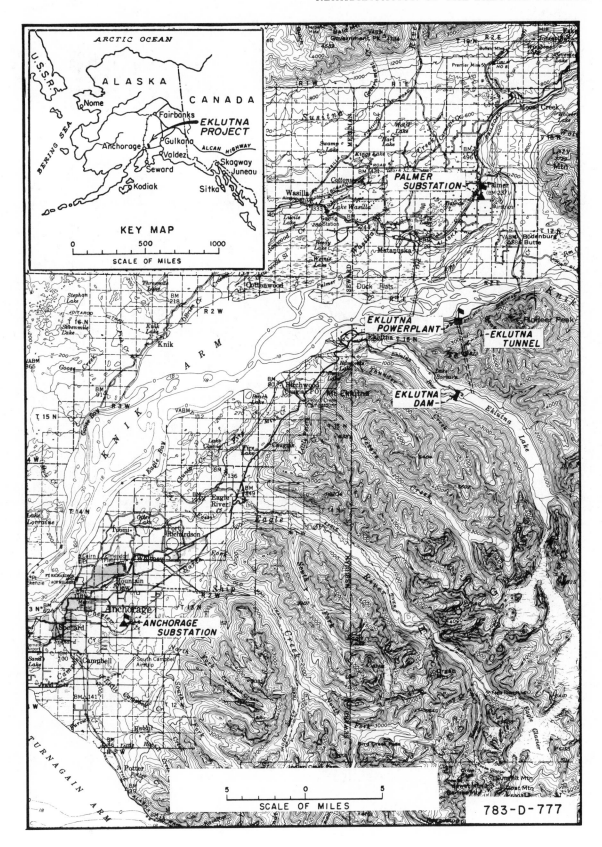

FIGURE 2   Location map, Eklutna project.

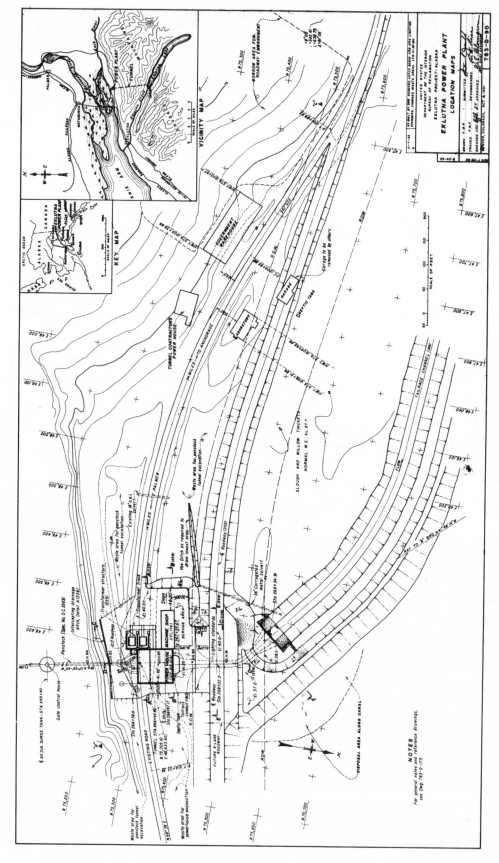

FIGURE 3 Eklutna power plant location maps.

460

it embodies two large flats—a valley floor and a coastal plain. The Cook Inlet and Chugach Mountains almost isolate these areas from each other; they are connected by a narrow strip of land bordered by a branch of the inlet—Knik Arm, a tidal estuary—and the mountains.

Anchorage lies on a low bluff overlooking Cook Inlet and is bounded on the north, south, and west by arms of the sea. To the east is a low plain extending to the Chugach Mountains. This enclosed area comprises about 75 mi². Matanuska Valley, through which flow the Matanuska and Knik rivers, covers an area of about 50 X 16 mi and is almost surrounded by the Alaska, Talkeetna, and Chugach ranges.

Trending northwest from the Chugach Mountains to Knik Arm is Eklutna Creek, which descends through a steep-sided troughlike glaciated valley about 27 mi long. Rugged peaks up to 8,200 ft in elevation rise sharply above short valleys tributary to the creek.

The project is intended for power production only. Firm energy has been estimated at 143 million kilowatt-hours (kWh) annually. Nonfirm energy, available only during certain hours in summer and early fall, is estimated to be more than 16 million kWh in the average year. Transmission lines north to Palmer and south to Anchorage have been constructed, along with substation facilities. These lines operate at 115 kilovolts (kV).

DESCRIPTION OF EKLUTNA DAMS

Three dams have been constructed at the Eklutna site; each in its time served to store water and provide head for power production. These dams are briefly described herewith:

Initial Structure

The first dam to provide water for power generation was built by private interests in 1929, on top of a natural glacial dam. The latter was left by an alpine glacier about 7 mi long, which, on receding, formed the glacial dam and Eklutna Lake behind it. The lake overflowed through Eklutna Creek below the dam. The natural glacial dam was raised with brush, clay, moss, logs, lumber, and rocks to provide a water supply for a small power plant that was placed in operation near Eklutna Village, about 8 mi downstream from the dam.

This initial dam was not very successful, because when the lake water level rose 4 or 5 ft above the level held by the natural dam, the slightest leak allowed the water to escape. Consequently, wood piling was driven across the inlet of the overflow channel to permit storage of water to a depth of 3 or 4 ft above the natural lake level.

Structure Existing at Time of Earthquake

In the fall of 1939, an earth and rock-fill structure was built incorporating portions of the initial structure. This dam had 15 open bays, each 10 ft wide, that could be flash-boarded to elevation 871.0 and a gated section with 19 spillway gates, each 6 ft 6 in. high by 5 ft wide, to control discharge and thereby provide a more dependable water supply for the existing power plant. The crest of the spillway gates, with the gates closed, was at elevation 867.5, the same as the crest of the ungated, open-bay section.

The dam was purchased by the City of Anchorage in 1943 and was sold to the federal government when the Bureau of Reclamation's Eklutna project was being built. In 1952, when the bureau constructed the pressure tunnel through Goat Mountain to the new Eklutna Power Plant, this dam was strengthened and reinforced. Principal improvements consisted of placing additional earth-fill embankment material on the existing embankment, driving and anchoring additional sheet piling, and placing riprap on the upstream and downstream faces.

This dam, as modified in 1952, had a crest length of 555 ft, a crest width of 15 ft, and a crest elevation of 875.0. It had 2:1 side slopes both upstream and downstream and a volume of 5,000 yd³. The 19 spillway gates were in such poor condition, because of aging, that they were required to be left permanently closed.

This structure, generally referred to herein as the existing structure, was still in place after the earthquake. Investigation, however, revealed that it was not safe, and a decision was made to replace it with a new structure about 1,400 ft downstream (U.S. Bureau of Reclamation, 1965); gates and excess timbers were removed from the existing structure to make it inoperative.

Replacement Dam Constructed after Earthquake

The replacement dam, constructed in 1965, consists of an earth and rock-fill embankment with a crest length of 815 ft, a crest width of 30 ft, and a crest elevation of 891.0. It has a 3:1 upstream slope, a 2:1 downstream slope, and a volume of 85,000 yd³. An ungated overflow spillway, with a crest width of 18 ft and a crest elevation of 871.0, is incorporated in the dam. Detailed dimensions and physical features of the dam and spillway are given later in the sections on "Replacement Dam" and "Spillway."

POWER CONDUIT AND APPURTENANCES

Water is conveyed northward from Eklutna Lake to the Eklutna Power Plant through a power conduit about 4½ mi long excavated through Goat Mountain (Figures 3–6). The principal elements of the conduit and appurtenances are described below. The dimensions are those of the original construction, and principal changes incorporated during the repair and rehabilitation are indicated in the discussion. Figure 5 shows a schematic plan and profile of Eklutna project power features as they were originally constructed, and Figure 6 shows the effects of the rehabilitation after the earthquake.

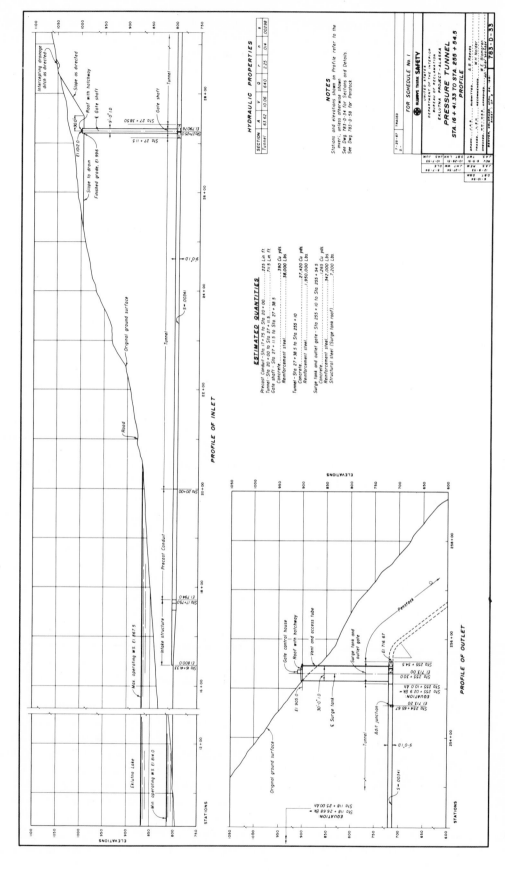

FIGURE 4 Profile of power conduit as originally constructed (including intake structure, intake conduit, pressure tunnel, gate shaft, and surge tank) from station 16+41.33 to station 255+54.5.

462

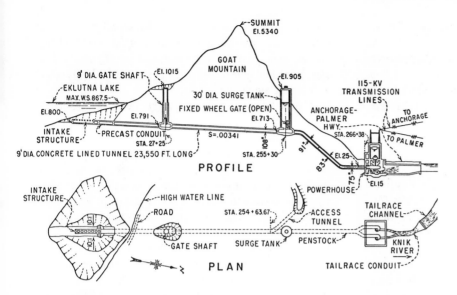

FIGURE 5   Schematic plan and profile of Eklutna project features before 1964 earthquake.

Intake Structure

Diversion from the lake is made through an inlet channel, 100 ft wide and originally about 500 ft long, excavated at the lake bottom at elevation 800 (about 70 ft below the maximum lake-surface elevation). In the original construction, an intake structure about 134 ft long extended from the inlet channel. Immediately downstream from the trashrack portion of the intake structure was a precast-concrete transition section about 14 ft long. The inside of this transition section tapered from a rectangular reinforced-concrete section approximately 9 × 23 ft to a circular section 9 ft in diameter. At the end of the square-to-round transition section was a bulkhead section 7 ft 6 in. long, from the end of which a 9-ft inside diameter precast-concrete pipe

225 ft long was constructed, extending to the entrance of Eklutna Tunnel. The pipe had walls 12 in. thick and was cast in 16-ft sections, each weighing about 40 tons.

The earthquake so severely disarranged the intake structure, the transition section, the bulkhead section, and the upstream 16-ft sections of precast-concrete pipe that eight of these sections had to be removed or abandoned and a new intake structure constructed for the pressure tunnel. This new intake structure connects to the remaining six precast-pipe sections, which have been repaired.

Tunnel

A circular concrete-lined pressure tunnel 9 ft in inside diameter and 23,550 ft long conveys water from Eklutna

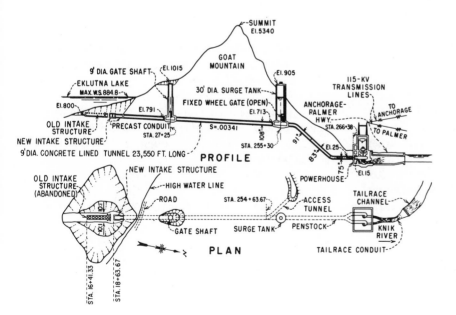

FIGURE 6   Schematic plan and profile of Eklutna project features after earthquake damage rehabilitation.

Lake to the penstocks leading to the power plant. The capacity of the tunnel is 640 ft³/sec at a velocity of 10.0 fps; the slope of the invert is 0.00341. The tunnel terminates in a surge tank, installed directly over the tunnel, 22,805 ft downstream from the bulkhead gate shaft. The surge tank, of the restricted-orifice type, has an inside diameter of 30 ft, a wall thickness of 18 in., and extends 176 ft above the tunnel.

The tunnel section beneath the surge tank contains one 9-ft long round-to-square transition and a similar square-to-round transition spaced 4.5 ft apart along the centerline. The 4.5-ft rectangular separation serves as a gate slot for the fixed-wheel gate used for emergency closure of the tunnel in the event of damage to the penstocks or to the turbines and for unwatering the penstocks for inspection and maintenance.

A tunnel adit is located at the outlet end of the tunnel near the surge tank. The adit, essentially the same size as the main tunnel, is approximately 300 ft long. The purpose of the adit is to provide a means of access to the tunnel for inspection and maintenance. It also acts as a free-flow conduit to convey drainage water from the tunnel when entrance into the tunnel is necessary. Access is by means of a watertight door from the adit to the tunnel.

Penstock

From the surge tank at the end of the Eklutna Tunnel, the power penstock conveys water to the power plant turbines. The overall length of the penstock is about 1,388 ft, installed in 30-ft sections. The penstock is a variable-diameter (91-, 83-, and 75-in.-outside-diameter) welded and coupled steel pipe encased in concrete in a tunnel extending from the surge tank to the power plant. Plate thickness of the penstock varies from 5/16 in. at the initial section to 1½ in. at the terminal section. In profile, the penstock roughly parallels the mountainside, descending for approximately 864 ft at an angle of 53°; it then levels off and continues through a horizontal section about 501 ft long.

At the power plant, the penstock bifurcates into two 51-in.-diameter, 23-ft-long branches that are connected to the spiral cases of the turbines. A 66-in. butterfly valve is installed in each penstock branch upstream from the turbines to provide means of unwatering the turbines for servicing or maintenance. These valves also serve as emergency shutoff valves in the event of damage to the turbines. Access to the penstock interior is obtained through the vent at the surge tank, through manholes in the power plant, and through the tunnel adit.

Power Plant and Switchyard

The power plant is a reinforced-concrete structure 149 ft long housing two vertical-shaft generating units. The Francis-type turbines are rated at 25,000 hp at a speed of 600 rpm and an 800-ft effective head. The generators are rated at 16,667 kilovolt-amperes (kVA), 3 phase, 60 cycles, 6,900 volts (V). The maximum operating head is 850 ft. There are two main power transformers rated at 3 phase, 60 cycles, forced-oil and forced-air-cooled, 20,000 kVA, 6,600–115,000 grounded wye-volts.

The switching equipment for the power plant is located at three different elevations. The switchyard equipment itself, consisting of the power circuit breakers, disconnecting switches, and main buses, is on the roof of the power plant at elevation 92.50. The main power transformers that step up the generator low voltage are in the transformer bay adjacent to and southwest of the power plant structure at elevation 41.25. The high-voltage bushings of these main power transformers are connected to the main switching equipment on the roof of the power plant.

The 115-kV bus structure on the power plant roof consists of two bays to supply the 115-kV lines to the cities of Palmer and Anchorage. In addition, there is a 12.47-kV line that supplies power to the government camp from a small transformer energized from the low-voltage generator leads. This transformer is in the transformer bay adjacent to and south of the power plant structure.

Tailrace

Water discharged from the draft tubes of the turbines in the power plant enters a 209-ft-long pressure tailrace conduit through which the water is conducted under the Glenn Highway to an open tailrace channel that discharges into the Knik River.

The tailrace conduit is made up of rectangular reinforced-concrete transition sections of varying widths and depths. The terminal section of the conduit is 50 ft long and flares outward in the downstream direction from a width of about 14 ft to a width of nearly 47 ft. This terminal section varies in depth and has five openings separated by 10-in. walls through which the water passes into the tailrace channel. Stop-log slots at the outlet of the conduit are available for use when it is necessary to dewater either the conduit or both draft tubes at the same time.

The banks of the open tailrace channel are built on a 2:1 slope and are lined with riprap at the junction with the tailrace conduit. The channel is about 75 ft wide at the top and 25 ft wide at the bottom. It is about 12 ft 6 in. deep and 2,000 ft long.

ASSESSMENT OF EARTHQUAKE DAMAGE

POWER PLANT

A quick survey of the power plant and switchyard by project personnel immediately after the earthquake indicated no apparent damage to either of the two generating units, but revealed major damage to two 115-kV air circuit breakers and bushing-type transformers serving the Anchorage and Palmer lines. The circuit breakers are located on the powerhouse roof at elevation 91.50. The free-standing hollow porcelain insulator columns, which are part of the circuit breakers, broke at the base, causing complete collapse of the contact mechanisms on the two breakers. Also, the two 20,000-kVA power transformers, located in the transformer bay southwest of the powerhouse, had shifted on their rails and had sunk several inches, as had the camp-line transformer. After the initial survey, the generator, which had been stopped for examination, was started and station service was restored at 5:55 p.m. A temporary bypass was installed around the damaged equipment, and the Anchorage line was energized through a bus tie switch at 10:00 p.m. Service was restored to Palmer at about 10 a.m. the next day.

Water pressures at the turbines of the power plant fluctuated during the night of March 27 and during the next day, indicating that some disruption of the facilities had occurred; a considerable amount of debris was noted in the tailrace at this time. At 2:40 p.m. on March 28, a shear pin failed on unit 1 wicket-gate drive, forcing a shutdown of the power plant. This shutdown was the first of a series of stoppages required to make repairs and to remove rock and debris from the intake structure, pressure tunnel, penstock, wicket gates, and spiral cases. After emergency repairs to the wicket-gate drive, operation continued on an intermittent reduced-output basis until May 9, 1964, when emergency repairs of the power conduit were undertaken. There were many shear-pin failures during this time, but a half-screen of 2-in. mesh chain-link fencing, installed between the butterfly valve and the spiral case of each unit, effectively intercepted many of the rocks before they got to the wicket gates and turbine runners. It also was soon learned that the large rocks did not move through the tunnel if the total load was kept below 18,000 kW (equivalent to a water velocity of about 5 fps). Consequently, this load limit was maintained so far as possible.

CONDUIT AND INTAKE STRUCTURE

After it was determined that debris had penetrated the tunnel and penstocks serving the power plant, an underwater survey was made on April 19, 1964, at the intake structure and conduit at Eklutna Lake. When this survey revealed that one joint in the precast-concrete intake conduit was badly damaged, a decision was made to repair this joint and immediately to make a further inspection of the intake structure, conduit, and tunnel.

On May 9, 1964, the pressure tunnel was unwatered by the contractor and an extensive inspection was made of the entire waterway, including an underwater inspection of the intake structure and of the precast conduit upstream from the tunnel headgate. This inspection revealed that some of

the conduit joints had been separated by as much as 10 in. and some of the conduit sections had been laterally displaced. It was subsequently determined that the movement resulted from a consolidation of materials in Eklutna Lake induced by the earthquake. The intake structure had moved approximately 44 in. toward the lake; the tensional forces in the precast conduit produced by this horizontal shift had caused separation of 10 of the 15 bell-and-spigot joints in the conduit (Figure 7). The opening of these joints allowed a quantity of rock, gravel, and debris, estimated at 1,200 yd^3, to enter this pipe and to be deposited throughout 3¼ mi of the pressure tunnel. The debris was cleaned from the tunnel and temporary repairs were made to the conduit sections.

TAILRACE

During the period when the power plant was shut down for repair of the intake, the 209-ft-long pressure tailrace conduit was inspected and cleaned. Cross-section measurements revealed a total of 110 yd^3 of rock and mud in the conduit, most of which is presumed to have been deposited following the break in the precast pipe section of the tunnel intake. The inspection also revealed considerable shifting of the sections nearest the power plant. General area subsidence raised the high-tide water level at the tailrace outlet approximately 3 ft.

Severe cracks developed in the ground surface (Figures 8 and 9) in the area adjacent and parallel to the 2,000-ft-long open-canal section of the tailrace. The cracks varied in width from a few inches to 5 ft and had the effect of squeezing in the sides of the channel. The invert was irregularly mantled by gravelly debris, ranging in depth from a few inches to several feet.

OTHER POWER FACILITIES

In addition to the damage at Eklutna power plant, the preliminary survey made after the earthquake revealed considerable damage to equipment at Anchorage substation, Palmer substation, and the Eklutna–Palmer transmission line; minor damage to Reed substation was also observed. One pole structure and two conductor spans in the Eklutna–Palmer transmission line were destroyed by a snowslide, three 115-kV lightning arresters at Anchorage substation were damaged, and one 115-kV bushing at Palmer substation was damaged. All equipment was immediately repaired.

EKLUTNA DAM

Eklutna Dam sustained considerable damage, one important aspect of which was that it did not appear until several weeks after the earthquake. The frozen ground near the surface apparently moved as a mass during the earthquake.

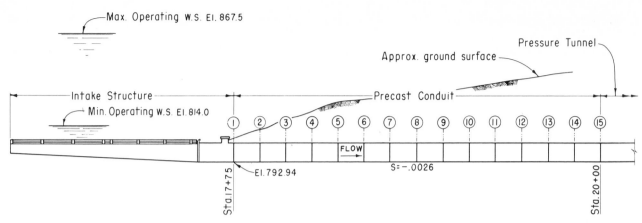

INTAKE STRUCTURE AND PRECAST CONDUIT
ELEVATION

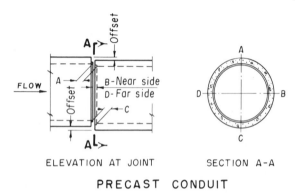

ELEVATION AT JOINT   SECTION A-A

PRECAST CONDUIT

PRECAST CONDUIT										
JOINT SEPARATIONS				OFFSET	JOINT SEPARATIONS					OFFSET
JOINT	A	B	C	D		JOINT	A	B	C	D	
1	1 7/8"	1 1/8"	3/8"	1 1/8"	0	9	1 3/4"	2"		1 3/4"	0
2	1"	1/2"	5/8"	7/8"	0	10	3 1/2"	3 1/4"	2"	2 1/2"	0
3	1 1/4"	1"	1 3/8"	1 1/2"	0	11	3"	3 1/2"		3 3/4"	0
4	1 1/4"	1 1/2"	1 1/4"	1 1/2"	0	12	1 1/2"	1 3/4"	2"	1 1/2"	0
5	2 1/2"	1 7/8"	7/8"	1 5/8"	0	13	2 3/4"	2 1/2"	1 1/2"	1 1/2"	0
6	10"	10"		10"	4"	14	3/4"	1 1/4"		1 1/4"	1
7	6 1/2"	6 3/4"		8"	4 1/2"	15	2 3/4"	2 1/8"		1 1/2"	0
8	3 3/4"	3"		3 3/4"	0						

FIGURE 7   Eklutna Power Plant intake structure and conduit. Joint separations after earthquake; temporary closures made on the ten ≥2 in.

Much later, when the ground thawed, it was found that the earthquake had consolidated the alluvial materials and had left a void under the spillway structure. This void caused settlement and cracking of the spillway and leakage through the dam that necessitated construction of a new dam and spillway.

AUTOMOTIVE REPAIR SHOP AND OTHER STRUCTURES.

The ground beneath the north end of the automotive repair shop, a wood-frame structure, settled up to 1 ft and moved approximately 10 in. horizontally along a tensional crack; this movement destroyed the floor and radiant-heating system in the floor slab, and lighting fixtures were torn loose from the wall. This structure had to be rebuilt at another location.

Several other structures that suffered minor damage included the machine shop adjacent to the powerhouse (the different periods of oscillation of these two structures caused the shearing of interconnecting drainage and electrical systems), the warehouse, the project office, and some camp housing facilities.

POWER PLANT YARD AND ROADWAYS

Cracks up to a foot wide and several feet deep (Figure 8) developed from a point west of the garage, extended eastward adjacent to the north wall of the warehouse, and thence across the roadway to the project office building. Cracks also extended from the garage to the southwest corner of the warehouse, and a similar but much larger crack occurred in State Highway 1 opposite the entrance to the project area. Back-filling the pavement cracks was a continuing operation for several weeks because adjustment along the cracks, believed to have been caused by the mechanics of thawing, continued to take place.

UNDAMAGED FEATURES

The powerhouse, supported on piles driven to bedrock (graywacke), was not visibly damaged by the earthquake. Other features that were apparently undamaged included the gate shaft, the pressure tunnel, the penstock, the surge tank, and the anchor block (Figure 5).

The concrete gate shaft, at station 27+25, was founded on competent rock and was reinforced to withstand in-

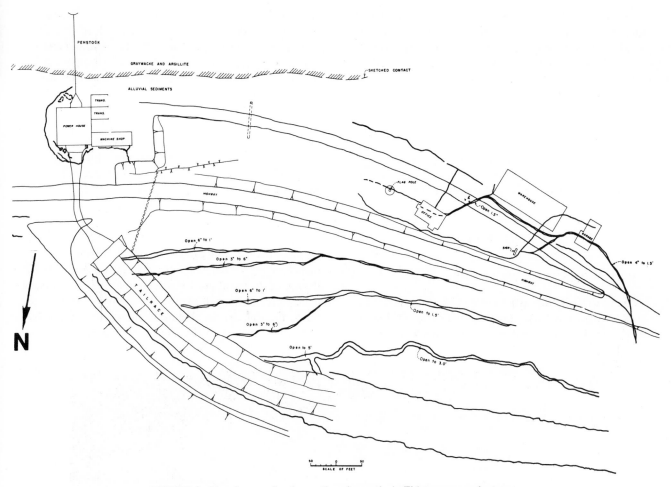

FIGURE 8   Sketch map of major earthquake cracks in Eklutna power plant area.

ternal bursting pressures. Possible vertical deflections of the shaft caused by earthquake motion were provided for by a number of horizontal joints. No damage to this structure was discernible.

Although much of the rock through which the 9-ft-diameter pressure tunnel was drilled is badly broken and shows numerous minor fault planes, no structural damage to the tunnel was found. Considerable quantities of water were encountered entering the tunnel through gate leakage, tunnel flap valves, and joint leakage, but this was not caused by the earthquake.

The entire length of the penstock tunnel was excavated in weathered rock except for a portion at the lower end where the tunnel section emerged to overburden material. This reach of tunnel was designed as a length of conduit supported at one end by the tunnel rock and at the other end by a pile-supported anchor block or bent. The penstock is of variable diameter, 75–91 in., and is constructed of steel pipe encased in concrete.

FIGURE 9   General view of Eklutna Power Plant after the earthquake. Cracks up to 5 ft wide along the banks of the 2,000-ft tailrace channel are visible below the power plant. The cracks had the effect of squeezing in the sides of the channel. The channel was cleaned by blasting and dragline operations.

The reinforced-concrete surge tank was constructed in badly fractured though reasonably stable rock. It was supported for its full height by 8-in. wide-flange H-beam structural-steel supports on 4-ft centers. The surge tank is at the downstream end of the pressure tunnel.

All evidence indicated that the penstock, surge tank, pile-supported anchor block, and powerhouse oscillated as an integral part of the area. Very little relative movement occurred between these features, although prominent surface settlement occurred in the anchor-block area. A maximum residual separation of 1/16–1/8 in. was measured in the penstock ports of the powerhouse wall.

GEOLOGICAL CONSIDERATIONS

GEOLOGY OF THE EKLUTNA AREA

The Knik River (Figure 10), Eklutna Lake, and Eklutna Creek lie in glaciated valleys covered with glacial till ranging in grain size from rock flour to large boulders. Where glacial and more recent streams have reworked this material, it has been sorted and somewhat bedded. In local areas, layers of nearly pure silt and clay are found interbedded with layers of coarser materials. In the present stream channels and flood plain of the Knik River, well-rounded gravel and clean sand are found to a depth of at least 15 ft. Several intermittent advances of alpine glaciers have left glacial terrace remnants at high elevations along the Eklutna Creek Valley. The steep-sided valleys and flat flood-plain area above the confluence of the Knik and Matanuska rivers are further evidence of a long period of glacial erosion.

GEOLOGY OF NEW EKLUTNA PROJECT FEATURES

Geologic data relating to the various Eklutna project features have been given in a previous bureau publication (U.S. Bureau of Reclamation, 1958). Logan (1967) also discusses in detail the geology of the various features in relation to the earthquake damage. Figure 11 shows the topography and surface geology of the project features. Some general

FIGURE 10   The Knik Glacier, one of the many active glaciers in the Chugach Mountains.

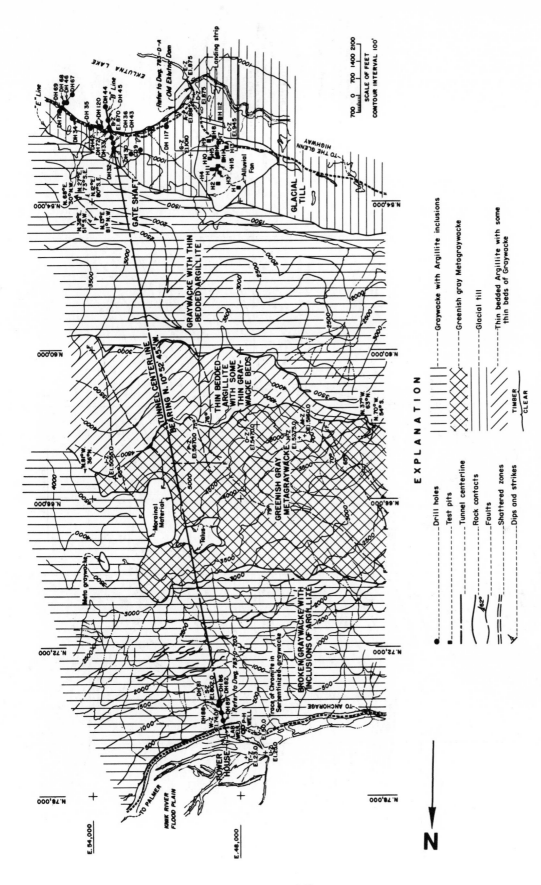

FIGURE 11 Topography and surface geology of Eklutna project.

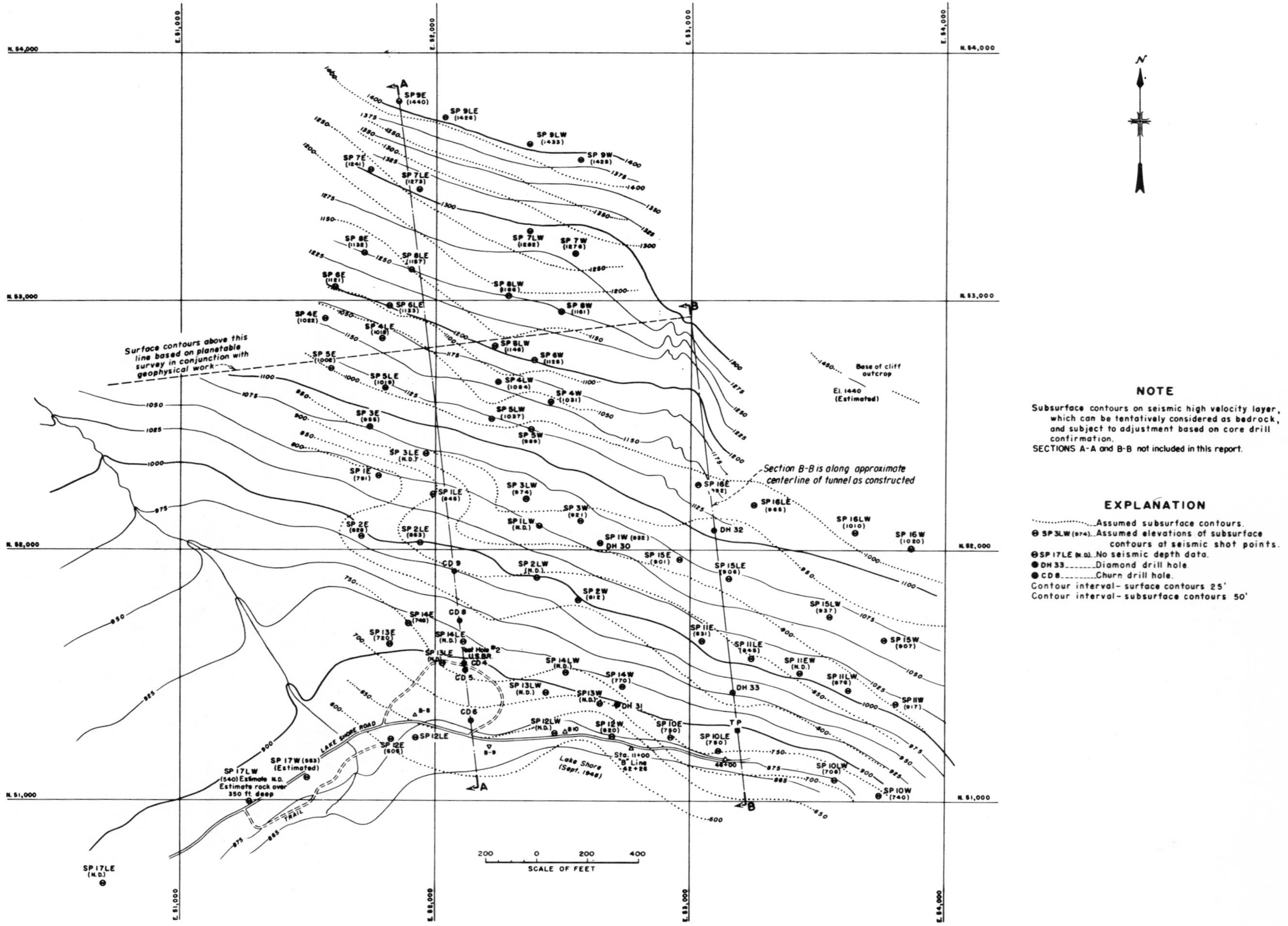

FIGURE 12 Bedrock contours from seismic data for intake area obtained in 1951.

470

information and geologic data relating to the rehabilitation of the intake structure and replacement of the dam follow.

INTAKE STRUCTURE

Surface topography and bedrock contours obtained in 1951 from seismic data in the vicinity of the intake structure are shown in Figure 12. Although foundation conditions in the area of the intake structure and conduit were well-documented during the original investigations in 1951, three additional holes (DHI-10, -11, and -12; see Figure 13) were drilled along the conduit line in September and October 1964 in an effort to detect possible fracturing or shattering of the compact glacial till resulting from the earthquake. This exploration revealed no significant changes in the till foundation, nor was any evidence of foundation failure observed during excavation for the new structure. Absence of structural damage to the existing intake structure and conduit segments indicates that the glacial-till foundation itself did not fail during the earthquake, but that consolidation of the bedding material under these structures resulted in a horizontal movement toward the lake, accompanied by a lesser amount of vertical displacement.

The new intake structure rests in firm glacial till. This material is a heterogeneous mixture of clay, silt, sand, gravel, cobbles, and boulders. It is extremely compact, and ripping was necessary before it could be removed by a dozer blade or dragline bucket. The location of exploration holes and surface geology in the area of the intake structure, obtained in 1951 and amplified in 1964, are shown in Figure 13.

DAM

The foundation exploration for a structure to replace Eklutna Dam began in August 1964 at a site near the downstream toe of the existing dam. An exploration program contemplating nine drill holes was formulated to determine the stratigraphic sequence of materials, competency of these materials, depth of stripping, and depth of the cutoff trench. Two of these holes (DH-1 and DH-2) were completed in the right abutment area and penetrated 30–50 ft of soft wet silts and clays overlying firm, well-compacted glacial till. Because the soft silts and clays were considered incompetent to support the proposed structures, the site was abandoned in favor of a location approximately 1,400 ft downstream. The selected site had previously been considered for a high dam and was investigated in 1951 by a series of drill holes and test pits (Figure 14). Two additional holes (DHS-13 and DHS-14) were completed along the proposed spillway alignment in October 1964. The locations of both the 1951 and the 1964 exploration holes, as well as the surface geology, borrow area, and rock source, are indicated in Figure 15.

The foundation at the selected site consists of firm glacial till with occasional thin discontinuous lenses of sand and clay. The till is overlain on both abutments by a bed of gravelly clay from 4 to 15 ft thick. This material has little stability when wet, and numerous small slumps were evident in the area of the left abutment before construction of the dam. These slumps resulted from seasonal saturation of the gravelly clay by water from muskeg swamps on the gently sloping bench above the damsite. Much of this clay was removed by excavation of the cutoff trench, and drains were provided to intercept water from the muskeg swamp. The clay was completely removed along the spillway alignment so that this structure would rest on firm glacial till.

EARTH DAM, SPILLWAY, AND INTAKE STRUCTURE

CONDITION OF EXISTING DAM

Immediately after the earthquake of March 27, 1964, the existing low dam at the outlet of Eklutna Lake was inspected. This and subsequent early inspections revealed no visible damage. The frozen ground near the surface apparently moved as a mass during the earthquake and the earth was not cracked in the area of the dam and spillway. Later inspections, however, revealed some consolidation of the alluvium beneath the frozen layer that had resulted in the development of a void. By July 1964, it became evident that the upper layers of alluvium under the spillway gate structure had begun to subside into the void. Two cracks about 1 in. wide had developed, one in the base of the spillway slab and one in the sill of the gate structure, and a large part of the base slab had obviously lost its foundation support as a result of the void. Figure 16 is a view of the spillway gate structure.

A representative was sent from the Denver office of the Bureau of Reclamation to inspect this damage and to determine what temporary repairs should be made and how the spillway could be operated, if at all, until permanent repairs could be made. He determined that the spillway could not safely resist water pressure against the gates and that it would be unsafe to hold the reservoir water level above the bottom of the gates. He concluded that the gates should be kept open until the structure could be replaced or repaired. Subsequent studies indicated that it would be less expensive to build a new dam and spillway near the downstream toe of the existing structure, than to repair the existing dam and spillway.

REPLACEMENT DAM

Explorations for a replacement dam near the location of the existing dam revealed highly plastic clay in the founda-

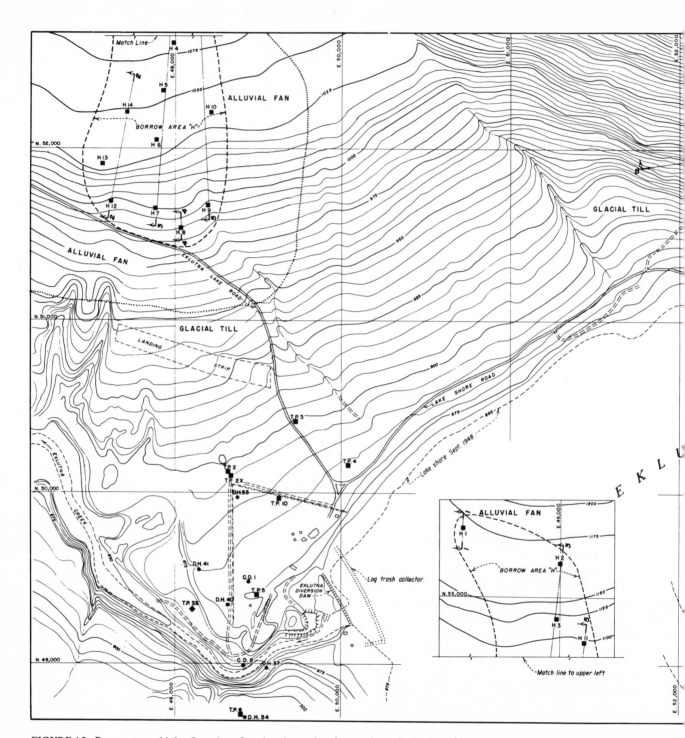

FIGURE 13   Pressure-tunnel inlet. Location of exploration and surface geology obtained in 1951 and amplified in 1964.

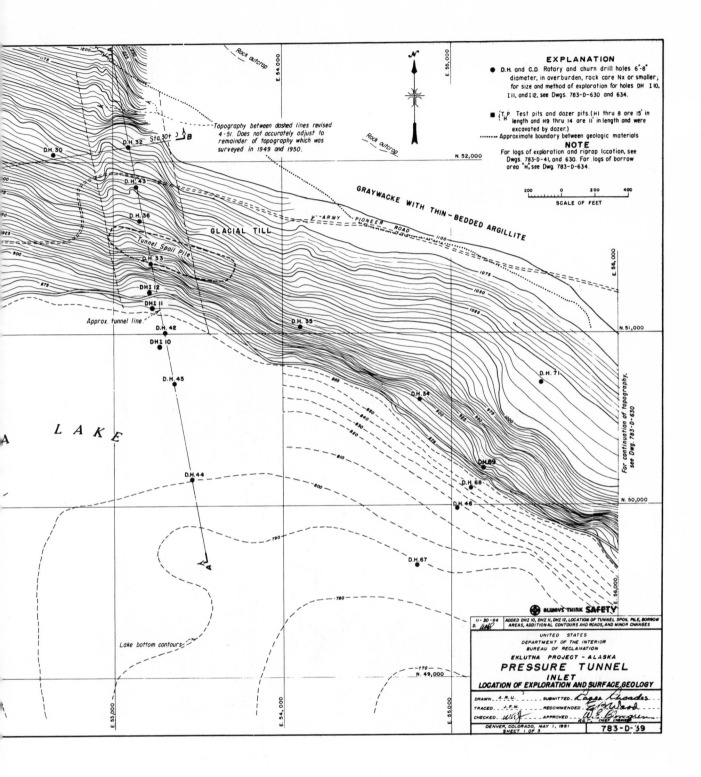

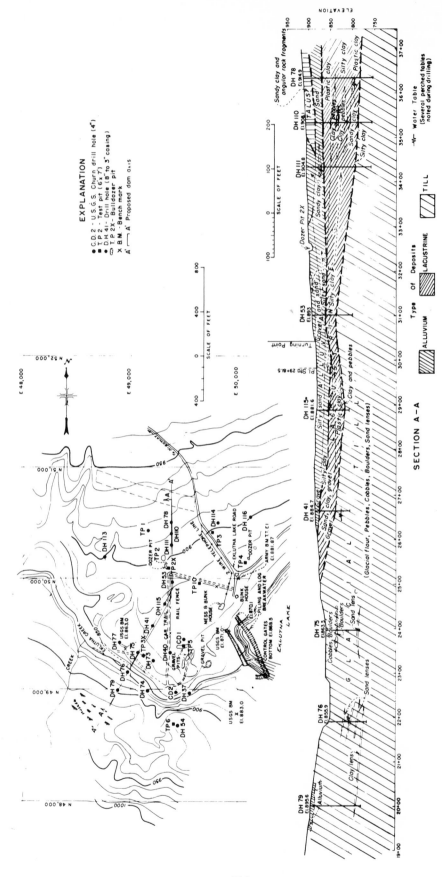

FIGURE 14 Location of exploration and a geologic section made in 1951 in the damsite area.

474

tion that would not support the spillway structure. A suitable foundation for the spillway was found about 1,400 ft downstream at a location that also simplified the diversion of Eklutna Creek; construction there would not interfere with the operation of Eklutna Lake.

On August 25, 1964, design and planning engineers from the Denver office of the Bureau of Reclamation and representatives from the bureau's Alaska District headquarters met to discuss the practicability of increasing the capacity of the lake or of altering the turbines or generators to provide additional peaking capacity. It was determined that it would be impractical to design the new Eklutna Dam to increase the capacity of the lake materially either initially or in the future. Also, changes at the generating plant would require a shutdown of the project, which could not be tolerated for several years, or until sufficient additional generating capacity was available in the area. Accordingly, the replacement dam was built with the spillway crest only 3.5 ft higher than the existing spillway (elevation 871.0), which raised the active storage capacity from 160,000 to 175,000 acre-feet. The crest of the new dam itself was, however, raised 16 ft, which greatly increased the surcharge storage capacity in the event of flood.

Principal Features

The principal features involved in the construction of the replacement structure for Eklutna Dam were an earth and rock-fill dam embankment and a reinforced-concrete spillway structure. The arrangement of the features is shown in Figure 17, and the location of the replacement dam with relation to Eklutna Lake (see Figure 18), Eklutna Tunnel, the existing dam, and the dam-embankment borrow areas is shown in Figure 15.

EMBANKMENT

The dam embankment is about 815 ft long at the crest, with a crest width of 30 ft and a crest elevation of 891.0, which is about 51 ft above the streambed. The dam has a 3:1 upstream slope and a 2:1 downstream slope. A rock-fill berm at elevation 856.5 extends 83 ft downstream from the dam to provide increased stability. The berm is about 15 ft thick and is a continuation of a rock-fill slope protection on the left abutment, which, it was considered, might be subject to movement. A cutoff trench, excavated to firm clayey soil, is provided just upstream of the centerline of the dam.

The zone 1 portion of the dam embankment consists of a central impervious core of selected clay, silt, sand, and gravel compacted by tamping rollers to 6-in. layers. Flanking the zone 1 portion both upstream and downstream is a zone 2 portion consisting of selected sand, gravel, and cobbles compacted in 12-in. layers by the treads of a crawler tractor. The outer or zone 3 portions of the dam embankment are composed of rock-fill material to 36-in. maximum size placed in 3-ft layers. There is no special slope protection other than that afforded by the zone 3 rock fill on the faces of the dam and the left abutment.

The area was explored for construction materials in 1951 in connection with designs for a dam with about three times the volume of the replacement dam. These investigations outlined an alluvial fan containing a silty clayey bouldery soil that could be processed to produce impervious material, talus deposits containing potential rock fill, and sand and gravel deposits of submarginal quality described as shingle gravel. In 1964, investigators of the site outlined gravel bars along Eklutna Creek that contained limited quantities of sand and gravel with more acceptable characteristics than the shingle gravel.

The stripping and processing required to produce zone 1 earth fill was estimated to make its cost nearly equal to that for gaining access to and hauling out zone 3 rock fill, or for stripping gravel bars along the river for zone 2. Consequently, it appeared that none of the three zones had any great economic advantage over any of the others as far as materials were concerned.

The embankment was so low that no inherent stability problem was anticipated, although a weak foundation underlies the site. In view of the Arctic conditions prevailing at this location, however, a rocky porous outer shell was desirable to ensure permanence of the neatlines and grades of the outer slope under Arctic freezing and thawing cycles without frequent maintenance.

On the basis of the preceding considerations, the embankment was zoned to have a minimum impervious earth-fill core (zone 1) and outer shells of talus rock (zone 3), with core and shell zones separated by a transition zone of minimum width (zone 2). Zone 2 was composed of sand and gravel of a gradation that will prevent the movement of fines from the earth fill into the rock fill.

Special Design Loadings

It was decided to increase horizontal embankment loads 20 percent on any part of the spillway for earthquake loading under normal conditions. The condition was to be met with a one-third increase in allowable stresses.

It was decided also to add a footing to the inlet channel at the crest structure to equalize base pressures at the junction of the crest structure and the conduit section, when there was no water against the crest.

SPILLWAY

The spillway consists of an approach channel, an inlet structure, a rectangular conduit, and a chute and stilling basin. The ungated crest of the spillway is constructed in the inlet structure.

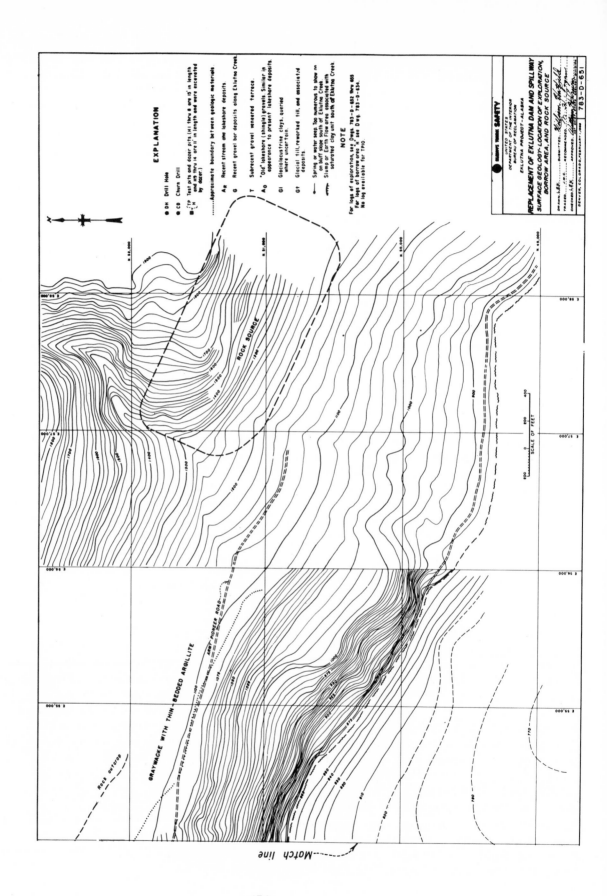

476

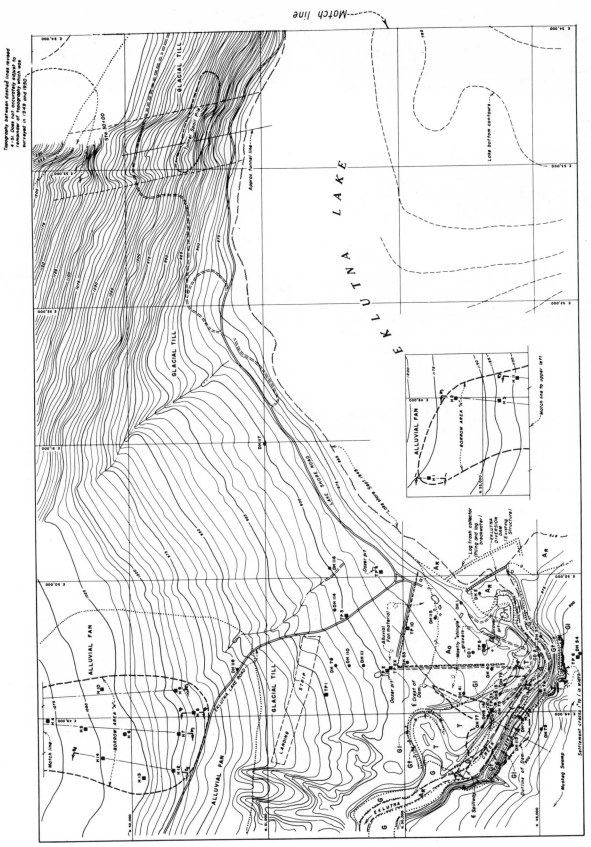

FIGURE 15 Topography, surface geology, location of exploration (both 1951 and 1964), borrow area, and rock source for the replacement dam.

477

FIGURE 16   View of spillway-gate structure of existing dam.

Because of the urgency of restoring the Eklutna Power Plant to full operation, no definite plan report was prepared and the design went directly into the specifications stage. The urgency of the work and the remoteness of the location also dictated that the specifications drawings be used as the final construction drawings. The final designs and specifications drawings were prepared in 1964 and 1965.

Eklutna Dam lies close to the permafrost line that crosses Alaska. Although permafrost probably does not occur at Eklutna Lake because of the warmth of the lake body, bureau personnel reviewed literature on construction in cold climates before deciding on the type of structure for the new spillway (U.S. Bureau of Reclamation, 1967). The reinforced-concrete spillway consists of an inlet structure 105.54 ft long, a rectangular conduit section 83.80 ft long, a chute 77.66 ft long, and a stilling basin 89.00 ft long. A general plan and sections of the spillway are shown on Figure 19. The entire structure is straight in alignment, has a constant width of 18 ft, and a total length of 356 ft. The entrance structure contains a second-stage concrete overflow crest and an adit for access to the hoist that controls a 30 × 30-in. drainage-outlet gate in the bottom of the crest section. The floor of the stilling basin, which is about 43 ft below the spillway crest, discharges the flow into Eklutna Creek.

The spillway crest is at the top of the conservation pool, elevation 871.0. For the reservoir water surface at maximum elevation 884.8, the spillway has a discharge capacity of 3,315 ft³/sec; Figure 19 shows the theoretical discharge curve for the spillway.

Special Protective Measures for Spillway Conduit Section

A butyl-rubber wrapping 3/32-in. thick was placed around the conduit section to prevent loss of foundation or embankment material through any cracks that might occur in the conduit.

Perforated sewer-pipe drains discharging in the downstream face of the chute blocks were installed to relieve uplift pressure under the floor slab during discharge.

INTAKE STRUCTURE

The original precast-concrete horizontal intake structure, 112 ft long and 26 ft 8 in. wide, with trashracked openings only on top, and the precast-concrete conduit had been placed under water on a prepared sand and gravel bedding in 1953. Investigation after the earthquake revealed that the earthquake had caused the shoreline materials, the intake structure, and the precast conduit to gravitate toward the center of the lake, thus opening the joints between many of the conduit sections and permitting large quantities of sand and gravel to enter the conduit. Accordingly, in the design of the replacement intake structure, the new structure was keyed well into the more compact glacial till below the structure to prevent any similar future movement. It was also located closer to the shoreline to reduce the number of conduit sections and to permit adequate working space inside a cofferdam for unwatering the site. Figure 18 shows Eklutna Lake in the vicinity of the intake structure.

The new intake structure is much more compact than the original one. It consists of a rectangular reinforced-concrete box structure, open and protected by trashracks on its top, front, and two sides. The trashracked portion is about 23 ft wide, 20 ft high, and 22 ft long in the direction of conduit flow. Overall length of the structure is 42 ft 4 in. A bulkhead opening is provided for emergency closure of the conduit.

EMERGENCY WORK AFTER THE EARTHQUAKE

REPAIRS TO ELECTRICAL EQUIPMENT AND FACILITIES

Immediately after the earthquake, Eklutna project forces made an inspection of the power plant and related facilities to assess the damage sustained. Most obvious was major damage to the two 115-kV air circuit breakers and bushing-type transformers serving the Anchorage and Palmer lines.

After a brief shutdown for inspection, station service was resumed at 5:55 p.m. The damaged circuit breakers were bypassed and other repairs were made that permitted resumption of service to Anchorage and Palmer by 10 a.m. the next day. Because of the urgency of the situation, it was impossible at that time to conduct extensive tests on each

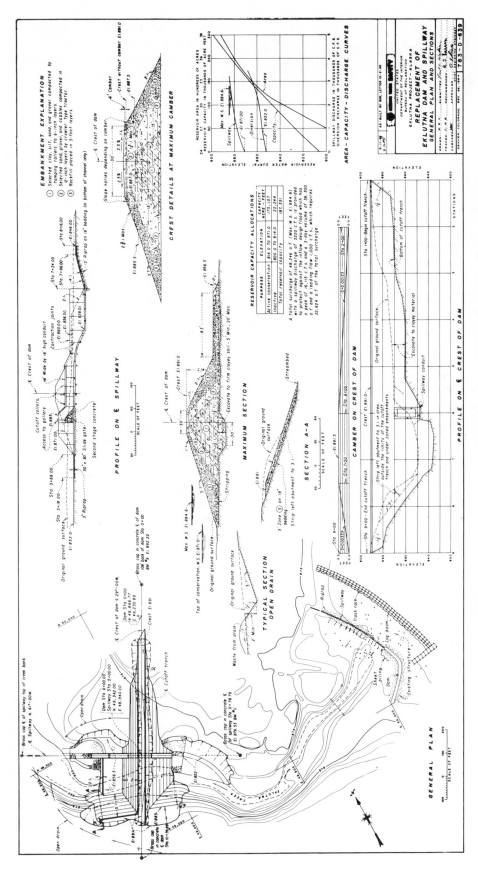

FIGURE 17 General plan and sections for replacement of Eklutna Dam and spillway.

479

FIGURE 18 View of shoreline of Eklutna Lake in the vicinity of the intake structure after the earthquake. Intake structure is located at left center of photograph on shoreline.

piece of equipment. Project personnel proceeded with caution and gradually raised the generated voltage from zero to its normal value. After the initial emergency work had been performed, the following work was accomplished on the electrical equipment and installations.

Eklutna Power Plant

Apparently, because the Eklutna Power Plant was founded on piles that were driven to bedrock, the earthquake caused only minor damage. The switchyard equipment on the powerhouse roof was the most severely damaged and considerable cracking occurred in the tailrace channel (Figures 8 and 9).

Two 121X auxiliary relays on the main control panel in the control room burned out, supposedly because of the mechanical failure of the 115-kV air circuit breakers on the powerhouse roof. Auxiliary contacts on the circuit breakers could not open to interrupt the operating current in these relays, and they became overheated. Both relays were replaced by similar units purchased and sent by air freight from Westinghouse Electric Corporation.

The main 20,000-kVA unit transformers, which had settled and moved from 3 to 5 in. on the track when tack-welded rail stops broke loose, and the government-camp transformer, which had settled badly, were raised and leveled. Broken conduit connections to the main transformers were repaired (Figure 20), and the conduit-entrance fitting for the low-voltage leads of the government-camp transformer was temporarily repaired pending receipt of a replacement unit.

The tap changers of all three transformers were operated and found to function freely. This trial operation indicated fairly conclusively, without an internal inspection, that the

core and coils had not shifted in the case. The oil levels and temperature in the bushings and tanks were normal.

Satisfactory results were obtained from Doble tests given to the three transformers and to the cables from the unit circuit breakers to the main transformers. Tests of the oil in all three transformers indicated a dielectric strength of more than 30 kV.

With the undamaged parts from the two 115-kV circuit breakers and with spare parts available, one complete circuit breaker was assembled and placed in operation. Another circuit breaker, which had been dismantled and flown to Alaska from the Gering substation in Nebraska, was also assembled and put in operation. Both these circuit breakers were given Doble tests. Consistent results were obtained for the various interrupters and for the three poles of the circuit breaker shipped from Gering. Test results from the other circuit breaker were not as consistent, but no information was available on the permissible variation for this equipment.

None of the switchyard structures appeared to have been racked or twisted, and all disconnecting switches were undamaged and operated easily. The 115-kV lightning arresters and capacitor potential devices appeared to be undamaged. This equipment did not receive a Doble test; it was considered more important to test the more vulnerable and more expensive equipment during the short time that the Doble-test set was available.

Only one electrical conduit was known to have been broken by the shifting of the machine shop in relation to the main power plant and that conduit was not in use. Other conduits and the circuit breaker air lines were protected at the building junction by embedded sleeves that permitted some movement or bending of the conduit.

The battery rack at Eklutna is equipped with sideboards, and therefore was not damaged. Individual cells had shifted slightly, but they were easily repositioned. With the exception of damage to two auxiliary relays, no damage to the power plant instrumentation or relays was found.

Anchorage Substation

The power transformers, which had shifted as much as 7 or 8 in. on their pads, were repositioned. Terminal boxes were damaged slightly by movement in relation to the embedded conduit, but this situation was remedied when the transformers were repositioned. The conduit connection to one transformer was broken at the ground level and was replaced. Three broken 115-kV lightning arresters were removed and new arresters were ordered. Operation without arresters is not considered particularly serious in this area because lightning incidence is very low. Tests of the oil in these transformers indicated a dielectric strength of more than 30 kV.

When the transformer shifted, a large force was exerted

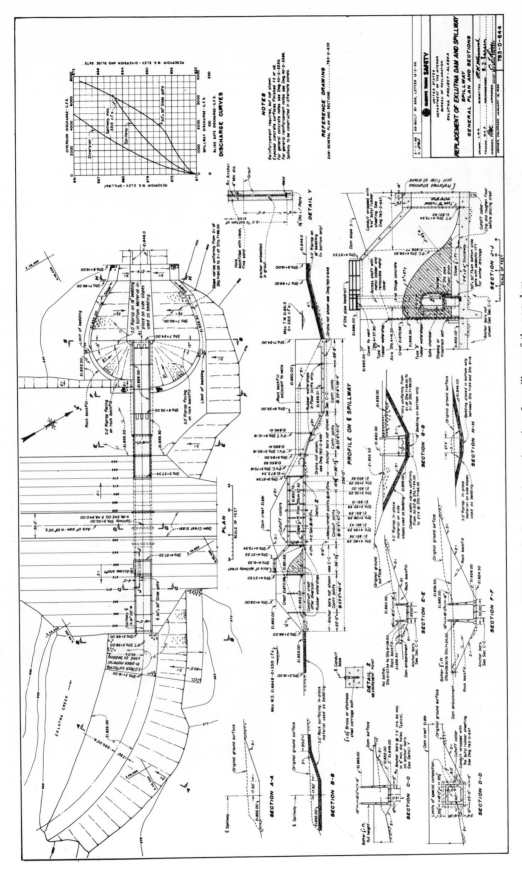

FIGURE 19 General plan and sections for spillway of the new dam.

481

FIGURE 20   View of 20,000-kVA transformer conduit and terminal box, showing damage caused by movement of the transformer during the earthquake. Rail stops, consisting of 1/4 × 1-in.-wide steel bars, were tack-welded to the rails. The welds broke and allowed the transformer to move on the rails.

by the low-voltage connections on the 34.5-kV bushings. One bushing on one transformer was left leaning at a small angle from its usual position. It was at first assumed that this bushing was damaged, but project personnel decided that the tank cover was bent by the force of the earthquake and that the bushing was probably not damaged. A further check was planned when the transformer could be taken out of service to install new arresters. It was thought that Doble testing of these transformers might not be possible, because the test set might not be available when a transformer outage could be scheduled. The oil levels in the transformer bushings and tanks were normal, as were the transformer temperatures and pressures.

No relays, instruments, or control wiring were damaged. The station battery rack had been installed with sideboards; consequently, there was some shifting of the cells but no damage. The entire rack, however, did move slightly on the control-house floor.

All circuit breakers operated properly; they were Doble-tested with satisfactory results. Also, all the disconnecting switches operated satisfactorily. None of the structures, the control house, or the cable trench were damaged; test equipment and miscellaneous tools and parts even remained on the shelves in the house. The 115-kV arresters on the transformer were of a sturdier design and therefore were not damaged.

Palmer Substation

The transformer at the Palmer substation shifted slightly on its pad. Also, one 115-kV bushing was found to be leaking

oil badly; it was replaced by the spare bushing, and the damaged bushing was returned to the manufacturer for repair. This transformer was given a Doble test during the week of May 18, 1964.

Circuit breaker operation was checked and found to be satisfactory; the circuit breaker was given a Doble test. The transformer structures did not appear to be racked or twisted, and all disconnecting switches were intact and operated easily.

Transmission Lines

There was no damage to the 115-kV Anchorage line, but the earthquake caused a snow and ice slide on the Palmer line near the Knik River bridge that swept away a three-pole guyed structure (No. 3/7) and an access road. This structure was located on the western edge of a large slide area, on top of a knoll. Previous slides had moved directly down the slope to a point just above the knoll and then veered off to the east. This slide was of such great volume and velocity, however, that a portion of the material rolled directly over the knoll and destroyed the structure. The loss of this structure was accompanied by the loss of about 7,500 ft of 397,500-circular-mil conductor, comprising the three phases of the two adjacent spans. Replacement of structure No. 3/7 was complicated by inclement weather and the mass of snow and ice that had to be traversed. An Army helicopter from Fort Richardson transported the poles to the site (Figure 21). The first of three poles was actually set by the helicopter crew, but efforts to set the remaining poles in this manner had to be abandoned be-

FIGURE 21   View of helicopter assisting in reconstruction of 115-kV transmission line. An Army helicopter crew cooperated with Bureau of Reclamation and Matanuska Electric Association line crews in rebuilding a section of the 115-kV line that was swept away by a snowslide released during the earthquake. April 3, 1964.

cause of the steepness of the mountainside. The helicopter, however, was used to deliver the remaining poles to the site.

The repair of the transmission line was completed on April 8, and service was restored on April 16, when repair work on the air circuit breaker at the Eklutna switchyard was completed. While the Palmer line was out of service, power was delivered to the Palmer substation from Reed substation (Anchorage line tap) over the Matanuska Electric Association (MEA) 34.5-kV line and the 12.47-kV Palmer area distribution system. To carry the Palmer load through the limited capacity of the Reed substation, it was necessary for the MEA to provide auxiliary cooling by means of truck-mounted fans.

Reed Substation

The transformer at this station is the property of the customer and was not damaged. The U.S. Bureau of Reclamation structures, switches, circuit breakers, instrument transformers, and instruments also showed no evidence of damage.

Mechanical Equipment Problems

A number of secondary mechanical problems developed as a result of the earthquake. These problems included the clogging of spiral-case and butterfly-valve drainlines by rocks, frequent clogging of cooling-water filters and coils with sand, and excessive wear of jet-pump diffusers by the extremely abrasive glacial rock flour. The problem of rock moving into the spiral cases was eased by limiting the plant output, but the sand continued to be a problem until the plant was shut down and the intake repaired.

Turbine-Generator Unit Checks

The generating units did not sustain any apparent damage as the result of the earthquake. As a precaution, however, alignment checks and bearing-clearance measurements were made by a maintenance specialist. Bearing clearances were satisfactory. Unit 1 was found to be leaning downstream 0.00067 in. compared with 0.00026 in. on unit 2. As a further precautionary measure, a half-screen of 2-in. mesh chain-link fencing was installed between the butterfly valve and spiral case of each unit to intercept rocks before they got to the wicket gates and runners. These screens proved to be only partly effective; some rocks did pass over them. From early experience, however, it was learned that the large rocks did not move through the tunnel if the total generating load was kept below 18,000 kW (corresponding to a water velocity of approximately 5 fps). Therefore, until intake repairs could be made and the rocks removed from the tunnel, this load limit was maintained insofar as other plants were able to make up the balance of the system load.

From the time rocks were first found to be entering the spiral cases, unit 1 was assigned the bulk of the power plant load to draw any rocks in the system in that direction, because this unit was scheduled for a major overhaul. (Unit 2 had been overhauled the year before.) Rocks lodging in the guide vanes and runners resulted in the loss of many wicket-gate shear pins, and necessitated a rush order for 24 pins from Newport News Ship and Drydock Co. and a special order for 6 specially fabricated pins.

INSPECTIONS OF POWER WATERWAY

Initial Inspection by Divers

When faulty operation of the generators after the earthquake revealed that foreign materials had found their way into the pressure tunnel and penstocks, a contract was negotiated with Associated Divers of Anchorage to make an underwater survey of the intake structure and as much as possible of the precast-concrete intake conduit to ascertain the extent of the damage.

The divers did not enter the conduit, and the inspection, made on April 19, 1964, revealed no damage to the trash-rack; one diver did, however, discover a gaping conelike hole in the lake bottom over the precast-concrete pipe section near the conduit inlet at approximately station 19+00 (Figures 4 and 5). A 10-in. opening in an exposed precast-pipe joint was discovered at the bottom of the cone, which was approximately 40 ft across the top and 15–20 ft deep.

After the underwater survey, a decision was made to repair the damaged section of the intake conduit and to make a detailed inspection of the intake structure, conduit, 4½-mi pressure tunnel, and penstocks as soon as a complete shutdown could be tolerated. The headgate would be closed to permit the unwatering of the tunnel and penstocks to facilitate inspection.

Detailed Inspections

By May 1, the Chugach Electric Association, City of Anchorage, and Elmendorf Air Force Base had their generating plants sufficiently restored for them to be reasonably sure of being able to handle the total area load for an extended period. A complete shutdown of Eklutna power plant for a thorough inspection of the waterway was now possible. On May 5, a representative from the Denver office of the Bureau of Reclamation negotiated with a contractor in Anchorage in the amount of $133,859.17 for a detailed inspection and repair, on a time-and-material basis, of known damage to the precast-conduit section of the tunnel intake. At the time of the negotiation, only one joint was known to be open.

On May 9, 1964, the Eklutna power plant was shut down and preparations for unwatering the tunnel began. Divers were sent into the headgate shaft before the gate was lowered to determine the condition of the gate slot (Figure 22).

FIGURE 22 Bureau of Reclamation and contractor's personnel lowering diving gear into headgate shaft in preparation for investigation of conditions in and around the headgate seat before unwatering tunnel.

The divers found deposits of sand and rock 1–2 ft deep both upstream and downstream of the gate, as well as at the gate pocket. Divers working in 40 ft of water required approximately 12 hours to clear the gate slot so that the gate could be seated.

Inspection of Pressure Tunnel

As soon as the headgate could be closed, unwatering procedures were completed and an inspection team walked the entire 4½-mi length of the pressure tunnel to ascertain the quantity of rock in the tunnel and to appraise any other damage. Rock was found deposited approximately 12–18 in. deep and was fairly uniformly distributed from the headgate (station 27+25) to station 103+00 (Figure 23). From station 103+00 to station 235+00 the rock was deposited in a series of bars of varying depth. The last mile was relatively free of debris. Cross-section measurements indicated that there was a total of 1,500–2,000 yd³ of material ranging from sand to an occasional football-sized rock, with most of the material under 1 in. in diameter. No structural damage to the tunnel was found.

Inspection of Penstocks

On May 18, a representative from the Denver office of the Bureau of Reclamation and the Bureau's Alaska District Manager made an inspection of the penstock from the base of the surge tank (elevation 716.67) to the power plant at elevation 24.0. This 863-ft length of penstock slopes at an angle of 53° to the horizontal, making inspection difficult. A unique method of descending this 6-ft-diameter pipe was devised. The penstock was filled with the tunnel-leakage water; the leakage was then diverted through the adit-tunnel door and a two-man life raft was floated down the penstock

(Figure 24). The rate of descent of the raft was controlled by releasing water from the penstock by the butterfly valves, wicket gates, and drain lines. Instructions to obtain the desired water discharge were relayed from the raft to the plant by a combination of telephone and radio. The entire penstock, from the tunnel to the generating units, appeared to have no permanent deformation that had been caused by the earthquake. Fine-line cracks in the overlapped painted surfaces at the coupled sleeve joints did, however, indicate that unusual pipe vibration had occurred.

Inspection of Intake Structure, Conduit, and Upstream End of Pressure Tunnel

When negotiations with the contractor were made, it was intended that work would be limited to the repair of the

FIGURE 23 Accumulation of debris in pressure tunnel as a result of earthquake damage to precast-concrete intake conduit. Rock in foreground is typical of that deposited throughout 3½ mi of the tunnel. View is looking upstream toward the loading end of the slusher unit. The drag bucket is being drawn toward the slusher from the gin pole in the center of the picture.

FIGURE 24 A two-man rubber raft being used for internal inspection of the 863-ft-long penstock that slopes at an angle of 53° to the horizontal. Descent of the raft was controlled by releasing water from the penstock drainlines. May 18, 1964.

one known opened joint of the precast-concrete intake conduit and to inspection and cleaning of the 1,000 ft of tunnel from the trashrack to the upstream face of the headgate (Figures 4 and 5). Bureau force-account labor would clean the $4\frac{1}{3}$ mi downstream from the headgate.

While force-account labor was working in the unwatered tunnel, the contractor began emergency underwater repair to the known break in the intake pipe and also undertook a detailed inspection of the inside of the precast-pipe section between the end of the drilled tunnel and the underwater intake. Entrance to the lake-bed portion of the tunnel was through an underwater manhole in the transition section at station 17+75. Six divers and their tenders were employed on three shifts, with two divers working on each shift. However, during the final inspection, when they were required to move through the entire 1,000 ft to the headgate, four divers were used to assist in handling the extended air lines.

Inspection by the divers revealed that 10 of the 15 bell-and-spigot joints had opened, some as much as 10 in. An order for changes covering repair of the additional joint separations was therefore negotiated with the contractor. A sketch of the affected sections of conduit and a chart showing their joint separations is shown in Figure 7. The final inspection also revealed that approximately 25 yd³ of rock, which could not be removed by divers, was distributed throughout the 500-ft portion of the tunnel, just upstream of the headgate.

EMERGENCY REPAIRS TO PRECAST INTAKE CONDUIT

Representatives from the Denver office of the Bureau of Reclamation were sent to Eklutna to help to work out the most expeditious temporary method of sealing the joints of the precast-concrete pipe.

Initial Operations

When the representatives from Denver arrived, a steel caisson had been lowered into the backfill material at joint 6, though not with complete success; it refused to go down the last 2 ft. Because of difficulties encountered in lowering the caisson, the decision had been made to attempt to uncover joint 7 without using a caisson. This work was then in progress. The crew consisted of two divers with about 10 supporting crafts for each of the three shifts. The divers were installing short curved steel plates on the inside across the opening at joint 6, securing them by 16-in. bolts and strongbacks outside the joint. These plates were installed around three fourths of the circumference, leaving a space at the top to allow muck to be removed from inside the pipe. The divers reported triangular openings at the ends of each plate. It was feared also that future shifting of the pipe sections could result in loosening the bolts and plates. The method was therefore later abandoned and the plates were removed in favor of the method of closure described later. An 8-in. airlift pump was used to remove sand and rocks from above joint 7 and also from within the pipe.

Subsequent Procedure

Bureau of Reclamation personnel, contractor personnel, and one of the more experienced divers discussed the best means of sealing the separated pipe joints. They finally decided to install expandable steel rings inside the pipe. Rings 12 in. wide would be used at the eight joints that had separations of 2–4 in. without offsets. Double 12-in. rings with flanges would be used at joints 6 and 7, which were separated 10 and 8 in., respectively, and were offset about 4 in. Each ring would be rolled to fit the 9-ft inside diameter of the pipe, and would be made in four segments of ¼-in. plates to keep the weight of each piece less than 100 lb, the maximum weight that it was considered the divers could handle. The rings were ordered from the Superior Machine Shop in Anchorage where a plate roll was available.

Removal of sand and gravel from within the pipe and from above joint 7 ran into difficulty. Fair progress was made until May 24, when a high wind and waves caused a sand slide that covered joint 7, partly filled the caisson at joint 6, and filled the inside of the pipe at both these joints. The same storm undermined piling supporting the contractor's crane, which was almost lost in the lake. When the crane was withdrawn to higher ground, its boom was too short, and the contractor was forced to obtain a larger crane to complete the work.

At this point, a decision was made to build a second caisson to be used at joint 7. This also was ordered from Superior Machine Shop and given priority over the expanding rings. The contractor continued to remove sand and gravel from inside the pipe and from above joint 7.

On the morning of May 26, a diver succeeded in cleaning sand from the top of joint 7 and in placing a 7-ft circular arc of steel plate over the joint. Additional arcuate pieces 4 ft long were later pushed down at each end of the 7-ft plate. Sand continued to slide into joint 7, however, and had to be pumped out of the pipe. The following evening a diver discovered that one of the 4-ft curved plates had been pushed down into the sand about a foot away from the joint. It was pulled out and replaced at the joint; the inflow of sand immediately lessened. On May 28, a top section of expandable ring was suspended inside joint 7, but a new sand slide made it necessary to remove the section on the swing shift.

On the morning of May 29, 17 sandbags were placed around the steel plates at joint 7, and a number of large rocks that protruded through the joint were removed. Swing-shift divers began to install the steel rings in joint 7. The large caisson was delivered at 9 p.m. This time, however, the complete double ring was successfully installed and the caisson was not used. The closing of joint 7 was completed on May 30, making it possible to clean all sand out of the pipe in that area and to gain unimpaired access to all other joints in the precast-concrete section. Installation of the single 12-in. rings in joints 5, 8, 9, 10, 11, 12, 13, and 15 proceeded at a rate of nearly two rings per shift.

On May 31, the graveyard shift completed installation of all the rings except the double ring for joint 6, which was still in the shop. This ring was installed the following day without the top pieces, to permit removal of some additional gravel.

It was concluded that the expanding steel rings, installed at separate joints in the precast-concrete pipe at the inlet to Eklutna Tunnel (Figures 25 and 26), would effectively prevent entrance of backfill material into the power conduit so long as there was no further appreciable movement of the concrete sections. The repair was considered to be only temporary. It was very expensive, as is all construction work in this area, but it permitted power production until permanent corrective work could be undertaken.

CLEANUP OF PRESSURE TUNNEL

By Force Account

The approach to the tunnel-mucking operation by force-account crews was complicated by the fact that the access to the tunnel at each end was less than 3 ft wide (Figures 27 and 28). There also was a considerable flow of water from headgate leakage, tunnel flap valves, and joint leakage. Rock-removal operations were started from both ends on a two-shift basis, using wheelbarrows and sluicing methods

through the adit-tunnel entrance downstream, and wheelbarrows and a ¼-yd³ bucket operating through the 220-ft headgate shaft at the upstream end.

Figure 29 shows a movable plywood dam being used to move debris toward the adit by means of the head developed by the leakage water.

By the end of the first week of rock removal by force-account hand labor, the rate of progress and daily cost indicated that mechanical means would have to be employed if the job was to be completed within a reasonable time. (Downtime for the Eklutna power plant is estimated to cost $4,000 per day.)

By Contractor Forces

Because the contractor was well experienced in tunnel-mucking operations and had equipment available, a decision was made to change the contract to include removal of the rock from the first 3½ mi of tunnel in addition to the rock that was deposited upstream of the headgate. Mobilization for this phase of the work was slow and tedious, because all equipment had to be broken down or cut into pieces that could be passed through the narrow space at the bottom of the headgate shaft (Figures 30 and 31). Bureau of Reclamation force-account crews were withdrawn for work in the tailrace and other critical areas after they had reached station 32+00 from the headgate end and station 189+00 from the adit-door end of the tunnel (Figure 4).

The contractor's mechanical mucking operations were accomplished using a diesel-powered 1½-yd³ haul unit and a slusher and drag-bucket combination (Figures 23 and 32). The empty drag bucket was drawn into the gravel debris by a cable attached to a gin pole that was jacked against the sides of the tunnel. The loaded drag bucket was drawn into the loading chute of the slusher unit, which discharged the material into the haul unit. The haul unit then delivered its load upstream to the headgate shaft where the rock was lifted to the surface in a ¾-yd³ bucket by a 45-ton motor crane.

Rock-removal progress was limited in the early stages of the operation by the travel time of the ¾-yd³ mucking bucket up the 220-ft gate shaft. As the slusher worked its way further into the tunnel, the travel time of the haul unit became the controlling factor; round trips eventually took approximately 45 minutes. Peak yardage was reached on the seventh day of operation, with an average of 50 buckets or approximately 40 yd³ per shift. As the contractor approached station 100+00 and a lighter concentration of material, the heavy slusher became increasingly difficult to advance. Force-account crews were again put to work from the downstream end. After 48 shifts, the contractor met the Bureau of Reclamation forces at station 157+00 at 12:30 a.m. on June 21. Figure 33 shows the second of two

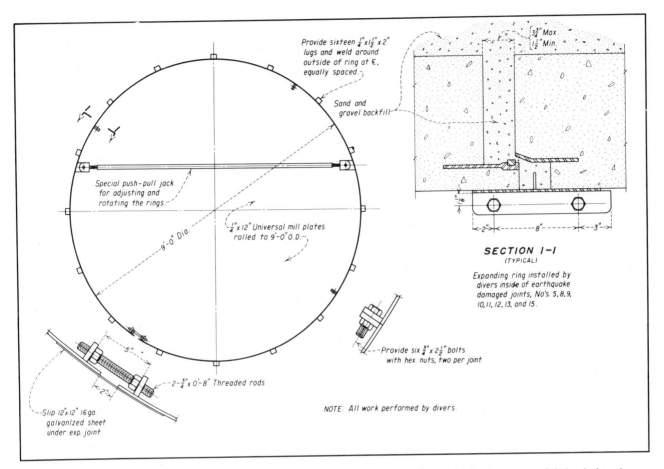

FIGURE 25   Steel expandable ring used for temporary repair of joints between sections of intake-structure conduit (typical case).

FIGURE 26   View of an expandable steel ring fabricated by the contractor for installation by divers to make emergency repairs to the precast-concrete-conduit-tunnel intake pipe. A single ring was used where there was no offset at the damaged joint. Where an offset existed, two rings were installed back to back.

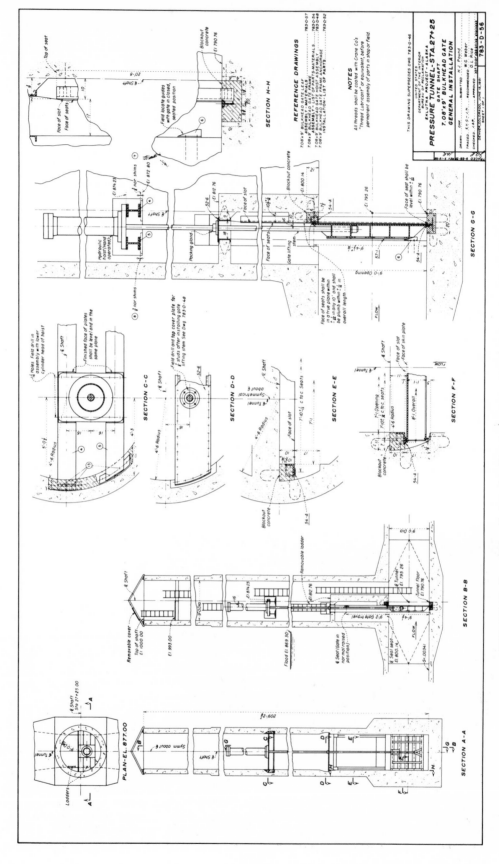

FIGURE 27 General installation of bulkhead gate in pressure tunnel, station 27+25 (gate shaft).

488

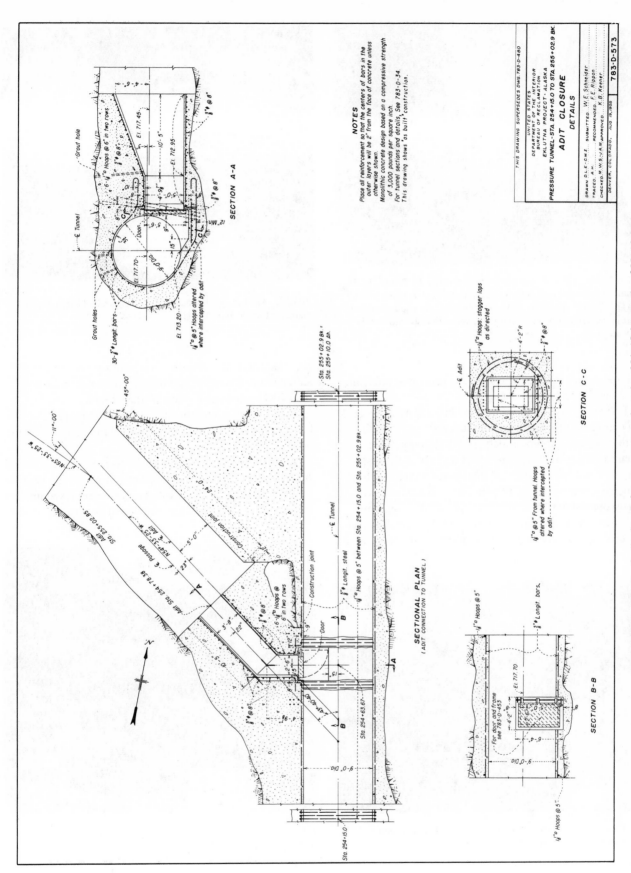

FIGURE 28 Details of adit closure for pressure tunnel, station 254+15.0 to station 255+02.9 Bk.

489

FIGURE 29   View of tunnel-mucking operation by Bureau of Reclamation force-account employees. Sand and rock is being moved toward the adit tunnel by means of a movable plywood dam utilizing the head developed by the leakage water to assist motivation. May 1964.

FIGURE 31   View of the haul unit being reassembled in the 9-ft-diameter tunnel. June 1964.

approximately equal piles of sand and rock removed from the headgate end of the tunnel.

Following final cleanup and demobilization of the mucking equipment, three heavy chain-link screens 4 ft high were installed at approximately 100-ft intervals downstream from the headgate. Each screen was made of 2-in. mesh wire with an additional strand interwoven to reduce the effective opening to 1 in. (Figure 34). The headgate was partly opened until the tunnel and penstock were filled, and then it was immediately closed and the tunnel was dewatered sufficiently to permit examination of the screens.

No rock had collected at the first screen at station 28+50, although the wire mesh had bulged somewhat, indicating there had been some impact. Workers found 1–2 yd^3 of rock deposited behind the second screen at station 29+50, but nothing was found lodged on the third screen at station 30+50.

After this small amount of rock was removed, the tunnel was again filled and the power plant was placed in operation for 48 hours. All possible customer load was picked up, in the hope that the remaining rock would be washed through

FIGURE 30   View of diesel-powered 1½-yd^3 haul unit being dismantled before lowering it into the tunnel through the headgate shaft. June 1964.

FIGURE 32   View of loading chute and drag bucket of the 15-hp electric slusher unit used by the contractor to remove accumulated gravel from the pressure tunnel. June 1964.

FIGURE 33   The second of two approximately equal piles of sand and rock removed through the headgate shaft during tunnel-mucking operations. The water spilling from the pipe at the left is the discharge from a high-lift pump installed behind the gate shaft and represents the leakage through the headgate seals.

the headgate and deposited against the screens. Following this 48-hour operation, the tunnel was again unwatered and approximately 23 yd³ of gravel were found deposited, with almost all the gravel being lodged behind the second and third screens. Less than 1 yd³ had been carried a short distance beyond the third screen. A second 48-hour generating period was conducted, and this time only 2 yd³ of gravel were collected. It was therefore assumed that the lake sec-

FIGURE 34   View of the second of three 4-ft-high screens installed at intervals of approximately 100 ft below the headgate. The screens were installed by the contractor after the sand and rock were removed from the 4⅓-mi tunnel. They were designed to stop the rock that remained in the tunnel between the headgate and the trashrack and that could not be readily removed by divers.

tion of the tunnel had been cleared of debris, and on July 2 the power plant was returned to normal operation.

MAJOR REHABILITATION AND REPLACEMENT WORK

REPLACEMENT OF INTAKE STRUCTURE AND REPAIRS TO CONDUIT

The replacement of the intake structure and permanent repair of the conduit leading to the pressure tunnel above Eklutna Power Plant were accomplished between February and May 1965. Components of the work required by the contract included caring for lake water and unwatering the site during construction, removing a portion of the existing precast-concrete pipe conduit at the intake of the pressure tunnel, earthwork and construction for a new intake structure and for installing stainless-steel joint-repair rings between sections of the remaining precast-concrete conduit, or construction of concrete encasements about these pipe joints. The contract also included furnishing and installing trashracks for the new intake structure, and placement of riprap in the excavation area to elevation 872.0.

INTAKE STRUCTURE AND CONDUIT FOR PRESSURE TUNNEL

The contractor began to move in equipment on February 26, 1965. On March 1, removal of ice 25 in. thick that had accumulated on the bank of Eklutna Lake above the inlet between elevations 847 and 812 was begun, using a ripper and three crawler-tractor bulldozers.

Excavation above the berm on the backslope above the intake was started, and the wet material was hauled to a waste area about 300 yd to the east of the centerline of the intake. Work on the cofferdam was started March 15 (Figure 35), and the area was ready to be drained on March 25. The tunnel was drained slowly during the day and the following night. On March 26, all water inside the cofferdam had drained out, exposing the intake structure and conduit (Figures 36 and 37). The cofferdam, which was 400 ft long, was built up to a crest width of 40 ft and a top elevation of 823.5. Pumping from a sump about 20 ft to the left of station 17+60 continued until construction was completed.

The inside joint rings, installed by divers immediately after the earthquake to exclude further sand and gravel intrusion were stripped off, and four damaged sections of the concrete conduit were removed. Four additional sections adjacent to the original intake structure, together with the intake structure, were abandoned but left in place (Figure 38). The six remaining pipe joints, which had been separated from ¾ in. to about 3½ in. by the earthquake, were

FIGURE 35   General view of construction of cofferdam and excavation for the new intake structure. March 23, 1965.

FIGURE 37   Two damaged joints on the existing 9-ft-diameter precast-concrete conduit. March 21, 1965.

sandblasted and dry-packed with concrete. Then the stainless-steel joint-repair rings, which the contractor elected to provide in lieu of concrete encasements about the joints, were installed. Three long screw jacks were used to facilitate installation of the rings. Some difficulties were encountered in fitting these rings because of irregularities in the shape of the existing pipe, but the work was completed by April 28, 1965. A view of one of the steel rings during installation is shown in Figure 39.

Concurrently with the work on the conduit, forms for the intake structure were prefabricated and were set in place on April 12. The reinforcing steel was also erected and con-

crete was placed in the base and the remainder of the intake structure (Figure 40). Figure 41 shows the completed intake structure, in front of the abandoned portion of conduit, and the original intake structure.

Final grading and placement of bedding and riprap below elevation 820 along the slope of the bank above the inlet (Figure 42) was accomplished concurrently with the concrete work for the intake structure.

Beginning on May 2, water was pumped from Eklutna Lake to the inlet-structure area enclosed by the cofferdam. By the following evening, the water had filled the area to elevation 803, and removal of the cofferdam was started the

FIGURE 36   Exposed top side (trashracked side) of original intake structure after removal of water. March 26, 1965.

FIGURE 38   General view of abandoned intake structure and conduit (in the background) and new intake structure nearing completion (in the foreground). April 28, 1965.

FIGURE 39 View of installation of steel rings inside the 9-ft-diameter precast-concrete conduit. April 16, 1965.

next day. By May 5, enough material had been removed from the cofferdam to permit the water depth to equalize on either side. Removal of the cofferdam was completed by May 7, and all work under this contract was accepted as complete on May 14, 1965.

The operation of the power plant was resumed with the production of power by one generator at 8 a.m. on May 18, 1965.

REPLACEMENT OF DAM AND SPILLWAY

Replacement of Eklutna Dam and the spillway structure was accomplished between April and November 1965. The

FIGURE 41 Completed new intake structure in front of remaining portion of conduit and old intake structure. May 3, 1965.

completed dam is shown in Figures 43 and 44. The contract completion date was October 8, 1966, but the contractor's proposed construction program estimated that all work would be completed by December 31, 1965.

The new dam is an earth and rock-fill structure with three zones composed of compacted material of varying porosity. A general plan and sections are shown in Figure 17.

The spillway for the new Eklutna Dam consists of an approach channel, an inlet structure with the crest of the spillway built into it, a rectangular reinforced-concrete conduit, and a chute and stilling basin.

Clearing Site and Removing Existing Structures

The prime contractor performed all clearing operations. Work started on April 6, 1965, and clearing in the dam-

FIGURE 40 New intake structure with concrete work completed and ready for installation of trashracks on the top, sides, and front. April 30, 1966.

FIGURE 42 Completed riprap in place on the back slope to the new intake structure. May 18, 1965.

FIGURE 43   View of completed Eklutna Dam, showing the upstream face and the spillway inlet.

construction area was essentially completed by May 1. Clearing in the source area for impervious zone 1 material, and removal of existing structures went on intermittently, the latter being nearly completed by September 1. Areas within the reservoir area below elevation 870, between the replacement damsite and the existing dam, were cleared of all growth that was more than 5 ft high and that had a butt diameter of more than 2 in. All timber structures, including timber gates with their stems and handwheels, were removed from the area of the existing dam. No problem was encountered with the level of the water in Eklutna Lake. As a result of the initial drawdown during the winter of 1964–

1965, the lake stood at elevation 812.0 on March 23, 1965, and rose to elevation 814.75 by May 18—a period during which no power was generated. When the generation of power was resumed, the lake level fell to 813.5 by June 19. A fairly steady rise then began, raising the level to elevation 826.0 on August 1 and to elevation 846.7 by September 30. A very gradual rise to elevation 847.2 continued until October 15. The level then dropped slowly and was at elevation 844.5 on November 15, 1965, the completion date. The gates on the old Eklutna Dam were kept open during the spring and summer and were removed in August 1965.

Excavation

Earthwork operations for the new Eklutna Dam were started in April 1965, when the contractor started stripping and excavating for the spillway and right abutment portion of the cutoff trench. The depth of cut varied from 5 to 35 ft in the spillway and from 0 to 15 ft in the cutoff trench; total spillway excavation was 35,959 yd^3, some of which was used later for zone 2 material. Concurrently with the spillway excavation, a major portion of the stripping and excavation on the left abutment was performed (Figure 45).

After the excavation for the spillway structure, earthwork operations were suspended to allow the concreting to proceed. Concrete placement had progressed sufficiently by the end of August to allow the contractor to complete the excavation of the left abutment and the remainder of the cutoff trench. The total volume of material excavated from the cutoff trench and left abutment was 27,255 yd^3, including stripping; the bulk of this material was wasted. Work progressed steadily on excavation and spillway construction, but embankment work was delayed until completion of the

FIGURE 44   View of the downstream face of the completed dam and spillway. October 21, 1965.

FIGURE 45   Excavating operations on the left abutment of the new dam. June 10, 1965.

concrete conduit section of the spillway on September 1, 1965. The entire spillway structure was completed by September 30.

Concrete Work

The only concrete construction related to the dam was in the spillway structure, because no river outlet other than the pressure-tunnel intake was provided. A total of 3,002 yd³ of concrete was placed: 792 yd³ in spillway floors at $80 per yd³; 1,105 yd³ in spillway walls at $140 per yd³; 873 yd³ in spillway conduit and cutoff collars at $180 per yd³; and 232 yd³ in second-stage concrete in spillway crest at $180 per yd³. The total cost was $416,923.40.

SUMMARY

Immediately after the earthquake, it was recognized that the Eklutna facility had sustained some damage. The generator was therefore stopped and an inspection was made; power generation was resumed within a half hour of the earthquake. During the next 2 months, however, operating difficulties were encountered and extensive damage to the power facilities and to the dam itself was revealed. An assessment of the damage led to the conclusion that it was more economical to build a new dam than to repair the old one. Accordingly, a new earth dam was constructed and the first power after rehabilitation of the waterway was put on the line May 18, 1965.

Table 1 summarizes the cost of the emergency work necessitated by the earthquake, the cost of rehabilitation of the intake structure and conduit for the pressure tunnel,

TABLE 1   Summary of Repair and Replacement Costs for the Eklutna Project

Item	Costs,[a] in dollars	
	Direct	
Construction by contract	2,259,311	
Materials furnished by government	87,678	
Purchased power	9,177	
Labor by government forces	111,245	
Subtotal		2,467,411
Service facilities		3,217
	Indirect	
Designs and specifications (Denver)	91,180	
Engineering and inspection	129,991	
Administration and general expense	185,502	
Subtotal		406,673
TOTAL[b]		2,877,301

[a] Shown in detail in Appendix B.
[b] Includes cost of emergency construction, rehabilitation of intake structure and conduit, and replacement of Eklutna Dam and spillway.

and the cost of replacement of Eklutna Dam and spillway. A more detailed cost summary, including contracts and purchase orders, is given in Appendix B.

Although damaged, the dam did not fail, but it was considered to be in an unsafe condition. Had the causative fault been closer to the dam, perhaps 20 mi distant instead of 110 mi, the intensity of ground shaking would have been two to three times as great; under these conditions the damage to the dam would have been correspondingly greater.

APPENDIX A   Summary of Important Statistics for the Eklutna Project

General Information

Purpose: To restore electric power to the Anchorage, Alaska, area for both civilian consumption and national defense installations after its disruption by the earthquake of March 27, 1964
Construction dates: 1964–1965

Reservoir (as modified)

Name: Eklutna Lake
Location: Approximately   5 mi southeast of Eklutna Power Plant and 30 mi northeast of Anchorage, Alaska
Reservoir statistics:
    Total live capacity: 213,271 acre-feet
    Active capacity: 174,798 acre-feet
    Present inactive capacity: 38,473 acre-feet
    Surface area (at total capacity): 3,420 acres
    High-water elevation (spillway crest): 871.0 ft
    Length: 7 mi
    Width: 0.7 mi
    Depth: 200 ft

APPENDIX A (Continued)

Dam (as replaced)

Type: Earth and rock fill
Foundation: Firm glacial till
Slopes: 3:1 upstream; 2:1 downstream
Slope protection: No special slope protection; rock-fill (zone 3) was placed in 3-ft layers on both upstream and downstream faces
Crest length: 815 ft
Crest width: 30 ft
Crest elevation: 891.0 ft
Volume: 85,000 yd^3

Spillway (as replaced)

Location: On right bank but almost midway between abutments of dam
Type: An ungated overflow crest with a rectangular reinforced-concrete conduit through the dam and a stilling basin energy dissipator
Crest elevation: 871.00 ft
Crest width: 18 ft
Capacity: 3,315 ft^3/sec with reservoir at maximum (surcharge) elevation 884.8

Intake Structure (as replaced)

Location: Eklutna Lake bottom
Type: Rectangular reinforced-concrete box structure, open and protected by trashracks on its top, front, and two sides
Dimensions: Trashracked portion about 23 ft wide, 20 ft high, and 22 ft long in direction of conduit flow; 42 ft 4 in. in overall length
Elevation of invert: 793.6 ft, which is 77.4 ft below the dam spillway crest
Inlet channel: 100 ft wide and about 720 ft long. (Original intake structure and portions of original intake conduit remain in inlet channel.)

Eklutna Tunnel[a]

Type: Circular, concrete-lined, pressure
Inside diameter: 9 ft
Length: 23,550 ft
Hydraulic properties:
  Area: 63.62 ft^2
  Velocity: 10.06 fps
  Capacity: 640 ft^3/sec
Slope: 0.00341 (80-ft difference in elevation between inlet and the outlet gate at surge tank)

Surge Tank[a]

Location: 22,805 ft downstream from bulkhead gate shaft and directly over tunnel
Height above tunnel: 176 ft
Inside diameter: 30 ft
Wall thickness: 18 in.
Type: Restricted orifice

Penstock[a]

Location: Downstream from the surge tank
Length: 1,388 ft
Variable diameters: 91-, 83-, and 75-in. outside diameters
Type: Welded and coupled steel pipe encased in concrete
Plate thickness: 5/16 in. for initial section and variable up to 1½ in. at terminal section
Profile: Descends 864 ft at an angle of 53° and then a horizontal run of 501 ft

Power Plant[a]

Location: Adjacent to Glenn Highway, 34 mi northeast of Anchorage, Alaska
Type: Reinforced concrete
Maximum head: 850 ft as originally constructed; 865 ft obtained with new dam
Number of units: 2
Installed capacity: 33,334 kVA
Turbines: Francis type, 25,000 hp at a rated speed of 600 rpm and an 800-ft effective head
Generators: Vertical-shaft type, 16,667 kVA at 90 percent power factor, 3 phase, 60 cycles, 6,900 V
Transformers: Two main power transformers, 3 phase, 60 cycle, forced-air cooled, 20,000 kVA, 6,600 to 115,000 grounded wye-volts

APPENDIX A   (Continued)

Switchyard[a]

Location: At three levels, on and adjacent to the power plant (roof elevation 92.50, intermediate roof elevation 58.54, and ground level elevation 41.25)

Number of units: Two 115-kV bays
                     One 12.47-kV bay

Tailrace[a]

Location: Extending north from power plant under the Glenn Highway

Type: Combination pressure and open channel. A reinforced-concrete pressure conduit 209 ft long and of various widths and depths discharges into an open channel with a bottom width of 25 ft, side slopes of 2:1, a depth of 12.5 ft, and a length of about 2,000 ft, which conveys the water into the Knik River.

[a]Note: These features have not been changed by the work discussed in this article, but are described here to complete the pertinent information on the power plant, tunnel, and related works.

APPENDIX B   Cost Summary for Emergency Work, Rehabilitation, and Reconstruction of Certain Eklutna Project Features Occasioned by Alaska Earthquake of 1964

A. EMERGENCY WORK AND REPLACEMENT OF AUTOMOTIVE REPAIR SHOP

Specifications or Invitation No.	Item; Contractor; and Contract No.	Total Cost to the Government, $	
Construction Contracts			
DC-6112	Repair of earthquake damage to Eklutna Tunnel (cleanup); Peter Kiewit Sons' Co.; Contract No. 14-06-D-5098	338,623	
DC-6270	Construction and completion of the automotive repair shop; Holiday Construction Co., Inc., Contract No. 14-06-D-5596	73,634	
	TOTAL, construction contracts		412,257
Supply Contracts and Purchase Orders			
(D) A-69, 455A	Turbine shaft sleeves and parts; Newport News Shipbuilding and Dry Dock Co.; Contract No. 14-06-D-5154	2,820	
64-1193	Equipment rental (pump, hose, compressor); Lottsfeldt and Kyzer; Contract No. 14-06-0906-22	1,121	
64-1194	Equipment rental (pump and hose); Shaw Tool Rentals; Contract No. 14-06-0906-23	113	
64-1195	Equipment rental (pump and hose); McDowell-Woodland Co., Inc.; Contract No. 14-06-0906-24	3,082	
64-1196	Electric pump rental; Equipment, Inc.; Contract No. 14-06-0906-25	265	
64-1197	Equipment rental (pump, gas engine); Bud's Service; Contract No. 14-06-0906-26	132	
64-1113	Inspection of intake structure; Associated Divers, Inc., by U.S. Army Corps of Engineers; Contract No. 64-76	8,737	

APPENDIX B   (Continued)

Specifications or Invitation No.	Item; Contractor; and Contract No.	Total Cost to the Government, $	
65-390	Diving service to recover diamond drill and associated equipment and inspection of Eklutna Tunnel intake; Associated Divers, Inc.; Contract No. 14-06-0906-27	3,448	
65-878	Replacement (Gering circuit breaker); Brown Boveri Corp.; Purchase order No. 703-65-483	14,688	
65-405	Equipment rental of compressor hose (gate shaft); Woodland Equipment Co., Inc.; Contract No. 14-06-0906-29	664	
65-1406	Equipment rental (compressor); Woodland Equipment Co., Inc.; Contract No. 14-06-0906-30	149	
DS-6309–66-657	Supplemental control and photogrammetric compilation of topographic map of Eklutna Lake; Air Photo Tech., Inc.; Contract No. 14-06-D-5667	6,430	
	Miscellaneous purchase orders	37,733	
	TOTAL, supply contracts and purchase orders		79,382
	TOTAL, contractual costs		491,639

Noncontractual Costs

Purchased power		9,177	
Labor by government forces		111,245	
Indirect costs			
Designs and specifications (Denver)		22,513	
Engineering and inspection		13,824	
Administrative and general expense		20,516	
TOTAL, noncontractual costs			177,275
TOTAL cost of emergency work and replacement of automotive repair shop			668,914

B. REPLACEMENT OF INTAKE STRUCTURE AND REPAIRS TO INTAKE CONDUIT

Construction Contract

DC-6212	Rehabilitation of intake structure and conduit for pressure tunnel; Manson-Osberg Co.; Contract No. 14-06-D-5444	652,416	
	TOTAL, construction contract		652,416

Supply Contracts and Purchase Orders

Miscellaneous purchase orders		2,289	
TOTAL, purchase orders			2,289
TOTAL, contractual costs			654,705

Noncontractual Costs

Indirect costs:			
Designs and specifications (Denver)		29,663	
Engineering and inspection		23,194	
Administrative and general expense		80,847	
TOTAL, noncontractual costs			133,704
TOTAL, cost of replacement of intake structure and repairs to intake conduit			788,409

APPENDIX B   (Continued)

Specifications or Invitation No.	Item; Contractor; and Contract No.	Total Cost to the Government, $	
C. REPLACEMENT OF EKLUTNA DAM AND SPILLWAY			
Construction Contract			
DC-6240	Eklutna Dam and spillway; A & B Construction Co.; Contract No. 14-06-D-5494	1,194,638	
	TOTAL, construction contract		1,194,638
Supply Contracts and Purchase Orders			
Miscellaneous purchase orders		6,007	
	TOTAL, purchase orders		6,007
	TOTAL, contractual costs		1,200,645
Noncontractual Costs			
Service facilities		3,217	
Indirect costs:			
Designs and specifications		39,004	
Engineering and inspection		92,973	
Administration and general expense		84,139	
	TOTAL, noncontractual costs		219,333
	TOTAL, cost of replacement of Eklutna Dam and spillway		1,419,978
Recapitulation:			
Cost of emergency work and replacement of automotive repair shop		668,914	
Cost of replacement of intake structure and repairs to intake conduit		788,409	
Cost of replacement of Eklutna Dam and spillway		1,419,978	
	TOTAL, cost of emergency work, rehabilitation, and reconstruction of Eklutna project features		2,877,301

APPENDIX C

FOREWORD TO U.S. BUREAU OF RECLAMATION TECHNICAL REPORT

"Rehabilitation of the Eklutna Project Features Following Earthquake of March 1964"

This supplement to the technical record of design and construction for Eklutna Dam, Tunnel, and Power Plant discusses the rehabilitation of the Eklutna project features following the severe Alaska earthquake of March 27, 1964. The presentation is divided into three parts. Part I is devoted to brief descriptions of the features as originally designed and as later rehabilitated, a brief account of the inspections and assessment of the earthquake damage, a summary of rehabilitation costs, and a description of the geology as it related to the earthquake. Part II contains two chapters on design, one dealing with the replacement of the intake structure and the repair of the conduit, and the other discussing the new dam and spillway. Part III contains three chapters related to construction, one on contract administration, one on emergency work to restore and maintain power generation immediately following the earthquake, and one on major repairs to intake conduit and replacement of the dam, spillway, and intake structure.

This presentation was prepared by the Technical and Foreign Services Branch of the Office of Chief Engineer in Denver, Colorado, from final design reports submitted by the field offices, numerous geological reports, and various other reports. Because of the large number of contributors, it has been found impractical to list or even determine the names of the contributors. However, the contribution of each person who in any way helped to prepare this publication is gratefully acknowledged.

B. P. BELLPORT, *Chief Engineer*
Bureau of Reclamation
Denver, Colorado

REFERENCES

Logan, Malcolm H., 1967. Effect of the earthquake of March 27, 1964, on the Eklutna hydroelectric project, Anchorage, Alaska *in* U.S. Geological Survey Professional Paper 545-A. Washington: Government Printing Office. p. 1–24.

U.S. Bureau of Reclamation, 1958. Technical record of design and construction for Eklutna Dam, tunnel and power plant. Denver: U.S. Bureau of Reclamation, March. 254 p.

U.S. Bureau of Reclamation, 1965. Final construction report on replacement of Eklutna Dam, Eklutna project, Alaska (unpublished report). Denver: U.S. Bureau of Reclamation, December.

U.S. Bureau of Reclamation, 1966. Eklutna and the Alaska earthquake. A report by the Alaska District Office. Juneau: U.S. Bureau of Reclamation, June. 165 p.

U.S. Bureau of Reclamation, 1967. Rehabilitation of Eklutna project features following earthquake of March 1964: A supplement to Eklutna Dam, tunnel and powerplant technical record of design and construction, March 1958. A Water Resources Technical Publication. Denver: U.S. Bureau of Reclamation, June. 111 p.

III
DAMAGE AND REPAIR

Introduction

The papers in this section describe the damage and repair of selected structures and facilities in the severely shaken region. Data are given on damage to a wide variety (Figure 1) of structures, on how they were repaired, and on the cost of making the repairs. An unusually comprehensive account is given of the effects of a major earthquake in terms of engineering, construction, and economics. Because the damage assessment and repairs described in these papers were handled by the Corps of Engineers, the authors had specially detailed knowledge of the structures and of the subjects that were studied. Such detailed information on United States earthquakes has never been published before.

The studies were prepared by staff members of the Engineering Division of the Alaska District Office, Corps of Engineers, under the guidance of the Chief, Engineering Division. The authors experienced the earthquake and, because the Corps of Engineers was made responsible for much of the reconstruction and rehabilitation, they were involved in the work of restoration that followed. In addition to the reports prepared by the staff members, two studies were made under contract to the Alaska District, and these, dealing with the performance of bridge foundations (Ross, Seed and Migliaccio, 1973), and nonstructural damage to buildings (Ayres, Sun, and Brown, 1973), appear elsewhere in this volume. Portions of a third study (Wilson and Tørum, 1968) performed under the direct management of the Coastal Engineering Research Center of the Office, Chief of Engineers, Corps of Engineers, with substantial support from the Alaska District, have been included in the Oceanography and Coastal Engineering volume.

The part of the state damaged by the earthquake was declared a disaster area by Governor William A. Egan and by President Lyndon B. Johnson. The President immediately established the Federal Reconstruction and Development Planning Commission for Alaska (Senator Clinton P. Anderson, Chairman) to plan and guide the reconstruction effort. The Commission was composed of the secretaries of most government departments and the heads of important commissions and agencies. Dwight A. Ink was named the Executive Director of the group, and he was assisted by Glenn V. Gibson of the Office of the Secretary of Defense.

The immediate tasks confronting the organizations designated to meet the problems were initially those of establishing order; providing food and shelter for the homeless and medical aid for the sick and the injured; caring for the dead; and establishing safe sanitation conditions, pure-water-supply points, and means of waste disposal. Large segments of the utility systems in the damaged towns had been either destroyed or rendered useless. Many industrial facilities and hundreds of homes had been destroyed, many more were severely damaged, and whole districts were without fuel, power, water, and sewerage facilities.

The Alaska District, Corps of Engineers, developed extensive data from those phases of the work for which it had prime responsibility. Consequently, many of the photographs used to illustrate this and other volumes come from this source.

The District also had considerable information to contribute toward the reports on highways, railroads, and airports, but were not actually responsible for their restoration. Much help was received by the District from the federal and state agencies who were directly responsible for the work, and this aid is gratefully acknowledged.

Thomas Gardner and Edmund J. McMahon, in their paper on the assistance provided by military bases, cover briefly the very large and vitally important contribution of the Alaskan Command, which controls the U.S. Army Alaska with headquarters at Fort Richardson, the Alaskan Air Command with headquarters at Elmendorf Air Force Base, and the Alaska Sea Frontier [Navy] Command with headquarters on Kodiak Island. Facilities of the first two commands border on the city of Anchorage, the largest city in Alaska and that which on a total-cost basis suffered the greatest damage. The Navy's command facility on Kodiak Island is adjacent to the city of Kodiak, which was also severely damaged. Although the damage appraisal and re-

FIGURE 1   This montage illustrates the variety of havoc wrought by this great earthquake. Views 1 and 2 show waterfront of Valdez before and after the event. Views 3 and 4 depict some of the destruction suffered by Anchorage. Views 5 and 6 show the tremendous destructive effect of the subaqueous slide and following tsunami waves at Seward; all harbor and waterfront structures were destroyed. View 7 shows the effect on one section of a large warehouse that held particular meaning on redesign procedures. View 8 gives an example of highway bridge response.

pair of some of the structures on these bases were undertaken by the Alaska District, much other work was done directly by the engineering staffs of these military commands. These commands also provided air and ground support to the affected areas both during the emergency period and during the subsequent restoration. Too much credit cannot be given to the commanding officers, staffs and personnel of these organizations for the strong support rendered.

A very damaging aspect of the earthquake is described in the paper on harbors and waterfront facilities by Norman L. Arno and Leonard F. McKinney. Alaska is a maritime state with a coastline almost two thirds as long as that of the rest of the United States. A sizable fraction of this coastline and its facilities were severely affected. South central Alaska, about 1,400 mi from Seattle by air, naturally depends on its harbors and docks as transportation bases for economic activities and communications. Water transportation between the many coastal communities in Alaska is far more important than in most other states because of the almost complete lack of developed access-road systems. In addition, Alaska lies in a region that encompasses one of the world's greatest fisheries, one that supplies large quantities of its products to the United States and that has attracted Russian, Japanese, and Korean fishing fleets. The harbor facilities of Alaska communities play an important role in the harvest of these resources, which are the mainstay of the economy. The fishing industry of Alaska represents a yearly return of over $200 million to the U.S. economy, and up to the time of the earthquake it was the commercial activity of greatest value to the state. After the immediate postearthquake needs of the affected communities (such as food, water, sanitation, and shelter) had been met, a maximum effort was made to reestablish the numerous harbor facilities. Funds were furnished for an extensive and immediate program of cleaning up the debris, establishing minimal emergency facilities, and proceeding with major restoration. The harbor facilities in all coastal communities within the affected zone were either badly damaged or totally destroyed.

Erwin L. Long, in his paper on landslides and related soil phenomena, addresses the subject of slides in general, including earth slides, snow and rock avalanches, and subaqueous slides. He describes in some detail the massive earth movements that occurred in the Anchorage area and discusses and analyzes the very destructive Fourth Avenue slide in the Anchorage business district; the highly destructive Turnagain slide in a prime residential area on the outskirts of Anchorage; and the L and K streets slide in another fine residential area of Anchorage. Numerous snow and rock avalanches were triggered by the earthquake, but fortunately generally not in locations where they could do any serious damage. Subaqueous slides and the tsunami-type waves generated by them were responsible for extensive damage to

several waterfront installations. The most disastrous of these slides were at Seward, Whittier, and Valdez. A great length of seacoast lay within the affected zone, and other such slides may have occurred on the faces of other deltas without known damaging effects. At Valdez, the slide and the tsunamis that followed caused the death of 30 persons.

The three papers by Warren George, Paul Knowles, John K. Allender, James F. Sizemore, and Duane E. Carson, describing the damage and repair of structures in the strongly shaken area, give a detailed description of the damage and repair of many typical Alaska structures. Up to the present, earthquake engineering has focused largely on designing to prevent collapse and loss of life; as such, a comparison of cost of damage to the cost of engineering to prevent damage has not been given the attention it deserves, mainly because of the difficulty in obtaining reliable figures on the cost of repairing damage. Accurate cost figures were available for the repair of many structures in Alaska, and they reveal valuable information on the true cost of earthquake damage. To design for earthquake forces is more difficult and time consuming than to design for gravity loads, and an adequate budget to cover comprehensive engineering analysis and design is an important factor in designing structures that will resist ground shaking without excessive damage. Increased attention to design can result in sizable returns in savings and safety. In general, those structures designed for military use survived the earthquake better than their civilian counterparts, because more attention was given to the problems of structural integrity both in their design and their construction; even these structures, however, could have profited from additional attention.

In the paper by Gary G. Sturman on the railroad, prepared with the cooperation of The Alaska Railroad, he describes the damage and repair of the rail lines and facilities. The land transportation facilities in Alaska are not highly developed. With the exception of a short section of the narrow-gage line from Whitehorse to Skagway, a Canadian-operated facility in the southeast panhandle section of the state, and a few relics of narrow-gage mining rail lines, The Alaska Railroad is the only railroad in the state. The main Seward–Anchorage–Fairbanks line, built and operated by the federal government, has a 12-mi branch to Whittier, and some other branch lines to coal mines and military facilities. The section of the line from Palmer south through Anchorage to Seward and the branch line to Whittier all lie within the zone affected by the earthquake. The damage sustained was extensive and provided valuable information on the effect of earthquakes on such facilities. Since World War II, the railroad had been brought up to recognized first-line standards, and therefore its reaction can be considered as a good example of earthquake resistance. Of necessity the roadbed through this area traverses the valleys and, therefore, to a considerable extent is built on an alluvial base. The bridges were generally founded on such material, as were many of the terminal facilities at the ports of Whittier and Seward. On the low-lying ground on both sides of Portage, at the head of the Turnagain Arm of Cook Inlet, a great deal of damage to roadbed embankment and bridge foundations occurred because of the low strength of the underlaying soils. Considerable damage also resulted from the general subsidence of the landmass in this area, which made it necessary to raise the roadbed to protect it from the high tides. The repair shops, warehouses, main depot, and general-administration buildings in Anchorage were all damaged; some received only minor damage, some were totally destroyed. The railroad-car unloading facilities at Whittier, a transfer point for cars transported by barge to and from the Seattle area, were rendered useless, but the Army dock was generally usable and was rapidly put into service. Two unlined railroad tunnels through the mountains, which together total 4 mi in length, were undamaged. Rockfalls and other disturbances found in these tunnels were inconsequential, although the in situ material was a highly fractured and fissured graywacke. The terminal facilities at Seward, the railroad yards, the warehouse, the docks, and port facilities, cranes, roundhouse, and the rolling stocks suffered almost indescribable damage from a subaqueous slide and a severe pounding by tsunamis in addition to the ground shaking.

Gary G. Sturman's other report on the Alaska highway system, prepared with the cooperation of the Alaska State Highway Department, summarizes the earthquake damage to the highway system. At the time of the earthquake, Alaska did not have an extensive network of surface communication. Most of the road systems could not be classified as more than good paved secondary roads. The bridges were of corresponding quality. About half the highway system was in the area affected by the earthquake. Those sections of the highway in the low-lying areas around Portage sustained severe damage to their roadbeds and bridges, mainly because of land subsidence, soil slumping, and fissuring. The high tides of Cook Inlet, acting against the weakened structures, caused additional destruction. The bridge foundations in this area were so severely affected that in many cases the superstructures collapsed, leaving sections of the road out of service for a long time. The new highway from Cordova, which was under construction on the old Copper River railroad embankments, sustained major damage, and the main bridge over the Copper River was partly destroyed. On the Cape Chiniak Road near Kodiak, 9 out of 14 timber bridges were destroyed by tsunamis.

In the paper on air traffic and control facilities, prepared by James M. Tanaka with the cooperation of the Federal Aviation Agency, the effect of the earthquake on the air-transportation system is described and certain deficiencies pointed out in the system's ability to resist earthquakes.

Because of the relatively undeveloped state of the highways and railroads, air travel in Alaska has developed as the principal means of transportation. For example, Alaska has far more private planes per capita than any other state. After the earthquake, when communication lines were broken and ground transportation had been rendered useless, the planes were able to operate and were of great value in ascertaining the extent of the damage, in assessing the needs for shelter, food, and medical aid, and in bringing in supplies. A number of the smaller airfields serving outlying communities were damaged to various extents from ground fissuring, but most could be used, and the necessary emergency repairs were quickly made by local operational crews stationed at the sites. The terminal building at the Anchorage International Airport was extensively damaged, and the control tower collapsed, killing one man. The ground control facilities for aircraft in the Anchorage area were temporarily out of service because of failure of communication systems (land lines, telephone, interphone, and teletype), but temporary service was reestablished within a few hours.

The paper by Claude B. Richardson on the damage and repair of utilities describes the effect of the earthquake on water-distribution systems, water-treatment plants, sewerage systems, electrical transmission and distribution facilities, and communication services. The massive earth slides were very damaging to buried systems and buried pipes were broken by fissures in frozen ground; in general, however, the buried systems were more earthquake resistant than might have been expected. The most severe damage to electrical distribution systems was sustained by the transmission line from the Cooper Lake hydroplant, where it crossed the tidal flats of Turnagain Arm on the way to Anchorage. Communication systems were disrupted by power failures, most of them temporary, and in certain instances serious interruption resulted from breakage in trunk-line cables. Because the public welfare is so immediately affected by damage to utilities, a special effort was made to repair the damage as quickly as possible. Especially thorough and interesting methods were used to ascertain the damage to buried pipe systems and ductwork so as to avoid possible hazards to health.

In his paper on the port of Whittier, David P. Belanger describes the effect on the developed port closest to the epicenter of the earthquake. Much engineering information was available on this facility because it had served as a military port during and after World War II. Most of the docks, buildings, and utilities systems had been built since then, and most were planned and designed by the Alaska District. There were large military tank farms, high-rise structures, and a wide variety of other buildings of masonry construction with different foundation conditions. All structures in this area had been designed for the zone 3 earthquake requirements of the Uniform Building Code. The Hodge Building, a 14-story reinforced-concrete structure resting on an alluvium base, withstood the earthquake with relatively minor damage. The massive six-story Buckner Building, resting part on rock and part on fill material and designed with a number of earthquake crumple joints, sustained only minor damage; however, nonstructural damage in this building was relatively severe. The dock structure, with steel piles and a concrete deck, capable of accommodating two large ships, resumed operations almost immediately. A combination of soil consolidation from the shaking and piping action of the sea waves caused some settlement of the adjacent warehouse structures, but they were still usable. The large steam and generating plant sustained only minor structural and nonstructural damage, and it was back on the line in a few hours, furnishing electric energy and steam to the community.

In his paper on the relocation of the town of Valdez, James M. Tanaka describes this unusual consequence of an earthquake. Valdez stood at the eastern end of Valdez Arm on deltaic fan deposits of streams fed by Valdez Glacier, about 50 mi from the epicenter. With a population of about 600, it is the nearest town to the east of the epicenter. Severe damage was caused by a combination of heavy shaking, repeated opening and closing of earth fissures that crisscrossed the frozen crust of the soil, and water-uplift pressures induced by seismic waves. A subaqueous slide and the resulting tsunami waves destroyed the waterfront, and, when the dock and warehouse-approach structures slid under the water, 30 persons lost their lives. After much investigation and study, the townsite was declared unsafe for a reconstruction effort, and a move was planned to a new location

4 mi west along the north shore of Port Valdez. This cooperative undertaking by federal and state agencies and community groups was accomplished successfully, despite many difficult problems, at a cost of approximately $37,000,000.

In retrospect, it seems that much of the earthquake damage could have been avoided, at little extra cost, by proper engineering. We found that tsunamis generated by an earthquake can cause more extensive damage to waterfront communities than can the ground shaking. We learned, too, that earthquake shaking can trigger destructive landslides and that prolonged shaking can result in displacements of large masses of soil.

WARREN GEORGE
U.S. Army Corps of Engineers District, Alaska

REFERENCES

Ayres, J. Marx, Tseng-Yao Sun, and Frederick R. Brown, 1973. Nonstructural damage to buildings in The Great Alaska Earthquake of 1964: Engineering. NAS Pub. 1606. Washington: National Academy of Sciences.
Ross, Grant A., H. Bolton Seed, and Ralph R. Migliaccio, 1973. Performance of highway bridge foundations in The Great Alaska Earthquake of 1964: Engineering. NAS Pub. 1606. Washington: National Academy of Sciences.
Wilson, Basil W., and Alf Tørum, 1968. The tsunami of the Alaskan earthquake, 1964: Engineering evaluation. Coastal Engineering Research Center Technical Memorandum No. 25. Washington: U.S. Army Corps of Engineers, May. 444 p.

THOMAS L. GARDNER
EDMUND J. McMAHON
U.S. ARMY CORPS OF ENGINEERS DISTRICT,
ALASKA

Assistance Provided by the Military Bases

The Alaskan Command (ALCOM) has three component commands: U.S. Army Alaska (USARAL), with headquarters at Fort Richardson; Alaskan Air Command, with headquarters on Elmendorf Air Force Base (AFB); and Alaska Sea Frontier with headquarters on Kodiak Island (Figure 1). Among the federal and state organizations providing liaison and support to the Alaskan Command are the following: the Federal Aviation Agency; U.S. Coast Guard Marine Inspection Office; Alaskan Communications Region; National Security Agency; American Red Cross; U.S. Army Engineer District, Alaska; Military Sea Transportation Service; and Alaskan Disaster Office.

MILITARY INSTALLATIONS IN SOUTH CENTRAL ALASKA

Elmendorf AFB (Figure 2), 3 mi northeast of Anchorage, on the east shore of Knik Arm of Cook Inlet, has a runway about 200 ft above sea level. All-weather paved highways run from Elmendorf to Anchorage, Fairbanks, Seward, Soldotna, and Wildwood Station, and The Alaska Railroad, which at the time of the earthquake was operated by the U.S. Department of the Interior, links the base with Seward, Whittier, Anchorage, Palmer, and Fairbanks. The air base uses the seaports of Seward, Whittier, and Anchorage; when the port of Anchorage is icebound during the winter months, the base depends on the deep-water ports of Whittier and Seward for its oceangoing freight.

The headquarters of USARAL is at Fort Richardson, about 8 mi northeast of Anchorage. The fort adjoins Elmendorf AFB, where the army post was originally located. On October 15, 1950, the Army released to the Air Force the land that is now Elmendorf AFB and constructed new facilities at Fort Richardson. The boundaries of Fort Richardson were later expanded to include an area north of Eagle River; the fort then comprised a total of 67,296 acres. Although installations at Fort Richardson sustained

ABSTRACT: Military bases in the region affected by the Alaska earthquake responded quickly to the direct impact of the shock on their own territory and on the civilian communities in the area. In many ways, these military bases were able to respond more speedily and more effectively than the civilian organizations, and they played a significant role in mitigating the disaster.

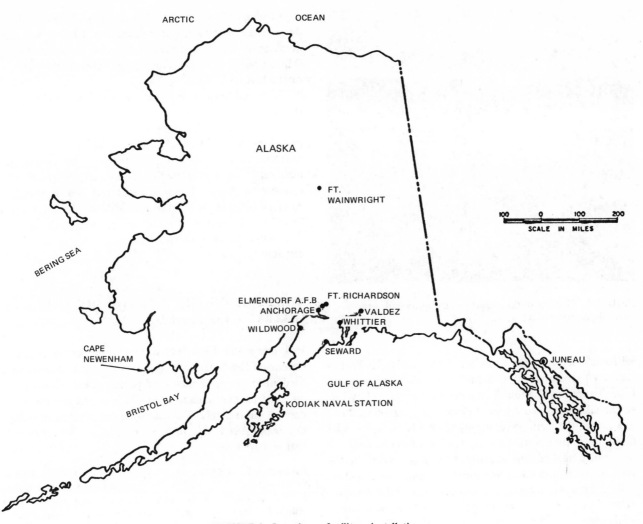

FIGURE 1 Locations of military installations.

U.S. Army Corps of Engineers

FIGURE 2 Aerial view of Elmendorf AFB showing family housing, the District Engineering building (foreground), and Knik Arm (background).

earthquake damage that was to cost about $17 million to repair, the command remained in all aspects operational.

Kodiak Naval Station, on Kodiak Island, is approximately 250 mi southwest of Anchorage and 670 mi west of Juneau by air. The island can be reached throughout the year by commercial aircraft, by the State of Alaska ferry system, and by commercial and private boats. Construction of the naval base was begun in September 1939. During the earthquake and subsequent tsunami, the primary source of electric power supplied to the naval station was completely lost. The power plant building was inundated, as shown by the oil slick marks in Figures 3 and 4, but emergency generators were immediately activated at all Kodiak sites. Normal power was restored to the on-base components on April 10, 1964. Although power-transmission lines and transportation routes suffered considerable damage from the earthquake and tsunami, the Naval Communications Station (NAVCOMMSTA) buildings all remained intact.

U.S. Navy

FIGURE 3 Flooding of the aircraft parking apron during the tsunamis, Kodiak Naval Station.

With the emergency power on line, NAVCOMMSTA Kodiak was able to maintain all its circuitry commitments with very little disruption. The fourth tsunami wave generated by the earthquake destroyed 2½ mi of power line (Figure 5). This line carried the main power supply to Holiday Beach in addition to communication cables. The loss of the communication cables resulted only in a loss of telephone service to the station; all other circuitry was routed by microwave, and the naval station was at no time out of operation. Emergency measures were undertaken immediately, and major repair work was completed within the same year.

The port of Whittier, about 60 mi southeast of Anchorage (Figure 1), is the terminus of a branch of The Alaska Railroad. The branch line passes through the Chugach Mountains in two tunnels between Portage and Whittier. No highways connect Whittier to other points within Alaska. When operational, the port of Whittier was a small self-contained community at the west end of Passage Canal, an arm of Prince William Sound. This pocket of land was isolated from the remainder of Alaska by its wall of mountains and could be reached only by water until the construction of the two railroad tunnels in 1943 by the Corps of Engineers. This World War II project made it possible to install a single-track rail line from Portage, about 50 mi southeast of Anchorage, to the port site. The Alaska Railroad acquired ownership and since World War II has operated trackage into the port. Alternate means of transportation made the port of Whittier no longer necessary as a military facility, and it was closed on December 1, 1960. A small civilian caretaker staff remained, and the port continued civil operations on a reduced scale.

Although 13 of the 52 residents in Whittier were killed during the earthquake, tsunami, and fire, Whittier was the quickest of the stricken towns to recover; cargo was being shipped out of town by train less than a week after the earthquake.

Wildwood Station, at about 60°34′ N and 151°16′ W, on the east side of Cook Inlet (Figure 1), although only 60 mi southwest of the Anchorage area by air, is about 160 mi away by highway. The southern boundary line of Wildwood runs along the border of the city of Kenai, just outside the main gate. The station itself has no airport, but the Kenai commercial airport, 3 mi to the east, provides aerial connections with the Anchorage area. Wildwood Station sustained minor damage, including the collapse of the elevated steel water-storage tank and breaks in the water and fuel-distribution systems.

ANALYSIS OF THE DISASTER BY THE MILITARY COMMAND

With communications almost nonexistent between Alaskan Command Headquarters and the south central Alaska areas hard-hit by the earthquake and tsunamis, only sketchy information was available with which to evaluate the damage immediately. The following report (U.S. Alaskan Command, 1964) was made on the basis of the information that was available:

An earthquake of 8.5 magnitude centered at 61N, 147.5W [later located at 61.04N, 147.73W] has occurred, causing extensive damage in southern Alaska and tidal waves. The major earthquake has been followed by numerous minor tremors. The Alaskan communities of Anchorage, Seward, Valdez, Cordova, Kodiak, and Kenai have re-

U.S. Navy

FIGURE 4 Oil slick marks 9 ft high indicate the height of tsunamis on the central power plant building, Kodiak Naval Station.

U.S. Navy

FIGURE 5 Damage caused by the tsunamis on the Holiday Beach Road, Kodiak Island.

ceived major damage. There are apparently some casualties in these communities, but the local civil authorities have not been able to determine estimated numbers.

The Alaskan Command has been in constant contact with Governor Egan, Anchorage Mayor Sharrock, and other civilian and Civil Defense authorities to determine what the military can do to assist in this disaster. The Alaskan Command is giving full available assistance to the stricken communities and will continue this aid as long as required to protect lives and property and to help in the recovery from this calamity.

Some examples of this assistance are: Troops and materiel support have been provided to the Anchorage area. Fissures in the road prevented our support convoy from reaching Seward. Troops and materiel will be sent to Seward by helicopter after daylight on 28 March. Weather prevented airlift of troops and materiel support from reaching Valdez. Barracks on Elmendorf Air Force Base have been made available to shelter civilians.

The Alaskan Command Headquarters will continue on a 24-hour operation during the present emergency to direct military support and assistance operations.

Elmendorf Air Force Base, Fort Richardson, and Wildwood Station have been damaged. The extent of the damage is currently being surveyed. However, the Alaskan Command is operational and capable of carrying out all assigned missions. A Strategic Air Command KC135 (Stratotanker) aircraft was sent from Eielson Air Force Base to Juneau to bring doctors and nurses to the Anchorage area. Alaskan Air Command has requested six 36-bed mobile hospital units be sent to assist the Command.

At daylight, 28 March, with weather permitting, aerial, visual, and photographic reconnaissance will be made of southern Alaska to fill in the incomplete reports that have been received.

MILITARY AID AND ASSISTANCE

MASSIVE AIRLIFT

As soon as communications were reestablished between military installations, state and city Civil Defense headquarters, and the devastated communities of south central Alaska, calls for help began pouring into the command post

of the Alaskan Command. Calls from the Greater Anchorage area received immediate attention, but response to communities in the outlying areas that required airlift support had to be postponed until the following morning because of bad weather and a lack of runway information and navigational aids at the airports of the stricken towns. As soon as it was light, the first of 17 Provider (C-123) transports of Elmendorf's 5017th Operations Squadron took off with relief supplies and equipment for Seward, Valdez, and Kodiak (Figure 6). Military Air Transport Service (MATS) had been notified, and Air Force transport aircraft from strategic locations throughout the United States were alerted to fly emergency requirements to Alaska.

During the next 21 days, this aerial transportation developed into a massive airlift that distributed over 3,700,000 lb of cargo to hard-hit areas. MATS broke its own disaster-relief cargo-hauling record by moving more than 2,750,000 lb of supplies in support of Operation Helping Hand. In addition, during the 2 weeks after the disaster, USARAL Aviation Battalion light aircraft flew 556 sorties for disaster relief, carrying 137,075 lb of cargo and 947 passengers. The Alaskan Air Command flew almost 200 sorties during the first 12 days after the earthquake, airlifting 560,300 lb of cargo and approximately 850 passengers including evacuees. Alaska Air National Guard flew nearly 160 hours, handling approximately 315,000 lb of cargo and more than 150 passengers.

DAMAGE SURVEYED BY AERIAL RECONNAISSANCE

Loss of communication facilities prevented early damage assessments of the Greater Anchorage area and outlying

U.S. Air Force

FIGURE 6 Essential supplies being loaded on aircraft to assist the stricken communities.

communities. Damage was so widespread that photo recon-naissance was needed to make a preliminary survey. Photo-reconnaissance aircraft in south central Alaska were airborne with the first favorable flying weather on March 28. In the 5 days after the earthquake, these planes flew missions over Seward, Whittier, Anchorage, Valdez, Wildwood Station, Kodiak, Seldovia, and Cordova and photographed 80 per-cent of the Seward Highway, as well as vital areas of The Alaska Railroad between Anchorage and Seward and be-tween Portage and Whittier. The planes flew 64 hours on 23 sorties in the first 2 weeks after the earthquake, and in the 12-day period ending April 10 made 2,400 aerial negatives, from which 29,040 prints were produced. Additional photo-reconnaissance planes were sent to Alaska where they spent some 87 flying hours on 11 direct-support photo missions using more than 4,200 feet of film to photograph the areas of Anchorage, Seward, Kodiak, Whittier, Valdez, Cordova, Gulkana, and the entire south central Alaskan highway complex.

TRANSPORTATION OF A HIGHWAY BRIDGE

One of the outstanding single airlift support operations was the combined effort of Alaskan Air Command and Alaska Air National Guard to airlift a Bailey bridge (Figure 7) for the Army Engineers from Elmendorf AFB to the Soldotna–Kenai area on the Kenai Peninsula. This bridge replaced the concrete structure destroyed by the earthquake at Cooper's Landing on the lower end of Kenai Lake. Army Engineers of the 562d Engineering Combat Company trans-ported the bridge by truck in sections over the Glenn High-

U.S. Army

FIGURE 7 Erecting a Bailey-type replacement bridge.

way from Eklutna to Elmendorf AFB. There it was loaded on a Military Air Transport Globemaster II (C-124) of the Alaskan Air Command, on Alaska Air National Guard Pro-viders (C-123), and on two Air Reserve Flying Boxcars (C-119) from March AFB, California, lent to Alaskan Air Command for the operation. Nearly 60 sorties were required for the 5-day operation that involved the airlift of about 520,000 lb.

Detachment 1, Western Air Rescue Center, commonly known in Alaska as the Rescue Coordination Center, on Elmendorf AFB, coordinated, controlled, and assigned all rescue missions conducted by the military, by Civil Air Patrol, and by federal agencies during the Helping Hand exercise.

COMMUNICATIONS

The earthquake put out of operation most of the public communications in the area affected by strong ground shak-ing. The military long-lines telephone system in Alaska, most of which was owned and operated by the Air Force Com-munications Service at that time, sustained only minor damage. The major terminals for the military system and for the commercial Alaska Communications System, which were within or near Elmendorf AFB, did, however, sustain some damage (Figure 8).

On the local scene, all available personnel and equipment were quickly mobilized for immediate recovery action. The former satellite points in various communications nets were now serving as major communications centers; Elmendorf and Fort Richardson taxis that formerly answered calls were now making calls. Radio-equipped taxi units were deployed to establish the first installation-wide communications net-work and were performing liaison services between Elmen-dorf and Fort Richardson. From Fort Richardson, the 56th Military Police Company radio net sent a squad car into Anchorage to establish the first postearthquake communica-tion link between the post and the city. The squad car was stationed at the Public Safety Building to relay damage re-ports and requests for assistance until wire communications could be reestablished. A point-to-point radio net was also established by the 33d Signal Battalion between USARAL and Civil Defense Headquarters in Anchorage. Similarly, the Alaska State Police sent a radio-equipped patrol car to stand by at the Rescue Coordination Center at Elmendorf to relay messages between the Rescue Coordination Center and Alaska State Civil Defense Headquarters. Within 5 minutes of the earthquake, the Army's Anchorage Area Air Defense microwave command and control system was completely restored and in operation. Within 90 minutes, 95 percent of the local communications of Fort Richardson and Elmen-dorf were restored to a limited degree, and the commercial Alaska Communications System was passing emergency and

U.S. Air Force

FIGURE 8   Emergency repairs were made in the battery room of the ACS toll center on Government Hill to permit restoration of telephone and teletype communications.

Civil Defense telephone traffic to the other states. Military Affiliate Radio System (MARS) on Elmendorf AFB went into operation on emergency power minutes after the earthquake. A mobile communications van that had been tested only the day before was used to supply emergency power. The MARS station and the Civil Defense net joined forces to establish a telephone patch between the command post of the Alaskan Air Command and Civil Defense Headquarters. During the first week of operation, this station received and delivered 3,000 MARS-grams and sent out 2,800 messages.

While emergency power was being restored at the MARS station, a MARS volunteer at Fort Richardson maintained communication between the station and Civil Defense Headquarters by means of the mobile radio rig in his automobile. The MARS station was on the air within an hour after the earthquake and maintained a 24-hour-a-day schedule until April 15.

Because of the increased communication traffic and the use of MARS frequencies and equipment for official as well as amateur messages, the MARS station at Fort Richardson handled the outbound messages, while Fort Wainwright and Wildwood Station received the inbound calls. By April 15, these three stations had handled a total of 9,379 messages.

At the Alaska Communications System toll center on Government Hill and at the telegram center in Anchorage, communications personnel worked to restore outside lines. Telephone communications were restored to Anchorage less than 2 hours after the earthquake, and limited telegraph service was provided shortly thereafter. Through the combined efforts of the 1929th Communications Group, American Telephone and Telegraph, the Pacific Company, Western Union, and Canadian telephone companies, 26 one-way circuits out of Alaska were hastily activated, thus permitting communications directly from Anchorage and Fairbanks to Chicago, San Francisco, and Dallas. Telegraph circuits between Anchorage and Seattle were made available for the Red Cross. Two teletypes and three telephones were set up 2½ hours after the earthquake in the lobby of the Alaska Communications System Building on Government Hill for the use of the general public.

Two cables connecting the city of Anchorage telephone utility to the Air Force-operated long-distance system were severed. Until these broken cables were repaired the following day, personnel in the city had to go to the Government Hill Telephone Toll Building to place long-distance calls and send telegrams. On Saturday, Air Force personnel were joined by Anchorage city telephone technicians in restoring the long-distance limited service to the City of Anchorage.

During the first 4 days after the disaster, 18,629 calls, of which 12,104 were completed, were made to other states through the toll building on Government Hill.

To ensure control and maintain liaison communications between Elmendorf, Fort Richardson, and Civil Defense and to fill the gap in local communications as well as to assist the rapidly repaired commercial facilities, Army communicators of the 33d Signal Battalion went on the air Friday night, substituting very-high-frequency (VHF) radio-relay equipment between switchboards that were separated by broken cable. VHF units were moved to Alaska State Civil Defense Headquarters to establish 12-channel relays between Civil Defense and Fort Richardson, and Civil Defense and Elmendorf AFB. Another 12-channel rig was installed to connect the Federal Aviation Agency installation at Merrill Field with the Alaska Communications System Building on Government Hill. To complete the local communication network, the communicators also installed a wire line between Civil Defense Headquarters and the Alaska State Highway Department.

To serve the outlying areas, the 33d Signal Battalion and the Signal Platoon, 172d Infantry Brigade (mechanized), established voice and radio-teletype connections between Fort Richardson and Seward and a radio connection between the Army post and Whittier. To install the voice link between Whittier and Portage, the signalmen pulled a 4-channel cable through the 2½-mi railroad tunnel into Whittier.

U.S. Army

FIGURE 9 Emergency water station in the Turnagain Heights residential area.

Communications between Seward and Fort Richardson had been increased by the 172d Infantry Brigade with the installation of a second voice and radio-teletype link. The radio teletype gave Seward its first communication link with the rest of Alaska since the earthquake and was Seward's sole means of communication with the rest of the state until late in the evening of March 31, when two telephone lines were opened. The 171st Infantry Brigade of Fort Wainwright established the radio-teletype communication circuit between the fort and the city of Valdez.

AID TO THE CITIZENS OF STRICKEN COMMUNITIES

Three hours after the earthquake, the 1st Battalion, 37th Artillery, reported to the Public Safety Building with five water trailers to aid Anchorage. From the night of the earthquake until the following Monday morning, March 30, six trucks shuttled water trailers back and forth from Fort Richardson to the city. As many as 33 of these trailers were stationed at hospitals, in school yards, at major public buildings, and in the Anchorage park strip (Figure 9). On Tuesday, March 31, four water-purification units arrived from the 4th Infantry Division, Fort Lewis, Washington. In coordination with officials of the civilian Public Health Service, the purification units were placed at four key locations within the city (Figure 9). Three days after the earthquake, the water hydrant at the Orah Dee Clark Junior High School in Mountain View was established as one of the primary water-distribution points. The water-supply assistance program continued until Sunday, April 5, when the city system had been sufficiently restored to provide potable

water to most of the city area. The assistance program involved about 52 men in addition to the crews manning the water-purification units.

Because utilities were inoperable immediately after the earthquake, the preparation and dispensing of food to feed hundreds of volunteer workers became a major problem. On Saturday morning, March 28, Fort Richardson began to operate four field mess halls. These mess halls operated continuously, serving hot C-rations, soup, and coffee (Figure 10). One mess hall served 7,462 meals and used 198 lb of coffee. Two other mess halls in midtown Anchorage served more than 800 meals a day during the 48 hours of operation.

Elmendorf's 5040th Food Service Squadron personnel also went on 24-hour shifts, and in the first 4 days after the earthquake they doubled the normal feeding schedule by serving 44,487 regular meals and 11,820 C-ration meals. The people fed included the 200–400 evacuees from the city of Anchorage to Elmendorf AFB. The loss of the civilian commercial bakeries in Anchorage forced the base bread bakery to operate 24 hours a day, commencing Saturday, with a maximum production of 14,000 lb of bread a day. Maximum production continued for 4 days to support troop dining halls at Elmendorf, Fort Richardson, and the USAF Hospital at Elmendorf, as well as to supply the base commissary. The bread baked included 3,960 lb of frozen raw loaves of bread that had been donated to Civil Defense by an Anchorage producer who was forced to suspend operations. The baked bread was returned to the Anchorage Civil Defense for distribution (Figure 11).

Emergency housing on Elmendorf AFB and Fort Richardson was immediately arranged for displaced military

U.S. Army

FIGURE 10 Field kitchen behind the Police Station in Anchorage.

U.S. Air Force

FIGURE 11   Fresh bread loaded on aircraft for distribution to the needy communities throughout south central Alaska.

and civilian personnel. Within 2 hours, buildings that were structurally safe for occupancy were identified, and adequate bedding, rations, and field kitchens were made available for about 5,000 people. The first buildings were available shortly thereafter and eventually some 2,000 displaced persons, mostly military, were provided with emergency housing.

The supply system of the Alaskan Command, in addition to satisfying the numerous military requirements, also managed to fulfill innumerable civilian requests. One of the major requests was for fuel distributors who eventually dispensed 244,000 gallons of diesel fuel to the local population. Other materials supplied in direct support of the civilian community and governmental agencies included 800 sleeping bags, 200 bunks, 450 air mattresses, 80 regular mattresses, several hundred blankets, 5,000 paper cups and plates, 2,900 ft of electric wire, and 2,240 lb of chlorinated lime.

Government inspection teams were supplied with tables, folding chairs, desks, typewriters, water cans, hard hats, file cabinets, and arctic clothing. Civil authorities were furnished

the sanitation kits that were stored and reserved in fallout areas. Radio receivers were supplied to the Civil Defense personnel, and pumps and small and large generator sets were given to The Alaska Railroad for use in the state emergency.

MEDICAL ASSISTANCE

About 3 hours after the earthquake, the Anchorage Police Department requested two Army ambulances, with emergency equipment and four airmen assigned to aid them in transporting casualties to Providence Hospital. Exactly 1 hour after the request was received, the crews and ambulances reported to the Police Department in the Public Safety Building, downtown Anchorage.

Almost immediately after the earthquake, the military installations began to provide the medical supplies and services to the Anchorage area (Figure 12). For example, six sanitarians were lent to the Civil Defense health authorities; a field autoclave was sent to Providence Hospital; and operators, standby power generators, and fuel to run the equipment were delivered to the Alaska Native Hospital, Providence Hospital, Presbyterian Hospital, and the Air National Guard facilities. When the decision was made to reopen Presbyterian Hospital, the Army troops assisted in cleaning the building and preparing it to receive the expected patients. Even the hospital's laundry had to be finished on the post because the damaged laundry facilities at the hospital were not usable for 4 days. During this time, the post laundry washed 1,472 items for the hospital and 124 bundles for the Red Cross.

When the decision was made to evacuate St. Mary's

U.S. Air Force

FIGURE 12   One of the military ambulances pressed into service to meet the emergency created by the earthquake.

Residence, 27 USAF Hospital personnel and 7 military ambulances were used to transfer 37 patients. The local military personnel were supplemented by a medical team composed of 5 doctors, 10 nurses, 2 anesthetists, and 20 enlisted medical specialists flown from Madigan Army Hospital, Fort Lewis, Washington. The team left Fort Lewis on Saturday and remained in the Anchorage area until April 2, when its help was no longer needed.

While their husbands and fathers worked 12-hour days and longer in the disaster-relief effort, the women and girls also helped. The Grey Ladies and teen-age nurses' aides were busy at the hospitals; one Fort Richardson senior Girl Scout spent 35 consecutive hours as a nurse's aide at Providence Hospital. Others, like the Red Cross volunteers, were busy in relief centers.

SEARCH AND RESCUE

Survey teams, each consisting of one city policeman, one Army medical corpsman, one engineer, and three infantrymen, searched all buildings in the damaged downtown area. The teams were backed up by ambulances of Fort Richardson's 514th Medical Company. When rehabilitation of Anchorage's Turnagain residential area was slowed because of lack of equipment (Figure 13), Elmendorf's motor pool responded with 20 trucks, a large wrecker, and two radio units with drivers and supervisory personnel.

The six-story control tower for the Anchorage International Airport collapsed as a result of the earthquake, killing one of the operators on duty and trapping the remaining two in the wreckage. When an urgent call was sent out for a crane large enough to lift the wreckage to free the entrapped men, Elmendorf's 5040th Civil Engineering Group responded with a 20-ton mobile crane.

Fuel spillage at Anchorage International Airport, caused by ruptured fuel tanks and lines, created a severe fire hazard. The Alaskan Air Command provided 100 5-gallon cans of foam to prevent the fuel from catching fire. In addition, the Alaskan Air Command civil engineers and fire-department personnel foamed the petroleum, oil, and lubricant areas of the port of Anchorage so that workers could get in to repair the dock and equipment as well as the adjacent tank farms, where ruptured fuel lines and split tank seams had saturated the area with thousands of gallons of mixed fuel oil and gasoline.

Army Engineers with mine detectors worked with city utility crews for 3 days locating water and sewerage mains.

Soldiers and military vehicles transferred goods from wholesale food warehouses that had collapsed during the earthquake. Cold-storage facilities for meat and other perishable foods were made available at Fort Richardson, because storage was not available within the city.

The military installations contributed heavy equipment to be used in the search and rescue operations and subsequent clearing of danger areas (Figure 14). Fort Richardson, for example, furnished two 20-ton cranes, eight bulldozers, a pile driver, and a variety of wheeled vehicles for the emergency. In addition, the post provided 261 wheeled vehicles, exclusive of jeeps and sedans, to the city of Anchorage during the first days after the earthquake.

ELMENDORF AFB RECOVERY OPERATIONS

IMMEDIATE RESTORATION PLANS

After the earthquake, the U.S. Air Force Alaskan Air Command and the 5040th Air Base Wing at Elmendorf made initial damage assessments and formulated recovery plans. The 41 strategically deployed auxiliary-power units and generators were energized throughout the base. Air Force command posts were operating immediately with emergency power and light amid the rubble of crumbled masonry, shattered light fixtures, and broken glass. As base power was restored to various areas, the 30 temporary emergency power units and operating personnel were moved to other locations where they were needed.

Military personnel and civilian employees reported to their duty stations after the earthquake and immediately went on 24-hour duty status. Off-duty air policemen and security guards reported to their headquarters within 30 minutes after the disaster and were dispatched to furnish necessary security and base assistance. Air Police mobile patrols on the base were utilized immediately to disseminate announcements of an urgent nature to the base population

U.S. Air Force

FIGURE 13   Removing belongings from damaged houses in the Turnagain Heights landslide area.

U.S. Army Corps of Engineers

FIGURE 14   Demolition of Hillside apartments. Troops, material support, and equipment, requested by Anchorage authorities, were lent to the city for cleanup operations and restoration programs.

via the public address systems mounted on their vehicles.

Some of the most essential and difficult jobs facing the base were the restoration of utilities and the inspection of buildings and facilities for safety. Large-scale programs of both temporary and permanent repairs were speedily put into operation by the 5040th Civil Engineering Group.

TEMPORARY TRAFFIC CONTROL

The base air traffic terminal and control tower with its glassed-in cupola was so damaged that it was inoperable (Figures 15 and 16), severely limiting incoming and outgoing

U.S. Air Force

FIGURE 15   Interior damage in MATS Terminal Building.

U.S. Air Force

FIGURE 16   Base air traffic control tower; badly twisted steel frame structure was deemed a total loss.

traffic. Radio equipment in a parked Provider (C-123) aircraft was used as a temporary means of maintaining air traffic control. A pilot-controller manned this makeshift expedient for almost 2½ hours until replaced by supervisory tower and communications operations personnel. Air Force Communications Service sped a mobile control tower and operating personnel from the 3d Mobile Communications Squadron at Tinker AFB, Oklahoma. The unit arrived on Easter Sunday and became operational within 3½ hours after landing at Elmendorf AFB.

Damage to aircraft was caused primarily by falling light fixtures and other overhead objects in the hangars. Sheet-metal workers and other specialists of the 5040th Consolidated Aircraft Maintenance Group worked continuously from 24 to 36 hours on repairs to make the aircraft ready to fly.

EVACUATION OF THE USAF HOSPITAL

The USAF Hospital because of extensive damage was forced to evacuate all patients and staff from the building (Figure 17). In just 18 minutes, 181 patients, 18 newborn babies, and 45 staff personnel were moved to the nearby nurses' quarters and to noncommissioned officers' and airmen's

U.S. Air Force

FIGURE 17 Extensive damage to the interior of USAF Hospital on Elmendorf AFB from which 181 patients were evacuated and housed in nearby quarters.

barracks. With the assistance of the 64th Field Hospital from Fort Richardson, which furnished field generators for power and lighting and a field kitchen, these buildings were rapidly turned into a field hospital with wards, treatment rooms, casualty rest areas, a major surgery suite, and a pediatrics and obstetrics area (Figure 18). The latter was needed immediately; within 1 hour, twins were delivered there by the light of a flashlight.

Anticipating a potentially large medical requirement, Alaskan Air Command requested assistance from the Air Force Surgeon General's Office. Tactical Air Command medical units were alerted and moved into place in reserve

at Eielson AFB by eight Tactical Air Command Hercules (C-130 turboprop) aircraft within 36 hours. These units consisted of a 100-bed casualty unit with 62 personnel from Pope AFB, North Carolina, one 36-bed hospital unit with 42 people from Shaw AFB, South Carolina, and another 36-bed unit with 55 people from Seymour Johnson AFB, North Carolina.

FORT RICHARDSON RECOVERY OPERATIONS

Communications at Fort Richardson were checked to assure command and control and to establish the extent of the damage that had been incurred. Survey and reconnaissance parties investigated the damage to military installations and to the city of Anchorage, and the Commanding Officer of the 172d Infantry Brigade had been alerted for possible commitment of other units (Figure 19).

Fort Richardson had sustained substantial but not crippling damage from the earthquake. One man suffered severe head injuries in the Fort Richardson Skyline Service Club when interior walls and ceiling supports gave way. He later died of his injuries and was the only earthquake fatality among U.S. Army personnel in Alaska.

DAMAGED BUILDINGS

Many buildings sustained spectacular, although not structurally severe damage. In troop barracks, nonbearing curtain walls cracked and gave way in many cases. Many buildings were evacuated as a safety measure, but a weekend inspection by engineers proved that no major structural damage had occurred.

U.S. Air Force

FIGURE 18 Temporary field medical units set up adjacent to the USAF hospital to be prepared for potential emergencies.

U.S. Army

FIGURE 19 At the request of civil authorities, guards were stationed throughout the city of Anchorage.

FIGURE 20 Partial collapse of one of the main supply warehouses on Elmendorf AFB required many man-hours for removal of salvageable equipment and supplies.

The post dispensary personnel were forced out of their building by the damage, and men of the medical battalion erected a Jamesway hut during the evening to house a field dispensary.

In warehouses, concrete block walls and some roof framing were damaged by the earthquake. Several bays on one Elmendorf AFB warehouse collapsed and smashed several jeeps that were parked next to the building (Figure 20). Crews went to work immediately, and by 8:30 p.m., Friday, scattered and jumbled goods were being moved from the damaged warehouses to meet urgent needs in Anchorage. By midnight, the warehouses were again fully operational.

Shelves in the post commissary collapsed, scattering groceries. Troops and commissary workers labored throughout the night to restock the shelves and opened the store on time on Saturday (Figure 21).

RESTORATION OF UTILITIES

As a safety measure, the electrical power was cut off immediately after the earthquake while the men on shift checked the huge boilers and turbines in the power plant. Cold-water feed lines had been broken, the water-treatment plant feeding the boilers was severely damaged, and steam pipes hung from broken supports. The plant remained operational, however, and by early Saturday morning it was producing at almost full capacity. Repairs were carried on by the regular shift crew who returned to the post when the earthquake had subsided. They were joined by a man who, after 3 years of retirement, came back to work all night and to return for the Saturday night shift. The electrical distribution system was damaged, and off-duty line crews hurriedly returned to the post to make the necessary repairs. Primary power lines to vital command and communications centers were restored

within an hour, and by 7:40 a.m., March 28, power was restored to all critical areas of the post, including family housing areas.

Domestic water supply also threatened to become a major problem. The water-purification plant furnishes Fort Richardson and Elmendorf AFB with potable drinking water, and the City of Anchorage filtration plant obtains most of its water from an Army reservoir on Ship Creek created by a concrete dam. Immediately after the earthquake, it was evident that there were leaks in the system because the water level in the post reservoir was dropping at the rate of 1½ ft an hour. The dam reservoir reached a potentially dangerous low level, although it never did go dry. Meanwhile, Ship Creek on the main post dried up entirely. The creek had been blocked by slides about 3 mi upstream from the water plant. Before engineers could be assembled and dispatched to clear this natural dam, the stream had breached the slide area and water was again available.

OPERATION HELPING HAND

After April 2, the scope of USARAL participation in Operation Helping Hand steadily diminished. Civil authorities in the disaster areas began to assume more responsibility for reviving their own communities once the worst of the wreckage had been cleared away, and the people had been clothed, fed, housed, and given medical treatment. On May 1, the last of the soldiers guarding the Turnagain Heights area were recalled to Fort Richardson. Finally, on May 7, Headquarters, USARAL, issued the following directive:

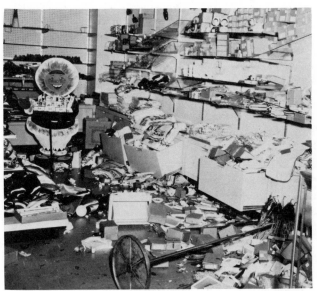

FIGURE 21 Interior disarrangement of base exchange supplies that had to be restocked and rearranged.

Emergency actions taken by this headquarters and major subordinate commands to render assistance to civil authorities during the recent earthquake and its aftermath are hereby terminated.

MILITARY ASSISTANCE TO OUTLYING CITIES

In addition to the city of Anchorage, many smaller towns in the area of strong shaking were given assistance by the military.

KODIAK CITY

The city of Kodiak was severely damaged, and the Navy undertook the rehabilitation of designated areas of the city. Specialists immediately started around-the-clock operations in the station power plant, while others began to work on the washed-out road to the nearby Naval Communications Station. Alternate routes were opened, river crossings were repaired, and vital road traffic began moving again. Military assistance to the city of Kodiak involved both material and manpower. Segments of the Navy's Mobile Construction Battalion NINE, based at Port Hueneme, California, were sent to help, as was the seaplane tender USS *Salisbury Sound* of the U.S. Pacific Fleet. This 150-man Seabee Disaster Recovery Team equipped with tools, rations, and cold-weather clothing, departed Port Hueneme on Saturday, March 28, within 6 hours of receiving notice. Their jet transports landed at Kodiak 4½ hours later. Power linemen of the unit worked for 3 days in the city until all power was restored. Meanwhile, welders and pipefitters of the unit helped repair the city's main crab-freezing plant, and crane operators helped clear the demolished sections of the city.

The unit remained in Kodiak for 12 days before returning to Port Hueneme. Five seabees, two linemen, two apprentice linemen, and one electrician worked a total of 310 man-hours, assisting the Kodiak Electric Association (KEA) in restoring service. The Navy also shipped in six KEA-purchased transformers weighing approximately 1,800 lb. The seaplane tender USS *Salisbury Sound* arrived in Kodiak from Oak Harbor, Washington, on March 31; 30 minutes later, her generators were completely linked to naval-station power lines and were providing power equal to one-fourth the capacity of the station's power plant. All ship's facilities, including hot showers and laundry, were made available to the restoration and repair crews.

The dock-landing ship USS *Alamo* arrived at Kodiak from San Diego, California, with a 160-ft pontoon dock, equipment, and operating personnel to assist in the rehabilitation of Kodiak's fishing fleet. In addition to Navy ships, the U.S. Coast and Geodetic Survey ships *Pathfinder* and *Surveyor* and the U.S. Coast Guard cutter *Bittersweet* were

assigned to the recovery project. The *Pathfinder* and *Surveyor* collaborated with Fleet Weather Central in gathering tidal data, charting the ocean floor, and relocating navigational aids. The Kodiak-based *Bittersweet* was first to undertake the job of redepositing buoys and replacing lost navigational markers.

The Coast Guard secondary radio station NOJ broadcast urgent marine messages, asking all vessels to proceed to the nearest villages to assist and to report their findings to the established control center. Less than 2 hours after the earthquake, five Coast Guard cutters were diverted to assist the areas that appeared to be the most severely damaged according to the meager communications available at that time. The cutters *Minnetonka, Storis,* and *Sorrel* were directed to Prince William Sound, the cutter *Bittersweet* to Seward, and the cutter *Sedge* to Valdez. On Sunday, March 29, aerial surveys of the disaster area concentrated on locating missing persons in the remote island areas. The cutters *Sorrel* and *Bittersweet* remained in the Seward area, with the cutter *Sedge* continuing assistance in Prince William Sound. The cutter *Storis* was diverted to Cook Inlet for ice-breaking duties for the port of Anchorage.

Personnel of the marine barracks at Kodiak maintained continuous security over the station operating areas during the tsunamis, although many of these areas were under water four times during the evening of March 27. After the initial tremor, marines were assigned to direct traffic in the city of Kodiak, to assist in evacuating people from low areas, and to patrol areas damaged by tsunamis. Another group of marines was sent into the city to assist in maintaining law and order and in protecting property in the damaged areas. During the first 10 days, 18 sentries were assigned to aid the city police for 24 hours a day. Navy personnel, numbering 1,135 men, contributed 190,374 hours toward the city's recovery effort.

The Navy and the Red Cross supplied blankets and sandwiches to the needy. A total of 1,080 blankets, the majority flown in by Navy aircraft from Seattle and Whidbey Island, Washington, were distributed throughout the city. During the first 48 hours, 12,000 meals were served to evacuees on the Kodiak Naval Station as well as to 350 people quartered at Kodiak High School, which was designated by Civil Defense officials as a refugee center. The 270 evacuees from Kodiak Island villages and from neighboring islands were fed at the naval station galley from Saturday, March 28, until Tuesday, March 31, when they were flown to Anchorage at the request of the Bureau of Indian Affairs. Navy chaplains and nurses looked after their well-being, and the galley served approximately 6,000 meals a day during the first 4 days after the disaster and 4,000 meals a day thereafter.

Items supplied by the Navy after the earthquake included generators, water pumps, manila rope, boat anchors, office supplies, telephone lines, assorted foodstuffs, disposable diapers, sleeping bags, medicine, mattresses, sheets, kitchenware, and many other sundry articles. Individual contributions and donations in unknown quantities were made by military and civilian families in the form of clothing, food, and shelter.

While the naval recovery parties were busy in downtown Kodiak, the USS *Kodiak* was helping boat owners move the fishing fleet to a safer anchorage, delivering cattle feed to isolated ranches, and evacuating the inhabitants of Old Harbor, Ouzinkie, and Kaguyak. Later, the ship was ordered to Homer to pick up floating piers and docking facilities for use in relocating undamaged Kodiak fishing boats in Gibson Cove. With her diesel engine still warm, the USS *Kodiak* put to sea once more—with bulldozers on board—and headed for Old Harbor to help work parties clear the village of debris.

At first light on Saturday, helicopters were used in the Kodiak area to evacuate stranded people and to make damage surveys. Some 15 special flights were made by Kodiak Naval Station Air Detachment aircraft during the first 10 days after the disaster. Transportation for donated materials from the lower 48 states required 704 military man-hours and 489 equipment-hours. Navy and Coast Guard aircraft and maintenance personnel at the station were forced out of their hangars and, with little or no protection from the wind and weather, faced the problem of keeping the aircraft operational.

A part of the MATS airlift servicing the Alaskan theater was diverted directly to Kodiak. Support included 3 Globemasters II (C-124's), two Cargomasters (C-133's), and one Stratolifter (C-135). Moreover, a Tactical Air Command Hercules (C-130) hospital aircraft, held in reserve at Eielson AFB, was used to pick up 6,000 lb of bread at Elmendorf AFB for the Kodiak population. On the return trip to Elmendorf, the aircraft evacuated Kodiak natives to Anchorage.

After 3 weeks, all major demolition in the downtown business district was completed, and military personnel moved to the outlying areas, where all health hazards had been removed by the first week of May.

In summary, within a few days, 512 persons were evacuated by air, 279 persons were billeted at the Naval Station, 3,500 typhoid inoculations were administered, and tons of supplies were flown day and night into the city of Kodiak. More than 156,624 man-hours were expended by the Coast Guard during Operation Helping Hand.

SEWARD

The City of Seward was severely damaged by the tsunami (Figures 22 and 23). The harbor was wiped out, rail and road transportation was disrupted, the utilities were damaged, and communications, including the town's only radio

U.S. Army Corps of Engineers
FIGURE 22   Seward before the earthquake.

station, were gone. The airstrip remained operational and was the only transportation link with the outside world.

When the earthquake struck, 21 soldiers from various USARAL units on special duty for the Army Recreation Center for the Seward "All American City" award and celebration were in the dining hall. They vacated the building, and on their way to higher ground they stopped to pick up children from houses near the camp. After recovering from the initial shock, the soldiers offered their services to the Seward Hospital and to other community agencies. For example, three cooks in the group operated the kitchen in the Jesse Lee Home, an orphanage, by cooking on Army

U.S. Army Corps of Engineers
FIGURE 23   Seward after the earthquake.

field ranges. In addition, the Army cooks from the recreation center established a mess hall in the local high school.

The cooks managed the kitchens all night and well into Saturday afternoon, feeding the children of the home and other people in Seward, using foodstuffs from damaged stores and from private homes. At the high school, the community kitchen provided an average of 800 meals a day for citizens and volunteer workers. To reduce the kitchen load, Company A established its own field kitchen to feed the soldiers on duty elsewhere throughout the city.

At daybreak on Saturday, March 28, other soldiers reported to the Chief of Police and formed a search party to probe the dock area and other hard-hit parts of the city. They worked throughout the day, searching for injured and dead. Guard posts were established along the dock areas, in the business district, and a roving downtown patrol was set up to assist the city police. Later in the day, 139 officers and men of Company A, 4th Battalion, 23rd Infantry, Fort Richardson, with the 216th Transportation Truck Company, Army National Guard, were flown by AAC and Air National Guard aircraft to assist the city of Seward in its cleanup operations. After 8 days of intensive effort on behalf of the city, Company A was withdrawn on April 4 and replaced by Company C (Airborne), 4th Battalion, 23rd Infantry.

The Corps of Engineers answered a call from Seward for assistance in restoring utility operations and water-distribution and sewage-disposal systems. Chugach Electric Association personnel performed the immediate repairs on the electrical power lines.

Petroleum tank farms along the Seward waterfront caught fire during the earthquake. The tsunamis that followed spread blazing gasoline and oil over part of the city (Figures 24–27), leaving much debris floating in Resurrec-

U.S. Army Corps of Engineers
FIGURE 25   Twisted Alaska Railroad tracks (foreground) at Seward.

tion Bay. City officials requested a demolition expert with experience in knocking down dangerous buildings, in blasting pits for sanitary use, and in similar tests that require the use of explosives.

A water-purification engineering unit was flown into Seward on Saturday and immediately installed its equipment at a small lake near the city's edge to fill the portable water trailers. On its first day of operation, the engineering unit produced 10,000 gallons of water. In addition, six water trailers were stationed at various points throughout the city to dispense potable water to the public. The mission of the water-purification unit was completed on April 9.

U.S. Army Corps of Engineers
FIGURE 24   Damaged storage tanks along the Seward waterfront.

U.S. Army Corps of Engineers
FIGURE 26   Steel graveyard of Alaska Railroad tank and freight cars at Seward after the earthquake.

U.S. Army Corps of Engineers

FIGURE 27   Damaged and partly submerged Alaska Railroad dock on the Seward waterfront.

On Easter Sunday, a 30-kW generator was flown in to provide emergency power for the Seward hospital, and two smaller 1½-kW generators were furnished for airfield control facilities.

In coordination with members of the local Civil Air Patrol, the USARAL troops established a control center to operate the airport and organized an air-depot detail to unload the many aircraft arriving in Seward. They also manned a petroleum-oil-lubricant depot at the field.

Despite damage to their own communities, Civil Air Patrol personnel of the Anchorage, Homer, Kenai, and Seward units flew search and rescue missions and transported passengers and cargo. During the early days of the disaster, the Civil Air Patrol airlifted thousands of pounds of foodstuffs, medical supplies, fuel, and equipment, as well as a large number of passengers to Seward and other parts of the Kenai Peninsula; they also evacuated people from Seward, Hope, and Portage.

The bulk of the intra-Alaska airlift support was in the Seward area. The Alaskan Air Command immediately released to the local inhabitants Air Force emergency supplies that were stored in the Seward safe-haven area. On Good Friday evening, an Alaskan Air Command Provider (C-123) departed from Elmendorf AFB with 10,400 lb of relief cargo for Seward.

Between 6 a.m., March 28, and 6 a.m., March 31, the Alaskan Air Command and Air National Guard Provider (C-123) aircraft delivered 168 passengers and 59,120 lb of cargo to the Seward area. In the following 24 hours the aircraft delivered 198 passengers and 127,700 lb of cargo. A special project during this period was the disposition of 60,000 lb of perishable food and 32,700 lb of equipment, unloaded from the steamship *Tonsina* at the port of Anchorage for delivery to Seward.

VALDEZ

"Valdez is a shambles" (U.S. Alaskan Command, 1964) was the first postearthquake news of this city received by the Alaskan Command. The need to send aid to Valdez was obvious, and the mission was assigned to the USARAL Yukon Command and to Fort Wainwright, near Fairbanks.

Communications between Valdez and Anchorage were temporarily maintained by an amateur radio operator in Valdez and an Air Force sergeant at Cape Newenham Air Force Station, on the west coast of Alaska. The Air Force Communications Service MARS operators at Elmendorf AFB, unable to reach Valdez on the MARS frequencies, asked the sergeant to make contact over the amateur radio band. The Valdez radio operator passed accounts of the disaster to the sergeant, who, in turn, relayed the information over the MARS network to Elmendorf, which retransmitted the data to Alaska State Civil Defense. This three-way contact continued until the Valdez operator was forced off the air by one of the tsunamis.

The first elements of the Valdez task force departed from the Fort Wainwright airstrip at 11:50 p.m. on Good Friday, less than 3 hours after the mission had been assigned. Because of bad weather, it was 7:30 a.m. before the party was finally able to land in Valdez. Additional men and equipment from Fort Wainwright were on the way to Valdez by way of the Richardson Highway.

Valdez was severely damaged (Figures 28 and 29). The waterfront was a tangle of smashed timbers, boats, and all kinds of debris. None of the waterfront installations survived the tsunami. The Union Oil tank farm was ablaze, the electricity was out, the water system inoperable, and the sewerage system destroyed.

U.S. Army Corps of Engineers

FIGURE 28   Bulk-asphalt tank farm surrounded by debris and mounds of ice carried inland by the tsunamis at Valdez.

U.S. Army Corps of Engineers

FIGURE 29   Bulk-storage tank farm at Valdez damaged by the mounds of ice tossed against the tanks.

The Army task force commander and his survey team met immediately with the mayor of Valdez, the local state policeman, and a doctor, and the decision was made to evacuate the city. On March 28, all but 40 men and 5 women were evacuated from Valdez. The 53 patients at the Harbor View Hospital, a mental institution, were flown by Air Force Provider (C-123) aircraft to the Alaska Psychiatric Institute in Anchorage.

Meanwhile, in Gulkana and Glennallen a follow-up team from Fort Wainwright helped to establish a dining hall at the Glennallen High School and to survey the entire area for living quarters for the evacuees. All available space in schools, lodges, private homes, and in garages and warehouses was enlisted. Civil Defense set up headquarters at Glennallen High School, and Alaska Communications System provided emergency communications.

The Army established a checkpoint near the junction of the Richardson and Glenn highways to meet the evacuees from Valdez and to guide them to the temporary quarters. Some 500 people were housed and fed under this arrangement for periods ranging from 1 to 6 days.

In Valdez, the soldiers went to work with the remaining civilians to clean up the devastated city. A mess hall was established to feed the workers and cleanup crews. A water-purification unit arrived from Fort Wainwright, and a tank truck delivered water to the hospital and to other buildings still in use. One of the first actions was to search the entire beach-area debris for the 32 persons who were listed as missing (Figure 30). To assist in the search, USARAL, Alaskan Air Command, Air National Guard, and Civil Air Patrol aircraft conducted numerous reconnaissance missions over the city and surrounding area in the critical first few days after the disaster.

Army engineers and signalmen worked with the Valdez city utility workers to repair the telephone lines and electrical system. Communications were temporarily out of order, but by Saturday morning two outgoing lines from Valdez were open, and limited electrical service was reestablished by Easter Sunday. The city's heavy equipment, which had been in storage for the winter months, was serviced and made available to clear the city of rubble and to fill in crevices at the airport.

The mayor organized the collection of all perishable foodstuffs from commercial outlets and private homes and stockpiled them at the evacuated hospital, where the city postmaster, who was also a cook, established a temporary kitchen to feed the community workers.

Three Army doctors and some medical aid men, with the help of the Valdez doctor and a public health nurse who had driven down the Richardson Highway, inoculated the city's inhabitants against typhoid.

The task force commander appointed a crew of dog catchers to capture deserted and stray dogs and place them in a compound. Here the animals were fed and watered and could be reclaimed by their owners.

The Richardson Highway into Valdez had sustained only minor damage in the earthquake, and supplies could be brought into the city by this route. The highway, however, also created the problem of controlling the entrance of sightseers and potential looters into the area. At the entrance of the town, the Army manned a checkpoint to turn back all but those people who needed to be there. The checkpoint also helped to keep track of Valdez citizens

U.S. Army Corps of Engineers

FIGURE 30   The ruins of the fish cannery in Valdez.

should any new tremors or waves cause further loss of life. A similar check was maintained at the airport. The mayor and task-force commander devised a pass system that permitted workmen into the city areas where they were needed and gave businessmen access to their establishments for salvage purposes. At the same time, it kept the curious and the would-be looters out and sealed off areas that had been declared unsafe.

At the peak of its activities, the Army had 114 officers and men in Valdez, including infantry, engineer, signal, and medical personnel. Another 85–90 Army personnel were deployed in the Gulkana–Glennallen area. When the community had recovered to some degree, the troops and equipment were returned to Fort Wainwright by air.

WHITTIER

The first plane to reach the isolated port of Whittier was an Army Shawnee helicopter, which arrived late on Saturday afternoon to pick up an Alaska Railroad employee, his wife, and their baby who had been killed in the earthquake. On his way back to Fort Richardson, the helicopter pilot picked up 16 more women and children along the Seward Highway between Portage and Anchorage.

The inhabitants of Whittier moved into the gymnasium because their quarters were badly shaken by the earthquake, and the aftershocks were continuing. Electricity was restored in 6 hours, and water was running within 10 hours. By the third day after the earthquake, the normal way of life in Whittier was generally restored, except that the community dining room continued to operate.

On the Thursday after the earthquake, the first cargo moved over the Whittier docks. Ships and barges continued to arrive and unload on the dock. By the time the first train arrived at Whittier, more than 80 carloads of cargo were waiting to be distributed.

The port of Whittier was operating on a very limited basis. A large amount of cleaning up had to be done. Structural damage to buildings had been minor, but there were many cracked and fallen curtain walls and, although the maintenance building was being used, one end of it was badly damaged.

The first military aid to the port was given by an Army engineer detachment from Fort Richardson, which was sent to probe and clear the tunnel. A detachment from the 33d Signal Battalion followed and installed a radio connection with Fort Richardson and a 4-channel telephone cable through the railroad tunnel to connect with Portage. An Army civilian communications engineer, assisted by Alaska Communications System personnel, restored service on the badly damaged local telephone system. Five men from the 56th Engineer Company helped to restore port utilities.

On April 6, Fort Richardson sent a composite platoon of 46 men to help with the heavy cleanup work. The men and three jeeps were lifted into Whittier by Army Shawnee helicopters and immediately began the job of cleanup and damage control. They tore down unsafe walls, cleared debris, and salvaged and restacked the safe-haven supplies that had been stored in the port area.

SUMMARY AND CONCLUSIONS

During the first 2 weeks after the earthquake, the military bases played a very important role in mitigating the effect of the disaster on civilian communities. They provided search and rescue capabilities, medical supplies and facilities, food and shelter, potable water, communications, air and ground transportation, emergency power supplies, technical services, construction equipment, rehabilitation teams, and helped in many other ways. The military bases were especially effective in these operations because they had ready a supply of trained manpower, including technical experts, efficiently organized and prepared to respond quickly in an emergency. They had good communications facilities with the ability to bypass malfunctioning components. In addition, they had available a strong air-transport system, particularly important in Alaska where highway and rail transportation are relatively undeveloped. Equipment, such as trucks, construction equipment, emergency power supplies, and water-purification units, that was particularly needed to cope with the disaster was also available. In addition, the military bases had on hand large quantities of food, fuel, and medical supplies and could quickly secure additional help from the states in the form of manpower and supplies. For example, hospital units were flown in and reconnaissance planes were provided.

The bases themselves received some damage from the earthquake, but were able to remain operational. The earthquake showed that special attention should be given to the protection of communications systems in general and airport traffic-control systems in particular from earthquake damage.

REFERENCE

U.S. Alaskan Command [1964]. Operation helping hand: The armed forces react to earthquake disaster. Alaskan Command Publication. Seattle: Headquarters Alaskan Command. 83 p.

NORMAN L. ARNO
LEONARD F. McKINNEY*
U.S. ARMY CORPS OF ENGINEERS DISTRICT,
ALASKA

Harbor and Waterfront Facilities

The work of the Corps of Engineers in restoring or rehabilitating waterfront facilities was concentrated primarily in south central Alaska, specifically on Kodiak Island and in the Cook Inlet and the Prince William Sound areas. The most extensive work on waterfront facilities was done in communities relatively close to the major fault line. A minor restoration project was accomplished in southeastern Alaska at Klawock on the west side of Prince of Wales Island. The location of the major cities and towns that were damaged is shown in Figure 1.

Just before the earthquake the populations of the main waterfront towns affected by the earthquake were as follows: Anchorage, 48,000; Cordova, 1,328; Homer, 900; Kodiak, 2,800; Seldovia, 470; Seward, 1,800; Valdez, 565.

Underwater slides caused by the earthquake were major factors in the waterfront destruction at Valdez, Seward, and Homer. Slides at Valdez and Seward totally obliterated the waterfront facilities on which the economy of the cities depended, and at Homer the breakwater protecting the small-boat basin failed in a slide. The slides at Valdez and Seward generated waves that caused further destruction in those areas.

Uplift or subsidence affected every waterfront town in south central Alaska, from Kodiak through Homer and Anchorage to Cordova. Subsidence affected all the towns except Cordova and Tatitlek. The maximum subsidence was almost 6 ft, and Cordova was uplifted about 6½ ft.

Ground shaking caused damage to the Army dock at Anchorage. Damage from fires occurred in both Valdez and Seward, where petroleum products burned.

Tsunamis were responsible for widespread damage, particularly at Kodiak, Seldovia, and Cordova. The tsunamis also added to the general destruction by spreading burning fuel at Seward; the damage would have been still greater if the tsunamis had occurred at high tide.

In most coastal areas, a combination of slides, uplift or subsidence, fires, and tsunamis caused the damage. Only at Tatitlek, where uplift occurred, and at Klawock, where damage was caused by tsunamis, can a single cause of dam-

ABSTRACT: The waterfront communities of Anchorage, Cordova, Homer, Kodiak, Seldovia, Seward, and Valdez were damaged severely by the effects of the 1964 earthquake; uplift or subsidence, ground shaking, tsunamis, landslides, and fires affected some or all of these towns to some degree. Tsunamis were especially damaging and demonstrated that they could cause almost total destruction where they struck. The harbors and waterfront facilities of these various communities were repaired, mostly by the Corps of Engineers, so that they could resume their occupations and restore their economies.

*Now with the Bureau of Land Management, Anchorage.

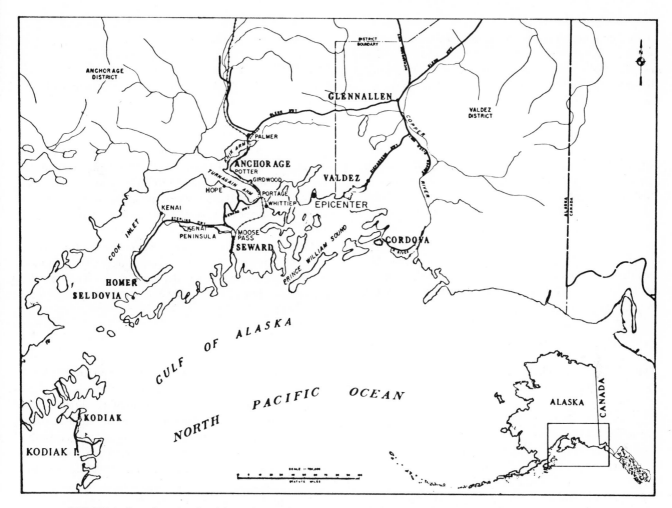

FIGURE 1   Location of major cities and towns in south central Alaska damaged by the earthquake of March 27, 1964.

age be identified; the other areas were damaged by two or more phases of the disaster.

In general, timber structures that were not heavily ice laden, not struck by the tsunamis, and not on slide areas, experienced only minor damage if any. Masonry structures whose foundations did not fail and that were not struck by a tsunami were also undamaged, indicating that, in general, the design of the structures themselves was adequate to withstand the forces imposed by the ground shaking.

DESIGN OF WATERFRONT FACILITIES

Technical criteria governing the design of waterfront facilities to be restored or replaced were taken from U.S. Army Corps of Engineers manuals (1960, 1963) or technical memoranda. Some criteria used in planning the small-boat basins were based on unpublished data developed in harbor-design conferences held by the Corps of Engineers in 1962, 1963,

and 1965. Two major categories of structures were restored or rehabilitated; they were fabricated structures, such as docks, floats, piers, warehouses, and buildings, and earthwork, such as breakwaters.

The "Preliminary Report: Tidal Datum Plane Changes, Prince William Sound, Alaskan Earthquakes" March–April, 1964 (U.S. Coast and Geodetic Survey, 1964b) was used to determine the elevation change of the landmass relative to sea level and to establish controlling elevations for the new or rehabilitated structures. Tidal datum planes defining normal and extreme high- and low-tide elevations, developed by the U.S. Coast and Geodetic Survey, were also used to establish controlling elevations on the structures.

ANCHORAGE

Anchorage harbor, one of the major ports in south central Alaska, lies on the eastern shore of Knik Arm at its confluence with the head of Cook Inlet (Figure 2). It has the distinction of having one of the largest tidal fluctuations in the world. The extreme range is 40.7 ft, from an extreme low tide of –4.9 ft to an extreme high of +35.8 ft. Mean tidal range is 27.4 ft, from mean low tide of +2.2 ft to a mean high tide of +29.6 ft, all with respect to mean lower low water (MLLW).

Cook Inlet and Knik Arm have open-water navigation for about 8 months of the year, i.e., from April to November. During the remaining 4 months, ice floes impede but do not prohibit shipping. In the spring, pan ice moves extensively. Tidal currents in the Anchorage harbor area are relatively strong and influence navigation. Most vessels utilize the 7-knot current to their benefit when entering and leaving.

All types of vessels use the harbor, from large oceangoing ships to small fishing and pleasure boats. Tankers, van-type freighters, and bulk-cargo freighters call regularly at Anchorage. During the winter, however, only deep-draft vessels use the port extensively.

WATERFRONT FACILITIES

A plan of the waterfront facilities before the earthquake appears as Figure 3.

Ocean Dock

Ocean Dock, with a connecting railroad spur 1 mi long from the Anchorage railroad yards, was designed and constructed by The Alaska Railroad in 1919. The open-pile structure was 77 × 355 ft, with a 30 × 300-ft approach and a 48 × 200-ft warehouse (Figure 4). It was used intermittently until 1924, when it was no longer needed. In 1930, a local cannery operator leased the facility; little or no maintenance was performed, and 1,100 ft of track along the approach was removed.

In 1941, the railroad regained title to the wharf, replaced the railroad spur, and leased the structure to the then War Department. The Army rehabilitated the structure and widened the entire wharf by 77 ft, placed additional trackage, and installed water and power lines. The dock was used extensively during the early war years, before railroad and docking facilities were constructed at Whittier and Seward.

Ocean Dock continued to be used primarily for handling Army freight. Until 1961, when the City of Anchorage completed construction of its own commercial dock, commercial carriers were permitted to use the dock only when it was not needed for military operations. Depths at the face of Ocean Dock were inadequate for deep-draft vessels because of shoaling; vessels therefore were unloaded over two breasting barges.

The Army was considering further dock extension and rehabilitation in 1964, when the dock was severely dam-

aged by the earthquake. On April 16, 1965, the dock was returned to The Alaska Railroad.

Permanente Dock

On August 26, 1949, Permanente Cement Company of Seattle, Washington, applied for a permit to construct docking facilities about 983 ft south of the Ocean Dock. The facilities consisted of a 75-ft-wide slip with a 355 × 60-ft timber-pile dock along the south side of the slip. Because the application conflicted with one made by the City of Anchorage, the site was moved to 1,150 ft south of Ocean Dock, and the application was resubmitted on November 15, 1949; the construction permit was granted on March 2, 1950.

On March 31, 1950, the Permanente Cement Company requested a modification of the permit to allow construction of a dock with face parallel to the shore; this was granted on April 12, 1950. The construction was completed in the same year.

Anderson Dock

On February 7, 1953, Captain Jack Anderson applied for a permit to construct a barge wharf near the mouth of Ship Creek. The facility planned was a 20 × 470-ft pile and plank retained fill with a 30 × 130-ft scow on piling parallel to the shore. At the face of this dock a grid was to be constructed to support barges during unloading operations. The permit was issued on March 27, 1953, and a wharf (85 × 400 ft) was constructed by Alaska Freight Lines under this permit and completed near the end of August 1953.

On October 29, 1956, Captain Anderson requested a permit to lengthen the dock 140 ft and widen it 65 ft; the permit was granted on November 30, 1956. At the time of the earthquake, the dock had been lengthened approximately 140 ft and had been widened about 50 ft.

Alaska Aggregate Corporation Dock

Alaska Aggregate Corporation applied on August 29, 1958, for a permit to construct docking facilities between the mouth of Ship Creek and Captain Anderson's dock on the north. After much disagreement, the permit was given on November 5, 1958.

During 1959, fill was hauled into the area and a bed was prepared to berth a ship for 360 ft of the bulkhead along the south side (Ship Creek side) of the property. On October 9, 1959, the placement of the ship and reinforcing with concrete and ballasting was completed. A crane was placed on the ship to unload cargo, and a berth was constructed on the south side of the grounded ship for cargo barges.

Asphalt Dock

On May 3, 1954, Rogers Construction Company and Babler Brothers applied for a permit to construct dock facilities

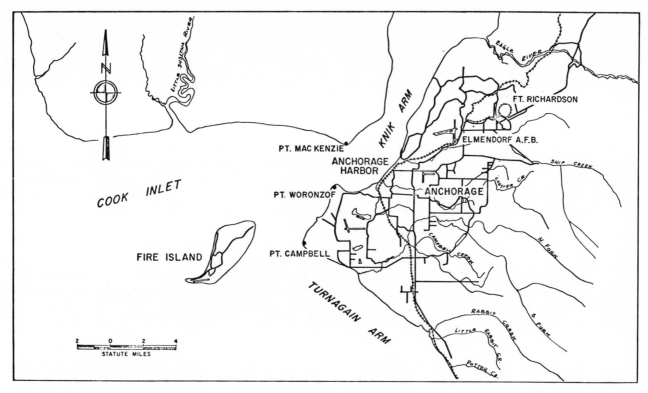

FIGURE 2   Anchorage harbor.

between the Alaska Fish and Game Dock and Permanente Cement Dock. The proposed facility was an earth-fill wharf about 450 × 330 ft, with fill contained by H piles between which were precast-concrete slabs. The permit was given on July 2, 1954, and construction was completed in October 1954.

A permit for extension of the wharf with a barge slip was requested by Rogers Construction Company and Babler Brothers on November 18, 1958. This proposed facility was approximately 550 × 470 ft with a 100 × 375-ft barge slip approximately in the middle of the dock. The proposed construction was the same as the original structure. A permit was granted on December 19, 1958, but the new work had not yet been done at the time of the earthquake in 1964.

On May 14, 1959, the permits originally issued to Rogers Construction Company and Babler Brothers were transferred to Union Oil Company, and the facility later became known as the Asphalt Dock.

City Dock

The permit for construction of the City Dock was applied for on June 1, 1956. The facility planned was a 600 × 300-ft structure consisting of a 212-ft-wide dock, a 98-ft-wide earth fill, and a 150 × 500-ft transit shed. The main dock was to be supported on 30-in. caissons filled with concrete.

Permit for construction was issued on September 14, 1956.

The facility constructed was supported entirely on piles, with two approach structures on the south end (Figure 5). There are 26 rows of piles parallel to the shore. The outboard piles are 42-in.-diameter caissons filled with concrete. The next four rows eastward are 24-in.-diameter steel piles; the next four rows, 20-in.-diameter; and the last 17 rows, 16-in.-diameter. The wall thickness of the piles is 7/16 in. The batter piles are steel side-flange members, size 14BP117, and tubular steel piles 20 in. in diameter. All piles are unfilled with the exception of the easterly row of the north dock extension and the outboard row. The dock is accessible by rail and truck on either side of the warehouse.

The firm of Tippetts–Abbott–McCarthy–Stratton (1965) describes the facility in the following terms:

The main pier is separated from access trestles and an apron extension to the north by expansion joints which allow stress relief from horizontal deck movements caused by changes in temperature, ship mooring and berthing forces, wind loads, or seismic forces. Under normal conditions, at 60 degrees Fahrenheit, these expansion joints separate adjoining components by 2 inches. In addition, stress relief in the main pier is obtained from inclusion of an expansion joint running on a line from north to south and adjacent to the east wall of the transit shed. This joint separates the structure of the main body of the pier into two parts, the eastern part measuring 74 feet 10 inches × 445 feet 6 inches, the western 196 feet 10 inches × 445 feet 6 inches. Under normal conditions this joint sepa-

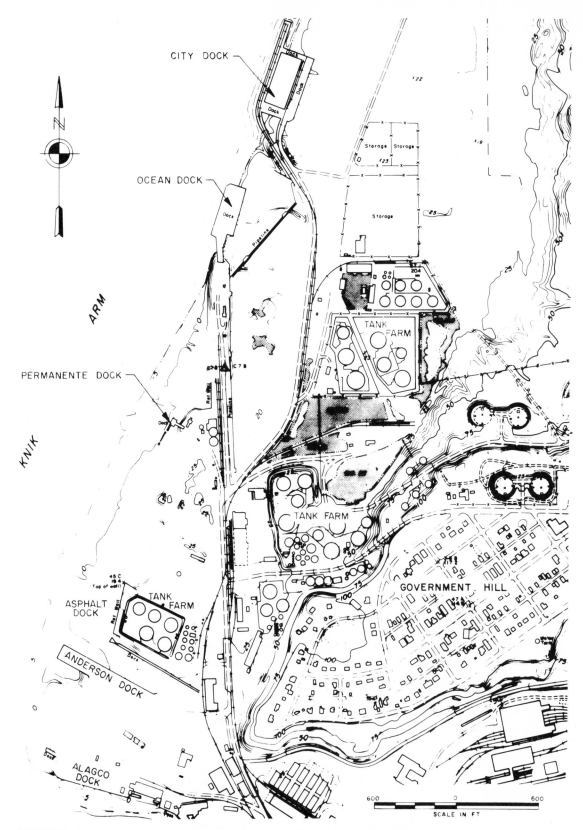

FIGURE 3 Plan of Anchorage waterfront facilities, showing development by city of Anchorage, federal government, and private enterprises.

FIGURE 4   The old Ocean Dock, Anchorage, about 1 year before the earthquake, with Elmendorf AFB and the Chugach Mountains in the background.

rates the two parts of the main pier by 2 inches. The larger section supports the transit shed including terminal offices, as well as cranes and appurtenant track work for handling ships' cargoes.

Optimum use of a marine terminal depends on the relationship of the structure to a tidal plane elevation, rather than ground elevations. Berthing vessel accessibility, protection from wave action, ice damage and other elements relate directly to vertical clearances from tidal plane elevations.

For locations protected from excessive wave action and not subject to damage from ice floes, such as Seattle, it is generally accepted that the surface of a pier or wharf should be at least 6 feet above the higher high water level. However, this general rule applies only to locations with normal tidal and climatic conditions. Extreme high tides have been recorded in Anchorage which, if accompanied by high winds of storm velocity, would cause the entire surface of the structure to become awash under application of this rule. For this reason and because of possible damaging action by ice floes, the original design placed the elevation of the deck a distance greater than 6 feet above mean higher high water. The deck surface at the west edge of the pier was set at elevation 40 feet above the reference plane. A gentle slope of the deck downward toward the more sheltered waters adjacent to the shore for purposes of drainage placed the deck along the east edge of the apron at elevation 38.75 above the reference plane. Hence, in the original design the deck surface at the exposed west edge of pier was 10.4 feet above mean higher high water and 4.2 feet above extreme high water; the sheltered east edge of the pier was 9.15 feet above mean higher high water and 2.95 feet above extreme high water.

The deck in the interior of the transit shed was sloped upward from elevation 40 at the west building line to elevation 43 at the east building line and was less critical to extreme ranges of tidal waters.

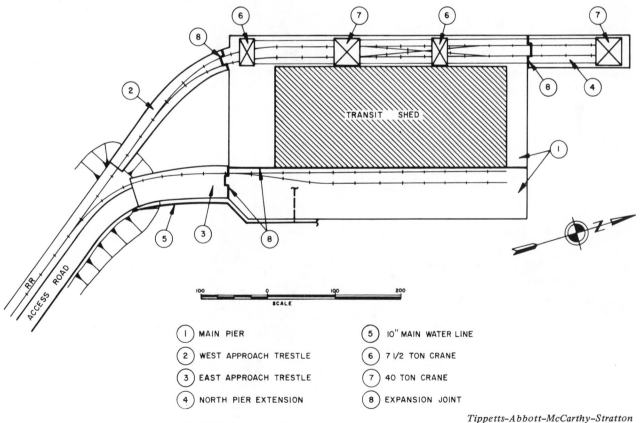

1   MAIN PIER
2   WEST APPROACH TRESTLE
3   EAST APPROACH TRESTLE
4   NORTH PIER EXTENSION
5   10" MAIN WATER LINE
6   7 1/2 TON CRANE
7   40 TON CRANE
8   EXPANSION JOINT

Tippetts-Abbott-McCarthy-Stratton

FIGURE 5   Port facilities of city of Anchorage: general plan.

DAMAGE TO WATERFRONT FACILITIES

Ocean Dock

The earthquake almost completely destroyed the Ocean Dock. Considerable heaving and lateral breakage occurred on the approach, particularly near the rock fill. The entire deck was uneven, with fractures up to 3 ft wide along the line where extensions to the dock were joined. In some instances, the capping and deck were lifted completely off the piling. All piling, buildings, and light poles canted seaward. The angle of the piling was about 8.5 degrees (Figures 6 and 7).

During past rehabilitation of the dock, additional pilings had been driven without removal of the old ones, leaving a mass of pilings beneath the dock in various stages of disrepair.

The massive accumulation of ice on the piling increased the mass and momentum of the dock and contributed to the extensive damage.

Permanente Dock

The Permanente Dock sustained only minor damage, but one cement-storage bin did collapse (Figures 8 and 9). Berg and Stratta (1964) of the American Iron and Steel Institute give the following description of the bin and failure:

At the entrance to the Army dock are located the storage facilities of the Permanente Cement Company. Here, a steel bin for cement storage collapsed and the top tore open. The bin was cylindrical, about 30 feet in diameter and 30 feet high, with a bottom cone about 15 feet high. A supporting ring at the base of the cylinder was carried on eight steel wide-flange columns which were

FIGURE 6 Anchorage: Damage to the Ocean Dock, showing separation of dock sections and undulating deck surfaces.

FIGURE 7   Anchorage: Ocean Dock, showing damage to railroad tracks (A) and piling leaning seaward (B).

supported by reinforced concrete pedestals. The columns were 14-inch wide-flange sections welded to 1¼-inch base plates. Each base plate rested on a 1-inch thick leveling plate and was anchored with four 2¼-inch anchor bolts.

In the earthquake the columns broke loose from the base plates and the bin fell. The welds connecting the columns to the base plates

Anchorage Daily Times

FIGURE 9   Anchorage: Cement-storage tank destroyed by the earthquake at Permanente Dock.

were completely inadequate. One of the base plates was cleaned and it was found that the weld was a 3/16-inch or smaller fillet over only part of the weldable length, and the red paint on the faying surface had not even been burned off by the heat of the welding process.

Anderson, Alaska Aggregate Corporation, and Asphalt Docks

The Anderson Dock was relatively undamaged by the earthquake (Figure 10).

The only damage to the Alaska Aggregate Corporation Dock was caused by the crane tipping over on it (Figures 10 and 11). One of the nearby cement-storage bins owned by the company collapsed (Figure 12).

The Asphalt Dock was also relatively undamaged.

FIGURE 8   Anchorage waterfront, March 1964, looking north. City Dock (top), Ocean Dock (center), and private dock (near bottom).

FIGURE 10   Aerial view of the southern part of the Anchorage waterfront, March 1964. Alaska Aggregate Corporation Dock is at the extreme bottom.

Anchorage Daily Times

FIGURE 11   Anchorage: Alaska Aggregate Corporation Dock after the earthquake, showing crane that tipped over.

City Dock

The following description of damage to the City Dock, port of Anchorage (Figures 13, 14, and 15) was taken from the Tippetts-Abbott-McCarthy-Stratton report (1965):

After the March 27 earthquake, changes in the normal joint openings indicated considerable movement and accompanying stress in the two parts of the main pier. Measurement on the north–south expansion joint showed a relative displacement of 17″ at the north end and 8″ at the south end over the normal separation of 2 inches. Total width of opening was 19 inches and 10 inches respectively. Comparison of structural damage between the eastern and western portions of the pier indicated that nearly all of the displacement occurred in the west part, or large portion, of the main pier. Translation to the west of this part of the pier, on the basis of joint mea-

FIGURE 13   Port of Anchorage dock (City Dock) on March 28, 1964. Photo taken from approach trestle shows cranes with counterbalances missing.

FIGURE 14   Anchorage: City Dock, from southwest, June 1964, showing repaired cranes and first dolphin for temporary POL dock and Ocean Dock.

Alaska Air National Guard

FIGURE 12   Anchorage: Collapsed cement-storage tank of Alaska Aggregate Corporation after the earthquake.

FIGURE 15   Anchorage: City Dock, June 1964. Counterbalances and support arms have been replaced on the cranes. Dolphin for temporary POL dock is in the foreground.

surement, was 12½ inches. Rotation in a counterclockwise direction accounted for an increase of 4½ inches at the north end and a decrease of the same magnitude at the south end.

Visible evidence of the pier displacement after the earthquake is the manner in which batter piles were deformed. The batter piles battered to the west were bowed and buckled while those battered to the east were relatively straight. Later investigations showed that most of the batter piles showed some degree of distress but that, in general, westward battered piles and eastward battered piles at the north end of the structure were damaged to a greater degree. The evidence is that the displacement of the pier, both translational and rotational, was developed and retained by buckling of the batter piles in the west portion of the main pier. [Figure 16 indicates probable modes of displacement under seismic-induced loading.]

The working of these batter piles against the large horizontal seismic forces indicated vertical loads at the pile heads which were transmitted into concrete pile caps above. Numerous cracks and areas of spalled concrete were developed in the vicinity of the heads of these batter piles.

The seismic forces further caused a swaying of the pier in a rotational and east–west direction, inducing bending moments and shears at the tops of vertical piles. These stresses in some cases caused shattering of the concrete cap and deck around the pile head [Figure 17]. In other cases the pile itself was sheared off at weld splices. Probable interaction of forces between the west and east portions of the main pier induced visible bows in vertical piles in the north end of the east part of the main pier. Shattering of the concrete curb in this vicinity was noted.

The displacement of the main pier is of particular significance from the structural standpoint because of its effect on the loading pattern of the piling.

The piles were originally designed to transmit the deck loads to

FIGURE 17 Anchorage: City Dock, showing damaged concrete pile caps.

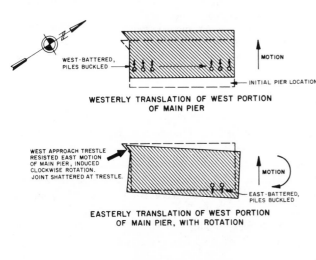

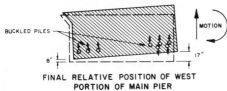

FIGURE 16 Anchorage: Probable motion of west portion of main pier under seismic loading.

the ground along their axis as a pure column. However, as a result of the earthquake, as stated earlier, the evidence indicates that the deck was displaced westward the same distance relative to its base. The effect of this displacement on the piles resulted in a stress condition which was one or a combination of the following:

1. *At the top of the pile:*
   a. The connection held rigidly, thereby inducing a bending moment at the cap.
   b. The connection held rigidly but the pile yielded, resulting in an indeterminable residual bending moment.
   c. The concrete cracked, causing the connection to rotate, resulting in very little or no bending moment at the top.
2. *At the base of the pile:*
   a. The soil held the base rigidly, thereby inducing a bending moment.
   b. The soil held the base rigidly but the pile yielded at some indeterminate point below the mud line, resulting in a residual moment.
   c. The pile rotated, relieving all or part of the bending moment.
3. *Along the length of the pile:* The pile yielded and deformed.

The resulting loading pattern on the piles is complex and varied. Piles that lost their rigidity at the ends but retained their straightness still were able to carry their loads along the axis but now exerted a horizontal load westward on the dock. The horizontal load was transmitted through the deck to the other piles. Piles that retained their rigidity at one or both joints and piles that were deformed carried their loads by a combination of axial stress and bending stress. The amount of bending stress was dependent upon the amount of horizontal load imposed by the deck, its degree of rigidity, and the amount of deformity.

The battered piles were designed, similarly to the vertical piles, to transmit their loads to the ground along their axis through compression and tension. The effect of the displacement on the piles battered north and south was similar to that of the vertical piles. The piles battered east and west bore the brunt of work in resisting the displacement. This was evidenced by the number of these piles that were visibly deformed. Other piles of this group were in all probability deformed under the mud line or were driven further into the ground.

The effect of the bending stresses created in the piles is to reduce their load-carrying capacity as columns. It was also feared that in time, because of creeping of the soil and the concrete and cracking of concrete due to weather and vibration, the bending moments on the ends of piles would be relieved, creating a horizontal force westward. This would induce greater moment on other piles and greater axial loads on the westward batter piles.

The west approach trestle suffered considerable damage as a result of the earthquake. Loads transmitted from the main pier induced shattering of the concrete at the expansion joint separating the trestle from the main pier [Figure 16]. The trestle's contribution to the resistance of motion of the main pier caused the shorter and less flexible piles near the access approach fill to rupture within the concrete cap embedding the pile heads. Buckling of several batter piles occurred in a general southeasterly direction. Translation of the trestle in a general southwesterly direction shattered concrete caps near the midpoint of the trestle. Several piles were also sheared off in this area. Rotational tilting of the deck because of the general southwesterly displacement of the battered frame raised the west side of the deck as much as three inches. The east side of the deck lowered as much as three inches. As a result of damage the trestle was barricaded to traffic until after repairs were effected.

The east approach trestle suffered comparatively little damage from the earthquake. Although some railroad track bolts were sheared and some shattering of concrete curb at the north end was noted, this trestle provided the only access to the pier immediately following the earthquake.

Translation and rotational movements due to seismic forces and interaction of the north pier extension with the main pier caused shattering and uplift of the concrete caps and deck at and over heads of all except one of the brace piles, both in the north–south and east–west directions. Six brace piles buckled. At the time the earthquake occurred a 40-ton crane and a 7½-ton crane were secured at the north end of the extension approximately as shown in Figure [5].

General overall damage to the transit shed, utilities, and cranes occurred under the action of seismic forces. Damage to the transit shed included ruptured connections between lateral bracing and perimeter roof members, severely cracked concrete encasement at the bottom of all steel columns, loss of holding capacity of nearly all metal siding screw fasteners, torn and separated fiber-glass siding, damaged rolling steel doors, collapsed concrete-block office partitions, and broken and torn roofing insulation and vapor barrier.

Damage to utilities included ruptured domestic and fire water-supply lines at the north–south expansion joint of main pier; loosened sprinkler heads; broken plumbing fixtures; broken water distribution, boiler, drainage, and sewer piping; bowed water-supply

line along east trestle; and a destroyed pipe-support bracket at the north end of the main pier. Numerous light fixtures and bulbs were destroyed. Electrical and telephone wires in conduit runs ruptured or broke loose from access or utility boxes and at numerous other junction points. The access ramp adjacent to the north pier extension was damaged.

Damage to cranes included loss overboard of boom counterweights from two cranes; deformed and sheared counterweight support arms, brackets and connecting hardware; sheared and loose ended structural bolts; a destroyed ladder safety guard; damage to all travel trucks; bent electrical travel feeds and misalined trolley duct; and ruptured and shorted-out wiring on travel trucks and rail clamps.

As a result of seismic forces, subsidence of the landmass in the Anchorage area caused a lowering of the dock relative to the water level. The elevation of the top of pier deck prior to the earthquake was approximately 40.0 feet above the reference plane of mean lower low water. Subsequent to the earthquake, the deck surface is approximately 36.3 feet above the reference plane.

Subsidence of the facility relative to tidal datum planes destroyed the former degree of protection of under-deck utility and fire-protection-system piping and electrical conduit runs against the ravages of floating and submerged ice. As a result of the 3.7-foot subsidence, there is insufficient clearance between the underside of the deck structure and the top of ice during winter. Freezing of moisture in the hairline cracks opened by seismic action or retained by capillary action in the pores of unbroken concrete, and uplift forces and abrasive action of winter ice will probably cause spalled concrete and increase yearly maintenance costs. The floating camel fendering system's effectiveness and usability at mean high and extreme high water is reduced. There is now little or no clearance below the overhang of the structure above. Movement of the floats on the cable anchor system is restricted, and vessels working alongside are held too far from the face of the pier for best operating efficiency during periods of high water.

At extreme high water, approximately 31% of the deck surface of the main pier would be inundated by water to a depth of 9 inches, and the entire east trestle would be completely covered by 9 inches of water.

Fuel-Storage Facilities

Many of the fuel-storage tanks in the dock area were damaged. Some tanks bulged outward at the bottom; in others, roofs and upper walls buckled. The Standard Oil Company of California reported two 100,000-gallon tanks leaking and a possible loss of 50,000 gallons of gasoline out of the approximately 300,000 gallons on hand. Union Oil Company reported no storage losses, with about 200,000 gallons on hand. Shell Oil Company reported light losses and about 11 million gallons of storage space available.

Shipping Congestion

Because of the loss of the railroad between Anchorage and Whittier, shipping to the port of Anchorage increased so greatly that a serious problem arose in scheduling the berthing of vessels. Many ships had to stand by in the inlet awaiting their turn at the dock.

All goods shipped by boat to Anchorage or destined for the interior of Alaska had to land at Anchorage, where the dock could accommodate at most two ships at one time. The tremendous petroleum requirements of Anchorage and of Elmendorf Air Force Base had to be met. With the destruction of the old Ocean Dock, which had been used as a tanker berth, the whole load fell on the City Dock. The City Dock had only one access to shore, and it was necessary to run the tractor trailers in a circular traffic pattern around the dock, which resulted in congestion and delays. An additional problem was created by the requirement for loading small boats for the oil-exploration activities that were increasing in the Anchorage area.

RESTORATION OF WATERFRONT FACILITIES

Very little restoration of damaged waterfront facilities at Anchorage was undertaken by the federal government. The City Dock access was repaired, covers on earthquake joints on the City Dock deck were replaced, and a temporary petroleum, oils, and lubricants (POL) dock was constructed to replace unusable facilities on the Ocean Dock (Table 1). For immediate off-loading of petroleum products to Anchorage, military forces installed pipelines on the City Dock by about the middle of April 1964.

City Dock

Restoration work performed by the City of Anchorage on the City Dock consisted mainly of redesign, relocation, and protection of portions of the pier facilities. The water-distribution system and the electrical system were pro-tected or relocated, and the floating ship-fendering system was reconstructed.

The Tippetts–Abbott–McCarthy–Stratton (1965) report for the City of Anchorage gives the following description of the restoration:

As a result of rehabilitation studies, it was decided to submit a contract for the rehabilitation of the pier. The basic proposal would include the work of restoring the west portion of the main pier to its original position. An alternate proposal was also added in which the contractor would rehabilitate the pier but would leave the east portion in its displaced position. The method of performance for the basic proposal was left to the discretion of the contractor but subject to the approval of the Engineer.

The analysis of the submitted bids revealed a very high cost for the basic proposal to restore the west portion to its original position without correcting the change in elevation. Considering this and after consideration of this factor as well as the other factors discussed heretofore, it was decided to award the contract on the basis of a revised alternate bid to repair the pier in place.

At the outset of the work, the slightly bowed piles were straightened by clamping a bracing beam (strong back) alongside the bent section and applying two to four hydraulic jacks on the pile. This worked quite effectively. In order to expedite the work, reduce the costs, and to avoid disruption of port activities which would be caused by splicing of piles or pile driving, this "strong-back" method was used to repair all the batter piles including those that were scheduled to be replaced with new sections by splicing or driving. Heat was applied to some badly distorted piles to bring them into line.

During the process of the work it became apparent that repairs to the cracked concrete would be more extensive than the original survey indicated. Scaffolding placed under the deck for the repair work permitted closer and more thorough inspection of the work. How-

TABLE 1 Anchorage Area Contracts

Project	Date Awarded	Date NTP[a]	Date Work Started	Completion Date Original Schedule	Actual	Amount Paid to Contractor (dollars)	Funding Agency
City Dock repair	Mar. 28, 1964	Mar. 28, 1964	Mar. 29, 1964	Apr. 1, 1964	Apr. 18, 1964	5,003	OEP[b]
Feasibility study and preliminary plan, off-loading facility, port of Anchorage	Apr. 8, 1964	Apr. 8, 1964	Apr. 9, 1964	June 1, 1964	June 1, 1964	18,000	OEP
Design and construction POL facility, port of Anchorage	Apr. 29, 1964	Apr. 30, 1964	Apr. 30, 1964	July 9, 1964	July 10, 1964	433,401	OEP
Harbor 1965 maintenance	June 18, 1965	June 21, 1965	June 21, 1965	July 30, 1965	Aug. 18, 1965	48,225	CE[c]
Harbor dredging (1966)	Apr. 20, 1966	Apr. 28, 1966	May 23, 1966	Sept. 15, 1966	Terminated for default	–	–
TOTAL						504,629	

[a] Date of notice to proceed.
[b] Office of Emergency Planning (later, Office of Emergency Preparedness).
[c] U.S. Army Corps of Engineers.

ever, the major reason was that hairline cracks that were considered normal cracking of concrete or of minor consequence had widened and other new cracks had appeared. These cracks can be attributed mainly to the distorted configuration of the pier. This subjects the pile caps to bending and horizontal stresses that were nonexistent previously. The work of repair redistributed these stresses, creating new strains, and resulted in cracking. The distortion also subjected the pier to greater displacements and vibrations from the impact of ships and ice floes which, coupled with the above mentioned internal stresses, added to the cracking, the detrimental effects of water and icing of cracks, compounded by the subsidence of the deck, served to widen the existing cracks.

The work of straightening the piles and repairing the concrete cracks in the main pier is now completed. This portion of the pier has been brought as nearly as possible to full operating status. However, the structural strength of the pier has not been restored on a permanent basis.

Temporary Petroleum, Oils, and Lubricants Handling Facilities

Because of interference with the unloading of restoration cargo and other delays, and the high cost of tanker standby, the feasibility of constructing a temporary POL dock was investigated.

On April 8, 1964, an architect–engineer contract was awarded for a feasibility study of a temporary POL dock to define the most economically feasible structure, the location, and the planned future expansion of the port. A facility was needed that could be constructed with readily available material in a short time with a life expectancy of about 2 years.

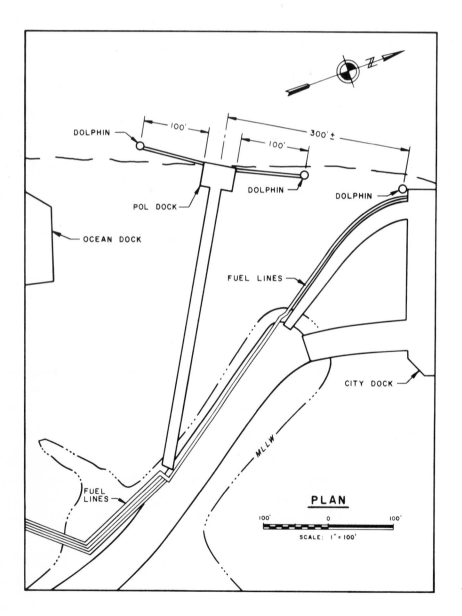

FIGURE 18   Plan view of temporary POL dock, constructed in 1964 for emergency facilities to unload fuel for Anchorage and vicinity.

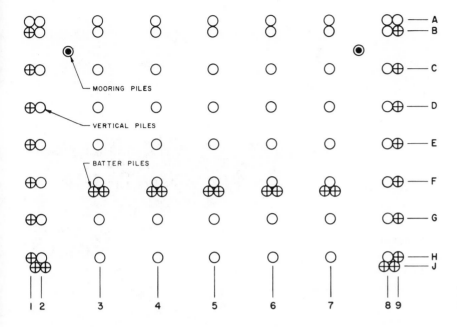

FIGURE 19 Pile layout for breasting platform, temporary POL dock, Anchorage.

Four plans for the POL dock were considered: a timber dock, a DeLong-type dock, a conventional steel-pile dock, and a north extension of the City Dock using one DeLong section.

The DeLong dock could not be used because too much time was required for preparation and towing to the site, and the cost was too high. Steel-pile construction also could not be used because of the high cost of construction.

A decision was therefore made to design and construct a temporary timber structure. The design was completed on April 20, 1964, and a contract was awarded for construction on April 29, 1964. The project was completed on July 10, 1964, at a cost of about $443,000.

The site chosen for the temporary POL dock was between the City Dock and the Ocean Dock, because no dredging was required in that area. Details of the dock are shown in Figures 18 and 19. Figures 14 and 15 are photos of the POL dock under construction. The POL dock, completed in August 1964, is shown in Figure 20.

The entire structure was not intended to last through the following winter; it was expected to fail because of the heavy loads imposed by the swiftly flowing drift ice along the Anchorage waterfront. A dock that would withstand these forces would have been more expensive and could not have been constructed for use in 1964.

The temporary dock lived up to its name; in February 1965, the dolphins for the dock were destroyed by floe ice (Figure 21), and the outer section was extensively damaged later. Figure 21 shows the massive accumulation of ice on the POL dock, indicating ice buildup on the structures at the time of the earthquake.

FIGURE 20 Anchorage: Temporary POL dock after completion in August 1964. Damaged Ocean Dock on right.

FIGURE 21 Anchorage: From bottom, damaged Ocean Dock, damaged POL dock, and City Dock, February 1965. The dolphins for temporary POL dock have been carried away, and ice floes and heavily ice-encrusted piling can be seen on oil docks.

Permanent Petroleum, Oils, and Lubricants Handling Facilities

While the design and construction of the temporary POL dock were being carried out, the City of Anchorage was planning a permanent facility. In the summer of 1965, the port of Anchorage began to construct it in the same location as the temporary dock. In the process of constructing the new dock, the northern 100 ft of the Ocean Dock was removed so that a dolphin could be installed.

The permanent POL dock was all but completed in fall 1965, but it was not until fall 1966, after the area in front of it had been dredged, that the fender piles were installed and tankers could actually use the dock. By this time, however, congestion at the City Dock had been relieved by repairs to the Anchorage–Whittier rail line, and an appreciable amount of cargo was moving over the Whittier dock, enabling tankers to use the City Dock without lengthy delays.

Demolition of Ocean Dock

The U.S. Army in Alaska (USARAL) controlled the Ocean Dock through a use permit from The Alaska Railroad. Because the dock was so badly damaged, USARAL requested that it be demolished, under authority of Public Law 875 or of the Corps of Engineers, as a hazard to navigation. The demolition project could not be funded by the Office of Emergency Planning (later the Office of Emergency Preparedness) (OEP) because the facility was owned by a federal agency, and the dock could not be demolished under the Corps of Engineers' authority because it was not at the time a hazard to navigation; it was only a potential hazard should it fall down.

In late August 1966, a portion of the Ocean Dock was removed (Figure 22) to permit dredging for access to the POL dock under a regular Corps of Engineers funded

FIGURE 23   Anchorage: Ocean Dock in October 1966, after portion of the face had been removed. Lower photo shows dock separation.

FIGURE 22:   Anchorage: Face of Ocean Dock during demolition on August 24, 1966.

maintenance-dredging project; 25 ft of the face, or about 7,600 ft^2, were removed under this contract.

During removal and dredging operations at the Ocean Dock, seaward movement was observed in the deck. The separation between the deck sections increased about 1 ft 6 in. in one week (Figures 23 and 24). The piles were leaning seaward at an angle of about 15 degrees. Because of the increased danger of collapse, another request was sent to the Office, Chief of Engineers (OCE) for permission and funds to demolish the dock before it became an actual hazard to navigation. Permission was subsequently granted.

The private facilities were repaired by the owners and were back in operation in a short time. The crane on the Alaska Aggregate Corporation dock was reinstalled in its original location (Figure 25). New fuel tanks were constructed and cement-storage bins replaced.

FIGURE 24 Anchorage: Damaged Ocean Dock, October 1966, showing condition of piling on interior of dock.

FIGURE 25 Looking north at the Anchorage waterfront, summer 1964, Alaska Aggregate Corporation dock can be seen in the foreground with crane set up. Tideflats at left are exposed at low tide. Ship Creek is in foreground.

CORDOVA

Cordova harbor is a partly protected area in Orca Inlet (Figure 26), a shallow strait between the Gulf of Alaska and Prince William Sound. This strait has shoaled in recent geologic time because of accumulation of fine-grained material carried to sea by the Copper River. The city of Cordova developed along the east shore of Orca Inlet. For vessels crossing the Gulf of Alaska from the inside passage of southeastern Alaska, Cordova provides the first developed and protected harbor.

Orca Straits provide a short route from the primary salmon-fishing grounds at the mouth of the Copper River to the home port and canneries at Cordova. The alternate and much longer route from the fishing grounds to Cordova is around Hawkins Island and through a narrow shallow channel between Hawkins and Hinchinbrook islands.

Tides at Cordova have an extreme range of 22 ft, from an extreme low of –5 ft to an extreme high of +17 ft. Mean tide range is 10 ft, from a mean low tide of +1.5 ft to a mean high tide of +11.5 ft. All elevations refer to the plane of MLLW.

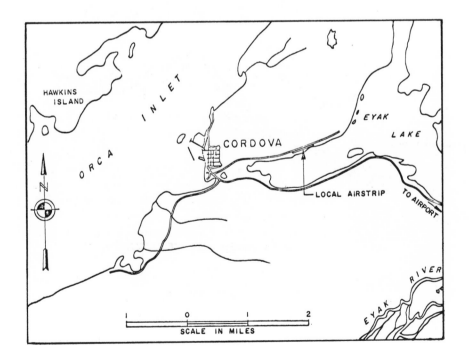

FIGURE 26 Vicinity map of Cordova.

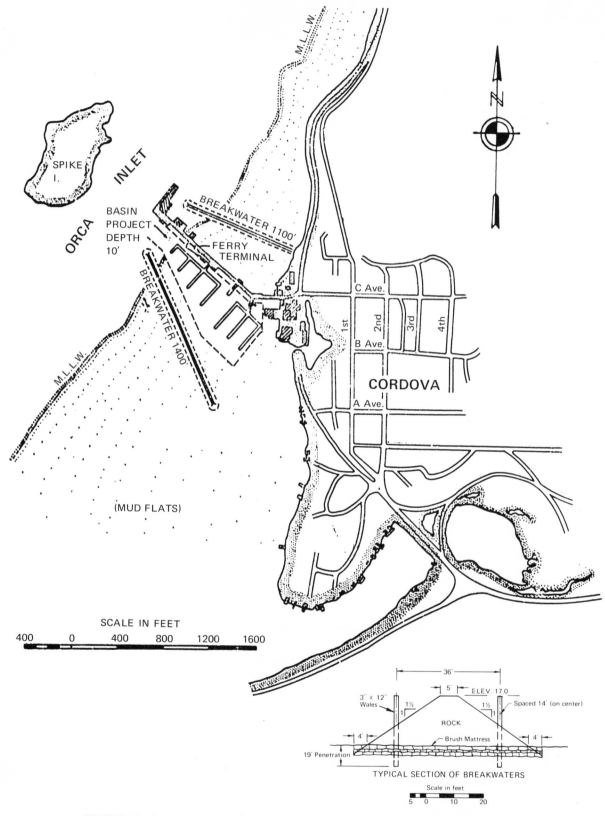

FIGURE 27 Cordova: Layout of small-boat harbor and breakwater section before the earthquake.

PREEARTHQUAKE WATERFRONT FACILITIES

Before the earthquake, Cordova had an 8.25-acre small-boat basin at a depth of 12 ft below MLLW. The basin was protected by a north breakwater about 1,100 ft long and a south breakwater about 1,400 ft long (Figures 27–29).

The breakwaters were constructed of a rubble mound with a crest elevation of 17 ft above MLLW. Because the foundation material was very unstable, the breakwaters were constructed on a brush mattress extending 4 ft beyond the toe of the fill (Figure 27).

The City Dock and approach structure was approximately 1,300 ft long and 20 ft wide and extended along the expansion area of the small-boat basin. The dock had a deck elevation of 23 ft above MLLW.

A ferry slip had been constructed in 1963 on the approach to the City Dock (Figure 30). The slip was 48 ft wide, 159 ft long, and lay at an angle of about 30 degrees to the City Dock approach. Three ramps, each 16 ft wide and at elevations of +18 ft, +14 ft, and +10 ft, were constructed at the end of the slip to permit loading and unloading at various tide levels. Sections of the ramps are shown in Figure 30.

The small-boat basin, built in 1938, was designed for 500 boats. Because of the increase of boat size since its construction, the basin had space for only 220 boats at the time of the earthquake (Figure 31) and was overcrowded. The Cordova fishing fleet consisted of about 400 boats; consequently, many boats used natural but inadequate coves and inlets for semiprotected moorage.

DAMAGE TO WATERFRONT FACILITIES

Damage at Cordova resulted in part from the tectonic uplift and in part from the tsunami that arrived some time later. No slides or fires occurred. The boats moored in the basin and the floats were not damaged.

Damage by Tectonic Uplift

Earthshocks caused little damage to structures, but differential movement of the ground did damage the sanitary-sewerage outfall by causing joint separation. In addition, tectonic uplift left the outfall discharging in the tideflats well above the MLLW line, creating a sanitation hazard and an obnoxious condition.

Uplift of 6.5 ft reduced the depth of the small-boat basin from 12 ft to 5.5 ft at MLLW, making the water too shallow at low tide for any but the smallest skiffs. In addition, the natural inlets that provided shelter for boats before the earthquake were rendered useless because of the uplift; the privately owned deep-draft Ketchikan Wharf Company dock about ½ mi north of town was similarly affected by the uplift.

FIGURE 28   Cordova small-boat harbor float facilities, City Dock, and boat-repair grid, summer 1961. Spike Island is in the background and the city of Cordova in the foreground. North is to the right.

Many small fishing boats were stored in the cannery at the Ketchikan Wharf Company dock. Because of the uplift, the area in which these boats were normally launched for the fishing season was dry, except at extreme high-tide stages, making it very difficult to launch the boats in preparation for the fishing season.

Damage by Tsunami

The earthquake-generated tsunami struck Cordova shortly after the earthquake. A Coast Guard ship tied to the City Dock when the tsunami struck moved violently, and the mooring lines pulled the dock seaward, leaving the wood piling leaning at an angle of about 15 degrees. In addition, the water surface rose above the deck of both the City and Ferry docks, pulling the pile caps loose from the drift pins. When the water level receded, many pile caps were dislocated. In addition to dock damage, a number of homes were destroyed along the waterfront.

FIGURE 29   Cordova small-boat harbor and City Dock, summer 1961. North is to the left.

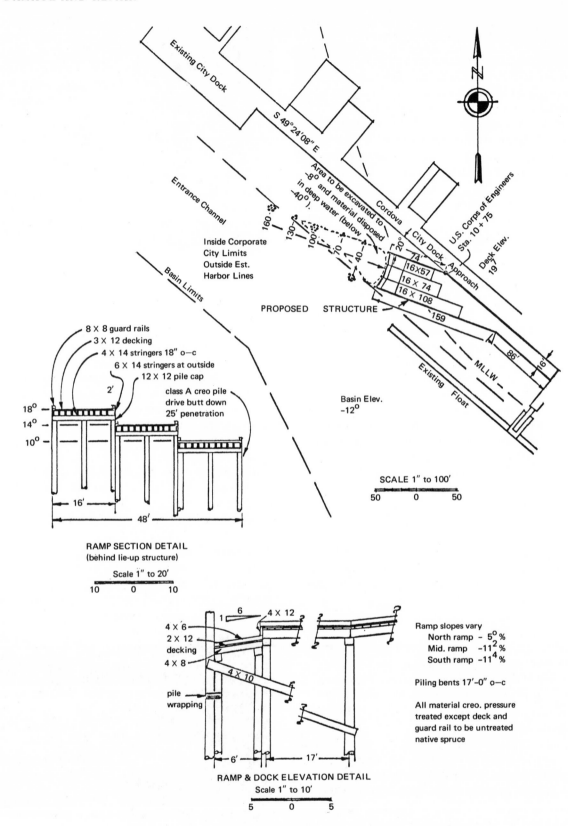

FIGURE 30 Plan and sections of the preearthquake ferry slip at Cordova.

FIGURE 31 Cordova small-boat harbor shortly after construction in 1938, looking toward Spike Island.

RESTORATION OF WATERFRONT FACILITIES

The Cordova waterfront facilities were restored with funds furnished by both the OEP and the Corps of Engineers. The state contributed by modifying a contract that was in existence at the time of the earthquake to make it coincide with the master plan developed for the harbor. The City of Cordova acquired the real estate necessary to allow the restoration efforts to proceed and installed temporary floats. Tables 2 and 3 list the items of work necessary for restoration and the source of funds for each item. In general, the Corps of Engineers financed the restoration of the previously authorized federal harbor projects, whereas OEP funded restoration of all publicly owned facilities (Table 4).

TABLE 2 Cordova Construction Contracts

Project	Date Awarded	Date NTP[a]	Date Work Started	Completion Date Original Schedule	Completion Date Actual	Amount Paid to Contractors (dollars)	Funding Agency
Repair to ferry dock, including new approach to dock	Apr. 6, 1964	May 9, 1964	May 9, 1964	May 15, 1964	June 23, 1964	75,800	OEP
Debris cleanup	May 18, 1964	May 22, 1964	May 25, 1964	July 13, 1964	July 8, 1964	36,449	OEP
Float removal and first-stage bulkhead construction	June 19, 1964	June 26, 1964	June 24, 1964[b]	July 21, 1964	Apr. 6, 1965	112,930	OEP
Float removal ($15,565)	—	—	Jan. 14, 1964	July 21, 1964	—	—	—
First-stage bulkhead construction ($81,440)	—	—	—	July 21, 1964	—	—	—
Outfall sewer repair and extension (south of small-boat basin, SBB)	June 22, 1964	June 30, 1964	June 29, 1964	Aug. 25, 1964	Aug. 29, 1964	54,000	OEP
Railroad street sanitary-sewerage outfall rehabilitation and storm-sewer extension north of SBB, including lagoon dikes and silt barrier	Aug. 21, 1964	Sept. 1, 1964	Sept. 1, 1964	Nov. 15, 1964	Dec. 8, 1964	344,147	OEP
Dredging SBB and ferry dock; rental of hydraulic pipeline dredge	June 19, 1964	July 14, 1964	Sept. 15, 1964	NA[c]	June 5, 1965	556,595	OEP and CE
Second-stage bulkhead construction, including blanket on north breakwater and repair to gravel blanket along inside of first-stage bulkhead	Nov. 10, 1964	Nov. 10, 1964	Nov. 12, 1964	Oct. 23, 1964	Apr. 24, 1965	249,331	OEP and CE

TABLE 2   (Continued)

Project	Date Awarded	Date NTP[a]	Date Work Started	Completion Date		Amount Paid to Contractors (dollars)	Funding Agency
				Original Schedule	Actual		
Auxiliary power plant for city of Cordova	Jan. 19, 1965	Jan. 19, 1965	Jan. 19, 1965	Apr. 20, 1965	July 19, 1965	3,133	OEP
North breakwater repair and entrance-channel slope protection	Nov. 25, 1964	Dec. 4, 1964	Nov. 23, 1964	Feb. 6, 1965	Apr. 5, 1965	143,355	OEP and CE
Road on north breakwater	–	–	–	Jan. 1, 1965	March 7, 1965	–	–
Ferry terminal facility, including bulkhead for approach ramp	Oct. 16, 1964	Dec. 1, 1964	Dec. 5, 1964	Jan. 2, 1965	May 1, 1965	52,510	OEP and CE
Removal of city dock approach and appurtenances, including removing obstacles in harbor	Jan. 14, 1965	Jan. 18, 1965	Jan. 19, 1965	Mar. 2, 1965	Feb. 16, 1965	182,425	OEP
Ferry terminal utilities	Feb. 18, 1965	Mar. 6, 1965	Apr. 19, 1965	May 1, 1965	May 8, 1965	20,593	OEP
SBB, inner-harbor facilities reconstruction including public loading dock	Mar. 31, 1965	Apr. 9, 1965	Apr. 21, 1965	June 30, 1965	Aug. 19, 1965	244,565	OEP
New city dock, including road widening	June 8, 1965	June 19, 1965	June 24, 1965	Nov. 15, 1965	July 15, 1965	424,900	OEP and CE
Float lighting transferred to city of Cordova					Feb. 5, 1965		
City dock transferred to city of Cordova					Nov. 15, 1965		
Entrance breakwater	Sept. 3, 1966	Sept. 7, 1966	Sept. 14, 1966	Nov. 16, 1966	Oct. 18, 1966	51,660	CE
Confine slurry within bulkhead	Oct. 18, 1965	Oct. 18, 1965	–	–	–	5,668	–
TOTAL						2,558,061	

[a] Date of notice to proceed.
[b] Contractor started work prior to notice to proceed.
[c] Not available.

An increase in depth from 12 to 14 ft at MLLW in the small-boat basin was necessary to accommodate the larger and deeper-draft vessels that currently are used for commercial fishing in the Cordova area. The basin area was also to be increased to 18.7 acres at a depth of 14 ft at MLLW to provide an area large enough for mooring 450 boats. Restoring the basin by dredging to preearthquake conditions would also have restored an even more pronounced overcrowding problem than before because of additional boats seeking basin protection owing to loss of natural mooring areas.

The restoration schedule was to interfere as little as possible with the ferry schedule and with the businesses near the dock. A new ferry terminal therefore had to be provided before the dock approach was moved. Before the ferry terminal facility could be constructed, however, the area in front of it and the slopes under it had to be dredged to make the water deep enough for maneuvering the ferry. Removal had to be timed so that the hired dredge, costing about $2,600 per day, would not be delayed.

Scheduling of work was further complicated because insurance companies required small boats to moor within the basin as a condition for maintaining their policies. To fulfill this condition, the floats could only be moved a few at a time while the new floats were being constructed within the basin. Some of the floats had to be removed, however, be-

TABLE 3   Cordova Supply Contracts

Project	Date Awarded	Date NTP[a]	Date Work Started	Completion Date Original Schedule	Actual	Amount Paid to Contractors (dollars)	Funding Agency
Piling and timber for first-stage bulkhead	–	–	May 27, 1964	–	May 29, 1964	28,000	OEP
Hardware for first-stage bulkhead	–	–	May 28, 1964	–	June 4, 1964	5,000	OEP
Second-stage bulkhead piling and timber	Sept. 9, 1964	NA[b]	Sept. 9, 1964	Sept. 21, 1964	Sept. 19, 1964	86,000	OEP
Ferry dock, lumber	Sept. 11, 1964	Sept. 17, 1964	Sept. 17, 1964	Oct. 3, 1964	Oct. 3, 1964	17,908	OEP
Ferry dock, piling	Sept. 11, 1964	Sept. 17, 1964	Sept. 17, 1964	Oct. 3, 1964	Oct. 3, 1964	17,026	OEP
Hardware for ferry ramp	Sept. 11, 1964	Sept. 17, 1964	Sept. 17, 1964	Oct. 3, 1964	Oct. 3, 1964	6,440	OEP
Off-loading lumber, hardware, and piling	Sept. 19, 1964	Sept. 19, 1964	Sept. 19, 1964	Oct. 3, 1964	Oct. 3, 1964	12,065	OEP
Second-stage bulkhead 6,500 ft wire rope	Dec. 21, 1964	Dec. 21, 1964	Dec. 21, 1964	Dec. 28, 1964	Dec. 28, 1964	4,733	OEP
TOTAL						177,172	

[a]Date of notice to proceed.
[b]Not available.

fore the dredge could start excavation in the expansion portion of the basin. Another complication was the requirement for maintaining access to and utilities for the Point Chehalis Cannery. Early in the schedule, an access road was

TABLE 4   Breakdown of Funding

Corps of Engineers	Office of Emergency Planning
RESTORATION FUNDING	Debris cleanup
First-stage bulkhead	City dock and dock approach removal
Dredging (existing small-boat basin)	Ferry terminal facilities
North breakwater repair	Dredging (landing area)
South breakwater repair	Retaining dikes
Entrance-channel slope protection	Dock replacement
Silt barrier	Utilities
Blanket north breakwater	Inner-harbor facilities
	Float removal
EXPANSION FUNDING	Float repairs and replacement
Second-stage bulkhead	Public loading dock
Dredging (expansion area)	Grid replacement
Entrance breakwater	Float approaches
	Float utilities
	North breakwater roadway
	Approach ramp bulkhead
	Storm sewer extension
	City dock replacement
	Adjacent dredging
	City dock utilities

constructed on the north breakwater and connected to the lock approach that had been built immediately after the earthquake. The old City Dock, extensively damaged by the tsunami, also had to be removed before the new City Dock could be constructed. The property of the Washington Fish and Oyster Cannery, which was on the old dock, had to be acquired; the City of Cordova purchased all necessary real estate through condemnation procedures, thereby permitting early demolition of the old City Dock and approach. An undamaged privately owned nearby dock was used by deep-draft and Coast Guard vessels while the new dock was under construction.

The restoration work had to be accomplished in the shortest time possible, protected moorage for the fishing fleet had to be maintained during construction, and Cordova's economy had to be protected as much as possible. These criteria were adhered to throughout the restoration program. The final schedule of restoration required removal of the dock, the dock approach, and commercial establishments abutting it; relocation of the dock and ferry terminal; removal and reinstallation of the float system; and repair of the ends of the breakwaters.

Temporary Repairs to City Dock, Approach, and Ferry Dock

The economy of the city of Cordova is centered in its small-boat harbor. Damage, caused primarily by tsunamis, had rendered this area unsafe for normal use and had made speedy repair of the harbor imperative. At the time of the earthquake, the State of Alaska had an active contract for extension of the City Dock, but the day after the earthquake it was obvious that the construction could not be continued as designed. The state halted construction until a master plan could be developed by the Corps of Engineers and then modified its contract to include the most-needed repairs to the dock and to begin construction of an approach from the dock to the north breakwater. When the funds available to the state were exhausted, the Corps of Engineers awarded a new contract utilizing OEP funds for rehabilitation of the dock and restoration of the ferry terminal.

The marine highway from Cordova to Valdez is the only surface-transportation link between the city of Cordova and the rest of Alaska. The state ferry *Chilkat* makes two trips a week. To maintain commerce, the ferry dock had to be repaired as soon as possible. The master plan required expansion and deepening of the harbor, necessitating removal of the dock approach and ferry dock. To accommodate the shipping requirements during the interim period, minimum repairs were made to permit use of the dock. The City Dock and Ferry Dock repair contract was completed on June 23, 1964.

Debris Clearance

The tsunami caused extensive damage to private piers and houses along the Cordova waterfront and deposited some debris that included an old scow, several skiffs, and some old dock piling. Demolition of several houses along the waterfront and cleanup of trash along the beach line was included in the debris-clearance contract. All burnable material was either burned in place or hauled away; the trash was buried along the beach line in pits from 8 to 10 ft deep.

The city of Cordova had a large rat population, especially along the margins of Odiak Slough and the city dump. A two-man rodent-control team from Fort Richardson, assisted by a man from the Fish and Wildlife Service who was familiar with the area, were dispatched to resolve this problem.

Small-Boat Basin Restoration and Expansion

Disposal of Dredged Material   A major problem in deepening and expanding the small-boat basin was disposal of dredged spoil. A total of about 535,000 yd³ of material had to be dredged, which included 140,000 yd³ in the restoration portion of the basin, 155,000 yd³ in the ferry-terminal area, and 240,000 yd³ in the expansion portion of the basin. Several areas were considered for disposal of material; an area south of the small-boat basin could be filled; the material could be taken by barge about 2.5 mi across Orca Inlet to a bay; or Odiak Slough or an area north of the north breakwater could be filled. The area north of the north breakwater was selected because it was closest and

most economical; however, a system had to be constructed to contain the dredged material. The system selected (Figure 32) consisted of a first-stage and second-stage bulkhead. The bulkheads were actually vertical timber walls acting as membranes to retain the dredged fill with rock facing to hold the slopes against wave actions.

First-Stage Bulkhead and Float Removal   A contract for the first-stage bulkhead and removal and stockpiling of existing floats was awarded on June 24, 1964. It was assumed that the dredging could be finished in 2–3 months and that the floats could be removed while most of the boats were on the fishing grounds when there would be the least need for mooring facilities. Problems in scheduling the dredging operation and in acquiring real estate delayed completion of the dredging. To expedite the construction of the first-stage bulkhead, two separate supply contracts were made—one for supplying piling and timber, the other for providing the hardware. These materials were ordered in late May and delivered in June to be available to the contractor for immediate construction of the first-stage bulkhead. Although the construction contract was not closed out until April 1965, the first-stage bulkhead was completed in mid-August 1964.

Second-Stage Bulkhead   The second-stage bulkhead was required to complete the disposal area for dredged material (Figure 32). The computed amount of dredging to be done determined that a top elevation of +15 ft MLLW was needed to accommodate all the material to be dredged from the small-boat basin and ferry-landing areas. The material underlying the area of the second-stage bulkhead was sandy silt, incapable of bearing the load that the required 17-ft-high wall would have imposed when filled with liquefied dredged materials. Extensive probing and analysis determined the most economical method of retaining the dredged fill; the final design of the bulkhead (Figure 33) consists of an extensive cable-tieback system to deadmen (Figure 34), a gravel layer to provide the filter requirements to retain the dredged spoil, a layer of quarry spalls, a facing of armor rock (Figure 35), and a strengthening of the first-stage bulkhead by adding stone to the seaward face.

On November 12, 1964, construction began on the second-stage bulkhead and on the strengthening of the first-stage bulkhead. To expedite completion of the second-stage bulkhead, a supply contract was negotiated to provide the piling and timber (delivered in September 1964) to permit construction to start as soon as the contract was awarded. During construction, another supply contract for 6,500 ft of wire rope was required to provide tiebacks; the rope was delivered in December 1964.

The second-stage bulkhead contract included blanketing the north breakwater with 2 ft of gravel to prevent seepage

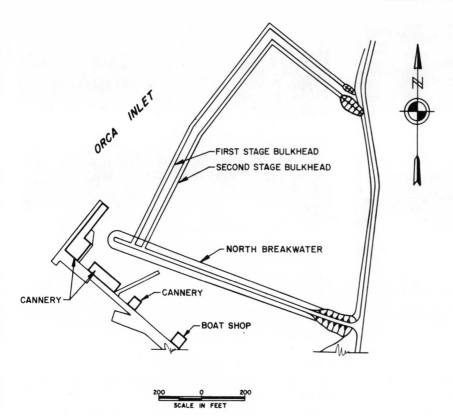

FIGURE 32 Plan view of the first- and second-stage bulkheads constructed to contain the material dredged from the small-boat basin, Cordova.

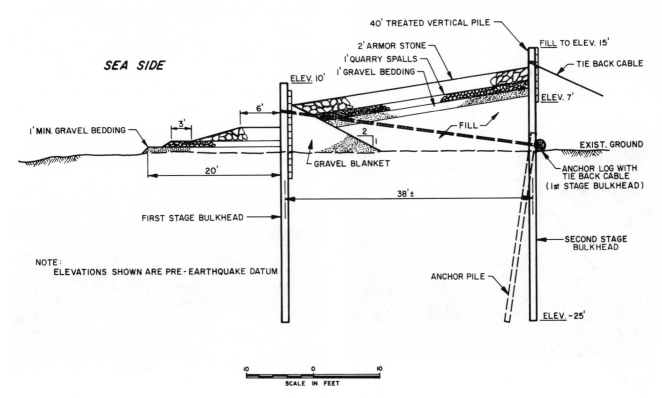

FIGURE 33 Typical section of the two bulkheads finally designed and constructed at Cordova.

FIGURE 34   Cordova: Dredged material being discharged into the north disposal area adjacent to the second-stage bulkhead (January 1965).

FIGURE 36   Cordova: Preearthquake view of the lagoon area east of the small-boat harbor, showing cannery, warehouse buildings, skiffs, and fishing scows.

of the fine dredged materials through the porous rubble-mound north breakwater. The work was completed May 10, 1965.

Tidal Lagoon   During design of the second-stage bulkhead, more accurate computations of the dredging quantities showed that the disposal area within the bulkheads would be insufficient to contain all the dredged material. The overage was estimated at 60,000 yd^3; a tidal lagoon within the city limits made an ideal disposal site for this material (Figures 36 and 37). Before the earthquake, all the city's storm drainage flowed into this area, which was inundated

twice daily, and the fresh water was mixed with salt water. As a result of the uplift, the lagoon was dry except at the highest tide stages. Before the lagoon could be filled with dredged material, storm drains had to be extended through the area to prevent glaciation of the storm runoffs that would threaten surrounding development. In addition, a dike had to be constructed across the mouth of the lagoon to contain the fill. The fresh water that flowed into the basin had been frozen at times to a depth of 6 in., damaging boats by springing the hull seams. The use of the lagoon as a disposal area accomplished the dual purpose of providing a nearby disposal site and of alleviating the icing problem within the small-boat basin.

FIGURE 35   Cordova: Rock slope protection placed between first- and second-stage bulkheads and at toe of first-stage bulkhead. Spillway through the bulkhead is on the left (May 1965).

FIGURE 37   Cordova: Lagoon area east of small-boat harbor was dry at all but the highest tides after the earthquake (April 1964).

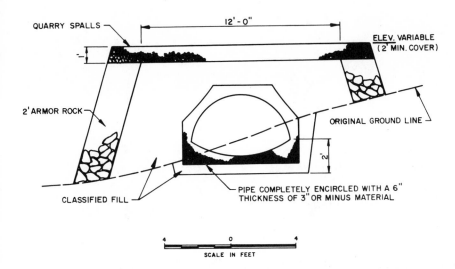

FIGURE 38 Cordova: Typical pipe section (arch type) of storm sewer crossing the mud flats south of the small-boat basin.

Storm Sewer The storm sewer was extended south of the small-boat basin, approximately parallel to the already existing sanitary sewer. The most economical method of construction was to provide a 72 X 44-in. corrugated-metal pipe and line, laid on the mud flats and covered with fill material protected by quarry spalls (Figure 38). This method of construction reduced the necessity for maintenance dredging within the small-boat basin by blocking the transport of sediment into the basin around the southeast end of the south breakwater. Only a low dike, which was called the silt barrier, was required to extend the south breakwater to the protective cover over the storm sewer.

The silt barrier was in an area that was subjected to waves only at extremely high tides. The design wave was determined by applying a shoaling coefficient (Beach Erosion Board, 1961) to the deep-water design wave from the southwest. Armor-stone requirements for the silt barrier and sewer line were as follows: thickness based on design stone size; maximum armor-stone size not to exceed 10 percent by weight. A typical section of the silt barrier is shown in Figure 39. On September 1, 1964, construction was started on the storm sewer, the lagoon dike, and the silt barrier; construction was completed on December 8, 1964.

North Breakwater Roadway During development of the plan, modifications were necessary to ensure retention of

the City Dock, particularly in the vicinity of the Point Chehalis Cannery, which was to be left standing. Although the temporary approach from the dock to the north breakwater had been completed, the only road access was over the city dock approach, which was soon to be removed. It was imperative that the cannery remain in operation because it was a major factor in the economy of Cordova, purchasing, processing, and shipping the local fish catch. An access road, therefore, was essential. The cannery is in operation 11 months of the year and is shut down during the month of January, the only time during which the access to the cannery could be closed.

A contract for a road on the north breakwater was awarded; work started on November 23, 1964. A typical section through the north breakwater after completion of the dredged fill and the roadway is shown in Figure 40, and a view of the finished breakwater appears as Figure 41. The contract included repair of the south breakwater, which was being undermined because of the relatively lower water level, and rock protection of the entrance-channel slope, which was installed after the channel had been dredged. The contract was completed on April 5, 1965 (Figures 40 and 42).

Dredging All restoration work was contingent on dredging. The areas that required excavation to provide sufficient

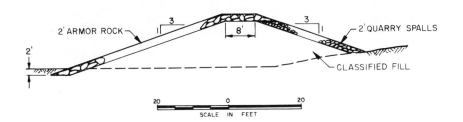

FIGURE 39 Cordova: Typical section of the silt barrier, which consisted of an extension of the south breakwater to the storm-sewer groin.

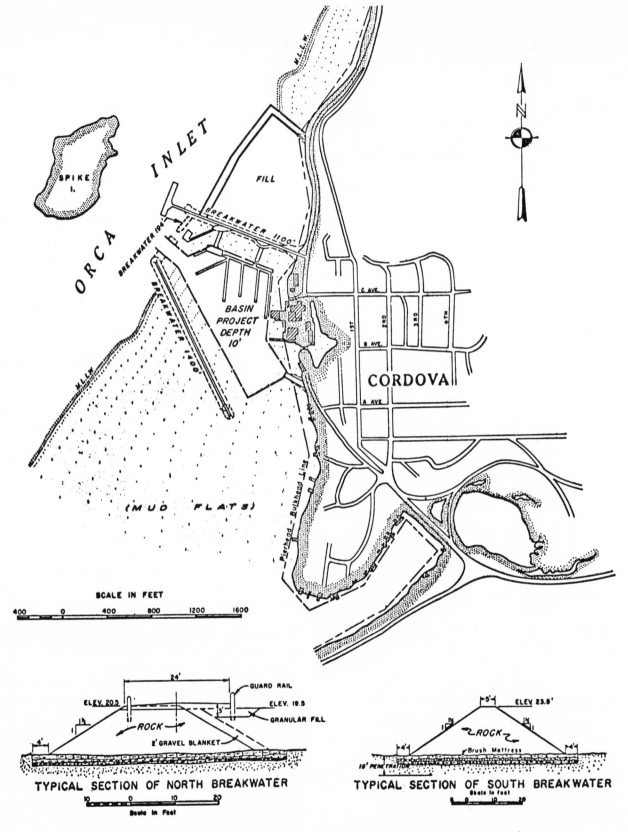

FIGURE 40 Cordova: Layout of the small-boat harbor after restoration and sections of the breakwaters.

FIGURE 41 Cordova: The north breakwater roadway, with float installations and float-approach construction under way on the left. Fill area on the right has been completed (June 25, 1965).

depth for navigation are shown in Figure 43. The area in front of the Ferry Dock had to be dredged so that the necessary rock protection for the fill could be placed. The dredge had been excavating a channel in Orca Inlet, 55 mi south of Cordova. Because of the bad weather conditions anticipated in Orca Inlet from January to April, dredging in the most essential part of Orca Inlet was completed before the dredge was brought into the protected waters of the Cordova small-boat basin. Dredging was started in the ferry terminal area on December 22, 1964, and was completed by the time the contractor required access.

The next area available for dredging was the expansion area of the harbor, but the dock approach had to be removed as the dredging proceeded. The critical portion of the dock approach was removed by the time access was required, and dredging was not delayed (Figure 44).

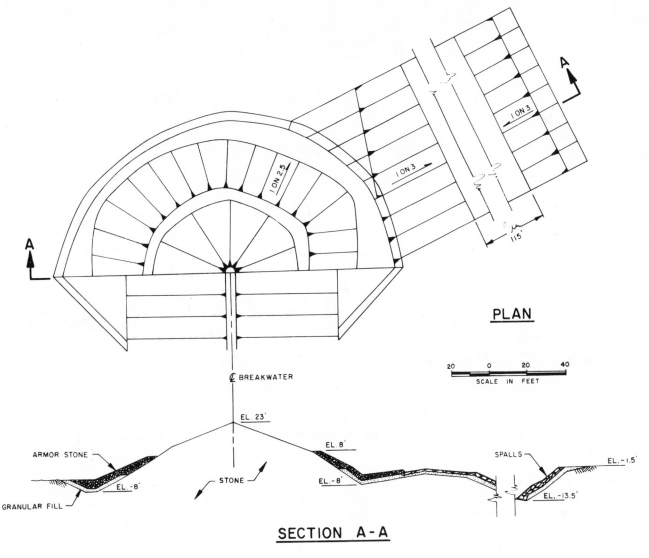

FIGURE 42 Cordova: Plan and section of repair to south breakwater and entrance channel.

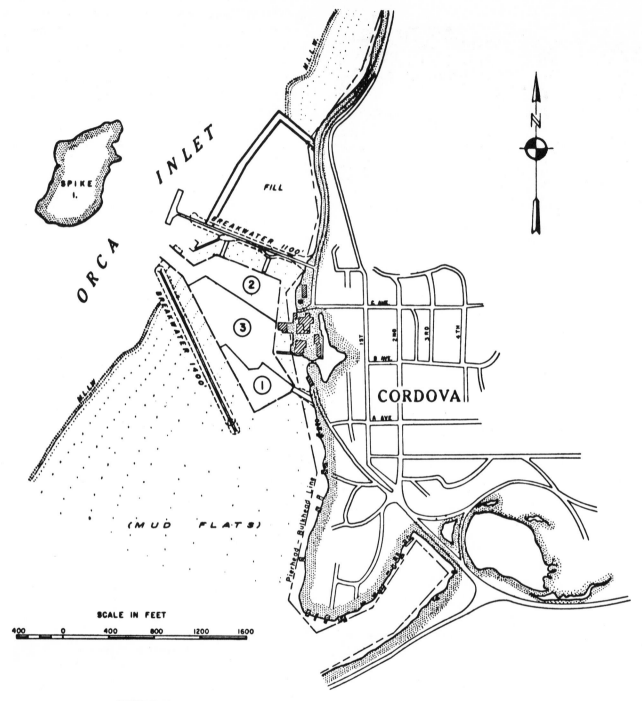

FIGURE 43 Plan of Cordova small-boat basin, showing areas to be dredged and priorities.

Fill Material from Excavation Material excavated from the Cordova small-boat basin and ferry dock area was used to fill the area north of the north breakwater and the diked lagoon area east of the small-boat basin. Spillways were provided at the north end of the bulkhead and at the south end of the lagoon to discharge the water pumped by the hydraulic dredge. About 10 percent of the solid dredged material was carried over these spillways but the bulk of the dredged material settled in the designated disposal sites, although a small amount was lost when the first-stage bulkhead blew out.

While the fill was being placed, it was in a relatively fluid

FIGURE 44 Cordova: Dredging is under way in the expansion area. The pile foundations are under construction for a boat shop and bar in the fill area. One third of the floats have been removed. The Ferry Dock in the upper-left-hand corner is complete (March 16, 1965).

state. The coarsest fraction of material settled closest to the discharge line, and the finest fraction was carried to the extremes of the disposal sites. The fill areas were at first unable to support a man on their surface.

In the lagoon fill area, material was discharged at the north end; the spillway, which discharged into the storm-sewer line, was at the extreme south end. This filling operation was completed in May 1965. By June 1965, a crust strong enough for a person to walk on with care had formed on the north end, but not on the south end. By late fall 1965, a person could walk anywhere on the north end but only with care on the south end, and the fill was still unstable in some places in summer 1966.

In the north fill area, dredged material was discharged in two places adjacent to the north breakwater; the fill operation was completed in April 1965. The north fill area, like the lagoon area, was relatively fluid when placed, developed a crust after some time, and was not fully hardened by the summer of 1966. A photograph taken in August 1965 shows tire tracks on the north fill (Figure 45).

As time progresses, the dredged fill is draining and becoming more stable, but engineers do not know when it will develop enough strength to support structures without substantial foundation preparation or special design.

Ferry Dock Replacement and Approach-Ramp Bulkhead

The design of the Ferry Dock was based on the State of Alaska design that had existed before the earthquake and tsunami; the only changes made were in the location and the fill bulkhead. The dock has three separate ramps terminating at various elevations; it is a standard pile-and-timber structure designed for H-20 loading (Figures 40 and 46).

The Ferry Dock construction contract was advertised December 5, 1964; the starting date of construction depended on an estimate of when the dredging in Orca Inlet would be completed. Work started on the Ferry Dock on December 5, 1964. The ferry was scheduled to be in dry dock at Seattle for about 3 weeks for the annual inspection, and the new Ferry Dock had to be completed during this time. Because of the short construction period, the materials had to be on hand for the contractor when work on the Ferry Dock began.

While the ferry was away, the City Dock approach was removed (Figure 47), and work started on the ferry landing on January 19, 1965. The Ferry Dock contract also included construction of a bulkhead to the new approach; concurrently with his work on the Ferry Dock, the contractor placed fill behind this bulkhead to connect the approach to the newly constructed road on the north breakwater. Work was completed in December 1964 on the continued access allowed to the Point Chehalis Cannery.

Temporary Utilities

With the forthcoming removal of the approach to the City Dock, the water and electric lines to the Point Chehalis Cannery had to be removed. Permanent utilities to the cannery were not to be installed until the new City Dock had been constructed (fall 1965); temporary water and power were therefore required to enable the cannery to keep operating. The technique of using 4-in.-diameter irrigation pipe to provide a temporary water supply had been developed by the City of Anchorage shortly after the earthquake and was used in Valdez during the summer of 1964. In January 1965, 3,000 ft of surplus irrigation pipe was shipped to Cordova and installed on the mud flats from the city water main to the Point Chehalis Cannery. It was still in use in

FIGURE 45 Cordova: North fill area has been completed. Tire tracks can be seen on the fill (August 1965).

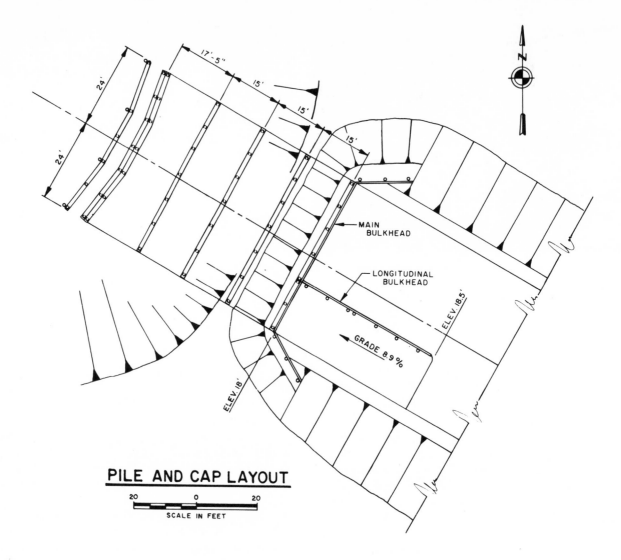

PILE AND CAP LAYOUT

SCALE IN FEET

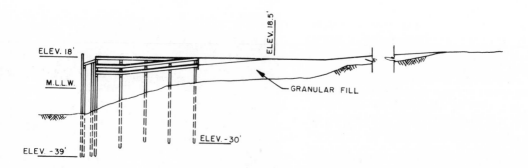

PROFILE

SCALE IN FEET

FIGURE 46 Cordova: Layout and profile of the new Ferry Dock.

FIGURE 47   Cordova, February 1965: Aerial view of bulkheads for disposal area (left). Removal of the City Dock approach and dredging are in operation. Storm-sewer protection is east of south breakwater.

March 1966. A 50-kW diesel-powered generator was installed at the cannery to furnish the temporary power with which to operate.

Completion of Dredging and Replacement of Floats

The floats could not be installed at the time planned because pile-driving equipment was not available. It was still necessary to moor boats within the small-boat basin while dredging was in progress, but the floats had to be removed so that the dredge would not be delayed. At the end of March, the City of Cordova volunteered to install the floats temporarily in the expansion portion of the basin while dredging continued in the restoration portion (Figure 48). Before permanent float installation could begin, a strong

north wind developed. The temporarily installed floats broke loose and drifted toward the south breakwater into the dredge-discharge line, which extended from the dredge, between the floats and the south breakwater, to the disposal area north of the north breakwater. The dredge discharge line kept the boats and floats from drifting into the south breakwater, which, because of its very rough surface, would have caused appreciable damage to the floats. Some of the boats and floats were damaged, but none were lost.

On April 21, 1965, construction began on the float installation (Figure 49). It included permanent installation of the old floats in the basin expansion area, a public loading dock to replace the City Dock approach (which also served as a dock), and installation of a boat-repair grid. The most easterly line of floats was found to be over a rock outcrop, which precluded pile-driving in this area. The new float configuration is shown in Figure 50. Extensive probings were made to determine the limit of the rock, which was found to extend to the stall floats on the second line of floats from the eastern limit. Because of the small-boat basin configuration, it was impossible to revise the float layout without jeopardizing its capacity and future float configuration. The float-installation contract was therefore modified to include drilling the rock to receive the necessary piles. The contractor was able to use his pile-driving equipment efficiently on those floats that did not require drilling and on the approaches and new public dock. This work was done while he was awaiting the arrival of rock-drilling equipment from Kodiak, about 300 mi away. As soon as the rock-drilling at Kodiak was completed, the drill barge proceeded to Cordova, but sank en route; the project was delayed until the contractor could purchase another drill barge and trans-

FIGURE 48   Cordova: Permanently installed portion of the north fill area and the small-boat harbor, May 1965.

FIGURE 49   Cordova: Float installation in progress, seen from new public loading dock. Float sections with styrofoam billets are shown in the foreground on the left side of the floats. Boats are tied to floats while float installation proceeds (June 26, 1965).

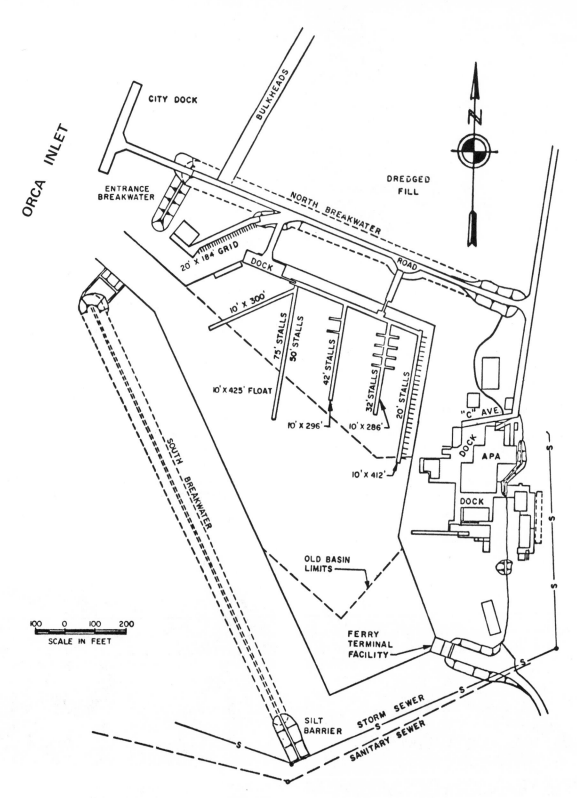

FIGURE 50   Cordova: Layout of inner-harbor facilities and City Dock after restoration.

port it to Cordova. The float installation was completed in August 1965.

City Dock Replacement and North Breakwater Roadway

The work remaining included construction of the new City Dock, repair of the north breakwater, completion of the second lane of the road on the north breakwater that supplied utilities to the dock, and finishing construction of the approach trestle. Selection of the site for the new City Dock was a major problem. To select the most economical and accessible location for the dock, local interests in Cordova were consulted, surveys were made of several sites, load tests were conducted, and soil-probing results were used to determine potential dock stability. One location considered was off-shore of the fill north of the north breakwater, but it was rejected because of high cost of construction there and doubts as to when the fill within the bulkhead would stabilize sufficiently to support the heavy traffic anticipated between the city and the dock. The site at the end of the north breakwater was finally selected (Figure 51).

The dock was designed to be 300 ft long and 30 ft wide with complete utilities. The deck elevation is 20.5 ft above MLLW, and the available depth is 30 ft below MLLW

(Figure 52). Timber cross bracing provided stiffness between elevation +7.5 ft and elevation +14.5 ft MLLW. The dock was designed as an all-timber structure, complete with fender pile and buffer logs to prevent floating debris from getting under the dock and damaging the cross bracing. Metal ladders, a lighting system, and a water-supply line were also included.

The size of the new dock was limited to that of the public section of the original dock, which, although longer and wider, had also accommodated the Washington Fish and Oyster Cannery, making that portion basically a private dock structure. Although the City of Cordova would have preferred a larger dock, it was unable to produce the additional money itself because of expenditures in acquiring real estate for the rest of the project. Construction of the dock was begun on June 24, 1965; although the contract was not completed until July 1966, the dock was transferred to the City of Cordova on November 15, 1965.

After the dock was put in service in November 1965, several contract modifications were found to be necessary. The dock was extremely flexible, causing some local concern, but this flexibility was not detrimental to the main dock structure. When a ship docked, the dock moved longi-

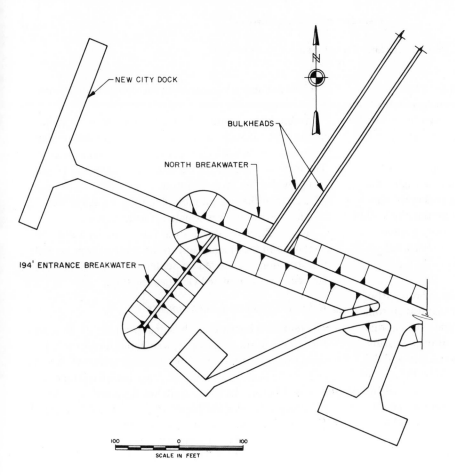

FIGURE 51 Cordova: Plan view of new City Dock location and entrance breakwater.

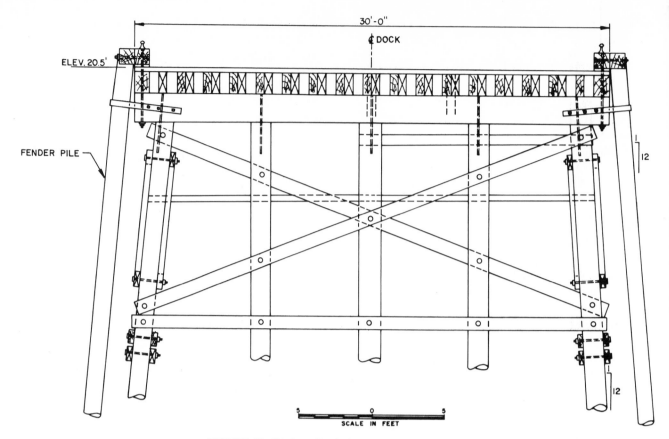

FIGURE 52 Cordova: Typical section of new City Dock.

tudinally up to 6 in., and flexible couplings in the 6-in. waterline between the approach and the dock were necessary to prevent breakage of the line. Although the dock is long, narrow, and flexible, it has proved to be a very satisfactory structure.

When construction of the dock was completed, the buffer logs installed to prevent debris from damaging the cross bracing were removed by operating personnel who considered that these logs, which would continually abrade the fender and bearing piles, were unnecessary because little floating debris was present in the Cordova area.

Entrance Breakwater

After the floats had been installed in the northern part of the small-boat basin, it became apparent that waves from the north caused more damage to boats and floats in that location than they had in the southern half of the harbor. This situation was unexpected because refraction and diffraction analysis indicated that there would be little or no wave action from northerly winds in this area, and sufficient wave energy was not expected to reflect from the south breakwater to cause damaging waves in the basin. During a storm in December 1965, waves from the north were found to diffract around the north breakwater and progress into the basin at about 90 degrees to the direction of incident wave travel.

Studies were conducted to determine the most economical site and cross section for the entrance breakwater, giving consideration to both cost and annual maintenance cost. The location selected for the entrance breakwater (Figure 51) provided the smallest entrance-channel gap and took advantage of the highest ground in the area. A rubble-mound breakwater was selected (Figure 53).

The entrance breakwater was funded under authority contained in the amendment to the Alaska Omnibus Act. Construction was started on September 14, 1966, and the structure was completed October 18, 1966.

Relocated Business Establishments

The relocated business establishments on the fill area, adjacent to the north breakwater, were built during the fill operation on a driven-pile foundation (Figure 54). A gravel and crushed-rock-fill access for construction traffic was provided before the dredged fill had been installed. After the dredged fill was completed to grade, a rock and gravel mat was placed atop it for a parking area.

The Point Chehalis Cannery was moved to a dock constructed off the bulkheads 400 ft north of the City Dock.

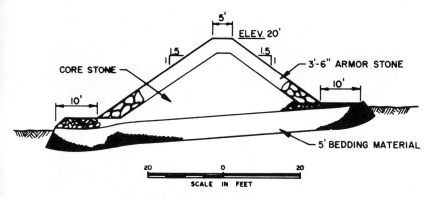

FIGURE 53   Typical section of entrance breakwater of the Cordova small-boat basin.

To provide access, a 4-ft-thick rock- and dirt-fill surface was placed on top of the dredged fill in February 1966.

HOMER

The City of Homer, at the southern terminus of the Sterling Highway that connects with the Anchorage–Seward Highway (Figure 55), has a deep-water ice-free port that accommodates tankers, freighters, and barges off-loading cargo at Homer's City Dock for transshipment to the lower Kenai Peninsula area. The Alaska State Ferry System had recently started service to Homer, carrying passengers, vehicles, and freight between Homer and Seldovia and between Homer and Kodiak on a regular semiweekly schedule.

Homer Spit is a unique landmark on the Kenai Peninsula. It is a long, low, narrow finger of land built up of littorally transported materials (Figures 56–59) lying immediately southeast of the city of Homer and extending about 4 mi, or halfway into Kachemak Bay. The tip (distal end) of the spit supports canneries, motels, restaurants, and all Homer's waterfront facilities, including the small-boat basin and the City Dock. The City Dock serves all deep-draft vessels calling at Homer and is open to general use on payment of wharfage charges. The original small-boat basin on the northeast side of the spit, about 0.4 mi from the tip of the spit, was dredged from the beach and was protected by a rubble-mound breakwater. It housed the Homer fishing fleet. Mooring facilities in the basin consisted of modern wood and polystyrene floats installed by the State of Alaska.

Homer is open for year-round shipping. Drift ice from the head of Kachemak Bay sometimes drifts down the bay to block the entrance to the small-boat basin, but deep-draft vessels could, if necessary, use the deep-draft dock when this occurs.

The extreme tide range at Homer is 31.1 ft, between an extreme high of +25.1 ft and an extreme low of −6.0 ft. The mean tidal range is about 16 ft between mean high water of +17.5 ft and mean low water of +1.6 ft. All elevations refer to the plane of mean lower low water (MLLW).

WATERFRONT FACILITIES BEFORE THE EARTHQUAKE

City Dock

The City Dock that existed at the time of the earthquake was completed on May 9, 1949. The dock was a 160 × 40-ft structure with a 14 × 240-ft access, supported on creosoted wood piling.

A 21-ft extension on the shoreward side of the dock was completed in September 1957. Later, a preengineered metal warehouse was installed on the dock for dry storage of goods subject to water damage.

This dock had experienced several earthquakes and, as in the 1964 earthquake, had sustained very little damage from the earthshocks.

Small-Boat Basin

The original Homer small-boat basin at the end of the spit (Figures 60–62) was about 180 ft wide and 672 ft long and was protected by a rubble-mound breakwater 1,260 ft long (Figure 63); the basin and breakwater were completed by

FIGURE 54   Cordova: Bar and outboard-motor shop under construction on the north fill area. North breakwater roadway is on the left (May 1965).

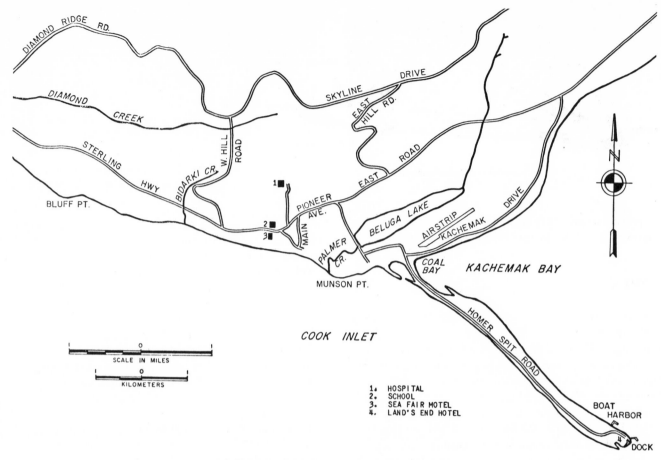

FIGURE 55   Vicinity map of preearthquake Homer.

the Corps of Engineers in September 1962. The breakwater section shown in Figure 64 consisted of gravel core, covered with quarry-run rock, which, in turn, was protected against wave action by armor stones.

Basic meteorological data for the original design were very limited—a common situation in Alaska. The Homer airport on the mainland 4 mi from the small-boat basin was the nearest climatological station. No wind data at the spit end were available. Design of armor stones for the original Homer small-boat basin was based on a 5-ft design wave from the north. According to the Hudson formula (Beach Erosion Board, 1961), the armor-stone gradation was set between 700 and 1,100 lb. During construction of the original breakwater, armor stones beyond these limits were placed. In December 1962 and March 1963, the breakwater was damaged by storms that had generated significant wave heights of 4.7 and 4.0 ft, respectively. In Figure 65, two typical sections of the damaged breakwater are shown.

In designing armor stone for repair of the breakwater that had been damaged by the waves, wind data recently obtained at the spit end were used. When they were compared with wind records at the Homer airport, the strongest

winds at the spit end were found to be about 30 percent greater than those at the airport. The most damaging waves were found to be those generated by winds blowing over the full 21.5-mi length of Kachemak Bay. The comparatively narrow width of Kachemak Bay reduced the actual 21.5-mi northeast fetch to an effective fetch length of about 10 mi.

By applying the effective fetch length (Saville, 1954) of 10 mi to the wind velocity-duration curve developed for Homer Spit, engineers calculated a significant deep-water wave height of 7 ft with a corresponding period of 5.5 seconds and a wave length of 155 ft (Beach Erosion Board, 1961, 1962). They anticipated negligible refraction at the breakwater because underwater contours seaward of the breakwater are nearly perpendicular to the angle of wave attack. At the design high tide, the underwater topography causes shoaling of the wave. As a result, the wave height is modified to 6.4 ft on the breakwater trunk and to 6.7 ft at the breakwater end. With the 6.7-ft wave and 1 on 1.75 breakwater side slope, the Hudson formula gave a design stone weight of 2,100 lb. The minimum armor-rock weight selected was 75 percent of the design stone weight. The

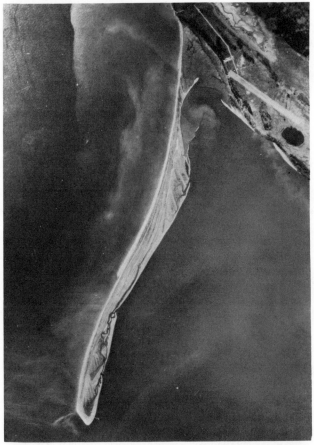

U.S. Army

FIGURE 56 Vertical aerial photograph of Homer Spit taken during World War II. Road from the spit to the airport had not yet been built. The old Cook Inlet Coalfield Company's dock was built in the early 1900's for delivering locally mined coal to steam-driven whaling and sealing ships. The hook configuration of the spit indicates transport of littoral materials around the tip of the spit.

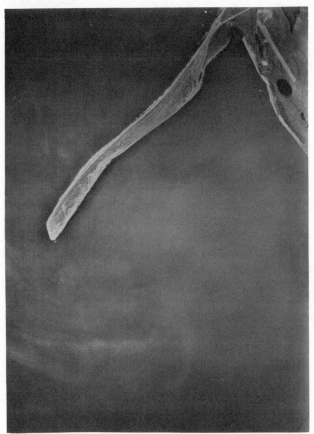

U.S. Army

FIGURE 57 Vertical aerial photograph of Homer Spit. Note different dock configuration from that shown in previous photograph (August 15, 1952).

FIGURE 58 Looking northwest toward Homer over middle of the spit (April 1964).

FIGURE 59 Aerial view of groin field near base of Homer Spit (July 5, 1966).

KACHEMAK BAY

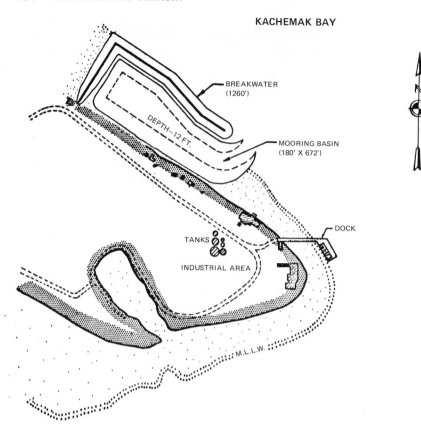

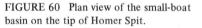

FIGURE 60 Plan view of the small-boat basin on the tip of Homer Spit.

maximum stone weight of 4,500 lb was selected to ensure economical quarry operation. A typical breakwater section as repaired and existing at the time of the earthquake is shown in Figure 65. Only the seaward leg had been completed; the landward leg had not been repaired.

Private Facilities

The private facilities on the spit were the Land's End Hotel, the Porpoise Room restaurant, Salty Dawg Saloon, Standard Oil Company tank farm, and two seafood-processing plants.

Damage to Waterfront Facilities

Earthquake damage to structures in the city of Homer was extremely light compared to the damage in some other

FIGURE 61 Homer: Construction of the original small-boat basin after dredging. The gravel core, which required dressing before the protective stone was deposited, is shown. The breakwater tip has already been covered with protective stone (spring 1962).

FIGURE 62 Homer: Completed small-boat basin, before installation of floats, at low tide of −5 ft M L L W (fall 1962).

FIGURE 63 Homer: Completed breakwater; slope-protection stone is in the foreground. Armor stone is wrapped around nose of breakwater (fall 1962).

towns in the earthquake-affected area. The unreinforced-concrete-block first floor of one small hotel was damaged and required extensive repair to make it fit for habitation. The Homer school sustained minor damage. Chimneys were knocked down and a few plate-glass windows were broken. The Homer economy, however, was severely affected by the subsidence of the spit, which damaged the improvements on the end of the spit. The spit subsided between 2 and 3 ft (Waller, 1966), and the granular material of which the spit is composed compacted; maximum compaction occurred at the tip. Except for 10-ft subsidence of a spoil pile remaining from the original small-boat basin excavation, the average drop at the end of the spit was about 5.4 ft at MLLW.

As a result of subsidence and compaction, the spit was awash at the higher tide stages, and the road leading from the mainland to the facilities at the seaward end was inundated. The large and very popular Land's End Hotel at the very tip of Homer Spit was flooded at extreme high tides. The newly completed Porpoise Room restaurant, which

was to have had its grand opening on March 28, 1964, was inundated at extreme high tides to about 3.5 ft above the floor level. The deck of the City Dock was awash at high tides. Storm waves attacking the Cook Inlet (southwest) side of the spit eroded the beach, carrying materials to the top of slope to form a new berm that covered the road with gravel. Because access to the spit depended on the tide levels and the businesses and the City Dock were threatened by high tides, Homer's economy was brought to a standstill.

The damage to the Seward-Anchorage Highway in the Portage area severed all road connection between Kenai Peninsula and Anchorage. Transportation was limited to airplane or boat, which put a tremendous strain on the airlines' capabilities.

The small-boat basin sustained severe damage. The basin (Figure 60) was dredged from the beach slope on the northeast side of the spit and protected by a rubble-mound breakwater. Figure 64 is a typical section through the basin and the original beach profile before construction of the small-boat basin. Results of a topographic and hydrographic survey of the small-boat basin area taken following the earthquake are shown in Figure 66. The last 500 ft of the breakwater leg paralleling the shoreline was destroyed by a landslide. The top of the breakwater from Stations 4+10 to 7+80 sloped from an undisturbed elevation of +28 ft to MLLW. Without its protecting breakwater, the basin offered no protection from the predominant northeast and east winds to moored boats. In the absence of nearby protected moorage areas, many boats that normally used the basin remained through the summer following its destruction by mooring to the piles that formerly held the float system in place (Figure 67). All Homer-based boats eventually were dispersed to other protective areas, including Seldovia and Halibut Cove, across Kachemak Bay from Homer.

Periodic inundation of the lower part of the privately owned fuel-storage tanks at the spit end made it necessary for them to be weighted with oil so that they would not float. The salt water accelerated rusting, necessitating excessive preventive maintenance and painting.

Although tsunamis and other waves associated with the

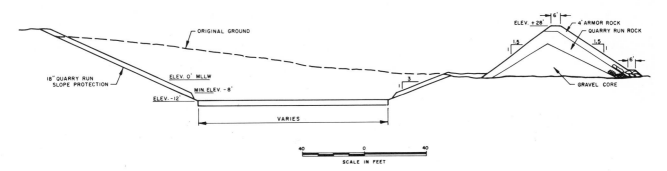

FIGURE 64 Homer Spit: Section through original small-boat basin and the beach profile before the construction of the basin.

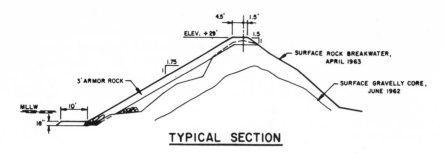

TYPICAL SECTION

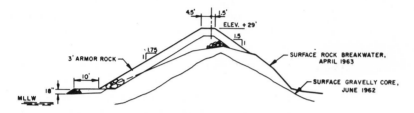

TYPICAL SECTION STATION 4+35 TO 5+40 &
6+28 TO 6+33

SCALE IN FEET

FIGURE 65   Homer Spit: Sections of damaged breakwater after two storms in winter of 1962–1963. Method of repair, which was only partly completed at the time of the earthquake, is shown.

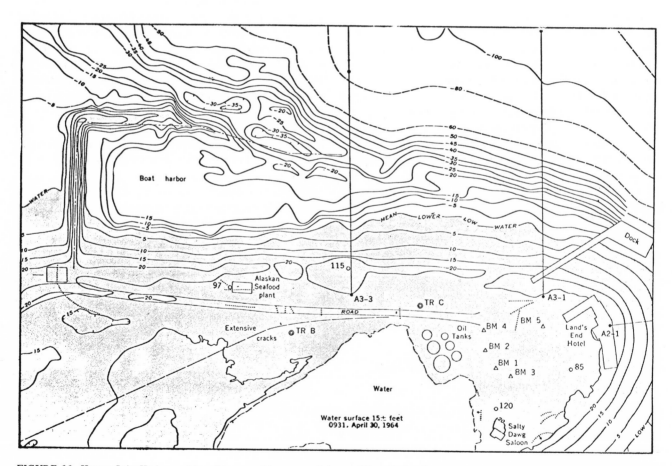

FIGURE 66   Homer Spit: Hydrographic and topographic survey of the small-boat basin after the earthquake. Note landslide at the outer end of the east breakwater.

FIGURE 67 Homer Spit: Original breakwater inundated by high tide. At highest tide stages the building behind moored boats had 3.5 ft of water on the floor (April 1964).

earthquake struck the Homer area, they caused no damage because of the low tide stages existing at the time (Waller, 1966).

No lives were lost at Homer in the earthquake and resulting tsunamis.

RESTORATION OF WATERFRONT FACILITIES

In comparison with losses in other earthquake-damaged areas in Alaska, the monetary loss at Homer was not large. Homer, however, was severely affected by the loss of all the facilities on which the economy of the town was based. To get Homer back on its feet, the City Dock and the small-boat basin had to be restored. Tables 5 and 6 list Corps of Engineers' restoration contracts. Although there was doubt at first that the integrity of the spit would be maintained (Waller, 1966), it was finally decided that the spit would retain its original configuration and would be rebuilt from natural forces. The stability of the end of the spit was still in doubt, however, and the 4-mi-long highway from the

mainland had to be raised and protected to provide continuous access to the business establishments and facilities at the end. While the Corps of Engineers was making studies to determine the spit's integrity and stability, other sites in the Homer area were examined to ascertain whether they would be suitable for waterfront facilities. In May 1964, however, all questions regarding access, stability, and integrity of the spit were resolved, and planning began for the rehabilitation of waterfront facilities at the end of the spit.

Restoration of Small-Boat Basin

The restored and expanded Homer small-boat basin (Figure 68) has a total area of 10 acres and is 12 ft deep over the 2.75 acres of the restored basin and 15 ft deep over 7.3 acres of the expansion portion of the basin. The basin is protected by a 1,018-ft-long rubble-mound main breakwater. The main breakwater incorporates a part of the damaged breakwater into its section. The 238-ft-long entrance breakwater was built on the landward leg of the breakwater that was constructed to protect the original small-boat basin. Basic criteria formulated for design specified that the basin was to be sited within the Homer Spit and near its distal end and was to contain 10 acres at project depth with sufficient room for expansion to 20 acres. The maximum allowable wave height within the mooring area was to be limited to 1 ft, although 0.5 ft maximum was preferable. The entrance channel depth was to be at least −15 ft MLLW. The entrance channel was to be as straight as possible to allow safe access for small boats. All the material dredged from the basin was to be utilized for land fill to stabilize the end of the spit. The plan was to be the most economical when interest and amortization on a 50-year project life were considered, as well as annual maintenance cost. Sufficient

TABLE 5 Homer Construction Contracts

Project	Date Awarded	Date NTP[a]	Date Work Started	Completion Date Original Schedule	Actual	Amount Paid to Contractor (dollars)	Funding Agency
SBB construction, including clearing operations, dredging and breakwater	July 30, 1964	Aug. 12, 1964	Aug. 13, 1964	Nov. 15, 1964	Sept. 12, 1965	1,581,514	OEP and CE
City dock: 60 × 130 ft dock with 400-ft approach trestle	Aug. 19, 1964	Aug. 24, 1964	Aug. 27, 1964	Oct. 15, 1964	June 9, 1965	368,477	OEP
SBB: inner-harbor facilities reconstruction	Mar. 23, 1965	Mar. 23, 1965	June 16, 1965	Aug. 11, 1965	Sept. 15, 1965	197,412	OEP
City dock fire protection	Apr. 12, 1965	Apr. 20, 1965	June 21, 1965	July 1, 1965	Sept. 30, 1965	50,712	OEP
TOTAL						2,198,115	

[a]Date of notice to proceed.

TABLE 6 Homer Supply Contracts

Project	Date Awarded	Date NTP[a]	Date Work Started	Completion Date		Amount Paid to Contractors (dollars)	Funding Agency
				Original Schedule	Actual		
City dock supply piling	Aug. 3, 1964	–	Aug. 3, 1964	Aug. 15, 1964	Sept. 20, 1964	142,734	OEP
Hardware for city dock	July 31, 1964	–	Aug. 7, 1964	Aug. 15, 1964	Sept. 27, 1964	6,965	OEP
	Aug. 17, 1964	–	Aug. 7, 1964	Sept. 3, 1964	Sept. 27, 1964	4,089	OEP
TOTAL						153,788	

[a]Date of notice to proceed.

fill area was to be provided adjacent to the basin for parking 250 cars and 30 car–boat trailer combinations. No additional parking facilities would, however, be provided. The icing conditions at Homer had to be taken into account in aligning the entrance channel; because ice generally moves from north or northeast, the entrance channel was to be oriented in an easterly direction and protected by a breakwater. A boat-launching ramp was to be provided where the associated traffic would not interfere with boat moorage within the basin.

The small-boat basin was restored with funds available to the Corps of Engineers from OEP under Public Law 875. The basin was extended and the boat-launching ramp constructed using funds allocated under the 1964 amendment to the Alaska Omnibus Act.

A typical section through the entrance breakwater and the landward leg of the main breakwater is shown in Figure 68 and a typical section through the seaward portion of the main breakwater in Figure 69. To reduce costs, the entrance breakwater incorporated a part of the original breakwater. The main breakwater was also built on top of the original breakwater at the outer portion, where a new section extended to land. Costs were further reduced on the main breakwater by using dredged fill on the shoreward portion. Figure 70 is a view of the small-boat basin under construction.

The wind data and design wave developed for the pre-earthquake repair were used in design of the small-boat basin rehabilitation. The breakwater sections include a core of quarry-run rock, protected with a layer of armor rock 5.5 ft thick. A rock blanket placed at the toe of the breakwater protects against undermining from wave action at low tides. The breakwater's top elevations were selected to preclude overtopping by the design waves at a normal maximum high tide of +23.5 ft. To prevent fine material in the core from being piped through the armor stone, it was specified that in a 5-ft zone adjacent to the armor rock not more than 10 percent by weight of the stones could be less than 25 lb. The remainder of the core rock could be quarry-run

rock, but oversize stones that could not be incorporated in the core rock section would not be used.

The armor-stone size was designed using the Hudson formula (Beach Erosion Board, 1961) for a two-layer-thickness rubble-mound pell-mell-placed angular quarry stone on 1 on 1.5 slopes and subjected to 6- to 7-ft wave. The minimum armor-stone size of 2,000 lb is approximately 75 percent of the design stone weight determined by the Hudson formula. The maximum size of 5,000 lb was selected not only to allow the use of most stones obtained from the quarry, but to allow that stone to be incorporated into the armor-stone section; 50 percent of the stones had to weigh more than 3,000 lb each. On the breakwater heads, the armor-stone weight was increased to preclude damage that had been observed on breakwater heads in other areas (Beach Erosion Board, 1961). Stones were required to weigh from 3,000 to 6,000 lb each, and 50 percent of the pieces were to be larger than 4,000 lb.

Slope-protection stone was placed on the 1 on 3 dredged slopes to prevent damage from wave attack. The slope-protection stone was placed only on the slopes of the entrance channel, not in the small-boat basin area; experience had shown that boat-generated waves from normal activity within the basin would cause very little damage to the unprotected slope.

The rock blanket at the toe of the breakwater and on the slopes was graded to prevent piping of the underlying fine *in situ* materials and to prevent damage by impinging waves. The size was set from a maximum of 300 lb to the minimum requirement that no more than 5 percent of the stones, by weight, could be less than 10 lb.

The top elevation of the seaward leg of the main breakwater was set at +30 ft MLLW to prevent overtopping by the design wave height at the normal maximum high tide of +23.5 ft. The top elevations of the landward leg of the main breakwater and of the entrance breakwater were reduced to +29 ft MLLW, because waves attacking these areas would be about 1 ft less than those from the northeast. Minor overtopping of the breakwaters would occur at extreme tide stages exceeding +23.5 ft. It was determined that this infrequent overtopping could be allowed because waves would affect only the entrance channel; accordingly, the extra cost of protecting against this eventuality was not warranted. The top width of the seaward portion of the main breakwater was set at 8 ft to accommodate three diameters of the

design stone as normally required where minor overtopping of the structure can occur. The top widths of the landward leg of the main breakwater and of the entrance breakwater were set at 7 ft.

The stability of the breakwater was determined with an IBM 1620 computer program for a stability analysis based

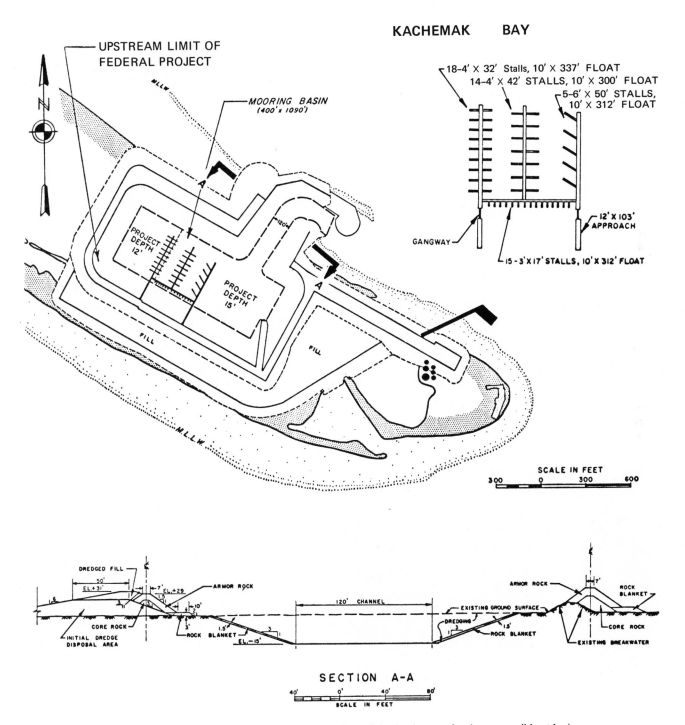

FIGURE 68   Homer Spit: Layout, plan view, and sections of the breakwaters for the new small-boat basin.

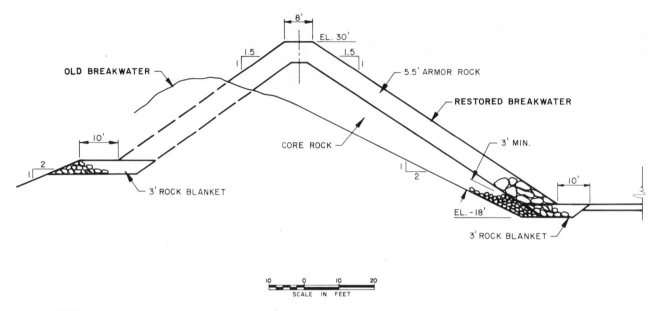

FIGURE 69 Homer Spit: Typical section of the seaward portion of the main breakwater of the restored small-boat basin.

on the circular-arc methods (U.S. Army Corps of Engineers, 1960). The criteria and assumptions for determining the stability of the breakwater were based on soil strength with $\tan\phi=0.700$ ($\phi=35°$) for sands and gravels; rock for the breakwater and slope protection was assigned a strength of $\tan\phi=0.840$ ($\phi=40°$). To determine at which tide elevation the lowest factor of safety would occur, a typical section was analyzed with tide elevations 0, +9, and +14 ft MLLW. The least factor of safety was found to occur at low tide (MLLW) and was used for the remainder of the analysis.

Three separate critical breakwater sections were exam-

FIGURE 70 The end of Homer Spit, showing the City Dock. Breakwaters are under construction, and dredging of the small-boat basin has started (September 1964).

ined with earthquake loads. It was found that most of the breakwater had a factor of safety greater than 1.25 for a 0.1 gravity seismic force. However, one relatively short portion of the main breakwater had a factor of safety of 1.00 with the 0.1 g seismic load. Because this particular section represented only a relatively short portion of the breakwater, and the assumed values for ϕ were conservative, it was felt that the breakwater would be stable under normal zone 3 earthquake loads of 0.1 g.

The entrance-channel width of 120 ft at a depth of −15 ft MLLW was selected to allow safe passage of boats passing in opposite directions through the bend. A sharp bend was required so that the main breakwater would provide adequate protection to the basin against waves, as well as to reduce the amount of ice entering the basin. Sharp bends in entrance channels are not normally recommended because they reduce the sight distance necessary for safe traversing and create navigation problems during wind conditions. In the case of Homer, however, the advantages of the sharp bend were found to outweigh the disadvantages.

The shoaling experienced in the original small-boat basin entrance channel also was expected to occur in the new entrance channel. One year after original construction, a minor deposit of littoral drift was found in the old entrance channel. Between May 1964 and November 1965, another deposit was found on the southeast side of the entrance breakwater. The accretion has not created a problem because the entrance channel is some distance from the area in which it occurred. A survey taken in August 1966 on that portion of the beach above MLLW near the entrance breakwater shows that very little change occurred.

After the basin was completed, observation during the winter of 1965–1966 indicated that approximately 4 in. of ice formed on the northwest end of the basin; this accumulation cannot be attributed to floe ice from Kachemak Bay because of the effectiveness of the ice barrier that was installed under the inner-harbor facilities contract. The ice had concentrated in the northwest third of the basin feathering from a maximum 4-in. thickness and existed for only a short time. Because there is no source of freshwater supply to the end of Homer Spit, which is 4 mi from the mainland, and because the salinity of the sea water in Kachemak Bay is about the same as that in the open ocean, snowfall is considered to be the principal source of fresh water from which the ice was formed. As greater boat traffic occurs in the area, the ice will continually break up and will not impede small-boat traffic.

Restoration of City Dock

About 6 ft of subsidence caused by the earthquake allowed the highest tides to totally inundate the Homer City Dock (Figure 71). Because road access from Anchorage and the Seward waterfront facilities had been destroyed in the earthquake, the dock was the only waterfront facility that could receive supplies from deep-draft vessels serving a large area in the lower Kenai Peninsula. Much of the tonnage scheduled for other ports was consigned to Homer; the dock could not therefore be removed from service, but extensive restoration or rehabilitation was evidently needed.

High tides accompanied by waves could seriously damage the dock with floating debris during storms. To prevent major damage to the dock, the Corps of Engineers recommended that the warehouse be removed, that the pile caps be tied to the piles, and that every sixth deck plank be removed during the highest tides to relieve uplift pressure. The City of Homer did the emergency work and was reimbursed by OEP with Public Law 875 funds.

The dock could be made into a usable structure either by raising it 6 ft to compensate for the subsidence, or by constructing a completely new dock. To raise the dock, the deck and stringers would have to be removed and 5-ft-long stub piles spliced on the caps on which additional pile caps would be added to support the new stringers and decking. Two valid objections were raised to this plan: The dock would be shut down during construction, imposing a grave hardship on the area; and the drift ice in Kachemak Bay could exert tremendous pressures on the dock. It was feared that the raised portion could not be attached firmly enough to the old piles to preclude ice damage. The alternative of constructing a new dock was obviously the most desirable, but OEP policies of providing restoration in kind at least cost to the government required a cost estimate to determine the relative merits of each alternative. The cost estimate showed that there was very little difference between building a completely new dock and raising the deck of the old dock. A new dock was therefore planned. The location selected for the new dock and its relationship to the old dock is shown in Figure 72.

Criteria used in selecting the site and design for the dock included replacing the dock with an equivalent dock area. The site should be on the northeast side of Homer Spit to protect docked vessels against the large waves generated on Cook Inlet that attack the southwest side of the spit. The dock was to be as near to the end of the spit as possible to take advantage of relatively close deep water. This would hold the dock approach to a minimum length to obtain the required 28 ft of water MLLW at the dock face. The site was to permit the dock face to be lengthened in accordance with future plans of Homer. The dock was to be constructed of creosoted pile and wood to prevent damage from marine borers. Adequate fire protection was to be provided on the dock. The angle of the dock approach to the shoreline was to reduce damage from drift ice. Buffer logs were to be installed to prevent debris from being carried under the dock and from causing damage to cross bracing. Adequate lighting on the dock was to be provided. The warehouse was to be moved off the dock and constructed on a special platform adjacent to the dock approach. An approach ramp was to accommodate two-way traffic, but no turn-around on the dock was to be included, nor were the fuel lines on the dock to be replaced.

The dock was designed and constructed in accordance with these criteria, and a typical section is shown in Figure 73. The dock design included stiffening to prevent excessive deflection from loads imposed by a deep-draft vessel mooring under adverse weather conditions and tide. No dolphins were considered necessary to provide adequate stiffness. Bids for construction of the dock were opened on August 17, 1964, and work was started on August 27, 1964.

FIGURE 71   Homer: City Dock nearly awash at high tide (December 1964).

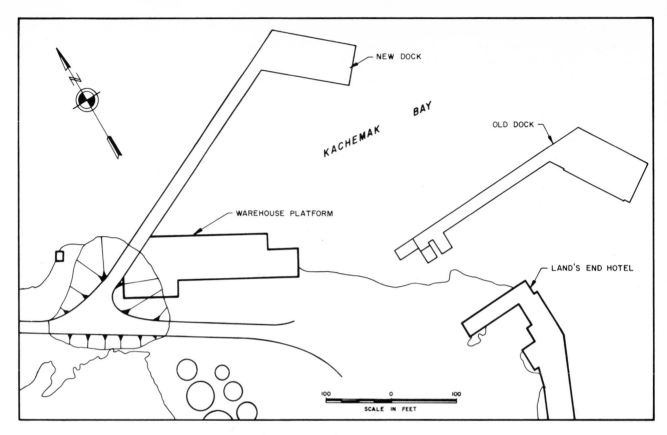

FIGURE 72   Location of new dock on Homer Spit.

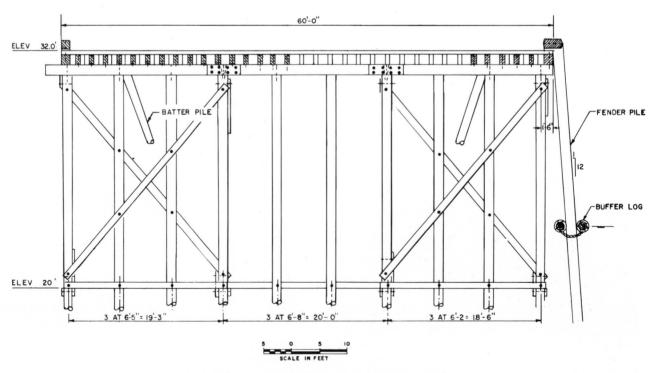

FIGURE 73   Typical section of the new dock on Homer Spit.

FIGURE 74   Homer: Completed City Dock and warehouse platform with warehouses installed. Remnant of old City Dock approach
is on left. Land's End Hotel is at extreme left (August 26, 1965).

The city's warehouse, which was originally on the old
City Dock, and a smaller warehouse on the old dock approach were placed on a platform adjacent to the new City
Dock approach. The materials for the platform were obtained by the City of Homer and the platform was constructed by the Corps of Engineers under the City Dock
contract (Figure 74). To expedite construction of the dock,
the government furnished materials such as piling, deck
materials, and such miscellaneous hardware as bolts,
washers, nails and spikes, wire rope, clamps, plates, angles,
bars, plate washers, and metal shoes. The contractor furnished such accessory items as ladders, hand grips, and cleats.

The dock was originally scheduled for completion in the
middle of October 1964. Because of a slow construction
start and damage during the winter to that portion already
constructed, the contract was not actually completed until
June 1965. By November 27, 1964, the contractor had
completed the dock approach to bent 29 and had partly
completed the approach to bent 35. In a storm on November 27, 1964, 10 piles at the end of the unfinished approach
were lost. On the night of December 30, 1964, and on the
morning of December 31, the dock was further damaged by
ice (Figure 75). At the same time, the old City Dock was
badly damaged. An inspection showed that all construction
on the new City Dock seaward of bent 27 was gone. Damage
to the old dock was confined mainly to the first row of
piles along the approach and dock adjacent to the bay.
A barge tied alongside the approach was forced through the
fender piling and under the dock by the ice. As the tide
rose, the barge raised a considerable portion of the decking
off its supports. It was estimated that 100 piles, including
the fender piling, were damaged beyond reuse and that repair costs would be about $50,000.

When the events leading to this damage were reconstructed, the damage was found to have been caused mainly
by an uncommon movement of the heavier than normal ice

pack. With the aid of a slight breeze, the ice on the Kachemak Bay side of the spit retreated with the tide a distance
of 3–4 mi from the spit. As the tide changed, so did the
wind (although maximum velocity of wind was estimated
at no greater than 15–20 mph) and the ice returned en
masse to the spit. The impact of the ice against the dock
and barge was the major cause of damage.

Repair of the old dock was not feasible because of the
hazards of winter construction, and the new dock would
have been completed by the time the old dock could be repaired. Homer had a 2-month supply of fuel oil, which was
not enough to last until the new dock was completed;
therefore, oil had to be trucked from Kenai at extra cost.

The dock contract required installation of fire walls on
the dock approach. The fire walls were constructed of
2 X 12-in. planks attached to the bearing piles at bents 14
and 30. One fire wall had been completed when the contractor shut down his construction activities in November
1964. During subsequent storms, waves striking the completed fire wall caused excessive motion in that bent,
threatening to damage the dock approach. The contractor
removed the fire wall, and the second fire wall was deleted
from the contract.

Construction on the new dock resumed in March 1965.
Because of the ice damage to both docks during the preceding winter, dolphins were placed in the new dock to resist
unusually large ice loads that exceeded those of a docking
ship. Normal ice loads, taken into account on the original
design, were less than the loads of a docking ship. The dolphins were installed at the two seaward corners of the dock,
well inside the face, so that the outer batter piles would not
protrude beyond the face of the dock.

FIGURE 75   Homer: Icing conditions at the end of the spit at high
tide. Completed warehouse platform is shown in addition to the
partly completed approach to new City Dock and the nearly inundated remains of the old City Dock (December 1964).

The dock has been in constant use since it was completed, serving deep-draft traffic to Homer by the Alaska State Ferry System. It has proved to be structurally sound and has sustained no damage since completion, except for a few broken fender piles.

Fire protection was provided for the Homer Dock by separate contract, awarded on April 12, 1965; work started on June 21, 1965. The originally scheduled completion date of July 1, 1965, was not met because construction was delayed by the dock construction contract, which was completed June 9, 1965. The fire-protection contract was completed September 30, 1965. After the contract had been awarded but before the start of construction, some local interests requested several changes in the distribution system that carried the water to the hydrants. The major change requested was for the pump to be located inshore, but this request could not be granted because it would necessitate either a deep well or a sump with a horizontal intake line to deep water. The additional cost could not be justified by OEP for a minimum facility under Public Law 875. Another request was that a diesel engine be used to drive the pump instead of a gasoline engine, but gasoline was found to be more reliable at winter temperatures, and the request was denied.

An alternate means of preventing the spread of fire along the approach had to be supplied to replace the fire walls. A fire curtain that was within the scope of a minimum facility was constructed at about the center of the approach; it consisted of a 2.5-in.-diameter galvanized line perpendicular to the approach structure between bents 19 and 20.

Inner-Harbor Facilities

Facilities that were restored included a complete boat-float system with 104 individual stalls and a transient moorage area, all of which required electrical utilities and firefighting equipment.

Although the original float system (Figures 76 and 77) at Homer was not destroyed during the earthquake and subsequent waves, the protecting breakwater was destroyed. It was feared that storm waves would destroy the float system before the small-boat basin could be completed. The floats could not be removed and stored at Homer because there was no protected area nearby, and it would have been too costly to transport the floats to high ground on the mainland, repair them, and transport them back to the new basin when it was completed. The floats were used in other areas with protected moorage but no available floats. The Navy transported most of the floats to Kodiak for installation at Gibson Cove; the rest were towed to Halibut Cove across Kachemak Bay from Homer and installed there (Figure 78).

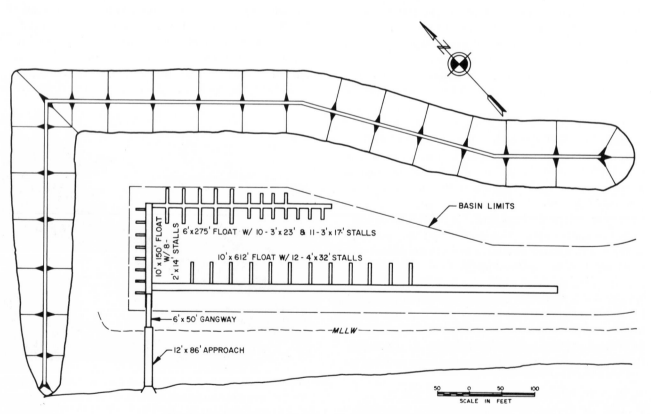

FIGURE 76   Homer Spit: Float layout in original small-boat basin.

FIGURE 77 Homer: Completed small-boat basin with floats in place (fall 1963).

The original float system had been constructed in 1963 by the State of Alaska. The floats were of wood buoyed by polystyrene billets. At peak periods, over 100 boats used the original basin by double and triple tying to floats that were designed to accommodate only 80 vessels. Because the original basin configuration was long and narrow, the float system was very inefficient. A distinct fire hazard existed at low tides, because boats could not enter or leave the stalls without going aground on the dredged slopes of the basin (Figure 76). In the restoration, floats capable of safely accommodating 115 boats were installed by using the available small-boat basin area more efficiently.

Development of the inner-harbor facilities was a joint effort of the State of Alaska and the Corps of Engineers, with the state furnishing detailed design criteria in the form of drawings and outline specifications. The state's design allowed for future expansion of the float system by the addition of floats for smaller boats in the far end of the basin and for larger boats nearer the entrance channel. The Corps of Engineers followed the state's design closely in developing final plans and specifications for advertisement. All the new harbor facilities were constructed of wood and the floats were buoyed by extruded polystyrene billets (Figures 68 and 79–81).

During construction of the small-boat basin in the winter of 1964–1965, when most of the breakwater had been installed, but before the plug was breached (Figure 82), ice was found to block the entrance channel. This situation indicated that ice could easily enter the basin, particularly during incoming tides when the velocities within the entrance channel would normally be on the order of 0.5 fps. Once it was inside the basin, the ice could not easily leave; consequently, an ice barrier of some sort was necessary to prevent ice from entering the basin (Figure 83).

During the winter of 1965–1966, the ice barrier kept drift ice from the basin and provided access for vessels. Local authorities, however, did not remove the ice barrier after the ice season was over; it was damaged when a barge ran over one side of it and was totally destroyed when another vessel hit the other side. If the ice barrier is to be replaced, the city or state must do it.

KODIAK

KODIAK HARBOR

Kodiak is situated at lat. 57°47′ north, long. 152°24′ west, on the northeastern corner of Kodiak Island in southwestern

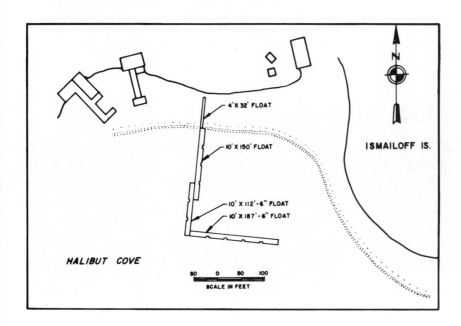

FIGURE 78 Float facilities moved from Homer small-boat basin to Halibut Cove, across Kachemak Bay.

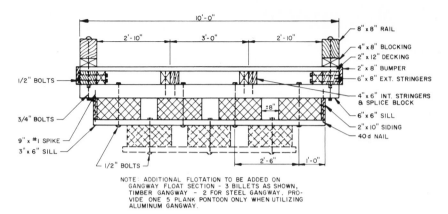

NOTE: ADDITIONAL FLOTATION TO BE ADDED ON
GANGWAY FLOAT SECTION - 3 BILLETS AS SHOWN,
TIMBER GANGWAY - 2 FOR STEEL GANGWAY. PRO-
VIDE ONE 5 PLANK PONTOON ONLY WHEN UTILIZING
ALUMINUM GANGWAY.

10' FLOAT SECTION

FIGURE 79   Typical float section for restored inner-harbor facilities in Alaska.

FIGURE 80   Homer: The small-boat basin during float installation.
New cannery is on left, adjacent to small-boat basin entrance channel, and new hotel is between approaches to float system (August
1965).

FIGURE 82   Homer: Small-boat basin and portion of spit at high
tide. The portion of the spit was effectively an island at extreme
high tide (December 1964).

FIGURE 81   Homer: Groin between Alaska Seafood's cannery and
small-boat basin. Ferry *Tustumena* is in background, tied to new
City Dock. One section of float system is being towed to basin after
being launched from shore (June 25, 1965).

FIGURE 83   Homer: The ice barrier before installation of boom
logs between piles and shore (August 14, 1965).

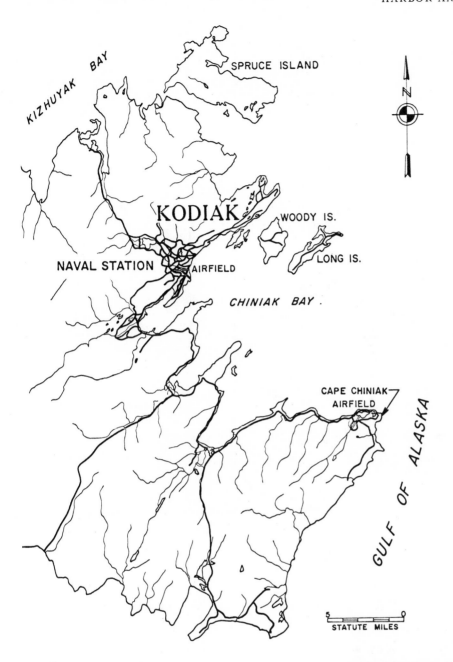

FIGURE 84   Vicinity map of Kodiak.

Alaska (Figure 84). Kodiak was approximately 50 mi north-west of the causative fault of the March 27, 1964, Alaska earthquake. Kodiak Harbor is the only developed harbor of refuge and is the principal point of repair and supply for vessels plying the 745-mi expanse of water between Seward and Dutch Harbor.

Kodiak Harbor is in the northeastern portion of St. Paul Harbor, a deep narrow strait between Near Island and the northeast coastline of Kodiak Island (Figure 85). A part of the harbor is protected from storms by Near Island and is used as a winter anchorage area. The most easterly portion of the harbor is the western half of a ¾-mi waterway forming the northerly passage into St. Paul Harbor. An

alternate approach channel to St. Paul and Kodiak harbors, known as the South Channel, connects directly with Chiniak Bay.

Tides at Kodiak have an extreme range of 17 ft, extending from an extreme low of –4.0 ft to a high of +13.0 ft. Mean tidal range is 6.6 ft from a mean low of +1.0 ft to a mean high of +7.6 ft, all referenced to MLLW.

WATERFRONT FACILITIES

The city of Kodiak has developed along the southeasterly shoreline delineating St. Paul Harbor, Kodiak Harbor, and North Channel (Figures 85 and 86). The waterfront facili-

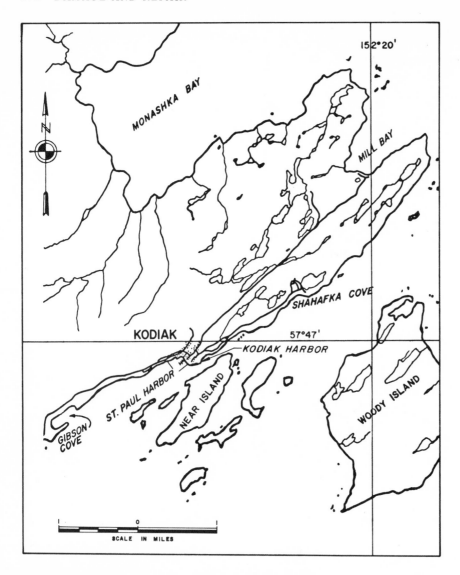

FIGURE 85 Map of the Kodiak area, showing the position of the harbors.

FIGURE 86 Kodiak small-boat harbor in about 1960, looking northeast. Mooring facility and built-up waterfront were all either destroyed or damaged extensively by the tsunamis following the earthquake. Ice can be seen in small-boat basin.

ties consisted of a city dock, a small-boat harbor, and some private businesses.

City Dock

The basic City Dock, constructed of timber by Kodiak Fisheries Company in the 1930's, lies about 0.5 mi southwest of Kodiak. In 1940, the facilities were purchased by the O. Kraft & Son Company. The wharf and warehouse were taken over in 1942 by the Army and a number of additions constructed. At the time of the earthquake, the dock was owned by the city, and the city warehouse, a cold storage plant, and a king crab processing plant had been constructed on the wharf. Float facilities for mooring small boats (Figure 87) were attached to the east end.

Small-Boat Harbor

The 11.7-acre small-boat basin was completed in 1958 by the Corps of Engineers (Figure 88). The basin was 8 ft and

FIGURE 87 City Dock, Union Oil Company dock and tanks, and the float facilities attached to the City Dock at Kodiak before the earthquake.

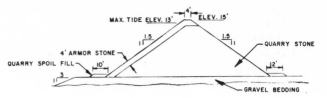

TYPICAL SECTION SOUTHWEST BREAKWATER

TYPICAL SECTION SOUTHEAST BREAKWATER

FIGURE 89 Kodiak: Typical sections of southwest and southeast breakwaters before the earthquake.

12 ft deep below MLLW and was protected by two rubble-mound breakwaters—one 1,250 ft long and the other 760 ft long.

The longer southwest breakwater was faced with armor stone and had a top elevation of +15.0 ft MLLW and a top width of 4 ft (Figure 89). It was faced and topped with a 4-ft layer of armor stone to protect the lighter core stones from wave attack damage. The armor stones weighed from 750 to 1,500 lb and had not been damaged during its 6 years of life. The core stones weighed a maximum of 1,500 lb, no more than 25 percent being less than 6 in. in least dimen-

sion. The southwest breakwater was sited on fine fill materials originally dredged from the basin area.

The shorter southeast breakwater, constructed exclusively of quarry stone, had a top width of 6 ft, a top elevation of +12.0 ft MLLW, and was sited on a natural rock reef (Figure 89). No armor rock was necessary because of the natural protection against large wind-generated waves and the

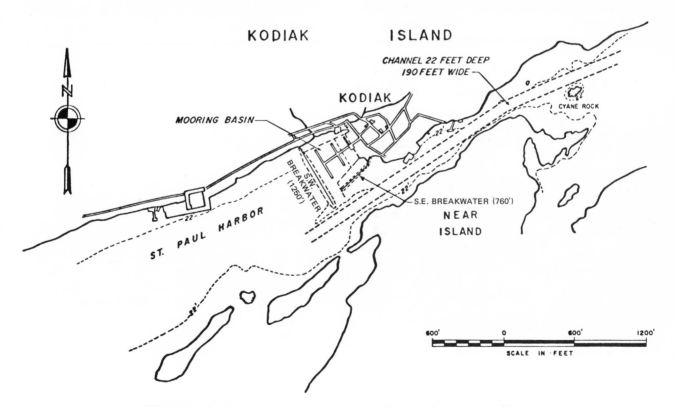

FIGURE 88 Configuration of the preearthquake 11.7-acre small-boat basin at Kodiak.

ability of the quarry stone to withstand boat-generated waves. The quarry stone had not been displaced during the 6 years that it had been there.

The floats and other facilities of the inner harbor that had been completed before the earthquake included approach ramps, finger and master floats, public loading dock, electrical and water utilities, a seaplane float, boat-repair grids, and a boat-launching ramp (Figure 90). These facilities had been installed intermittently by the State of Alaska and local authorities. All structures within the basin were of timber, and the floats were buoyed with a polystyrene flotation material.

A 60,000-ft² parking and service area on the northeast side of the small-boat harbor had been developed by the City of Kodiak on fill placed by the Corps of Engineers during construction of the small-boat basin in 1957 and 1958.

Private Facilities

Alvine's Marine Repair facilities consisted of a drydock to accommodate vessels up to 250 tons, a 68 × 118-ft boathouse, a 52 × 75-ft marine-repair shop, about 4,000 ft² of wharf area, and a 20 × 40-ft boat elevator. Living quarters were constructed on the shoreward side of the facilities. In February 1964, a fire fanned by gusts of wind reaching 50 knots gutted the shops, destroyed the dry dock and living quarters, and leveled a home across the street.

The U.S. Fish and Wildlife Service dock facilities consisted of a warehouse about 28 × 50 ft, a dock approach 10 × 130 ft, and a dock 14 × 67 ft roughly perpendicular to the approach.

Kodiak Airways, Inc., facilities consisted of a gravel ramp for amphibious aircraft, a hangar, and an 80 × 95-ft parking lot. The company owned a number of aircraft.

Muller Dock and Cannery facilities consisted of a 40 × 82-ft building that housed the main cannery, a 34 × 34-ft cold-storage room, a 20 × 24-ft steam room, a 20 × 20-ft ice house, and a 20 × 116-ft dock.

Halferty Canneries, Inc., facilities consisted of a large wharf with Standard Oil Company as a tenant, a cannery, and a store with clothing, grocery, and hardware departments. Standard Oil Company also maintained floats on the eastern end of the wharf.

Union Oil Company POL dock facilities consisted of a 14 × 250-ft dock approach, a 12 × 175-ft pipeway, a 41 × 73-ft wharf, a warehouse, mooring dolphins, and a small float. The wharf and approach were of creosoted fir pile and timbers, and the dolphins were constructed of creosoted fir piles.

The preearthquake conditions at Kodiak are shown in Figures 91–93.

Damage to Private Waterfront Facilities

Heavy damage was inflicted on Kodiak in three stages. The first stage was the earthquake, the second was a series of tsunamis that swept through the waterfront and low-lying areas of town, and the third was a wind storm with 100-knot winds several days later.

The earthquake did relatively minor damage to structures. Almost all the waterfront structures were of wood frame and were resilient enough to withstand the shocks. The city is sited on or near bedrock; consequently, the general ground motion may have been less severe than in areas

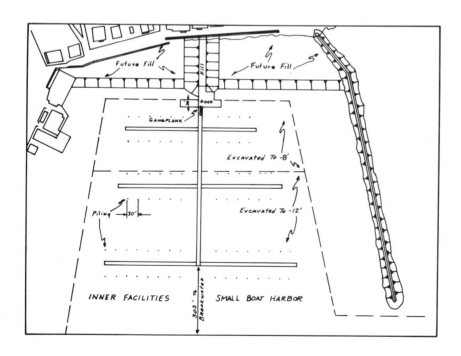

FIGURE 90 Kodiak: Layout of the inner-harbor facilities before the earthquake and tsunami.

FIGURE 91   Small-boat harbor and inner-harbor facilities at Kodiak just before the earthquake and tsunami.

FIGURE 93   Looking down Alaska Street, Kodiak, before the earthquake and tsunami.

that were sited on alluvium. The southwest breakwater, however, settled as much as 10 ft. Minor appurtenances, such as brick chimneys, were damaged, and the rock on which the city of Kodiak is founded subsided 5.8 ft during the earthquake. Even if the tsunami had not caused such devastation, this subsidence would have made it necessary to raise most dock and shore-side facilities.

In Kodiak, the series of tsunamis caused serious losses and damage (Tudor, 1964): 25 people were killed; 40 percent of the business district and many houses were destroyed; 75 percent of food supplies were lost; 77 fishing boats were destroyed, badly damaged, or missing; and some floated inland and grounded. Three canneries were lost, and the City Dock was damaged. The warehouse and harbormaster building were missing; numerous piers, piles, anchors, and lines were damaged; breakwater armor stones were displaced; and all inner-harbor facilities in the small-boat basin were destroyed, including the boat-moorage floats, ap-

proaches to floats, public loading dock, and grid (Figures 94–107).

Damage would have undoubtedly been greater if the highest tsunami had occurred at high tide. Not all the vessels moored in the small-boat basin were extensively damaged or destroyed by the tsunami; many escaped with little or no damage. With the loss of all mooring facilities in the Kodiak area, boat owners were forced to anchor their vessels elsewhere. Many boats anchored west of the small-boat basin and seaward of the City Dock. Three days after the earthquake, when a storm with winds of from 80 to 100 knots arose during the night, many of these vessels were not boarded for an anchor watch. As a result of the high wind, the boats dragged anchor, and 18 vessels were sunk or driven aground, causing extensive damage.

DAMAGE BY THE EARTHQUAKE AND TSUNAMI

City Deep-Draft Dock

Damage to the dock was caused primarily by the series of tsunamis that swept along the waterfront. These, in conjunction with the subsidence of the area, ripped some of the decking from the stringers. Stringers that were driftpinned to the pile caps were lifted off and moved laterally as much as 9 in.; where the connections held, piles were lifted from 5 to 7 ft. The east approach to the dock, including about 20 piles, was washed away.

Wood structures on the dock sustained very little damage as a direct effect of the earthquake. Subsequent periodic wave action damaged but did not destroy the buildings.

The entire first floor of the Kodiak Ice and Cold Storage Company building was covered with 8 ft of water. The foundation structure under the cold-storage area was destroyed, and the waves flooded and silted all the machinery, storage facilities, and electrical equipment on the first floor. Similar

FIGURE 92   The Kodiak public dock in the small-boat basin before the earthquake and tsunami.

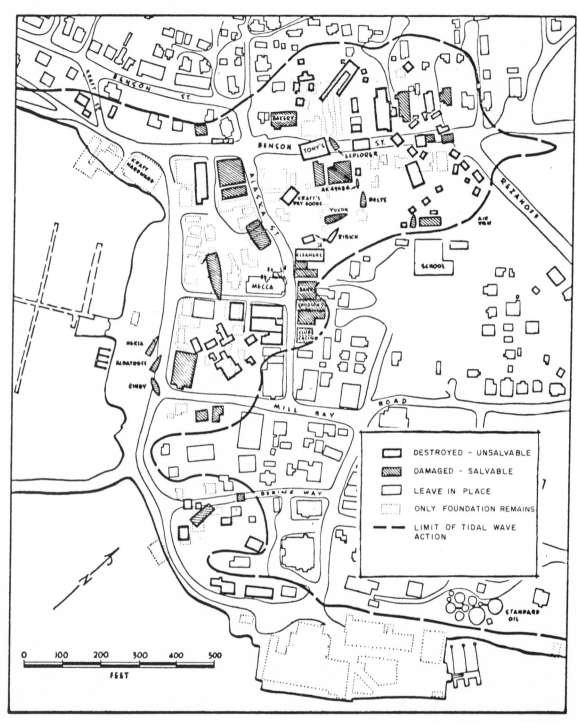

U.S. Navy

FIGURE 94 The extent of tsunami damage to the city of Kodiak.

U.S. Navy

FIGURE 95   A Kodiak store destroyed by the tsunami. The sidewalk has heaved, and building foundation has been destroyed.

U.S. Navy

FIGURE 96   Alaska Street, Kodiak, after the disaster. Building that was on the left has been completely destroyed.

U.S. Navy

FIGURE 97   Kodiak, after the tsunami had swept through the city.

FIGURE 98   Kodiak waterfront. Buildings above tsunami wave height are undamaged.

U.S. Navy

FIGURE 99   One of the Kodiak fishing vessels destroyed by the tsunami. Float section in background has been completely torn loose.

U.S. Navy

FIGURE 100   Kodiak: The *Victory Maid* after the tsunami. Float section has been completely torn loose.

FIGURE 101   Kodiak: The *Mary Ruby*, grounded on the water-front, has a hole in her side, and siding has been stripped from the building on the right.

U.S. Navy

FIGURE 104   Two of Kodiak's fishing vessels deposited by the tidal wave at the intersection of Mill Bay Road and Marine Way.

U.S. Navy

FIGURE 102   Kodiak: Looking toward small-boat harbor. Scattered buildings have boats deposited among them.

FIGURE 105   A cannery tender, deposited near the Kodiak school at elevation +42 ft M L L W, is being prepared for refloating.

FIGURE 103   Kodiak waterfront, May 1964, showing high tide caused by tectonic subsidence. Fishing boat, the *Mary Ruby*, has been deposited on the shore. High-water marks can be seen on the building at the right, and corner between first and second story has been chipped by a boat.

FIGURE 106   Kodiak: Sunken fishing boat outside the small-boat basin breakwater. City dock and king crab processing plant are in the background.

FIGURE 107   Downtown area and sea wall, Kodiak waterfront. The roadway is flooded at high tide.

Small-Boat Harbor

Some of the townspeople who had climbed the hills with flashlights related that when the four waves came onto land, the impact of the ships being swept into the city produced grinding and thudding noises. The second wave, in particular, came with a roar, and numerous piles, anchors, lines, and piers snapped and broke as the harbor became a dizzy whirlpool.

The harbor-master's building was completely destroyed when a large fishing boat collided with it at about 15 knots. The 6–8 ft of submergence by the higher tsunami wave buoyed the public loading dock's decking off the pile caps to which the deck stringers were attached only by driftpins. The vertical motion accompanied by lateral movement destroyed the decking. When the bulkheads and more than two dozen piles under the approach to the public dock were destroyed, the approach decking floated away; the warehouse with its equipment was also swept from its foundation.

During the earthquake, the southwest breakwater subsided generally (Figures 108–110). About 5.8 ft of the total

damage was sustained by other buildings on the dock. The mooring floats for small boats on the east end of the dock were also damaged. When the tides stabilized, extreme high tides were approximately 15 in. from the original deck level.

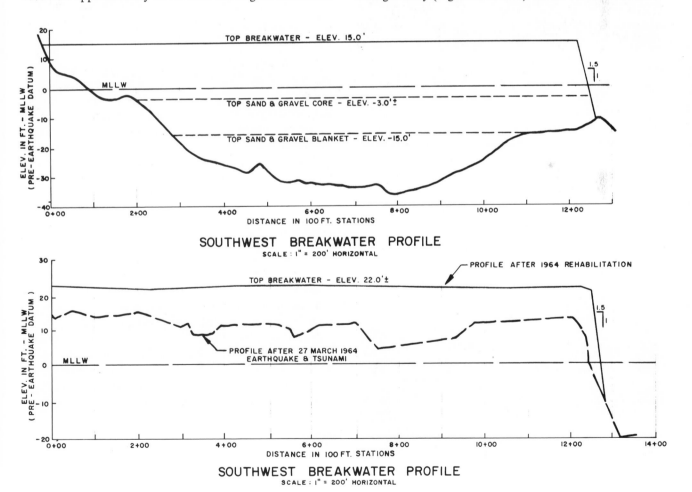

FIGURE 108   Profile of southwest-breakwater center line after the earthquake with profile of new breakwater superimposed (Kodiak).

FIGURE 109 Kodiak small-boat basin at high tide. Southwest breakwater was damaged by subsidence and overtopping tsunami.

subsidence was caused by general tectonic deformation, and the remainder was caused primarily by localized foundation failure during the earthquake and displacement of stones during overtopping by the tsunami; up to 10 ft of the maximum of 15.8 ft of subsidence can be attributed to foundation failure. Determination of the tsunami damage to the southwest breakwater is not possible, but the damage was believed to be minor.

During an inspection after the earthquake, a large percentage of the elongated armor stones common to the

FIGURE 110 Kodiak small-boat basin—southwest breakwater at high tide, showing damage by subsidence and overtopping tsunami.

southwest breakwater were observed to have been realigned so that the long axes of the stones were nearly perpendicular to the breakwater center line. This vane effect was most noticeable near the crest and on the seaward side of the breakwater, indicating that the tsunami's force was directed perpendicular to the southwest breakwater and was strongest as the wave crest approached.

The southeast breakwater was affected by the 5.8 ft of tectonic subsidence. Appreciable damage was done to the breakwater (Figure 111). Most of the damage was apparently caused by overtopping during the tsunami (Figure 112). Postearthquake surveys indicate, but do not confirm, that the strongest force from the tsunami was to the north toward the small-boat basin.

The earthquake did little damage to the inner-harbor facilities, but the series of tsunamis completely destroyed them. The tremendous noise of grinding and crashing heard during the tsunami was indicative of the violence of the damage. The parking lot near the small-boat harbor did not appear to have been damaged except for the tectonic subsidence and slope ravelling caused by the tsunami's overland flow. A road along the northwest side of the basin that provided access to the seaplane float was damaged to about the same extent as the parking lot.

Private Waterfront Facilities

The force of the tsunami waves was sufficient to level a bowling alley at the edge of the small-boat harbor to the foundation slab. Only a few reinforcing rods that had extended into the concrete-block walls protruded from the floor slab.

One cannery, with its floor system driftpinned to a timber-pile foundation, was entirely removed. The driftpins remaining on the center row of piling pointed in the direction in which the second wave swept away the cannery. Another timber cannery was floated from its foundation and was carried more than 1 mi into the harbor, where it was lodged on the breakwater (Tudor, 1964).

A welding shop near the harbor's edge, with corrugated-steel roofing and siding, was extensively damaged. The sides were torn away, but the heavy welding equipment and steel stock inside were not dislodged (Tudor, 1964).

The Kodiak Island side of the narrow channel between Kodiak Island and Near Island was lined with docks, canneries, machine shops, flight services, and associated facilities to serve the fishing industry and transportation needs. The tsunami destroyed almost all these structures (Figure 113).

DAMAGE TO WATERFRONT FACILITIES

The Navy and the Corps of Engineers cooperated to restore facilities to preearthquake conditions in the city of Kodiak.

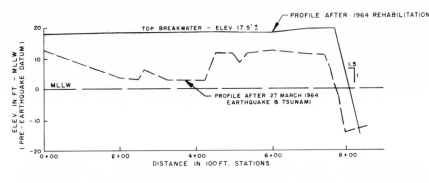

FIGURE 111 Kodiak: Profiles of southeast breakwater before and after the earthquake.

Immediately after the President's declaration of a "major disaster," the OEP requested the U.S. Navy's Bureau of Yards and Docks to clear debris and make the necessary emergency repairs to public utilities, streets, and buildings in the city. The Navy was also asked to lend a pontoon dry dock to the city for the repair of privately owned fishing vessels. OEP requested the Corps of Engineers to perform the necessary work on the inner-harbor facilities. This work included construction and installation of floats with piling, construction of a dock and approach from land to the float facilities; reinstallation of electrical and water facilities with appurtenances and other supporting work; restoration of the parking-lot area to a proper grade at its original pre-earthquake site; and restoration of the access road on the northwest side of the small-boat harbor to a grade that would facilitate access to the floating inner-harbor facilities.

The debris from the channel and small-boat basin area was cleared, and the breakwaters were reconstructed in Kodiak Harbor by the Corps of Engineers. Table 7 lists the contracts administered by the Corps of Engineers on the Kodiak waterfront.

Debris Clearance

Debris removal was the first step necessary in the restoration of the waterfront facilities to restore the economy of the area. Wrecks and debris were cleared from the small-boat basin and from the channel between Kodiak and Near Island by the Corps of Engineers under the authority of Section 20 of the River and Harbor Act of March 3, 1899. The debris-removal contract included sweeping to locate obstructions, diving to identify the obstructions, and the removal of the obstructions hazardous to navigation. The work supplemented the Navy's shore-side clearing project and included removal of all wrecked boats, automobiles, and other debris that were in shallow water and were considered to be a menace to navigation. The sweeping and diving in the harbor exposed debris such as boats, automobiles, machinery, pipes, scrap metal, hardware, rope, cable, and bottled goods. Debris had been scattered over the entire waterfront, some of which had been carried long distances by the tsunami. For instance, a boat was found near the east entrance to the north channel opposite Holiday Island. Cars, machinery, pipes, and other miscellaneous objects were found in a cove outside the main channel on the Near Island side. It was assumed that the bodies of those missing and presumed dead would be found during the debris clearance, but none were.

City Deep-Draft Dock

The dock could not be used in its damaged condition. To make the dock usable, many of the driftpins on the pile caps had to be cut off, and the deck had to be moved back to the approximate original position with a bulldozer. New piling had to be driven and decking replaced. Within 10 days, the dock was operational again at a cost of about $7,000; the work was done by the city.

In November 1964, when the annual high tides began, it was feared that wind-driven tides would again damage the dock; 15,000 sandbags therefore were obtained from the U.S. Army through the Corps of Engineers (2,000 of the bags were returned to the U.S. Navy for borrowed bags). The bags were filled and placed on the dock by volunteer city workers. Eligible costs for the emergency work were reimbursed by the Corps of Engineers under Public Law 99.

FIGURE 112 Kodiak: Southeast breakwater, showing damage caused by overtopping tsunami and subsidence.

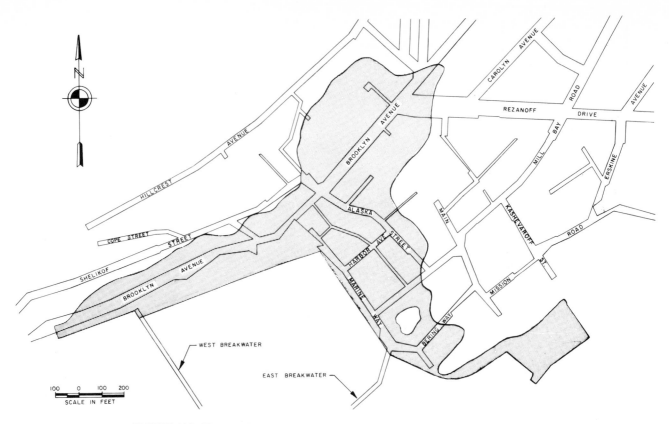

FIGURE 113 Plan showing extent of damage to city of Kodiak and waterfront facilities.

Small-Boat Harbor

Small-Boat Basin The small-boat basin was restored with funds available to the Corps of Engineers under PL 99, 84th Congress; the work was limited to repairing and to raising the two breakwaters protecting the small-boat basin. This waterfront-facility restoration contract was the first to be advertised after the earthquake. Solicitations for offers were made on April 22, 1964, and proposals were opened on April 30, 1964. Because the necessary equipment was at Kodiak, and because of the extreme urgency of this project, the contractor started work 2 days before being issued the official notice to proceed (Figure 114).

Criteria for design were only slightly different from those

TABLE 7 Kodiak Construction Contracts on Small-Boat Basin

| Project | Date Awarded | Date NTP[a] | Date Work Started | Completion Date | | Amount Paid to Contractors (dollars) | Funding Agency |
				Original Schedule	Actual[b]		
Clearing harbor of wrecks	Apr. 21, 1964	Apr. 22, 1964	Apr. 22, 1964	May 22, 1964	May 15, 1964	63,360	CE
Raising breakwaters	May 6, 1964	May 20, 1964	May 18, 1964	July 25, 1964	Aug. 16, 1964	431,500	CE
Reconstruction of parking lot and access road	July 30, 1964	Aug. 10, 1964	Aug. 15, 1964	Oct. 10, 1964	Oct. 29, 1964	194,073	OEP
Reconstruction of inner-harbor facilities	Aug. 7, 1964	Aug. 24, 1964	Aug. 31, 1964	Nov. 15, 1964	Jan. 26, 1965	538,419	OEP
TOTAL						1,227,352	

[a] Date of notice to proceed.
[b] Time extension granted for additional drilling.

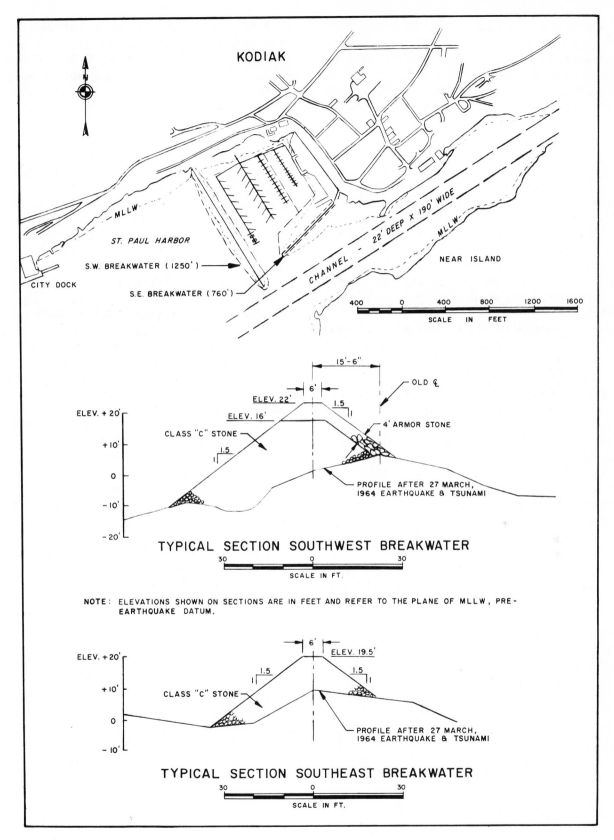

FIGURE 114 Sections of southeast and southwest breakwaters and breakwater locations that were reconstructed at Kodiak.

used in the original breakwater design. The rehabilitated southeast breakwater had the same alignment as the original breakwater. The side slopes of 1 on 1.5 were unchanged. The top width, however, was increased from 4 ft to 6 ft to reduce the need for maintenance because of overtopping during extreme high tides. The top elevation was originally +12 ft MLLW and was rebuilt to a top elevation of +14 ft MLLW to preclude overtopping during the normal maximum high tide of +13 ft MLLW. The southeast breakwater was reconstructed from quarry-run rock of the same size used in the original structure. Gradation originally included a maximum size of 1,500 lb and was limited to not less than 25 percent under 6 in. in least dimension. No damage was evident on the southeast breakwater before the earthquake, so the original gradation was maintained; maximum allowable size was, however, increased to 3,000 lb, 25 percent of the stones by weight could be smaller than 10 lb, and 10 percent of the stones by weight had to be larger than 100 lb.

The reconstructed southwest breakwater had the same base alignment as the southeast breakwater, except that the center line was moved 15.5 ft landward (Figure 114). The realignment was necessary to reduce the amount of armor stone required by allowing the toe of the armor stone to abut the original breakwater. The original top elevation of +15 ft MLLW was increased to +16.5 ft MLLW. The increase was to preclude overtopping by all but the highest anticipated storm waves at normal maximum high tides of +13 ft MLLW. It was considered improbable that the extreme high tide of +15 ft MLLW and the maximum design wave would occur simultaneously. The top width of 6 ft was held and was based on the diameter of three stones of the design armor-stone size. The original side slopes of 1 on 1.5 were not changed. Original armor-stone size was graded between 750 and 1,500 lb. In the rehabilitation of the southwest breakwater, the minimum size of 750 lb was retained, but the maximum size was increased to 3,000 lb to allow a reasonably wide gradation and to lessen costs of quarrying by reducing the amount of waste stone. In accordance with criteria used for rehabilitation, at least 50 percent of the stones were to exceed 1,150 lb.

Inner-Harbor Facilities Inner-harbor facilities were restored to include a complete boat-moorage float system with 208 individual stalls and a transit moorage area; a seaplane float, attached to the boat-float system, to accommodate four seaplanes; a 28 X 180-ft public loading dock that also serves as access to the float system; a second access ramp; a 24 X 224-ft boat-repair grid; all water and electrical utilities; and fire-fighting equipment on the float system.

The original float system at Kodiak was totally destroyed by the tsunami. The harbor configuration and area were not changed in the restoration. Because the original float system

had been constructed piecemeal as funds became available to the State of Alaska, the preearthquake configuration was inefficient and to some extent unsafe because of the system of mooring boats bow-on to the floats with their sterns held in place by piles. The floats installed under restoration authority were much safer and used the available small-boat area more efficiently.

Development of the inner-harbor facilities was a joint effort of the State of Alaska and the Corps of Engineers; the state furnished detailed design criteria in the form of sketch drawings and outline specifications. The Corps of Engineers followed the design closely in developing final plans and specifications for advertisement. All the new inner-harbor facilities were constructed of timber with the floats buoyed by polystyrene billets (Figure 114). A typical float section is shown in Figure 79. The seaplane-float facilities were originally in the west corner of the basin but, to reduce conflict between boat and plane traffic, they were moved as close to the entrance as possible. Boat repair grids have been widely used in Alaska for many years, but the concept of the sloping grid was introduced in the earthquake restoration to allow use by boats of all sizes, the deeper-draft vessels grounding on the lower end of the grid and the smaller vessels grounding at the higher elevation. Many fishermen using this facility have praised the ease of docking and the versatility that allows them more latitude as to the tide stage at which they must arrive (Figure 115).

During reconstruction of the inner-harbor facilities, several changes were introduced to meet needs not apparent in original design. The navigation markers at the toe of the rock slope west of the southeast breakwater to warn boats of the existence of the rock reef were replaced and 3 X 6-in. wood sills were added for each tier of 10-ft polystyrene flotation planks to give more support at the center. It was found that the original 6-ft-span polystyrene was not strong enough and tended to crack and break under the loads applied during use of the floats.

In the course of the construction, the contractor found that in several areas the 15-ft penetration required for support piles could not be obtained because of a rock bottom. He was instructed to drill into the rock, to install the prenotched piles, and then to backfill to keep the piles in place. Twenty-six of these holes were required (Figure 116).

The water system had to be modified to include flexible joints in areas where significant movement occurred. The fire hydrants, which were attached to the side of the floats, needed a special guard to reduce damage from docking boats.

The completed inner-harbor facilities are shown in Figures 117 and 118.

Parking Area, Access Road, and Erskine Creek Diversion
The preearthquake parking area next to the small-boat basin covered an area of about 60,000 ft² and had an elevation of

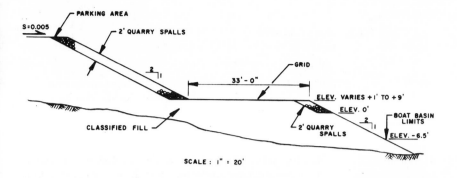

FIGURE 115   Typical section of boat-repair grid constructed at Kodiak.

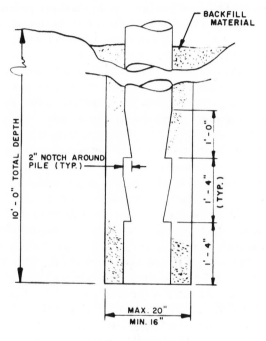

FIGURE 116   Kodiak: Typical section of piling for retention of the floats. The piles are inserted in holes drilled in rock on the bottom of the small-boat basin.

FIGURE 117   Boats in restored small-boat harbor, Kodiak.

FIGURE 118   Looking north from the seaplane ramp, Kodiak. The finished floats.

about +13 ft MLLW, preearthquake datum. Because of the general subsidence, the parking area had to be reconstructed. Reconstruction, funded by OEP, consisted of raising the area to elevation +14.2 ft MLLW (+20 ft preearthquake datum) and installing 2 ft of stone protection on the basin slope. The top elevation was established to allow about 1 ft of freeboard at the normal extreme high tide of +13 ft MLLW. The preearthquake limits of the area were changed slightly because of the realignment of a street (Marine Way). The surface area was increased to about 69,000 ft^2 to best coincide with the master plan. Excavation in the area of the boat-repair grid and construction of the embankment for the boat-launching ramp adjacent to the southeast break-water were included in the contract. No special surface was installed in the parking area, but it was sloped to drain toward the small-boat basin. No special surfacing was put on the boat-launching ramp. Slope-protection stone was 2 ft thick (Figure 119) and consisted of quarry spalls well-graded to a maximum size of 250 lb. Between 10 and 25 percent of the stones, by weight, were less than 5 lb, and 50 percent were larger than 25 lb. The slope-protection-stone gradation was selected to preclude damage by boat-generated waves within the basin and also to prevent leaching of the under-lying classified fill of sand, gravel, and broken stone. The

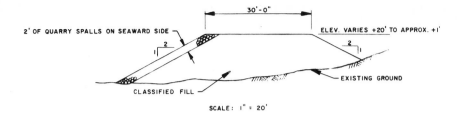

FIGURE 119 Typical section of boat-launching ramp, Kodiak, showing armor stone on seaward side.

thickness was selected to accept about two maximum-size stones.

An access road was built along the northwest side of the small-boat basin to replace the preearthquake road (Figure 120). The restored access road includes a fill with top elevation of +20 ft MLLW, a top width of 30 ft, and side slopes of 1 on 2. No slope-protection stone was used on this road because the float system itself protected the area against the larger boat-generated waves. Only small boats would navigate close to the access road and the minor waves generated by them would not cause damage to the fill.

Before the earthquake, the fresh waters of Erskine Creek flowed into the northern corner of the small-boat basin, causing icing conditions within the northwest half of the basin during the winter months. The City of Kodiak had attempted to prevent icing by installing a bubbler system to agitate the water mechanically by mixing the underlying salt layer with the overlying fresh water. The bubbler system was effective in the immediate area of the installation but did not prevent formation of ice in the remainder of the basin. Diversion was considered to be the best and least expensive way of preventing a recurrence of this icing condition within the restored basin. This would prevent the fresh waters of Erskine Creek from entering the basin during the winter months. The diversion consisted of a 36-in.-diameter pipe laid parallel to Marine Way and discharging outside the southeast breakwater. A concrete diversion structure was constructed at the north corner of the basin to allow discharge of the flood flows into two 72 × 44-in. corrugated-metal-pipe arches. The diversion manhole included a stop-log structure to be operated manually by the City of Kodiak.

Stop logs installed at the end of the flood season provided the necessary diversion to the 36-in. line. The construction sequence of the diversion line and the flood-overflow pipes was complicated because the Navy had fill work to do later landward of the parking area. Stubouts from the diversion manhole were provided so that the Navy's contractor could tie in to the system later. The Navy contract was completed before the extremely cold winter of 1965–1966, and the system functioned satisfactorily during that winter; no icing was apparent within the small-boat basin.

Temporary Waterfront Facilities Between the time of the destruction of all inner-harbor facilities by the tsunami and the time when usable facilities were completed under the rehabilitation program, temporary moorage facilities were installed by the Navy at Gibson Cove, 1.75 mi west of the city of Kodiak. Gibson Cove is a natural, comparatively shallow cove, roughly circular in shape, part of which is naturally protected against wave attack (Figure 121). The moorage facilities consisted of a single line of floats in the most protected portion of the cove; mooring dolphins were installed in the less-protected area. The floats were salvaged by the U.S. Navy from Homer and transported to Kodiak. The floats were at first installed on the north side of Gibson Cove, but wave conditions there proved to be too severe for safe moorage, and the floats were moved to the more protected area. The piles driven for the original float installation were left in place as mooring dolphins. Use of Gibson Cove as a permanent small-boat basin was discussed,

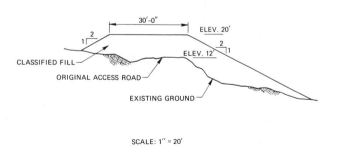

FIGURE 120 Typical section of the rehabilitated access roadway to the southwest breakwater, Kodiak.

FIGURE 121 Kodiak: Temporary moorage for boats in protected Gibson Cove.

but was rejected because construction of the necessary entrance breakwater would be too expensive. There was also some question of the possibility of excessive resonance in the circular harbor if the entrance channel were closed off.

SELDOVIA

Seldovia is near the southern end of the Kenai Peninsula on the south shore of Kachemak Bay, near the mouth of Cook Inlet (Figure 122). It is situated at tidewater on the northwestern slope of the Kenai Mountains on Seldovia Bay, an arm of Kachemak Bay that indents the northwestern coastline of the Kenai Peninsula.

The extreme tide range is 29 ft between an extreme high of +23 ft and an extreme low of −6 ft. The mean tidal range is 15.4 ft between mean high water of +17.0 ft and a mean low water of +1.6 ft. All elevations refer to the tidal datum plane of MLLW.

King crab fishing is excellent in the Seldovia area, and three canneries process the catch. In addition to crab, the area has a minor shrimp and salmon fishery.

The Seldovia waterfront was almost completely devel-

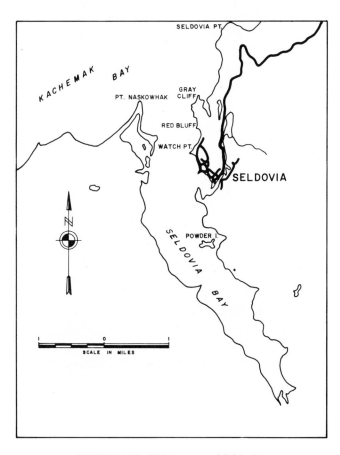

FIGURE 122 Vicinity map of Seldovia.

oped with a small-boat harbor, City Dock, large private dock with petroleum unloading facilities, and several canneries. Most of the business area was constructed on piers that abutted the unique boardwalk that served as Seldovia's main business street. The city and petroleum docks were capable of accommodating deep-draft vessels and, with the addition of the improved navigation channel into Seldovia in 1961, were very adequate for existing ocean-steamer commerce, such as the import of food, dry goods, petroleum products, and other necessities of life, as well as supplies for the canning industry in town. Exports included the locally processed fish and crab.

Seldovia was open for year-round shipping. No ice formed in the deep-draft portion of the harbor; a small amount of sheet ice formed within the small-boat basin but did not impair navigation.

SMALL-BOAT BASIN

The configuration of the preearthquake Seldovia small-boat basin and the two protecting breakwaters is shown in Figure 123. The basin dimensions were approximately 300 × 700 ft at a depth of 12 ft below MLLW. The original harbor was dredged and the breakwater constructed as a regular Corps of Engineers navigation project authorized by Congress. Construction was completed in December 1962. The small amount of sheet ice that formed within the small-boat basin is attributed to a supply of fresh water from a small creek entering the tidal slough that drains into the south end of the small-boat basin.

Typical sections of both the north and south breakwaters as they existed before the earthquake are shown in Figure 123. The rubble-mound breakwaters were constructed with a gravel core (Figures 124–126). Both breakwaters were protected by armor stones designed to withstand the 5.5-ft design wave from the north. Armor-rock size was determined from the criteria in the Beach Erosion Board Technical Report No. 4 (1961).

The contract for the original breakwaters specified that the core material be well-graded gravel and sand, with at least 40 percent by weight of the particles retained on the No. 4 sieve, and with no more than 10 percent by weight passing the No. 22 sieve. The quarry-run rock between the core and armor was to consist of stones of random sizes, except that those that were less than 6 in. in least dimension were not to exceed 25 percent of the total weight. Armor rock on the seaward face of the north breakwater and at the head of the south breakwater was to weigh between 1,500 and 3,000 lb with a 5-ft minimum thickness. On the remainder of the south breakwater, the armor rock was specified to weigh between 500 and 1,500 lb and be 4 ft thick. The armor-rock thickness in all cases was selected to be a minimum of 2 design-stone sizes thick.

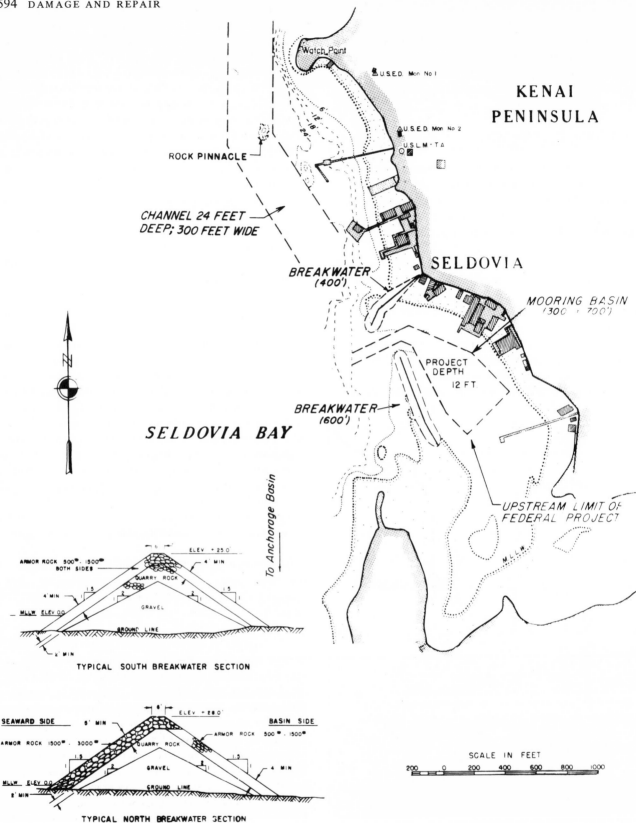

FIGURE 123 Configuration of breakwaters and cross sections before the earthquake and tsunamis at Seldovia.

FIGURE 124 Seldovia: North breakwater during construction. Core rock has been placed at the top of the breakwater over the shaped gravel core.

FIGURE 126 Seldovia (summer 1961): Small-boat basin under construction. The gravel core is in place for the south breakwater (right), and rock protection has been placed on north breakwater (left). City Dock is on the far left.

The crest width of 6 ft was selected to provide interlocking of 3 design-weight armor-stone diameters. The top elevation of 28.0 ft above MLLW for the north breakwater was selected to preclude overtopping by the 5.5-ft design wave at all but the highest tide stages. The top elevation of 25.6 ft above MLLW for the south breakwater was selected to preclude overtopping at all except the highest tide stages of the 2.6-ft design wave from the west. Side slopes of 1 on 1.5 had been selected to hold quantities to a minimum and were the steepest allowable to maintain a stable slope. The breakwaters were founded on either rock or gravel, and no subsidence caused by the weight of the structures had been noted before the earthquake.

OTHER FACILITIES

The layout of the inner-harbor facilities before the earthquake is shown in Figure 127. The boat and seaplane floats and their approach ramps had been completed by the State of Alaska before the earthquake, but electrical and water utilities had not been installed. At the time of the earthquake, the harbor was in full use. All structures within the harbor were of timber, and the floats were buoyed with a plastic flotation material. A boat-repair grid and marine railway were situated outside the harbor before the earthquake (Figures 128 and 129).

DAMAGE TO WATERFRONT FACILITIES

Damage at Seldovia was caused by the earthquake and by the tsunamis that came a few hours later. Damage from the earthquake itself was limited to that caused by the 3.5-ft subsidence that exposed the docks, canneries, boardwalk, and the structures along it to flooding during seasonal high tides (Figures 130–132). Tides in the area are normally highest from September to November. Breakwaters protecting the small-boat basin were affected by the subsidence, because overtopping could occur at ordinary high tides, exposing inner-harbor facilities to greater wave action and the breakwaters to potential damage.

The tsunamis struck Seldovia several hours after the earthquake. Low tide of 1.7 ft occurred at 7:29 p.m. on March 27, 1964; high tide of +19.5 ft was due at 1:39 a.m. on March 28. The first wave started at 10:25 p.m. on March 27 when the predicted tide was +9.1 ft. Seldovia radio reported, "tide slowly coming in." At 10:28 p.m., Seldovia radio reported, "tide coming fast." At 10:37 p.m., "water going back out," was reported. It was apparently the first wave that damaged the floats within the Seldovia small-boat basin. The float system was damaged by the tsunamis; many of the piles that held the floats in place broke and allowed the floats to drift free; some remained within the

FIGURE 125 Seldovia: North breakwater during construction. Core rock has been placed at the top of the breakwater over the shaped gravel core.

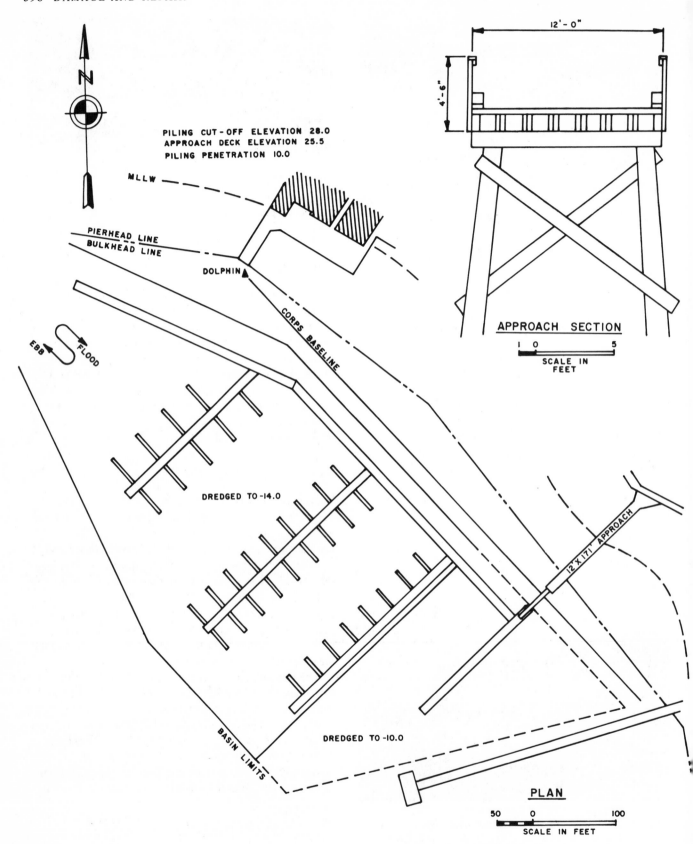

FIGURE 127 Layout of float facilities in the small-boat basin at Seldovia.

FIGURE 128   North end of Seldovia boardwalk with sandbags placed to prevent damage. The marine railway and boat-repair grid can also be seen (March 1964).

harbor, but most drifted out to Seldovia Bay (Figure 133). No damage to boats was reported and only minor structural damage was sustained by the floats. Although the tsunami inundated the boardwalk to a depth of several feet, the boardwalk did not require major repairs. Several business establishments adjacent to the boardwalk were flooded to a minor extent and required only cleanup and very minimal repairs as a result of the water damage.

Inner-harbor facilities were only slightly damaged during the earthquake, but they were badly damaged during the first tsunami after the earthquake (Figure 133). Most of the piles that had originally held the small boat floats in place and that broke during the tsunami had been placed in holes drilled in the rock bottom of the harbor and backfilled with the excavated crushed rock. These piles had a penetration of

FIGURE 129   Seldovia: The City Dock after being raised 5 ft. Boat-repair grid is in the foreground (February 1965).

FIGURE 130   Seldovia boardwalk at high tide. Hotel on left had several inches of water on floor at this tide stage. Approach to small-boat harbor had been raised, and a ramp to the boardwalk had been installed (October 1964).

FIGURE 131   Seldovia residents walking on boardwalk at extreme high tide.

FIGURE 132   The Seldovia waterfront at high tide.

between 8 and 10 ft. To prevent the buoyant force at high tide from overcoming available friction, the piles had been notched about 1½ in. at various elevations similar to the notching shown in Figure 116. The upper notch was cut near the point of maximum moment and caused a stress concentration there.

There was no loss of life at Seldovia because of the earthquake or the tsunamis. Damage would undoubtedly have been greater, however, if the tsunami had occurred at high tide rather than at the lower stages.

Bank Erosion

The city of Seldovia was on a peninsula with Seldovia Bay on one side and a small tidal slough on the other. Because of the general area subsidence of 3.5 ft, velocities of ebb and flood tides in the slough were increased. The banks of the slough vary in height from just a few feet to 15 ft or more. A narrow but important roadway parallels the slough on the Seldovia side atop the bank, and a 10-in. wooden water main had been buried about 2 ft under the center of the road. One section of the bank, about 600 ft seaward of the airport access bridge across Seldovia Slough, had sloughed because of water saturation from the leaking water main that had been damaged in the earthquake. The slide section was about 75 ft long and ranged from 4 to 8 ft in width. This section of the bank was supported by an old bulkhead constructed of native timber. The settling portions of the roadway placed stress on the water main, causing additional leakage that further endangered the stability of the remaining roadway. Erosion also occurred along the bank on each side of the airport-access-bridge abutment. Several small slide areas were noted along the slough bank upstream, but no immediate property or utility damage was expected.

RESTORATION OF WATERFRONT FACILITIES

The Corps of Engineers was designated by OEP to restore the Seldovia waterfront facilities to preearthquake conditions. OEP directed the Corps of Engineers to consider raising the existing boardwalk and approach for protection against tidal action caused by land subsidence in Seldovia area. They were also instructed to investigate the intent of private-property owners to elevate their structures to meet the grade of the proposed elevated boardwalk. In addition, the engineers were to remove damaged inner-harbor facilities and to reconstruct piling, floats, and approaches. The City Dock was to be raised to avoid damage from overtopping and waves. The state-owned dock was considered to be eligible under the boardwalk authority because the dock was leased to the city.

Table 8 lists the contracts administered by the Corps of Engineers in the restoration of the Seldovia waterfront.

To provide continued protection to the small boats

FIGURE 133   Seldovia waterfront the day after the earthquake. Some of the floats are still in place, and two sections are floating loose within the harbor; the remainder had been carried into Seldovia Bay. Snow can be seen on top of the north breakwater and the extreme south end of the south breakwater, indicating the height of the highest tsunami during the night of March 27–28.

moored in the basin, it was necessary to raise the breakwaters to preearthquake elevations relative to the water surface. Funds available to the Corps of Engineers under PL 99, were used for this work, which was limited to raising the two breakwaters. This was the second waterfront-facility-restoration contract advertised after the earthquake.

Typical sections of both the north and south breakwaters after they had been raised 4 ft to compensate for the subsidence that had occurred at Seldovia are shown in Figure 134. At the time of the new design, the exact amount of subsidence had not been determined, but it was known to be somewhere between 3 and 4 ft; for safety, therefore, the breakwaters were each raised 4 ft. Three different types of stone were used to raise the breakwaters: armor stone, class B stone, and class C stone (defined in next paragraph); the increase in cross section was all on the basin side of the breakwaters (Figure 134) to reduce the amount of armor stone required. If the section had been increased on the seaward side, only armor stone could have been used, which would have greatly increased the unit price, because all the material quarried would not then have been usable within the contract.

In the design for raising the breakwater, no changes were made in the criteria used for the original breakwaters. The armor-stone gradation remained between 1,500 and 3,000 lb, with the further stipulation that at least 50 percent of the stones be larger than 2,300 lb. Class B stone gradation remained between 500 and 1,500 lb, with at least 50 percent of the stones to be larger than 1,000 lb. Class C stone gradation was set at a maximum of 1,500 lb; 25 percent of the stone, by weight, could be smaller than 25 lb, but 10 percent must be larger than 100 lb. The relatively wide gradation on class C stone was to allow an economical quarry operation and to reduce waste to a minimum.

TABLE 8 Seldovia Construction Contracts

| Project | Date Awarded | Date NTP[a] | Date Work Started | Completion Date | | Amount Paid to Contractors (dollars) | Funding Agency |
				Original Schedule	Actual		
Small-boat basin, raise breakwaters	May 20, 1964	May 22, 1964	May 22, 1964	Sept. 15, 1964	Oct. 10, 1964	307,493	CE
Airstrip and access-road rehabilitation and reconstruction of harbor floats	July 31, 1964	Aug. 14, 1964	Aug. 14, 1964	Oct. 10, 1964	Nov. 6, 1964	128,835	OEP
Small-boat basin, reconstruction of float facilities, schedule B	July 21, 1964	Aug. 17, 1964	Sept. 8, 1964	Oct. 14, 1964	Dec. 15, 1964	118,174	OEP
Dock rehabilitation	Nov. 9, 1964	Nov. 9, 1964	Nov. 13, 1964	Dec. 31, 1964	Mar. 1, 1965	45,975	OEP
Road-erosion control and water-distribution system	Dec. 15, 1964	Dec. 15, 1964	Feb. 1, 1965	Mar. 15, 1965	Mar. 15, 1965	72,830	OEP
Urban renewal number 26, including boat grid and seaplane-float ramp; repair floats and reconstruct boardwalk	July 14, 1965	July 24, 1965	Aug. 5, 1965	Aug. 28, 1966	–	1,998,506[b]	URA[c] and OEP
boat grid	–	–	–	Sept. 7, 1965	Sept. 19, 1965	–	–
seaplane float	–	–	–	Nov. 21, 1965	Sept. 22, 1965	–	–
schedule A	–	–	–	Nov. 21, 1965	Dec. 6, 1965	–	–
schedule B	–	–	Aug. 28, 1966	June 1, 1967	–	–	–
TOTAL						2,671,813	

[a]Date of notice to proceed.
[b]Total on schedules A and B.
[c]Urban Renewal Administration.

During restoration of the breakwaters, the north breakwater was extended shoreward 50 ft to fully protect the harbor at all tide stages (Figures 135–137).

Inner-Harbor Facilities

Inner-harbor facilities restored with Public Law 875 funds, included a complete boat-float system reconstructed to its preearthquake design (Figure 138). Damaged floats were repaired and reinstalled; destroyed floats were replaced.

Development of the design for the replacement of inner-harbor facilities at Seldovia was a joint effort by the State of Alaska and the Corps of Engineers. The Engineers closely followed detailed design criteria supplied by the state and developed final plans and specifications before the contract was advertised. All the new inner-harbor facilities were constructed of timber, and the floats were buoyed by polystyrene billets (Figure 79).

The approach to the float system was too low after the earthquake because of the general 3.5-ft subsidence in the area. To conform to the elevation set for the new boardwalk and surrounding areas, the approach was raised 6 ft (Figure 139). The boardwalk was razed in the urban-renewal project.

The seaplane float lies immediately southeast of the boat floats. It was rather old and sustained heavy damage from the tsunami. Cost estimates made of repair versus replacement showed that it would be less expensive to replace the old seaplane float than to repair it. The replacement float, 24 X 36 ft with ramps at each end, was held in place by two piles installed on the landward side so that they would interfere as little as possible with seaplane traffic using the float. The original contract, which included float installation without ramps, was completed on December 15, 1964; the ramps were added and construction completed on September 22, 1965 (Figure 140).

The original seaplane float was found to have orientation deficiencies; these were rectified in the restoration. The new float was rotated 30 degrees counterclockwise to allow

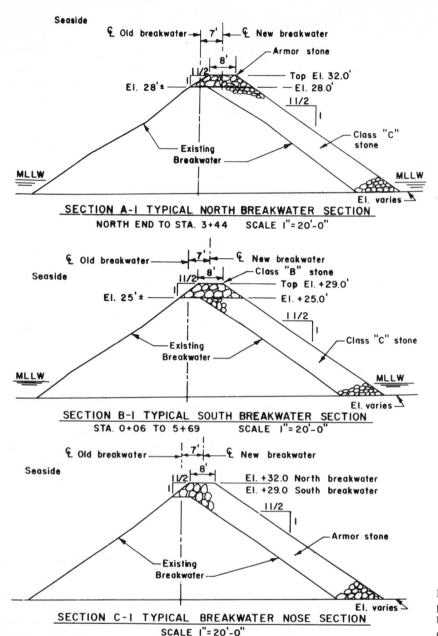

Seaside

℄ Old breakwater ⟶ 7' ⟵ ℄ New breakwater

Armor stone

Top El. 32.0'

El. 28.0'

El. 28'±

8'

1 1/2

1

Existing Breakwater

Class "C" stone

1 1/2

1

MLLW   MLLW

El. varies

SECTION A-1 TYPICAL NORTH BREAKWATER SECTION
NORTH END TO STA. 3+44   SCALE 1"=20'-0"

℄ Old breakwater ⟶ 7' ℄ New breakwater

Class "B" stone

Top El. +29.0'

El. +25.0'

Seaside

8'

1 1/2

1

El. 25'±

Existing Breakwater

1 1/2

1

Class "C" stone

MLLW   MLLW

El. varies

SECTION B-1 TYPICAL SOUTH BREAKWATER SECTION
STA. 0+06 TO 5+69   SCALE 1"=20'-0"

℄ Old breakwater ⟶ 7' ℄ New breakwater

Seaside

8'

1 1/2

1

El. +32.0 North breakwater
El. +29.0 South breakwater

1 1/2

1

Armor stone

Existing Breakwater

El. varies

SECTION C-1 TYPICAL BREAKWATER NOSE SECTION
SCALE 1"=20'-0"

FIGURE 134   Typical sections of the repaired breakwaters for the Seldovia small-boat basin. The increase in cross section was on the basin side.

easier access. Piling at the end of the old float had interfered with seaplane use; in the new float construction, the piling was installed on the landward side of the float to avoid interference.

The grid and the marine way outside the small-boat basin were rendered unusable by the subsidence; in addition, they had to be demolished to make way for an urban-renewal project. The OEP authorized construction of a replacement grid inside the harbor to meet the minimum requirements of boat owners and operators for a minor repair facility. The grid, installed on the south side of the float approach (Figure 138), was about 110 ft long and 20 ft wide and was

constructed of five-pile bents (Figure 141), each capped with a 12 × 14-in. 22-ft timber.

The sloping boat-repair grid used in the reconstruction of Kodiak Harbor had been well received. The Seldovia grid was therefore also designed to slope at the 4 percent grade used at Kodiak. The landward pile cap was set at elevation of +9.4 ft MLLW, and the seaward pile cap was set at elevation +5.0 ft MLLW. The large tidal range at Seldovia permitted the relatively high grid elevations. As a result, the grid is usable for a large portion of each day.

During rehabilitation of the floats, 21 flotation billets were found to have been broken. Ten of these billets were

FIGURE 135   Seldovia: The north breakwater at a medium tide stage, before it was raised (April 1964).

FIGURE 136   North breakwater at Seldovia, after it had been raised. The armor rock has been carried around the breakwater head about 50 ft on the basin side. The breakwater has also been extended 50 ft to connect it to the shore.

FIGURE 137   Seldovia, August 12, 1965: South breakwater (foreground) and north breakwater (background) after increases in height.

in the section built under the inner-harbor facilities contract, and 11 were found in the remaining sections built previously by the State of Alaska. Breakage was attributed to an unusually heavy snowfall during December 1964 and early January 1965 that deposited about 1 ft of ice on the floats. This period coincides with the peak of the king crab fishing activity. Fishermen had stacked crab pots and other heavy gear on the ice-laden floats and this additional load is believed to have been responsible for the breakage. Because the adverse conditions could recur, an intermediate support was added on all flotation billets under the 10-ft-wide master and finger floats. About 104 sills, 3 in. × 6 in. × 10 ft, were added (Figure 142). In the area of the broken billets, 21 sills had already been added, by change order to the original inner-harbor facilities restoration contract.

City Dock

The dock is of vital importance to the canneries at Seldovia because much of the finished produce is shipped from this dock and many of Seldovia's supplies are delivered there.

The dock sustained no structural damage during the

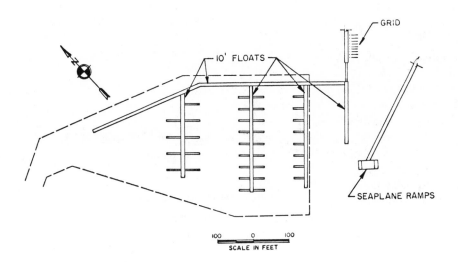

FIGURE 138   Seldovia: Configuration of floats in the restored small-boat basin. The seaplane ramps have been turned 30 degrees.

FIGURE 139   Seldovia: The raised approach to the float system and the sloping ramp leading to the damaged boardwalk (October 1964).

earthquake, but it subsided about 3.5 ft. As a result of this subsidence, the dock was flooded at high tides and was threatened with damage if waves occurred at higher tide.

To rehabilitate the dock, it was necessary either to raise the old structure or to construct a new one. In contrast to the situation at Homer, the most economical and most reasonable rehabilitation measure was to raise the dock. This was possible because drift ice is not a problem in Seldovia Bay. In addition, the dock had subsided only 3.5 ft, whereas at Homer it had subsided between 5.5 and 6 ft; and the dock could be out of service while construction was in progress because other docks were available in Seldovia if needed. The dock was raised about 5 ft to allow more freeboard than existed before the earthquake (Figure 143); 4-ft-creosoted pile stubs were set atop the old pile caps to raise the deck. New pile caps were set over the pile-stub extensions, and the old stringers and decking were replaced at the higher elevation. The pile-stub extensions were drift-pinned to both the old and new pile caps to resist the anticipated horizontal forces, and the new stringers were drift-pinned to the pile caps.

Access to the raised dock from the boardwalk was provided by means of a long sloping ramp at about 4.7 percent grade. This grade was designed to allow easy transit by the forklifts and small tractors that are used to transport the processed fish products to the dock for loading on freighters.

Bank Erosion

Repair of the erosion at the airport access-bridge abutment was considered to be of primary importance to maintain the integrity of the bridge. The erosion was repaired using end-dumped slope-protection stone (Figures 144 and 145).

The slide area 600 ft seaward of the bridge was repaired with a metal bin retaining wall.

SEWARD

HARBOR

Seward is at the northern end of the western shore of Resurrection Bay, a narrow arm of the Pacific Ocean that extends about 12 mi north into the mountainous Kenai Peninsula. Mountains rise abruptly from the eastern and western shores of the bay to elevations of 3,000–5,000 ft within 2 mi of the coast. From Resurrection Bay, a valley extends northward over a low divide to Kenai Lake and also northwestward along the Resurrection River, which empties into the bay through a braided channel.

The head of Resurrection Bay is protected against ocean swells by its curved configuration and by a chain of islands at the mouth, which reduces the wave energy entering from the Gulf of Alaska.

The city of Seward developed on the alluvial fan deposited by Lowell Creek (Figure 146). As the city grew, periodic flooding by Lowell Creek became intolerable; an earth dam was constructed 0.76 mi upstream from the creek

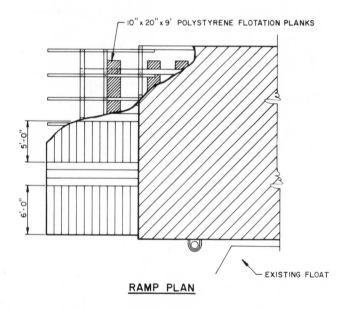

RAMP PLAN

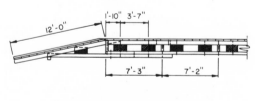

RAMP ELEVATION

FIGURE 140   Seldovia: Details of the seaplane-ramp addition after restoration.

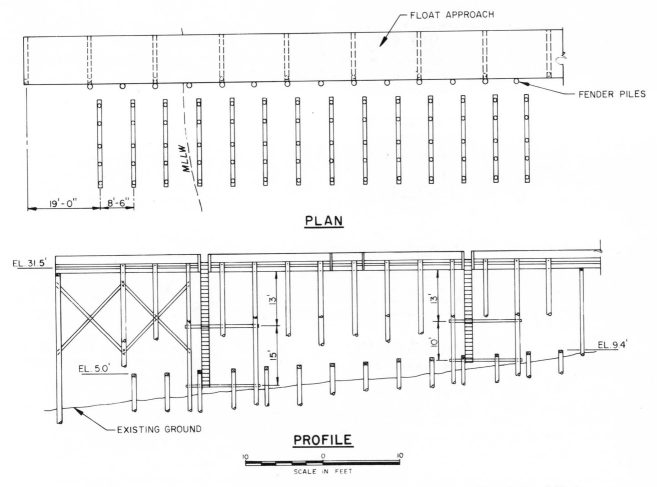

FIGURE 141   Plan and elevation of the new boat-repair grid constructed inside the small-boat basin at Seldovia.

mouth, and the water was diverted to the southwest in a concrete-lined tunnel through a mountain ridge.

Seward is the ocean terminus of the Seward–Anchorage Highway and of The Alaska Railroad, which extends through Anchorage to Fairbanks. It is an ice-free harbor and a major port serving the interior of Alaska. Seward's waterfront was highly developed, with railroad marshaling yards, several marginal wharfs, petroleum-product unloading docks, a cannery dock, and a small-boat basin (Figure 147). The deep-draft docks were owned by The Alaska Railroad and by the U.S. Army. The petroleum-product unloading docks were privately owned, but the small-boat basin and its protecting breakwaters had been constructed by the Corps of Engineers.

SMALL-BOAT BASIN

The original small-boat basin at Seward (Figures 148 and 149) was immediately north of the town, near the confluence of the Lowell Creek alluvial fan on which Seward

stands and the alluvial fan built up by the Resurrection River. Two rock breakwaters and two wood breakwaters incorporated a total area of about 8 acres, of which about 4.7 acres had been dredged to a depth of 12.5 ft below MLLW. Over 210 boats used the original basin, mooring to the floats that had been installed by the State of Alaska. A public loading dock lay within the protected area. The south breakwater was constructed in 1931, the basin was dredged in 1932, and the north breakwater was added in 1937. In 1956, the two pile breakwaters were added and the south breakwater was raised. Maintenance dredging of the basin had been completed in 1952 and again in 1962, when 2 ft of advanced maintenance dredging created an overall depth of 14.5 ft below MLLW in the basin.

INNER-HARBOR FACILITIES

The layout of the inner-harbor facilities at Seward before the earthquake (Figure 150) and the addition of the wood and polystyrene floats by the State of Alaska from time to

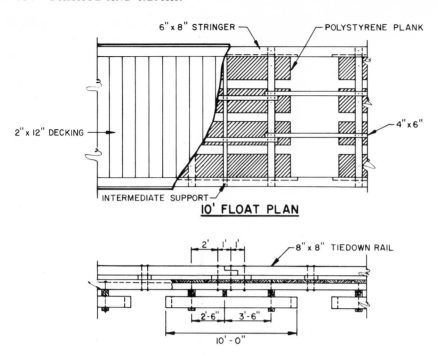

FIGURE 142 Seldovia: Plan and elevation of a typical float section, showing added intermediate support.

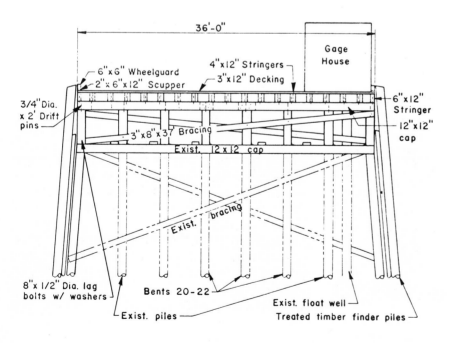

FIGURE 143 Seldovia: Section of restored City Dock, showing method of increasing height.

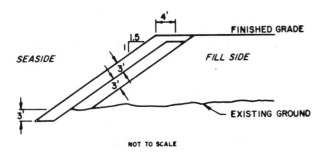

FIGURE 144 Section showing slope protection for roadway along slough at Seldovia.

FIGURE 145 Seldovia: View toward northwest, showing tidal slough (foreground) with completed slope protection in three locations on the slough banks. The raised breakwaters and completed float system can also be seen.

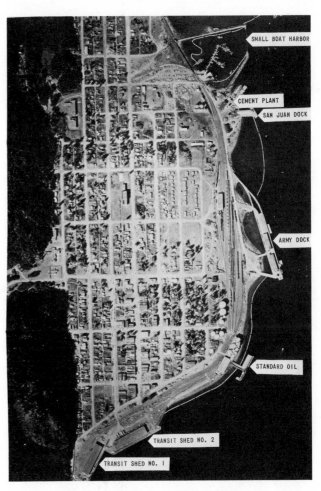

FIGURE 147 Seward before the earthquake.

FIGURE 146 Looking southwest at the city of Seward from above the mouth of Resurrection River (1962). Maintenance dredging was going on in the small-boat basin at the time. Highway to Anchorage leaves photo at lower right.

FIGURE 148 Seward: The small-boat harbor during maintenance dredging in 1962.

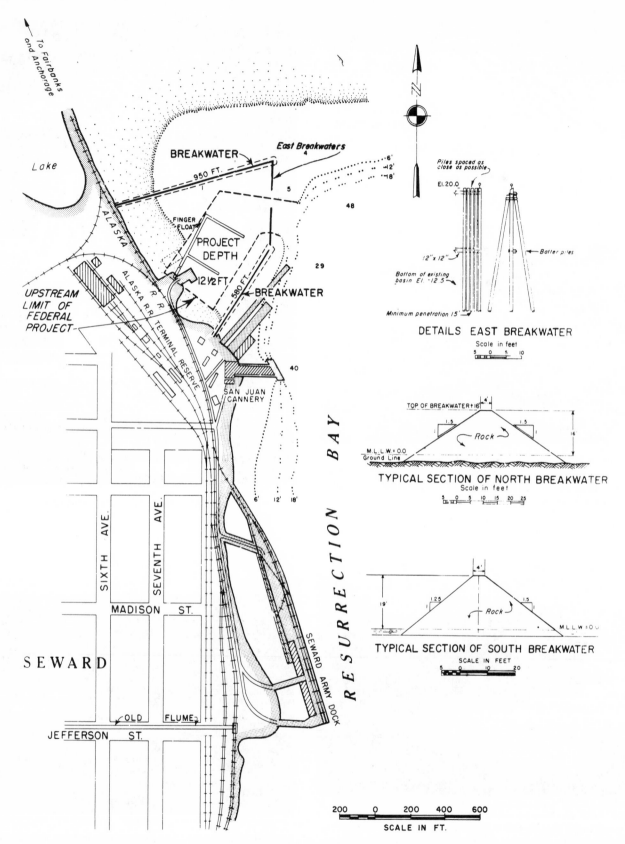

FIGURE 149 Plan and sections of the small-boat basin breakwaters at Seward before the earthquake and tsunami.

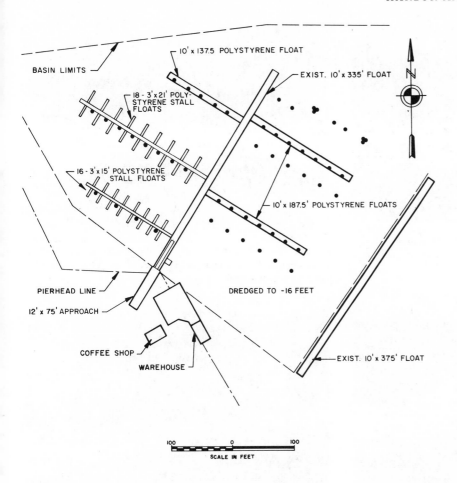

FIGURE 150 Plan view of the inner-harbor facilities of the small-boat harbor at Seward before the earthquake.

time as the need arose had created an inefficient float configuration before the earthquake. The moorage system was also unsafe because of overcrowding. Over 210 boats used the original floats, many of them moored two and three abreast or bow-to on the floats. During very crowded periods, boats were also beached in the shelter of the basin. Utilities on the original float system included water and electrical service.

DAMAGE TO WATERFRONT FACILITIES

The city of Seward was severely damaged by the earthquake and the resulting tsunamis. Its economy came to a halt because the waterfront facilities had been almost totally destroyed; 13 lives were lost in the calamity. The destruction was caused by slides, fires, locally generated waves, and tsunamis. Submarine slides caused massive destruction of facilities along the waterfront and destroyed virtually all the marginal wharfs and POL facilities. An immediate result of the seismic shock was the rupture of fuel-storage tanks. The leaking fuel caught fire as it flowed into the bay. Shortly after the earthquake, waves generated by underwater slides occurred, carrying the burning fuel inland and toward the

head of the bay. The waves not only spread the fuel, setting more buildings on fire toward the north end of town along the perimeter of the waterfront, but in addition carried houses, boats, mooring floats, piling, and a tremendous amount of debris northward, depositing it in the tidal lagoon and well above high tide into the trees at the head of Resurrection Bay (Figures 151–158). Only one 35-ft pleasure boat escaped damage because it was being used at the time for fishing at the mouth of the bay.

About 150 ft of the western part of The Alaska Railroad wharf at the south end of town was the only dock structure that remained at Seward. All other structures were destroyed, leaving no visual evidence that they had ever existed. The tremendous damage inflicted is apparent in Figures 159–168.

A hydrographic survey (Figure 168) made in the area of the original small-boat basin gives an indication of the tremendous change in the Seward waterfront. The end of the south breakwater was originally founded in about 8 ft of water (MLLW); after the earthquake, the water at this location was about 120 ft deep. While the hydrographic survey of the Seward waterfront was being made, from April 3 to April 7, 1964, the surface of the water adjacent to the

FIGURE 151   Debris carried by the tsunami to the head of Resurrection Bay. Seward–Anchorage Highway is on extreme right (April 1964).

Alaska Air National Guard

FIGURE 154   Seward: Debris deposited in residential area near the intersection of Third Avenue and D Street. House, oil drums, and piling have been moved.

FIGURE 152   Houses and debris deposited in the freshwater lagoon to the west of the Seward–Anchorage Highway (April 1964).

FIGURE 155   Debris deposited in residential area near the Standard Oil Co. tank farm, Seward. Oil barrels were deposited by tsunami after being transported from Standard Oil Co. storage area. Note chimneys left standing after buildings burned.

FIGURE 153   Oil-soaked debris deposited in freshwater lagoon west of Seward–Anchorage Highway.

FIGURE 156   Boats and debris deposited by the tsunami at the head of Resurrection Bay. Old Jesse Lee Home for Orphans and Bayview Elementary School are in the background.

FIGURE 157 Debris near Texaco Tank Farm, Seward. Note collapsed and exploded storage tanks. Remains of docks are included in debris.

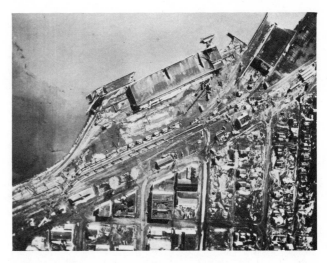

FIGURE 159 The railroad transit sheds at Seward. Note missing portion of transit shed number 1 and destroyed portion of the wharf at transit shed number 2.

FIGURE 160 Destroyed transit shed number 2, Seward. Gantry on the right was moved to the new railroad dock (April 1964).

FIGURE 158 Seward: Boats were among the items carried to the head of the bay. Some of them were relatively undamaged.

FIGURE 161 Destroyed transit shed number 2, Seward (April 1964).

FIGURE 162   Damage to marshaling yards on Seward waterfront; rails were stripped from the railroad ties.

T. Van Valkenberg

FIGURE 165   Damage to Seward waterfront: the burned-out city powerhouse is in the center, and remaining Standard Oil tanks are on the right.

FIGURE 163   Damage to old marshaling yards, Seward. In some cases, rails have been stripped from ties.

Alaska Air National Guard

FIGURE 166   Tsunami damage near railroad wye, Seward. Dock remains can be seen on right. The *Rich Queen*, a boat belonging to the Army Recreation Center, is in the foreground.

Alaska Air National Guard

FIGURE 164   Damage to railroad rolling stock in the vicinity of the city equipment yard, Seward. The railroad engine house is in the background.

FIGURE 167   Small-boat harbor, Seward, after the earthquake and tsunami. Fires on water are from burning fuel leaking from submerged tanks and tank cars.

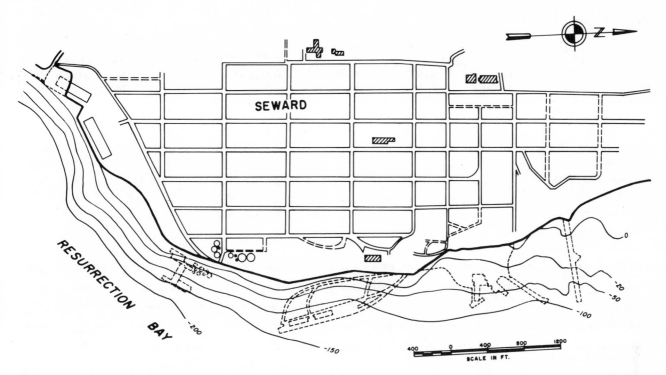

FIGURE 168   Seward: Postearthquake hydrographic survey shows the increased water depths in the vicinity of the old waterfront facilities.

waterfront was covered with petroleum products. Gasoline was seen bubbling to the surface, indicating that leaking pipelines or tanks were underwater. Because of the tremendous fire hazard to the community, the waterfront area was placed under round-the-clock armed guard.

RESTORATION OF WATERFRONT FACILITIES

All waterfront facilities restored by the Corps of Engineers at Seward were replacements for those destroyed during the earthquake. All permanent restoration was made north of Seward in the tideflats at the head of Resurrection Bay, because the Seward waterfront was considered a high-risk area subject to future slides. This high-risk designation extended landward to Seventh Avenue and extended from the intersection of Seventh Avenue and Monroe Street to near the lagoon area. The high-risk designation was based on the results of soil studies made by the Corps of Engineers under assignment from OEP.

The major waterfront rehabilitation projects completed by the Corps of Engineers included construction of a new small-boat basin, a new City Dock, inner-harbor facilities for the basin, and a new deep-water railroad dock with adjacent marshaling yard and support buildings. The contracts awarded at Seward for construction and for supply of services and materials are listed in Tables 9 and 10. Restoration could not proceed, however, until suitable areas from the standpoint of stability and size were found on which

the new facilities could be constructed.

All the restoration projects were interdependent because of the dredging. Each restoration project involved a large amount of dredging: 1,700,000 yd³ for the railroad dock, 400,000 yd³ for the City Dock, 200,000 yd³ for the restoration portion of the small-boat basin, and 380,000 yd³ for the expansion portion. Originally, two dredges were considered necessary at Seward, but the dredges could not be obtained. Dredges available on the West Coast of the United States had already been obligated to major projects planned before the earthquake. It was not economically feasible to import a dredging plant from the East Coast of the United States or from a foreign country.

Debris Removal

A measure of the amount of destruction that occurred was the cost of removing debris. Waterfront cleanup and debris removal was an absolute necessity before any construction on the waterfront could be started. The debris included houses, buildings, railroad engines, railroad cars, tracks, ties, large oil tanks, cars, boats, piling, timber, telephone poles, trees, household goods, and many other items. The existence of this debris not only hindered repairs and construction in the area but created a great safety hazard for operations.

Debris cleanup and repair was let in two separate contracts. The first started on April 4, 1964, and the second on May 21, 1964. The contractors did the following work:

TABLE 9   Seward Construction Contracts

Project	Date Awarded	Date NTP[a]	Date Work Started	Completion Date Original Schedule	Completion Date Actual	Amount Paid to Contractors (dollars)	Funding Agency
Debris cleanup and phase I repairs	Apr. 4, 1964	Apr. 4, 1964	Apr. 6, 1964	June 20, 1964	June 20, 1964	1,161,855	OEP
Debris cleanup and phase II repairs	May 21, 1964	May 28, 1964	May 28, 1964	Sept. 25, 1964	Oct. 16, 1964	1,648,434	OEP and ARR
Breakwaters and boat-launching ramp	Aug. 12, 1964	Aug. 12, 1964	Aug. 13, 1964	June 28, 1965	June 17, 1965	1,068,064	OEP
South breakwater by	–	–	–	Nov. 15, 1964	May 7, 1965	–	–
Small-boat basin, city dock and ARR dredge rental	Aug. 12, 1964	Aug. 12, 1964	Aug. 28, 1964	–	Nov. 2, 1965	2,228,655	OEP
ARR facility clearing	Aug. 21, 1964	Aug. 21, 1964	Aug. 25, 1964	Sept. 20, 1964	Sept. 20, 1964	69,200	ARR
City Dock	Aug. 28, 1964	Sept. 12, 1964	Sept. 8, 1964	June 19, 1965	July 15, 1965	171,369	OEP
Usable facility by	–	–	–	Dec. 4, 1964	Nov. 20, 1964	–	–
ARR restoration	Sept. 18, 1964	Sept. 18, 1964	Sept. 28, 1964	Oct. 14, 1965	June 15, 1966	5,890,802	ARR
Inner-harbor facility reconstruction	Nov. 24, 1964	Dec. 8, 1964	Mar. 8, 1964	May 31, 1965	July 2, 1965	392,874	OEP
Fish facility	Jan. 8, 1965	Jan. 11, 1965	Jan. 20, 1965	Feb. 15, 1965	Feb. 25, 1965	63,282	OEP
Water supply (schedule A) Fire protection (City Dock) (schedule B), and Sewer repairs (schedule C)	Jan. 8, 1965	Jan. 12, 1965	Jan. 18, 1965	Feb. 19, 1965	Mar. 1, 1965	84,530	OEP
Utility installation, ARR dock	May 5, 1965	May 13, 1965	July 1, 1965	July 13, 1965	July 31, 1965	101,060	OEP
ARR transit shed offices	Nov. 22, 1965	Nov. 26, 1965	Apr. 20, 1965	Feb. 8, 1966	July 4, 1966	147,590	ARR
ARR engine house	May 17, 1966	May 18, 1966	June 1, 1966	Dec. 4, 1966	Jan. 27, 1967	304,889	ARR
Harbor-master's office and shop	May 26, 1966	May 31, 1966	June 1, 1966	Oct. 28, 1966	Dec. 16, 1966	120,900	OEP
TOTAL						13,453,504	

[a]Date of notice to proceed.

Removed debris on the waterfront, in the lagoon area, at the airfield, and in Crawford Subdivision at the head of Resurrection Bay.

Rehabilitated three water wells and repaired water main from old Fort Raymond to the city center.

Installed a temporary 4-in. aluminum irrigation pipeline to Forest Acres Subdivision with connectors for each residence.

Installed 20 cesspools on existing outfall-sewer lines to temporarily solve the waste problem.

Repaired the water and sewer systems south of the lagoon.

Graded and placed fill for emergency repair of the existing streets and roads of the main city and cleaned drainage ditches.

Provided improvements to Vista Street west of the lagoon area for an emergency evacuation route.

Cleaned up floating debris consisting of timbers, nearly submerged piling, and power poles on the bay.

Provided operation of the local airport to maintain commercial freight and passenger service.

Stabilized the runway by overlaying with gravel.

Constructed channel in slide north of the city and diversion groin to preclude washout of the slide and subsequent flooding of a housing area.

Placed riprap around power pole on the bank of Snow River to prevent washout.

Removed severely damaged Railroad Shop Repair Building.

Demolished the old city-owned State Building that was used as a city hall before the earthquake.

Salvaged the railroad gantry that toppled from the dock into the bay at the railroad dock.

Disposed of the railroad engine near the lagoon.

Removed underwater obstruction that constituted a potential navigation hazard (–40 ft MLLW).

Demolished The Alaska Railroad docks.

Demolished damaged portion of transit shed 1 and the whole of transit shed 2.

Removed oil-saturated gravel and soil.

Demolished burned-out powerhouse and electrical shop.

Removed underwater obstruction projecting from the face of the railroad dock at berth 2 and removed 10 tank cars that protruded above –40 ft MLLW.

Drove five test piles 80 ft to determine soil condition at the head of Resurrection Bay. Ran load test and pulled the piles.

The contracts were completed on October 16, 1964, at a final cost of $2,810,000. The Seward waterfront after it had been cleaned up is shown in Figure 169.

OEP was not permitted to finance work on federal projects. Therefore, under the terms of the first debris-removal contract, the contractor was required to exert a minimum of effort in disposing of the government-owned Alaska Railroad property. Damaged railroad property was to be moved a minimum distance out of the way of the debris-clearance operations; if it did not obstruct debris clearance, it was to be left in place. Railroad tracks that were pulled

TABLE 10 Seward Supply Contracts

Project	Date Awarded	Date NTP[a]	Date Work Started	Completion Date Original Schedule	Completion Date Actual	Amount Paid to Contractor (dollars)	Funding Agency
Piling for city dock	Aug. 5, 1964	–	Aug. 7, 1964	Sept. 24, 1964	Oct. 3, 1964	133,808	OEP
Hardware for city dock	Aug. 5, 1964	–	Aug. 7, 1964	Sept. 21, 1964	Sept. 24, 1964	43,423	OEP
Pipe and piling for ARR dock	Aug. 10, 1964	–	Aug. 11, 1964	Sept. 25, 1964	Oct. 30, 1964	952, 361	ARR
Steel pipe piles for ARR dock	Aug. 20, 1964	–	Aug. 20, 1964	Oct. 17, 1964	Oct. 30, 1964	213,634	ARR
Rails #6 double cross-over for paved areas	Sept. 1, 1964	Sept. 24, 1964	Sept. 24, 1964	Dec. 24, 1964	Apr. 15, 1965	67,750	ARR
ARR dock load, transport and discharge 1,053 tons 65-ft steel H-piles from Seattle to Seward	Sept. 11, 1964	–	Sept. 11, 1964	Sept. 25, 1964	Sept. 22, 1964	17,500	ARR
Off-loading steel piles	Sept. 16, 1964	Sept. 16, 1964	Sept. 16, 1964	Oct. 3, 1964	Oct. 3, 1964	27,145	ARR
Off-loading steel piles	Sept. 18, 1964	Sept. 18, 1964	Sept. 18, 1964	Sept. 21, 1964	Sept. 25, 1964	3,092	ARR
Off-loading piling and hardware	Oct. 2, 1964	Oct. 7, 1964	Oct. 7, 1964	Oct. 7, 1964	Oct. 24, 1964	6,271	OEP
Cleanup underwater debris	Oct. 23, 1964	Oct. 23, 1964	Oct. 26, 1964	Nov. 5, 1964	Nov. 5, 1964	5,125	OEP
Pipe and fittings for small-boat harbor	Dec. 11, 1964	Dec. 11, 1964	Dec. 11, 1964	Jan. 5, 1965	Jan. 12, 1965	9,225	OEP
Steel pipe and H-piles for ARR dock	Jan. 25, 1965	–	–	Apr. 10, 1965	Mar. 17, 1965	14,068	ARR
Steel piling for ARR dock	Jan. 29, 1965	–	–	Apr. 10, 1965	Mar. 24, 1965	108,595	ARR
ARR dock-radiographic testing of welding	Apr. 9, 1965	Apr. 9, 1965	Apr. 12, 1965	May 22, 1965	May 30, 1965	11,009	ARR
ARR dock-bearing H-piles	June 7, 1965	June 7, 1965	June 7, 1965	July 21, 1965	July 15, 1965	239,242	ARR
ARR dock-bearing H-piles	June 7, 1965	June 7, 1965	June 7, 1965	June 28, 1965	June 22, 1965	16,193	ARR
TOTAL						1,868,441	

[a]Date of notice to proceed.

away from ties and intermingled with debris were removed.

The second debris-removal contract contained provisions for clearance and demolition of the destroyed Alaska Railroad property. The railroad contributed almost $95,000 for this work.

One of the most unusual and difficult jobs in the underwater debris clearance was the removal of a large section of the front wall and foundation of the railroad dock at berth 2. This ell-shaped concrete section, approximately 40 ft long and weighing about 240 tons, had tipped over and was blocking the one remaining area at Seward that could be used by large ships. It was a distinct hazard with its sharp projections that could easily puncture the hull of a vessel.

Several methods of removing the section were considered. Blasting to break it into more easily handled pieces was ruled out because of the potential damage to the remaining portion of the dock that would be usable once the section had been removed. The contractor tried but failed to drag it to deeper water with a barge, using block and tackle. The wall section was finally moved by attaching a large barge to it at low tide and letting the tide lift the barge. The barge was floated to deeper water and the section released.

When all cleanup operations were apparently completed, a sweeping operation was conducted to determine whether any more material was present on the bottom above −40 ft MLLW. Divers reported that several partly buried railroad cars that had not been visible during previous inspections still lay in the area. Local current velocities had apparently removed enough material to make these obstructions visible. The contractor removed these last remaining objects.

Restoration of Small-Boat Basin

Restoration of the basin in its original position was obviously impossible because of the underwater slide that had occurred there. A new site was therefore selected at the head of Resurrection Bay adjacent to the Seward–Anchorage Highway. This site was chosen because of its stability, accessibility to town, protection, and because of the availability of large areas for shoreside facilities for expansion of the basin. Before the earthquake, the basin was so overcrowded that the economic development of the city was hindered. Several new industries requiring additional space were being developed in Seward at the time of the earthquake, and basin expansion was being planned. In planning the harbor restoration, present and future needs, economy of design, and maximum utilization of the area and dredged material were considered. The basin was expanded from 4.7 acres to 17.2 acres, including 4.7 acres of berthing area at project depth of −12.5 ft MLLW and 12.5 acres of anchorage area at project depth of −15 ft MLLW. Total basin capacity in berthing and anchorage areas was increased to about 465 boats. The plan included two rubble-mound breakwaters (one on the south and one on the east) to pro-

FIGURE 169   Seward after cleanup, looking north (January 1965). Alaska Railroad piers 1 and 2 are at lower left.

tect the basin and the City Dock, which was to be built in the same general area as the basin. The material from excavation was disposed to the west and north of the basin not only because economical disposal areas were available, but also because land could be developed for shoreside facilities and parking. The disposal site to the west of the basin was the saltwater lagoon between the old railroad grade and the Anchorage–Seward Highway.

Criteria established for the design of the small-boat basin stipulated that the basin was to be built in an area that would not conflict with the development of railroad facilities and on a site that was stable against zone 3 earthquake loads (0.1 *g* horizontal load). The basin was to contain 17.2 acres at project depth with sufficient room for expansion to 28.5 acres at project depth. The contractor was to dredge 12.5 acres to −15 ft MLLW and the remaining 4.7 acres to −12.5 ft MLLW. The maximum allowable wave height within the basin area was limited to 1 ft, although a 0.5-ft maximum was preferable. The entrance-channel depth was to be −15 ft MLLW and as even as possible to reduce navigation hazard to boats. Breakwaters were to be designed to prevent overtopping at all but highest tides. Surface flow of freshwater was to be excluded from the basin. All material dredged from the basin was to be utilized for land fill adjacent to the basin.

The plan was to be the most economical with regard to interest, amortization, and annual maintenance on a 50-year project life. The lagoon west of the highway was not to be filled because it was to be used by spawning salmon. An access to the lagoon was to be constructed from an area outside the basin. Existing drainage through culverts under the road had to be plugged to preclude seepage through the fresh fill.

Sufficient area was to be available around the basin for

shoreside facilities and parking, and an easily accessible boat-launching ramp was to be included in the design as near to the entrance channel as possible to conflict the least with moored boats or with boats moving to and from the mooring area. The boat-launching ramp was to be four lanes wide to replace the ramp that existed before the earthquake.

In developing the layout of the basin, the major problem was to provide a relatively straight entrance channel while protecting the basin against severe wave action and holding the length of the entrance channel to a minimum, but these criteria were observed. Adequate hydrologic and meteorologic data were available for the development of the plan, and no problems were expected to arise during construction; sufficient subsurface data were also obtained for the design.

Close coordination with the City of Seward ensured that the design was satisfactory to the city authorities. One modification that resulted from this coordination was the installation of the small-boat-launching ramp at the extreme south end of the basin adjacent to the south breakwater rather than near the center as originally planned.

All planning and design of the basin were finished before the expansion of the basin was authorized. There was a possibility that the expansion would not be authorized and that only rehabilitation of the original basin would be allowed. If only 4.7 acres of the basin could be constructed, the south breakwater was to be built to full height and dimensions, but the east breakwater was to be built to its full height and dimensions at the outer end only, with a low section extending to shore. The low section would have been overtopped during any tides above half tide and was therefore designed with a wide flat section capped with armor stone so that it would suffer the minimum of damage from overtopping waves. This section, however, was considered necessary to give some protection to the City Dock, which was to be at the north end of the basin area. Although the plan was seriously considered, it was realized that the breakwater would have to be brought to full height later when the expansion was approved at an additional cost of about $200,000. The expansion of the Seward and other small-boat basins was provided for in an amendment to the Alaska Omnibus Act, which was signed into law by the President on August 19, 1964. When the basin work was advertised on July 30, 1964, there was every indication that the expansion would be approved. The OEP therefore authorized the breakwater contract to be advertised for both breakwaters built to the full design heights and sections that would be necessary for the expanded basin. The contract was awarded August 12, 1964, and work actually started the next day, 6 days before the amendment to the Alaska Omnibus Act became law.

Wind data from 1924 to 1963 were used to determine the design wave height used in the design of the breakwaters for the basin. The predominant wind directions are north and south, determined by instruments located at the southeast end of the northwest–southeast runway at the Seward Airport. The airport is 2 mi northeast of the town of Seward, and because of the rugged and irregular terrain it is often subject to differing winds, particularly the north winds funneling out of Resurrection Bay Pass. A curve of maximum wind velocity versus duration for the period 1954–1963 was used to forecast the deep-water design wave. The method was obtained from the Beach Erosion Board Technical Report No. 4 (1961). The most critical generating area for waves attacking the basin breakwaters is from the south–southeast over a 12.2-mi fetch. The maximum significant wave height of 4.6 ft was found for wind velocities of 33 mph with 1.8 hours' duration. The corresponding wave period is 4.75 seconds, and deep-water wavelength is 116 ft. Winds from other directions were smaller because of the limited fetch over which the waves could be generated. Because of the underwater topography seaward of the breakwaters, the wave would be modified by shoaling. At extreme high tide of 14.64 ft, the water depth would be about 15 ft and the wave height would be modified by shoaling to about 4.2 ft. This wave then was used to determine the armor-rock sizes and the breakwater height needed because of runup; a maximum high tide of 13.5 ft MLLW was used because simultaneous occurrence of the design wave and extreme high tide would be so infrequent that it would be uneconomical to design against this occurrence.

Because the angle of wave attack on the east breakwater is less than 90°, the runup would be reduced (Alaska Department of Public Works, 1966). When waves generated between south–southeast and east–southeast, and their respective runups were compared, it was found that the critical waves for determining runup were from a southeast wind. These waves had a shoal height of 3.4 ft in 12 ft of water at maximum high tide, and the runup was determined to be 3.6 ft (U.S. Army Corps of Engineers, 1963). Again, using a design high tide of 13.5 ft, the top elevation of the north leg of the east breakwater was determined to be +17 ft MLLW. The configuration of the breakwaters and the top elevations are shown in Figure 170. For the south breakwater, top elevations were 18 ft, except for the most northerly 200 ft adjacent to the entrance channel, which sloped to +16 ft because wave heights are reduced by diffraction around the nose of the east breakwater. On the east breakwater, the southern 550 ft was set at +18 ft, the next 750 ft at +17 ft, and the northern 435 ft at +16 ft. The variations in top elevation were allowed because shoaling reduces wave heights in these areas. Top widths of the breakwaters were set at 5 and 6 ft, respectively, to preclude damage from minor overtopping at the highest tide stages. The criteria used were based on three armor-stone diameters.

Typical sections through the breakwaters (Figure 170) show them to be basically of rubble-mound construction

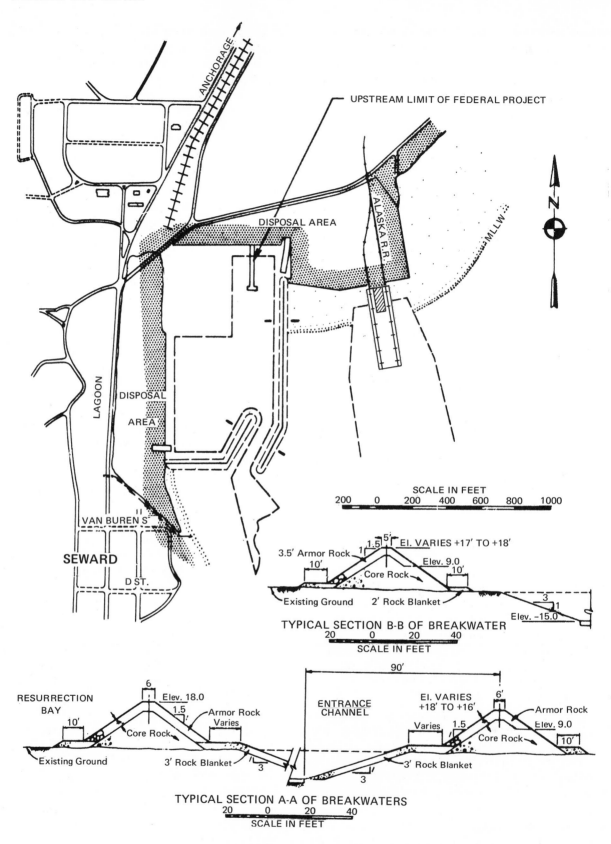

FIGURE 170 Configuration of breakwaters, including sections for new small-boat basin at Seward.

with a toe-protection blanket to prevent damage from erosion of the *in situ* materials by wave action at the toe. The breakwater section includes a core covered with armor rock. The core rock was specified to be pit run, but oversized stones that could not be incorporated in the core-rock section were not to be used. In a 5-ft zone adjacent to the armor rock, not more than 10 percent, by weight, of stones could be less than 25 lb to avoid piping of fine materials through the voids between the armor layer stones. The rock blanket at the toe of the armor rock and on the slopes was designed to preclude piping of the finer underlying materials through it. Rock blanket placed on horizontal surfaces was required to be well graded, with a maximum size not to exceed 300 lb and no more than 5 percent of the stones, by weight, less than 10 lb. Gradation of material for the rock blanket placed on sloping surfaces was 75 percent of stones from 200 to 800 lb, 30 percent larger than 400 lb, and not more than 10 percent smaller than 25 lb. The larger stone on the slope was to prevent damage to the slope protection stone from wave attack. In Figure 171, armor stone has been placed on the extreme southern end of the east breakwater and on the northern end of the south breakwater. Two large oil tanks inside the basin, one grounded on each side of the City Dock, had floated free during extremely high tide and had drifted into the basin where they went aground. They were subsequently removed.

During construction of the breakwaters (Figure 172), the contractor made an enlargement near the bend in the east breakwater so that rock-hauling equipment could turn around. The armor rock was placed by land-based equipment and no floating plant was required.

Two separate armor-rock gradations were set for use on the breakwaters. The south breakwater and the south 550 ft of the east breakwater had armor stone graded between 1,000 and 3,000 lb, with 50 percent of the pieces to be larger than 1,500 lb. On the remainder of the east break-

FIGURE 172   Seward: Railroad dock (right) and small-boat basin (left). The dredge is widening the channel to the City Dock. The completed fish-passage facilities are shown on the left. Immediately below and to right of the fish-passage facilities is the submerged north breakwater of the old small-boat basin.

water, the size of the armor stone varied between 350 and 1,500 lb, with 50 percent of the pieces larger than 700 lb. On the basin side, the armor stone was carried to elevation +9 on both breakwaters, below which the core rock was not protected. This was done to reduce the amount of armor rock required and yet preclude damage from overtopping. On the east breakwater, armor stone was wrapped around the head of the breakwater and carried northward 200 ft on the channel side.

Also included in the breakwater contract was the preparation of the area in which the grid was to be placed by another contractor. To the dressed 1:3 slope, 18 in. of quarry spalls were added to prevent damage by wave action. These were graded from a maximum size of 150 lb to a minimum requirement that no more than 20 percent, by weight, of the stones could weigh less than 5 lb, and 50 percent of the stones, by weight, could be larger than 25 lb.

A separate contract awarded for dredging the basin (Figure 173) included dredging in the City Dock and railroad dock areas. During dredging, the area adjacent to the south breakwater on the basin side was overdredged, and stability computations, following the procedure outlined by U.S. Army Corps of Engineers (1960) *Engineering Manual* 1110-2-1902, showed that the undermined south breakwater would consequently be unstable during a seismic zone 3 earthquake. At the lowest tide of elevation −3 ft MLLW, the lowest safety factor with zone 3 earthquake loads of 0.1 g was 1.13. Because the normally accepted safety factor of 1.25 could only be obtained by adding material to the slope, the breakwater contract was modified to include the placement of granular fill along 1,000 ft of

FIGURE 171   Seward small-boat basin's south breakwater (left) and east breakwater under construction (right), January 1965. City Dock is in the background. Large fuel-oil tanks are on beach in small-boat basin where they were pulled ashore.

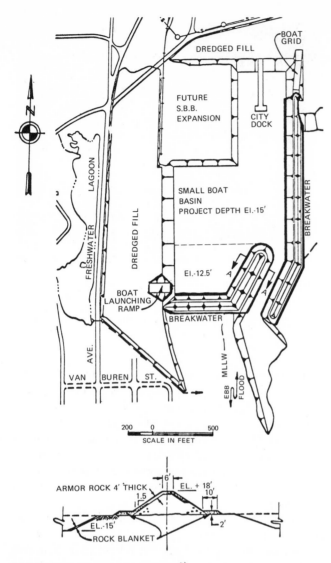

FIGURE 173 Seward: Plan of small-boat basin, showing area and depth to be dredged and disposal areas.

the over-excavated portion of the south breakwater. The fill was hauled along the breakwater in rock buggies and placed with a crane and clamshell-bucket attachment.

Since the breakwaters were completed, the structures have been subjected to severe storms, but no damage has been detected during subsequent inspections.

Included in the breakwater contract was the construction of a four-lane small-boat-launching ramp adjacent to the south breakwater (Figures 173–176).

Icing of Alaska's small-boat harbors in the winter is a common occurrence. The problem at Seward has been minor; ice reached maximum thicknesses of only 1 in. in the float area in the winter of 1965–1966. Some ice also was seen in the expansion area in the northwest corner of the

basin before expansion dredging was finished, and a very small amount was present adjacent to the grid in the northeast corner. This ice is believed to form from freshwater contributed by snowfall and groundwater flow. Although ice can be expected to form during colder periods, icing is not expected to become a serious problem at Seward.

After completion of the basin dredging and construction of breakwaters, the fill was found to be insufficient to bring the lagoon area up to an elevation above high-tide level. The 8.3-acre area in the northwest corner of the basin that had been reserved for expansion was dredged to −15 ft MLLW so that the lagoon area could be used by light industry as an area for development adjacent to the basin.

Fish Facility

In the early stages of planning the small-boat harbor, it was proposed that both the freshwater lagoon west of the Seward-Anchorage Highway and the saltwater lagoon east of the highway be filled to create land adjacent to the harbor and additional ground for development by the City of Seward. Coordination with the State of Alaska Department of Fish and Game and with the Regional Director of the Bureau of Commercial Fisheries revealed that they planned to continue to use the freshwater lagoon west of the highway as a spawning and rearing area for salmon. An average escapement into this area was reported before the earthquake of 321 adult silver salmon in 1 year. Because these salmon had an egg potential of over a million, this area was considered a major production source for the Resurrection Bay silver salmon fishery. The Department of Fish and Game wished to maintain the lagoon as a rearing area for the juvenile salmon, which spend from a few months to a year in the lagoon before migrating to salt water. To maintain the fishery in the 1964 spawning season, the contractor who was removing debris decontaminated the freshwater lagoon by removing the polluted soil and silt deposited in the lagoon by the tsunami. Up to 2 ft of gravel was added to the floor of the lagoon to provide a spawning area. Because the small-boat basin was in the northwest corner of Resurrection Bay, the lagoon's freshwater discharge had to be moved to an area outside the basin to prevent icing. However, the discharge channel also had to serve the needs of migrating and spawning salmon by allowing access to the lagoon at the higher tide stages while holding the lagoon's salinity to a minimum. At first, it was proposed that a culvert with gates be installed under the Seward-Anchorage Highway and an open channel carried from there to Resurrection Bay; the invert elevation of the culverts would have been at approximately mean high tide. The State Highway Department planned to modify the highway in the lagoon area but had not made definite plans by the time the Corps of Engineers was ready to complete design of the fish facility. To maintain flexibility, the control was moved from the

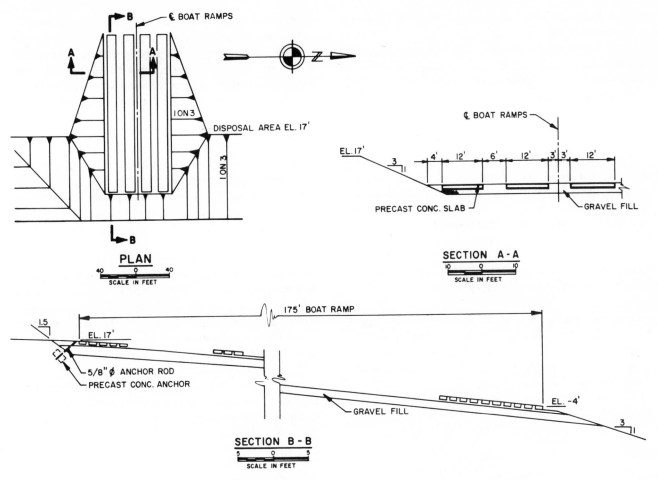

FIGURE 174   Plan and details of the four-lane launching ramp at the Seward small-boat basin.

FIGURE 175   Seward: Charter boat using small-boat launching ramp (August 3, 1965).

FIGURE 176   Small-boat basin in full use on August 17, 1965. The dredge is excavating materials from the approach to the new Alaska Railroad Dock. The freshwater lagoon is in the foreground.

highway to an area at the downstream end of the ditch next to Resurrection Bay.

After the freshwater lagoon had been restored, the bottom elevation ranged from +2.5 to +4.5 ft MLLW with a water surface at +6.5 ft MLLW, which provided the desired depth. Because of this new criterion, it was impossible to install the culverts at mean high tide; an alternate plan was therefore developed using the following criteria:

The freshwater lagoon's normal water surface was to be maintained at +6.5 ft MLLW, and culverts were to be installed at the downstream end of the channel adjacent to Resurrection Bay. The salinity of the freshwater lagoon was to be held to a minimum, and the maximum discharge of 6 cfs was to be allowed to pass during flood stages.

Sufficient water was to be maintained in the channel at minimum flow of 1 cfs to allow passage of salmon from Resurrection Bay to the freshwater lagoon.

It would be desirable to adjust the salinity of the lagoon by controlling the inflow of seawater from the bay (newly hatched salmon require freshwater, but silver salmon ready to leave the lagoon should be conditioned to saline water before entering the sea).

The plan and sections of the fish facility are shown in Figure 177. The alignment of the fish ditch appears at first glance to require an excessively long channel from Resurrection Bay to the freshwater lagoon. This alignment was selected to provide sufficient parking space for a large number of cars and trailers near the small-boat-launching ramp during peak periods, such as the Seward Salmon Derby. This plan would also hold the discharge far enough from the south breakwater to prevent littorally transported materials trapped against the south breakwater from eventually plugging the intake to the fish facility.

Details of the fish facility, including the 24-in. corrugated-metal pipe through the dike with a combination slide and flap gate on the bay end of the pipe, are also shown in Figure 177. The gate can be opened to admit spawning salmon and controlled amounts of seawater. The pipe has zero slope with inverts set at +6.25 ft MLLW to keep the pond at +6.5 ft minimum elevation even at small flows on the order of 1 cfs. A sloping 48-in. corrugated-metal pipe with invert elevation at the intake of 6.75 ft and fitted with a flap gate at the bay end is located adjacent to the 24-in. pipe to pass anticipated flood runoff. The lagoon ditch is level with invert elevation of +5.5 ft to always contain at least 1 ft of water for fish passage at minimum flow. Two 48-in. pipes run through the highway with invert elevations of +5.5 ft MLLW. Armor rock was placed for 200 ft on the bay side of the dike fill that replaced the washed-out area of the old railroad grade.

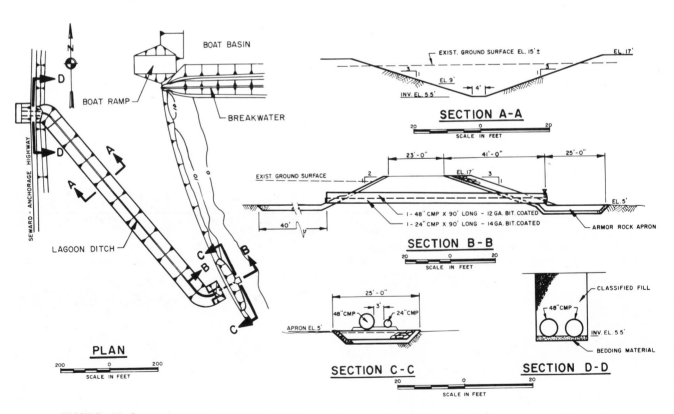

FIGURE 177 Plan and sections of the fish facility that provides access for spawning to the freshwater lagoon at Seward.

Gradation of armor stone on the Resurrection Bay side of the dike was between 25 and 1,000 lb, with the provision that at least 75 percent of the stone weigh from 200 to 1,000 lb and that at least 30 percent of the stone, by weight, be in sizes larger than 500 lb. Spalls less than 25 lb could not exceed 10 percent, by weight. One foot of quarry spalls was placed under the 2½-ft armor layer to provide a filter to prevent migration of the finer underlying materials through the slope-protection stone. The quarry-spall gradation ranged from 2 in. to 12 in., with at least 50 percent, by weight, in sizes larger than 6 in. Rocks smaller than 2 in. could not exceed 10 percent of the total, by weight. The wave attack in this area is considerably less than on the small-boat basin breakwaters because it is protected by the Lowell Creek alluvial fan on which the town of Seward is built and by the basin breakwaters immediately to the north. Wave attack across Resurrection Bay from the east is considered to be so infrequent, by available wind records, that it could be ignored. The completed fish ditch and the freshwater lagoon west of the Seward–Anchorage Highway are shown in Figure 172.

City Dock

Public docking facilities at Seward were totally destroyed in the slides generated by the earthquake. A new public loading dock existed within the small-boat basin as a portion of the City Dock before the earthquake. That portion of the city-owned dock outside the breakwater was leased to a cannery but was open to the public because of overcrowded conditions at the public dock.

Criteria for design of a new dock included a 300-ft long, 35-ft-wide dock with staging area near the end. Draft on both sides and end of dock was to be at least 15 ft below MLLW. The dock was to be located so that one side would be usable under all weather conditions and so docked vessels on either side would not interfere with normal navigation in the small-boat basin or entrance channel. Deck elevation was to be at least 4 ft above the highest tide. The recommended plan was to be based on an austere design as required by Public Law 875. It was to be located so that boats up to 110 ft long could use the dock with adequate navigation channels on each side. The necessary utilities were to be provided on the dock, including electricity, potable water, and fire protection.

The site finally selected for the dock allowed boats entering directly from Resurrection Bay to cause the least possible interference with small basin traffic. A large shoreside backup area was available for development of industries and other commercial enterprises dependent on the dock, and the navigation channel would also serve boats entering or leaving the moorage or anchorage areas within the small-boat basin.

The wood dock selected was the most economical both from the standpoint of first cost and total annual costs based on a 50-year life. Two other types of construction considered were steel pile with a wood deck and steel pile with a concrete deck.

In a public meeting held at Seward on July 9, 1964, the dock and its relation to the overall planning of the small-boat harbor were discussed. A request was made by local businessmen for construction of two marginal docks, each about 2,000 ft long, to support nearby cannery operations, but because this dock was to be a city-owned facility for public use, it was explained that it could not be constructed for the specific benefit of any one industry or company. Also, no private buildings could be constructed on the dock because of the provisions of the OEP directive authorizing a public facility. The dock location (Figure 173) was not ideal, but the general location was accepted as satisfactory if the dock were moved slightly west; this was done. The dock's location with regard to the dredged fill area to the north, placed to support industry and fishery-oriented commercial enterprises, and a detailed plan are shown in Figure 178. The figure also shows a typical section through the dock and design details that include the six-pile bents with two batter piles, fender piles, buffer logs, and the deck details. The dock was designed for an H20-S16 design load and with adequate cross bracing and batter piles to withstand the docking loads imposed by the largest ship likely to use the dock. The staging area at the end of the dock was designed and constructed as a separate entity. A ½ × 12 in. steel plate spans the 4-in. gap between the two structures to provide a safe driving and walking surface.

Two fire walls were constructed on the dock to slow the spread of any potential fire. One was placed at about the middle of the main dock and one at the end of the main dock where it joins the T section. The fire wall was constructed of two layers of 2 × 12-in. tongue-and-groove lumber with staggered joints. The first layer was horizontal, the second layer vertical, with 4 × 16 in. blocking between the stringers directly above the fire-wall planking. The fire wall extends from the deck to elevation +2 ft MLLW.

The dock was constructed of creosoted piling, timbers, and decking to protect against marine-borer attack and rotting. The piling and hardware for the City Dock were obtained by supply contract ahead of the contractor's notice to proceed to expedite construction of the dock. Because docking facilities at Seward were virtually nonexistent, the City Dock contract required that a portion that included the dock approach, the dock (excluding the T section), fender piles, blocking between fender piles, decking, ladders, and temporary grab bars be completed by November 30, 1964. The contractor completed this portion by November 20, 1964, by prefabricating the deck sections on land and installing them on the predriven piling with a

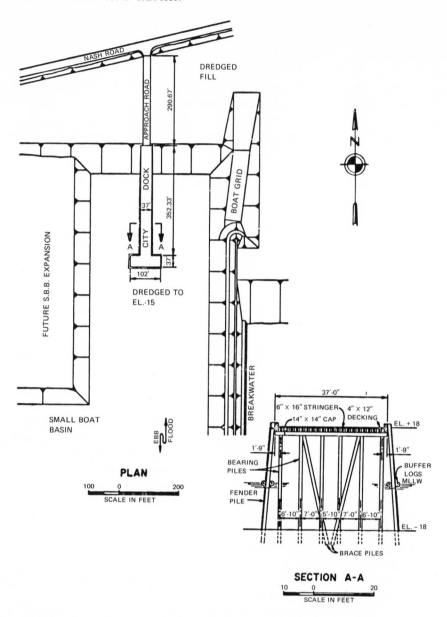

FIGURE 178   Plan and details of City Dock and its location in relation to the small-boat basin at Seward.

crawler-mounted crane. He continued to work after the priority completion date and had practically completed the dock by the end of December 1964. The contract was not closed out, however, until July 15, 1965, when the remainder of the fender piles were driven, the bull-rail installation was completed, and the 2-in. domestic water line and the electrical service were installed.

Since its completion, the dock has been used primarily by vessels associated with the fishing industry at Seward. A photo taken during January 1965 shows the use to which the dock was put as soon as it could safely be used (Figure 179).

In 1965, the Halibut Producers Association constructed a processing and sharp-freeze plant alongside the approach to the City Dock. Since then, the fishing fleet has off-loaded all its catch over the City Dock to the plant.

Inner-Harbor Facilities

A different float configuration was installed in the new basin within the 4.75-acre portion that constituted the restoration of the small-boat basin. The new configuration was both efficient, because of its rectangular shape, and safe, because it was designed with an individual stall for each boat. The inner-harbor facilities were restored, using funds provided by OEP under Public Law 875. The development of the design was a joint effort of the State of Alaska and the Corps of Engineers. Restoration included a complete boat-float system with two approaches,

FIGURE 179 Seward: The unfinished City Dock in use in January 1965.

A boat-repair grid was installed in the northeast corner of the dredged area on the slope east of the City Dock. It is a sloping grid almost identical to that installed at Kodiak, 22 ft wide and 224 ft long, constructed of 5-pile bents on 8-ft centers capped with 12 × 14 in. × 22-ft pile caps. A catwalk alongside provides support for the boats using the grid and an access from the approaches (Figure 181). The grid slopes from a maximum elevation of +8 ft MLLW at the north end to −1 ft MLLW at the south end. Two 20-ft-wide approaches to the grid were installed over which machinery and parts could be transported to the boats being repaired on the grid.

Harbor-Master's Office and Shop

Before the earthquake, Seward had a harbor-master's office in operation on the public dock in the small-boat basin. Living quarters and a shop were located in a two-story building near the west end of the north breakwater; the first floor was 30 × 60 ft and the second floor was 24 × 30 ft. All these facilities were destroyed by the waves that struck Seward.

Under Public Law 875, the city was eligible for replacement of the facility. The rooms and services that were required included a maintenance shop area for one 30-ft boat, an office and a sleeping room for the harbor master, men's and women's toilets, and a small enclosure around the furnace.

Three types of construction were considered for the 32 × 108-ft basic structure: a wooden building faced with

potable water, electrical service, and fire protection (Figures 180–181). All the new inner-harbor facilities were of timber construction with the floats buoyed by polystyrene billets (Figure 181). A 24 × 36-ft seaplane float with a ramp on one end was built near the entrance channel at the end of the longest finger float. Its design was identical to that previously installed at Seldovia.

The gangways from the approach docks to the floats were of the standard design developed for all the restored inner-harbor facilities. They were constructed of steel and wood; the handrail served as the top member of a truss (Figure 182).

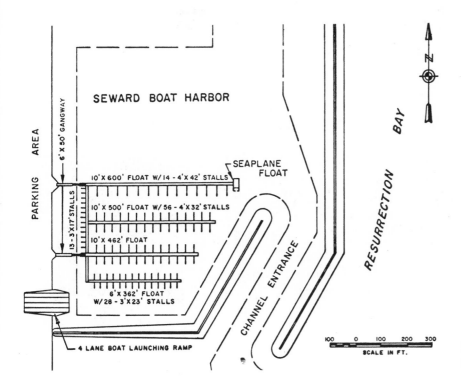

FIGURE 180 Configuration of float facilities for new small-boat basin at Seward.

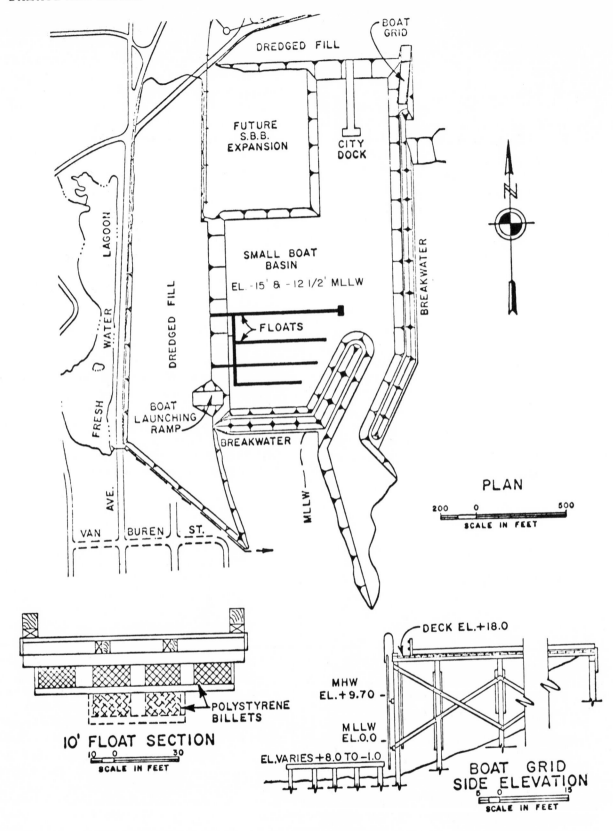

FIGURE 181   Seward: Plan of small-boat harbor showing inner-harbor facilities. Sections of a float and the boat grid are also shown.

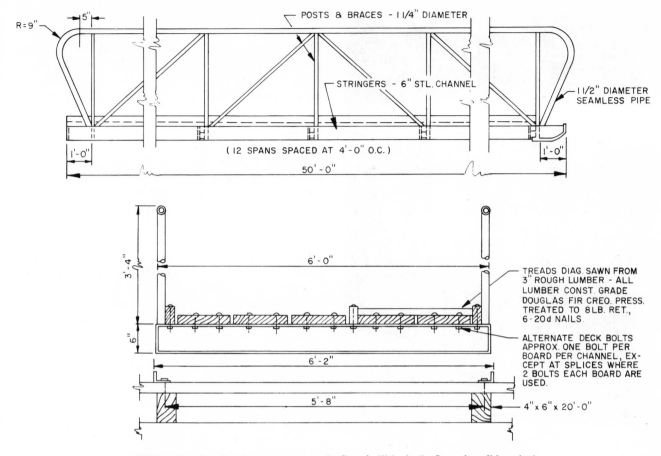

FIGURE 182   Details of the gangways to the float facilities in the Seward small-boat basin.

native stone, a concrete-block building, and a preengineered metal building. The metal building was estimated to be the most economical.

During work on design, the city asked that the following items be included, the funds for construction to be furnished from its treasury: a raised concrete slab for the portico; a north bay for the portico (roof and truss, 42 X 60-ft); north and west glass curtain walls in the lobby; east and west doors in the lobby; roof and structural support to allow construction of an apartment later; and a flagpole and monument.

The site of the building is on the west side of the small-boat basin, centered between the two approaches to the boat floats. A contract for construction was awarded on May 26, 1966, which was scheduled for completion on October 28, 1966.

Alaska Railroad Dock and Related Facilities

Relocation, design, and construction of the new railroad dock and related facilities in Seward are described in this volume (Sturman, 1973).

VALDEZ

The old Valdez townsite was situated at tidewater on a glacial-outwash plain at the head of Valdez Arm immediately west of the confluence of Lowe River and streams from Valdez Glacier (Figures 183 and 184). The town was encircled by a rubble-mound dike to protect it from floods and to prevent the stream channels from migrating into town. Figure 184 is an aerial view of Valdez and the waterfront facilities.

The port of Valdez is the ocean terminus of the Richardson Highway and is a major port serving the interior of Alaska (Figure 185). Before the earthquake, two privately owned wharfs for deep-draft vessels were open for general use by the public on payment of mooring and wharfage charges. These facilities were adequate for existing ocean-steamer commerce. The wharfs provided dockside moorage for three large deep-draft oceangoing vessels at one time. Warehouses on the deep-draft docks were used to store goods until they could be transshipped. Petroleum transfer facilities, a cannery, and a ferry terminal were also located

FIGURE 183   Valdez and the waterfront area before the earth-quake and tsunami.

on the docks. East of town, a petroleum unloading dock with two pile dolphins serviced a tank farm. Shortly before the earthquake, a small state-owned ferry had initiated service to Cordova, carrying passengers, vehicles, and freight

between the two ports on a regular semiweekly schedule.

A small-boat basin had been dredged from the Lowe River flats at the head of Valdez Arm by the Corps of Engineers and had an area of 3 acres (Figure 186). The basin was protected by a 530-ft-long timber-pile breakwater on the southwest side and by a rock-and-gravel breakwater about 475 ft long on the southeast side. Project features also included diversion of a small creek from the basin. Dredging of the basin was completed in October 1939 and all breakwater work was completed in October 1957. Modification of the pile breakwater to include a rock-and-gravel protective base was accomplished in 1960. Maintenance dredging was carried out in fiscal year 1952 and again in 1962. Federal funds spent on the small-boat basin before 1964 amounted to $426,000, and the State of Alaska had dredged an additional 1.5 acres. The controlling depth within the basin was 14 ft below MLLW (Figures 187–189).

Valdez, the most northerly ice-free port in Alaska, was available for all-season shipping. At times, some sheet ice would form within the small-boat basin, but never enough to hinder its use. The extreme tide range at Valdez was 22.0 ft, varying between an extreme high of +17.0 ft and an extreme low of –5.0 ft. The mean tidal range was 9.4 ft, varying between mean high water of +10.9 ft and mean low water of +1.5 ft. All elevations are measured from the plane of MLLW.

DAMAGE TO WATERFRONT FACILITIES

The city of Valdez was severely damaged by the earthquake. The single most disastrous event was the submarine landslide along the waterfront. Thirty lives were lost when the dock area disappeared and the waves generated by the slide swept onto the Valdez waterfront from the bay. All

FIGURE 184   Valdez before the earthquake and tsunami. The large amount of Wharfing is shown in the foreground.

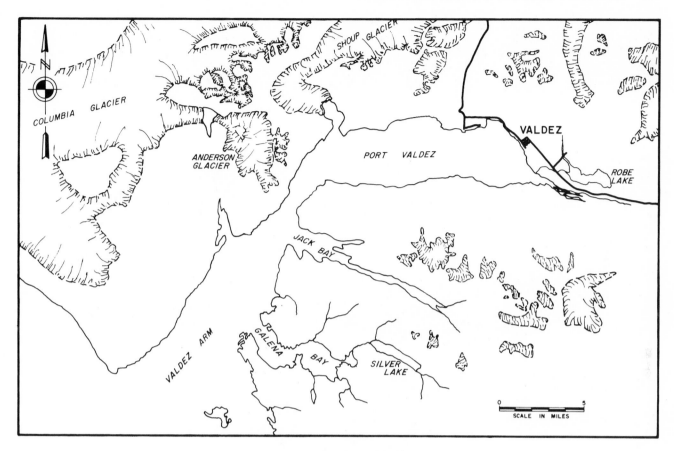

FIGURE 185   Vicinity map of Valdez.

the docks, piers, terminals, and small-boat-harbor facilities were completely destroyed. All that remained of the local fishing fleet was two boats that were away from port at the time of the disaster. A large part of the business district and a smaller part of the residential district were destroyed. Power, sewer, and water systems were entirely disrupted. Several hours after the earthquake, fires broke out in a group of fuel-oil storage tanks immediately east of the small-boat basin and destroyed the tank farm (Scientific and Engineering Task Force, 1964). The effect of the earthquake and waves on Valdez is vividly portrayed in pictures (Figures 190–202).

The first wave, which appeared minutes after the earthquake stopped and reached well into the town, was caused by the localized slide of the Valdez waterfront. Tsunamis continued to arrive throughout the night but caused very little additional damage (Scientific and Engineering Task Force, 1964).

The slide that destroyed the waterfront was estimated to be about 4,000 ft long and 600 ft wide. A hydrographic survey of the waterfront area after the slide shows that the water depth at the dock face increased from 35 to 110 ft.

An area near the small-boat basin, formerly exposed at low tide, was covered by approximately 70 ft of water (Scientific and Engineering Task Force, 1964).

The Alaska Steamship Company freighter, S.S. *Chena*, was unloading cargo at one of the docks at the time of the earthquake. Within 2 or 3 minutes after the start of the earthquake, the ship was reported to have lifted 30 ft above the pier on an incoming wave and to have heeled over landward 45 or 50 degrees into a turbulent area where the pier had been immediately before. The ship was slammed to the bottom by a rapid succession of waves and rolled wildly. The skipper of the *Chena*, Captain Merrill Stewart, nevertheless was able to get the ship under way and moved it to deep water (Coulter and Migliaccio, 1966).

Nine longshoremen were working aboard the *Chena* when the earthquake occurred. Two of these men were killed when they were struck or crushed by the falling and shifting cargo in the plunging ship, and a third was badly injured with multiple fractures of both legs and a crushed torso. The third mate on the *Chena* suffered a heart attack and later died.

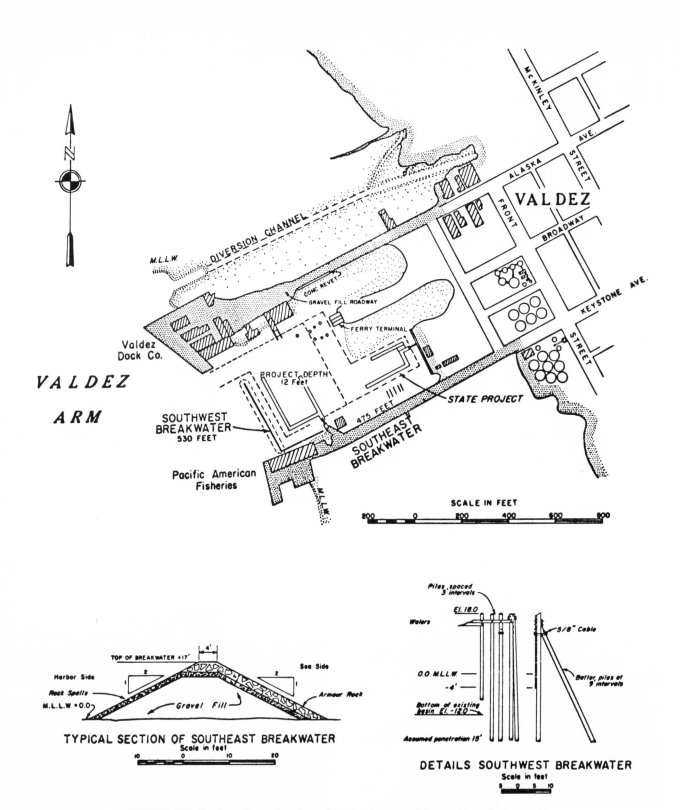

FIGURE 186   Configuration and sections of the breakwaters of the small-boat basin at Valdez.

FIGURE 187   Small-boat harbor at Valdez before the earthquake.

FIGURE 190   One of many fuel-storage tanks that were destroyed at Valdez by the earthquake (April 1964).

FIGURE 188   Seaward side of southwest breakwater of the small-boat basin at Valdez before the earthquake.

FIGURE 191   Valdez, spring 1964, after the earthquake: Road on left served the northwest dock. Building on right is a bar that was destroyed by the waves.

FIGURE 189   Basin side of southwest breakwater of the small-boat basin at Valdez before the earthquake.

FIGURE 192   Valdez: Wave damage to wood frame structure. April 1964.

FIGURE 193   Valdez, wave damage, spring 1964: Metal racks in foreground were used to support petroleum lines from dock to storage tanks. Bent petroleum lines can be seen off the racks.

FIGURE 196   Burning fuel tanks, damaged by the earthquake at Valdez.

FIGURE 194   Damage done by the earthquake and tsunami to tank farm at Valdez.

FIGURE 197   Damaged and shored business establishment at Valdez.

FIGURE 195   Debris on the beach in the area of the docks at Valdez (April 1964).

FIGURE 198   Wave damage to tank farm at Valdez.

FIGURE 199 Damaged fishing boat grounded at Valdez.

FIGURE 201 The roadway to the east dock on the southeast breakwater of the small-boat basin; Valdez waterfront after the earthquake and tsunami.

TEMPORARY RESTORATION OF WATERFRONT FACILITIES

Debris Removal

Immediately after the earthquake, the city of Valdez was a shambles. Ice chunks blocked the streets, buildings were totally or partly destroyed, and debris littered the entire area. Utilities service had been interrupted because of numerous breaks throughout the city. All docking facilities had been destroyed. Fuel tanks were destroyed, and the fuel was burning. Many safety hazards existed.

The townspeople responded to the emergency with food, supplies, materials, and services to provide temporary facilities. On March 29, 1964, a Valdez contractor was awarded a contract for $142,105 for debris removal. Under the terms of this contract the contractor reimbursed the people of the city for their work, supplies, and materials in the amount of $17,000. The following work was accomplished:

• Mess facilities were set up to operate until April 30, 1964.

• Sewers were repaired where possible, and septic tanks were installed where repair was not feasible.

• The supply line from the water tank to the power house was repaired.

• The hospital and schools were repaired for emergency use and the utilities were repaired.

FIGURE 200 Damage by the earthquake and tsunami to a Valdez motel.

FIGURE 202 Valdez: Debris left on the waterfront by the tsunami. A pleasure boat is grounded in the background.

• Ice and debris was removed from all streets.

• Power and telephone lines were repaired.

• The firehouse was repaired, and city property that was in a hazardous condition was demolished.

• The garbage dump was reopened, and an area at the edge of town was cleared for the stockpiling of salvageable material.

• A temporary ferry slip was constructed.

• Debris west of McKinley Street, which included autos, trucks, vans, boats, timbers, piling, and other personal property, was cleared, hand-sorted for salvageable items, and the remainder hauled to the dump.

• Private property endangering life and property was demolished.

• Storm drains were installed on Broadway Avenue between McKinley Street and the small-boat basin.

• Minor repairs were made to the airstrip.

The contract was completed on June 18, 1964, at a final cost of $215,773.

To maintain the economy and commerce of Valdez, three temporary facilities—a ferry slip, a barge terminal, and an open warehouse—were needed immediately. As a measure of expediency, these temporary facilities were constructed at the existing townsite though plans were under way to relocate the entire town because of the high-risk category of its existing location. The high-risk category was based on the results of soil studies made by the Corps of

TABLE 11   Valdez Construction Contracts

Project	Date Awarded	Date NTP[a]	Date Work Started	Completion Date Original Schedule	Actual	Amount Paid to Contractor (dollars)	Funding Agency
Debris removal	Mar. 29, 1964	Mar. 29, 1964	Mar. 29, 1964	Apr. 30, 1964	June 18, 1964	215,773	OEP
Temporary barge terminal and cannery dock	Apr. 23, 1964	Apr. 24, 1964	Apr. 24, 1964	July 10, 1964	July 1, 1964	107,454	OEP
Small-boat basin	July 30, 1964	Aug. 11, 1964	Aug. 17, 1964	June 7, 1965	July 15, 1965	1,429,644	OEP and CE
Priority work, including provision for breakwaters, a ferry slip, and dredging of the west two-thirds of the small-boat harbor	–	–	–	Nov. 15, 1964	May 14, 1965	–	
City Dock Construction of dock, placement of rock fill, armor rock, and gravel surfacing, and installation of guard-rail	Aug. 14, 1964	Aug. 18, 1964	Aug. 20, 1964	Nov. 30, 1964	May 15, 1965	1,247,000	OEP
Modification to temporary ferry dock	Sept. 24, 1964	Sept. 28, 1964	Sept. 30, 1964	Oct. 12, 1964	Oct. 2, 1964	11,654	OEP
Restore warehouse No. 1	Aug. 14, 1964	Aug. 17, 1964	Oct. 29, 1964	May 15, 1965	June 15, 1965	345,249	OEP
Erect warehouse No. 1	–	–	–	Dec. 31, 1964	June 15, 1965	–	–
Furnish warehouse No. 2	–	–	–	May 15, 1965	May 15, 1965	–	–
Ferry terminal facility	Nov. 3, 1964	Nov. 4, 1964	Nov. 10, 1964	Dec. 24, 1964	July 1, 1965	63,009	OEP
Small-boat basin, inner harbor facilities	May 20, 1965	May 21, 1965	June 7, 1965	Aug. 31, 1965	Sept. 25, 1965	357,080	OEP
Warehouse No. 2, and erecting temporary partitions in warehouse No. 1	Sept. 20, 1965	Sept. 24, 1965	Sept. 25, 1965	Dec. 30, 1965	July 1, 1966	224,377	OEP
	–	–	–	Oct. 19, 1965	Oct. 19, 1965	–	–
TOTAL						4,001,240	

[a]Date of notice to proceed.

TABLE 12 Valdez Supply Contracts

Project	Date Awarded	Date NTP[a]	Date Work Started	Completion Date Original Schedule	Actual	Amount Paid to Contractor (dollars)	Funding Agency
Exploration of new townsite	Apr. 30, 1964	–	Apr. 30, 1964	May 14, 1964	May 14, 1964	9,943	OEP
Piling for city docks	Aug. 5, 1964	–	Aug. 7, 1964	Sept. 24, 1964	Oct. 3, 1964	350,959	OEP
Lumber for docks	Sept. 11, 1964	Sept. 17, 1964	Sept. 17, 1964	Oct. 3, 1964	Oct. 3, 1964	17,280	OEP
Piling for docks	Sept. 11, 1964	Sept. 17, 1964	Sept. 17, 1964	Oct. 3, 1964	Oct. 3, 1964	17,869	OEP
Hardware for docks and ferry ramps	Sept. 11, 1964	Sept. 17, 1964	Sept. 17, 1964	Oct. 3, 1964	Oct. 3, 1964	6,164	OEP
Piling for dock	Oct. 23, 1964	Oct. 23, 1964	Oct. 23, 1964	Nov. 14, 1964	Nov. 14, 1964	10,584	OEP
Piling for dock	Oct. 31, 1964	Oct. 31, 1964	Oct. 31, 1964	Nov. 14, 1964	Nov. 14, 1964	9,216	OEP
Piling and lumber for City Dock	Dec. 24, 1964	Dec. 24, 1964	Dec. 24, 1964	Jan. 12, 1965	Jan. 12, 1965	8,252	OEP
TOTAL						430,267	

[a]Date of notice to proceed.

Engineers under assignment from OEP. A more detailed discussion of the studies and the relocation and permanent restoration of the waterfront facilities at Valdez is given elsewhere in this volume. The contracts for construction and for supply of services and materials are listed in Tables 11 and 12.

Temporary Barge Dock

Temporary docking facilities for barges were required at the original townsite to maintain a flow of waterborne goods to Valdez. A minimal facility was therefore designed and constructed (Figure 203). The dock was 25 ft wide, 200 ft long, and was located next to what remained of the southeast breakwater; materials readily available in the town were used.

The dock was built of treated timber piling with 12 × 12-in. untreated caps parallel with the short dimension, 4 × 12-in. stringers 16 in. on centers to support the 3-in. deck. The pile bents were cross-braced with 3 × 12-in. timbers on alternate bents. A timber bulkhead extended for about half the length of the dock on the south side. The bulkhead is tied back with two cables per bent to anchors buried in the remains of the original south breakwater.

Two timber dolphins were constructed seaward of the temporary dock, a 15-pile dolphin about 25 ft from the dock in line with the face, and an 8-pile dolphin 100 ft northwest of the first in a line perpendicular to the dock. These were installed to aid the docking operation during adverse wind conditions. All piles were 20 ft long with penetrations of 26 ft for the first dolphin and 20 ft for the

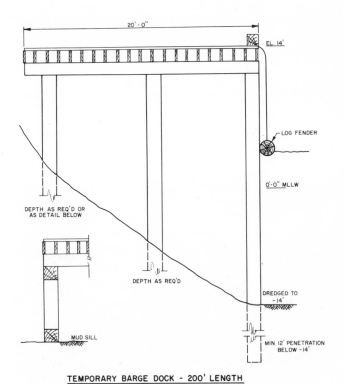

FIGURE 203 Section of the temporary barge dock at the old Valdez townsite.

second. The piles were driven with a single-acting steam hammer rated at 7,600 lb. Piles in the first dolphin had a driving rate in the last five blows of from 0.5 to 1.0 in. Piles in the second dolphin had a driving rate in the last five blows of from 0.5 to 1.5 in.

Controlling water depth at the dock was 14 ft MLLW, which was inadequate for deep-draft vessels. At high tide, however, deep-draft vessels did use this dock. Some dredging was required to provide even this minimum depth. The general waterfront area on which the temporary dock was built was known to be unstable. In June 1964, the area in front of the newly constructed dock sloughed in and a boat grounded. Additional dredging was therefore necessary to provide a usable facility (Figures 204 and 205).

Temporary Warehouse

An open-storage shed was constructed on the waterfront to provide storage space for supplies delivered over the temporary barge dock. The warehouse, 45 ft wide and 165 ft long, was constructed using post and beam construction; roofing and siding were of corrugated sheet metal. Construction was completed in June 1964 (Figure 206).

Temporary Ferry Terminal

Because Valdez is the nearest road terminus to Cordova, it was essential to continue ferry service between these two towns. A landing site for the ferry was therefore required. The ferry has a ramp built into its bow that can be dropped for loading and unloading—a system similar to that used on military landing craft. The length of the ramp allows the ferry to accommodate fluctuations in tides of about 6 ft. To allow landings at all tide stages, a three-ramp ferry dock was used before the earthquake. Because of the decision to

FIGURE 205   Valdez: Alaska Steamship lines freighter, *Susitna*, at the temporary barge terminal. Freighter was very lightly loaded but still could not pull into the dock because of shallow water at the dock face (September 1964).

provide only minimum facilities pending completion of projects at the new townsite, only one ramp was constructed. It was located on what remained of the road access to the preearthquake northwest dock (Figure 207). A minimum of dredging was accomplished to provide adequate depth only at the higher tide stages. The temporary ferry terminal was completed in the middle of April 1964.

In August 1964, the state requested dolphins to provide lateral support when the ferry was moored during the impending winter weather. Before the dolphins were installed, the ferry's own power was required to hold it in place. In calm weather there was no problem other than safety, but

FIGURE 204   Valdez: The old townsite, with barge dock, ferry dock, and the temporary warehouse completed (March 1965).

FIGURE 206   Valdez: Temporary warehouse at high tide. Road access to the temporary facilities has been cut by flooding (September 1964).

FIGURE 207 Valdez: Approach road to temporary ferry dock at the old townsite at high tide (August 1965).

serious problems were anticipated in bad weather. In addition, the state reported that the mooring area was rapidly silting-in and that dredging was required to clear the area. It also was reported that the road leading to the ferry was being seriously eroded during the high tides which overtopped that road. This condition made costs abnormally high to maintain operation of the facility.

Because safe moorage of the state ferry was necessary, pile dolphins were installed (Figure 207). Minimum dredging provided the required depths. This work was completed on October 2, 1964, and the project was transferred to the State of Alaska for operation and maintenance. To comply with the concept of providing only a minimum facility, however, no work was done on the roadway. Maintenance of the roadway was continued by the state.

New community facilities have been constructed at the new city of Valdez on the Mineral Creek site approximately 4 mi from the old town, which is to be completely abandoned.

GIRDWOOD

The old townsite of Girdwood was on Turnagain Arm, Cook Inlet, 37 mi southeast of Anchorage (Figure 208), at the mouth of Glacier Creek between the railroad on the north and the highway on the south. The town was established as a mining camp, but at the time of the earthquake only about 50 people lived there. Most of those working were employed by the State Highway Department or The Alaska Railroad.

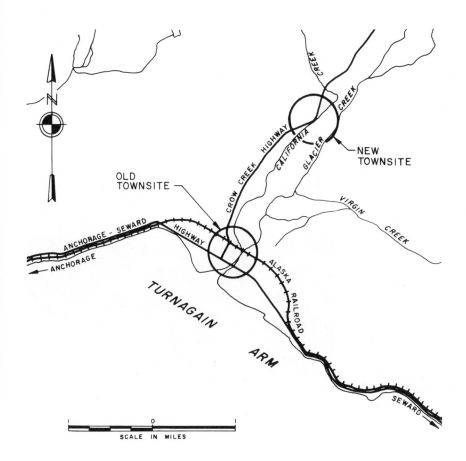

FIGURE 208 Vicinity map of Girdwood, showing the old and new townsites.

FIGURE 209 Old Girdwood townsite after the earthquake and tectonic subsidence, showing extent of flooding at high tide. Village was entirely flooded at extreme high tides.

There were and are no waterfront facilities at Girdwood; supplies are taken overland from Anchorage.

EARTHQUAKE DAMAGE

Damage to Girdwood was caused from flooding after the 5–6 ft of earthquake-induced subsidence of the area (Figures 208–210). Buildings and their contents were soaked by the silt-laden salt water. Wells were polluted by the flood water, and sewage-collection systems were made inoperative. Erosion on Glacier Creek also became a problem.

RESTORATION

There was no restoration of the old town of Girdwood; the townsite was moved, and the new location and layout are shown in Figure 211. The Corps of Engineers, under authority of PL 875, moved the community hall and drilled a well.

The community hall was moved in October 1964 at a cost of $2,800. A local house-moving firm moved the building the 2.5-mi distance to the new townsite. The building was set on cribbing because a permanent foundation could not be constructed at that time of the year. To make the building habitable during the winter, a purchase order for $1,000 was awarded for repairs.

On April 7, 1965, a contract was awarded to construct a permanent foundation for the community hall. This contract provided for construction of piers, removal of existing supports, setting the building on the foundation, and constructing skirting around the crawl space with ventilation and an access panel. The work was completed on May 19, 1965, at a cost of $2,139.

A contract was awarded on November 10, 1964, for construction of an 8-in.-diameter well at the new Girdwood townsite (Figure 211). Construction was completed on February 14, 1965, at a cost of $7,307.50. The depth of the well at the bottom of the screen is 79.4 ft. A pumping test was maintained for 20 hours at 350 gallons per minute with a drawdown of 36.7 ft. Within 17.5 hours after the test was stopped, the groundwater had recovered to the original level.

HOPE

Hope is on the southwest shore of Turnagain Arm, Cook Inlet, at the mouth of Resurrection Creek. The town is 88.5 mi from Anchorage by road or about 25 mi by air.

Established in 1896, Hope was the scene of the first recorded gold strike in Alaska. At one time, over 5,000 gold seekers lived there in temporary shelters. The inhabitants, who now number about 60, make their living from agriculture or by working for the State Highway Department. A number of recreation homesites have been developed on a wooded ridge nearby. There were no boat-docking facilities.

EARTHQUAKE DAMAGE

Most of the damage to Hope resulted from flooding because of the 5-ft subsidence, as in the case of Girdwood. Two houses were made uninhabitable by the high tide, and about 10 others were flooded. Other minor damage included fallen chimneys and destruction of electrical wiring in the school. The school water well was also contaminated, and the water supply was partly interrupted.

FIGURE 210 Old Girdwood townsite at low tide after the earthquake and tectonic subsidence.

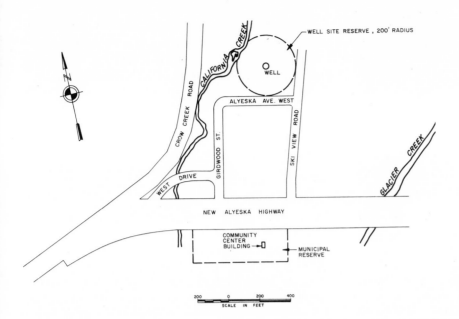

FIGURE 211 Layout of new townsite of Girdwood.

REPAIR AND RESTORATION

On September 14, 1964, a contract was awarded in the amount of $3,203.14 for rewiring the Hope School. The work consisted of replacing a 50-A circuit breaker and installing wiring in surface-installed conduit; this work was completed on September 30, 1964.

A contract was awarded on November 10, 1964, for construction of a 6-in. well (Figure 212), which was completed on February 15, 1965, at a cost of $5,065. The depth of the well to the bottom of the screen is 70 ft. A pumping test was maintained at 10 gallons per minute for 24 hours with an 11-ft drawdown.

KLAWOCK

The town of Klawock, on Prince of Wales Island in southeastern Alaska, is about 60 mi northwest of Ketchikan on the Pacific Ocean side of the island.

The extreme tide range is 18.5 ft between an extreme high of +14.5 ft and an extreme low of –4.0 ft. The mean tidal range is 8.1 ft between a mean high of 9.4 ft and a mean low of 1.3 ft. All elevations refer to the tidal datum plane of MLLW.

WATERFRONT FACILITIES BEFORE
THE EARTHQUAKE

The waterfront facilities consisted of floats for mooring fishing boats, a city dock, a boat-repair grid, and some private docks and canneries.

The float facilities consisted of 516 ft of timber and polystyrene floats 10 ft wide with a 12 × 150-ft approach (Figure 213). Lighting was the only utility on the floats. During the fishing season, a machine shop was available at the cannery for repair of the fishing boats.

The city dock is 28 × 60 ft in area with a 12 × 221-ft approach and is constructed of timber on wooden piles and timber (Figure 214). An 18 × 68-ft boat-repair grid was located on the south side of the approach.

WATERFRONT DAMAGE AND REPAIR

The damage caused by the tsunami was light in comparison to that caused in other coastal cities in south central Alaska. The only reported damage was to the float facilities. The float approach structure and the seaplane float were destroyed, floats were damaged, piling broken, and the gangway displaced.

On June 18, 1964, a contract for repair of the floats was awarded in the amount of $23,954. The items of work were as follows:

- Remove and dispose of existing approach structure.
- Construct new 12 × 150-ft approach structure.
- Construct and install new 24 × 46-ft seaplane float.
- Drill three pile holes and place three piles.
- Furnish and drive six piles for the seaplane float dolphins.
- Rehang the existing 6 × 50-ft gangway.
- Repair and relocate existing 10 × 120-ft float.
- Replace end pontoon and four polystyrene planks on the main float.

FIGURE 212   Vicinity map of Hope town-site, showing the location of the school and the well.

• Repair minor damage to the pile collars on the connecting float.

• Replace four wolmanized handrail posts and handrails on the gangway.

• Provide ramp suitable for vehicular traffic from the approach structure to the parking area.

The deck of the approach structure was constructed at +16 ft MLLW. The piling for the floats placed in drilled holes was firmly seated butt-down in the bottom of the holes and backfilled with ⅜-in. and smaller-sized material. The tops were cut off at +22 ft MLLW. Construction was completed on August 18, 1964.

ORCA INLET

Orca Inlet runs in a southwest to northeast direction and extends from the Gulf of Alaska to the head of Orca Bay north of Cordova. The width of the inlet varies from about 1½ mi to 3 mi; the depth varies from zero to several hundred feet. The general configuration of the area of that reach between Shag Rock and west of Bluff Point in the vicinity of Big Point is shown in Figure 215.

Before the earthquake and the resulting land upheaval, the channel through Orca Inlet had controlling depths of about one fathom. Although some difficulty was previously experienced at low tide stages, the normal flow of traffic

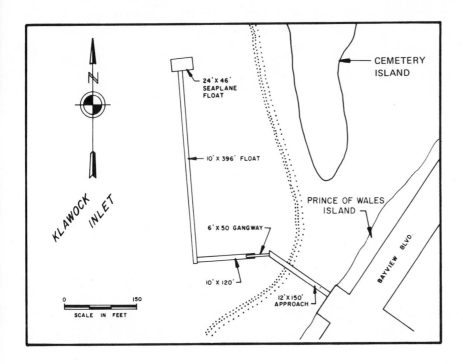

FIGURE 213 Layout of float facilities at Klawock before the earthquake and as they were restored.

has used this route since the inception of the Cordova fishery. The alternate route is north from Cordova to Orca Bay, west and south around Hawkins and Hinchinbrook islands, and then easterly to the Egg Island area. This route is not only 80 mi longer but exposes the boats to the open waters of the Pacific Ocean and the Gulf of Alaska and is usually impossible for the smaller craft to navigate.

The earthquake caused land upheaval of about 6 ft in the area of Cordova; a similar rise had occurred in this reach. Where controlling depths were from 1 to 1½ fathoms at MLLW, they were about 0 fathom at MLLW after the earthquake.

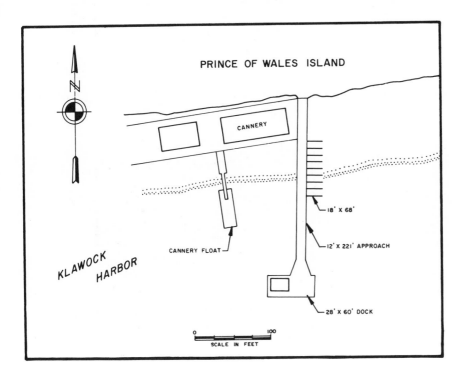

FIGURE 214 Plan view of City Dock and boat-repair grid at Klawock before the earthquake and tsunami.

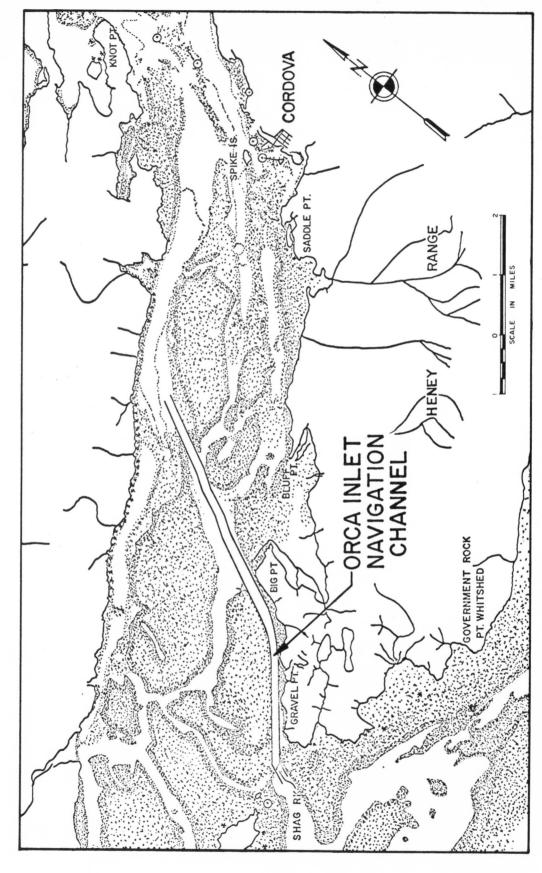

FIGURE 215 Vicinity map of Orca Inlet, showing portion to be dredged.

RESTORATION OF THE CHANNEL

Restoration of the navigation route consisted primarily of dredging a shallow-draft channel with a project depth of –8 ft MLLW and a width of 100 ft. Slopes were maintained at a 1:12 pitch. The dredged material was pumped to disposal areas a sufficient distance from the navigation channel to prevent reentry. The Shag Rock channel spoil was pumped to the rocky shoal area in the vicinity of Shag Rock.

The first dredging contract was awarded on August 12, 1964, and was completed on December 10, 1964, at a cost of $439,930. A channel 50–75 ft wide was dredged at a depth of –7 ft MLLW over a distance of 10,000 lin-ft.

The second contract was awarded on July 15, 1966, and completed on September 13, 1966, at a cost of $344,467. The work consisted of increasing the depth and width of the channel to 8 ft MLLW and 100 ft, respectively.

TATITLEK

Tatitlek, at latitude 60°52′ north and longitude 146°41′ west, is 23 mi southwest of Valdez, 38 mi northwest of Cordova, and 110 mi east of Anchorage. It lies 47 mi southeast of the epicenter of the March 27, 1964, earthquake. The townsite is on the east shore, near the south entrance of the Tatitlek Narrows that connect Valdez Arm and Port Fidalgo. An Indian village in the center of the excellent fishing waters of Prince William Sound, Tatitlek is not connected to the Alaska highway system, and all transportation to and from the village is by boat or seaplane. There are no roads or airports at Tatitlek.

Before the earthquake, a natural mooring basin adjoining

FIGURE 217 Tatitlek waterfront at high tide, showing increase in elevation of landmass.

the town was used by boats for semiprotected moorage. Several shallow reefs protected the area from the large ocean swells refracted into Prince William Sound from the North Pacific Ocean. The villagers engaged in fishing under the management of the Bureau of Indian Affairs, selling their catch to cannery tenders from Cordova. The fishing industry was and is the sole source of income for the villagers who use their own fleet of small boats.

Tides at Tatitlek have an extreme range of 22.0 ft, from an extreme low of –5.0 ft to a high of +17.0 ft. Mean tidal range is 10.0 ft, from a mean low tide of 1.5 ft to a mean high of 11.5 ft. All elevations refer to the tidal datum plane of MLLW.

DAMAGE TO WATERFRONT FACILITIES

The damage to Tatitlek was limited to the loss of mooring depth because of the uplift of about 4.6 ft in the area (Figures 216 and 217). The controlling depth in the natural mooring basin before the earthquake was about 1 fathom at MLLW; with the uplift, no usable depth was left. After the earthquake, vessels attempting to anchor as before were grounded at low tides. Space for swinging on the anchor was more limited because of the restrictive reefs in the area.

The Indian village of Chenega, 75 mi southwest of Tatitlek on Knight Island Passage, Prince William Sound, was destroyed by the tsunami following the earthquake; 53 former residents of Chenega village were moved to Tatitlek. Their boats and others that they planned to buy added to the congested and hazardous conditions existing in the area.

RESTORATION

Harbor

To provide adequate anchorage depth in the harbor at Tatitlek, OEP authorized and funded a dredging contract under Public Law 875 (Table 13). A 2½-acre anchorage area at project depth of 8 ft below MLLW was authorized.

FIGURE 216 Tatitlek waterfront after the earthquake, showing increase in elevation of the landmass (summer 1964).

TABLE 13   Tatitlek Construction Contract

Project	Date Awarded	Date NTP[a]	Date Work Started	Completion Date		Amount Paid to Contractor (dollars)	Funding Agency
				Original Schedule	Actual		
Harbor restoration and dredge rental	Sept. 15, 1964	Sept. 15, 1964	Sept. 27, 1964	Oct. 15, 1964	Oct. 9, 1964	70,625	OEP

[a]Date of notice to proceed.

FIGURE 218   Dredge at work in Tatitlek harbor; increase in elevation of the land can be seen along the waterfront (summer 1964).

A 200-ft-wide entrance channel was required for access to the anchorage area (Figure 218). Excavated material was deposited in shallow water west of the excavation. The proposed basin is shown in Figure 219. Because no probings were taken in the area, it was not possible to define the exact limits to be anticipated in dredging, but a hydraulic dredge was brought in to provide as much area as possible up to the maximum of 2½ acres. During construction, the overlying sands and gravels were dredged off as much as possible, and the anchorage area formed was L-shaped. Although the resulting area was not quite as satisfactory as anticipated, it has proved to be very usable for anchorage and partial protection of the fishing boats. Several seiners and skiffs anchored off Tatitlek can be seen in Figure 220.

After completion of the dredging project, the village requested that a breakwater be constructed south of the anchorage basin to provide further protection. The request had to be denied because it was not economically feasible.

Housing Construction

No housing was available for the Chenega residents who were moved to Tatitlek. New housing was constructed by the Bureau of Indian Affairs (Figure 220).

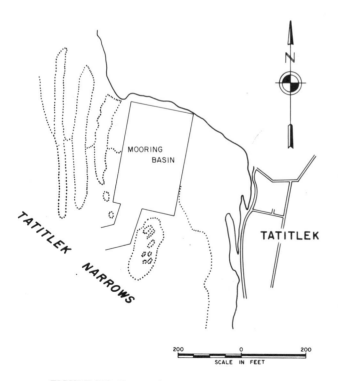

FIGURE 219   Proposed mooring basin at Tatitlek.

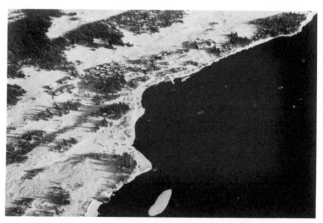

FIGURE 220   Tatitlek after dredging of the area in which boats and skiffs are anchored. New housing, constructed for the residents of Chenega who moved to Tatitlek after their village was destroyed, can be seen (February 1965).

ACKNOWLEDGMENT

Except as otherwise stated, all figures are credited to the U.S. Army Corps of Engineers.

REFERENCES

Alaska Department of Public Works, 1966. Alaska directory of state harbor facilities. Juneau: State of Alaska, Division of Waters and Harbors.

Beach Erosion Board, 1961. Shore protection planning and design. Technical Report No. 4. Washington: U.S. Army Corps of Engineers.

Beach Erosion Board, 1962. Waves in inland reservoirs. Technical Memo No. 132, November. Washington: U.S. Army Corps of Engineers.

Berg, Glen V., and James L. Stratta, 1964. Anchorage and the Alaska earthquake of March 27, 1964. Report of the American Iron and Steel Institute. New York: American Iron and Steel Institute. 63 p.

Coulter, Henry W., and Ralph R. Migliaccio, 1966. Effects of the earthquake of March 27, 1964, at Valdez, Alaska. U.S. Geological Survey Professional Paper 542-C. Washington: Government Printing Office. 36 p. Also in The Great Alaska Earthquake of 1964: Geology. NAS Pub. 1601. Washington: National Academy of Sciences, 1971. p. 359–394.

Saville, T., 1954. The effect of fetch width on wave generation. Beach Erosion Board Technical Memo #20, December. Washington: U.S. Army Corps of Engineers.

Scientific and Engineering Task Force, 1964. 30 Day Report of the Scientific and Engineering Task Force. (Task Force No. 9.) Washington: Federal Reconstruction and Development Planning Commission for Alaska. 52 p.

Sturman, Gary G., 1973. The Alaska Railroad in The Great Alaska Earthquake of 1964: Engineering. NAS Pub. 1606. Washington: National Academy of Sciences.

Tippetts–Abbott–McCarthy–Stratton, 1965. Evaluation of physical damage to Anchorage port and terminal facilities resulting from the March 27, 1964 earthquake (unpublished report for City of Anchorage). Seattle: Tippetts–Abbott–McCarthy–Stratton, Consulting Engineers and Architects, July.

Tudor, W. J., 1964. Tsunami damage at Kodiak, Alaska, and Crescent City, California, from Alaskan earthquake of 27 March 1964. U.S. Naval Civil Engineering Laboratory Technical Note N-622. Port Hueneme, California: U.S. Naval Civil Engineering Laboratory. 131 p.

U.S. Army Corps of Engineers, 1960. Stability of earth and rockfill dams. U.S. Army Corps of Engineers Engineering Manual 1110-2-1902, December 27. Washington: U.S. Army Corps of Engineers.

U.S. Army Corps of Engineers, 1963. Design of breakwaters and jetties. U.S. Army Corps of Engineers Engineering Manual 1110-2-2904, April 30. Washington: U.S. Army Corps of Engineers.

U.S. Coast and Geodetic Survey, 1964a. Preliminary report–Prince William Sound, Alaskan earthquakes March–April 1964 (second printing). Seismology Division Report. Washington: U.S. Coast and Geodetic Survey. 101 p.

U.S. Coast and Geodetic Survey, 1964b. Preliminary report: Tidal datum plane changes, Prince William Sound, Alaskan earthquakes March–April, 1964. Office of Oceanography Report. Rockville [Maryland]: U.S. Coast and Geodetic Survey. 5 p.

Waller, Roger M., 1966. Effects of the earthquake of March 27, 1964, in the Homer area, Alaska (with a section on Beach changes on Homer Spit, by Kirk W. Stanley). U.S. Geological Survey Professional Paper 542-D. Washington: Government Printing Office. 28 p. Also in The Great Alaska Earthquake of 1964: Geology. NAS Pub. 1601. Washington: National Academy of Sciences, 1971. p. 461–488.

ERWIN L. LONG
U.S. ARMY CORPS OF ENGINEERS DISTRICT,
ALASKA

Earth Slides and Related Phenomena

Slides and area-wide settlement caused by the consolidation of soil were major factors contributing to the destruction of property and loss of life during the Alaska earthquake. Tsunamis were the greatest single cause of loss of life, but slides caused the second largest number of casualties. In the Anchorage area, earth slides were responsible for much of the damage that occurred to one- and two-story buildings during the earthquake. Damaging slides occurred in Turnagain, Fourth Avenue, L Street, and Government Hill.

Damage resulting from earthquake-caused avalanches was negligible. Very favorable frost conditions and a lighter than normal snow pack may have materially decreased the potential damage from snow slides, and few improvements other than highways and railroads existed in the avalanche areas.

Three weeks after the earthquake, Ralph B. Peck was retained as consultant on slide investigations to the Alaska District Corps of Engineers. Shortly thereafter, Thomas Thompson, consulting engineering geologist, and Laurits Bjerrum of the Norwegian Geotechnical Institute were also retained as consultants to the Corps of Engineers on the earthquake-induced soil failures at Anchorage, Seward, and Valdez.

The firm of Shannon & Wilson, Inc., was retained on April 25, 1964, to assist in the analysis of these slides, to make investigations, and to recommend remedial measures. H. Bolton Seed was retained by Shannon & Wilson as special consultant on earthquake dynamics of soils.

Before investigation by the Corps of Engineers, the Engineering Geology Evaluation Group and the Arctic Alaska Testing Laboratories of Anchorage conducted inspections of the Anchorage area slides. The initial study was sponsored by the Alaska State Housing Authority (ASHA), the City of Anchorage, and the Urban Renewal Administration. Lidia Selkregg, aided by Ruth Schmidt, conducted the study for ASHA. Their reports were analyzed and relevant parts were included in the reports prepared by Shannon & Wilson.

Slides and related phenomena resulting from the 1964

ABSTRACT: Ground vibrations initiated many earth slides in the regions strongly shaken by the 1964 Alaska earthquake. Some of the large destructive slides were the consequences of soil liquefaction, whereby a stratum of soil lost nearly all its strength after undergoing oscillatory earthquake strains. A reduction in soil strength, resulting from oscillating earthquake-induced stresses, was responsible for the large soil movements. Slides similar to the large Turnagain Heights landslide did not occur elsewhere, although many miles of coastline with apparently similar soil conditions were shaken with equal or greater intensity. Liquefaction-associated phenomena of cohesionless gravels, sands, and silt soils were commonly observed under low overburden pressures, but were not observed in similar materials under large gravity loads. Major economic losses resulted from settlement of soils, some of which were related to liquefaction, consolidation, or a combination of consolidation and horizontal stretching of substrata. All major rock avalanches occurred adjacent to glaciers. Failures of snow, ice, and rock that produced avalanches may be related to gradual decreases in strength through brittle-failure crack progression, pore-water pressure increases, and partial melting of ice, but very little field data are available to support any positive conclusions concerning the mechanics of failure.

Alaska earthquake are of numerous types and occurred in many different places. We classify them in this study as soil slides, subaqueous soil slides, avalanches, crustal movements, and settlements. We recognize that some slides have gone unobserved in uninhabited areas affected by the earthquake.

Eyewitness accounts (Alaska District Corps of Engineers, 1964), reports by Seed and Martin (1965), and other portions of this and other reports tend to substantiate the interdependence of soil failures on the duration of the earthquake. Within the immediate Anchorage area, slide failure and graben development seem to have begun well after the shock waves commenced. The testimony of eyewitnesses varies as to the length of time, but a common estimate was 1½ to 2 minutes.

SCOPE

The purpose of this chapter is to review earth displacements related to this earthquake. The displacements discussed are classified as soil slides (which include rotational, horizontal translatory, and liquefaction slides), subaqueous slides, and avalanching of snow, ice, and rock. Crustal movements that are of insufficient magnitude to come under any of the foregoing headings but that could be destructive are also covered in this chapter.

SOIL SLIDES

The location of the three types of soil slides in the Anchorage area is shown in Figure 1. To permit a more rapid evaluation of slide danger from earthquake forces, Laurits Bjerrum, Office Chief of Engineers consultant, conducted a field survey and compiled a list and chart (Figure 2) of slopes that failed and slopes that did not fail, both of which were overlying Bootlegger Cove Clay. Slopes with some form of natural buttressing and those with other pertinent characteristics were noted. This information formed the basis of a slope-stability chart (Figure 5 on Plate 7.1, Shannon & Wilson, Inc., 1964b) that served as one means of evaluating the possibility of future sliding of existing slides and future need for stabilization.

ROTATIONAL SLUMPS

Rotational-slump soil failures occurred at the following locations (Varnes, 1958) in the Anchorage area: along the north side of lower Ship Creek, south and east of the Corps of Engineers Alaska District office building (Figure 3); along Chester Creek on Romig Hill near West Anchorage High School (Figure 4); on Third Avenue east of Post Road (Figure 5); on the north side of Government Hill (Figure 6); at Cairn Point (Figure 7); across Knik Arm from Cairn Point, northeast of Sleeper landing strip (Figure 8); along the bluff southeast of Point Campbell (Figure 9); and as an integral part of the graben development in the complex Turnagain slides (Figures 10–12). As grabens deepened, rotational failure of the oversteepened graben slopes probably occurred during the tensile or crack-opening phase of the earthquake cycles. There was also an indication that some of the rotational slides along the north bluff of Ship Creek may have involved partial or complete liquefaction in the lower portion of sliding. The four rotational slides immediately north and east of the Sleeper landing strip also appeared to involve some liquefaction of lower layers with horizontal spreading (Figure 8).

Elmendorf–Ship Creek Slides

A series of seven slides occurred along the north bluffs of Ship Creek east of the Government Hill slide (Figure 3). The most westerly slide was directly in front of and south of the Corps of Engineers Alaska District office (Figure 13), and the most easterly slides were ½ mi ENE of the West Elmendorf Power Plant. The four most westerly slides (Figure 14) could be classed as slumps. There was some indication of liquefaction and runout at the toe. Figures 15 and 16 show the stratigraphic sequence of the soils adjacent to the West Elmendorf Power Plant on the east end of these slides. Water seeps along this section of bluff were generally about 5–10 ft above railroad grade at the west end and about 5–10 ft below railroad grade at the east end, or at approximate elevations of 85–95 ft mean sea level (MSL). The Alaska Railroad grade varied in elevation from 78 to 100 ft. The point of toe failure closely approximates the line of water seepage. This zone would be weaker than zones further upslope because the frost penetration would have been least in the saturated toe area. The saturated sands and coarse granular soils are also subject to liquefaction. The four more prominent westerly slides had heavy silty gravel, either as natural Naptowne outwash or as fill, overlying the Bootlegger Cove Clay deposits. All these slide areas had some oversteepening of the upper slopes from the placement of fill. The top-of-slope elevations vary only slightly from 135 ft MSL. The indications of liquefaction imply possible failure in the sand or gravelly sand strata interbedded with the stiff Bootlegger Cove Clay below the present slope toe. A 10- to 15-ft soft sensitive clay stratum does exist under this area, but its top is at about elevation 45 ft, or 37–55 ft below the toe of the slope.

The road grade was rebuilt across the top of the slides between the Corps of Engineers Alaska District office building and the power plant as shown in Figure 17. The middle three slides (Figure 18) continued to drop several inches at the scarp line during the year after the earthquake. As a result of scarp-line movement, the warehouse road north of

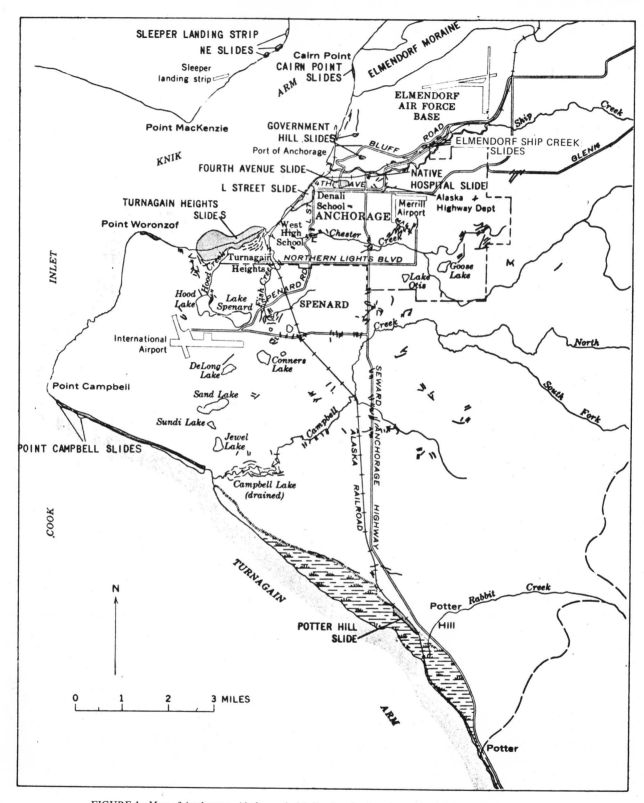

FIGURE 1 Map of Anchorage, Alaska, and vicinity showing location of landslide and ground cracks.

Shannon & Wilson, Inc.

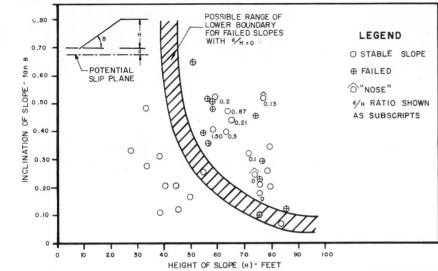

FIGURE 2   Bjerrum slope-stability chart.

Alaska State Housing Authority

FIGURE 3   Stereo pair showing a series of eight rotational-slump slides along the bluff on the north side of Ship Creek, Anchorage (April 4, 1964). Scale: 1 in. = 2,000 ft. (Note: A number of the other aerial views in this paper are given in stereo pairs to provide a three-dimensional effect when viewed through a stereo viewer).

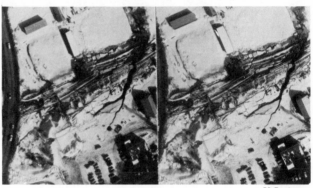

U.S. Army

FIGURE 5   Rotational-slump slide on Third Avenue, east of Post Road and north of State Highway Complex, Anchorage (April 4, 1964). Scale: 1 in. = 200 ft.

FIGURE 4   Rotational-slump slide on Romig Hill on the south bank of Chester Creek and north of West Anchorage High School (May 20, 1964).

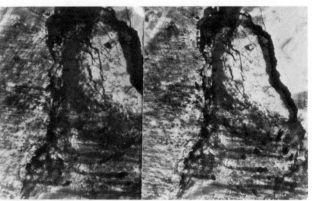

U.S. Army

FIGURE 6   Rotational-slump slide on the north side of Government Hill, Anchorage. Passive zone below slide (April 4, 1964). Scale: 1 in. = 200 ft.

T. Tice, Army Corps of Engineers

FIGURE 7   Rotational-slump slides on Cairn Point, north of the Port of Anchorage (March 29, 1964).

U.S. Coast and Geodetic Survey

FIGURE 8   Rotational-slump slides northeast of Point MacKenzie and Sleeper airstrip (March 30, 1964). Scale: 1 in. = 1,500 ft.

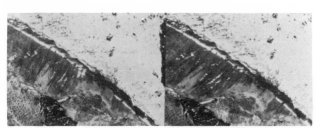

Alaska State Housing Authority

FIGURE 9   Rotational slump at Point Campbell. Scale: 1 in. = 500 ft.

FIGURE 10   Rotational slump within a graben in the west Turnagain retrogressive translatory slide (April 19, 1964).

FIGURE 11   Rotational slump in Turnagain translatory slide, north side of Lynn Ary Park (May 13, 1964).

FIGURE 12   Rotational slump into graben northeast of McCollie and east Turnagain Parkway (April 12, 1964).

the Alaska District office building was extended east to the Bluff Road, so that the main thoroughfare would bypass the slide area.

The two more easterly slides, one immediately east of the power plant (Figure 19) and the other ½ mi ENE (Figure 20) of the power plant, were rotational-slump failures of more limited movement. The slide area of Figure 19 had been filled primarily with ash. This slide area had cracking

and small displacements extending across the road into natural Naptowne gravel outwash and fill. The two most easterly slides in Figure 20 were not as high; the slide adjacent to the railroad fill was less than 10 ft high. Of the many slides that occurred as a result of the March 27, 1964, earth-

FIGURE 13 Rotational-slump slide, south of the Corps of Engineers Alaska District office building. This slide overlaps an old slide scar to its left (west) (March 30, 1964). Scale: 1 in. = 500 ft.

FIGURE 14 Four rotational slides along the north side of Ship Creek (March 30, 1964). Scale: 1 in. = 500 ft.

quake, all those exhibiting horizontal translatory sliding failed in soft sensitive clay or sand strata in the Bootlegger Cove Clay formation. The depth of these layers below the base of the bluff permitted the lower terrace to act as a buttress, resisting the formation of that type of failure along the Elmendorf–Ship Creek bluffs.

The slope-stability chart (Figure 2) indicates that the slope adjacent to the West Elmendorf Power Plant was within the zone of possible failure. The natural buttressing of the toe, however, provides adequate restraint to prevent such deep-seated failures. The power plant is not considered to

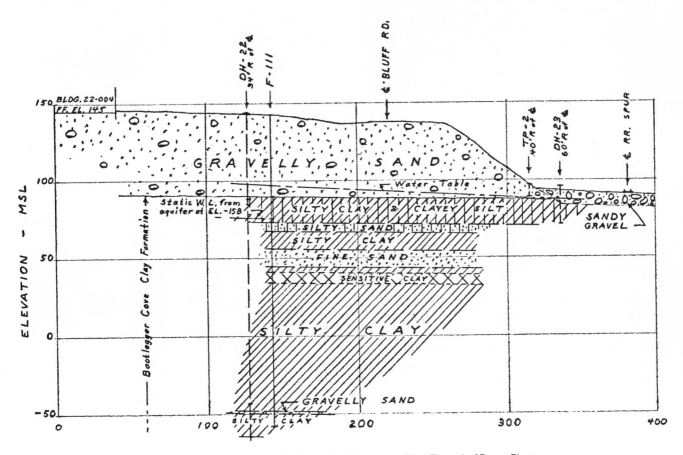

FIGURE 15 Geologic section for soil-stability study, West Elmendorf Power Plant.

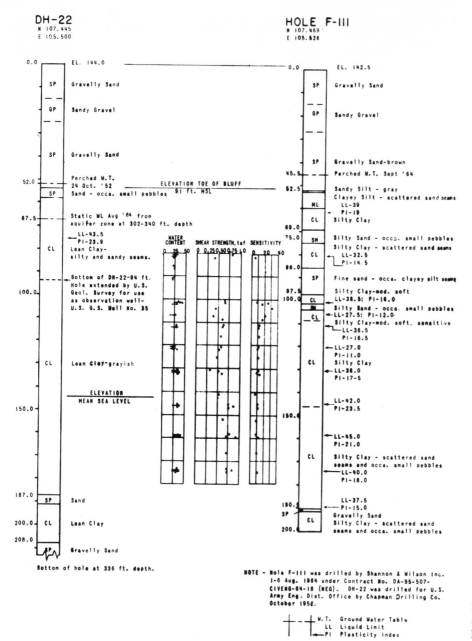

FIGURE 16   Logs of test holes for soil-stability study, West Elmendorf Power Plant.

be in danger from slide failures, and a no-risk classification of the plant was recommended.

As a result of the combined effects of the steep slope, the low permeability of the soil existing along the slope, and hydrostatic pressures from the confined water table, the reconstructed bluff line is subject to local shearing and sliding. The construction of a berm, either along the toe of the bluff or along the flattening of the toe face, to a slope of approximately 1:3 would reduce or eliminate local shearing and sliding in the event of another major earthquake. Settlement or slumping would be reduced but not eliminated.

Romig Hill Slide

The Romig Hill slide was a rotational slide of limited movement. Although small, it was important in the evaluation of the Romig Hill soils. The soil condition was a critical factor in determining whether the earthquake-damaged portions of the West Anchorage High School (within 200 ft from the head of the slide) should be reconstructed or rebuilt at another site. Figure 21 shows the West Anchorage High School and Hillcrest Drive at the head of the slide and Chester Creek meandering along the base of the slide. The soils in-

Air Photo Tech, Inc.

FIGURE 17 Rotational-slump slides along the north side of Ship Creek after rebuilding of Bluff Road across the top of several slides and removal of the toe of one slide from the railroad tracks (June 1, 1964). Scale: 1 in. = 850 ft.

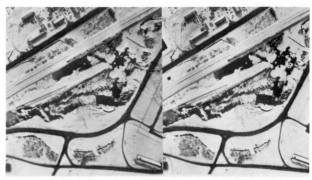

Alaska State Housing Authority

FIGURE 19 Rotational-slump slide east of West Elmendorf Power Plant in ash fill along Bluff Road (March 30, 1964). Scale: 1 in. = 500 ft.

Alaska State Housing Authority

FIGURE 18 Three rotational-slump slides east of the Corps of Engineers Alaska District Office building and southwest of the West Elmendorf Power Plant along the north bank of Ship Creek (March 30, 1964). Scale: 1 in. = 500 ft.

Alaska State Housing Authority

FIGURE 20 Rotational-slump slides in bluff and in a low fill adjacent to the railroad along entrance to Elmendorf AFB (March 30, 1964). Scale: 1 in. = 500 ft.

vestigations and stability analysis showed that the bluff was of marginal static stability before the earthquake. The clay soils varied in strength from 0.4 to 0.7 ton/ft^2, with slightly lower strengths closer to the bluff. Approximately 0.5 ton/ft^2 average strength was required for static equilibrium. The West Anchorage High School was found to be far enough back that slope-flattening for stabilization or future bluff-sliding would present no danger to the school. Adjoining bluff areas did, however, reveal some cracking from slippage of the frozen crust along the oversteepened slopes. A more detailed description of the Romig Hill slide and recommended stabilization requirements are given in section II, Shannon & Wilson's report to the Corps of Engineers (1964b).

Third Avenue and Post Road Slide Area

This slide is immediately north of the State Highway Department district office and shop area (Figure 22). Exploration of the slide (Figure 5) indicated that failure resulted from

Alaska State Housing Authority

FIGURE 21 Romig Hill rotational-slump slide on the north side of West Anchorage High School and bordering on Chester Creek (March 30, 1964). Scale: 1 in. = 500 ft.

overloading the edge of an old horst block with the highway embankment. This particular failure separated the main natural-gas line into Anchorage and probably helped to eliminate fire as an aftermath of the earthquake. Investigations indicated that the bowl area (2,500 ft long and 1,200

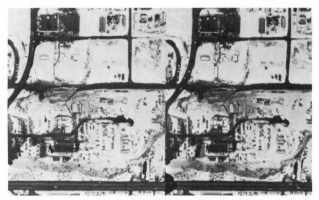

Alaska State Housing Authority

FIGURE 22   Rotational-slump slide north of State Highway Complex, adjacent to Post Road and crossing Third Avenue. District Administration Building is lower left north of Fifth Avenue (March 30, 1964). Scale: 1 in. = 500 ft.

ft wide) encompassing this slide (Figure 23) probably resulted from a very old, earthquake-induced translatory slide. Before the area was leveled, it had the horst and graben configuration common to recent and older Anchorage failures. Some of this horst and graben configuration could still be seen in 1950 (Figure 24). Damage to the Highway District Administration Building from soil cracks progressing through the building appeared to be a result of differential settlement. The north end of the building is over the south edge of a horst block, whereas the south end of the building is over a graben with a 40-ft depression in the clay surface (Figure 25). This slide was probably protected from renewed sliding by the lower gravel terrace formed by the Ship Creek channel in the years following the original sliding. The original plane of sliding appears to have been near elevation

U.S. Coast and Geodetic Survey

FIGURE 23   The bowl area north of Fifth Avenue and east of Ingra Street is probably an old earthquake slide area with horst and graben configuration. The Alaska Native Hospital translatory slide is to the left of Ingra Street and south of First Avenue (northeast of hospital at left center of photo) a rotational-slump slide is to the right of Post Road and crosses Third Avenue (April 3, 1967). Scale: 1 in. = 1,300 ft.

U.S. Geological Survey

FIGURE 24   Preearthquake photo of Alaska Highway Complex bowl area. Horst blocks and grabens can be seen midway between the Alaska Native Hospital (lower right) and the State Highway Complex above the curve in Post Road (August 8, 1950). Scale: 1 in. = 1,650 ft.

42 ft MSL. The lower terrace is at elevation 51 ft in the vicinity of Second Avenue.

Subsidence occurred just west of the Highway Department facilities on Post Road. A photograph taken on March 30, 1964 (Figure 26), shows a sand boil, possibly resulting from sand liquefaction and extrusion from the subsided area. Figure 24 indicates that the subsidence and boil were in a common graben of the older sliding discussed above. An old offset crack, possibly caused by settlement of soils in the same old graben on the western side of the horst block, is on the Third Avenue Hill between the Alaska Native Hospital area and the State Highway Complex and is shown crossing Third Avenue in Figure 24.

The preearthquake concentration of water in the point adjacent to the Alaska Native Hospital was probably a result of groundwater migrating along a graben around the head of this old slide and draining away below the point adjacent to the hospital. The water table in the graben under the Highway Administration Building measured 6.5–8 ft below the ground surface. Grabens such as those disclosed by the exploration documented in Figure 25 and shown in a 1950 photo (Figure 24) and a 1952 photo (Figure 27) would have limited the migration of water downslope through the old slide area.

Stability of the old slide area was analyzed with the slope-stability chart (Figure 2). The most critical slope was 75 ft high and had an inclination (tangent beta) of 0.09. The plotted point falls on the lower left boundary for failed slopes with d/H value equal to zero; however, an actual buttressing effect from overburden soils indicates a d/H value of 0.15–0.35, which was sufficient to provide an adequate margin of stability against shear failure. Under seismic motion similar to the earthquake of March 27, 1964, localized failures could again occur in the slope north of East Third Avenue, and excessive ground motions could again cause fissures

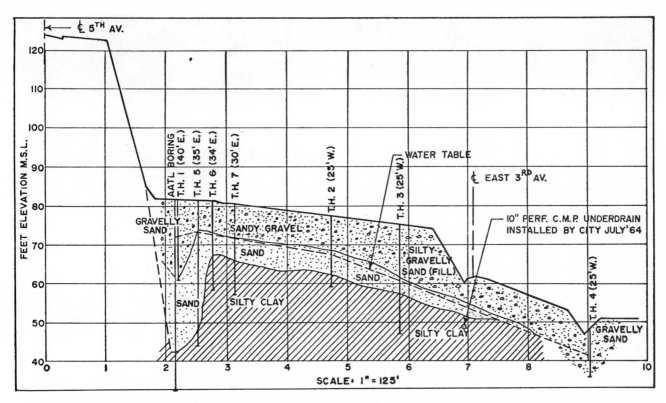

FIGURE 25   Alaska State Highway Complex. Geologic profile, north–south section 1,250 ft east of Medfra Street. Scale: 1 in. = 125 ft.

in the vicinity of the Alaska State Highway Department Administration and shop buildings.

Ground motion and surface cracking during an earthquake can be reduced by lowering the groundwater level by drainage. Resistance to failure of the Third Avenue highway fill can be improved by downhill buttressing of the north side of Third Avenue, or by an overall flattening of the slope.

Knik Arm Slides

The Knik Arm slides included the rotational slump on the north side of Government Hill (Figure 6), the Cairn Point slides northwest of the Elmendorf runway (Figures 7 and 28), and a series of one compound slide and two single slides across Knik Arm from Cairn Point (Figures 8 and 29) north-

U.S. Army

FIGURE 26   Sand boil (center) probably resulting from subsidence of road fill crossing an old graben at intersection of Post Road and Fourth Avenue (bottom). Third Avenue is at top of picture (March 29, 1964). Scale: 1 in. = 180 ft.

Jack Karterman, Alaska Railroad

FIGURE 27   Graben and horst configuration in bowl area between Highway Complex (Alaska Road Commission) and Alaska Native Hospital; Post Road is the prominent highway feature (January 10, 1952).

FIGURE 28 The larger of the rotational-slump slides on Cairn Point (March 29, 1964). Scale: 1 in. = 670 ft.

east of the Sleeper airstrip. Figure 30 gives a preearthquake view of this area. Although the airstrip slides have not been investigated in detail, stratigraphic features from previous investigations (Figure 31) show these bluffs to have a strong similarity to the bluffs and soils of Anchorage. Mrs. Lyman Woodman, of 117 East Cook, on Government Hill, saw two of these slides across the Knik Arm about two thirds of the way through the earthquake. She described one landslide as having occurred "all at once," and the other slide as gradually sliding in a "jerky fashion." Figure 28 shows the larger Cairn Point slide after the earthquake, and Figure 32 shows Cairn Point as it appeared in 1950. The rotational slump on the north side is described in more detail in the Shannon & Wilson (1964b) report.

Point Campbell Slides

Point Campbell had two slides: one (Figure 9) occurred on the northwest end of sand dunes on top of the Turnagain

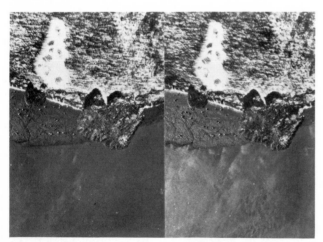

FIGURE 29 Three of the rotational-slump slides northeast of Sleeper airstrip across the Knik arm from Cairn Point. Predicted tide would be approximately 11 ft relative to the postearthquake MLLW (April 3, 1964). Scale: 1 in. = 1,500 ft.

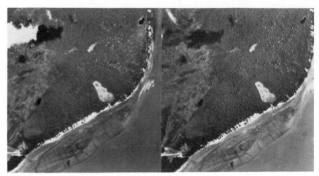

FIGURE 30 Preearthquake view of Cairn Point northeast of Sleeper airstrip at low tide. The airstrip is in the lower left-hand corner (August 12, 1961). Scale: 1 in. = 3,300 ft.

Arm bluff. The second (Figure 33) occurred 2,500 ft southeast of the first, along the same bluff; it apparently also failed in the sand dunes, and the debris accumulated at the toe of the slope. The water table in this area is approximately 10 ft MSL.

HORIZONTAL TRANSLATORY SLIDES

Horizontal translatory soil failure, which characteristically shows horizontal spreading and graben development, could also be considered as a modified wedge failure. These failures in 1964 appear to have resulted from liquefaction of a nearly horizontal layer reaching a depth of 60–80 ft adjacent to the slide scarp. This kind of slide seems to be characteristic of the Alaska earthquake and also of the 1811 New Madrid earthquake (Davison, 1936). Some slides of this type retrograded to such an extent that portions developed into earth flows. A characteristic of this kind of slide is a certain degree of uniformity of the graben-spacing to other grabens and to the adjoining bluff face. Slides of this type were confined to the Anchorage area and included the slides at the First Avenue Alaska Native Hospital (Figure 34), Government Hill School (Figure 35), Fourth Avenue (Figure 36), L Street (Figure 37), and Turnagain (Figure 38). Soil failures in these areas occurred along bluff faces; the ground surface behind the slide was generally level with very gradual horizontal changes in soil types and thicknesses. These failures have been attributed to liquefaction of sand layers and liquefaction of clay.

First Avenue Slide

The First Avenue slide, a horizontal translatory slide adjacent to the Alaska Native Hospital complex, intersected an older graben on the opposite face of the northeast point (Figure 34). Sliding did not seem to disturb the base terrace, but gave the impression of overriding it (Figure 39); swirls of clay were contained in sand layers at an elevation of 50 ft,

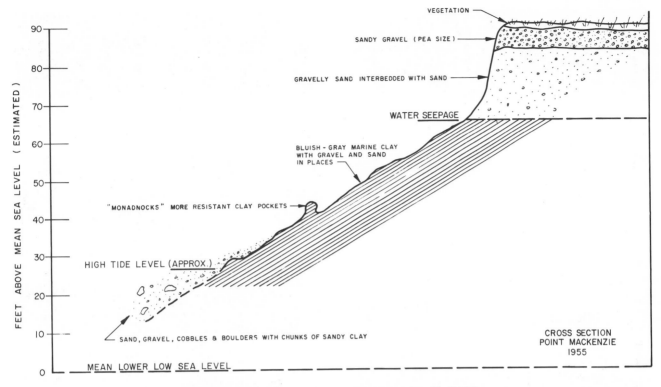

FIGURE 31 Cross section, Point MacKenzie soil profile (1955).

U.S. Geological Survey

FIGURE 32 Preearthquake view of Cairn Point (August 8, 1950).
Scale: 1 in. = 3,400 ft.

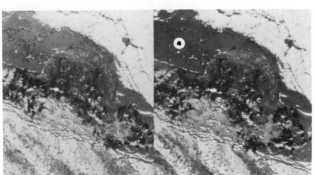

Alaska State Housing Authority

FIGURE 33 Point Campbell slide, 2,500 ft southeast of the slide
shown in Figure 9. Partial liquefaction may have resulted from pore
air pressure (April 1, 1964). Scale: 1 in. = 500 ft.

U.S. Army

FIGURE 34 First Avenue horizontal translatory slide (April 4,
1964).

suggesting shear failure. Failure may have taken place either
in soft clay or by sand liquefaction, with the failure plane
between elevation 40 ft and elevation 50 ft. A characteristic
feature of the cracks behind the slide was that they tended
to go around Alaska Native Hospital. Although large earthquake joints separated the wings from the central core,
ground cracking did not connect these areas of less foundation restraint. The bluff area immediately west of this slide

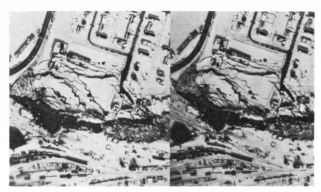

Alaska State Housing Authority

FIGURE 35   Government Hill horizontal translatory slide (March 30, 1964). Scale: 1 in. = 500 ft.

T. Tice, U.S. Army Corps of Engineers

FIGURE 36   Fourth Avenue horizontal translatory slide (March 28, 1964).

T. Tice, U.S. Army Corps of Engineers

FIGURE 37   Southwest portion of the L Street translatory slide (March 28, 1964).

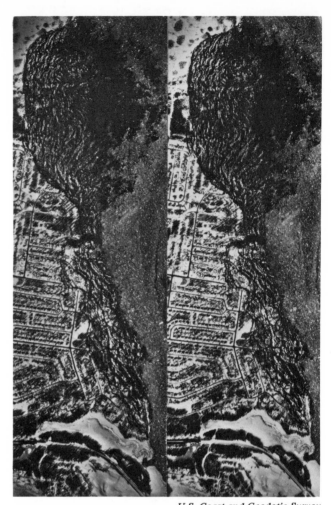

U.S. Coast and Geodetic Survey

FIGURE 38   Turnagain retrogressive translatory slide. Hood Creek intersects the slide at the center of the picture and roughly divides it into the east and west Turnagain slide areas (April 3, 1964). Scale: 1 in. = 1,780 ft.

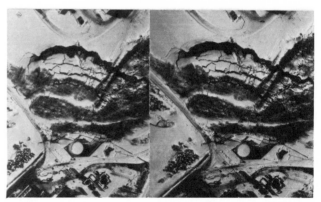

U.S. Army

FIGURE 39   First Avenue horizontal translatory slide. Passive zone at base appears to override the lower terrace (April 4, 1964). Scale: 1 in. = 300 ft.

Alaska State Housing Authority

FIGURE 40   First Avenue horizontal translatory slide. Older slide intersects along north slope; the cirque-like configuration on the west (right) side suggests another older slide area (March 30, 1964). Scale: 1 in. = 470 ft.

looks like an old slide area (Figures 23, 24, and 40). The area east and southeast is a very large old horizontal translatory slide area. A cross section of the First Avenue slide with a possible old graben near the toe is shown in Figure 41. A detailed report of the slide and stabilization require-

ments appears in section 12 of the Shannon & Wilson (1964b) report.

Government Hill School Slide

The principal Government Hill slide occurred adjacent to the Government Hill Elementary School (Figures 35 and 42). The Government Hill School slide was primarily a horizontal translatory slide that had retrogressed to a secondary failure condition (Figure 43). The Government Hill area did, however, include a partly circular slump slide on the north side of Government Hill (Figure 6). The toe portion of the Government Hill School slide did show a flow configuration (Figure 44). Sliding was possible in the fine sand layers at elevations of 50–55 ft with streamers of clay providing an indication of possible liquefaction failure. Failure was also possible in the soft to medium-strength clays at elevations of 20–40 ft. Overall evaluation indicates the most probable zone of failure to be at an elevation of 38 ft. Failure of this slide progressed to the point that a good toe berm exists and the slide could be both statically and dynamically stable with some regrading. Preearthquake slide conditions are shown in Figures 45 and 46.

A small circular slump occurred along the bluff immedi-

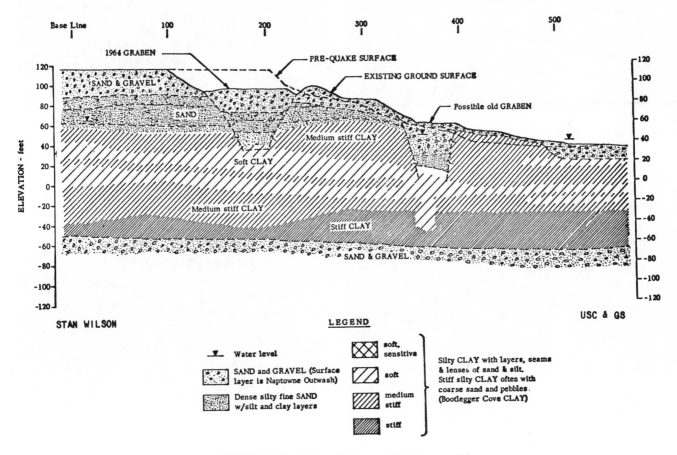

FIGURE 41   Geologic profile through First Avenue slide.

FIGURE 42   Government Hill horizontal translatory slide. Retrogression had developed into a secondary failure condition (April 4, 1964).

FIGURE 43   Government Hill horizontal translatory slide shows intersection of grabens that developed separately (April 30, 1964).

FIGURE 45   View of Government Hill before 1939; 1964 slide was to the right of upper portion of road, up on the bluff behind The Alaska Railroad terminal yards.

FIGURE 44   Government Hill horizontal translatory slide. Flow configuration is evident along base of slide (March 30, 1964). Scale: 1 in. = 500 ft.

FIGURE 46   View of Government Hill (left) in 1953. Graded area immediately above largest railroad building is being prepared for trackage that was later covered by the Government Hill slide (July 11, 1953).

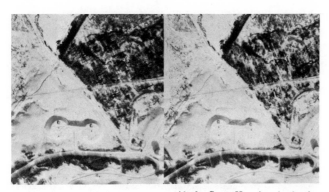

Alaska State Housing Authority
FIGURE 47   Old slide failures on north side of Government Hill. A graben extended under a portion of the tank foundation area (March 30, 1964). Scale: 1 in. = 500 ft.

ately north of the Army petroleum, oil, and lubricant (POL) tank farms on the north side of Government Hill (Figure 6). This slide, which shows characteristics of rotational failure, is next to a very large old slide area that had stabilized itself. Preearthquake exploration had shown graben development along the slopes of this old slide. The tanks in Figure 47 were constructed partly on a gravel-filled graben and partly on a horst block of very sensitive clay.

Another old slide existed on the west side of Government Hill (Figure 48). A postearthquake view of this slide area appears as Figure 49; the area is now the site of a tank farm. The south side of Government Hill west of the present new slide also shows grabens from old sliding (Figure 50); the Government Hill road seemed to act as a buttress against further sliding, especially when it was well-frozen. Wreckage

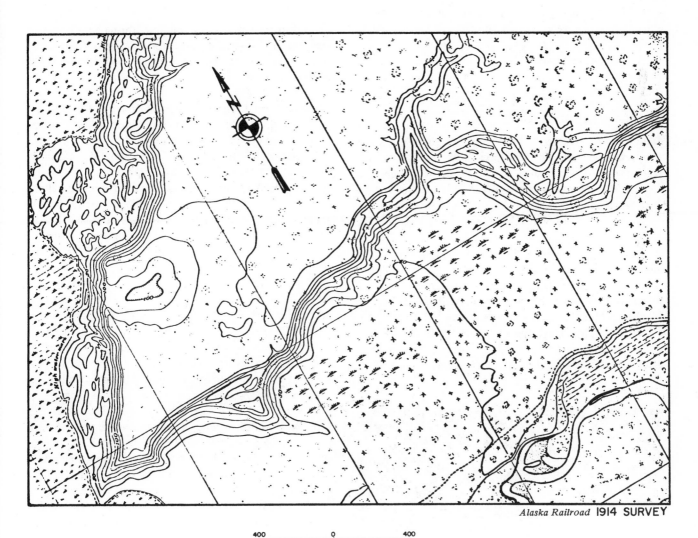

Alaska Railroad 1914 SURVEY

```
400            0            400
       SCALE IN FEET
```

FIGURE 48   Government Hill slide area.

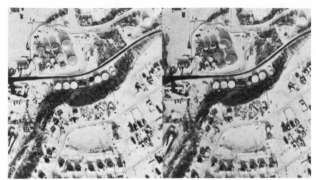

Alaska State Housing Authority

FIGURE 49 Old slide area at west end of Government Hill. Area of slide shown on the 1914 map is Figure 47 (March 30, 1964). Scale: 1 in. = 500 ft.

U.S. Geological Survey

FIGURE 51 View of downtown Anchorage before the 1964 earthquake. Old slide scars are evident along the bluff, including the bowl area from First to Fourth avenues and from C to E streets (August 8, 1950). Scale: 1 in. = 650 ft.

in the slide area has since been removed, and the broken-up areas have been graded to drain; the slide toe still remains in place.

A more detailed evaluation of the slide and recommended stabilization measures appear in section 13, Shannon & Wilson (1964b).

Fourth Avenue Slide

Slide Analysis Before the 1964 Alaska earthquake, the area now described as the Fourth Avenue slide area already had features now associated with earthquake-induced slides (Figure 51). Figure 52 is a 1914 Alaska Railroad map showing a bowl-shaped incision in the south Ship Creek bluff. Figures 52 and 53 show that Ship Creek had a large meander within its south bank along the north side of the present First Avenue, between D and E streets, where the present Alaska Railroad depot stands. If the meander existed at the time of the earlier slides, sliding may have occurred at a much lower elevation than was possible with the meander filled in and buttressing the lower strata of soil. Figure 54 is a fairly early photograph (possibly 1916) of the Fourth Avenue slide area from across Ship Creek. Figure 51 is an aerial view of the same area before the construction of D

U.S. Coast and Geodetic Survey

FIGURE 50 Indications of old graben formations along south side of Government Hill (bottom) and to the west (left) of the new slide (April 3, 1964). Scale: 1 in. = 1,390 ft.

Street and Second and Third avenues through the bowl area; indications of early translatory sliding of lesser displacement to the east and west can also be identified in this picture. An excavation made in 1966 showed the north scarp of an old slide, identified by the offset in the surface of the clay strata. The old scarp was observed 140 ft east of the center line of F Street and approximately 100 ft north of the center line of Third Avenue. Borings drilled in 1964 between C and F streets along Third Avenue also indicated the possibility of an old graben in that area. Evaluation of eyewitness reports indicated that the Fourth Avenue slide started 1½–2 minutes after the beginning of the earthquake and ceased at the termination of strong earthquake motion. The translatory horizontal slide was retrogressive to the point that a second graben had formed east of C Street (Figures 55–57) and terminated under the center of the block north of Third Avenue between Barrow and A streets. At the end of the earthquake, another graben was just beginning to form between the Fourth–Fifth avenue alley and Fifth Avenue on D Street. The graben can be traced in a southeasterly direction from its west end at F Street and Third Avenue, toward Fourth Avenue, and then in an east-northeasterly direction to its termination on Second Avenue between A and Barrow streets (Figures 55–57). The passive zone or toe of the slide can be traced from Third Avenue and E Street northeasterly to Second Avenue and D Street (Figure 58), then east across the intersection of Second Avenue and C Street (Figure 59), beneath the warehouse northeast of that intersection (Figure 60), thence east along the face of the steep bluff, apparently terminating north of the intersection of A Street and Second Avenue (Figures 61–63). Volume-displacement computations, analysis of soil strengths, and zones of disturbance indicate that the sliding probably occurred in or near the base of a sand layer close to elevation 45 ft MSL; if sliding had not first

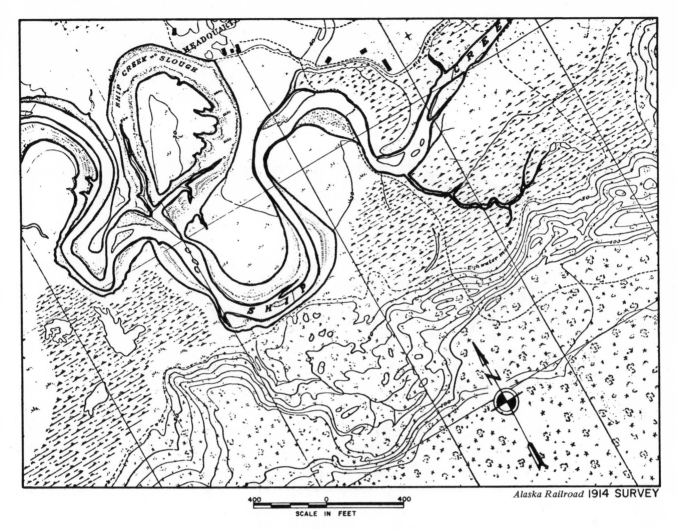

FIGURE 52 Fourth Avenue slide area.

occurred in the sand, it probably could have occurred in the underlying soft sensitive clay. The plane of sliding was locally translated downward by the frozen crust and broke through the surface along a line of heated structures west of B Street (Figure 64). The slide-toe elevation varied from possibly as low as 25 ft MSL to 94 ft MSL over its full length, but varied between elevation of about 37 ft MSL and 53 ft MSL between B and D streets. The nature of the sliding was such that the slopes came to rest in a static but potentially unstable configuration under loading of another earthquake with at least 2 minutes' duration of strong motion. No retaining berm of consequence was formed at the toe of the slide that would have stabilized it against long-duration strong earthquake motion. Evaluation and analysis indicated that the slide could be most economically and effectively stabilized by the construction of a gravel retaining buttress (Figure 65), extending from E Street to Barrow Street, with its toe along the alley between First and Second avenues and

its head between Second Avenue and the alley between Second and Third avenues. Figures 66 and 67 show the completed buttress in November 1967. The Third and Fourth avenue graben areas provide a natural depression in the clay surface for the accumulation of groundwater. Figure 68 is a profile of the Fourth Avenue slide soil strata and grabens. Drainage of these grabens was provided in the stabilization project to improve stability of the upper soil strata.

An area bordered by First and Third avenues and G and K streets presented an independent problem relating to the Fourth Avenue slide area. This slope was well within the failure zone of the slope-stability chart as evaluated from other areas (Figure 2). Investigation showed the plane of greatest weakness in the clay to be at elevation 20 ft MSL, which is near the toe of the slope. The lower slopes had been used as a disposal area for silty gravel from street and building excavations. This fill in a frozen condition limited failure at elevations above the slide base. Thermal analysis indicated

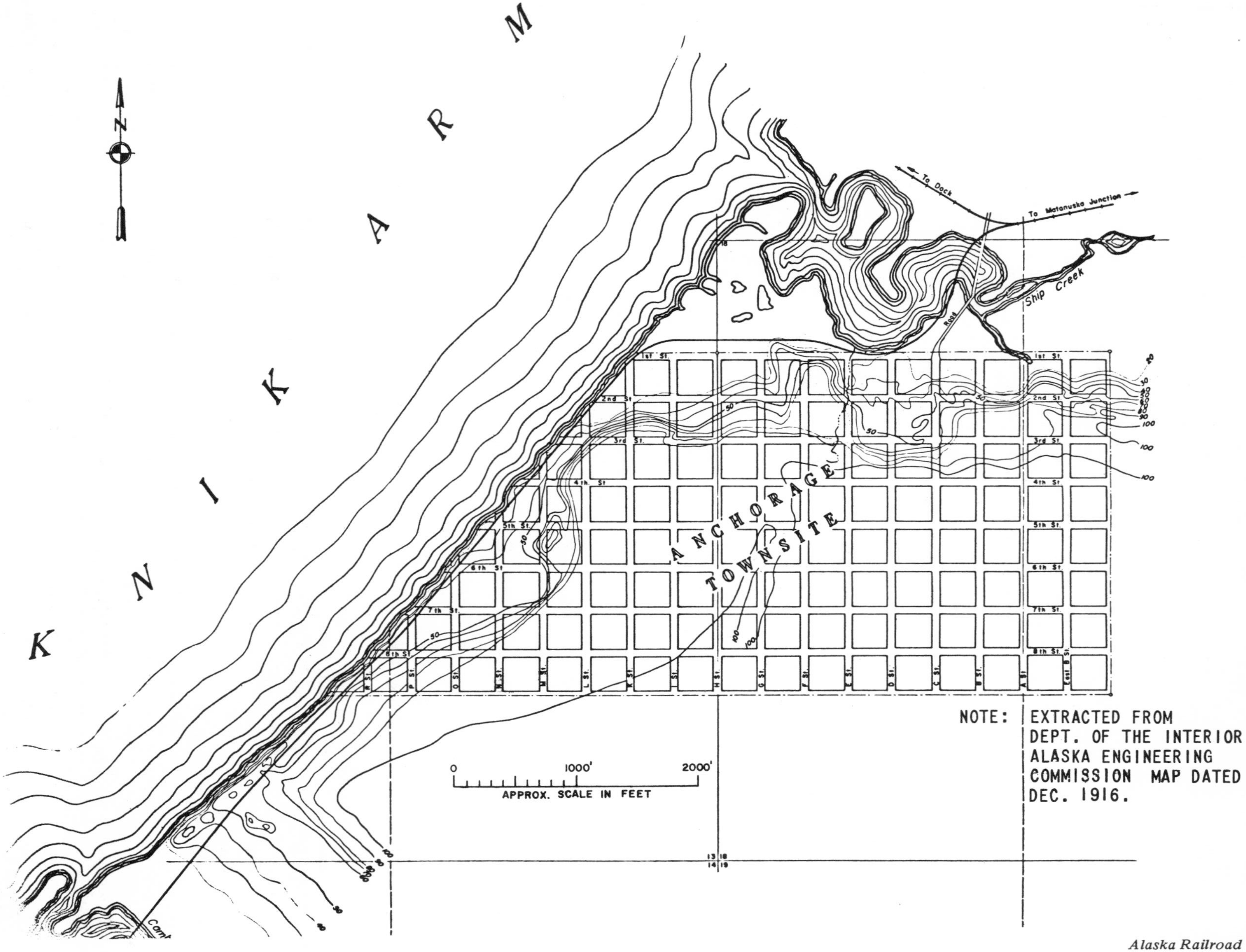

FIGURE 53 Anchorage townsite topography.

Lu Liston

FIGURE 54 Anchorage, in about 1916, looking south over Ship Creek: First Avenue runs along the base of the opposite hill, and the present C Street goes up the hill. The meander was along First Avenue in the vicinity of D and E streets.

the presence of 6 ft of seasonal frost, which was the most probable strengthening element at the toe of the slope.

A more detailed evaluation of the Fourth Avenue slide and recommended stabilization measures appear in section 8 of the Shannon & Wilson, Inc. (1964b) report.

Slope-Stability Evaluation   The slides, which were all statically stable after the earthquake, could not be analyzed for future potential earthquake failure by standard methods of analysis. The most direct method of earthquake-stability evaluation of slopes was developed by Bjerrum (Shannon & Wilson, Inc., 1964b) and is shown as Figure 2. This slope-stability chart facilitates the rapid evaluation of potentially unstable slopes and shows that a number of potentially unstable slopes that did not fail were observed to be naturally buttressed (see $d:H$ ratio). The noses or points of many

U.S. Army

FIGURE 55 Fourth Avenue slide retrogresses to the formation of a second graben east of C Street. Fourth and Sixth avenues at lower left (March 29, 1964). Scale: 1 in. = 170 ft.

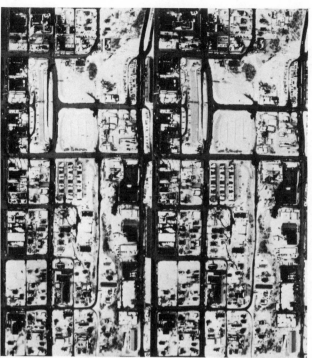

Air Photo Tech, Inc.

FIGURE 56 Fourth Avenue horizontal translatory slide, extending from Fourth Avenue on the left to First Avenue on the right and from Barrow Street (second up from bottom) to E Street (second down from top) (March 30, 1964). Scale: 1 in. = 470 ft.

steeper bluffs remained stable, apparently because of better drainage conditions. Drainage has other effects, such as the degree of saturation with its effect on liquefaction; the influence on salt leaching from the clay, with its effect on both the undisturbed strength and remolded strength; and the influence on effective stress. With the aid of the slope-stability chart, it was determined that a flatter slope would be required to provide stability to the Fourth Avenue slide area.

The G–K street bluff area (Figure 69) was originally categorized as a slope that was potentially susceptible to failure (Figure 70). It, however, did not fail during the earthquake.

A second method of stability evaluation considered was a static-wedge analysis using the probable remolded shear strengths along the plane of sliding. If earthquake forces are assumed to be transmitted into the slide block from below, these forces would be equal to the vertically transmitted earthquake forces across the plane of sliding and could not exceed the average remolded shear strength multiplied by the area of the slide plane. The net unbalancing force would be equal to the earth pressure at the head of the slide. This method of analysis indicated that failure should have occurred at the deepest-possible failure plane rather than at

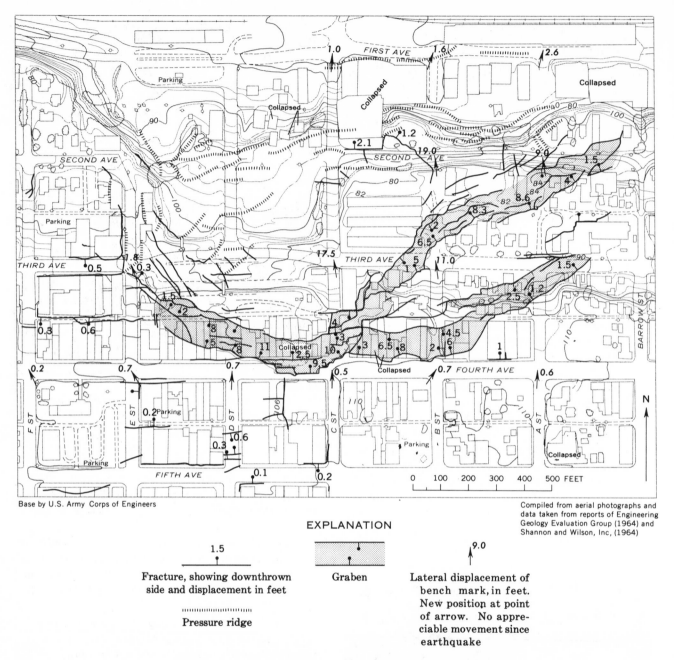

EXPLANATION

1.5

Fracture, showing downthrown
side and displacement in feet

Graben

9.0

Lateral displacement of
bench mark, in feet.
New position at point
of arrow. No appre-
ciable movement since
earthquake

Pressure ridge

Base by U.S. Army Corps of Engineers

Compiled from aerial photographs and
data taken from reports of Engineering
Geology Evaluation Group (1964) and
Shannon and Wilson, Inc, (1964)

FIGURE 57 Fourth Avenue slide area with grabens and pressure ridges.

the shallowest-possible plane, where failure actually
occurred.

As a result of the obvious magnitude of resistance required to satisfy a normal wedge analysis, Wilson and Seed
conducted laboratory tests to investigate and refine the
probable mechanisms of the dynamic translatory failure
(Appendixes C, D, and E, Anchorage Area Soil Studies,
Shannon & Wilson, Inc., 1964b). Seed and Martin (1965)
also worked out three methods of dynamic stability
analysis for buttress design.

Buttress Design Design of a buttress was initiated following
the submittal of the preliminary report on the Fourth Avenue slide area by Shannon & Wilson (1964a) and was essentially complete in September 1964. A number of methods,
including freezing, were evaluated and rejected as being unsuitable (Shannon & Wilson, Inc., 1964b). As a result of a
very tentative proposal based on limited evidence made to
the city of Anchorage by Linn Forrest and the Fourth Avenue Property Owners Association, the Corps of Engineers
was requested to evaluate the freezing method further, and

T. Tice, U.S. Army Corps of Engineers

FIGURE 58 Passive zone of Fourth Avenue slide continues from lower right-hand corner along the north (left) side of Second Avenue, crosses C Street and continues east (March 28, 1964).

FIGURE 61 Fourth Avenue slide passive zone east of the intersection of C Street and Second Avenue (right center) (March 28, 1964).

FIGURE 59 Fourth Avenue slide passive zone at intersection of C Street and Second Avenue (March 28, 1964).

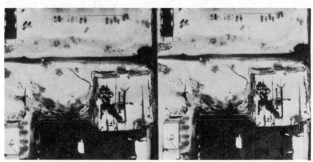

U.S. Army

FIGURE 62 Fourth Avenue slide passive zone and demolished warehouse north of Second Avenue and east of C Street (March 29, 1964). Scale: 1 in. = 180 ft.

FIGURE 60 Fourth Avenue slide passive zone on C Street hill, looking south from First Avenue toward Second Avenue (March 28, 1964).

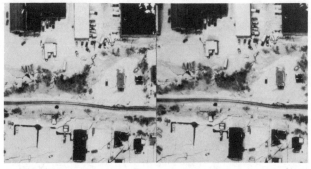

U.S. Army

FIGURE 63 Eastern termination of Fourth Avenue slide passive zone on north side of Second Avenue. The A Street right-of-way is between two buildings at upper right (March 29, 1964). Scale: 1 in. = 180 ft.

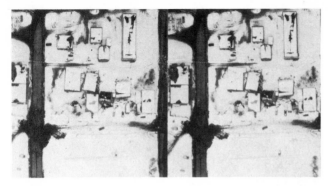

U.S. Army

FIGURE 64   Fourth Avenue slide passive zone broke through a series of heated structures along the north side of Second Avenue between C Street on the right and D Street on the left (March 29, 1964). Scale: 1 in. = 180 ft.

Air Photo Tech, Inc.

FIGURE 65   Completed Fourth Avenue buttress extends just west of E Street to Barrow Street on the east (June 2, 1967). Scale: 1 in. = 2,000 ft.

this was done in considerable detail. The greatest advantage of the proposal was the elimination of government-sponsored real-estate redevelopment, but detailed evaluation disclosed that freezing would cost more than a gravel buttress and the refrigeration system would require continuous maintenance. A buttress design that would resist earthquake forces equivalent to those of March 27, 1964, was eventually selected. On the basis of the evaluation of the various stability analyses the buttress would be required to resist 180 kips/lin ft. The buttress was designed to resist that force, using gravel with an angle of internal friction of 40° at the designed placement density of 140 lb/ft^3 (98 percent of *Alaska District Corps of Engineers Modified Maximum Providence-Vibrated Standard Density*). The gravel buttress would resist the force through intergranular shear strength along an extension of the slide plane through the buttress.

The design of the buttress project provided for the drainage of seepage waters from the new graben as well as from the older graben on Third Avenue (Figures 71 and 72). Where elevations permitted the required invert slope, perforated 12-in. paved corrugated metal pipe (CMP) was trench-laid. This pipe intercepted and drained the new grabens. Because the surface of the clay in the old graben was at a much lower elevation, special manholes were specified and drains were jacked horizontally into the base of the Naptowne outwash overlying the clay in the old graben. Drainage from these horizontal drains and from the 12-in. paved perforated CMP drains were then collected in an 18-in. paved corrugated metal pile, carried to the base of the buttress (Figure 71), and collected in a 24-in. paved-pipe drainage line. Groundwater was picked up in 5-in. semicircular pipes paralleling the 18- and 24-in. collection lines. The base

FIGURE 66   Panoramic view of the Fourth Avenue slide area looking east, with completed buttress and urban-renewal redevelopment area (December 20, 1967).

FIGURE 67   Panoramic view of the Fourth Avenue slide area looking west, with completed buttress and urban-renewal redevelopment area (December 20, 1967).

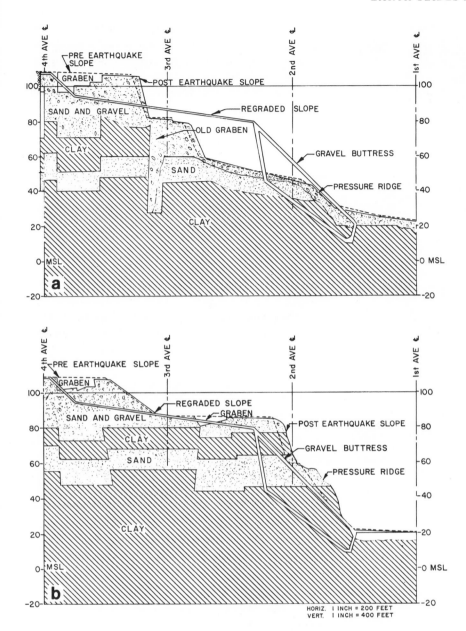

FIGURE 68   Fourth Avenue slide and buttress profiles. (a) C–D Street profile; (b) B Street profile.

HORIZ. 1 INCH = 200 FEET
VERT.   1 INCH = 400 FEET

of the buttress was below higher tide levels (7 ft below extreme high water). To limit the influx of tidal waters into the drain system, a tide gate was used at the outfall into Ship Creek.

Limitations   To minimize the risk of damage to the structures in the event of future earthquakes, limitations on future construction on the slide area were recommended in a joint release by the U.S. Army Engineer District, Alaska, and the Federal Reconstruction and Development Planning Commission for Alaska's Scientific and Engineering Task Force (Task Force 9): Final recommendations on risk classifications, Anchorage and vicinity, September 8, 1964, and

an accompanying map of the same date, outlining those areas discussed in the release; and Report on Anchorage area soil studies, Alaska, to U.S. Army Engineer District, Alaska, August 28, 1964, by Shannon & Wilson, Inc., Seattle, Washington. The recommendations limiting design and use of the buttress project area covered in these reports are as follows:

Hereinafter, all references to grades are to the grades as established in the Fourth Avenue stabilization design. It was recommended that the urban-renewal area be limited to the area between the north side of Fourth Avenue and the toe of the 20 percent slope immediately north of Fourth Avenue: Buildings are to be limited to two-story structures of

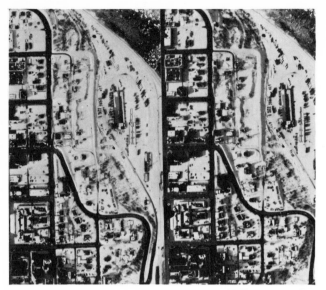

Air Photo Tech, Inc.

FIGURE 69   G–K Street slope area that did not fail. The six streets (from bottom to top) are F, G, H, I, K, and L. From left to right are Fourth, Third, and Second avenues and Christensen Drive. North is to the right (March 30, 1964). Scale: 1 in. = 480 ft.

light construction such that the net increase in soil loading over the limits of the building area will not exceed an average of 500 lb/ft^2. Above-grade structural floors should not exceed 125 lb/ft^2 live load; buildings were to be limited to a height not to exceed two stories over the highest elevations adjacent to the structure; the amount of fill not to exceed the quantity removed first by excavation within that area; and the maximum depth of excavation was not to exceed 10 ft.

We recommend the following criteria for construction

and site grading in the area bounded by the lower toe of the upper 20 percent slope and the upper elevation of the lower 20 percent-slope buttress on the south and north sides, respectively, and by Barrow and E streets on the east and west sides, respectively. The maximum depth of cut and the maximum height of fill not to exceed 5 ft, except for temporary excavations for placement of footings and footing subgrade, the temporary excavations to be backfilled and compacted immediately after completion of footing construction; the average depth of cut and height of fill not to exceed 3 ft; buildings to be limited to two-story structures of light construction so that the net increase in soil loading within the building area will not exceed an average of 400 lb/ft^2; above-grade structural floors should not exceed 125 lb/ft^2 live load. No basement is to be allowed in this area; all excess excavation is to be removed from the site; utilities may be constructed throughout the area, but in each case proper backfilling and compaction are to be rigidly enforced.

The following criteria shall apply to the lower buttress slopes (the lower buttress slope is the 20 percent slope that is located 170–470 ft south of First Avenue between Barrow and D streets and extends northwesterly west of D Street. The lower buttress also includes the 20 percent slope bounded by First Street, Christensen Road, Second Street, and K Street). No cut is to be permitted on the slope or within the limits of the lower buttress construction except on a temporary basis to permit construction of footings or utilities; no basement to be permitted in this area; no fill to be permitted on the buttress slope unless the fill slopes are at a 20 percent or flatter slope; construction of fills with 20 percent or flatter side slopes over and north of the toe of the buttress increases the effectiveness of the buttress and is permissible and desirable; buildings to be limited to two-story structures of light construction such that the net

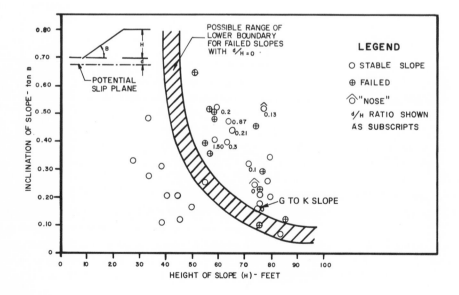

FIGURE 70   G–K Street slope-stability chart.

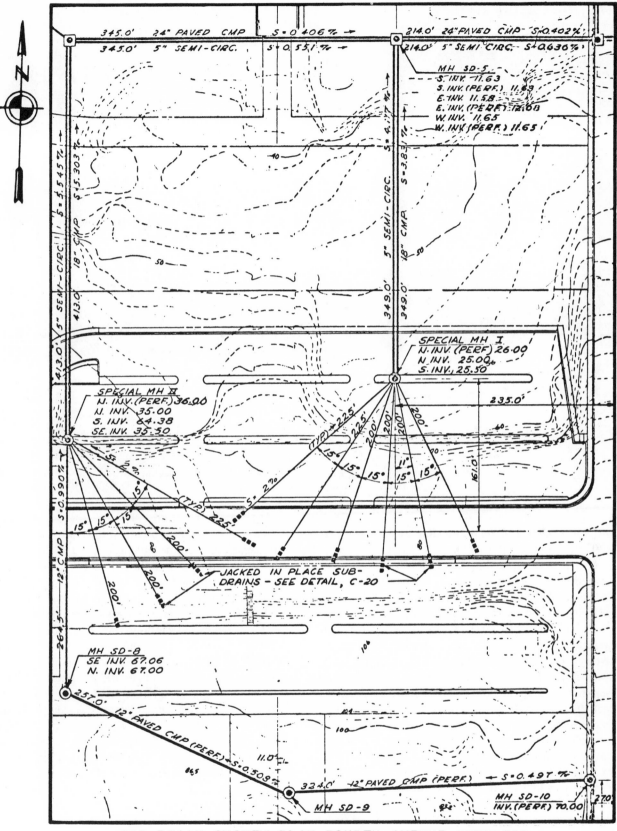

SUB-DRAIN SYSTEM PLAN FOURTH AVENUE BUTTRESS

SCALE IN FEET

FIGURE 71   Subdrain system plan for Fourth Avenue buttress.

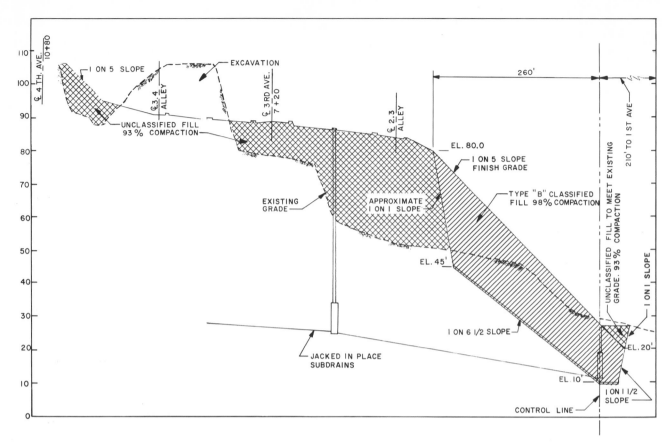

FIGURE 72 Fourth Avenue buttress section and subdrain system.

increase in loading within the building area shall not exceed 400 lb/ft², a two-story structure will be interpreted as two floors, columns required to support the first floor shall not be considered in limiting the height of the structure; and building heights in the area south of the G to K buttress will be restricted only by individual stability analysis.

The following additional criteria shall apply to all construction within the urban-renewal development area: Mandatory requirements for builders to furnish all structural and foundation seismic-design calculations for buildings over one story in height and of any structure with a design live load in excess of 100 lb/ft² above the ground floor; all seismic-design calculations, drawings, and specifications to be made by registered professional structural and foundation engineers (this is probably the most important consideration of all given to the safety of any individual structure); all construction to have qualified inspection to ensure that buildings are constructed within the intent of approved drawings and specifications; continuous review and updating of seismic-code provisions as found necessary for structures and foundations; if a higher classification seismic zone is ever established, this area should be included; adequate hori-

zontal and vertical reinforcement to be provided to resist stresses imposed on the building and foundation by the effect of soil movement on the structure; basement walls to be designed as retaining walls to withstand statically and dynamically induced earth forces; and special consideration to be given to harmonic motion developed in buildings of extreme lengths and widths during an earthquake.

The construction of the buttress fill and improvement of drainage will increase the vertical load on the slide-disturbed materials. This will result in erratic settlements of the regraded slope for a period of several years or more. In addition, a future earthquake of intensity and duration comparable to that of March 27, 1964, may result in permanent lateral movement up to approximately 1 ft. Because of these anticipated lateral movements, pile or pier foundations should be considered unsuitable unless carefully tied together at the base and at intermediate points by approved ties. Floor slabs should be structurally tied to the foundation walls, to prevent their separation by ground motion.

To provide further guidance, our consultants have recommended that the following Joint Release of Alaska Task Force 9, Alaska Reconstruction Commission, and the U.S.

Army Engineer District: Final recommendation on risk classification, Anchorage and vicinity, dated September 8, 1964, be quoted:

When the stabilization work is completed, all of that area will be returned to Nominal Risk. In the slide area below Fourth Avenue and between Barrow and E Streets, however, construction should be limited to parks, parking areas, and light occupancy structures not over two stories in height. Even for such structures, certain restrictions must be imposed on depths of excavations or fills and on weights of buildings to prevent an unbalance of the buttress which could impair or destroy its effectiveness.

In all of the Fourth Avenue slide area between Barrow and I Streets, bounded on the south by a line running from Barrow Street to F Street, midway between Fifth and Sixth Avenues, and along Fourth Avenue between F Street and I Street, it is anticipated that normal consolidation of the underlying soils will result in some vertical and horizontal movements. Because this condition can be expected to result in localized differential movement, both horizontal and vertical, particular attention must be given to the design of structures and their foundations so that such movements may be accommodated without undue damage to the building.

In further discussion of the foregoing paragraphs, the calculations should be submitted to the agency responsible for review and control of the seismic-code provisions. Ordinarily the city would undertake this function. We would assume that the city intends to supplement the Building Code, 1964 edition, with the enclosed recommendations. Alternatively, the city could develop a completely new code. We would recommend that the city employ a well-recognized consulting firm if a new code is to be drafted.

L Street Slide Analysis

Sliding before 1964 in the L Street area is evidenced by a preearthquake photograph of the Anchorage area (Figure 73). The relationship of slide features to the bluffs, streets, and railroad is shown in Figure 74. Postearthquake photography (Figure 75) shows evidence of the old slide scars

Alaska State Housing Authority

FIGURE 73   Photograph of Anchorage area taken before 1964 from which evidence of previous slides can be identified (August 8, 1950). Scale: 1 in. = 5,400 ft.

along with the more recent (March 1964) movements. Graben and horst configuration of the topography was identified on the south side of Fifth Avenue between L and M streets and along the toe of the bluff northeast of the intersection of Eleventh Avenue and R Street. An extension of the Eleventh and R graben was revealed during the excavation of the waterline connection into the house on the northwest corner of the intersection. The graben was between the south property boundary and the south wall of the house and extended westward. Excavation in the bowl-shaped depression south of Eleventh Avenue and west of K Street indicate the area to be an old slide area. Figures 76 and 77 show the relation of the old slide scars to the remainder of the L Street slide area. This area was probably protected during the 1964 earthquake by the retention of the old failure toe and by tidal deposition in the area immediately to the south. No postearthquake cracks of consequence were noted in that area.

According to eyewitness accounts, the L Street slide moved toward the end of strong earthquake motion. It was a horizontal translatory slide, and probably failed between elevation 40 and 50 ft in sand layers or at elevation 40 ft in soft sensitive clay in the area from Fifth Avenue South, terminating between Eighth and Ninth avenues, and also between the toe of the bluff and the railroad (Figures 78–80). The active toe landward of The Alaska Railroad occurred between elevation 42 ft and elevation 60 ft. The toe of the active slide, landward of the railroad, was restricted by the Fifth Avenue and Ninth Avenue access roads. The areas buttressed by Fifth Avenue and Ninth Avenue failed north of Fifth Avenue and south of Seventh Avenue, near elevation 15 ft MSL, seaward of the railroad embankment (Figures 81 and 82). The depth of coarser material underlying the roads and the greater depth of frost penetration seemed to form a reinforcing buttress landward of the railroad that forced the failure seaward of the railroad embankment. It may be more than coincidental that the zone of passive failure in the central portions of the slide was totally confined to the area landward of the more heavily traveled streets with less snow (Figures 83 and 84). This road was underlain by a greater depth of gravel and would have had deeper frost penetration than adjoining areas.

The graben area between Eighth and Ninth avenues and between L Street and N Street is of special interest because the grabens seemed to avoid three large structures that were founded on well-reinforced foundations. Although the graben tends to parallel the bluff to N Street, it is abruptly offset 150 ft to the north (Figure 37). If the southern end of the graben had remained a uniform distance from the bluff, as it did north and east of L Street and Eighth Avenue, it would have intersected St. Mary's Residence (Figures 78, 85, and 86). A well-reinforced foundation appeared to limit the failure necessary for the progressive dropping of

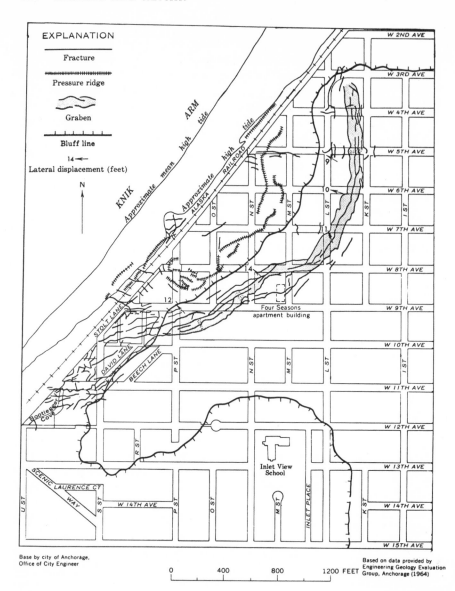

FIGURE 74 L Street slide area, Anchorage, Alaska. Plan of grabens and pressure ridges.

Alaska State Housing Authority

FIGURE 75 L Street slide area. Postearthquake photograph showing older slide scars (May 23, 1964). Scale: 1 in. = 2,000 ft.

U.S. Coast and Geodetic Survey

FIGURE 76 L Street slide bowl-shaped area (in center) northeast of the Chester Creek tideflats is probably an old slide area (July 24, 1966). Scale: 1 in. = 2,600 ft.

U.S. Coast and Geodetic Survey

FIGURE 77   L Street slide bowl-shaped area showing evidence of older sliding on the right side (south) (April 3, 1964). Scale: 1 in. = 1,320 ft.

a graben, as it did in the Fourth Avenue and Turnagain horizontal translatory-slide areas. Figure 87 shows the relative effect of unreinforced and reinforced foundations on the formation of grabens. The ridges of earth that formed at the slide toe were generally 3–5 ft high and 10–20 ft wide (Figures 81, 83, and 84). They were not of sufficient magnitude to form a resisting berm to buttress against future failures. Buttressing by the strengthening or reinforce-

ment of the existing soil or by the addition of soil, would be required to prevent a recurrence of sliding in another earthquake with strong motion of equivalent duration. At present, the economic prospects of stabilization do not look too favorable. The construction of gravel buttresses to limit failure would require the removal of all buildings in the construction area. The railroad grade would also have to be raised to provide sufficient protection against failure

Alaska State Housing Authority

FIGURE 78   L Street slide, showing the graben at the head of the slide and pressure ridges along the toe of the passive zone (March 30, 1964). Scale: 1 in. = 480 ft.

T. Tice, U.S. Army Corps of Engineers

FIGURE 79   L Street translatory slide. Southwest end between Ninth and Tenth avenues crossing P Street (March 28, 1964).

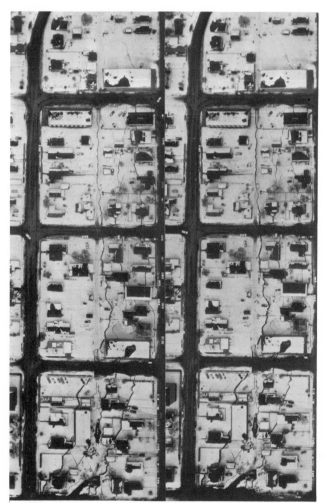

U.S. Army

FIGURE 80   L Street translatory slide. Graben between K and L streets and **Third to Seventh** avenues (bottom) (March 29, 1964). Scale: 1 in. = 175 ft.

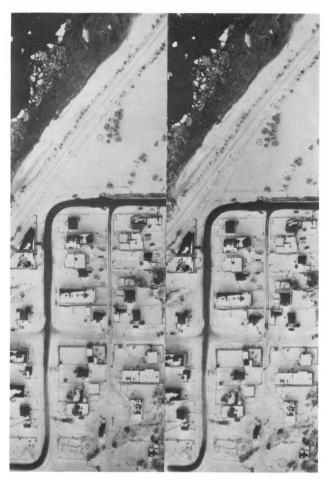

U.S. Army

FIGURE 81   L Street translatory slide, Fifth Avenue and N Street. The passive zone, indicated by the pressure ridges, follows the structures up the center of the picture, then terminates on crossing Fifth Avenue. From Fifth Avenue north a pressure ridge formed seaward of the railroad tracks (March 29, 1964). Scale: 1 in. = 175 ft.

along the railroad. Stabilization with sheet-pile cells or by the maintenance of permafrost at elevations that would intercept zones of possible failure have been evaluated. These methods were considered necessary because requirements for a gravel buttress, including the acquisition of land, appear excessive in cost.

Turnagain Slide Area Analysis

The sliding before 1964 seems to have been confined to the bluff line and was associated with a steady erosion of the bluff toe and recession (Figures 88–90). Older earthquake slides, if they existed, were probably removed by beach erosion. The evidence of a very old slide was encountered in drill hole C101-66, drilled near the mouth of Hood Creek. The drill-hole samples show a $37°$ dip of the clay from the top strata of the Bootlegger Cove Clay formation to the bottom of the hole that was at elevation –19 ft M S L.

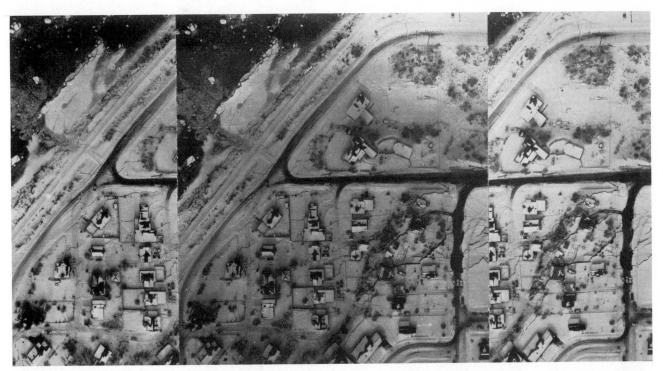

FIGURE 82   L Street translatory slide Ninth Avenue and Stolt Lane. The passive-zone pressure ridge is seaward of the railroad tracks at the southwest end of the slide area. P Street is along the right edge of the center and right pictures (March 29, 1964). Scale: 1 in. = 175 ft.

FIGURE 83   L Street translatory slide passive area. The pressure ridge runs between the toe of the bluff and the streets that are relatively free of snow. Greater frost penetration permitted these roads to act as a buttress. Greater buttressing along the toe would probably have caused failure further seaward (upper left). Seventh Avenue is above center of picture; Eighth Avenue is below the center. N Street is to the right center and O Street to the left (March 29, 1964). Scale: 1 in. = 175 ft.

FIGURE 84   L Street slide. Closeup of passive zone and pressure ridge at intersection of N Street and Seventh Avenue. Pressure ridge lifted log cabin structurally intact (April 13, 1964).

FIGURE 87   L Street translatory slide offset graben southwest of M Street. The well-reinforced foundation of the failed Four Seasons apartment building (background on the right) stopped graben progression beneath it while unreinforced foundation of the frame house permitted graben development (March 28, 1964).

T. Tice, U.S. Army Corps of Engineers

FIGURE 85   L Street translatory slide graben is offset at M Street and Eighth Avenue just as it approached the Four Seasons apartment building. The foundation of the failed Four Seasons was not offset or separated (March 28, 1964).

Air Photo Tech, Inc.

FIGURE 88   Pre-1964 Turnagain slide failures caused by oversteepening of the bluffs from toe erosion. Diagonal line at left is city limits. Larger slides are to the left (west) of Hood Creek (May 20, 1963).

T. Tice, U.S. Army Corps of Engineers

FIGURE 86   L Street translatory slide graben crossing Seventh and Eighth avenues and L and M streets. Graben shows 15 ft offset to left at M Street (March 28, 1964).

Eyewitness accounts indicated that sliding in the Turnagain area began approximately 2 minutes after the start of the earthquake. Some witnesses thought the duration of strong earthquake motions was as short as 1 minute in the Turnagain area, whereas timed records indicate the duration to be between 4 minutes 25 seconds and 7 minutes in the Anchorage area. It is conceivable that the duration of perceptible strong motion varied considerably in different areas. The partial or complete liquefaction of a soil stratum at depth may have greatly reduced the perceptible surface motion. The longer-period motions were also harder to per-

FIGURE 89   Pre-1964 Turnagain slide failure is to the right (east) of Hood Creek (May 20, 1963).

FIGURE 91   Turnagain slide area. The former residence of Lowell Thomas, Jr., is within the slide in background. Chilligan Drive at lower right (April 12, 1964).

ceive, but could have contributed to a continuation of soil failure.

Observations within the West Turnagain slide area (Figure 91) by Mrs. Lowell Thomas, Jr. (1964), indicated that sliding and failure of this large area ceased when the strong ground motions stopped. Observations by Brook Marston, however, in the vicinity of McCollie and Turnagain Parkway (Hansen, 1965, and Geology volume) which is behind the slide scarp, indicate that sliding continued after cessation of earthquake motion (Figure 92). Because earthquake motion continued at a lower level for several days, the magnitude of the earthquake at which major ground motion ceased would be of great interest; unfortunately, however, it is not known.

The first surveys were distance measurements to temporary benchmarks along Turnagain Parkway to detect any horizontal movement. These measurements were made in early April 1964, and a slope indicator was installed in Lynn Ary Park soon thereafter. No movement was recorded after these initial surveys and slope-indicator observations.

The east 600 ft of the Turnagain slide shows a pronounced pressure ridge at the toe (Figures 93 and 94). The existence of such a pressure ridge could indicate that the depth of littoral material overlying the slide plane was greater than that to the west. Pressure ridges were also evident along the beach line adjacent to Hood Creek and in Hood Creek itself (Figure 95). The Hood Creek pressure ridge may have resulted from the western movement of the east Turnagain slide. A sloping wedge failure (Figures 96 and 97) occurred in a small area on the west side of the large west Turnagain slide area. The zone of failure was well above the failure plane to the east between elevation 20 and 30 ft MSL. Samples obtained from the bluff adjoining this area indicate the clay to be stronger than normal, with possible strengths of about 0.5–1.0 ton/ft^2. Elsewhere in the Turnagain area, minimum undisturbed strengths were about 0.2–0.4 ton/ft^2.

Except for the limited areas already discussed, the Turnagain slide failures had characteristics of the horizontal translatory slides and were highly retrogressive in nature,

FIGURE 90   Pre-1964 Turnagain slide failure (upper right). This slide occurred in May 1957, following a heavy rain.

FIGURE 92   Eastern part of the Turnagain slide area north of McCollie Drive and along Turnagain Parkway (April 9, 1964).

T. Tice, U.S. Army Corps of Engineers

FIGURE 93   Turnagain retrogressive translatory slide: Passive-zone pressure ridge along eastern 600 ft of eastern part of Turnagain slide (March 28, 1964).

Alaska State Housing Authority

FIGURE 94   Turnagain retrogressive translatory slide: 600-ft passive-zone pressure ridge at eastern end of Turnagain slide (March 30, 1964). Scale: 1 in. = 475 ft.

Alaska State Housing Authority

FIGURE 95   Turnagain slide area: Pressure ridges at mouth of Hood Creek and along the creek (March 30, 1964). Scale: 1 in. = 690 ft.

FIGURE 96   Western part of the Turnagain slide, where the sloping-wedge failure occurred at a higher elevation than elsewhere in the slide.

whereas the Fourth Avenue and L Street slide areas developed horst blocks of considerable width and negligible vertical displacements within the limits of the blocks. The Turnagain horst blocks were recognizable as sharp ridges that generally paralleled the scarp lines (Figures 38, 97–99). In most cases, the upper Naptowne outwash had slid into the graben. The ridges could be recognized as horst blocks by their nearly horizontal bedding planes; development of large cracks and grabens permitted secondary circular and wedge-block failure of the oversteepened faces (Figures 94, 95, and 100).

A number of areas within the Turnagain slide area had more pronounced horst-block configurations than others. One area was between McKenzie Drive and Hood Creek (Figure 101); another was the northwest corner of Lynn Ary Park (Figure 102). These areas, although relatively intact, experienced vertical displacement and surface distortion. An area 100 × 250 ft in east Turnagain, north of the Marston Drive and Loussac Drive intersection, moved relatively intact with minor vertical displacement (Figures 94 and 95). Another small horst block, which retained its original surface cover, was in the southeast section of the large west slide. The area settled 2–3 ft (Figure 103).

Evaluation of the test data of soil beneath the area of sliding and behind the slide scarp, where soil movement, stretching, and pronounced cracking occurred, indicates a nearly horizontal plane of sliding. The elevation of the weakest plane possibly varied between elevation 0 and 10 ft MSL seaward of the slide scarp on Turnagain Parkway and elevation 0 and 5 ft landward of the slide scarp.

Exploration revealed evidence of sand intrusion into a

FIGURE 97   Western part of the Turnagain slide: Sloping-wedge failure to the left (east) of intact bluff. A greater soil strength in the intact area may have limited the magnitude of failure (May 20, 1964). Scale: 1 in. = 470 ft.

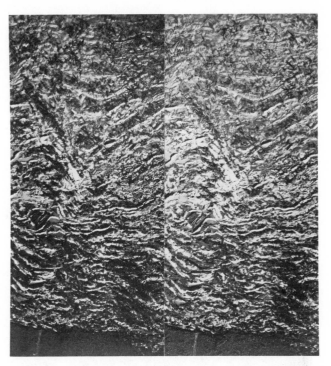

FIGURE 99   Western part of the Turnagain slide: Graben and horst blocks down the middle of the slide. Some portions of the slide moved much faster than others and in slightly different directions (see Figure 38) (May 20, 1964). Scale: 1 in. = 470 ft.

vertical crack in hole A-316-3.5 (Figure 104). The limited number and thickness of sand layers and the lack of continuity of these layers or lenses indicate that the failure of the soft sensitive clay was primarily responsible for the plane of sliding, although the liquefaction of thin sand layers may have contributed to the failure.

The area immediately behind the slide scarp settled as

FIGURE 98   Eastern part of the Turnagain slide: Graben and horst blocks typical of the Turnagain slide areas adjacent to Turnagain Parkway and Lynn Ary Park. The area was later used for stabilization studies (May 1964).

much as 2 ft, the magnitude of settlement decreasing to the south. Analysis of all horst blocks within the Turnagain slide area indicates settlements from 2 ft to possibly more than 20 ft. Most of the consolidation could be explained by the extrusion along or the wearing away of the sliding surface as it moved seaward. The declination of the sliding plane and the degree to which the slope of the failure plane affected the beginning and continuation of the slide are uncertain. From the exploration data, it appears that a series of sloping planes could have developed within the soft clay layers; the plane of weakest soil and overall progression of failure, however, appears to have been nearly horizontal (Figure 105).

Behind the slide, the potential failure plane of very soft soil is more nearly horizontal than the actual bedding planes of adjoining strata. This condition leads to a possible conclusion that the failure plane resulted from the strong repetitious horizontal earthquake motions parallel to the ground surface, whereas secondary failure blocks could have failed on a definite slope within the layer above the primary failure plane. Subsidence of horst blocks from soil extrusion and horizontal displacement became greater as the seaward movement progressed and, therefore, gave the impression of a failure plane at a steeper slope than may actually have existed.

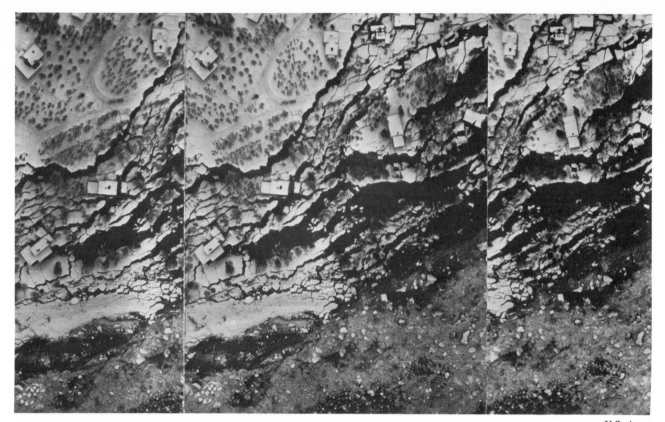

U.S. Army

FIGURE 100   Grabens and horst blocks in the eastern part of the Turnagain slide. The house on the left (east) edge is on a typical narrow horst block. The horst block at upper right is larger than most in the Turnagain slide area (March 29, 1964). Scale: 1 in. = 230 ft.

The formation of cracks and the slide scarp show the lines of least resistance followed by the cracks. Most of the house foundations in the Turnagain area were constructed of unreinforced concrete; most of the garages were slab-on-grade construction and were attached to the house. The heat loss from the houses was sufficient to keep the tem-

perature in the garages above freezing and relatively dry during the colder months. Many of the houses had basements with uninsulated walls. The penetration of frost in the Turnagain housing area during the time of the earthquake was 4–6 ft; the light snow cover contributed to the

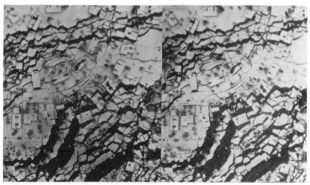

U.S. Army

FIGURE 101   Large horst block at west end of the eastern part of the Turnagain slide area, between McKenzie Drive and Hood Creek (March 29, 1964). Scale: 1 in = 350 ft.

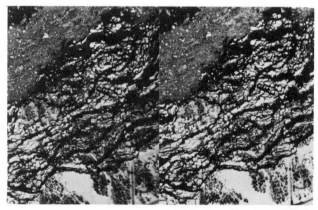

Alaska State Housing Authority

FIGURE 102   Large horst block moved northwest from its former position on the north side of Lynn Ary Park (bottom center) (March 30, 1964). Scale: 1 in. = 485 ft.

FIGURE 103 Only intact horst block in southeast portion of large western part of the Turnagain slide area (upper left) (April 19, 1964).

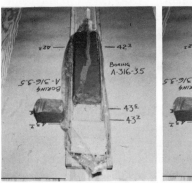
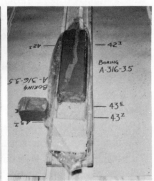

FIGURE 104 Bootlegger Cove Clay sample, Lynn Ary Park, Turnagain slide area. Sample separated on depleted horizontal sand lens that intruded into vertical crack. Horizontal lens at +1.9 ft MSL (January 19, 1966).

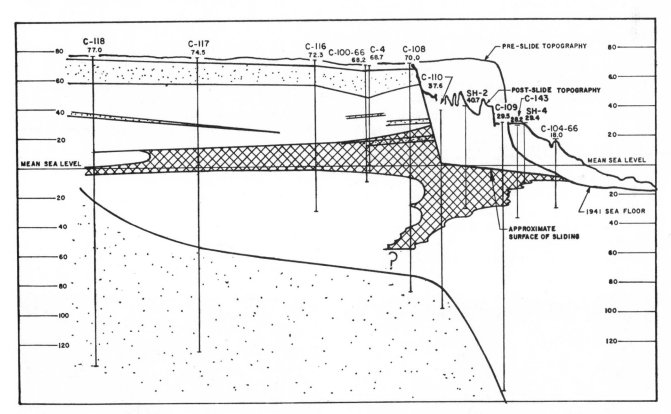

LEGEND

C-104-66   BORING LOCATION

18.0
T   SURFACE ELEVATION OF BORING

[⋯] RELATIVELY PERMEABLE, COHESIONLESS SOIL

[XXXXX] ENVELOPE OF SOFT AND VERY SOFT SILTY CLAYS, SHEAR STRENGTH LESS THAN 0.34 TONS/FT^2

FIGURE 105 Turnagain Parkway, north–south section A. Envelope of remolded silty clay strengths. Scale: 1 in = 50 ft vertical; 1 in. = 500 ft horizontal.

substantial frost penetration. Cracks tended to interconnect between the thawed areas around most house foundations (Figures 106 and 107). Larger cracks usually ran along the foundation wall under the garage slab, resulting in the outward movement of the garage (Figure 106). Houses with the longer unreinforced foundation wall perpendicular to the direction of crack progression sustained considerably more damage than similar houses with the longer foundation wall parallel to the direction of crack progression. The Swalling home, a large L-shaped house at the east end of the Turnagain slide, had a well-reinforced, uninsulated concrete foundation. Very large cracks and differential displacements developed around the house, but the foundation was not damaged (Figures 108 and 109). The soil had been pushed away ½–1 in. on all sides of houses with uninsulated basements; there was usually 1–4 in. of relative settlement around these houses. Cracks generally crossed the streets perpendicular to the center line, usually at an expansion joint in the curb or at a driveway entrance. Cracks also tended to avoid crossing the larger roots radiating from a trunk but would frequently parallel these larger roots, often going directly under the center of the tree and splitting its trunk. The house in Figure 110 shows the effect of graben development on a split-level house with an unreinforced basement foundation. Two houses at the seaward end of Sonstrom Drive at the mouth of Hood Creek had identical, although reversed, plans. These rectangular houses had well-reinforced concrete footings and block-foundation walls. Sliding in this area caused a 20–30 degree tilt of the two houses (Figure 111); portions of the foundations and footings were cantilevered as much as 10 ft without damage. The only damage to the buildings was to the front entrance steps and to the structurally weaker basement-garage entrances on the south or depressed side.

We can conclude that damage to houses both in and behind the slide area would have been less if the ground had not been frozen and if the foundations had been reinforced.

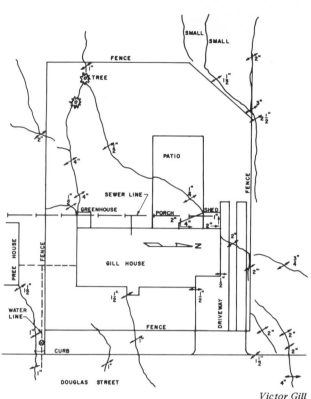

Victor Gill

FIGURE 107   Gill House, Turnagain. Cracks tended to interconnect thawed areas adjacent to most house foundations and to avoid crossing large roots, but they would travel radially to and from a tree. The soil next to fence lines and utility lines usually had less frost penetration and served as lines of weakness for crack progression.

The same earthquake occurring when little or no frost was in the ground might have caused a more closely spaced crack pattern and the translation of sliding farther inland.

Analysis of soil-strength test data indicates a gradual increase in soil strength of the weak soil layers to the south of

FIGURE 106   Crack pattern crossing between houses and beneath garages (April 30, 1964).

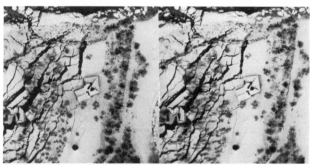

U.S. Army

FIGURE 108   Swalling residence with a well-reinforced foundation, at the eastern end of the Turnagain slide. Cracks extend to house without foundation or structural damage; a graben is nearby (March 29, 1964). Scale: 1 in. = 240 ft.

FIGURE 109   Ground level view of the Swalling residence. Cracks surrounded house but did not penetrate well-reinforced foundation (April 30, 1964).

the slide scarp (Figures 105 and 112). The piezometric gradient becomes less with depth (Figures 113 and 114) and would tend to concentrate seepage and the saline leaching of the Bootlegger Cove soil toward the bluff line. If the sensitivity of the clay is influenced by the leaching of saline, this could tend to limit the extent of sliding in a single earthquake. After sliding, new subsurface flow configuration would result, and new plains of weakness could then develop.

Stabilization Studies   The initial soil studies indicated that the sensitive clays at depths of potential failure extend a considerable distance behind the present bluff. If the earthquake had lasted longer, failure could have progressed at least to the limits of soil stretching and crack formation— approximately that area bounded on the east by Fish Creek, on the south by Knik Avenue, west to Hood Creek, and then roughly parallel to the west slide and a considerable distance behind the west slide scarp (Figure 115). Sta-

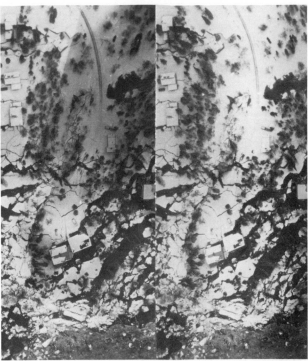

U.S. Army

FIGURE 111   Turnagain slide area at Hood Creek: Two houses at upper end of Sonstrom Drive had reinforced-block foundations that sustained negligible damage from a tilt of 20–30 degrees (March 29, 1964). Scale: 1 in. = 210 ft.

bilization by retention of the slide toe seaward of the original shoreline as a buttress was found not to be feasible, because of the probability of immediate loss of that area in another earthquake. This decision was based on strengths along the plane of sliding of 0.05 ton/ft^2 and strengths at the slide elevation behind the slide scarp of 0.125 ton/ft^2. Because of the probable loss of the seaward berm of the slide after the initial series of earthquake shocks, stabilization was deemed necessary to prevent further sliding in the event of another earthquake of equivalent intensity and duration.

Stabilization could be accomplished by an increase in shear strength over a large area or by a substantial strengthening of a limited buttressed area. Although strengthening a large area was considered impracticable, several possible methods of stabilization were considered (Shannon & Wilson, Inc., 1964b).

The first method proposed was the excavation and placement of a gravel buttress; this method was disapproved because of its high cost in relation to the value of the benefiting property. Chemical grouting, or physiochemical hardening, was considered and rejected because the soil was too impervious to permit acceptably economical and lasting treatment. Freezing was considered feasible, but the need

FIGURE 110   Turnagain slide area: House on West Marston Drive. Graben scarp developed at juncture of this split-level house (April 5, 1964).

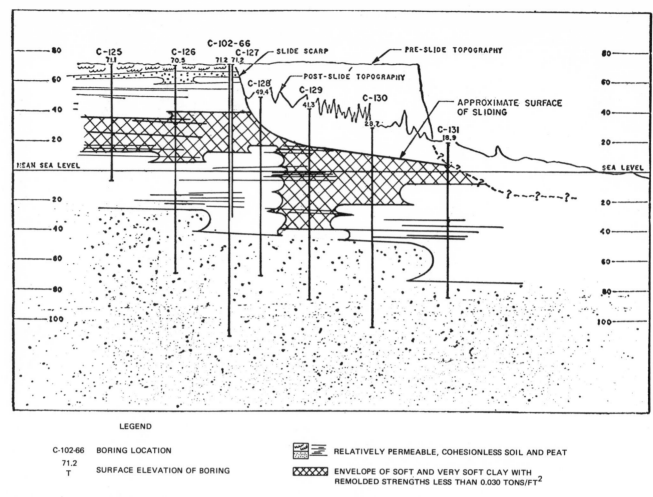

LEGEND

C-102-66   BORING LOCATION

71.2
T   SURFACE ELEVATION OF BORING

RELATIVELY PERMEABLE, COHESIONLESS SOIL AND PEAT

ENVELOPE OF SOFT AND VERY SOFT CLAY WITH
REMOLDED STRENGTHS LESS THAN 0.030 TONS/FT^2

FIGURE 112   West Turnagain: North–south section B. Envelope of silty clay remolded strengths. Scale: 1 in. = 50 ft vertical; 1 in. = 500 ft horizontal.

for controlled and continued maintenance of the soil in a permanently frozen state was considered a disadvantage if other more practical methods could be found.

Sand-drain stabilization, incorporating remolding of materials and subsequent reconsolidation, was considered feasible. Analysis indicated that the probable method of remolding was by delay-sequence firing of explosives. This could be done more easily in the slide area in front of the new scarp and behind the original shoreline because of the absence of structures and other improvements. Surcharging would be necessary to obtain the required consolidation pressure. A model test section was recommended to permit evaluation of the degree of remolding, the degree of reconsolidation, the decrease in sensitivity, and the increase in strength that might be attained.

The Corps of Engineers was authorized by the Alaska State Housing Authority (ASHA) to develop a program and conduct studies to stabilize the Turnagain slides and housing areas that would be endangered by possible future sliding.

On the basis of the recommendations of the Board of Consultants, investigations were begun on the feasibility of blast remolding and consolidation of the Bootlegger Cove Clay. The firm of Shannon & Wilson, Inc. was retained to conduct the investigations and report on the findings. Figure 116 shows the area used for the model tests immediately following the earthquake and Figure 117 shows the area as it had been regraded before beginning the subsequent model tests.

Evaluation   The change in soil properties was evaluated from strengths obtained from boring samples using torsional-vane strength tests and by cone penetrometer measurements of the *in situ* soil. The following conclusions were reached from the study of remolding the Bootlegger Cove Clay with explosives:

• A single charge of 30 lb disturbed the residences within the Turnagain area excessively.

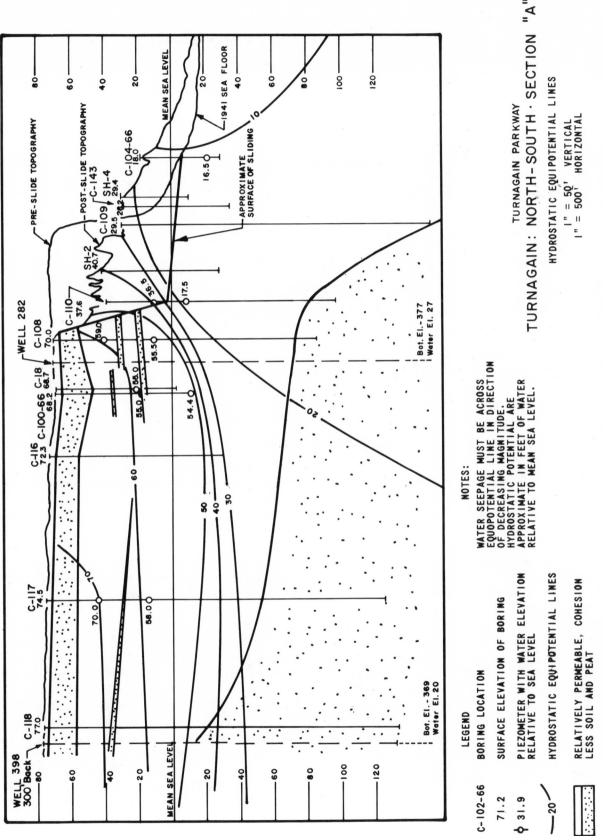

FIGURE 113 Turnagain Parkway, Turnagain: North–south section A. Hydrostatic equipotential lines. Scale: 1 in. = 50 ft vertical; 1 in. = 500 ft horizontal.

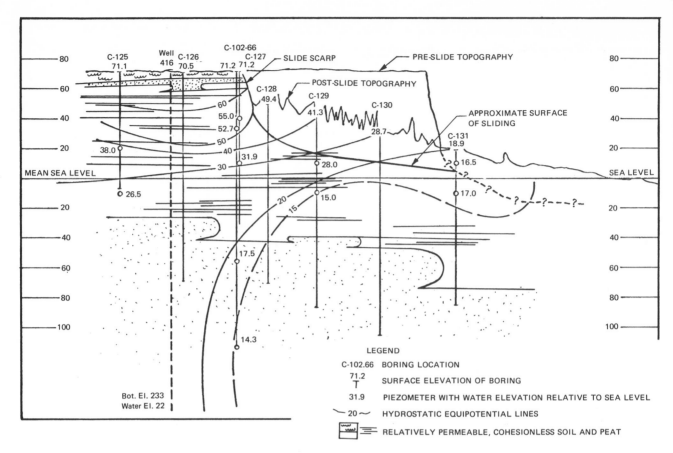

FIGURE 114   West Turnagain: North–south section B. Hydrostatic equipotential lines. Scale: 1 in. = 50 ft vertical; 1 in. = 500 ft horizontal.

• A series of small charges with a delay of more than 0.05 second between each charge was found to be more effective than a single large charge in disturbing the clay structure, but the process still disturbed the local residents.

• A significant increase in strength of the sensitive clay could be attained if the disturbed soil were subjected to an overburden stress of approximately 3 tons/ft². Treatment would require a disturbance of at least 50 percent.

• Laboratory dynamic-stress reversal tests performed on the remolded and reconsolidated clay indicated no change in the sensitivity of the soil.

• It was considered feasible, on a large-scale project, to obtain a 50 percent or greater degree of remolding by using a series of small delayed charges placed in holes 8–10 ft apart. The overall cost of surcharging required to consolidate the area when added to the cost of remolding eliminated this method. The disturbing effect of blasting on the residents in the area also contributed to the decision against using this procedure.

Electroosmosis was also considered as a method of stabilization, but was not pursued in initial analysis because the ability of the process to stabilize sand lenses was doubtful.

At a Board of Consultants meeting in January 1965, however, it was agreed that electroosmosis should be considered as a possible method of stabilizing the soil. After reevaluation of all data, the sands were found to be sufficiently discontinuous and to vary enough in elevation to make this process worth considering. Because failure is attributed basically to clay layers, the width of a potential buttress could be widened sufficiently to compensate for the effect of the sand lenses. Because electroosmosis had not yet been used as a permanent method of stabilization on similar clays, a model study was initiated to determine the degree of effectiveness of the treatment. The test section was located so that it could become a part of an overall stabilization project (Figures 116 and 117) if it proved successful. Leo Casagrande and Richard Loughney were retained as consultants for the application of electroosmosis, and Shannon & Wilson, Inc. was asked to conduct the soil tests and report the results. Figure 118 shows anode 1, which was extracted 129 days after start of treatment. The sculptured effect of the steel surface is a result of localized corrosion of the rail steel. Figure 119 shows the model test area as it appeared at the completion of tests.

Electroosmosis treatment of the Bootlegger Cove Clay

U.S. Coast and Geodetic Survey

FIGURE 115   Turnagain slide areas: Line indicates extent of possible sliding if earthquake had lasted even longer (April 3, 1964). Scale: 1 in. = 1,350 ft.

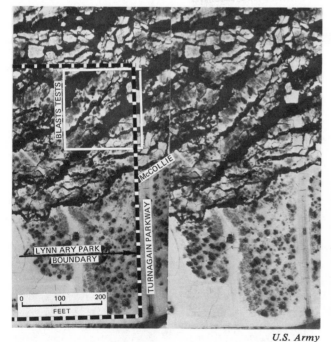

U.S. Army

FIGURE 116   Lynn Ary Park model test area, selected for stabilization investigations in Turnagain slide. Blast tests were along the left (west) side of the square outlined; electroosmosis tests were conducted within the square (March 29, 1964). Scale: 1 in. = 150 ft.

did not produce the desired strength increase; however, the sensitivity of the highly sensitive soil was reduced. No significant change in the moisture content, liquid limit, plastic limit, or plasticity index of the clay was noticed.

The greatest rate of settlement occurred during the first 20 days of treatment. The settlement for the entire test period averaged 1.8 in. and ranged from 1.0 to 3.5 in.

Piezometers within the treated area showed a significant

U.S. Coast and Geodetic Survey

FIGURE 117   Lynn Ary Park model test area in relation to the remainder of the slide area. Much of the Turnagain slide has been regraded to improve sanitation (July 24, 1966). Scale: 1 in. = 2,500 ft.

FIGURE 118   Electroosmosis treatment of rail pile 1, extracted after 129 days and 25,000 ampere-hours of treatment. Upper rail 64–65 ft depth, lower rail 33–34 ft depth.

drawdown in the first 20–30 days after treatment started. A drawdown of about 50 ft was observed in a piezometer near the center of the test area; however, high pore pressure was recorded in a piezometer located close to cathode 4. The water level in slope-indicator wells within the treatment area remained at a depth of 7 ft throughout the test. The groundwater perched on top of the clay probably flows into the area faster than it can be removed by electroosmosis treatment. The eductor-well system appears to have been only partly effective in removing groundwater from the area, and it did not appreciably affect the pore pressures near cathode 4. Observations in wells near eductor installations, however, indicate that they did effectively remove the water within the sand filter surrounding the cathode.

Salt concentration of the soil varied from 1 to 5 g/liter. The pH of the soil varied from 6.4 to 10.5, and the eductor-system water showed a variance in pH of 9.5–11.5. During preparation of samples for x-ray diffraction studies, treated samples were found to remain in suspension longer than untreated samples.

Laboratory resistivity measurements made on samples of the Bootlegger Cove Clay before electroosmosis treatment was started showed specific resistance of the order of 1,500 ohm-cm, whereas measurements made late in the test program gave a specific resistivity of 2,500 ohm-cm. The ground resistance of the steel electrodes increased from 1.3 ohms at the start of treatment to about 20 ohms at the end of the test. When the current was turned off to permit soil sampling, the resistance would drop back almost to its original value. Potential gradient readings between electrodes indicate a drop of 94 percent in the first 3 ft from an aluminum anode and a 75 percent drop from a steel anode. The high resistance of the ground adjacent to the electrodes and the extreme and rapid fluctuation in the resistance during periods when the current was cut off is not consistent with electroosmosis experience on other projects.

Although the reason for the unsuccessful results of the electroosmosis treatment is not certain, the high voltage drop near the anodes was thought to be a contributing factor; this, however, was considered an effect and not the basic problem. Other factors influencing the negative results were the loss of surcharge as a result of sliding that reduced the effective consolidation pressure, recirculation of pore water through sand or silt lenses back to the anode, and high pH of the soil.

When the model tests had been completed, additional borings were put down to further delineate the changes in soil strength of disturbed layers following the earthquake and to broaden the information on hydrostatic pressures around and in the slide zone. Additional subsurface investigations also were conducted to obtain detailed information on areas that did not fail, to permit a more comprehensive review of the probable mode of failure when considering other possible means of stabilization.

Figures 120–126 are logs of this additional exploration. Figures 113 and 114 are cross sections at locations shown in Figure 127 that give soil strata and the contour of piezometric elevations. Because the direction of water seepage is approximately normal to these piezometric contours, the direction of seepage is obviously downward from the surface and continues either toward the bluff or toward the highly permeable layers underlying the gravel.

The possibility of a peptizing dispersing effect from any humic acid present in waters seeping down from surface peat deposits was considered (Söderblom, 1960) together with the possibility of a slight difference in the molecular composition of soil layers of different strengths. X-ray and infraspectrographic analysis of selected samples with appreciable differences in strength and physical locations were made and the results are included as Appendix D to Shannon & Wilson's (1966) report on the electroosmosis field test.

The evaluation of soil consolidation and drainage charac-

FIGURE 119   Electroosmosis and eductor-well-system installations (November 1965).

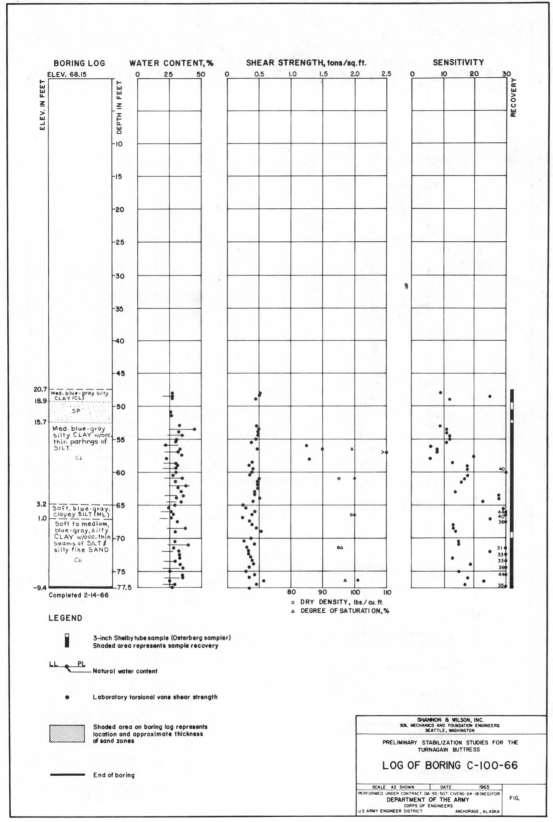

FIGURE 120 Log of boring C-100-66.

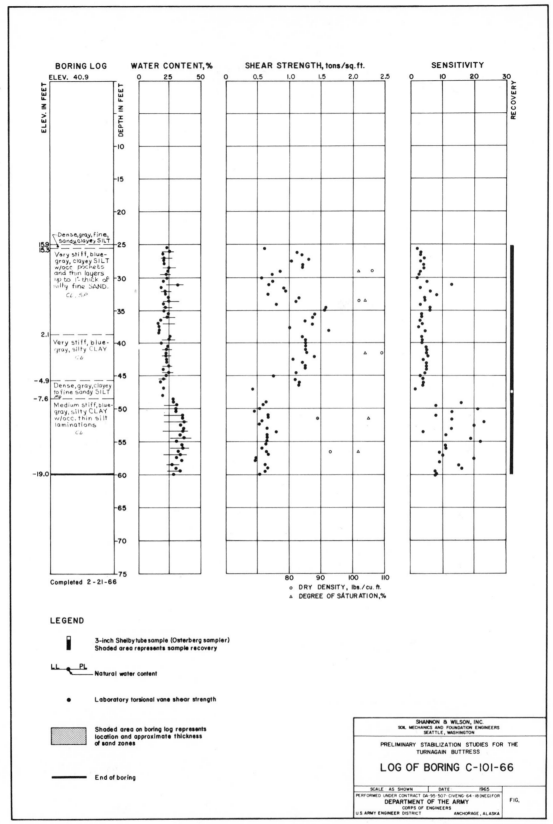

FIGURE 121   Log of boring C-101-66.

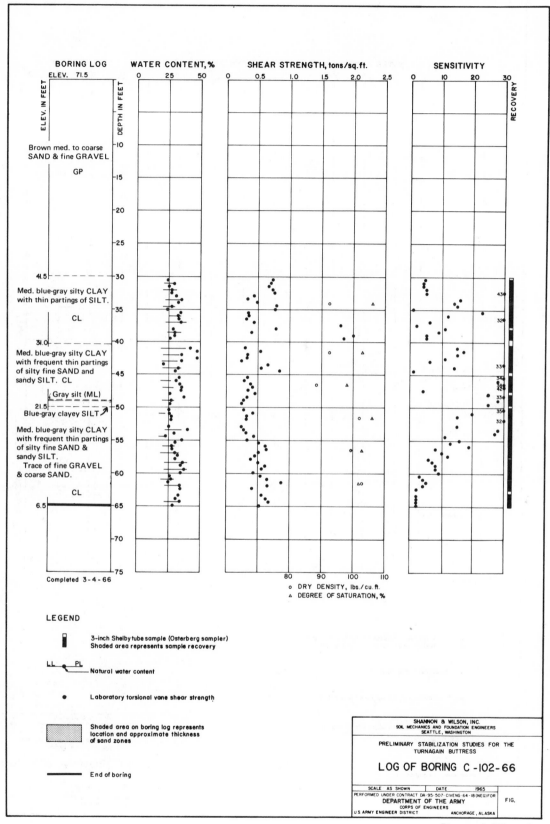

FIGURE 122   Log of boring C-102-66.

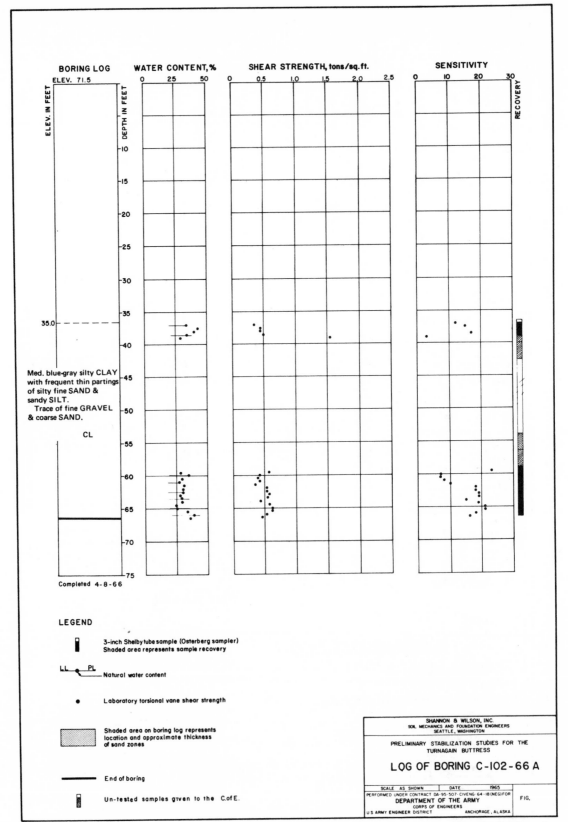

FIGURE 123   Log of boring C-102-66A.

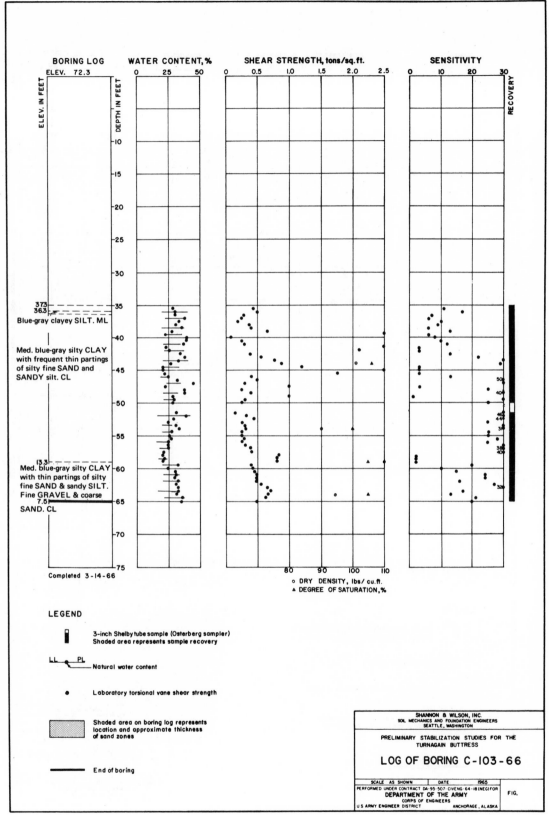

FIGURE 124   Log of boring C-103-66.

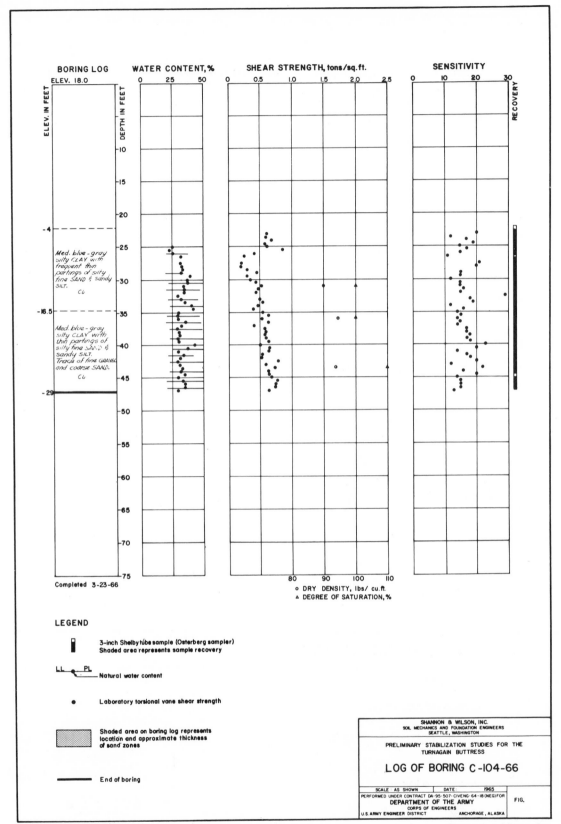

FIGURE 125   Log of boring C-104-66.

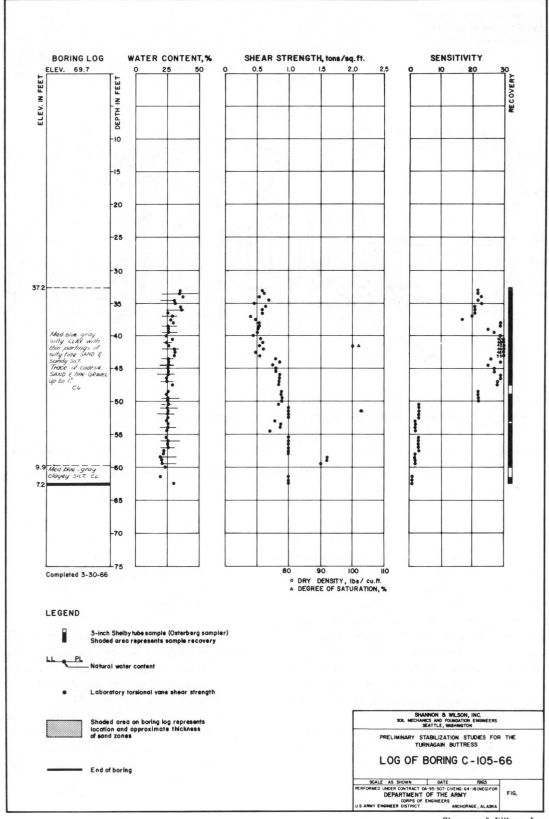

FIGURE 126   Log of boring C-105-66.

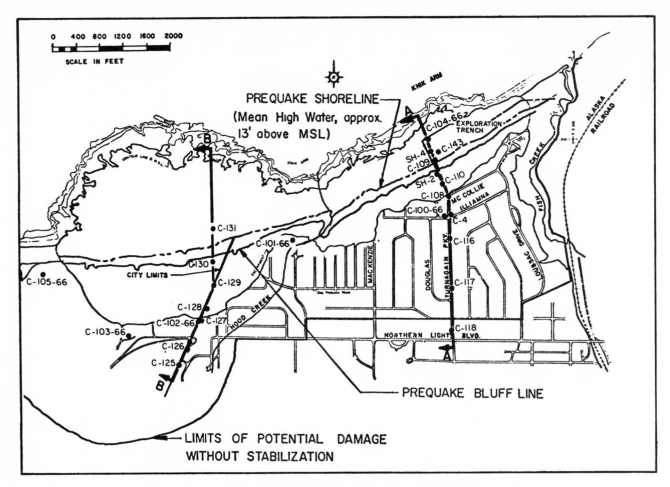

FIGURE 127   Turnagain slide area exploration section and 1966 exploration locations.

teristics indicated that a gravity subsurface drain system installed behind the postearthquake bluff was technically feasible and within reasonable cost if surface settlements of 6 in. to 2 ft could be tolerated.

The experience of the Corps of Engineers in the freezing and maintenance of frozen soils provides adequate data for a feasibility study of a frozen buttress within the slide area. The study revealed that it was economically feasible to freeze and maintain a frozen buttress. Maintenance costs would have been kept to a minimum by installing one of several natural refrigeration methods now available that store additional cold during the freezing period and thereby maintain a permafrost regime.

Because of the indicated strength gains in the disturbed zones, the slide material serving as a natural buttress was reconsidered in detail. The following factors were believed to be critical:

• The probable stability of the existing slopes, considering various permanent toe locations, evaluated with the slope-stability chart compiled by L. Bjerrum (Figure 2)

• The soil strength-to-depth relationship

• The present strength of the clay underlying the slide toe seaward of the original shoreline

• The relation of in-place vane shear testing and laboratory torsional vane test

A careful analysis of the data indicated that tideland soils seaward of the old shoreline and beneath the slide debris possessed strength characteristics at their respective elevations within the same magnitude as the soil beneath the present bluff line (Figure 128). The in-place vane shear tests showed slightly higher soil strengths than comparable soil strata tested with the torvane (torsional vane shear apparatus) on undisturbed tube samples.

As a result of the ability to depend on higher soil strengths seaward of the preearthquake shoreline, the seaward toe of the slide could be considered part of a buttress, and the flatter angle of inclination indicated the slope to be stable (Figure 2). The stability, however, would require erosion-control measures to maintain a toe seaward of the preearthquake shoreline.

After reexamination of all data, the Board of Consultants agreed that the natural slope of the slide material, in view of existing strength gains, provides an adequate natural buttress if the slopes are protected against beach erosion. Following this meeting, a concept study on Turnagain area beach erosion stabilization was prepared and transmitted to the Alaska State Housing Authority for their use and that of the City of Anchorage.

Conclusions In the interval since the March 27, 1964, earthquake, the strength of the zone of failure in the Turnagain area has been increasing and has reached, or will soon reach, its original value. The slope of slide material that now exists forms a natural buttress that should withstand an earthquake of similar intensity and duration to the great Alaska earthquake.

For the slide to remain stable, the beach materials at the existing toe must be protected from erosion by ice rafting, tides, and waves. A rock-protected toe is recommended.

The reevaluated stability of the Turnagain slide area has encouraged lending agencies to refinance existing homes behind the slide scarp. Methods of financing and the construction of beach-erosion protection are being studied by the City of Anchorage.

EARTH FLOWS

Earth flows that occurred as a result of the earthquake seemed to have originated from the liquefaction of horizontal strata of sand, silt, or clay 10–20 ft or more thick. The thickness of the liquefied soil seemed to increase with the duration of the earthquake. Because of the thickness of the particular strata that are subject to liquefaction and the movement of the slide, in some places a major portion of the slide appeared to be in a fluid state. The Potter Hill (Rabbit Creek) railroad-embankment slide (Figure 129) was

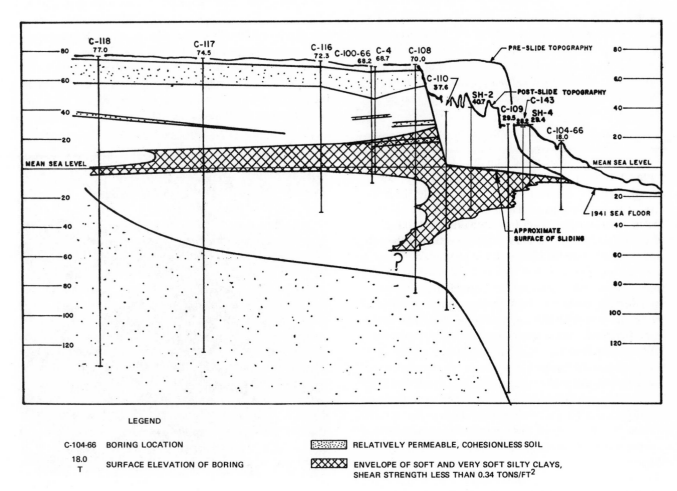

FIGURE 128 Turnagain Parkway, Turnagain: North–south section A. Envelope of soft silty clays. Scale: 1 in. = 50 ft vertical; 1 in. = 500 ft horizontal.

FIGURE 129   Potter Hill slide along Mile 103–104 of The Alaska Railroad.

of this type; terminal portions of the Turnagain slide (Figure 38), Government Hill slides (Figure 35), Sleeper airstrip slides opposite Cairn Point (Figure 8), Cairn Point slide (Figure 7), and one of the Elmendorf slides on the north side of Ship Creek (Figure 3) were partly of this type. The Point Campbell slide (Figures 9 and 33) might also be classed as earth flows.

Potter Hill Slide

Potter Hill is a railroad grade 3 mi northwest of the Potter railroad station (Figure 129). The slide area is approximately 1 mi long between Alaska Railroad Mile 103 and 104. This slide is of particular interest because the failure occurred in stratified sands that were subjected to some hydrostatic pressure and because a 150-ft section of the railroad subgrade also failed in the 1954 earthquake. The stratified sands in which liquefaction occurred continued under a much higher and steeper bluff without failing.

After the earthquake, an old railroad employee, Mr. Haag, wrote to John Manley, Alaska Railroad general manager, that after a duck-hunting trip on the Potter flats in 1916, he climbed the bluff immediately west of Rabbit Creek and noticed many fallen trees to the northwest. Several years earlier, in 1912, a series of earthquakes had occurred in south central Alaska; the fallen trees may have resulted from sliding after those earthquakes.

The October 3, 1954, earthquake in the Cook Inlet area occurred at 1:19 a.m. The following Sunday morning, a boy walking along the railroad tracks discovered that a 150-ft section of the railroad grade had disappeared at Potter Hill. A photograph taken on August 3, 1950 (Figure 130), shows the preearthquake Potter Hill area. Figures

131, 132, and 133 are pictures of the area that failed, taken on October 4, 1954, after it had been refilled. The embankment materials in the filled areas were partly submerged in a quick liquefied fine gray sand. The failure occurred in the railroad embankment at the toe of the bluff, but it did not cause the bluff slope to fail. Other sections upgrade of the flow sections slumped as much as 1 ft as a result of the same earthquake.

After the 1954 earthquake, horizontal drains of 2-in.-diameter perforated pipe were installed near the base of the railroad fill. The horizontal drains did not produce water, although water did percolate to within 4 ft of the surface in auger holes drilled in the ditch next to the bluff. A longitudinal perforated drain was also placed in this ditch but did not produce water.

The 1964 earthquake caused the failure of 4,000 ft of railroad grade and toe slumping of an additional 2,500 ft of grade. Figures 134–139 show the areas of the slides before and after the earthquake.

An unpublished report on landslides between Mile 103 and 104 on The Alaska Railroad following the earthquake of March 27, 1964, prepared for The Alaska Railroad by McCulloch and Bonilla of the U.S. Geological Survey in 1964, describes the Potter Hill slides. McCulloch and Bonilla examined aerial photographs of the slide area and transferred pressure ridges, cracks, and scarps delineated on the photographs to a transparent overlay (Figure 140). They also examined the slides in the field and mapped a profile,

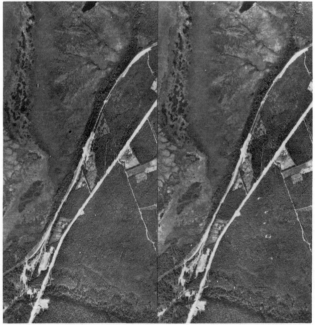

FIGURE 130   Potter Hill before the October 3, 1954, liquefaction earth-flow slide (August 8, 1950). Scale: 1 in. = 2,150 ft.

U.S. Coast and Geodetic Survey

FIGURE 131   Potter Hill between the 1954 and 1964 slides. Arrow shows location of 1954 slide (August 30, 1960). Scale: 1 in. = 2,400 ft.

measured across the slide at location A–A′, using a transit to determine horizontal and vertical measurements (Figure 140).

Bank Material   In the Potter Hill slide area, glacial till overlay glacial outwash. The till and outwash deposits dipped at a low angle to the north, so that the till formed an appreciable part of the visible section of ground above the tracks at the north end of the slide area (near Mile 104) (Figure 141). At the south end of the slide area (near Mile 103), a coarse gravel overlay the till, which was composed principally of sandy silt with some cobbles and boulders. Although it could maintain a steep-cut face, the till was not very compact or blocky and was quickly gullied by water running across the face. The upper part of the outwash beneath the till was a very silty fine sand with thin silt horizons. At station 2886+22, about 10 ft of pebble gravel lay just beneath the 18-in.-thick track ballast. Underlying the gravel, 15 ft of fine sand with a few silt beds was exposed.

Although no good exposures of the material lower in the bluffs were found, the blue-gray fine sand that formed the greater portion of the material visible on the slide surfaces and the similar fine sand found in a crack at the junction of the bluff face and the adjacent lowlands near Mile 104.2 indicate that the lower portion of the bluffs is composed of fine blue-gray sand.

FIGURE 132   October 1954 Potter Hill slide, Mile 103 The Alaska Railroad. New embankment already installed. Sand in foreground was quick (October 3, 1954).

FIGURE 133   October 1954 Potter Hill slide, Mile 103 The Alaska Railroad (October 4, 1954).

Air Photo Tech, Inc.

FIGURE 134   Potter Hill slide area less than 1 year before March 27, 1964, slides (1963). Scale: 1 in. = 1,310 ft.

A water well 900 ft east of station 2886+22 encountered the top of a 20-ft bed of "blue mud" at a depth of 175 ft, 2 ft above MSL and 18.5 ft above mean lower low water (MLLW). From this elevation to a depth of about 550 ft (375 ft below MSL), the well alternately penetrated thick beds of sand and blue clay.

Groundwater   Evidence suggests that there is ample groundwater throughout most of the depth of the Potter Hill bluffs. There are many permeable beds in the sediments that constitute the bluffs, and because water levels of between 240 and 30 ft above sea level are reported in wells east of the slide area, groundwater is probably discharged into the slide area at several levels.

The lower portion of the bluffs in the slide area is composed of permeable fine sand that occurs near the high-tide level and is probably kept nearly saturated by groundwater.

McCulloch and Bonilla (1970) pointed out that a system to drain the slide area thoroughly would have to keep sur-

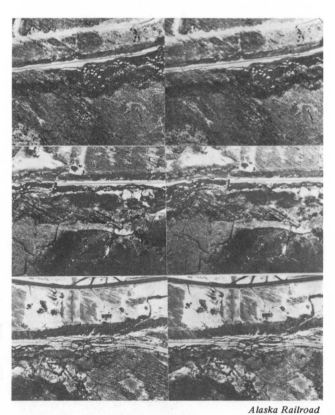

Alaska Railroad

FIGURE 136   Three stereo-pair segments of the Potter Hill slide from northwest to southeast, reading from top to bottom (April 1, 1964). Scale: 1 in. = 830 ft.

Alaska Railroad

FIGURE 135   Potter Hill slide: Slope failure continues well west of main slide (bottom). Railroad grade rises to west.

Alaska Railroad

FIGURE 137   Potter Hill slide from west end of main embankment failure, looking east.

Alaska Railroad

FIGURE 139   East end of Potter Hill slide shows cracking along base of bluff and embankment but not into bluff.

face water from infiltrating and eroding the bank. It would also have to contend with groundwater that was probably discharged laterally into the slide area at several levels throughout the height of the bluffs and with groundwater that saturated the base of the slide area.

History of the Potter Hill Slide Area   The section of the line from Mile 103 to 104 had been destroyed by slides at least three times within a 35-year period. The slides occurred in benches cut into the natural bank material and in the fills.

Bert Wennerstrom, chief accountant of The Alaska Railroad, recalled that in the late 1920's and early 1930's, heavy rains had caused sliding along this section (Mile 103–104). The largest slide took out about 1,000 ft of track and was the result of heavy rains. The failures involved cuts in the natural bank material.

Alaska Railroad

FIGURE 138   Middle section of Potter Hill slide.

In October 1954, an earthquake caused landsliding that again destroyed the line in the same area. An unpublished report, by James A. Morrison, on the slides between Mile 103 and 104 after the earthquake is on file at The Alaska Railroad Office. Although the report mentions only failures in the fills, failures might also have occurred in the natural bank material. The grade was described at the time of the earthquake as being "considerably drier than normal in the autumn of 1954."

On March 27, 1964, landsliding affected both cuts in natural bank material and fills from south of Mile 103 to north of Mile 104. The ground was frozen at the time of the earthquake, and, presumably, there was very little surface runoff; however, sand-rimmed holes on the slides, resulting from the expulsion of water, suggest that the landslide material had a high water content.

Both grade fills and benches cut into the natural bank material were therefore removed by these three landslides and failure has occurred as the result of heavy rain, earthquakes, and high and low surface runoff.

The Landslides   The Potter Hill landslides extended for about 4,200 ft along the railroad between Mile 103 and 104. At two places, several hundred feet of track and roadbed were destroyed. At other places along this section of track, the landslides have so far only affected the shoulder of the roadbed.

The landslides all consist of long narrow slump blocks that break into many units as they move downslope. In the lower parts of the landslides, the movement is by flowage and involves the estuarine silt of Turnagain Arm. Conspicuous, well-defined pressure ridges are more or less parallel to the face of the bluff, but consist of a series of arcs where

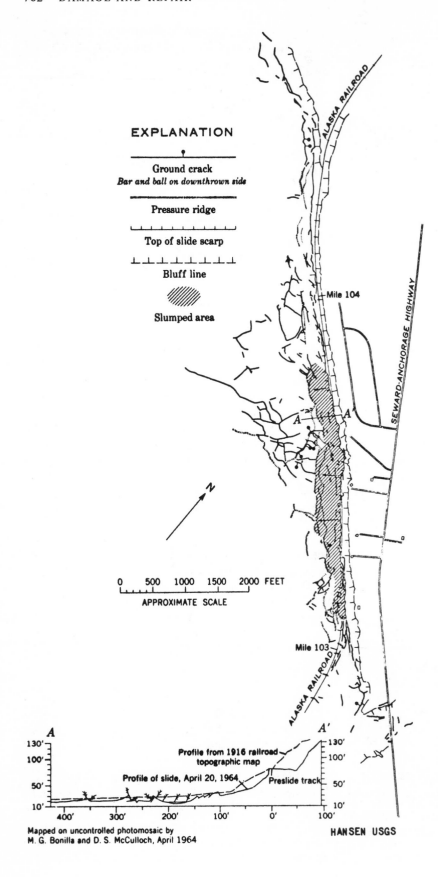

EXPLANATION

Ground crack
Bar and ball on downthrown side

Pressure ridge

Top of slide scarp

Bluff line

Slumped area

Mile 104

ALASKA RAILROAD

SEWARD-ANCHORAGE HIGHWAY

N

0   500   1000   1500   2000 FEET
APPROXIMATE SCALE

Mile 103

ALASKA RAILROAD

A   A'
130'   130'
100'   Profile from 1916 railroad   100'
topographic map
Profile of slide, April 20, 1964   Preslide track
50'   50'
10'   10'
400'   300'   200'   100'   0'   100'

Mapped on uncontrolled photomosaic by
M. G. Bonilla and D. S. McCulloch, April 1964

HANSEN USGS

FIGURE 140   Map and profile of the Potter Hill slide.

FIGURE 141   Potter Hill sediments. Glacial till and coarse gravel overlies stratified sands with interbedded gravel and silt layers. The Naptowne outwash overlies the Knik outwash with gravel content that increases with depth (June 1967).

the landslide movement has been great. The larger pressure ridges are within 400 ft of the track, but a few low ridges extend one-third mi from the track. The low ridges probably formed by essentially horizontal transmittal of stress from the lower parts of the landslides through the frozen upper layer of estuarine silt and thus are only indirectly related to the landslides.

Marginal cracks roughly paralleling the face of the bluff were found in the natural bank material, in the fill up to the level of the tracks, in the roadbed, and in the drainage ditch on the east side of the tracks. At the south end of the bluffs near Rabbit Creek, where the tracks diverge from the bluff face, cracking occurred nearly to the top of the face of the bluff. Cracks were observed and photographed by James A. Morrison on the surface of the bluff about 400 ft east of the edge, approximately opposite station 2886+00. Sand issued from these cracks shortly after the earthquake. North of the point where the tracks turn eastward off the face of the bluffs, marginal cracking, minor landsliding, and pressure ridges occurred along the bluffs and down onto the adjacent flat plain.

Mechanics of the Landslides   The mechanics of the landslides are not known, but from their field observations, McCulloch and Bonilla (1970) assumed that the slide was initiated by flowage of material near the base of the slope and that this resulted in slumping and disintegration of the higher parts of the slope. Flowage may have occurred either in the modern estuarine silt that forms the flat plain at the base of the slope and that carries part of the weight of the roadbed fill, or in the fine silt and sand that forms the lower part of the bluffs. Because the material that accumulated at the base of the slope and on the adjacent flat plain was substantially less than the amount of material removed from the slope by landsliding, they believed that there was flow-

age in the estuarine silt. Pressure ridges in the frozen surface layer of the estuarine silt extended to one-third mi from the base of the slope, suggesting that there was some lateral flowage in the silt. From these observations, McCulloch and Bonilla concluded that the landslides did not occur as a simple rotational failure.

Remedial Measures   If the landslides had been entirely rotational slumps, placing fill on the toe would have helped to stabilize them; because the lower parts of the landslides were flows, however, that treatment would not have avoided recurrent failure and might even have caused future slides. The form and dimensions of the landslides indicated that the estuarine silt had a very low strength and would not provide a suitable foundation on which to rebuild the subgrade. Dumping of fill on the downhill side of the track would have encouraged landsliding because the heads of many of the slides were immediately downhill from the tracks, and the fill would have increased the downhill driving force on the estuarine silt below.

Two alternative methods were suggested for avoiding future failure on this section, which had failed twice during earthquakes and at least once as the result of heavy rains. The first suggestion was to adopt a new alignment well east of the original line. The second suggestion was to retain the present alignment if a thorough soils investigation showed that the cost of building stable grades and the possible purchase of adjacent real estate were not prohibitive. The investigation of the existing alignment was to include an exploratory drilling program, laboratory testing of soils samples, slope-stability analysis, and design of cuts, fills, and drainage systems.

McCulloch and Bonilla (1970) indicated that there could be no satisfactory compromise between these two alternatives if additional failures were to be avoided. The rail laid across the slide area immediately after the earthquake was to be considered only as a temporary measure to be rectified as soon as possible.

The area adjacent to the railroad right-of-way was to be developed into a residential subdivision, which meant that failure along the slope might prove to be costly.

The Alaska Railroad contracted with Clair A. Hill & Associates, civil engineers, to conduct exploration and prepare plans for reconstruction of this section of the railroad. Plans were submitted in August 1964. Figures 142 and 143 are location and topography plates of the slide area, with 10-ft contours showing stationing and boring-hole locations. Figures 144–151 give the auger-hole logs and their legends. Water-bearing strata, where identified, and the elevation of water in the borings after their completion are recorded.

Slide stabilization consisted of the installation of a very comprehensive under-drain system paralleling the new railroad alignment. An interceptor ditch and bench were used

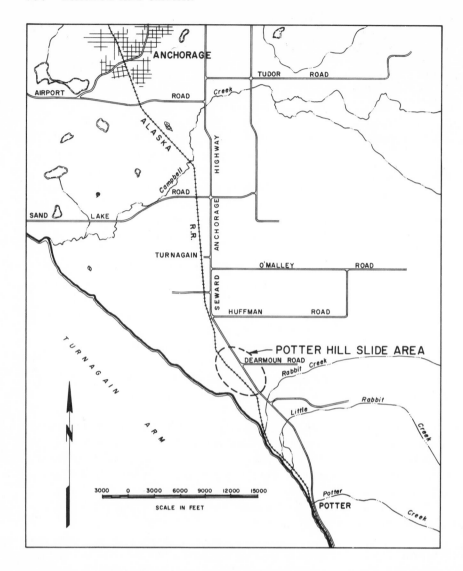

FIGURE 142   Vicinity map of the Potter Hill realignment, The Alaska Railroad.

to prevent surface waters from flowing over the bluff face and washing soil into the ditch directly over the subdrain (Figures 150–152). There was some water seepage from the hillside above the railroad grade before the 1954 earthquake. No seepage occurred between 1954 and 1964, but after the reconstruction was completed, it again became a problem; an additional cribbing and drop inlet was installed to take care of this added flow and to limit bank erosion. The completed construction in 1967 is shown in Figures 151–154.

SUBAQUEOUS SLIDES

Subaqueous slides, which are frequently caused by earthquakes, include the Lowe River Delta slide in Valdez harbor and the Yakutat Bay slides that resulted from the Yakutat Bay earthquake of 1899. Because the great Alaska earthquake occurred in an area surrounded by deposits that were susceptible to liquefaction, it is not surprising that the most

pronounced slides resulting from the earthquake were subaqueous slides. Very large submarine slides were observed at Valdez, Seward, and Whittier. Observations of water boils characteristic of submarine slides were also reported in other portions of the Prince William Sound area. Submarine cable breaks, such as those that occurred in southeastern Alaska, usually result from submarine slides. The mechanism of lacustrine slides at the east end of Kenai Lake as well as at Tazlina Lake, Beluga Lake, Eklutna Lake, and many others, is identical to that of the submarine slides along the seacoasts; these slides are all termed subaqueous slides.

The earthquake-affected area has a large number of inland lakes as well as many hundred miles of coastline, with numerous river and stream deltas, and hundreds of square miles of marine and lacustrine deposits of fine-grained soils that are susceptible to liquefaction. Studies of the Port Valdez slides by Coulter and Migliaccio (1966, and Geology volume), the Seward slides by Shannon and Hilts

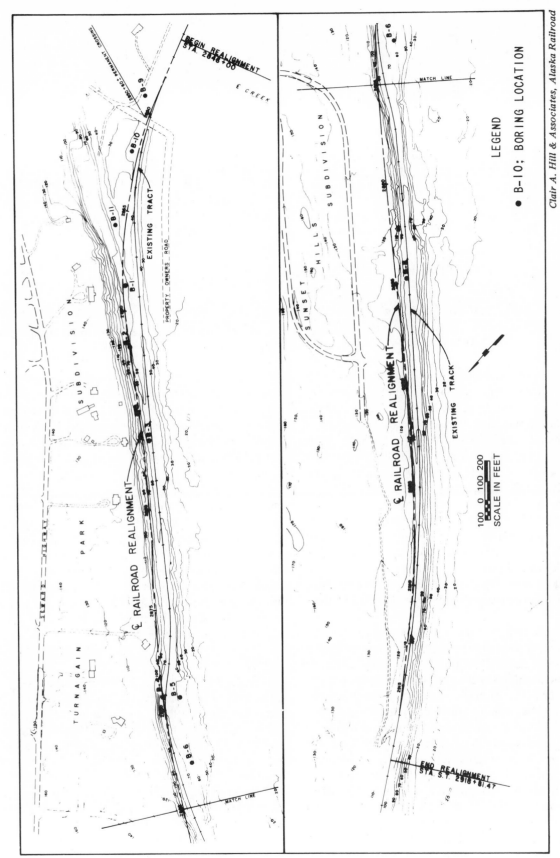

FIGURE 143 Slide topography of the Potter Hill realignment, The Alaska Railroad.

Clair A. Hill & Associates, Alaska Railroad

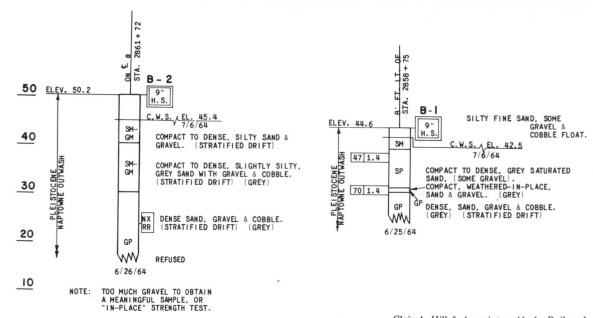

Clair A. Hill & Associates, Alaska Railroad
FIGURE 144   Log of test borings B-2 and B-1, Potter Hill realignment, The Alaska Railroad.

(1973, this volume) and Lemke (1967, and Geology volume), the Kenai Lake slides by McCulloch (1966, and Hydrology volume), the Whittier slides by Kachadoorian (1965, and Geology volume), the lake slides of the Copper River basin by Ferrians (1966), and the Martin–Bering River area lake slides by Tuthill and Laird (1966), all indicate a strong correlation between the subaqueous slides and destructive waves in the lakes, bays, and fiords. In many cases, the highest water and greatest amount of inundation was known to have been preceded by a major submarine slide, followed by waves of declining amplitude. Earthquake-induced subaqueous slides are of particular concern because of the loss of lives and property directly attributable to the even greater destruction that can result from the waves induced by the slides.

Terzaghi and Peck (1953) and Terzaghi (1956) discuss in detail the type of spontaneous liquefaction that can be associated with the submarine landslides. Such slides can be triggered by the initiation of a normal circular slide from delta deposits oversteepening a face (Terzaghi, 1956). Seepage pressures are also an accepted cause of many slides and have the effect of reducing the slope angle at which failure can occur. Nearly all the subaqueous slides resulting from the 1964 Alaska earthquake were subject to seepage pressure originating from groundwater from adjoining mountain slopes and from streams flowing down the valleys that seep into the deltas and adjoining alluvium. In addition, all submarine slides were subjected to the seepage pressures resulting during ebbtide. The tides at areas of submarine failure were near the mean lower low water elevation on the

ebb cycle. At the Valdez, Whittier, and Seward submarine-slide areas, the tide had ebbed 12–13 ft, with strong groundwater seepage in each case. Although the Homer slide was farther from the center of earthquake activity, the spit experienced minor sliding during ebbtide of 17 ft below the previous high tide.

Lacustrine sliding of lake-delta deposits was usually more severe near an active stream channel. The lake-delta deposits are usually formed with very little fluctuation of the water level. Under these conditions the delta deposits can be expected to be in a looser state than delta deposits affected by the fluctuation of the water surface and therefore more sensitive to spontaneous liquefaction. The magnitude of the Beluga Lake lacustrine slide, 145 mi from the epicenter, is an example of the sensitivity of lake deltas to liquefaction and is discussed further later.

Valdez

During the earthquake, the old town of Valdez lost most of its waterfront and the adjacent Lowe River Delta to subaqueous sliding. Further damage was caused by ground subsidence and earth cracking. Figures 155 and 156 show Valdez and the Lowe River Delta before and after the earthquake. The sources of damage influenced the community's decision to move to the Mineral Creek townsite.

Coulter and Migliaccio (1966) reported that the great Yakutat earthquake of 1899, which took place 250 mi east-southeast of Valdez, caused submarine landslides in the Lowe River Delta. The 1899 Yakutat earthquake was reported by Davison (1936) as having had a Richter magni-

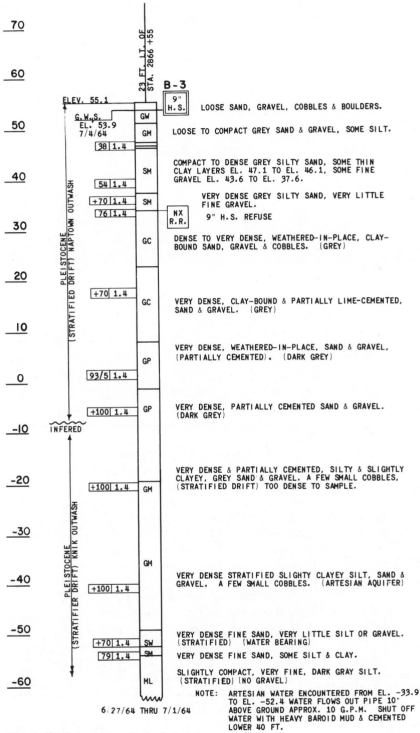

FIGURE 145   Log of test borings B-3,
Potter Hill realignment, The Alaska Railroad.

Clair A. Hill & Associates, Alaska Railroad

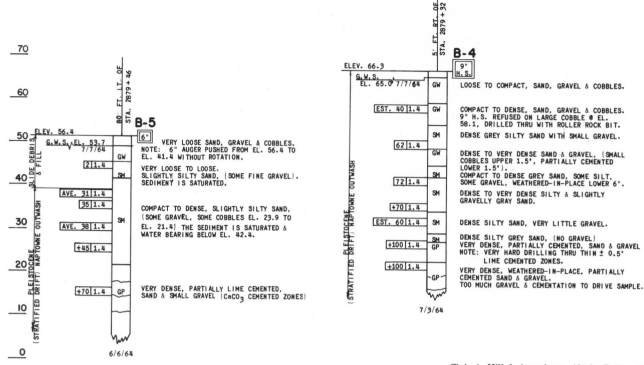

Clair A. Hill & Associates, Alaska Railroad

FIGURE 146   Log of test borings B-5 and B-4, Potter Hill realignment, The Alaska Railroad.

tude greater than 8.5. Heck and Eppley (1958) described it as having a Modified Mercalli Intensity of 11. Tarr and Martin (1914) described the duration as "vigorous shaking continued through three weeks." Valdez was within 40 mi of the epicenter of the 1964 Prince William Sound earthquake. Submarine sliding of the Valdez waterfront began soon after the beginning of the earthquake, according to witnesses and the report by Coulter and Migliaccio (1966):

As the *Chena* was rising, the Valdez dock was in violent motion. Within seconds of the first tremors, the dock broke in two, and the warehouse flipped forward and vanished into an extremely turbulent sea. *Chena* crewmen watched men, women, and children on the dock struggling desperately to get off or to find something to hold on to. None had time to escape.

The repeated raising and bottoming of the SS *Chena* at the Valdez dock may indicate successive sliding in the port area or submarine sliding elsewhere in the Valdez area. Coulter and Migliaccio (1966) give a detailed description of the submarine landslide and the present stability of the Valdez waterfront. Figures 157 and 158 give logs of borings and distribution of cracks and borings in the Valdez area. The massive submarine slide triggered by the earthquake involved 98 million yd³ of material and destroyed the harbor facilities and nearshore installations.

The predicted tide at the time of the earthquake was

approximately 6.2 ft below MSL, or 0 ft MLLW, the water having ebbed 12 ft from the previous high tide. The subaqueous sliding was generally limited to surface elevations below +15 ft MLLW.

Figure 159 shows the preearthquake waterfront in 1963; the immediate postearthquake waterfront is shown in Figure 160. From these photographs, it can be seen that the waterfront structures on piles were lost as part of the slide, whereas the approach fills remained intact. A fill area approximately 200 ft in diameter immediately west of the dock also disappeared with the slide. USC&GS soundings show that sliding was not confined to the Valdez waterfront but included the adjoining Robe River Delta (Valdez is built on older portions of this delta) and the interlaced Lowe River Delta immediately southeast (Figure 156).

The relation between soil density, overburden pressures, and liquefaction is a matter of concern in soil mechanics. The Valdez waterfront slide had a very unusual chance to show the effect of these parameters. At the time of the earthquake, three large stacks of 75-lb railroad rail, salvaged from the Copper River Railroad, were lying on the outer edge of the south end of the West Dock approach fill (Figures 159–161). Neither this heavily loaded approach fill nor the last dock approach fill failed as a result of the earthquake, although a comparison of a picture taken in 1954 (Figure 162) to a picture taken after the earthquake (Figure 163) indicates that 750 ft of the end of Shoup Spit failed. A 500-ft-wide section near the base of the spit also failed. Shoup Spit is located at the west end of the north side of Valdez Arm.

Whittier

The predicted tide at the time of the earthquake at Whittier was approximately –6.5 ft MSL or –0.2 ft MLLW and had ebbed 13 ft below the previous high tide. The Whittier-Passage Canal area before the earthquake is shown in Figures 164 and 165; a postearthquake view of the area is

shown in Figures 166–168. The subaqueous sliding included the east end of the airfield and a piece of land adjoining the FAA facility, both of which extended into the west end of Passage Canal. On the south side of the canal, two docks and their approach causeways were lost by the slide or by the tsunamis that followed.

The submarine landslides have been described by Kachadoorian (1965).

The profiles of the slides and submarine slopes are shown in Figure 169, and the changes in degree of slope are shown in Figure 170 (Kachadoorian, 1965).

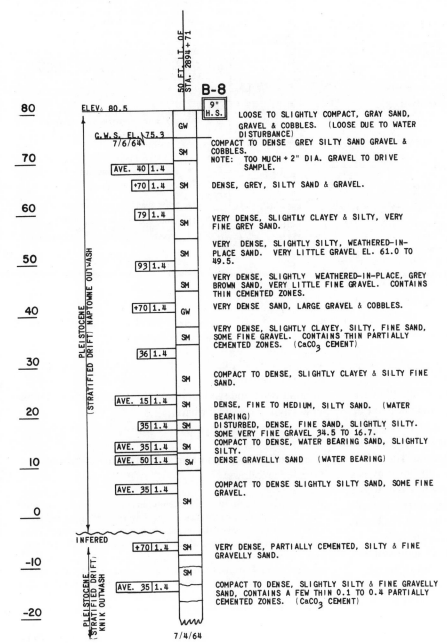

FIGURE 147 Log of test borings B-8, Potter Hill realignment, The Alaska Railroad.

Clair A. Hill & Associates, Alaska Railroad

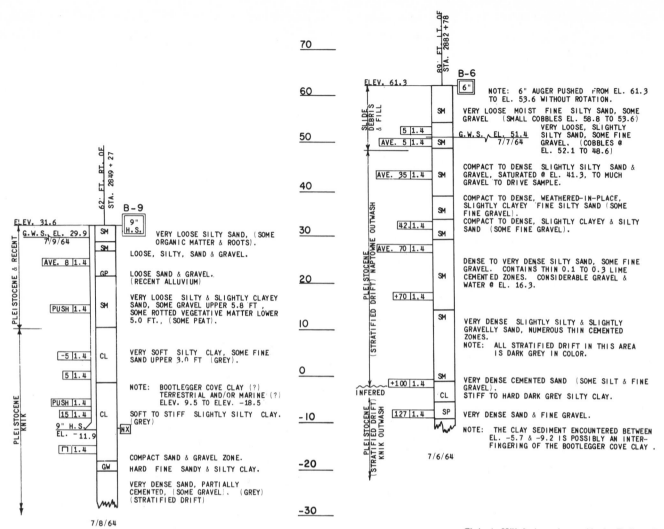

Clair A. Hill & Associates, Alaska Railroad

FIGURE 148   Log of test borings B-9 and B-6, Potter Hill realignment, The Alaska Railroad.

In Figure 169, the slide off the east side of the Whittier fan can be seen centered at approximately the midpoint of the marginal wharf. During construction of this wharf by the Corps of Engineers, the loss of bearing with lagged 14-in. H pile indicated high subsurface water pressure. The existence of high subsurface flows was partly confirmed by negligible salinity and by the very low preconsolidation, which had been indicated by undisturbed samples of stratified silt and fine sand layers obtained from a depth of 75 ft. Wharf piling was extended in depth and the amount of lagging was increased to develop the required bearing. Examination of the wharf since the earthquake has shown that it has not been affected by the subaqueous slides. The most easterly slide shown in Figure 169 failed at the portion of the marginal wharf that showed the least pile resistance during construction. This closest slide undoubtedly took place in co-

hesionless silt and sand and possibly in some gravel that also underlay the marginal wharf.

Seward

Shannon & Wilson report on subsurface investigations (1964c) as follows:

An extensive and massive subaqueous landslide caused by the Good Friday earthquake occurred along the Seward waterfront and was responsible for much of the damage to waterfront structures. The slide and seismic sea waves which followed completed the destruction of the waterfront.

The subaqueous landslides are believed to have started as conventional circular slides, which then liquified and became flow slides moving large distances and distributing the slide debris as a thin layer over the floor of the bay at depths too great to detect its presence. It is considered probable that failure was progressive and thus successive slides developed as the earthquake continued through its unusually long 4-minute duration. The Seward waterfront is presently stable under static conditions with the exception that beach flattening will occur within the tidal range, including some localized sliding in oversteepened slopes. Under dynamic conditions the Seward waterfront is considered unstable. The cracked and fissured ground landward of the present waterfront roughly outlines an area which may be engulfed in a future slide triggered by another great earthquake. Another area of subsidence and cracking similar in extent also probably will develop behind a future slide.

At the head of Resurrection Bay, planned new port facilities in the northwest sector should be located with adequate setback from the existing scarp of the subaqueous landslide to allow for the occurrence of additional earthquake-triggered slides. A future great earthquake will result in land subsidence of the order of several feet with significantly greater subsidence of ground on which heavy earth fills are placed.

Somewhat better subsurface conditions may exist in the northeast sector of the bay, but further explorations are required if this area is developed.

Forest Acres, a subdivision of Seward, was damaged in the earthquake by fissuring and sand boils. This area is considered stable under static conditions but susceptible to a repetition of fissuring and sand boils during another great earthquake.

The earthquake and subaqueous sliding followed a predicted tide of –0.5 ft MLLW or –6.0 ft MSL; the tide had ebbed 11.6 ft since the previous high tide. Failure of the waterfront soils was limited to soil with surface elevations below 20 ft relative to MLLW. The failures occurring in the northwest sector of Resurrection Bay had surface elevations at or below MLLW.

Seward and the northwest corner of Resurrection Bay 1 year before the earthquake are shown in Figure 171. Figures 172–174 are views of Seward and its waterfront after the earthquake. A comparison of the failure scarp in the Army dock area before and after the earthquake is shown in Figure 175. The postearthquake point of land protruding from the shore adjacent to the intersection of Jefferson Street with the shoreline shows a remarkable similarity to the point formed by the Lowell Creek flume (Figure 176), which preceded the diversion of Lowell Creek south of Seward through a tunnel and which also preceded the construction of the Army dock. Figure 177 shows the effect of the subaqueous sliding and tectonic settlement on

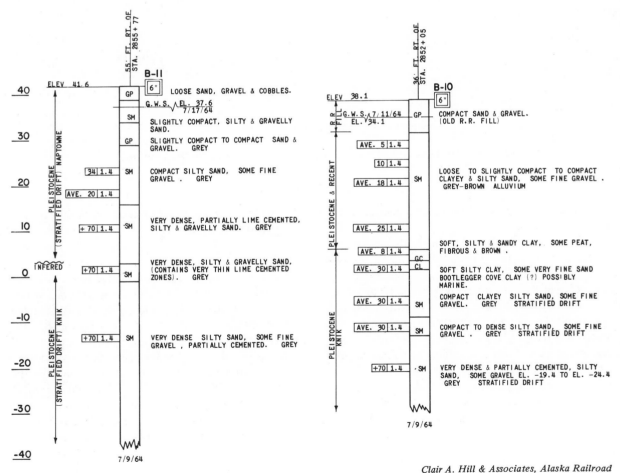

Clair A. Hill & Associates, Alaska Railroad

FIGURE 149   Log of test borings B-11 and B-10, Potter Hill realignment, The Alaska Railroad.

ROTARY - BORING

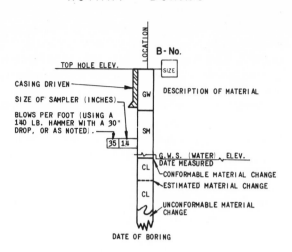

SOIL CONSISTENCY CLASSIFICATION

CONSISTENCY		BLOWS PER. FT.
GRANULAR	COHESIVE	
VERY LOOSE	VERY SOFT	0 TO 5
LOOSE	SOFT	5 TO 10
SLIGHTLY COMPACT	STIFF	10 TO 20
COMPACT	VERY STIFF	20 TO 35
DENSE	HARD	35 TO 70
VERY DENSE	VERY HARD	70

* (STANDARD PENETRATION TEST)
BLOWS PER FT. (140 LB. HAMMER,
30" FREE-FALL BLOW USING A 2"
O.D. X 1 3/8" I.D. SAMPLER).

LEGEND OF DRILLING, SAMPLING & TESTING OPERATIONS

- ● PLAN OF ANY BORING
- (SIZE) PENETROMETER (FLUSH-COUPLED)
- ● 2 1/4" CONE PENETROMETER
- [SIZE] SAMPLER BORING (DRY)
- [SIZE] ROTARY BORING (WET)
- [SIZE] AUGER BORING (DRY)
- [SIZE] JET BORING
- ◇ DIAMOND CORE BORING
- [ ] TEST PIT

BIT SIZES; (O. D.): "AX" = 1 13/16", "BX" = 2 9/32", "NX" = 2 29/32".

CASING SIZES; (O. D.): "BX" = 2 7/8", "NX" = 3 1/2".

NOTES:

H. S. = HOLLOW STEM AUGER

R. R. = ROLLER ROCK BIT

CLASSIFICATION BY THE UNIFIED SOIL CLASSIFICATION SYSTEM.

Clair A. Hill & Associates, Alaska Railroad

FIGURE 150   Log of test boring legends, Potter Hill realignment, The Alaska Railroad.

the waterfront area of the small-boat harbor and the San Juan dock.

The Alaska Railroad dock was rebuilt in the northwest corner of Resurrection Bay (Figure 178). Figure 179 shows the same area 10 months before the earthquake. A longitudinal profile of the dock subsoil is shown in Figure 180. The discontinuity in soil structure shown between bents 15 and 20 extended across the structures and may represent an old graben or a trench where a stream channel cut through the denser surface soils and later refilled with finer material. Pile-driving resistance is depicted graphically; split-spoon penetration resistance and soil types are represented by applicable numbers and letters, respectively. The piles, similar to those used for the construction of the Whittier dock, were 14-in. 73-lb steel H piles with 12 X 14-in. spruce lagging on each side of the web; piles were driven with a model D-520 link-belt diesel hammer. The dock area was far enough north to ensure that another slide similar to the one in 1964 would

not include the dock area. Densification of the dock subsoil from pile-driving would also limit future liquefaction of soils.

Homer

Submarine sliding at Homer was limited to the outer end of the small-boat harbor. The small-boat harbor at low tide before the earthquake is shown in Figure 181, and a similar view at low tide after the earthquake in Figure 182. Another small submerged slide may have occurred at the end of the spit. Figure 183 was taken at a higher tide elevation 18 days after the earthquake. At the time of the earthquake, the tide was at 2.7 ft MLLW or −6.9 ft MSL. The tide had ebbed 17 ft from its previous high. Both slides occurred in areas of recent deposition of littoral sand and gravels and along the steeper seaward slopes. Equally steep slopes between the two slide areas had experienced some erosion in recent years after the construction of the small-boat harbor and possibly were not affected by as much recent littoral drift. Explora-

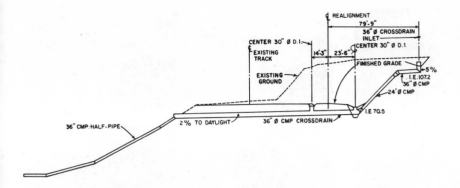

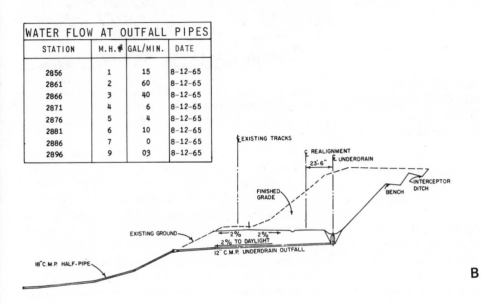

WATER FLOW AT OUTFALL PIPES			
STATION	M.H.#	GAL/MIN.	DATE
2856	1	15	8-12-65
2861	2	60	8-12-65
2866	3	40	8-12-65
2871	4	6	8-12-65
2876	5	4	8-12-65
2881	6	10	8-12-65
2886	7	0	8-12-65
2896	9	03	8-12-65

SCALE IN FEET

FIGURE 151 (A) Station 2894+00 and (B) a typical underdrain outfall profile. Potter Hill realignment, The Alaska Railroad.

Clair A. Hill & Associates, Alaska Railroad

FIGURE 152 Interceptor ditch and bench, Potter Hill railroad re-alignment, locking downgrade to southeast (June 1967).

FIGURE 153 Drop inlet along interceptor ditch near west upgrade end of Potter Hill railroad realignment (June 1967).

Air Photo Tech, Inc.

FIGURE 154   Potter Hill realignment after completion.

tion indicated that failure probably occurred at a depth of
10–25 ft in sand with scattered pebbles. The underlying soil
was probably sandy gravel or gravelly sand.

The breakwater had a maximum elevation of 27 ft above
MLLW with a top width of 8 ft and side slopes of 1.5 : 1.

The Homer Spit is discussed by Waller (1966, and Geology volume).

Kenai Lake

Sublacustrine slides occurred at numerous locations around
Kenai Lake. Most of these slides were investigated by
McCulloch (1966) and are of interest because of their size
and their nearness to the road, railroad, and adjoining home
sites and because they initiated waves in the ice-covered
lake that had greater damage potential than the slides
themselves.

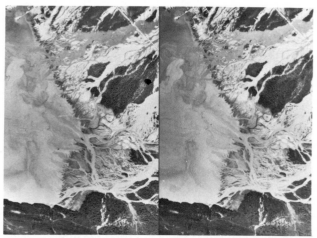

U.S. Coast and Geodetic Survey

FIGURE 155   Valdez waterfront, with Robe and Lowe River deltas,
10 years before the 1964 earthquake (July 27, 1954). Scale: 1 in. =
3,400 ft.

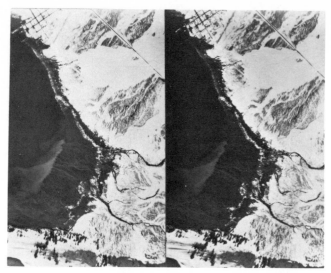

U.S. Coast and Geodetic Survey

FIGURE 156   Postearthquake Valdez with Robe and Lowe River
deltas (April 4, 1964). Scale: 1 in. = 3,400 ft.

In the past, many waves that may have been caused by
earth slides may have been incorrectly attributed to seiche
effects. Seiches are periodic oscillations of a body of water
that can be caused by many factors including earthquakes.
Seiches in Kenai Lake were generated by a 3-ft tilting of the
lake bed combined with earthquake oscillations. McCulloch
calculates from observations by Mrs. Hadley Roberts at
Lawing (east end of east–west section of Kenai Lake) that
seiche waves reached a height of 10 ft; he also reports that
backfill waves from the sublacustrine slides reached a height
of 30 ft at Lawing. Seiche waves on the west side of Ship
Creek Delta (south side, central section of Kenai Lake)
reached a height of 30 ft. Backfill waves from sublacustrine
sliding on the east side of this delta reached a height of 26
ft, whereas the far-shore wave from this same slide, impinging on the north Kenai Lake bank opposite the Ship
Creek Delta, reached a height of 72 ft. Nearly all the creek
and river deltas experienced sublacustrine sliding or slumping with slides at Ship Creek (Figure 184); Trail River
(Lawing) (Figures 185–186); and Rocky Creek (Boulder
Creek) and Lakeview (Victory Creek) deltas (Figure 187–190),
which were particularly large. All the deltas were composed
of coarse-grained materials with a predominance of gravel-
sized material. Aerial photographs (Figures 185–188) show
a predominance of broken ice in all the areas of subaqueous
sliding. This characteristic was used in evaluating other major
slide areas in which bottom topography was not available.

McCulloch and Bonilla (1970) observed that a sublacustrine landslide at Kenai Lake had removed 261 ft of
track and roadbed (from station 1126+39 to station 1126
+00) from the alluvial fan at Rocky Creek (also known as
Boulder Creek). Several other smaller landslides occurred at

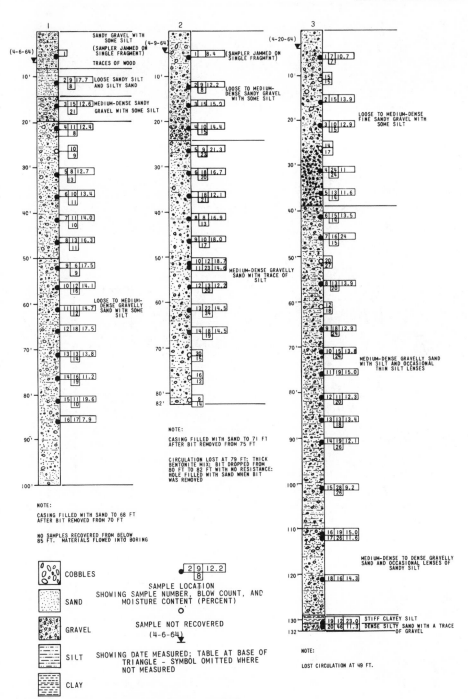

FIGURE 157   Logs of borings in the Valdez area.

Henry W. Coulter and Ralph R. Migliaccio, USGS

the margin of the fan, and the fan was severely fractured (Figure 191). The roadbed on either side of the slide passes through the zone of deep fractures.

Remedial Measures   Because of the steep underwater slope shown by soundings and because the roadbed adjacent to the slide ran through the zone of deep fractures, McCulloch and Bonilla strongly recommended that a new alignment be adopted on or east of the line indicated on Figure 191. Because of the very doubtful condition of the roadbed adjacent to the slide, any temporary use of the present alignment was discouraged. Rolling stock running over this portion of the roadbed might have produced an additional and perhaps rapid landslide. They warned that waste material from cuts should not be placed on the fractured ground because it might initiate new landslides.

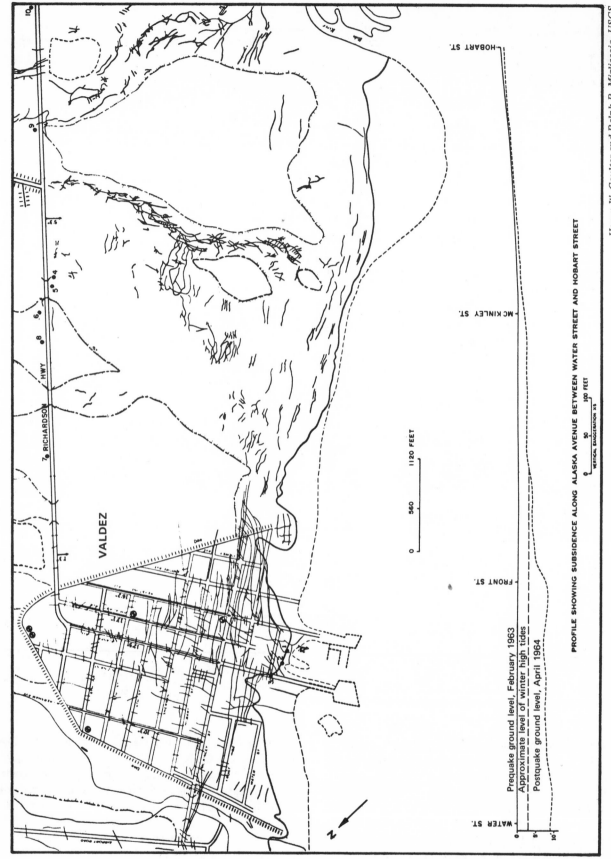

PROFILE SHOWING SUBSIDENCE ALONG ALASKA AVENUE BETWEEN WATER STREET AND HOBART STREET

VERTICAL EXAGGERATION X5

———— Prequake ground level, February 1963
— — — Approximate level of winter high tides
–·–·– Postquake ground level, April 1964

FIGURE 158 Plan showing distribution of cracks and boring locations, Valdez area.

Henry W. Coulter and Ralph R. Migliaccio, USGS

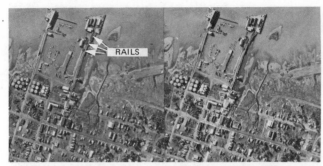

Bureau of Land Management

FIGURE 159   Valdez waterfront 6 months before the 1964 earthquake. Railroad rails are stacked on the west dock-approach fill (September 23, 1963). Scale: 1 in. = 1,000 ft.

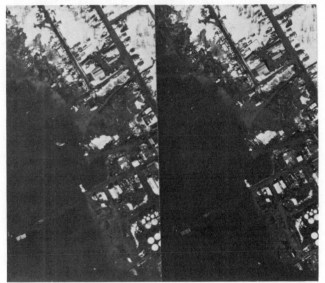

Alaska State Housing Authority

FIGURE 160   Valdez postearthquake waterfront at MHHW. Rail stacks protrude above submerged fill (April 11, 1964, 11:52 a.m.). Scale: 1 in. = 500 ft.

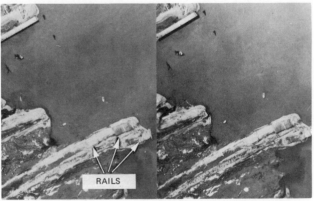

Air Photo Tech, Inc.

FIGURE 161   Valdez postearthquake waterfront. Approach fill supporting stacks of rail piling did not fail (June 13, 1964). Scale: 1 in. = 250 ft.

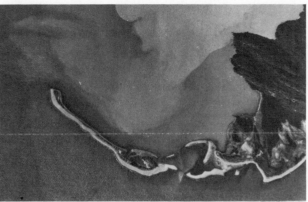

U.S. Coast and Geodetic Survey

FIGURE 162   Shoup Spit, Valdez Arm, before the earthquake (July 27, 1954). Scale: 1 in. = 1,300 ft.

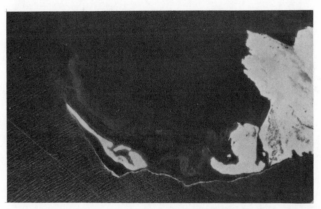

U.S. Coast and Geodetic Survey

FIGURE 163   Shoup Spit, Valdez, after the earthquake, +2.4 ft MLLW predicted tide. Apparent loss of 750 ft from end of spit and up to 500 ft of width near the base of the spit (April 4, 1964). Scale: 1 in. = 1,200 ft.

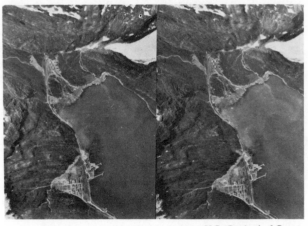

U.S. Geological Survey

FIGURE 164   Head of Passage Canal and Port of Whittier during construction (August 7, 1950). Scale: 1 in. = 4,000 ft.

FIGURE 165   Port of Whittier 6 months before the 1964 earthquake (September 23, 1963). Scale: 1 in. = 1,000 ft.

The fracturing changed progressively from the margin of the fan toward its apex. At the edge of the fan, landsliding occurred along the fractures. Just behind the fan's edge, the fractures were deep and bounded blocks that had been dropped down.

Further up the slope, as far as the highway, the fractures were relatively shallow and probably indicated downslope movement of the surface layer, which was frozen at the time of the earthquake.

A profile of the soundings that were made offshore from the landslide that removed the roadbed is shown in Figure 192.

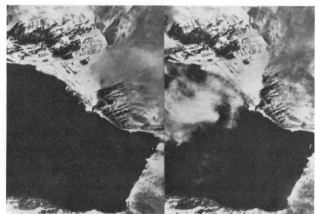

FIGURE 167   Head of Passage Canal and Port of Whittier after the earthquake. Subaqueous slides originated along port delta and the head of Passage Canal at the lower right. Point protruding into water is remnant of Whittier airstrip. Toe of Leonard Glacier avalanche is at the lower right (April 3, 1964). Scale: 1 in. = 3,400 ft.

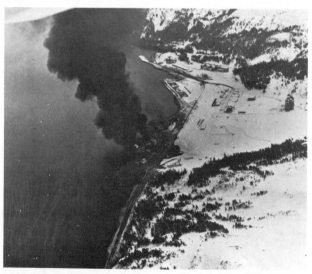

FIGURE 166   Port of Whittier after destruction of commercial port facilities by subaqueous sliding and tsunamis. The waves that caused the greatest destruction probably originated as a backfill wave from the subaqueous sliding (March 29, 1964).

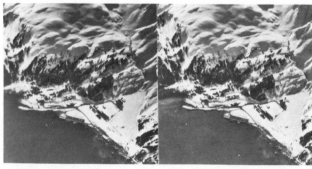

FIGURE 168   Port of Whittier after the earthquake. Subaqueous sliding occurred along entire delta face. Subsoil varied from coarse cohesionless silt to coarse gravels (April 15, 1964). Scale: 1 in. = 3,200 ft.

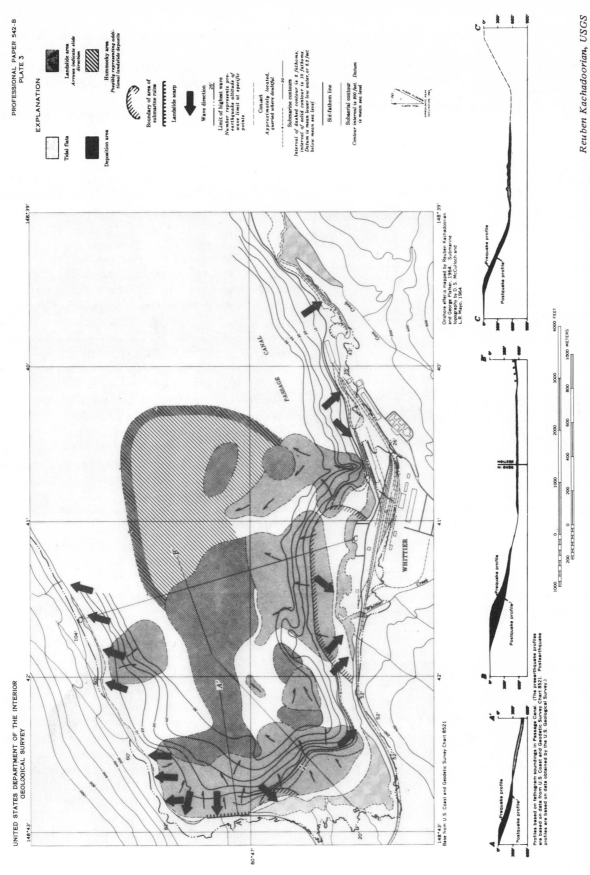

UNITED STATES DEPARTMENT OF THE INTERIOR
GEOLOGICAL SURVEY

PROFESSIONAL PAPER 542-B
PLATE 3

EXPLANATION

Tidal flats

Deposition area

Landslide area
Arrows indicate slide direction

Hummocky area
Possibly representing additional landslide deposits

Boundary of area of submarine ruins

Landslide scarp

Wave direction

26'
Limit of highest wave
Number represents prequake altitude of wave limit at specific points

Contact
Approximately located, queried where doubtful

Submarine contours
Interval of dashed contour is 8 fathoms, interval of solid contour is 10 fathoms. Datum is mean low water, or 6.5 feet below mean sea level

Six-fathom line

Subaerial contour
Contour interval is 200 feet. Datum is mean sea level

Base from U. S. Coast and Geodetic Survey Chart 8521

Onshore effects mapped by Reuben Kachadoorian and George Plafker, 1964. Submarine topography by D. S. McCulloch and L. R. Mayo, 1964

Profiles based on fathogram soundings in Passage Canal. (The prequake profiles are based on data from U. S. Coast and Geodetic Survey Chart 8521. Postearthquake profiles are based on data obtained by the U. S. Geological Survey.)

Reuben Kachadoorian, USGS

FIGURE 169 Map of Whittier, Alaska, showing postearthquake submarine topography, wave height, wave direction, submarine ruined areas, and profiles.

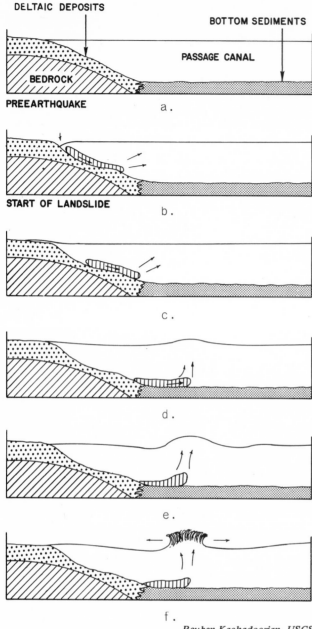

DELTAIC DEPOSITS

BOTTOM SEDIMENTS

PASSAGE CANAL

BEDROCK

PREEARTHQUAKE

a.

START OF LANDSLIDE

b.

c.

d.

e.

f.

Reuben Kachadoorian, USGS

FIGURE 170 Waves formed by subaqueous sliding.

be extremely difficult to place and maintain a fill in the area removed by the slide.

Realignment and reconstruction of damaged and lost portions of the railroad track at Rocky (Boulder) Creek were completed in 1965.

Profiles of the slide from fathometer soundings are shown in Figure 185 (line A–A') for the Trail River-Lawing area, in Figure 193 for the Lakeview (Victory Creek; line 72+94) and Rocky (Boulder) Creek area (line 89), and in Figure 194 (lines 53, 56, and section A–A') for the Ship Creek area. McCulloch (1966) has tabulated the physical characteristics and potential energy of the slides (Figure 195).

Bradley Lake

Bradley Lake is the site of a proposed hydroelectric project. It is in the Kenai Mountains northeast of Homer with a lake-surface elevation of 1,090 ft. The east end of the lake in 1950 is shown in Figure 196. Severely broken ice in the vicinity of the only major river delta that extends into the lake is shown in Figure 197 (taken May 30, 1964). The exposed soil at the mouth of the glacial river is predominantly sand and silt. Although the lake level is lower because of less runoff in late winter, Figure 197 shows that the delta has noticeably retreated from the location shown in Figure 196. The part of the delta most affected is adjacent to the present river channel as it enters into the lake. The ice was not broken at the west or outlet end of the lake. The epicenter of the earthquake was approximately 140 mi to the northeast. The interpolated zone plane of rupture, however, was 60–70 mi southeast of the lake.

Beluga Lake

Figure 198 shows broken ice and soil fracturing, possibly related to sublacustrine sliding of the Triumvirate Glacier river delta, at the west end of Beluga Lake. These slides occurred 145 mi from the epicenter of the earthquake and an equivalent distance from the closest portion of the interpreted zone of rupture. This large delta consists primarily of sand and gravel and shows little evidence of silts. Failure appears to have been magnified along the delta near the present stream channel.

Eklutna Lake

Eklutna Lake, fed by glacial streams and approximately 6 mi long, is a source of hydroelectric power. It lies 30 mi northeast of Anchorage in the Chugach Mountains and approximately 53 mi north-northwest of the epicenter of the earthquake. During the winter, when stream flows are at a minimum, the water level of the lake is lowered as much as 50 ft for power generation. Several slides occurred along the north shoreline of the lake (Figure 199) that were not associated with an existing stream flowing into the lake, but seem to have occurred at the base of a talus and old alluvial cones.

At the preearthquake center line of the track, the track was about 12 ft above the water, which was 9 ft deep; at the former shoreline the water was 52 ft deep. The lake bottom sloped away from this point at a slope of about 32 percent for approximately 100 ft and had a 27 percent slope for an additional 150 ft.

A slope of 32 percent is either equal to or slightly steeper than the stable slope for unconsolidated sediments deposited under water. Subaqueous stable slopes are thought to be nearer 28 percent. Because of the steep slope found by the soundings, McCulloch and Bonilla concluded that it would

FIGURE 171   Seward and vicinity 10 months before the 1964 earthquake. Tidal elevation is 4.1 ft M L L W, or −1.4 ft M S L (May 29, 1963). Scale: 1 in. = 1,800 ft.

FIGURE 172   Seward after the earthquake. Subaqueous sliding along waterfront and destruction by tsunamis (April 15, 1964). Scale: 1 in. = 1,300 ft.

FIGURE 173   Seward waterfront after destructive subaqueous sliding and tsunamis.

FIGURE 174   Seward waterfront scarp line from subaqueous sliding after the earthquake (1964).

U.S. Army and Bureau of Land Management

FIGURE 175   Before and after views of Army Dock area at foot of Jefferson Street, Seward. A preearthquake view of the Army Dock is at left; the postearthquake point of land (right photos) approximates the outfall location of the Lowell Creek flume (May 29, 1963). Scale: 1 in. = 330 ft.

Tazlina Lake

Tazlina Lake, on the north slope of the Chugach Mountains, is 20 mi long; its southern end is approximately 63 mi north-northeast of the earthquake epicenter. The lake is fed from the south by braided streams from the Tazlina Glacier. The Nelchina River enters Tazlina Lake at its northwest

Robert Zentmire

FIGURE 176   Seward alluvial fan in 1939, before construction of the Lowell Creek flume, with torrential deposition from Lowell Creek after a flood. Note similarity of shape to the portion that did not fail at the foot of Jefferson Street in Figure 175 (1939).

quadrant; the outlet of the lake is at the east end of the northeast arm of the lake. The delta at the south end of the lake within 1.5-2 mi of the glacier is expected to consist of coarse material; no failures were evident in that portion of the lake. The Nelchina River Delta is 40-50 mi from the Nelchina Glacier and has a gradient of approximately 600 ft along 45 mi of river between the glacier and Tazlina Lake. The Nelchina River Delta is 68-70 mi from the earthquake epicenter.

Ferrians (1966) describes the sublacustrine failures of the Nelchina River Delta in Tazlina Lake as follows:

The position and character of the water–delta interface in 1948 as compared with the position and scalloped character of the postearthquake interface indicate that not only was there subsidence but large segments of the delta front slid into the lake. This sublacustrine landsliding generated large waves that severely fractured the ice on the northern part of the lake and stranded large blocks of ice above water level along the shore. Large quantities of sediment and ice were discharged through the outlet of the lake into the channel of Tazlina River. *Similar sublacustrine landsliding occurred off the fronts of deltas in Klutina Lake and in Tonsina Lake.* [Figure 200].

The Nelchina River Delta in Tazlina Lake after the earthquake is shown in Figure 201. A point opposite and east of the Nelchina Delta with a slide area just south of the point is shown in Figure 202. The ice fracturing indicates that this was a subaqueous slide that retrograded into the stream delta. Heavy shore-ice breakage and shoreline scarps at other places along the shore could indicate other small subaqueous slides.

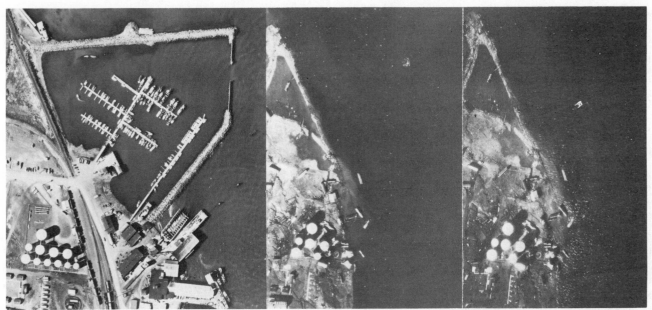

U.S. Army and Bureau of Land Management

FIGURE 177   Before and after, Seward small-boat harbor and San Juan Dock. The main line of the railroad closely approximates the scarp line of the subaqueous failure north of the Lowell Creek Delta (May 29, 1963). Scale: 1 in. = 330 ft.

Martin–Bering River Areas

Subaqueous landslides in the Martin and Bering river area east of the Copper River (Figures 203–205) are described by Tuthill and Laird (1966):

Lakes in the Martin-Bering Rivers area have been divided into two types on the basis of their bathymetric configuration. Lakes of the first type have slopes of about 10° or more around most of their shorelines and have average depths of 70–120 feet. Their bottoms are relatively flat. Tokun Lake, Lake Charlotte, and Kushtaka Lake are examples of this type. The second type of lake is extremely shallow throughout, depths rarely exceeding 6 feet. These lakes have been filled by outwash sediments from either the Martin or the Bering River. Bering Lake and Martin Lake are examples.

Little Martin Lake is intermediate between the two types. The western half of the lake is filled by outwash sediments from the Martin River to within 6–15 feet of its surface, and the eastern half

Bureau of Land Management

FIGURE 178   New Alaska Railroad Dock on the east side of the new small-boat harbor and ferry terminal. The dock was built closer to the shore so that a future subaqueous failure would not encroach on the dock (May 28, 1966). Scale: 1 in. = 800 ft.

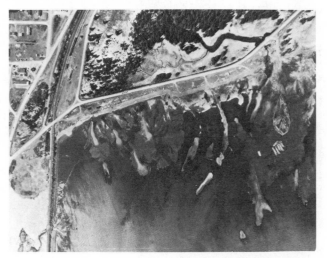

Bureau of Land Management

FIGURE 179   Preearthquake view of northwest Resurrection Bay at location of new small-boat harbor, constructed in 1965, and the new Alaska Railroad Dock, constructed in 1966 (May 29, 1963). Scale: 1 in. = 350 ft.

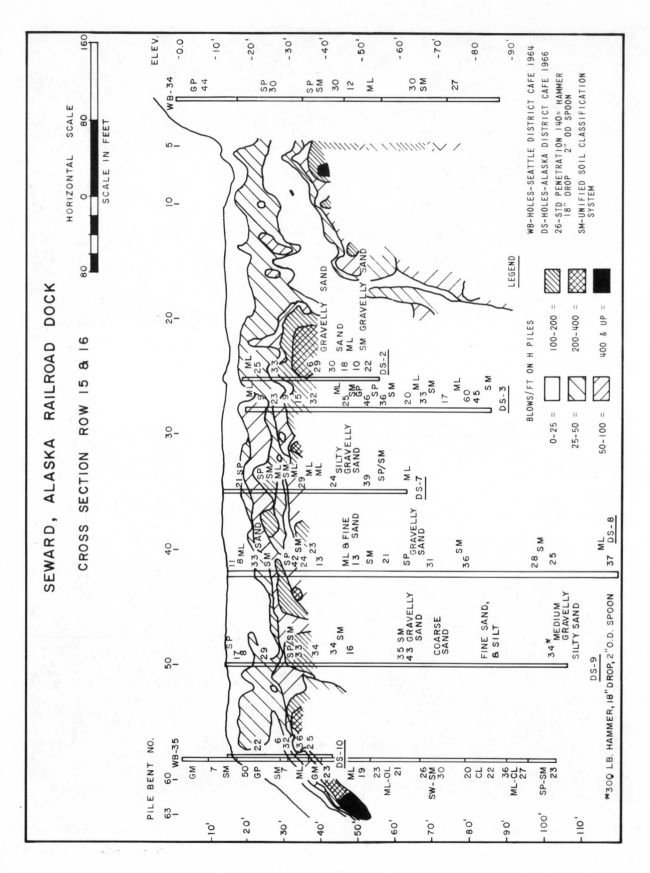

FIGURE 180 Seward, Alaska Railroad Dock. Longitudinal profile of the dock subsoil.

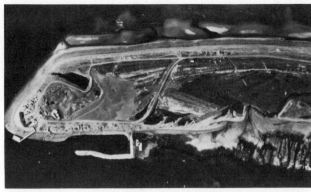

U.S. Coast and Geodetic Survey

FIGURE 181   End of Homer Spit and small-boat harbor before the earthquake. Littoral drift is from the top right (northwest) around the end of the spit. Drift to the right of the small-boat harbor is sand; gravel drift is still present (left) (July 1, 1962). Scale: 1 in. = 630 ft.

attains depths of 50 feet. Slopes in the eastern part of the lake are as high as 18°.

Subaqueous landslides occurred in the deltaic sediments of all lakes of the first type. The most detailed study was made of Tokun Lake [Figure 203]. The western shore of Tokun Lake consists of outwash sediments and in 1963 had a very low gradient. The north and south shores are steep and are composed of angular boulders and cobbles. Three streams enter Tokun Lake and have formed deltas having steep distal faces. All these deltas slid, presumably triggered by the earthquake. The largest slide in Tokun Lake involved the sediments deposited by Tokun Creek in the eastern quarter of the lake.

The landslides generated waves which fractured lake ice and modified the shores by overturning many flagstones along the southwestern shore. Algae which normally grow on the upper surface of submerged rocks were found on the lower side of these rocks, and dead aquatic insect pupae and larvae were observed on their upper surface. Lake ice and water set in motion by the subaqueous landslides in the opposite (eastern) end of the lake probably overturned the flagstones.

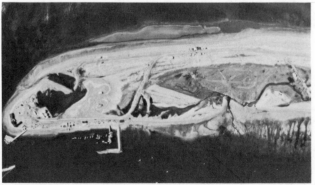

Bureau of Land Management

FIGURE 182   End of Homer Spit and small-boat harbor after the earthquake. End of the small-boat harbor breakwater that failed because of subaqueous sliding. Failure probably occurred in the more recent littoral-drift materials of lower density. Tide is −0.7 M L L W, which is equivalent to 5.0 M L L W preearthquake tide (July 1, 1964). Scale: 1 in. = 630 ft.

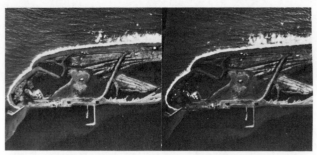

U.S. Coast and Geodetic Survey

FIGURE 183   End of Homer Spit and small-boat harbor 18 days after the earthquake (April 14, 1964). Scale: 1 in. = 1,270 ft.

Lake Charlotte has six inlet streams. The largest of these is the melt-water distributary from the Lake Charlotte lobe of the Martin River glacier at the northeastern end of the lake; a large subaqueous slide in its delta lengthened the shoreline 80 feet and increased the area of the lake by approximately 5.1×10^4 square feet (2.1 percent of the 1962 area). In 1962 the shoreline was 29,385 feet in length. The sliding of the delta front of the outwash plain at the northeast end of the lake increased the shoreline by 165 feet. The sliding of other deltas built out into the lake reduced the shoreline by 120 feet so that the 1964 shoreline measured 29,430 feet. . . . [The bathymetric changes in the northeast part of the lake are shown in Figure 204.]

At the extreme southeastern end of the shore a delta of angular gravel and sand slid. Mature Sitka spruce trees remained upright and rooted in the proximal part of the subaqueous slide—the upper parts of their trunks remaining above the surface of the lake.

A wave generated by this slide caused lake ice to strike the boles of trees and scuff and strip off the bark 3–6 feet above the scarp of the slump, and approximately 11 feet above the July 6 water level.

All the other deltas in Lake Charlotte slid. The one formed by the stream which drains the lake at an altitude of 319 feet, north of Lake Charlotte, modified the bathymetry of the central part of the lake.

Kushtaka Lake, like Lake Charlotte is formed behind a terminal moraine and is fed by melt-water streams from the Kushtaka lobe of the Martin River glacier. In late July 1963 the delta formed by this drainage had slopes (based on depths 100 meters from shore) as high as 11°. The entire front of this delta slid, and slopes were changed to about 40° by this one subaqueous landslide. . . . [Figure 205 shows bathymetric modifications of northern end of Kushtaka Lake and front of delta.]

The shallow lakes of the second type exhibited some settling of gravel bars and deltas, but showed no indication of subaqueous slides. The lack of steep free slopes on the distal faces of these bars and deltas no doubt explains their stability even during what must have been rather severe shaking.

SNOW AVALANCHING

Snow avalanching (La Chapelle, 1968), a common occurrence in alpine areas, occurred through most of the earthquake-affected area but was most prominent in the Prince William Sound area and adjoining mountains (Figures 206 and 207). Extensive avalanching also occurred along The

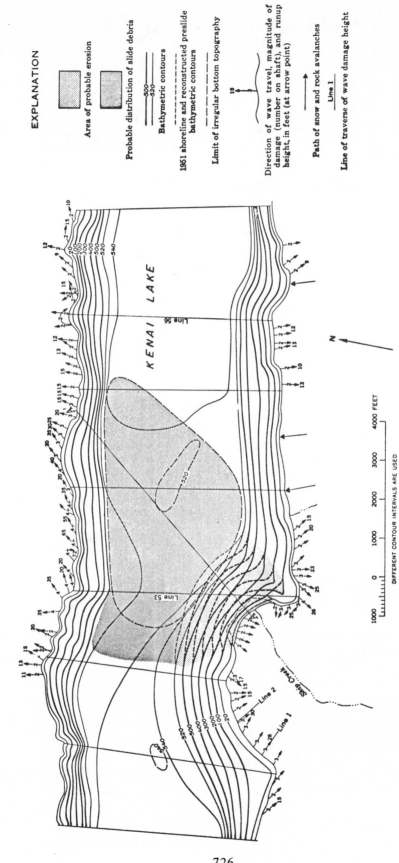

EXPLANATION

Area of probable erosion

Probable distribution of slide debris

———500——— Bathymetric contours
———520———

1951 shoreline and reconstructed preslide bathymetric contours

Limit of irregular bottom topography

Direction of wave travel, magnitude of damage (number on shaft), and runup height, in feet (at arrow point)

Path of snow and rock avalanches

——— Line 1 ———
Line of traverse of wave damage height

KENAI LAKE

Ship Creek

DIFFERENT CONTOUR INTERVALS ARE USED

1000   0   1000   2000   3000   4000 FEET

FIGURE 184 Ship Creek Delta on Kenai Lake. (See profiles on Figure 194.)

David S. McCulloch, U.S. Geological Survey

726

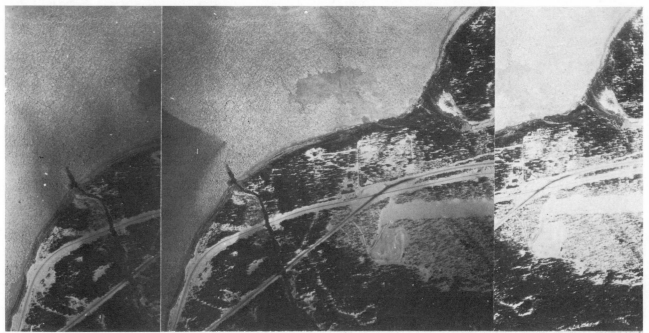

U.S. Army

FIGURE 185   Lawing (Trail River) subaqueous slide area. Trail River is to the right (north) and Ptarmigan Creek is to the left (March 30, 1964). Scale: 1 in. = 1,000 ft.

Alaska Railroad (Figures 208–210) and near Seward. Lemke (1967) describes the Jap Creek avalanches (Figure 211) near Seward as follows:

A snow avalanche, which contained some rocks and other debris, moved downslope across Jap Creek a few hundred feet downstream from the major rockslide and continued a short distance up the opposite valley wall. In both places, Jap Creek continued to flow under the slide masses, and no water was impounded.

During the winter preceding the earthquake, the snow inland was not as deep as usual. Anchorage had only 85 percent of its normal snowfall at the time of the earthquake. Following is a tabulation of accumulated snowfall, in inches, from September 1963 to March 27, 1964, and the normal accumulated fall between these dates:

	Anchorage	Valdez	Cordova	Seward	Yakutat
Sept. 1963–Mar. 27, 1964	54	231	149	75	237
Sept.–Mar. 27 normal	64	234	131	60	217
Percentage of normal snowfall	85	99	113	125	109

During February, high winds from the south further reduced the depth of the snow pack in the mountains im-

mediately east of Anchorage; the mountains were nearly bare of snow by March 21.

The snow avalanches triggered by the earthquake traveled much further than normal from the base of the mountains. A slide east of Kern Creek on Turnagain Arm destroyed a forested area with 20- to 50-year-old trees (Figure 212). The Pioneer Peak snowslide at the head of the Knik Arm near Palmer normally terminates at the road near the base of the mountain. After the great Alaska earthquake, the slide extended nearly one-quarter mi from the base of the mountain and ended in the Knik River (Figure 213), in spite of a very light snow pack. Snow avalanches resulting from a large earthquake can be expected to extend well beyond their normally defined toe and to engulf areas not previously affected.

Many of the avalanches were combined snow and rock slides and will be discussed in the section on rock avalanches.

Tarr and Martin (1914) described the avalanches associated with the 1899 series of earthquakes at Yakutat Bay as follows:

Alaska shook down a great series of avalanches of snow and ice into the upper portion of the Galario Valley (near Yakutat), and their seams were easily recognized in company photographs taken in 1905 as compared with those taken in 1899.

The great Yakutat earthquake of 1899, the Alaska Range earthquake of 1912, and the 1964 great Alaska earthquake

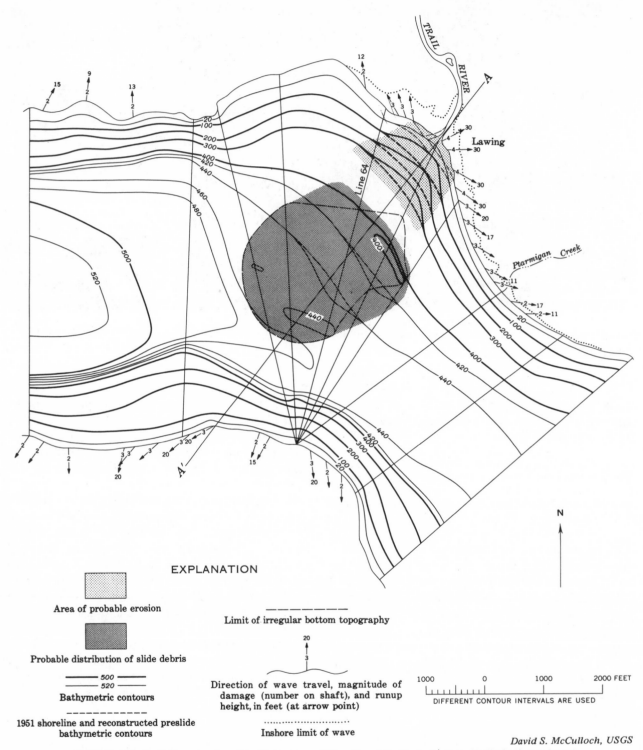

EXPLANATION

Area of probable erosion

Probable distribution of slide debris

——— 500 ———
——— 520 ———
Bathymetric contours

— — — — — — —
1951 shoreline and reconstructed preslide
bathymetric contours

— — — — — — —
Limit of irregular bottom topography

Direction of wave travel, magnitude of
damage (number on shaft), and runup
height, in feet (at arrow point)

....
Inshore limit of wave

1000   0   1000   2000 FEET
DIFFERENT CONTOUR INTERVALS ARE USED

David S. McCulloch, USGS

FIGURE 186   Trail River, Lawing slide. (Fathogram of Line 64 and Profile A–A′ on p. 60, Hydrology volume.)

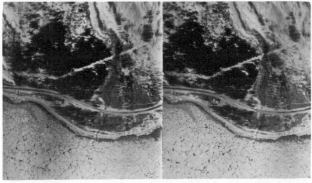

U.S. Army

FIGURE 187   Rocky (Boulder) Creek Delta area of subaqueous sliding on Kenai Lake. Sliding took out sections of Alaska Railroad tracks. Exposed soil in scarps consists of sandy gravel and cobbles (March 30, 1964). Scale: 1 in. = 1,000 ft.

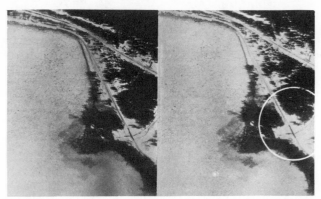

U.S. Army

FIGURE 188   Lakeview (Victory Creek) Delta area of subaqueous sliding on Kenai Lake. The railroad bridge crossing Victory Creek is circled (March 30, 1964). Scale: 1 in. = 1,000 ft.

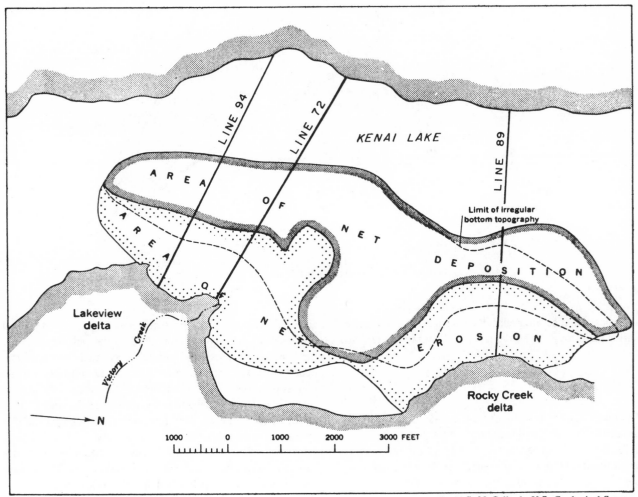

David S. McCulloch, U.S. Geological Survey

FIGURE 189   Lakeview (Victory Creek) and Rocky (Boulder) Creek slide areas on Kenai Lake. (See profiles on Figure 193.)

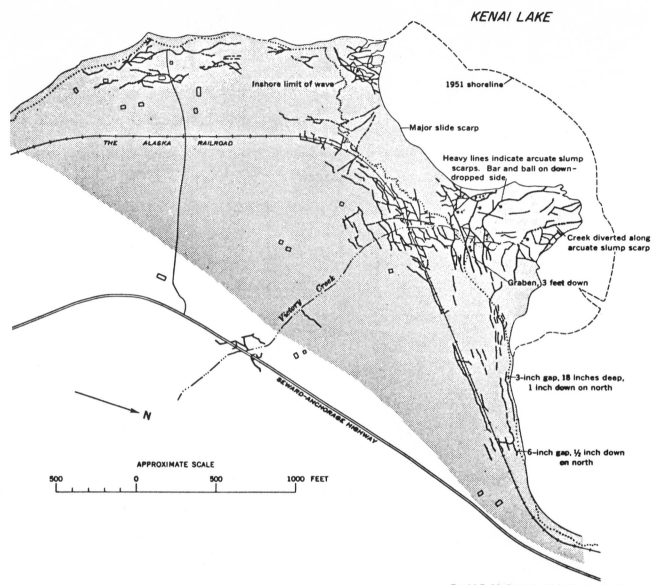

David S. McCulloch, U.S. Geological Survey

FIGURE 190   Lakeview (Victory Creek) Delta slide area.

all indicate that severe avalanching is a natural occurrence during major or great earthquakes in mountainous regions.

ROCK AVALANCHES

The long duration and intensity of seismic motion during the earthquake initiated many rockslides that might not have occurred in an earthquake of a shorter duration and less intensity. Of particular interest are the less numerous, but more devastating, high-velocity rock avalanches that could cause catastrophic destruction of villages, transportation arteries, and communication lines. The larger, cata-

strophic avalanches occurred adjacent to glaciers. In general, rock sliding may have been limited by the well-frozen crust in late March. Rockslides and debris avalanches seem to have been more widespread in the more poorly indurated rocks on Kodiak, near the southern end of the earthquake-affected area (Plafker and Kachadoorian, 1966, and Geology volume). Ground temperatures would be warmer in this area and it would have a seasonal frost depth of only 2–4 ft at lower elevations. Debris rockslides and avalanches were less noticeable in the northern sector of earthquake areas. The Seward area had numerous debris avalanches near the city and south of it (Figure 211). The larger rock avalanches occurred in the upper Prince William Sound area. Table 1 is a tabulation

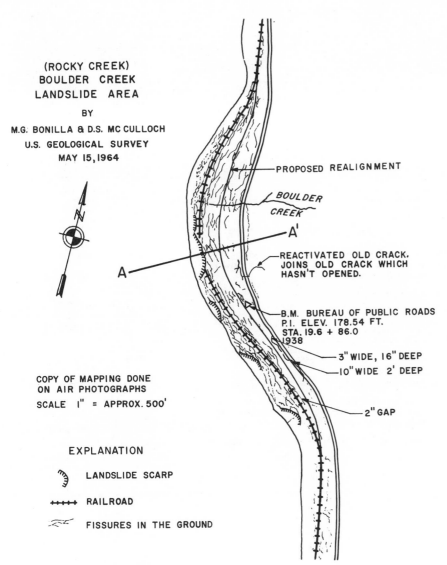

(ROCKY CREEK)
BOULDER CREEK
LANDSLIDE AREA

BY

M.G. BONILLA & D.S. McCULLOCH
U.S. GEOLOGICAL SURVEY
MAY 15, 1964

PROPOSED REALIGNMENT

BOULDER CREEK

A'

REACTIVATED OLD CRACK.
JOINS OLD CRACK WHICH
HASN'T OPENED.

A

B.M. BUREAU OF PUBLIC ROADS
P.I. ELEV. 178.54 FT.
STA. 19.6 + 86.0
1938

3" WIDE, 16" DEEP
10" WIDE 2' DEEP

2" GAP

COPY OF MAPPING DONE
ON AIR PHOTOGRAPHS
SCALE 1" = APPROX. 500'

EXPLANATION

LANDSLIDE SCARP

RAILROAD

FISSURES IN THE GROUND

FIGURE 191   Rocky (Boulder) Creek landslide area. (See profile of section A–A' on
Figure 192.)

M. G. Bonilla and D. S. McCulloch, U.S. Geological Survey

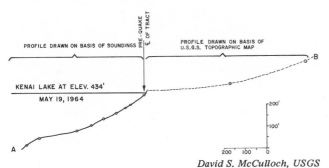

FIGURE 192   Profile across alluvial fan and landslide at Rocky
(Boulder) Creek, Kenai Lake. (See section A–A' on Figure 191.)

David S. McCulloch, USGS

of earthquake-induced rock avalanches listed by Post (1967,
and Hydrology volume), all of which occurred adjacent to
glaciers. Locations of these avalanches along with the axis of
related geomorphic features are presented in Figure 214.

The major avalanches listed are from 0.6 to 4 mi long and
are 1¼ mi wide or less (Ragle and others, 1965; Tuthill and
Laird, 1966; Post, 1967). They are all close to the axis of
maximum subsidence and the axis of maximum uplift (Figure 215) and are between the Chugach Mountains and
Yakataga geosynclines (Figure 214).

Although most of the glaciers have declined in elevation

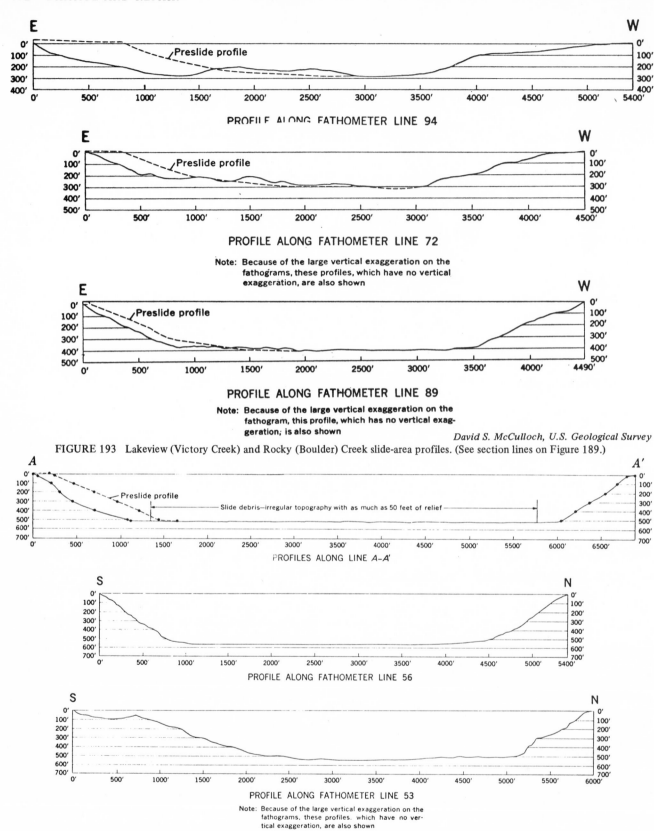

PROFILE ALONG FATHOMETER LINE 94

PROFILE ALONG FATHOMETER LINE 72

Note: Because of the large vertical exaggeration on the fathograms, these profiles, which have no vertical exaggeration, are also shown

PROFILE ALONG FATHOMETER LINE 89

Note: Because of the large vertical exaggeration on the fathogram, this profile, which has no vertical exaggeration, is also shown

David S. McCulloch, U.S. Geological Survey

FIGURE 193   Lakeview (Victory Creek) and Rocky (Boulder) Creek slide-area profiles. (See section lines on Figure 189.)

PROFILES ALONG LINE A–A'

PROFILE ALONG FATHOMETER LINE 56

PROFILE ALONG FATHOMETER LINE 53

Note: Because of the large vertical exaggeration on the fathograms, these profiles, which have no vertical exaggeration, are also shown

SHIP CREEK DELTA SLIDE AREA PROFILES   *David S. McCulloch, U.S. Geological Survey*

FIGURE 194   Ship Creek Delta slide-area profiles. (See section lines on Figure 184.)

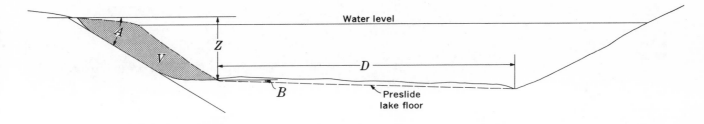

Slide	Volume (cu ft)	Potential energy (10⁶ ft lbs)	Normalized potential energy (potential energy ÷ volume)	Scarp slope (angle A, in degrees)	Depth (Z, in feet)	Lake-floor slope (angle B, in degrees)	Distance of debris travel (D, in feet)
Lakeview	226,875	[1] 17,285.97	76,191	10.5	220	3	1,280
Lawing	74,125	9,390.15	126,679	20	400	2	2,100
Ship Creek	198,250	28,079.59	148,372	25	520	0	4,750
Rocky Creek	66,375	6,998.55	105,439	25	380	2.5	600

[1] Because some material was moved upward by rotation at the Lakeview slide, the potential energy of the material raised to the level of the lake floor has been subtracted from the potential energy of the material above the level of the lake floor.

David S. McCulloch, USGS

FIGURE 195   The volume, potential energy, scarp slope, and distance traveled by the slide debris of the four major slides. The volume and potential energy are calculated for a vertical slice having a thickness of 1 ft as measured from reconstructed preslide bathymetric contours along fathogram lines 89 and 94 (Figure 193) and profiles A-A' (Figures 186 and 194).

as well as in length in recent years, surveys of sufficient accuracy to define changes in the elevation of glaciers adjacent to mountain slopes that failed are not available. The general slope of the mountains adjoining glaciers and older glaciated valleys does indicate that glacier erosion steepens the bases of the mountains. The retreat or declining thickness of gla-

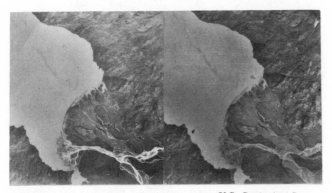

U.S. Geological Survey

FIGURE 196   Bradley Lake: Preearthquake view of river delta; top of photo is north (August 9, 1950). Scale: 1 in. = 3,400 ft.

ciers adjacent to these mountains exposed these mountain faces whose stability is critical.

Investigation after the earthquake disclosed several old rockslide avalanches where no new avalanches had occurred. Figure 216 shows an old avalanche or rockslide scar that was observed along the north side of the Upper Ship Creek basin. Figure 217 shows old rockslides, one superimposed on another, that occurred in the cliffs northwest of Homer. Whether these slides resulted from an early earthquake is uncertain, the absence of rock avalanching in this area, where snow cover was light and frost penetration deep, makes it doubtful that avalanching would have occurred if the frost penetration had been less or absent, or if underlying rocks had a higher degree of saturation.

Precipitation records for Anchorage and Cordova for September and October 1963, the period of fall rains, their comparisons with normal and extremes of precipitation, and the monthly mean temperatures are given in Table 2.

Seepage of water from the rocks and soil may have been limited by an early sharp freeze during November 1963 throughout the Anchorage, Valdez, Cordova, and Seward areas. The average November and December 1963 temperatures for Anchorage and Cordova and their comparison with the normals are as tabulated:

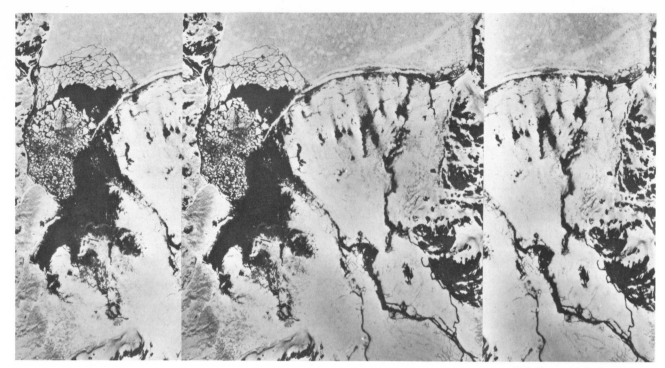

U.S. Coast and Geodetic Survey

FIGURE 197   Subaqueous sliding of Bradley Lake stream delta indicated by the areas of broken ice. Bradley Lake is 27 mi northeast of Homer at elevation 1,090 ft in the Kenai Mountains (May 30, 1964). Scale: 1 in. = 1,450 ft.

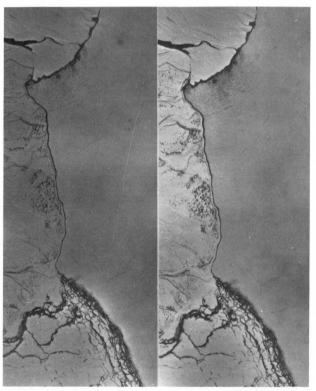

U.S. Coast and Geodetic Survey

FIGURE 198   Beluga Lake subaqueous sliding on the delta of the Triumvirate Glacier river tributaries. These slides are 145 mi west of the earthquake epicenter (May 31, 1964). Scale: 1 in. = 3,000 ft.

	Temperature (°F)	
	1963	Normal
Anchorage		
November	12.1	22.2
December	24.8	14.3
Cordova		
November	25.2	31.1
December	32.9	25.6

Precipitation and temperature records indicate a late fall condition, i.e., below normal precipitation followed by a sharp freeze condition in November. At the elevation of the rock avalanche, the temperatures would have been 10–20°F cooler. The sharp freeze in November may have contributed to a greater than normal ice-wedging of the rock. Because the snow cover in the area bordering on the Gulf Coast was greater than normal by the time of the earthquake, total frost penetration may have been limited. The shear resistance would have been least in the unfrozen zone of rock, whereas the frozen zones would have had high internal stresses conducive to failure. Inland areas also experienced a sharp freeze, followed by a snowfall that was well below normal near sea level and, from observations, was probably considerably below normal at the higher altitudes. Interior areas were more likely to have permafrost at higher altitudes and to have refrozen to the depth of seasonal thaw, which could account for a lack of the larger deep-seated slides on the inland drainages.

U.S. Army

FIGURE 199 Subaqueous slides and slumps in Eklutna Lake. The largest failures associated with talus and alluvial cones extend into the lake along its north shore. The lake is a source of hydroelectric power and is drawn down well below its normal level by late winter (April 8, 1964).

The Sherman Glacier avalanche was one of the largest of the rock avalanches. It occurred 21 mi east of Cordova along the southern flank of the Chugach Mountains, probably near the axis of uplift (Figure 218; Plafker, 1965) and the probable axis of an abnormal geanticline connecting the Montague Island uplift to the St. Elias fault (Post, 1967;

U.S. Army

FIGURE 200 Tonsina Lake. Broken ice indicates major subaqueous slides of delta deposits (April 8, 1964).

Figure 215). The earthquake caused the collapse of newly named Shattered Peak on the east side of a south-trending tributary of the Sherman Glacier. Figure 219 shows the slopes that failed before the earthquake, and Figure 220 shows these slopes after the earthquake. Figures 221–223 show Shattered Peak, which was 4,300 ft high and was reduced to a height of 3,800 ft by a failure 2,100 ft wide and 3,000 ft in the direction of slip (Marangunic and Bull, 1968). A 40°–45° slope is reported by Bull and Marangunic (1967). Plafker (1964) reports the preearthquake slope of the rock that failed as being 50° with an oversteepened toe of more than 75° (Figure 219). Figure 220 also shows a mountain on the west side of the same tributary glacier where smaller rock avalanches occurred after the earthquake. Figure 223 shows that portion of the avalanche as it approached the other slide in its travel down the glacier. An avalanche on another easterly tributary of Sherman Glacier (Figure 224) and another on Saddlebag Glacier originated from the same heavily faulted Shattered Peak that was the source of the largest avalanche (Figure 218). The combined area of the three slides originating from Shattered Peak is 4.8 mi². The rock debris flowed a distance of more than 3½ mi on slopes as flat as 1.5°. Much of the glacier area traversed was flatter than 4° (Field, 1965; Figures 225–227). The slide material consisted of rock and an estimated equal volume of snow. The rock consisted of quartzite, slate phyllite, and some graywacke. Closeups of the avalanche ma-

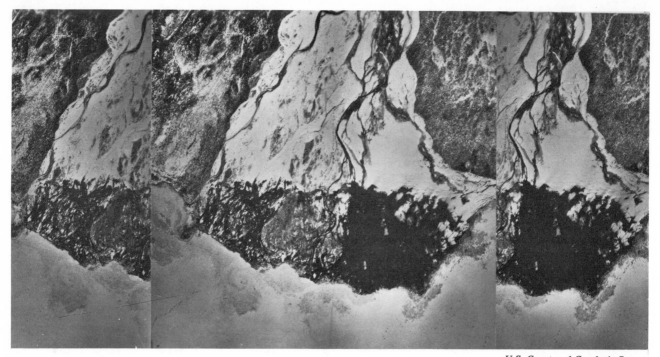

FIGURE 201   Subaqueous failure of Nelchina River Delta in northwest quadrant of Tazlina Lake (April 10, 1964). Scale: 1 in. = 2,500 ft.

terial are shown in Figures 228–230. The terminus of this glacier has retreated approximately ¾ mi since 1890, and ¼ mi since 1950 (Figure 231). The elevation of the tributary glacier would be expected to have diminished with the recession of the main glacier. The preearthquake oversteepened lower slope of the rockslide area was probably left exposed by the glacial recession, which contributed to

increased stresses in the rock. Sherman Glacier tributaries to the east and to the west of the tributary that had the major rock avalanche had lesser rock avalanches (Figures 223 and 224). The rock avalanche on the east side was 1½ mi long and 0.4 mi wide, nearly covering the full width of its valley. Saddlebag Glacier, just over the ridge and south of the south tributaries of the Sherman Glacier, had numerous avalanches, the largest being equivalent in size to the third largest Sherman Glacier rock avalanche.

The avalanches on opposite sides of the peak (Figure 232) indicate that although direction of bedding of the rock may have affected the magnitude of avalanching, it could not have been the sole cause. The area-wide distributions of the avalanches indicate that avalanching could not have resulted from a fault.

The possibility of permafrost and of the avalanching rock voids being nearly saturated exists under the local climatological and terrain conditions.

The Surprise Glacier avalanche is closer to the ports of Whittier and Anchorage than the other major avalanches already discussed. It, however, is located in a remote area southwest of the upper end of Harriman Fiord, 19 mi north of Whittier and 48 mi east of Anchorage. This avalanche area is adjacent to the axis of maximum subsidence (Figure 215), and along the Chugach Mountain geosyncline (Figure 214). Figure 232 (taken in 1957) shows the mountains on which avalanching later occurred. Figures 233 and 234 are oblique views of the mountains from which avalanching

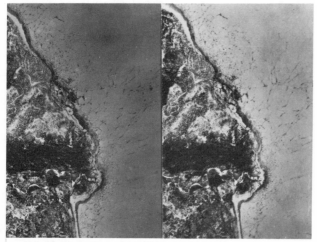

FIGURE 202   Tazlina Lake. Subaqueous slide on south branch of stream delta along the northeast sector of the lake. Slide retrogressed well inshore (April 8, 1964). Scale: 1 in. = 2,500 ft.

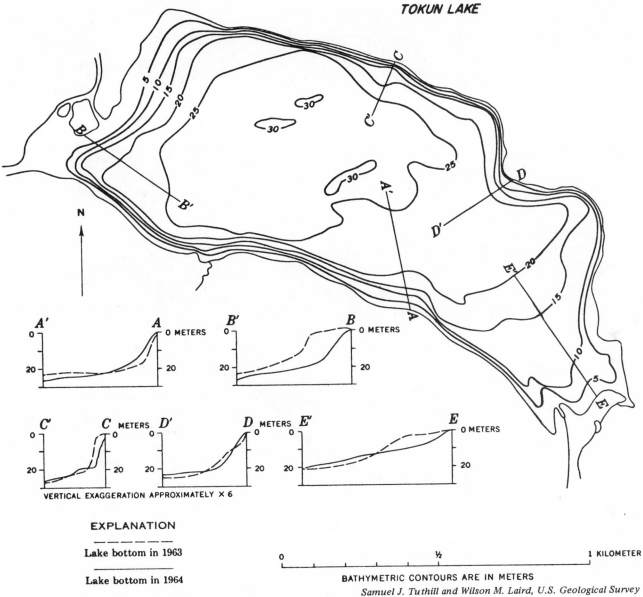

FIGURE 203   Map of Tokun Lake, showing bathymetry and profiles of bottom configurations in 1963 and 1964.

Samuel J. Tuthill and Wilson M. Laird, U.S. Geological Survey

originated. The coarser materials were confined in a trough of the Surprise Glacier, 2 mi long and ½ mi wide (Figures 235 and 236). Activity and sliding were continuing on this mountain and on a prominent peak at the head of Eklutna Lake when they were observed during the summer of 1964.

The Surprise Glacier terminus, which was entirely within the tidal zone, retreated 2,000 ft between 1899 and 1910. Photographs in 1957 show that the location of the terminus was essentially the same as in 1910 (Tarr and Martin, 1914, Plate CXXIX) when it was described by Tarr and Martin as aground on rock on its east side. The degree of change in elevation or thickness of the glacier is unknown.

Ranney Glacier avalanche, which terminated in the headwaters of Unakwik Inlet (Figure 237), was the closest avalanche to the earthquake epicenter. Figure 238 shows the Columbia Glacier avalanche approximately 12 mi east of Ranney Glacier avalanche.

Other major earthquake-induced avalanches on glaciers are listed in Table 1, and maps of them appear as Figures 239 (Schwan), 240 (Martin and West Steller), 241 (Slide, Johnson, and Miles), 242 (Allen), and 243 (Bering and Steller).

The Leonard Glacier avalanche is a debris avalanche along the west side of the Leonard Glacier. The accumulated debris

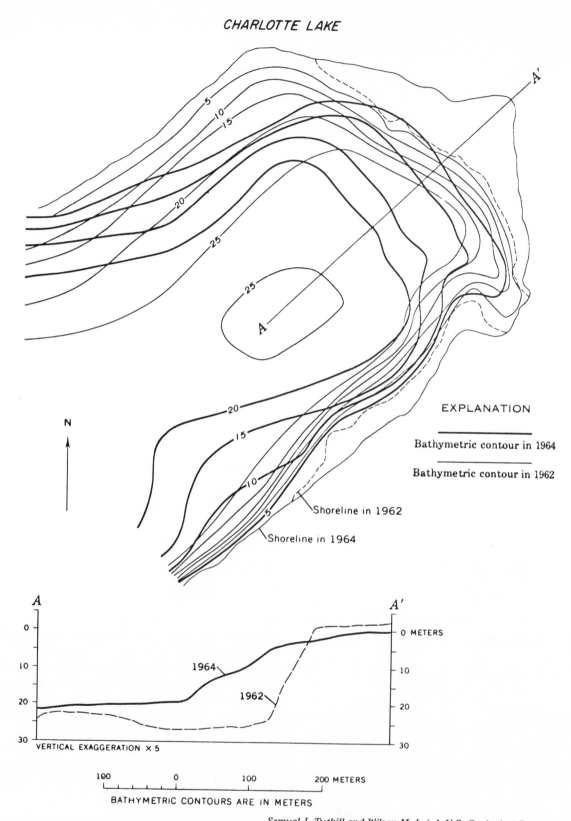

FIGURE 204   Bathymetric map and profiles, showing bottom configurations in northeast part of Lake Charlotte in 1962 and 1964.

KUSHTAKA LAKE

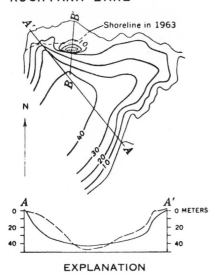

Shoreline in 1963

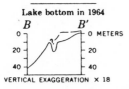

EXPLANATION

– – – – – –
Lake bottom in 1963

———
Lake bottom in 1964

VERTICAL EXAGGERATION × 18

0   1   2 KILOMETERS

BATHYMETRIC CONTOURS ARE IN METERS

*Samuel J. Tuthill and Wilson M. Laird,
U.S. Geological Survey*

FIGURE 205   Bathymetric map and profiles, showing bottom configurations of the
northern part of Kushtaka Lake in 1963
and 1964.

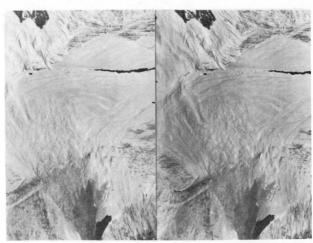

Air Photo Tech, Inc.

FIGURE 207   Snow and rock avalanches west of Valdez. Mineral
Creek constricted by avalanching (April 11, 1964). Scale: 1 in. =
500 ft.

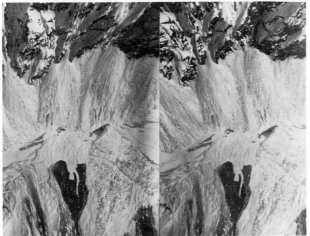

Air Photo Tech, Inc.

FIGURE 206   Snow and rock avalanches west of Valdez in Mineral
Creek Valley. Snow avalanches blocked mining road and caused a
temporary restriction of creek flow (April 11, 1964). Scale: 1 in. =
1,000 ft.

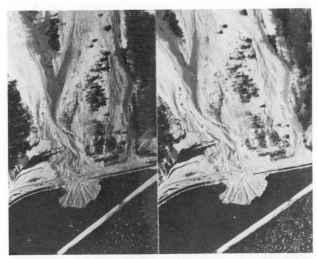

U.S. Army

FIGURE 208   Turnagain Arm snow avalanches. Kern Creek slide;
road and railroad have been cleared. New road crosses Arm beyond
slide area but was later inundated by high tides as a result of land
subsidence. Road was reconstructed at a higher elevation (March 30,
1964).

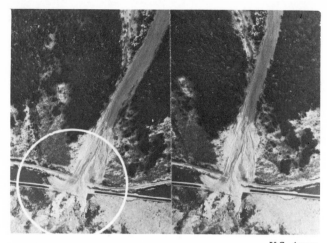

U.S. Army

FIGURE 209   Turnagain Arm snow avalanches along north side of
Arm below Kern Creek. Railroad along toe of slope, highway on
edge of tideflats (March 30, 1964). Circle shows area where transportation routes are blocked.

Art Kennedy, U.S. Forest Service

FIGURE 210   Turnagain Arm snow avalanches along north side of
the Arm between Kern Creek and Portage. Railroad is along toe of
slope; road is below, with new road crossing the tideflats beyond
the avalanche toe.

FIGURE 211   Snow and rock avalanches on Jap Creek, Seward (April 15, 1964). Scale: 1 in. = 1,200 ft.

U.S. Army

FIGURE 212   Snow avalanche below Kern Creek on Turnagain
Arm which took out many trees (April 1964).

Willard M. Knoppe

FIGURE 213   Debris remaining from Knik snow avalanche. During
years of normal snowfall, the slide would not extend past the toe of
the slide; this slide occurred with a very light snow pack and extended 1/4 mi into the Knik River. Bordenberg Butte is in background (late April 1964).

TABLE 1   Earthquake-Induced Rockslide Avalanches

Glacier Name	Area (km²)	Avalanche No.	Latitude	Longitude	Slides No.	Area (km²)[a]	Length (km)	Direction Traveled
			° ′	° ′				
Sherman	57	1	60 33	145 10	1	*8.5*	6	NW
		2	33	06	1	1.5	2.5	N
		3	31	08	1	1.5	3	N
		4	32	10	1	.5	1.5	NE
Schwan	140	1	60 53	145 11	1	*9*	6	NNW
		2	57	08	1	.5	1.5	W
Martin River	290	1	60 36	143 36	1	*5*	3	NNW
		2	36	38	2	*11.5*	4	NW
		3	38	35	2	*6.5*	5	S, SSE
		4	37	39	1	*8.5*[b]	5	SSE
		5	34	38	1	1.5	3.5	SW
		6	33	44	1	1	2.5	S
Bering	5,830	1	60 32	143 17	1	3	5	S
		2	30	10	1	2.5	6.5	S
		3	29	06	1	2.5	5	S
		4	29	04	1	1	1.5	SSE
		5	28	142 27	1	1.5	2.5	N
Steller	Branch of Bering Glacier	1	60 35	143 17	1	*7.5*	6.5	N
		2	33	31	1	1	2.5	SE
		3	33	32	1	.5	2.5	SSE
		4	32	34	1	1	4	SSW
		5	32	39	1	1	2.5	S
Slide[c]	—	1	60 32	144 19	1	*3*	4.5	S
		2	34	18	5	1	1	1 NW, 3 SW, 1 SE
		3	32	18	1	1	1	NW
Johnson	26	—	60 34	144 21	4	2.5	2.5	1 W, 3 NW
Unnamed	8	—	60 36	144 21	2	1.5	1.5	N, SE
Van Cleve	62	—	60 42	144 13	2	1	1	N
Saddlebag	10	—	60 31	145 06	4	2.5	2.5	1 SSE, 2 SW, 1 NE
Fickett	3	—	60 33	145 01	1	1	3	NNE
Allen	230	1	60 46	144 50	1	2	3	N
		2	45	45	1	1	2.5	NW
		3	47	55	1	1	1.5	N
Scott	155	—	60 43	145 08	3	1.5	1	SE
Rude	26	1	60 47	145 11	1	2	5	NW
		2	47	08	1	1	2	NW
Tasnuna	31	—	61 02	145 27	1	1.5	2.5	WNW
Columbia	1,370	1	61 13	147 14	1	1	1.5	SW
		2	13	16	2	1	1.5	ESE
Ranney	4	—	61 11	147 34	1	1	2	SE
Serpentine	26	—	61 09	148 16	1	.5	2.5	S
			06	18	1	.5	2	E
Surprise	70	—	61 02	148 31	2	3	3	ESE
Harriman	49	—	60 56	148 28	2	1	2.5	N
Pigot	16	—	60 54	148 30	1	.5	4	E
Twentymile	49	1	60 57	148 38	1	2	2.5	W
		2	56	38	3	1.5	1.5	1 W, 2 NW
Contact	10	—	60 28	148 28	4	3	1.5	NE
Unnamed	11	—	59 48	149 57	3	1.5	1.5	W
	4	—	59 42	150 03	2	2.5	1.5	W, SW
	4	—	59 44	150 15	1	.5	1.5	E

[a] Slide area: more important slides in italic (Post, 1967).
[b] Dust.
[c] Changed from Sioux Glacier by Board on Geographic Names (USGS).

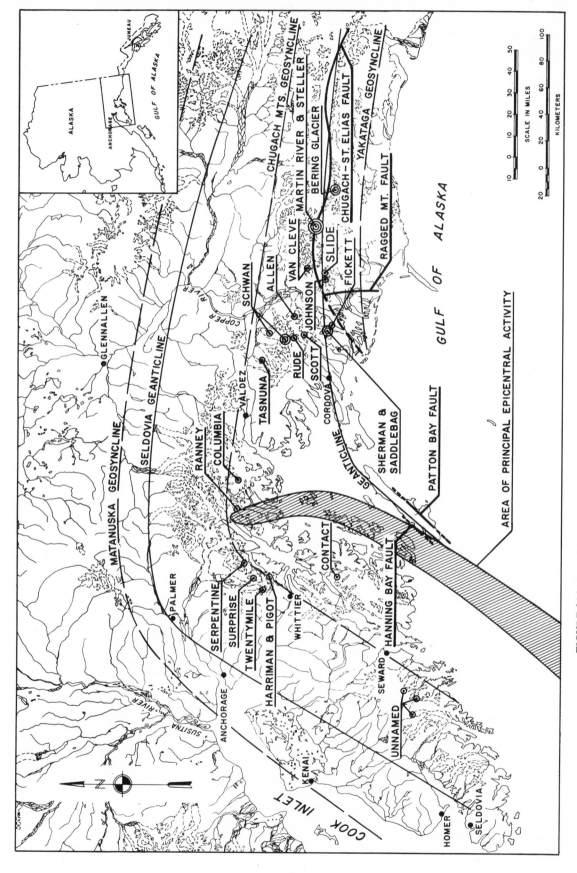

FIGURE 214 Location of major rock avalanches and possibly related geomorphic features.

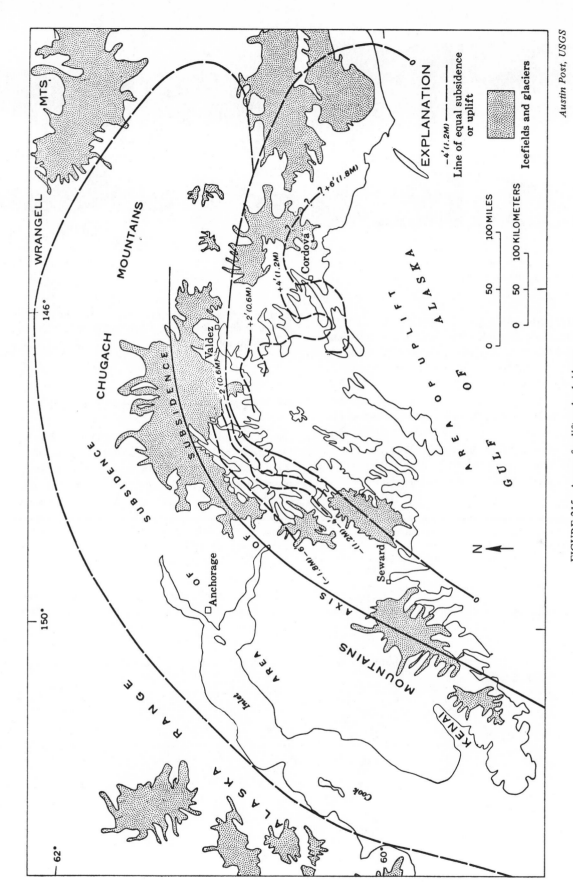

FIGURE 215 Areas of uplift and subsidence.

FIGURE 216 An old rock-avalanche scar on the north side of Ship Creek Valley east of Anchorage. Most of the snow shown fell at the time or immediately after the earthquake (early April 1964).

FIGURE 217 Old rockslides in cliffs northwest of Homer. The back portion of the slide appears from the tree cover to be of a later origin (April 1964).

covers a large part of the terminal moraine of the Leonard Glacier (Figures 244 and 245). The avalanche area is close enough to Whittier for residential construction on this moraine to be considered in another 100 years. The Leonard Glacier terminus has retreated 1,500 ft since 1939 and 3,000 ft since 1914 (Barnes, 1943).

The Portage Lake avalanches are also debris avalanches. The avalanche shown in Figure 246 appears to be the largest of many in this area. Art Kennedy (1964), one of a party conducting research on Portage Lake when the earthquake occurred, described the avalanche as follows:

In the distance the roar of avalanches ripping away the mountain sides became louder. By this time the vibrations and heaving of the ice seemed to have reached a plateau, but the distant roaring of avalanches continued to gain in intensity. . . . I decided to snowshoe back to the lake and view the site of our ordeal of the night before. Taking Howard Smith with me, I started off. Everywhere the snow was cracked and covered with dirt. We reached the lake after 45 minutes of walking. Evidence of the quake's dynamic force was everywhere. Great sections of rock had broken

loose causing black streaks on the once pure white mountains. Portage Glacier was no longer a sheer face of 250 feet but was now a gently sloping grade to the lake.

CRUSTAL MOVEMENTS AND SETTLEMENT OF UNCONSOLIDATED MATERIALS

The crustal soil sliding was indicated by the slipping of the frozen crust on steep bluff slopes of Turnagain Arm (Figure 247), the lateral displacement of the frozen ground surface overlying saturated alluvium along lower Ship Creek (Figure 248), and the lateral displacements and cracking in the unsaturated surface soils overlying the deep saturated deposits in the Portage (Figure 249), Knik River, Girdwood (Figure 250), Seward (Figure 251), Valdez (Figure 252), the Martin, Bering, and Copper river areas east of Cordova, and the Anchorage–Kenai areas (Figure 253). This type of movement would include all those areas involving appreciable amounts of soil fissuring without a

TABLE 2 Normal and Extremes of Precipitation in Anchorage and Cordova Compared to September and October 1963 and Monthly Mean Temperatures

	Precipitation (in inches)				Temperature (°F)	
	1963	Normal[a]	Max.[b]	Min.[b]	1963	Normal[a]
Anchorage						
September	0.98	2.50	5.43	0.52	52.0	48.0
October	1.01	1.87	6.43	0.26	36.8	35.8
Cordova						
September	7.57	12.51	c	c	50.9	47.6
October	10.44	11.90	c	c	41.5	39.8

[a] 1931–1960.
[b] 1916–1963.
[c] Not available.

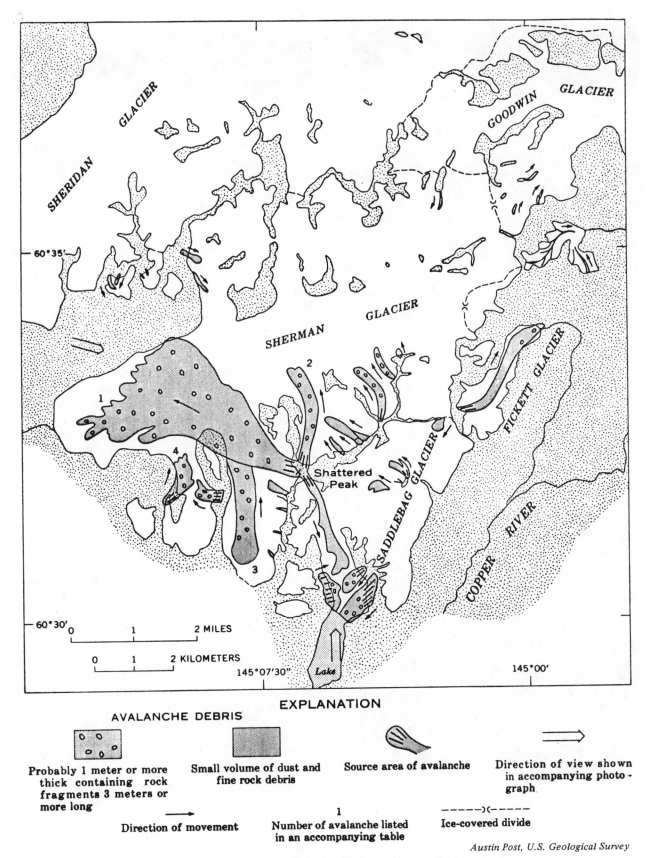

EXPLANATION

AVALANCHE DEBRIS

Probably 1 meter or more thick containing rock fragments 3 meters or more long

Small volume of dust and fine rock debris

Source area of avalanche

Direction of view shown in accompanying photograph

Direction of movement

1
Number of avalanche listed in an accompanying table

Ice-covered divide

Austin Post, U.S. Geological Survey

FIGURE 218   Sherman Glacier, Saddlebag Glacier, and Fickett Glacier avalanches.

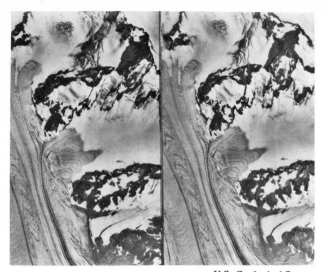

U.S. Geological Survey

FIGURE 219 Preearthquake photo of Sherman Glacier (Shattered Peak). Shattered Peak is the highest peak near the upper right side (August 5, 1950). Scale: 1 in. = 4,200 ft.

Arctic Institute of North America

FIGURE 221 Shattered Peak: Origin of Sherman Glacier avalanche (April 16, 1964).

marked subsurface plane of sliding. The horizontal retrogressive translating slides were preceded by these crustal movements (Figure 254).

Crustal movements almost invariably involve settlement, because any stretching of a mass of soil would normally have an associated settlement; however, settlement

of soil also resulted from a vibratory or dynamic consolidation effect on saturated and unsaturated cohesionless granular soils (Figure 255). This type of settlement must be distinguished from tectonic subsidence of the base rock. Settlement from stretching was evident landward of the Turnagain slide and was somewhat less evident behind the Fourth Avenue slide and other slide areas. Settlement from soil consolidation was particularly evident in the Portage area, at Valdez, and on the Homer Spit.

ANCHORAGE AREA

An appreciable amount of crustal movement developed in the sandy soils overlying the Bootlegger Cove Clay in the Turnagain area. The prominent crack pattern that developed from crustal movement generally paralleled the Knik Arm bluff line and intersected Fish Creek bluff at right angles (Engineering Geology Evaluation Group, 1964). Crustal movement cracks tended to connect with the unfrozen soils underlying the heated basements and garages (Figures 81 and 106). Crack displacement and crack development was limited by homes founded on well-reinforced basements, such as the Swalling home, which had negligible damage despite the size and displacement of the cracks around it (Figures 108 and 109).

During the initial stages of the earthquake, a crack developed across Northern Lights Boulevard, a half block east of Turnagain Parkway. This crack extended under the carport of an adjoining house where it was observed by the owner to open 4 ft before closing and caused the collapse of the posts supporting the west edge of the carport. After the earthquake, this crack was closed tight, and compressive

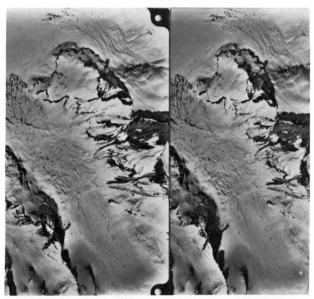

U.S. Coast and Geodetic Survey

FIGURE 220 Sherman Glacier avalanche. Principal origin of sliding is Shattered Peak on right edge of photo. Smaller avalanches originated along the knife-edge ridge at the lower left (west side of tributary) (May 30, 1964). Scale: 1 in. = 3,600 ft.

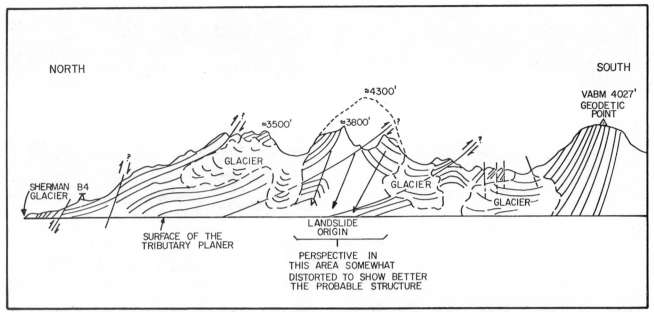

Colin Bull and Cedomir Marangunic, The Ohio State University

FIGURE 222   Sketch of ridge from which slide material originated seen from west side of tributary glacier. Scale is distorted to allow geological structure to be shown more clearly.

failure of the asphaltic concrete pavement across Northern Lights Boulevard was evident. Similar crack closures, with indication of compressive failure of adjoining materials, were observed along L Street between Third and Fifth avenues.

Soil-displacement cracking associated with subsoil liquefaction and stretching was common in the low flood and tidal plains. Figure 248 shows typical soil cracking along the lower Ship Creek valley, and Figure 256 shows displacement cracking along the Knik Arm tidal plain.

Settlement of soil was evident in isolated areas throughout the Anchorage area where buildings were constructed on sand or gravel deposits. Settlement was most evident in the thawed soils next to basements or below grade struc-

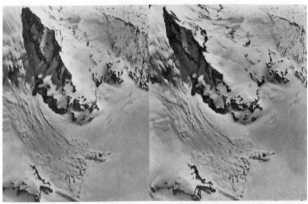

U.S. Coast and Geodetic Survey

FIGURE 223   Sherman Glacier avalanches. Small avalanches developed on west side of tributary when larger avalanche occurred. Origin of avalanching is the mountain at the upper left (May 30, 1964). Scale: 1 in. = 3,600 ft.

U.S. Coast and Geodetic Survey

FIGURE 224   Smaller Sherman Glacier avalanche from glacier tributary northeast of major avalanching. Shattered Peak was the source of this avalanche and of another avalanche traveling down Saddlebag Glacier to the southeast (May 30, 1964). Scale: 1 in. = 2,700 ft.

Arctic Institute of North America

FIGURE 225   Sherman Glacier avalanche, originating in tributary glacier; Shattered Peak on the left. Much of the distance traversed was flatter than 4° grade (April 16, 1964).

Marion T. Millett

FIGURE 228   Sherman Glacier seen slightly south of west toward terminus and point A (Figure 231) on lower tip of slide. Helicopter is resting on the ice surface directly in front of the slide (October 1, 1964).

W. O. Field, American Geographical Society

FIGURE 226   Sherman Glacier avalanche crossing Sherman Glacier on slopes as flat as 1½° and much of the distance flatter than 4°.

W. O. Field, American Geographical Society

FIGURE 229   Sherman Glacier seen east from point A (Figure 231) on lower tip of slide. The lower edge of the southern side of the slide is in the middle distance and Shattered Peak, the source of the slide, is at the upper right (October 1, 1964).

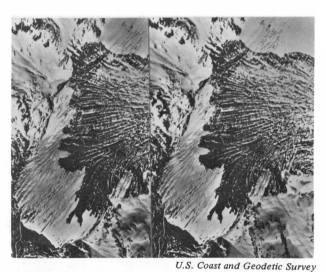

U.S. Coast and Geodetic Survey

FIGURE 227   Sherman Glacier avalanche; the flatter portions of the avalanche spread out over a width of nearly 2 mi (May 30, 1964). Scale: 1 in. = 3,600 ft.

W. O. Field, American Geographical Society

FIGURE 230   Large rock fragment on Sherman Glacier slide originated on Shattered Peak and traveled 2.5 km down glacier (July 11, 1965).

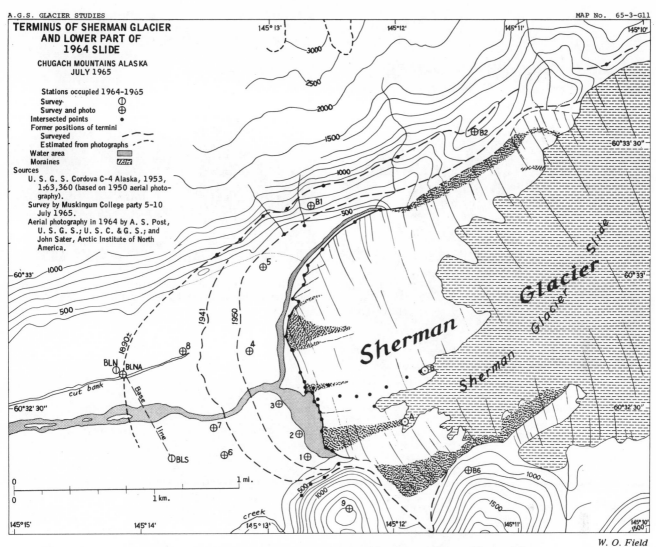

**TERMINUS OF SHERMAN GLACIER
AND LOWER PART OF
1964 SLIDE**

CHUGACH MOUNTAINS ALASKA
JULY 1965

Stations occupied 1964-1965
   Survey·
   Survey and photo
  Intersected points
  Former positions of termini
   Surveyed
   Estimated from photographs
  Water area
  Moraines
Sources
  U. S. G. S. Cordova C-4 Alaska, 1953,
   1:63,360 (based on 1950 aerial photo-
   graphy).
  Survey by Muskingum College party 5-10
   July 1965.
  Aerial photography in 1964 by A. S. Post,
   U. S. G. S.; U. S. C. & G. S.; and
   John Sater, Arctic Institute of North
   America.

W. O. Field

FIGURE 231   Sherman Glacier retreat 1910-1964 and terminus of Sherman Glacier slide.

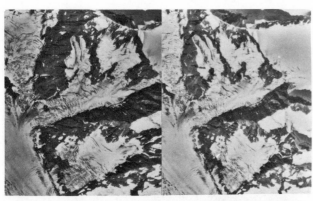

U.S. Geological Survey

FIGURE 232   Surprise Glacier Mountain, on which avalanching later occurred, is in center of photo (July 12, 1957). Scale: 1 in. = 4,000 ft.

Austin Post, U.S. Geological Survey

FIGURE 233   Surprise Glacier avalanche along west side of glacier that flows into Harriman Fiord from the south (1964).

Austin Post, U.S. Geological Survey

FIGURE 234   Surprise Glacier avalanche: Mountain from which slide originated, with faults evident on both sides of slide (1964).

Austin Post, U.S. Geological Survey

FIGURE 235   Surprise Glacier avalanche and dust, looking up the glacier from the northeast (1964).

Austin Post, U.S. Geological Survey

FIGURE 236   Surprise Glacier avalanche and dust, looking down glacier toward Harriman Fiord. Other smaller slides are also evident (1964).

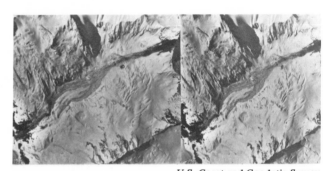

U.S. Coast and Geodetic Survey

FIGURE 237   Ranney Glacier avalanche terminates in Unakwik Inlet near earthquake epicenter (April 4, 1964).

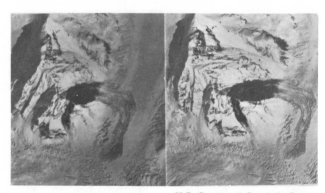

U.S. Coast and Geodetic Survey

FIGURE 238   Columbia Glacier avalanches approximately 20 mi northeast of the earthquake epicenter (April 4, 1964).

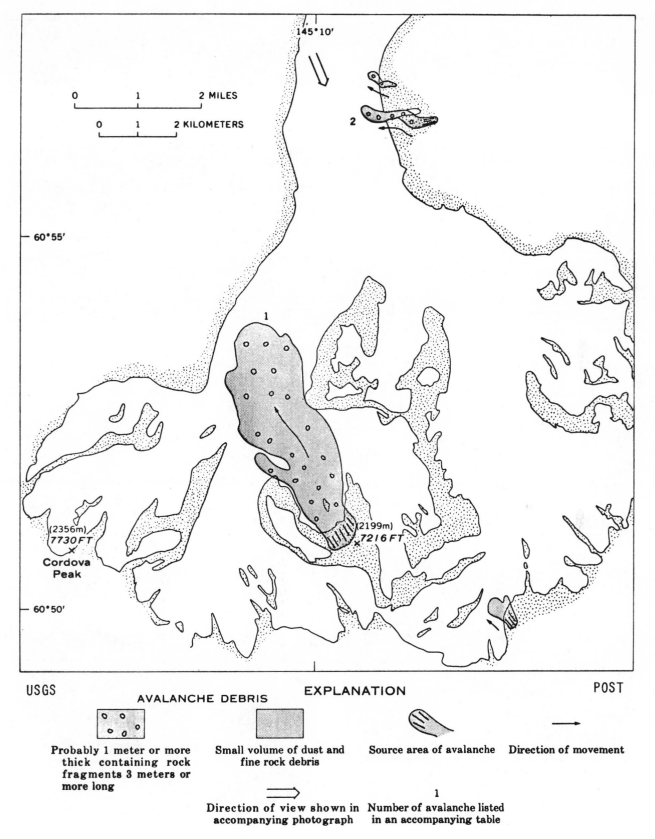

FIGURE 239   Map of rockslide avalanche on Schwan Glacier.

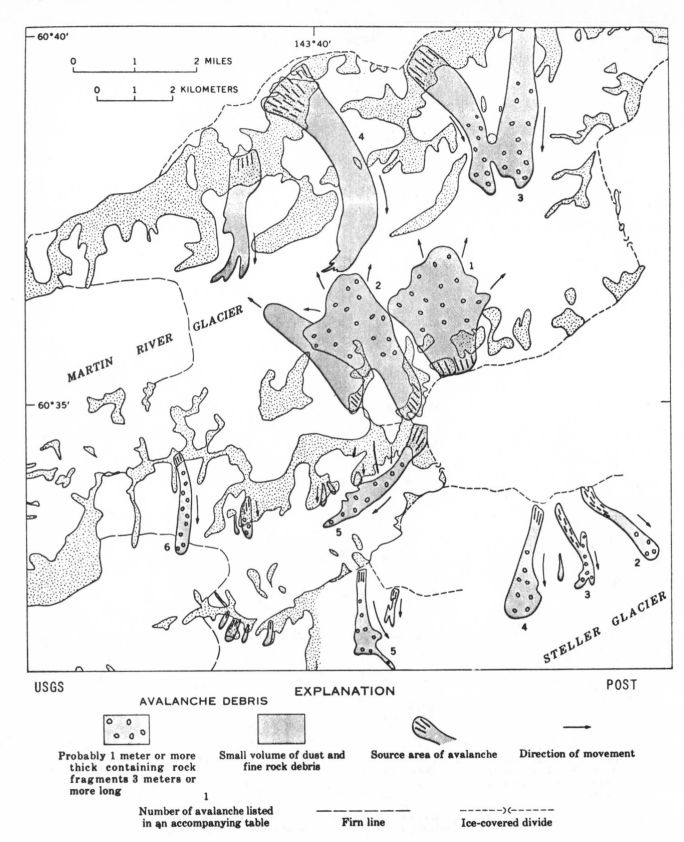

FIGURE 240 Map of rockslide avalanches on the Martin River and West Steller glaciers.

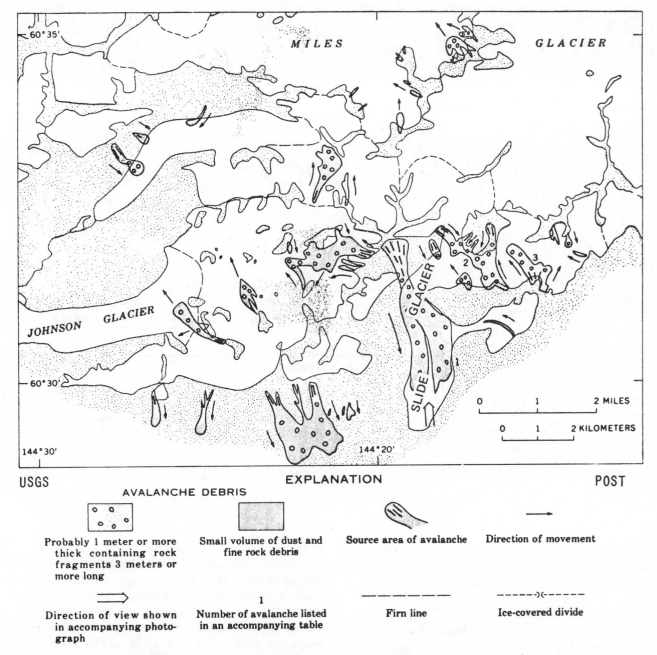

FIGURE 241   Map of rockslide avalanches in the region of Slide, Johnson, and Miles glaciers.

EXPLANATION

AVALANCHE DEBRIS

Probably 1 meter or more thick containing rock fragments 3 meters or more long

Small volume of dust and fine rock debris

Source area of avalanche

Direction of movement

Direction of view shown in accompanying photograph

1
Number of avalanche listed in an accompanying table

Firn line

Ice-covered divide

USGS   POST

tures. Settlements of 1–2 in. were common on the rather shallow (15 ft deep) Turnagain sands, and approximately 4 in. of settlement was observed around the West Elmendorf Power Plant. Within the power plant, the building foundation and floor slabs settled more than the deeper turbine and generator foundations. The turbine and generator foundations had been compacted to 100 percent of Modified AASHO (American Association of State Highway Officials) Density (approximately 145 lb/ft³, compared to

95 percent of Modified AASHO Density for building foundations and slabs). Some of the measured differential settlement adjoining slide areas might be attributed to stretching and thinning of underlying Bootlegger Cove Clays as well as to the liquefaction and horizontal flow of saturated sand strata in the Bootlegger formation.

Numerous slopes experienced downslope movement of the frozen crust materials. This movement occurred at both sides of lower Chester Creek, causing a 2- to 3-ft-high com-

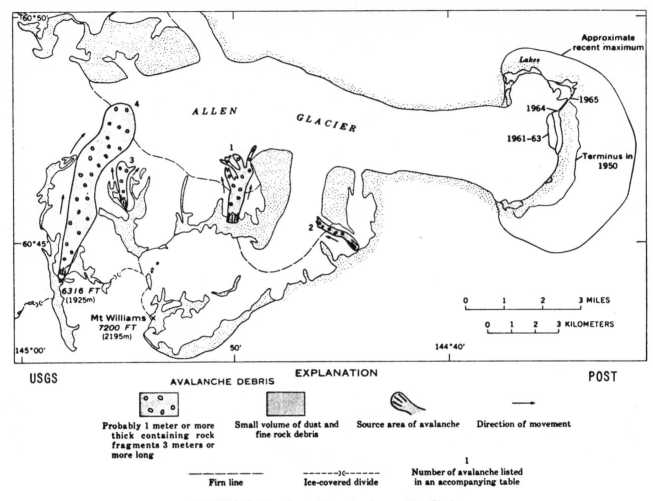

USGS EXPLANATION POST

AVALANCHE DEBRIS

Probably 1 meter or more thick containing rock fragments 3 meters or more long

Small volume of dust and fine rock debris

Source area of avalanche

Direction of movement

Firm line

Ice-covered divide

Number of avalanche listed in an accompanying table

FIGURE 242 Map of rockslide avalanches on Allen Glacier.

pression ridge of the highway fill crossing Chester Creek. Similar slippage was observed along the Elmendorf bluffs east of the port of Anchorage, at Point Woronzof (Figure 257), and along Turnagain Arm bluffs, between Rabbit Creek and Point Campbell (Figure 247). The slippage was also observed on a steep slope adjoining the Anchorage Sand and Gravel pit north of Merrill Field. The upper portions of the slopes mentioned are very well drained and consist generally of sand or gravel below the surface mantle of silt.

UPPER SHIP CREEK BASIN

The upper Ship Creek basin is that portion of Ship Creek in the Anchorage area that is above the water intake of the concrete impounding dam at the base of the Chugach Mountains. For a number of hours after the earthquake, the Ship Creek reservoir was nearly emptied of water, although the water-intake facilities and dam were undamaged

by the earthquake. This depletion of water supply probably resulted from the temporary damming of the creek channel by the cracking and downslope movement of frozen topsoil materials into the creek channel (Figure 258). Further restriction of the channel may have resulted from an accumulation of broken ice forming a more extensive dam. Figure 259 shows one of a number of sand boils observed along the lower slopes of the Ship Creek Valley. Liquefaction of these sandy materials resulted from consolidation during the period of earthquake movement.

PORTAGE

Crustal movement and settlement probably was as great in the Portage area as in any other part of the earthquake-affected area. Although surface topography is quite flat and stream channels are relatively shallow, earth cracks in the Portage area were the largest observed; many were 4–6 ft wide when examined (Figures 260–262). Figures 263–266 are additional views of ground cracks in the Portage area that resulted from crustal movements. Figure 267 shows the crack pattern that formed on a point of land extending into Portage Lake, located at the head of Portage Valley midway between Portage and Whittier. Figure 268 is a close-up of the same crack formation. Figure 269 shows the lateral displacement of the gravel soil from a building foundation. This displacement had occurred on all sides of the building foundation and resulted from the movement of the foundation against the adjoining soil. To permit such movement, the soil beneath the foundation may have partly liquefied.

Settlement in the Portage area is illustrated by Figures 270 and 271, which show the area after a spring high tide.

Although tectonic settlement may account for 5–6 ft of settlement, many additional feet of settlement undoubtedly occurred in the saturated silts, sands, and gravels overlying the bedrock. The water table in this area was 4–8 ft below the surface. It is probable that the severe crustal movements and settlement resulted from large-amplitude seismic surface waves in combination with liquefaction of the base soils (Figures 272 and 273).

SEWARD

The severity of crustal movement and the degree of settlement that occurred in the Seward area are indicated by the large earth cracks, ranging from a few inches to 2½ ft wide,

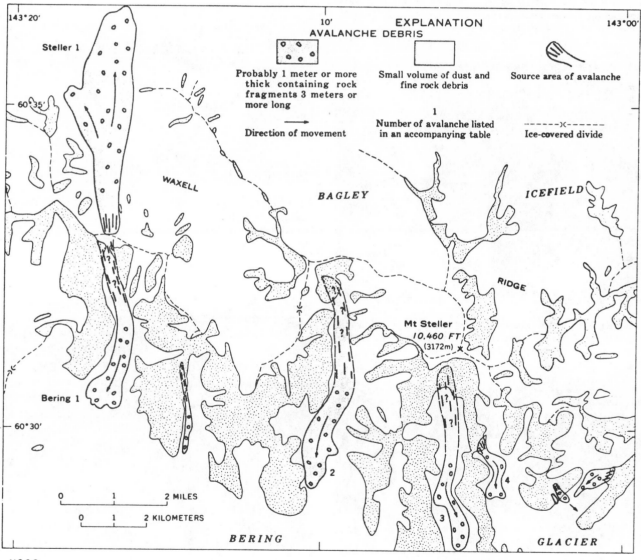

FIGURE 243 Map of rockslide avalanches in the Waxell Ridge region, Bering, and Steller glaciers.

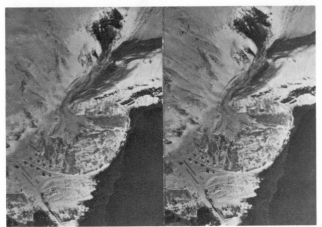

U.S. Coast and Geodetic Survey

FIGURE 244   Leonard Glacier debris avalanche terminates 1,500 ft north of the Whittier tunnel portal. Avalanche covered with fresh snow (April 15, 1964). Scale: 1 in. = 1,800 ft.

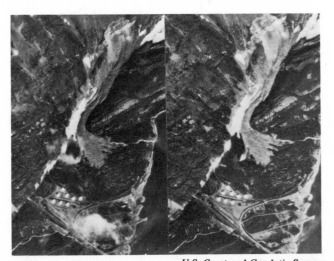

U.S. Coast and Geodetic Survey

FIGURE 245   Leonard Glacier debris avalanche. The remainder of the Whittier airstrip is at lower right; the railroad tunnel is at lower left (August 15, 1964). Scale: 1 in. = 1,650 ft.

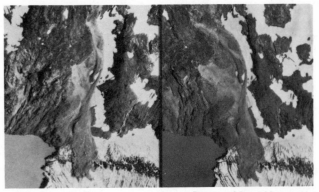

Bureau of Land Mangement

FIGURE 246   Portage Glacier debris avalanche at the north terminus of Portage Glacier (July 7, 1964). Scale: 1 in. = 1,000 ft.

Alaska State Housing Authority

FIGURE 247   Slipping of the frozen crust on steep slopes of the bluff along Turnagain Arm between Point Campbell and Campbell Lake (April 3, 1964). Scale: 1 in. = 540 ft.

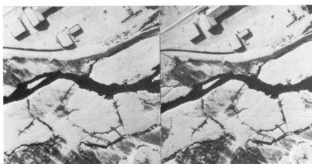

U.S. Army

FIGURE 248   Cracks caused by ground motion along Ship Creek, immediately upstream of the Chugach Electric Association–Alaska Railroad dam. Frozen crust overlying saturated alluvium (April 4, 1964). Scale: 1 in. = 520 ft.

U.S. Army

FIGURE 249   Portage: Soil-displacement cracking related to drained surface soils overlying saturated soils subject to liquefaction (March 30, 1964).

FIGURE 250   Girdwood townsite; unsaturated soils overlying saturated soils. Displacement cracks along railroad embankment and on townsite plain. Water-table level was 4–8 ft below this plain at the time of the earthquake (late April 1964).

and by the differential settlement adjacent to the earth cracks landward of the shoreline (Figures 251, 274, and 275). The extent of severe cracking is outlined on Figure 276. Considerable ground cracking and displacement took place in the Forest Acres subdivision in north Seward, although it was not close to a bank or failure scarp. The Forest Acres area was developed along Jap Creek on the alluvial deposits in the Resurrection River Valley (Figure 277). The soils in this area are composed of sand and gravels with smaller amounts of interbedded fine sand and silt occurring

Bureau of Land Management
FIGURE 252   Valdez crustal movements; displacement of unsaturated surface soils overlying saturated granular soils subject to liquefaction (McKinley Street east) (late March 1964).

more frequently in the fractured area. The water table in the fractured area was found to be at a depth of 6.3 ft and 12.5 ft (TP-1 and TP-2, Figure 278, Lemke, 1967); the distance to water increased with distance from the river and in the direction of the unfractured area. An exploratory hole drilled 250 ft outside the fractured area (Boring F.A.2, Figure 278) had a water level 22.0 ft below ground surface (Lemke, 1967). Figure 279 shows the pronounced ground

Bureau of Land Management
FIGURE 251   Seward: Soil-displacement cracks west of destroyed small-boat harbor and north of Texaco oil-storage tanks (late March 1964). Scale: 1 in. = 300 ft.

T. Tice, U.S. Army Corps of Engineers
FIGURE 253   Anchorage port area: Soil-displacement cracks east and above tidewater. Frozen crust is generally gravel fill overlying tide-deposited silt clays (March 28, 1964).

FIGURE 254   West Turnagain slide area: Soil cracking and displacement of the type preceding horizontal retrogressive translatory slide failure (April 19, 1964).

cracking along Jap Creek north and west of Forest Acres; Figure 280 shows the part of Jap Creek near the highway and railroad bridges. Some of the cracks, such as those along the toe of high fills, obviously relate to differential settlement, but the greater numbers of cracks generally occurred in lower ground with a high groundwater table. Figures 278, 281 and 282 show the relation of the ground cracking to the surface elevations; they also show the manner in which the cracks connect to the frost-free soil surrounding the Forest Acres homes.

VALDEZ

Crustal movements and settlement were quite pronounced in the Robe River and Lowe River deltas. The severe

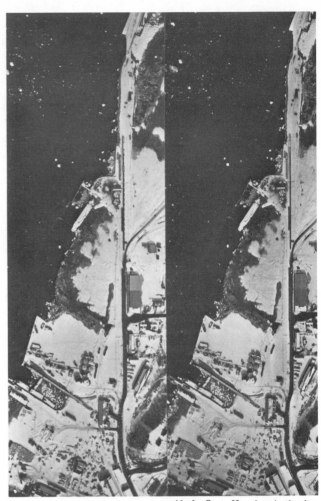

Alaska State Housing Authority

FIGURE 256   Anchorage port area: Displacement cracking in the granular soil and silt-clay slopes paralleling Knik Arm (March 30, 1964). Scale: 1 in. = 575 ft.

FIGURE 255   Girdwood townsite submergence after settlement of landmass combined with a spring high tide. Settlement was a combination of tectonic (bedrock) settlement and soil consolidation and stretching displacement toward tidewater (April 1964).

ground cracking on these deltas is shown in Figures 283 and 284. Coulter and Migliaccio (1966) have described in detail the extent of ground fissuring; the cracks opened from a few inches to 2 ft in width, and subsidence reached a maximum of approximately 19 ft at the waterfront. Figure 158 shows the pattern of ground cracking in the Valdez area as well as a settlement profile along Alaska Avenue between Water Street and Hobart Street (Coulter and Migliaccio, 1966). The cracking was more frequent and severe near the waterfront; cracking is noticeably less frequent across the dike and in the higher ground areas. The riverbeds and the portions of the dike that are penetrated by roads that reduced its height show the development of a considerable number of cracks.

Because the Valdez area has a very heavy snowfall and had a snowcover of 19½ ft on March 28, 1964, frost penetration would be minimal except under cleared areas such as

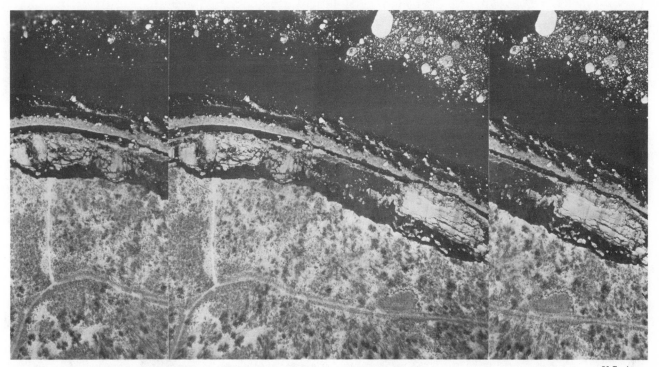

U.S. Army

FIGURE 257   Point Woronzof on lower Knik Arm west of Anchorage. Downslope movement of frozen crust material overlying drained sand and gravel soils (March 29, 1964). Scale: 1 in. = 530 ft.

FIGURE 258   Upper Ship Creek showing downslope slippage of frozen crustal materials that caused temporary damming of stream (April 8, 1964).

FIGURE 260   Portage: Soil-displacement cracks between Seward Highway and railroad station on floodplains at the head of Turnagain Arm.

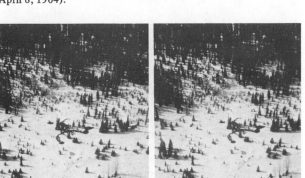

FIGURE 259   Sand boils, upper Ship Creek valley. A number of these were noted in the narrow floodplain paralleling Ship Creek (April 8, 1964).

FIGURE 261   Portage: Soil-displacement cracks on the Turnagain Arm side of highway. Railroad station in background (April 8, 1964).

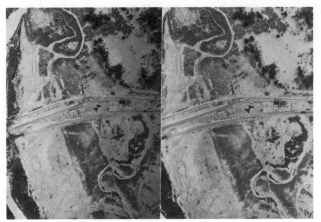

U.S. Army

FIGURE 262   Twentymile River and Portage railroad terminal. Cracks in Figure 261 can be seen on upper (east) side of highway embankment beside railroad depot (March 30, 1964).

FIGURE 263   Highway failure east of Kern Creek, toward Portage. Lateral displacement of road fill where it overlay tideflat alluvium (April 8, 1964).

U.S. Forest Service

FIGURE 264   East approach to Twentymile River highway bridge at Portage. Railroad station is in background.

U.S. Army

FIGURE 265   Displacement and cracking of soils along Portage Creek just south of Portage. Junction at right connects Seward Highway (paralleling railroad) to Portage Glacier Highway to the east (March 30, 1964).

U.S. Forest Service

FIGURE 266   Soil-displacement cracks south of Portage, following along highway center line and shoulder (early April 1964).

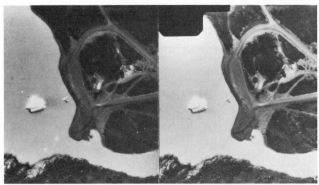

U.S. Coast and Geodetic Survey

FIGURE 267   Soil-displacement cracks on point of land extending into Portage Lake outlet. Stress distribution of soil under point should be less than along adjacent shoreline. Cracking may also reflect a lower soil density in the point materials. Lower soil stress and lower densities would both contribute to earlier soil liquefaction (August 29, 1964). Scale: 1 in = 600 ft.

FIGURE 268   Displacement cracks in point of land on Portage Lake shown in preceding figure (late March 1964).

U.S. Forest Service

FIGURE 270   Portage area after spring high tides; subsidence was a combination of tectonic settlement and settlement resulting from consolidation and of lateral stretching of underlying granular soils and interbedded silts (April 1964).

FIGURE 271   Portage area: Inundation of road and railroad embankments. Tectonic subsidence accounted for 5–6 ft of the settlement; soil consolidation and stretching accounted for the remainder (April 1964).

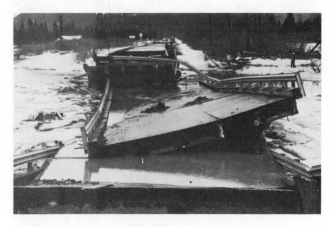

U.S. Forest Service

FIGURE 269   Portage area: Lateral displacement of soil adjoining foundation and concrete entrance stairway. Similar displacements were noted along the foundations of houses behind the Turnagain slide area (April 1964).

FIGURE 272   Portage area highway bridge; failure may have resulted from liquefaction of the soils in which bridge piers were embedded as well as from lateral displacement of the surface soils and seismic ground waves. (early April 1964).

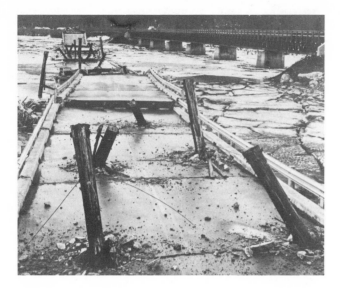

FIGURE 273   Twentymile River highway and railroad bridges. Both bridges show compression failure of soil from lateral displacement of embankments at the abutments. Subsoil liquefaction and seismic ground waves may also have contributed to failure of the highway bridge (mid-April 1964).

roads, parking areas, and windblown areas. Holes 1 and 3 (Figure 158), just north of the small-boat basin, show groundwater elevations of 4–6 ft below ground surface 2 months after the earthquake. Holes 7 and 10, on the highway fill east of town, show that groundwater existed at 14- to 23-ft depths. Air photographs show evidence of ground fractures and extruded sand in the vicinity of hole 10 and in those areas of shallower water table.

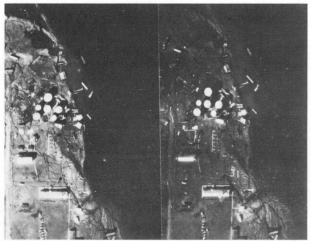

U.S. Army

FIGURE 274   Seward: Ground cracking and settlement. North end of railroad yards, Texaco oil-storage tanks, and former location of San Juan Dock (April 14, 1964). Scale: 1 in. = 340 ft.

FIGURE 275   Seward: Ground cracking and settlement. Railroad yards adjacent to Resurrection Bay. Submarine slides occurred along severe cracks in downtown Seward (May 20, 1964).

HOMER

Ground cracking and small submarine soil failures at the end of the Homer Spit caused some concern about the stability of the spit. The subsidence was sufficient to cause inundation of the spit during the higher tides after the earthquake (Figure 285). Approximately 2.5 ft of the subsidence was caused by consolidation of soils, and an additional 2.3 ft was considered to be tectonic subsidence.

The tidal elevation along the Homer Spit at the time of the earthquake was approximately −7.1 ft MSL, or 2.5 ft relative to MLLW.

The end of the Homer Spit before the earthquake is shown in Figure 286; the end of the spit after the earthquake is shown in Figures 287 and 288. High tides and storms caused the shoreline to recede and to build up the spit (Figures 289 and 290). Gravel excavated from the new small-boat harbor was also used to raise the surface elevation of the spit (Figure 291).

U.S. Coast and Geodetic Survey

FIGURE 276   Postearthquake Seward after waterfront had been cleared and regraded. Hatched area shows limit of severe ground cracking (August 29, 1964). Scale: 1 in. = 3,600 ft.

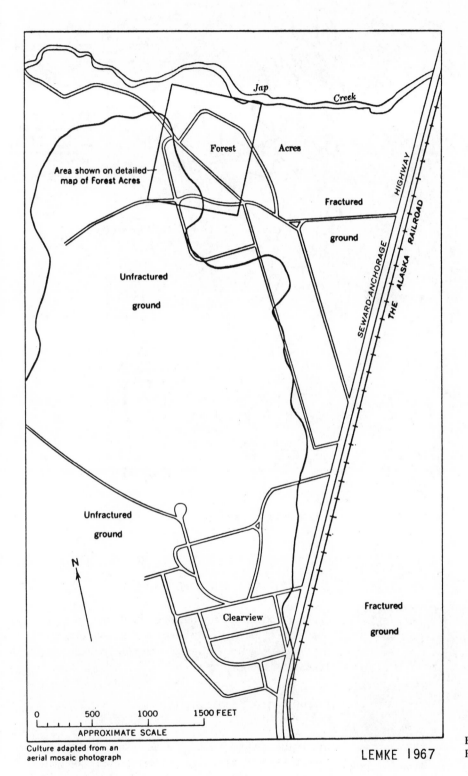

FIGURE 277 Limits of fractured ground in Forest Acres and Clearview subdivisions.

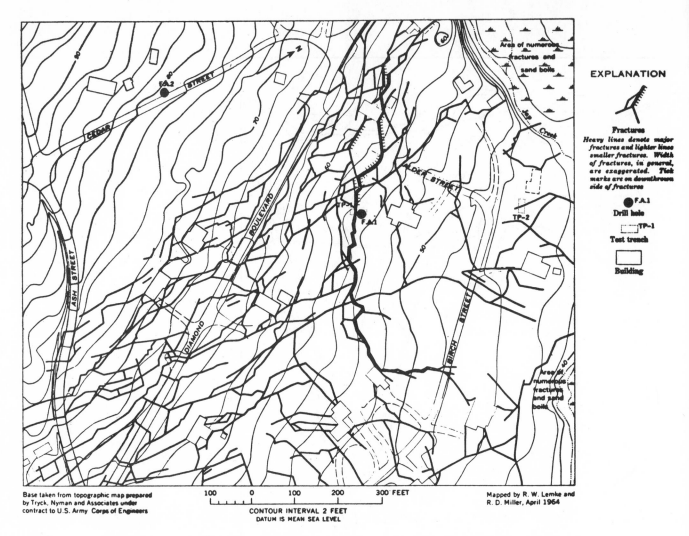

FIGURE 278   Ground fractures, drill-hole and test-trench locations, Forest Acres subdivision, north Seward.

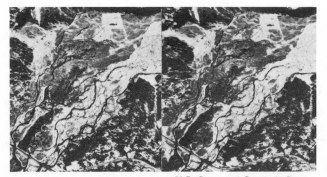

U.S. Coast and Geodetic Survey

FIGURE 279   Jap Creek ground cracking west of Seward Highway and railroad. Part of Forest Acres subdivision is along the left center of photo (April 3, 1964). Scale: 1 in. = 3,000 ft.

INVESTIGATIONS AND REPORTS

A major study of the soil failure in the Anchorage area was begun in May 1964 by Shannon & Wilson, Inc., under the direction of Warren George, Chief of the Engineering Division, Alaska District.

EXPLORATION AND LABORATORY INVESTIGATIONS

Initial studies of surface features and mapping of the grabens, cracks, and other pertinent features were conducted immediately after the earthquake by the Engineering Geology Evaluation Group, organized and supervised by Lidia Selkregg under the auspices of the Alaska State Housing Authority (ASHA). Ruth Schmidt coordinated fieldwork and prepared the survey and evaluation reports. These re-

U.S. Army

FIGURE 280   Seward Highway and railroad crossing Jap Creek northeast of Forest Acres subdivision, Seward. Cracks are more prominent in areas of lower ground (higher groundwater) and paralleling high fills (April 15, 1964). Scale: 1 in. = 570 ft.

ports were valuable guides in outlining areas for required exploration and testing. At the request of the Urban Renewal Agency, a division of the Housing and Home Finance Agency, ASHA arranged to obtain measurements and to conduct exploration and testing; piezometers and slope indicators were installed immediately after the earthquake. The work was performed by the Arctic Alaska Testing Laboratories under the supervision of Bud Adams. The

U.S. Army

FIGURE 282   Fractured ground in Forest Acres subdivision south (lower left) of area shown in preceding photo; ground cracks seem to relate to lower areas (April 15, 1964). Scale: 1 in. = 300 ft.

U.S. Army

FIGURE 281   Fractured ground in Forest Acres subdivision, with Jap Creek floodplain upper right. Crack displacement is greatest in upper center of photo; this slightly depressed area may be an old meander of Jap Creek. No ground cracks at upper left. Water table by road at upper left was 22 ft below surface. Water table by crack in center of photo was 12.5 ft below surface. Water table by house right of center of photo was 6.3 ft below surface. Scale: 1 in. = 340 ft.

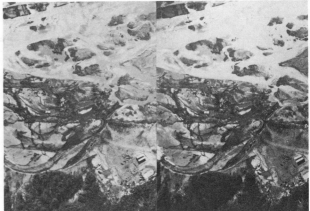

Air Photo Tech, Inc.

FIGURE 283   Ground fractures along the Robe River Delta east of Valdez. No cracks appear on the higher bench (lower left) (June 13, 1967). Scale: 1 in. = 540 ft.

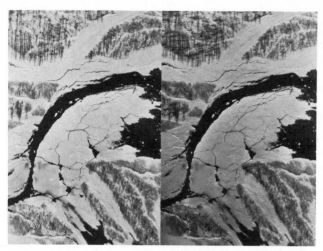

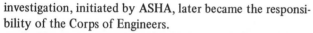

Alaska State Housing Authority

FIGURE 284   Ground fractures in Lowe River Delta east of Valdez. Fractures are more frequent along lower ground where water is nearer the surface (April 11, 1964). Scale: 1 in. = 500 ft.

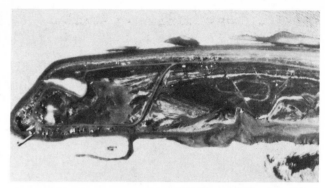

U.S. Coast and Geodetic Survey

FIGURE 286   End of Homer Spit before the earthquake at a midtide water elevation (June 17, 1962). Scale: 1 in. = 600 ft.

U.S. Coast and Geodetic Survey

FIGURE 287   End of Homer Spit after earthquake at a midtide water elevation (April 14, 1964). Scale: 1 in. = 630 ft.

investigation, initiated by ASHA, later became the responsibility of the Corps of Engineers.

On May 5, 1964, the crews of Arctic Alaska Testing Laboratories were combined with those engaged by Shannon & Wilson, Inc. to initiate soil exploration. In May, the results of two Failing-1500 drills and a drilling crew sent from the Mobile District, Corps of Engineers, were incorporated with the Shannon & Wilson data (Figure 292). A list of the drill rigs used in the exploration phase of the contract is presented in Table 3.

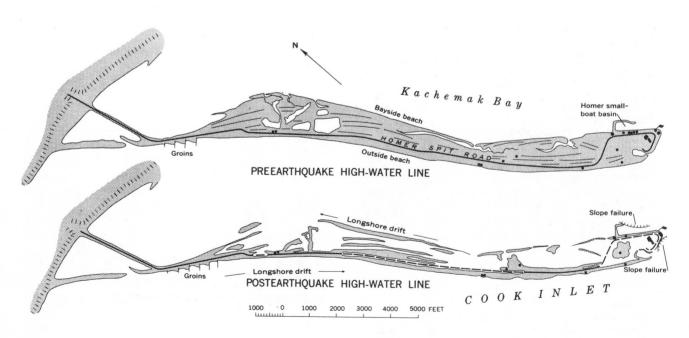

Roger M. Waller and Kirk W. Stanley, USGS

FIGURE 285   Effect of land subsidence on Homer Spit.

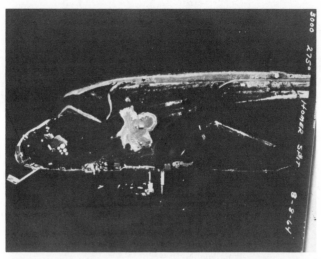

FIGURE 288 End of Homer Spit during a high tide. Predicted tide
was 20.1 ft MLLW or 10.5 ft MSL (August 8, 1964). Scale: 1 in. =
570 ft.

FIGURE 289 Homer Spit, Cook Inlet side, showing buildup from
the first storm that occurred during the high tides in spring 1965
(May 8, 1965).

FIGURE 290 Homer Spit: Buildup of south end from storm that
occurred at high tides. Subsidence of spit during earthquake inundated the first floor of Land's End Motel (background). Motel has
been raised above high-water elevation.

FIGURE 291 Homer Spit after earthquake subsidence. Land had
been raised by waves and by the disposal of gravel from small-boat
harbor excavation (May 8, 1965).

FIGURE 292 A Failing-1500 rig drilling exploratory hole C-116 in
Turnagain slide area (May 30, 1964).

Bucket-auger holes were used to obtain undisturbed
block samples of soil, to observe soil conditions directly,
and to obtain vane-shear strengths in the horizontal plane.
Vane-shear testing in place provided more reliable information on the *in situ* strength of the soils and determined the
degree of disturbance that may have resulted in the soil-
sampling operations. A special housing was designed to
protect the geologist making tests in the bucket-auger hole
(Figure 293).

Groundwater observations were obtained from 50
piezometer installations by Arctic Alaska, Shannon &
Wilson, Inc., and by the Corps of Engineers. Cased wells
and slope-indicator installations were observed to evaluate
the groundwater conditions.

Geophysical seismic exploration was conducted to
evaluate the velocity characteristics of the soil in an attempt to determine the depth of sliding and of soil-crack-
ing. Electrical resistivity was used in an attempt to differ-
entiate between the various zones of soil disturbance, and
geophysical studies were conducted in a number of drill

TABLE 3   Drilling Rigs and Owners or Operators Engaged in Postearthquake Anchorage Area Soil Exploration Tests

Drill Rig		Owner/Operator
Mayhew-1000 rotary	#1292	United Geophysical Service
Mayhew-1000 rotary	#1436	United Geophysical Service
Mayhew-1000 rotary	#1444	United Geophysical Service
Mayhew-1000 rotary	#1516	United Geophysical Service
Mayhew-1000 rotary	#1517	United Geophysical Service
Mayhew-1000 rotary	#1602	United Geophysical Service
Mayhew-1000 rotary	#1656 Norwell	United Geophysical Service
Mayhew-1000 rotary	#1691 Norwell	United Geophysical Service
Mayhew-1000 rotary	#1827 Norwell	Western Geophysical/Corps of Engineers
Mayhew-1000 rotary	#2008 Norwell	Western Geophysical/Corps of Engineers
Mayhew- 500 rotary	#1636 Norwell	Western Geophysical/Corps of Engineers
Failing- 1500 rotary	#1	Soil Sampling Services
Failing- 1500 rotary	#50	Corps of Engineers, Mobile District
Failing- 1500 rotary	#52	Corps of Engineers, Mobile District
Failing- 1500 rotary	—	Woodland-McDowell
Calwell bucket auger	#292	Corps of Engineers, Seattle District/Shannon & Wilson
Calwell bucket auger	#430	Corps of Engineers, Alaska District/Shannon & Wilson
Bucyrus-Erie churn 22W	#113687	Clemenson Drilling Company

FIGURE 293   Bucket auger rig with specially designed housing to protect geologist sampling the sides of the hole.

holes. Spontaneous potential electrical resistivity, microlog resistivity, and gamma-ray logs were also analyzed.

Where practical, test trenches were used to observe and sample the problem soils in an attempt to determine the mechanism of failure.

Slope-indicator casing was set and observations taken to determine whether additional soil movement was taking place.

A detailed description of Anchorage area soil studies was prepared by Shannon & Wilson, Inc. (1964a, b, 1966).

SURVEY CONTROL

Immediately after the earthquake, at the request of the Engineering Geology Evaluation Group, benchmarks were established and targets installed by J. L. Hayes of Tryck, Nyman & Hayes. The targets were installed to obtain distance measurements between the roof of the Catholic Junior High School (Figure 294 and Table 4) and the roofs of the Anchorage-Westward Hotel, the Knik Arms Apartments, and St. Mary's Residence. The first two measurements were taken on April 2 and 3 with a tellurometer; all additional measurements were taken with a geodimeter from April 3 to May 6. The Bureau of Land Management, which owns the geodimeter, claims an accuracy of ±0.06 ft for night readings. The manufacturer claims an accuracy of 0.04 ft for distance over 50 ft. Because of the target location, none of the observed changes is considered a result of subsurface movement.

Angular measurements were also taken from the Catholic Junior High School, with a line to St. Mary's Residence established as a base line. Angular measure-

Bureau of Land Management

FIGURE 294   Tellurometer making distance measurements to buildings in downtown Anchorage. Measurements were also taken from location on the mountain in the background.

ments were made with a Wilt T-2 theodolite with a 1-second accuracy. Angles were measured to the Knik Arms Apartments, the Anchorage-Westward Hotel, the Public Safety Building, and Providence Hospital. Micrometer readings on Anchorage area buildings from April 3 to

TABLE 5   Differences in Angular Measurements from St. Mary's Residence (0°00'00") to Selected Buildings in the Anchorage Area, from Theodolite Locations at Catholic Junior High School, between April 3 and May 6, 1964

Date	Knik Arms Apartments	Anchorage-Westward Hotel	Public Safety Building	Providence Hospital
April 3	2°41'19"	21°34'16"	–	128°55'32"
April 3	2°41'18"	21°34'15"	–	128°55'33"
April 6	2°41'19"	21°34'13"	32°47'59"	128°55'32"
April 7	2°41'22"	21°34'16"	32°48'00"	128°55'32"
April 8	2°41'20"	21°34'12"	32°47'56"	Not visible
April 9	2°41'20"	21°34'14"	32°47'58"	128°55'32"
April 11	2°41'21"	21°34'18"	32°48'01"	128°55'35"
April 13	2°41'21"	21°34'17"	32°48'01"	128°55'39"
April 15	2°41'22"	21°34'19"	32°48'01"	128°55'38"
April 18	2°41'21"	21°34'18"	32°48'01"	128°55'36"
April 21	2°41'22"	21°34'18"	32°48'03"	128°55'36"
April 28	2°41'22"	21°34'16"	32°47'59"	128°55'39"
May 6[a]	2°41'20"	21°34'17"	32°48'02"	128°55'29"

[a]Raining; measured one set only because of poor visibility.

May 6, 1964, are given in Table 5. Although some of the variations in the readings are in excess of instrument errors, they are not considered significant. At the request of the Engineering Geology Evaluation Group, Mr. Hayes also furnished distance measurements from a site in the Chugach Mountains east of Anchorage to monuments in the Spenard area, to compare with measurements to eight stations on which preearthquake measurements had been obtained in 1963. These measurements were taken with a tellurometer with first-order capability and an accuracy of 2 in. ±1 in 300,000. The measurements on Figure 295 are to stations in the Turnagain, International Airport, and Sand Lake areas. Differences in distance measurements vary from 0.3–0.9 ft immediately east and south of Anchorage International Airport to differences of 1.6–2.7 ft north of the International Airport. The maximum increase in distance of 2.7 ft was to a monument at Chillagen Drive and Clay Products Road, the only monument adjacent to a slide area (Turnagain) with preearthquake tellurometer measurements.

TABLE 4   Differences in the Distance from Catholic Junior High School Station (Fireweed Lane at Arctic Boulevard) to Selected Anchorage Area Buildings between April 2 and May 6, 1964 (Measured in Feet)

Date	Anchorage-Westward Hotel	Knik Arms Apartments	St. Mary's Residence
Tellurometer			
April 2	7078.23	6304.44	–
April 3	7078.55	6304.30	–
Geodimeter			
April 3	7078.46	6304.50	5525.77
April 5	–	6304.42	5525.61
April 6	7078.36	6304.31	5525.75
April 7	7078.39	6304.23	5525.69
April 8	7078.49	6304.41	5525.70
April 9	7078.37	6304.38	5525.62
April 11	7078.37	6304.37	5525.64
April 13	7078.39	6304.35	5525.64
April 15	7078.35	6304.33	5525.61
April 18	7078.35	6304.36	5525.58
April 21	7078.39	6304.32	5525.62
April 28	7078.33	6304.30	5525.58
May 6	7078.38	6304.34	5525.64
Mean Distance	7078.39	6304.36	5525.65

CONCLUSIONS

The numerous landslides and the consolidation, settlement, and cracking of soils were major features of the Alaska earthquake. This experience indicates that if the conditions are right, earthquake-induced soil failures can produce a disaster. The soil failures in the Anchorage area were produced by ground shaking that was not extraordinarily

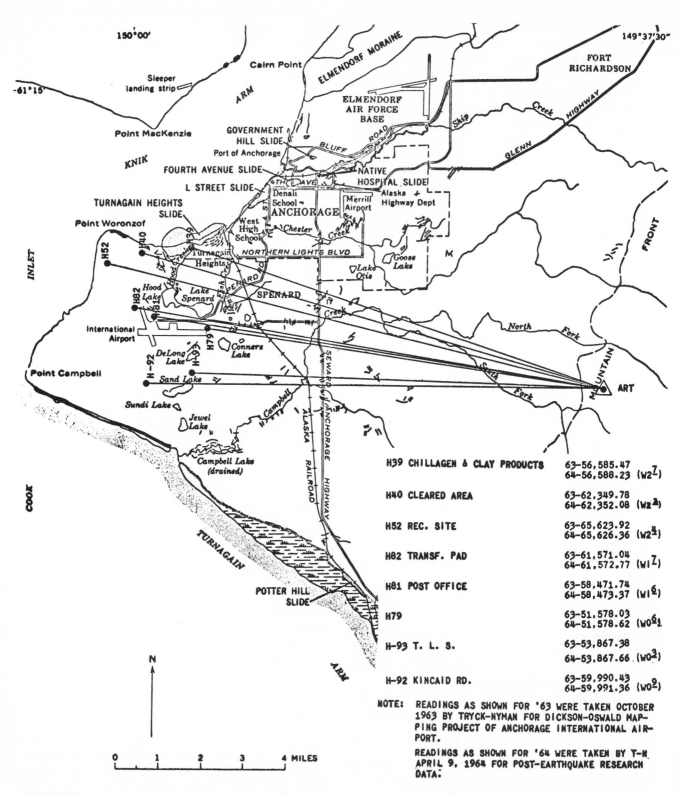

H39 CHILLAGEN & CLAY PRODUCTS	63-56,585.47	
	64-56,588.23	$(W2^Z_\frac{1}{1})$
H40 CLEARED AREA	63-62,349.78	
	64-62,352.08	$(W2^4_2)$
H52 REC. SITE	63-65,623.92	
	64-65,626.36	$(W2^{\frac{3}{4}}_1)$
H82 TRANSF. PAD	63-61,571.04	
	64-61,572.77	$(W1^Z_2)$
H81 POST OFFICE	63-58,471.74	
	64-58,473.37	$(W1^6_8)$
H79	63-51,578.03	
	64-51,578.62	$(W0^8_1{}_1)$
H-93 T. L. S.	63-53,867.38	
	64-53,867.66	$(W0^3_2)$
H-92 KINCAID RD.	63-59,990.43	
	64-59,991.36	$(W0^2_2)$

NOTE: READINGS AS SHOWN FOR '63 WERE TAKEN OCTOBER 1963 BY TRYCK-NYMAN FOR DICKSON-OSWALD MAPPING PROJECT OF ANCHORAGE INTERNATIONAL AIRPORT.

READINGS AS SHOWN FOR '64 WERE TAKEN BY T-N APRIL 9, 1964 FOR POST-EARTHQUAKE RESEARCH DATA.

FIGURE 295 Distance measurements from a site in the Chugach Mountains to stations in the Turnagain, Anchorage International Airport, and Sand Lake areas.

intense; the motion was not more severe than had been experienced on numerous occasions in California and other regions of the United States. The duration of shaking at Anchorage, however, was unusually long; the strongest phase lasted about 1 minute, and appreciable ground motion was felt for 3–4 minutes. The prolonged oscillatory straining of the soil in many cases is thought to have produced a degeneration of the strength that led to failure. Landslides were known to have occurred along the bluffs in the past, and additional sliding was to be expected during an earthquake. It was not expected, however, that numerous slides might be activated, or that very large masses of soil might be involved that might travel such large distances. It is still not known why more slides like the Turnagain Heights slides did not occur along the coastal bluffs, nor is it possible at present to assess the likelihood of sliding during future earthquakes of those bluffs that did not slide during the 1964 shaking. More precise methods are needed for assessing the possibility of soil failure during earthquake stressing.

Conclusions that were drawn about the slides and related phenomena follow:

1. The soil-slide failure mechanism appears to be related to the initial soil strength of the soils, the duration of strong ground motion, and the degree of loss of soil strength.

2. Rotational slumps, or circular slides, are thought to have been related to groundwater seepage along the pre-slide toes and were associated with an absence of any toe buttressing. Groundwater seeps coincided with a layer of sand overlying the Bootlegger Cove Clay formation in the Anchorage area. Sliding occurred along steep slopes. Progressive failure did not take place behind the initial slump failure; instead, failure generally flattened the slope and improved slope stability.

3. Horizontal translatory failure was related to the liquefaction of sand layers or to the reduction of strength in soft sensitive layers of clay. Groundwater pressures and direction of percolation were controlled from surface-water sources and were not artesian from sources upslope. The sensitivity of the clays may be related to very long-term leaching of salts by percolating waters. The presence of sand lenses would increase the horizontal permeability of soil strata and could increase the sensitivity of interspersed and adjoining clay layers. Failure occurred in the weakened soil layer closest to the surface. This shallow failure condition may have resulted from a relatively large soil oscillation from seismic action closer to the surface.

4. Earth-flow liquefaction was most pronounced in the Potter Hill railroad slide. Other forms of landslides, as well as subaqueous slides, showed earth-flow characteristics. The Potter Hill railroad embankment appears to have failed as a result of the liquefaction of underlying stratified clean sand and cohesionless silt layers under artesian water pressure. Failure diminished as the height of the fill increased, and it was totally absent under much higher bluffs immediately behind and to the west of the area that failed.

5. Subaqueous-slide failures were common to areas with cohesionless silt, sand, and gravel deposits, even at distances of more than 145 mi from the earthquake epicenter. Failures were most frequent in more recent deposits, in those with artesian groundwater pressure produced by stream gradient or by a lowered tide elevation, and in deposits under lower overburden or confining pressure.

6. Avalanching was observed very soon after the start of the earthquake and continued throughout the duration of the strong motion. Initial failure possibly resulted from direct seismic forces, whereas later or continuing failure may have resulted from progressive brittle failure of rock and ice and a progressive lessening of the shear strength with earthquake duration.

7. Crustal movements and settlement of unconsolidated material appear to have been influenced directly or indirectly by the following factors:

• Strains associated with seismic ground waves that caused consolidation and cracking of soils
• The long duration of the earthquake that permitted progressive cracking and movement of the soils
• Liquefaction of underlying soils permitting greater soil movement and accelerated cracking of the surface soil
• Greater cracking along stream channels and other depressions
• Settlement of soils that was most noticeable in cohesionless soil deposits, with the magnitude of settlement probably related to the type of material, density, and depth of deposit
• Short distance downslope frozen crust sliding along steep bluffs—a condition common to steep slopes with various soil conditions and appeared unrelated to groundwater conditions.

ACKNOWLEDGMENTS

Except as otherwise noted, figures are credited to the U.S. Army Corps of Engineers.

REFERENCES

Alaska District Corps of Engineers, 1964. Eyewitness accounts. Anchorage: U.S. Army Corps of Engineers.
Barnes, F. F., 1943. Geology of the Portage Pass area, Alaska. U.S. Geological Survey Bulletin 926-D. Washington: Government Printing Office.

Bull, Colin, and Cedomir Marangunic, 1967. The earthquake-induced slide on the Sherman Glacier, south-central Alaska, and its glaciological effects, *in* Physics of snow and ice. Proceedings of the International Conference on Low Temperature Science, Sapporo, Japan, 1966, Vol. 1, Part 1. Sapporo: Institute of Low Temperature Science. p. 395–408.

Coulter, Henry W., and Ralph R. Migliaccio, 1966. Effects of the earthquake of March 27, 1964, at Valdez, Alaska. U.S. Geological Survey Professional Paper 542-C. Washington: Government Printing Office. 36 p. Also *in* The Great Alaska Earthquake of 1964: Geology. NAS Pub. 1601. Washington: National Academy of Sciences, 1971. p. 359–394.

Davison, Charles, 1936. Great earthquakes. London: Thomas Murby and Company. 276 p.

Engineering Geology Evaluation Group, 1964. Geologic report: 27 March 1964 earthquake in Greater Anchorage area (unpublished report). Anchorage: Alaska State Housing Authority and City of Anchorage, 1964. 47 p.

Ferrians, Oscar J., Jr., 1966. Effects of the earthquake of March 27, 1964, in the Copper River basin area, Alaska. U.S. Geological Survey Professional Paper 543-E. Washington: Government Printing Office. 28 p. Abstract *in* The Great Alaska Earthquake of 1964: Geology. NAS Pub. 1601. Washington: National Academy of Sciences, 1971, p. 282–283.

Field, William O., 1965. Avalanches caused by the Alaska earthquake of March 1964, *in* International Symposium on Scientific Aspects of Snow and Ice Avalanches. International Association of Scientific Hydrology Publication 69. Gentbrugge [Belgium]: International Association of Scientific Hydrology, 1966. p. 326–331.

Hansen, Wallace R., 1965. Effects of the earthquake of March 27, 1964, at Anchorage, Alaska. U.S. Geological Survey Professional Paper 542-A. Washington: Government Printing Office. 68 p. Also *in* The Great Alaska Earthquake of 1964: Geology. NAS Pub. 1601. Washington: National Academy of Sciences, 1971. p. 289–357.

Heck, N. H., and R. A. Eppley, 1958. Earthquake history of the United States, Part 1: Continental United States and Alaska (exclusive of California and Western Nevada). U.S. Department of Commerce, Coast and Geodetic Survey. Washington: Government Printing Office. 80 p.

Kachadoorian, Reuben, 1965. Effects of the earthquake of March 27, 1964, at Whittier, Alaska. U.S. Geological Survey Professional Paper 542-B. Washington: Government Printing Office. 21 p. Also *in* The Great Alaska Earthquake of 1964: Geology. NAS Pub. 1601. Washington: National Academy of Sciences, 1971. p. 439–459.

Kennedy, Arthur [1964]. U.S. Forest Service research party weathers quake at Portage Glacier (unpublished personal account). 13 p.

LaChapelle, Edward R., 1968. The character of snow avalanching induced by the Alaska earthquake *in* The Great Alaska Earthquake of 1964: Hydrology. NAS Pub. 1603. Washington: National Academy of Sciences. p. 355–361.

Lemke, Richard W., 1967. Effects of the earthquake of March 27, 1964, at Seward, Alaska. U.S. Geological Survey Professional Paper 542-E. Washington: Government Printing Office. 43 p. Also *in* The Great Alaska Earthquake of 1964: Geology. NAS Pub. 1601. Washington: National Academy of Sciences, 1971. p. 395–437.

McCulloch, David S., 1966. Slide-induced waves, seiching, and ground fracturing caused by the earthquake of March 27, 1964, at Kenai Lake, Alaska. U.S. Geological Survey Professional Paper 543-A. Washington: Government Printing Office. 41 p. Also *in* The Great Alaska Earthquake of 1964: Hydrology. NAS Pub. 1603. Washington: National Academy of Sciences, 1968. p. 47–81.

McCulloch, D. S., and M. G. Bonilla, 1964. Report on a landslide at Mile 21.4 Kenai Lake, resulting from the earthquake of March 27, 1964 Unpublished Administrative Report to The Alaska Railroad. 4 p.

McCulloch, David S., and Manuel G. Bonilla, 1970. Effects of the earthquake of March 27, 1964, on The Alaska Railroad. U.S. Geological Survey Professional Paper 545-D. Washington: Government Printing Office. 161 p. In part *in* The Great Alaska Earthquake of 1964: Geology. NAS Pub. 1601. Washington: National Academy of Sciences, 1971. p. 543–640.

Marangunic, Cedomir, and Colin Bull, 1968. The landslide on the Sherman Glacier *in* The Great Alaska Earthquake of 1964: Hydrology. NAS Pub. 1603. Washington: National Academy of Sciences. p. 383–394.

Plafker, George [1964]. Sherman Glacier rockslide avalanche triggered by the Alaska earthquake of March 27, 1964 (Abstract). Menlo Park [California]: U.S. Geological Survey. 2 p.

Plafker, George, 1965. Tectonic deformation associated with the 1964 Alaska earthquake, *Science*, 148 (June 25), 1675–1687.

Plafker, George, and Reuben Kachadoorian, 1966. Geologic effects of the March 1964 earthquake and associated seismic sea waves on Kodiak and nearby islands, Alaska. U.S. Geological Survey Professional Paper 543-D. Washington: Government Printing Office. 46 p. Also *in* The Great Alaska Earthquake of 1964: Geology. NAS Pub. 1601. Washington: National Academy of Sciences, 1971. p. 177–226.

Post, Austin, 1967. Effects of the March 1964 Alaska earthquake on glaciers. U.S. Geological Survey Professional Paper 544-D. Washington: Government Printing Office. 42 p. Also *in* The Great Alaska Earthquake of 1964: Hydrology. NAS Pub. 1603. Washington: National Academy of Sciences, 1968. p. 266–308.

Ragle, Richard H., John E. Sater, and William O. Field, 1965. Effects of the 1964 Alaska earthquake on glaciers and related features. Arctic Institute of North America Research Paper 32. Washington: Arctic Institute of North America. 44 p.

Seed, H. Bolton, and G. R. Martin, 1965. An analysis of the Fourth Avenue and L-Street slide areas, Anchorage, Alaska. Appendix D *in* Remolding of Bootlegger Cove Clay with explosives. Preliminary stabilization studies for the Turnagain buttress for U.S. Army Corps of Engineers. Seattle: Shannon & Wilson, Inc. 180 p.

Shannon & Wilson, Inc., 1964a. Preliminary report to U.S. Army Corps of Engineers on 4th Avenue slide, Anchorage, Alaska. Seattle: Shannon & Wilson, Inc. 10 p.

Shannon & Wilson, Inc., 1964b. Report on Anchorage area soil studies, Alaska, to U.S. Army Engineer District, Alaska. Seattle: Shannon & Wilson, Inc. 300 p.

Shannon & Wilson, Inc., 1964c. Report on subsurface investigation for city of Seward, Alaska, and vicinity, to U.S. Army Engineer District, Anchorage, Alaska. Seattle: Shannon & Wilson, Inc. 77 p.

Shannon & Wilson, Inc., 1966. Electro-osmosis field test section. Preliminary stabilization studies for the Turnagain buttress for U.S. Army Corps of Engineers, Alaska. Seattle: Shannon & Wilson, Inc. 153 p.

Shannon, W. L., and D. E. Hilts, 1973. Earthquake-caused submarine landslide at Seward, Alaska *in* The Great Alaska Earthquake of 1964: Engineering. NAS Pub. 1606. Washington: National Academy of Sciences.

Söderblom, Rolf, 1960. Aspects on some problems of geotechnical chemistry. Reprints and Preliminary Reports No. 2–Supplement to the "Proceedings" and "Meddelanden" of the Institute. Stockholm: Swedish Geotechnical Institute.

Tarr, R. S., and Lawrence Martin, 1914. Alaskan glacier studies of the National Geographic Society in the Yakutat Bay, Prince William Sound, and lower Copper River regions. Washington: National Geographic Society. 498 p.

Terzaghi, Karl, 1956. Varieties of submarine slope failures. Article 3, Proceedings, 8th Conference of the Soil Mechanics and Foundations Division, Texas.

Terzaghi, Karl, and R. B. Peck, 1953. Soil mechanics in engineering practice. New York: John Wiley & Sons, Inc. 566 p.

Thomas, Mrs. Lowell, Jr., 1964. An Alaskan family's night of terror. *National Geographic Magazine*, 126 (July), 142–156.

Tuthill, Samuel J., and Wilson M. Laird, 1966. Geomorphic effects of the earthquake of March 27, 1964, in the Martin–Bering rivers area, Alaska. U.S. Geological Survey Professional Paper 543-B. Washington: Government Printing Office. 29 p. Abstract *in* The Great Alaska Earthquake of 1964: Geology. NAS Pub. 1601. Washington: National Academy of Sciences, 1971. p. 284.

Varnes, David J., 1958. Landslide types and processes *in* Landslides and engineering practice. Highway Research Board Special Report 29. NAS-NRC Pub. 544. Washington: National Academy of Sciences. p. 20–47.

Waller, Roger M., 1966. Effects of the earthquake of March 27, 1964, in the Homer area, Alaska (*with a section on* Beach changes on Homer Spit, by Kirk W. Stanley). U.S. Geological Survey Professional Paper 542-D. Washington: Government Printing Office. 28 p. Also *in* The Great Alaska Earthquake of 1964: Geology. NAS Pub. 1601. Washington: National Academy of Sciences, 1971. p. 461–488.

WARREN GEORGE   JAMES F. SIZEMORE
PAUL KNOWLES   DUANE E. CARSON
JOHN K. ALLENDER
U.S. ARMY CORPS OF ENGINEERS DISTRICT,
ALASKA

Structures in Anchorage

The primary objective of the structural design of buildings to withstand earthquakes has been one of preventing collapse and saving lives; analyses of cost of engineering and construction, compared to damage losses, have not been given the attention they deserve. The data required for such analyses are usually very difficult to collect because they are scattered throughout the files of building owners and government agencies. The damage assessment and rehabilitation of many structures after the Alaska earthquake were handled by the Alaska District Office of the Corps of Engineers, making information on costs readily available. This paper describes the damage and repair of selected buildings in Anchorage and comments on the influence of design and construction on the occurrence or absence of damage. Cost information is presented where available.

Figure 1 is a map of the area affected by the earthquake. The severity of the damage was undoubtedly increased by the relatively long duration of strong shaking. However, a review of the structures damaged indicates that slight additional attention to seismic design could have greatly increased the earthquake resistance of many structures with little increase in cost.

The variety of damage to structures described in this paper provides an indication of the many different kinds of damage caused by an earthquake. Nevertheless, the buildings studied represent only a small fraction of those damaged.

Information has been abstracted from many kinds of reports, including scientific, engineering, and economic reports as well as from newspaper and magazine articles, and from the files of private firms and the federal government (Blume and Associates, 1966; Committee on the Alaskan Earthquake, 1965; U.S. Army Engineering Division, 1964).

Two companion papers describe the effect of the earthquake outside of Anchorage: one on Structures in Small Communities (George and others, 1973, page 847, this volume), which describes the damage to buildings in the towns of Seward, Valdez, Homer, Palmer, Moose Pass, Kenai, Hope, and Girdwood; the other on Structures on Military

ABSTRACT: A review of the earthquake damage sustained by a selected group of buildings illustrates the performance of various types of structures and points out structural weaknesses and the different types of earthquake damage. Improved seismic design could have greatly increased the resistance of the buildings to earthquakes without much increase in construction cost.

The cost of repair was high and indicated that, in designing buildings for earthquake-prone areas, the cost of repairing potential damage should be considered and should be kept within reasonable limits.

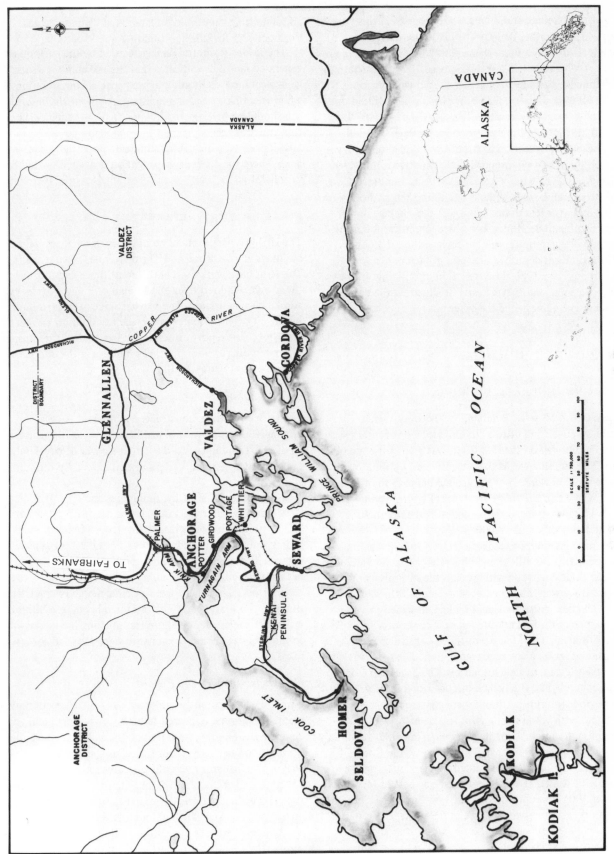

FIGURE 1   South central Alaska.

Installations (George and others, 1973, page 873, this volume), which describes damage at Fort Richardson and Elmendorf Air Force Base. Damage to Whittier is described in Port of Whittier (Belanger, 1973, page 1074, this volume).

Earthquake damage to buildings ranged widely from none at all to complete collapse. We have concentrated on structural damage; Ayres and others (1973, page 346, this volume) have dealt with Nonstructural Damage to Buildings. Because the selection of structures to be described was based on their damage, proportionate coverage is not given to structures with little or no damage. Many buildings suffered structural damage without collapsing and without causing injury or loss of life. Although this damage represented significant economic loss, these structures did meet the prime design requirement for safeguarding the public.

The structures described here and in the companion papers represent a typical cross section of buildings in the earthquake area, and they do serve to illustrate the nature of earthquake damage and the extent of repair costs.

STATE-OWNED BUILDINGS

MINES AND MINERALS BUILDING

The Mines and Minerals Building, 329 Second Avenue (Figure 2), consisting of two buildings joined together by a common doorway on the first floor, was damaged beyond repair. The building was in the area affected by the Fourth Avenue slide; movement of the ground beneath the footings caused severe damage to the structure (Figures 3 and 4). The building was consequently demolished early in June 1964 at a cost of about $8,000.

The original building, constructed in 1953, had a concrete foundation and floor and concrete basement walls. The first floor was wood with asphalt tile over plywood; the first-story walls consisted of wood studs with metal siding. The new portion of the building, designed in 1963, was completed on January 21, 1964. It contained 3,088 ft² of interior area and was of wood-frame construction with metal siding set on a concrete foundation. The roof was built up with 2 in. of rigid insulation. The basement floor was of concrete and the first floor consisted of asphalt tile on plywood. Interior partitions were constructed of gypsum board with wood doors, sash, and trim.

Because the original building was in an area that required extensive stabilization for earthquake safety, the Corps of Engineers designed and constructed the new building for the State of Alaska at a different location—east of Merrill Field, at 3001 Porcupine Drive. The new building (Figure 5), a one-story structure with an area of 5,950 ft², has exterior walls of concrete block with interior wood-stud and plaster-finish partitions. The roof is composed of 4-in. tar and

gravel decking supported on laminated wooden beams. Contract cost for this new building was $165,000.

The severe structural damage caused by the earthquake-generated landslide indicates that the possibility of such geological hazards should be given special consideration when selecting a site for a building. A potentially hazardous site should be investigated by qualified soils engineers before construction is planned. Zoning maps, issued by the city concerned which should indicate potentially hazardous areas where special soils investigation is needed, would be very helpful.

STATE HIGHWAY DEPARTMENT COMPLEX

The Highway Department complex consists of several small buildings at Post Road and Third Avenue (Figures 2 and 6). The structures were built at different times and most of them were acquired from the Bureau of Public Roads when Alaska became a state. The site has since been surrounded by the city. The complex was evidently built on an old landslide. This report discusses the two main structures, the office building and shop; other buildings in the complex are shown in Figures 7–10.

Office Building

The Office Building, constructed in the late 1940's, was originally a warehouse and had been remodeled for use as an office. The damage to this structure was of two kinds: that caused by lateral forces and that caused by differential settlement.

The main portion of the building is about 40 ft wide and 97 ft long; together the three stories comprise 10,287 ft². The bottom two stories have reinforced-concrete floors, beams, and exterior walls (Figures 11 and 12 for typical exterior elevations). The third story was added later and has light structural-steel framing with wood siding.

Information on the original seismic design of the Office Building is not available. The reinforced-concrete floors and walls performed adequately in transmitting the lateral loads to the foundation and presumably were designed for lateral loads.

Earthquake Damage and Repairs

This site was apparently subjected to localized earth movement. The ground appeared to lurch to the north and to elongate the building foundation. The building above the second floor also moved north, and as a result the south wall of the first story was out of plumb. All the exterior concrete walls were cracked, and Figures 13–15 show the typical cracking patterns. The first-floor slab-on-grade settled and cracked; the maximum differential settlement was 6 in. at the north end of the building (Figure 16). The second floor had a high point at one interior column, indicating that the entire building settled except for this point. The location of this column is shown in Figure 17; it was at a pit in the boiler room, and presumably its footing extended deeper into the subgrade than did the footing of the other columns. Some of the building settlement might have occurred before the earthquake. The structural beams, slabs, and columns showed minor cracking and spalling (Figure 17). This building resisted ground shaking. Two boilers shifted slightly, stressing the steam headers and causing misalignment of flues and draft fans. Water piping around the boiler room ruptured, as did some piping under the floor, and some lighting fixtures were damaged.

A breakdown of the costs of the repairs performed by the State Highway Department is not available, but the estimated total repair cost was $40,000.

Maintenance Building

The maintenance shop is a two-story steel-frame structure with a mezzanine level between the first and second floors over approximately 40 percent of the building area (Figures 18 and 19). The building was originally designed by The Alaska Railroad for the Alaska Road Commission in the late 1940's as a shop building with minor office area and with a second floor approximately 20 ft above the shop floor. The second floor was for parts storage and is served by a hydraulic elevator and an open stairwell. Later, an intermediate floor was constructed in the west portion. This and the west portion of the original second floor were developed as office space. The building, which has 19,494 ft² of gross floor area, sustained more structural damage than did the other buildings within the complex. The nonstructural damage was also severe.

The basic structure is a steel frame set on a reinforced-concrete perimeter wall approximately 5 ft high. Insulated steel siding and large steel sash areas are above the concrete wall. The mezzanine floor and second floor are of concrete on steel decks. The beam-to-column connections are generally simple shear connections but may have acted as moment resisting connections.

Members that were resistant to lateral forces were not included in the original design. The structure contained no shear walls and no diagonal bracing in the exterior walls, and it was further weakened by a large expanse of window and door openings in the insulated metal panels. The second floor probably acted as a diaphragm, and the loads were transferred to the foundation by a combination of column bending and siding shear resistance.

Earthquake Damage This building swayed and racked severely during the earthquake. The large movement caused many welded beam connections to fail, and at the second-floor level some of the structural-steel column flanges were distorted at connections to the deep beams. Large shear forces ruptured connections, and column bases were badly damaged (Figures 20–24). The column anchor bolts fractured, and the concrete walls and piers at the column lines were badly shattered, exposing the reinforcing. The foundation and floor slab received only minor damage.

The large building movements caused many windows to fall or shatter, and the wall panels buckled and pulled loose. Large areas of the steel sash fell out, and the frames for the large doors sagged and were deformed. About 20 fluorescent-light fixtures were badly damaged, and many others were loosened. A few pipes were damaged enough to required repair.

Repair of Earthquake Damage The structural repairs performed by the State Highway Department included installation of cross bracing in the walls and repair of the column bases and of all connections. The structural repair was performed to meet the zone III criteria of the *Uniform Building Code*. All broken windows were replaced and all spalled concrete was repaired.

The estimated total repair cost was $72,000, but a breakdown of costs is not available.

Conclusions

This complex of buildings is an excellent example of how buildings of various designs react to the same earthquake motion. The maintenance building sustained less permanent foundation displacement than did the office building, but it did sustain extensive structural damage from shaking because no lateral-force resisting members had been provided. The office building, in which lateral-force resisting members had been provided, showed little damage caused by shaking. The cost of earthquake repairs for the maintenance building far exceeded the money saved by not considering earthquake forces in the original design.

ALASKA PSYCHIATRIC INSTITUTE

The Alaska Psychiatric Institute, approximately 3 mi southeast of downtown Anchorage, next to the new Providence Hospital, is a newly built, modern multistoried structure, with a capacity of 225 hospital beds and contains, among other facilities, a gymnasium (Figure 2). The building has 134,000 ft² total floor area and was completed in 1962 at a cost of $6,000,000; it received only minor damage (Metcalf and Eddy, 1964).

The building is divided into five units (Figures 25 and 26). Unit 1, in the main part of the complex, is four stories high. Unit 2 is a Y-shaped wing two stories high connected to the west side of unit 1. Unit 3 is connected to unit 1 on the east. Unit 4 is a gymnasium to the south of unit 1. Unit 5 is a one-story service building south of unit 4 and connected to it by a passageway.

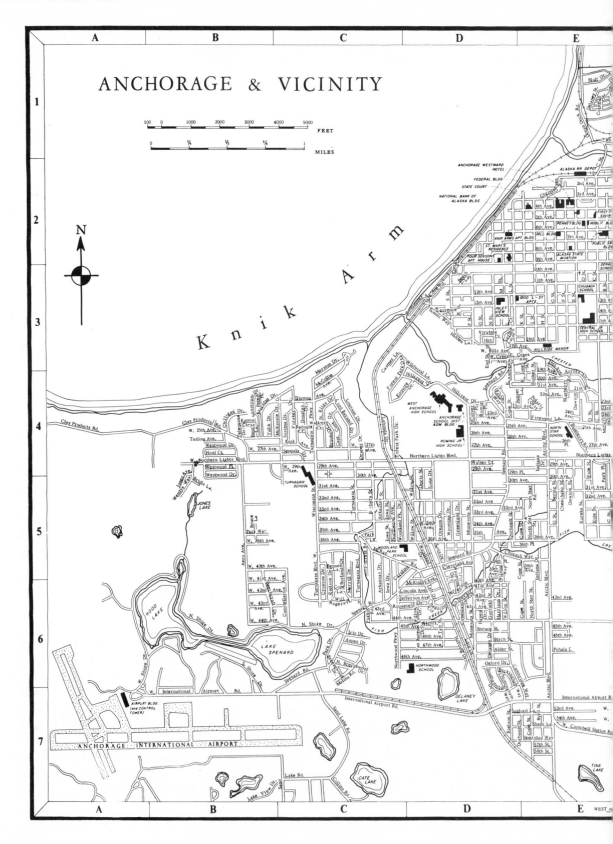

FIGURE 2   Preearthquake Anchorage.

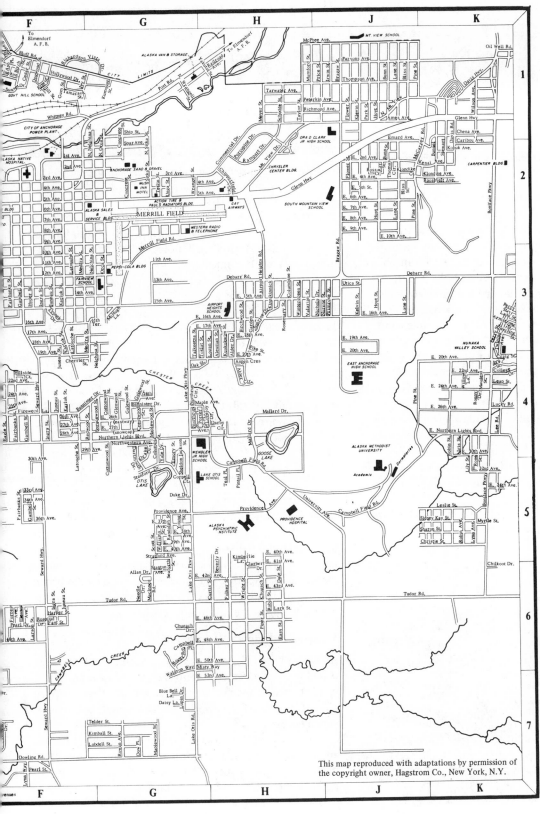

This map reproduced with adaptations by permission of
the copyright owner, Hagstrom Co., New York, N.Y.

FIGURE 3   South side of the Mines and Minerals Building showing some of the earthquake damage.

FIGURE 5   Completed Mines and Minerals Building (fall 1966).

Steel columns spaced at intervals of about 20 ft in both directions are the major features of the structural frame. The floors and roofs are of reinforced concrete formed on metal decking; the exterior consists of metal curtain walls, with the exception of the concrete shear walls (Figures 27, 28, and 29). The Y-shaped wings and the passageway are separated from the main building by 2-in. seismic joints. The gymnasium has open-web joists and a concrete roof. Most of the interior partitions are stud walls, and ceilings are gypsum board or gypsum board with attached acoustical tile. The Y-shaped wings have reinforced-concrete walls at the corridors (Figures 25 and 26). Figure 30 shows a typical section through the building.

The building was designed in accordance with the zone 3 requirements of the *Uniform Building Code*, but the design calculations were not available. The lateral loads were transmitted by the roof and floor systems to concrete shear walls and then to the foundation (see Figures 25–27 for shear-wall locations).

The concrete walls in the corridors of the Y-shaped wings are unusual in that the walls are penetrated at very frequent

intervals by door openings, and the ratio of openings to wall area is relatively high. The placement of the reinforcing bars in these walls was specifically noted on the drawings, however, indicating that much attention was given to the seismic design.

Earthquake Damage

In general, this building sustained only minor damage. Structural damage was limited to small cracks and some spalling of the exterior shear walls, stair walls and elevator-shaft walls (Figures 31–33). Most of the wall cracks observed were at the first-floor level. Cracking occurred less frequently above and below this floor. Minor cracking occurred in the floors, and heavier cracking was apparent at the stair walls and at the seismic joints between unit 1 and units 2 and 3. Most of the cold joints in the concrete walls showed evidence of working. Cracking and spalling were most pronounced in the shear wall at the northeast corner of unit 1, at the first floor (Figures 34–37). The interior shear wall along the corridors of the Y-shaped wings was not damaged.

Nonstructural damage included cracked ceiling and floor tile, cracks in the interior gypsum board and displaced caulking around the metal-panel curtain walls. In addition, some mechanical equipment and some hospital equipment broke loose, causing minor damage. Water damage occurred from a broken pipe in the third-floor ceiling.

Repair of Earthquake Damage

All cracks over 1/32-in. wide in the concrete walls were repaired with either an epoxy grout or an epoxy resin. The concrete wall at the northeast corner of unit 1 was chipped out and grouted (Figure 13). The slab-on-grade was repaired where necessary.

The entire building was restored to its original condition, and all mechanical and electrical systems were tested. The metal curtain-wall panels were resealed under a separate repair contract. Table 1 shows the breakdown of repair cost.

This structure is an example of a well-designed and well-constructed building with an unusual layout withstanding severe earthquake loads with only minor damage.

FIGURE 4   Portion of Fourth Avenue slide showing the slide effect on the Mines and Minerals Building.

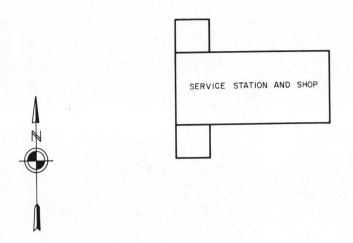

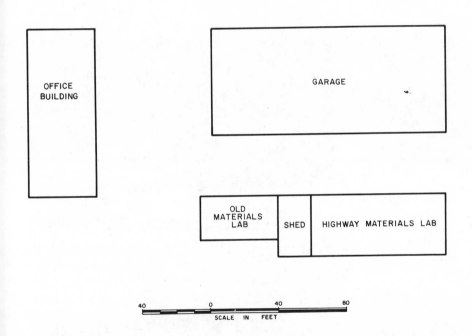

FIGURE 6   Plot plan of State Highway Complex, Anchorage.

TABLE 1   Summary of Damage Repair Costs in Alaska Psychiatric Institute

Type of Repair	Repair Cost
Structural repair	$ 80,800
Architectural repair	60,500
Mechanical-electrical	8,500
Painting	12,200
TOTAL	162,000
Original cost	6,000,000

CITY-OWNED BUILDINGS

WATER-TREATMENT PLANT

The water-treatment plant (Figure 38) is about 1,000 ft east of mile 5 on the Glenn Highway, about 5 mi northeast of the city hall of Anchorage. Ship Creek water is piped to the plant from a federally owned dam and intake structure at Fort Richardson. The primary function of the dam and intake structure is to supply water to Fort Richardson and to

FIGURE 7   Service Station Building, also known as the Service Shop, was designed by the Alaska Road Commission in 1955 and has 3,341 ft^2 of gross floor area. After the earthquake this building appeared to be in good condition; only minor cracks were observed in the concrete slab.

FIGURE 8   The Highway Materials Laboratory, also referred to as New Materials Laboratory, was designed by the Alaska Highway Department and constructed before the earthquake. Photo was taken in June 1964. This building suffered no structural damage; minor cracking did occur in the reinforced-concrete-block exterior walls.

FIGURE 9   Warm Vehicle Storage Building, constructed of wood on a concrete-block foundation, contains 13,619 ft^2 of gross floor area. Structural damage was minor, consisting of some loosened and open-jointed concrete blocks in the north end wall and a crack in the floor slab adjacent to the north end wall.

FIGURE 10   Postearthquake view of the maintenance building (right) and the office building (background). New Materials Laboratory is at left.

FIGURE 11   East elevation of office building after the earthquake.

FIGURE 12   North elevation of office building (June 1964).

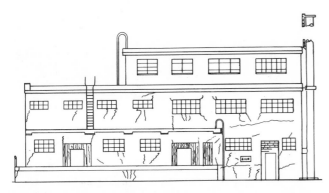

FIGURE 13   West elevation of office building in the State Highway Complex, Anchorage, showing cracks in concrete walls. Top story is constructed of structural-steel framing and wood siding. Damage is similar on east side.

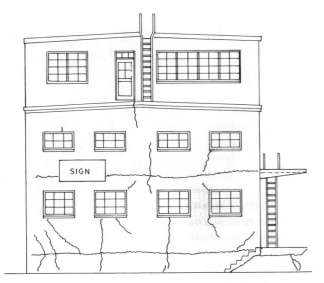

FIGURE 14   North elevation of office building, showing cracks in concrete wall.

FIGURE 15   South elevation of office building in State Highway Complex, showing cracks in the concrete wall. The south wall was left slightly out of plumb when the ground and the building moved north.

Elmendorf AFB. In general, the plant survived the earthquake with minor damage to beams, columns, and floor slabs, but with extensive damage to a shear wall. The plant did not lose its capacity to function and resumed operations as soon as electrical power was made available.

The plant measures about 190 × 200 ft in plan, and the length of the building runs north and south. The plant consists of five main areas (Figure 39): the headhouse, clear well, filters, pump room, and the area that houses the fluctuating, sedimentation, and skimming tanks (referred to as the sedimentation tanks).

The headhouse, about 60 × 70 ft in plan, occupies the

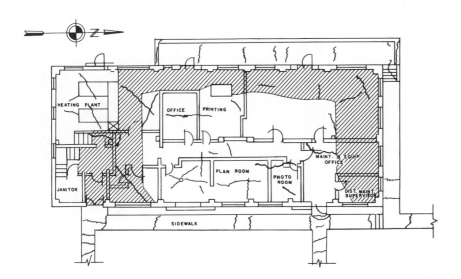

FIGURE 16   First-floor plan of office building of State Highway Complex. Cross-hatched area indicates floor area to be leveled. Wavy lines indicate cracks in floor slab.

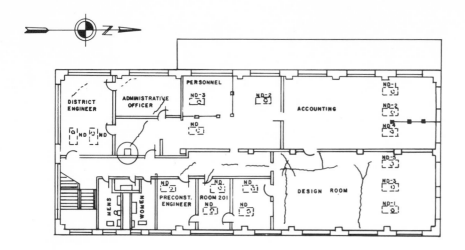

FIGURE 17   Second-floor plan of office building, State Highway Complex. Circled column indicates high point in floor that evidently did not settle as much as the rest of the building.

FIGURE 18   West elevation of maintenance building. Spalled concrete at the left corner was caused by the flexing of the structure during the earthquake.

FIGURE 20   Failure at column anchor bolts at column line B in the maintenance building.

FIGURE 19   North elevation of maintenance building. Broken windows were caused by the movement of the structure during the earthquake.

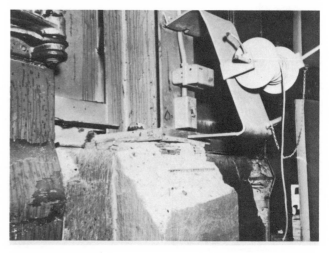

FIGURE 21   Failure of concrete at column line D in the maintenance building.

FIGURE 22 Failure of concrete pier and wall at the intersection of the exterior walls in the maintenance building.

FIGURE 24 Broken concrete at one of the column piers next to the large-vehicle entry doors in the maintenance building.

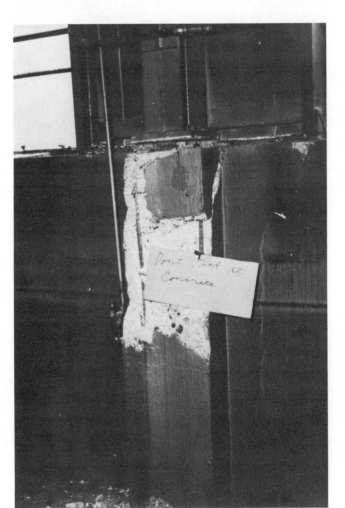

FIGURE 23 Failure of concrete column pier in the maintenance building.

northeast corner of the plant. It is a two-story structure with the clear well, which is located below the first floor and is used mainly for the storage of chemicals; the second floor houses the laboratory, offices, and chemical feeders.

The clear well and the exterior walls below the second floor are of poured-in-place reinforced concrete. The first and second floors are reinforced-concrete one-way rib and slab construction. The exterior walls above the second floor are 6-in. reinforced-concrete block with insulated vertical metal siding on the exterior. Partitions on the second floor are of reinforced-concrete block. The roof system consists of steel framing with a metal roof deck.

The filters occupy a 70 X 80-ft section of the building in the northwest corner of the plant. In this two-story section, the filters are on the second floor and the pumps on the first floor. The section is constructed of poured-in-place reinforced concrete, except for the roof over the filters, which consists of prestressed precast-concrete T-beams. The exterior walls consist of precast panels between poured-in-place concrete columns.

The sedimentation tanks, about 125 X 165 ft in plan, occupy the south end of the plant. The area contains open reinforced-concrete tanks, about 15 ft deep, and are located substantially below the outside finish grade. This tank area is covered by a roof constructed of prestressed precast-concrete T-beams about 10 ft above the tanks. The exterior walls around the tanks are constructed of precast panels about 16 ft long and 10 ft high between poured-in-place reinforced-concrete columns.

The prestressed T-beams over the sedimentation tanks are 8 ft wide and about 60 ft long and span the area in two 60-ft spans from north to south. An expansion joint (Figure 39) runs north and south at the center of the roof. The interior (center supports) ends of the tees are supported on a

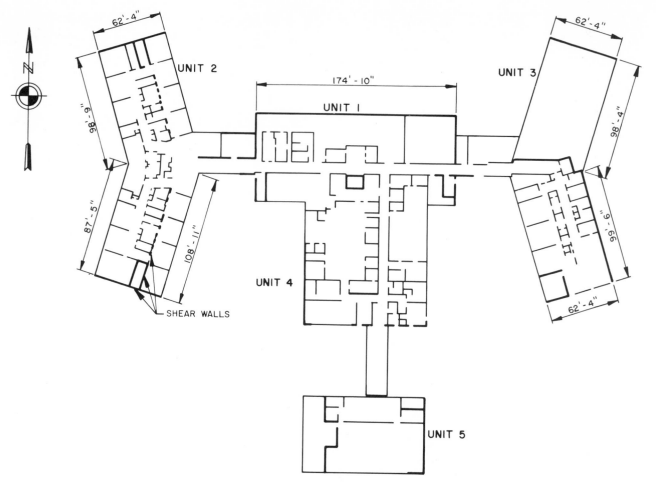

FIGURE 25 Ground-floor plan of the Alaska Psychiatric Institute.

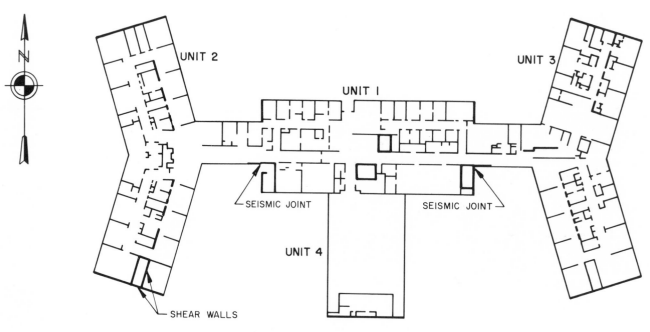

FIGURE 26 First-floor plan of the Alaska Psychiatric Institute.

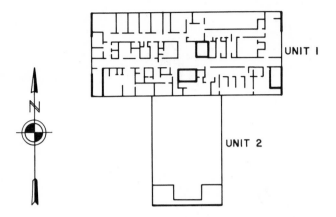

FIGURE 28 Front view of Alaska Psychiatric Institute, Anchorage. This well-designed building sustained little earthquake damage.

SECOND FLOOR PLAN

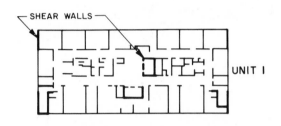

THIRD FLOOR PLAN

FIGURE 27 Second- and third-floor plans of the Alaska Psychiatric Institute.

FIGURE 29 Rear view of Alaska Psychiatric Institute.

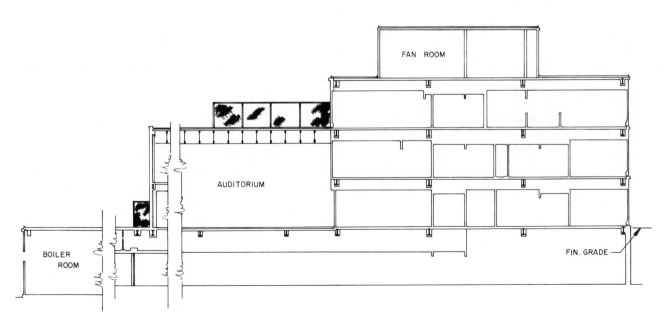

FIGURE 30 Section through Alaska Psychiatric Institute (no scale).

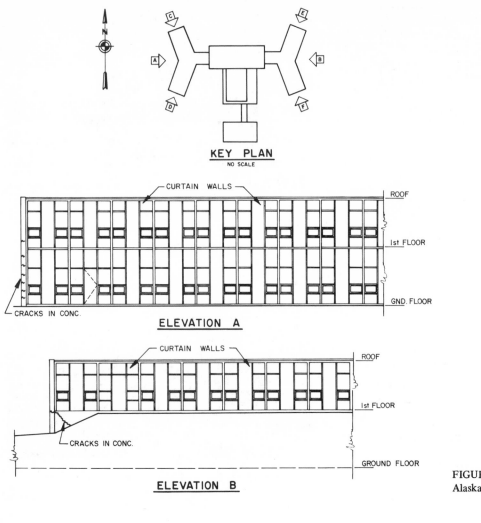

FIGURE 31   Plan and elevations A and B, Alaska Psychiatric Institute.

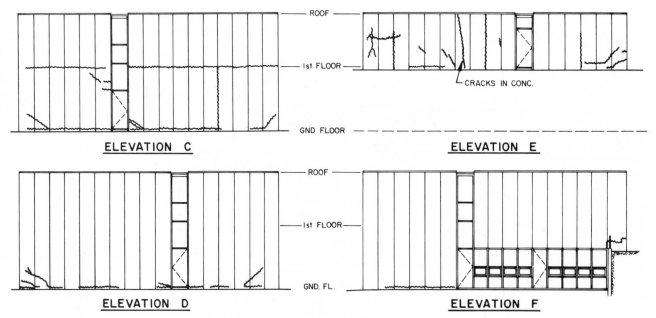

FIGURE 32   Elevations C, D, E, and F, Alaska Psychiatric Institute.

Gray, Rogers, Myers and Morgan

FIGURE 33   View of spalled concrete at the vestibule on the west end of unit 1, Alaska Psychiatric Institute.

Gray, Rogers, Myers and Morgan

FIGURE 35   View of damaged end wall of northwest corner of unit 1, Alaska Psychiatric Institute.

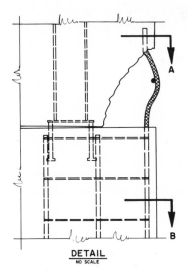

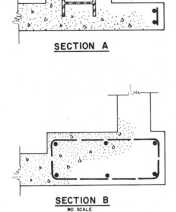

FIGURE 34   Details of damaged end wall in Alaska Psychiatric Institute.

Gray, Rogers, Myers and Morgan

FIGURE 36   View of damaged end wall at northeast corner of unit 1, Alaska Psychiatric Institute.

FIGURE 37   View of end wall of unit 1 after repairs, Alaska Psychiatric Institute. This wall was damaged at the ground line.

FIGURE 38 Exterior of Anchorage Water-Treatment Plant, seen from northwest corner of building (fall 1966).

north span are supported on precast-concrete columns 8 ft on centers. All columns are doweled into the concrete tank walls and into the stem of the T-beams.

Four reinforced-concrete shear walls, 8 in. thick and 8 ft long, run both north to south and east to west, parallel to the east–west axis and about 30 ft inboard from the exterior walls. In addition to these four shear walls, two more shear walls, 10 in. thick and 16 ft long, run parallel to the east–west axis and about 30 ft inboard from the exterior walls. These poured-in-place shear walls are under the precast inverted T-beam that runs east and west through the center of the tanks and supports the T-beams in the roof. Parallel to the north–south axis of the tanks is one 10-in.-thick by 20-ft-long shear wall at the center of each of the exterior east and west walls of the tanks.

Along the outer edge of the flanges of the T-beams of the roof are metal anchors, 6 ft apart, to which the precast exterior-wall panels are attached. The individual tees are also tied together by welding of the flanges at these anchor points. At the ends of the tees and flush with the soffit of the stems, a flat steel plate is anchored into the concrete stem by steel straps. Similarly, a plate is anchored into the

precast inverted T-beam that runs continuously east and west across the tanks. This inverted T is supported by concrete columns spaced at 16 ft on centers and by two shear walls (Figure 40 gives a section through the tanks, showing the T-beam supports). The stems of the T-beams at the south end of the south span and at the north end of the

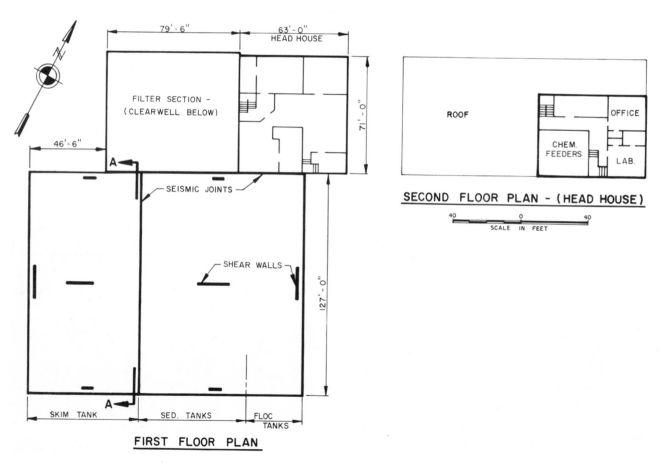

FIGURE 39 Floor plan, city of Anchorage Water-Treatment Plant.

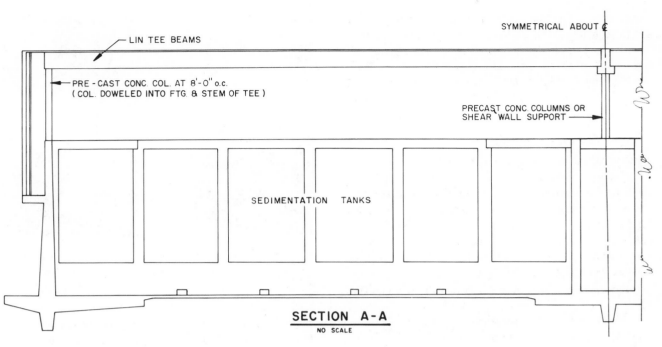

FIGURE 40 Section A-A (shown on Figure 39) showing framing system used in water-treatment plant.

precast inverted T-beam that supports the roof T-beams at the center of the tanks. The roof tees are anchored to the precast inverted T-beam by welding. This tying together of the roof system permits it to act as a horizontal diaphragm. The roof system over the filters is similar to that over the sedimentation tanks, except that the T-beams are about 35 ft long instead of 60 ft long.

The plant—designed by Alenar Associated, Anchorage, Alaska, and Stevens and Thompson, Portland, Oregon—was completed in 1962.

Seismic design was in accordance with the 1958 edition of the *Uniform Building Code*.

Earthquake Damage

Structural damage was not extensive; minor cracking and spalling appeared in some of the structural elements, but the only total failure was one shear wall near the northeast corner of the sedimentation tank, which was severely damaged. The eastern shear wall under the inverted T-beam, which runs east and west across the center of the tanks, was spalled at the bottom and developed many cracks. The tops and bottoms of the precast-concrete columns under the stems of the T-beams over the sedimentation tank were spalled at the north end of the north span. There was some cracking (vertical) and spalling in the stems of the roof tees at the ends where they are anchored to the inverted concrete T-beam. Many of the welded shear connectors that tied the flanges of the roof tees together and connected them to the walls failed. In general, these connections were

made by welding together the ends of hairpin reinforcing bars that were anchored into the members. In most cases, the reinforcing bars, rather than the welds, broke (Figure 41).

It appeared that the entire roof over the sedimentation tanks shifted slightly toward the northeast and rotated slightly in a counterclockwise direction. The expansion joints in the roof were damaged by movement between the

FIGURE 41 Some shear plates were installed where the original connections failed. Connection had been made by welding together embedded reinforcing steel bars; in most cases, the bars failed and not the weld. Heavier connection bars should be used if such members are to be used in roof construction (water-treatment plant).

sections of the building. Some very minor cracking occurred in the concrete elsewhere in the building; a few hairline cracks were visible in the joints of the concrete-block walls in the office area. In the clear well, some of the wooden baffles were torn loose, and some cracking occurred in the bottom of the sedimentation tanks (Figure 42). No reports of nonstructural damage were received.

Repair of Earthquake Damage

The shear wall, damaged beyond repair, was replaced by a new reinforced-concrete wall. Figure 43 shows a column repaired with nonshrink grout, a method similar to that used to repair the spalled inverted T-beams. Cracks in these T-beams were repaired by epoxy pressure grouting. Figure 42 shows the floor cracks in the concrete slabs that also were repaired by routing and grouting. Figure 41 illustrates how the welded hairpin reinforcing connectors were replaced by shear plates, bolted top and bottom by four ½-in.-diameter bolts.

An $86,565 contract for repairs was awarded on October 2, 1964, and was completed on May 10, 1965. The original construction cost of the plant was not available for this report, but it represented an investment of about $1,800,000.

Much of the damage could be attributed to inadequate joint connections at the ends of structural elements. Where massive precast-concrete elements are used, more attention should be given to the design of connections.

The plant remained operational, although it had sustained some structural damage; for a structure with unusual features, the earthquake damage was not excessive.

PUBLIC SAFETY BUILDING

The Public Safety Building is situated on C Street, between Sixth and Seventh avenues (Figure 2), and consists of a

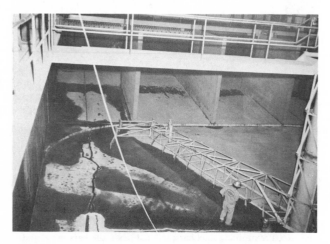

FIGURE 42   Repairs being made to bottom of sedimentation tank (water-treatment plant).

FIGURE 43   The dark area on the column shows where the concrete spalled and was repaired with nonshrink grout (water-treatment plant).

police station, firehouse, and jail (Figures 44 and 45). This building, which relies on the diaphragm action of the roof and concrete or concrete-block shear walls to transmit horizontal forces to the foundation, sustained a moderate amount of cracking in its reinforced-concrete and concrete-block walls.

The firehouse is a two-story section with a single-story garage. In the garage is a concrete training tower. The construction of the firehouse is similar to that of the police station, except that the exterior walls of the two-story section are constructed of insulated metal panels.

The police station is one story high and has a basement under part of it. The reinforced-concrete floor over the basement is supported on reinforced-concrete beams and columns. The roof consists of concrete fill on metal decking and is supported on open-web steel joists that are supported by structural steel columns. The ceilings are acoustical tile and the interior walls are plaster. The exterior walls consist of precast-concrete panels and insulated metal panels.

FIGURE 44   Public Safety Building (from west) after earthquake repairs. Fire station is at right and police station is at left.

FIGURE 45   Public Safety Building (from southeast) after repairs.

The jail is a one-story section with a slab-on-grade floor. The roof is constructed of precast-concrete T-beams that are supported by the exterior precast-concrete panels and poured-in-place concrete interior walls. Some interior walls are constructed of concrete block; the exterior walls are insulated and plastered.

Earthquake Damage

This building sustained no serious structural damage. The exterior precast panels were cracked at the joints between the panels and in the panels near the joints. Minor cracks were found in the structural floor slab and the slab-on-grade. The training-tower walls were cracked in some places, and the construction joints showed movements. Small cracks were made in the exterior and interior bearing walls for the concrete T-beams, and the concrete fill between the T-beams and walls was loosened.

The major nonstructural damage consisted of plaster cracks and tile damage; the ceiling tile was also lightly damaged.

Repair of Earthquake Damage

See Figures 46–50 for repairs. Quantities and costs of some repairs are as tabulated:

Cost of Earthquake Repairs for the Public Safety Building

Crack Repair	
Nonstructural walls and ceilings	1,800 lin ft
Structural concrete walls	800 lin ft
Floor slab	1,625 lin ft
Concrete-block walls	500 lin ft
Plaster	1,150 lin ft
Patch plaster	5 ft^2
Structural	$27,400
Architectural	20,229
Mechanical-electrical	3,600
TOTAL	$51,229

No obvious defects were apparent in the design and construction of this building.

CITY WAREHOUSE

This warehouse is at First Avenue and Latouche Street (Figure 2). The basic structure is about 55 ft wide and 200 ft long with a 10-ft-wide loading dock along one side and a 13-ft-wide loading dock along one end. The damage to this structure consisted mainly of cracks in reinforced-concrete walls and roof.

The roof is cantilevered 7 ft over the dock on the side and 9 ft over the dock at the end of the building (Figure 51). The roof is an 8-in. reinforced-concrete flat slab, supported by reinforced-concrete columns (see Figure 52 for bay spacing). Exterior walls, containing the overhead doors, are reinforced concrete and all other exterior and interior walls are concrete block. The first floor is 4 ft 8 in. above grade, and the roof is 12 ft above the floor (see Figure 52 for typical section through the structure).

The seismic design criteria are not available. In the longitudinal direction the horizontal loads were transferred to the exterior walls by the roof slab. In the transverse direction the horizontal loads were transmitted to the foundation by the end walls and the frame action of the columns and roof.

Earthquake Damage and Repair

The entire built-up roofing and the insulation were damaged, but no electrical or mechanical damage was noted. Figures 53–56 show the extent of damage.

Cracks in the concrete were repaired with an epoxy resin. Damaged masonry was replaced or repaired, new roofing and insulation were installed, and the exterior was painted.

A list of some repair quantities and costs follows:

Crack Repair	
Foundation wall	155 lin ft
Roof-slab	160 lin ft
Floor-slab	950 lin ft
Concrete-block joint	450 lin ft
Replacement of loading-dock slab	1,080 ft^2
New roof	12,300 ft^2
Painting	10,000 ft^2
Costs	
Structural repair	$12,496
Architectural repair	17,260
TOTAL	$29,756

The cracks in the foundation wall, floor slabs, and loading dock probably indicate some ground settlement. The damage to this building was similar to that sustained by many of the small buildings in Anchorage.

MERRILL FIELD CONTROL TOWER

The Merrill Field Control Tower (Figure 2) is a three-story concrete structure with a glassed-in control room above.

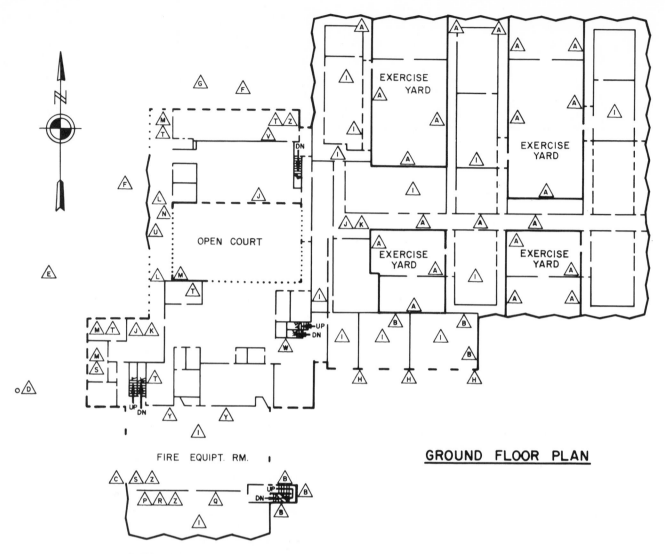

GROUND FLOOR PLAN

FIGURE 46   Damage-repair plans for Public Safety Building (see Figure 50 for symbols).

The tower is about 29 ft square and has an additional office area on the west side. It is constructed of reinforced-concrete walls, floors, beams, and columns, and it sustained only minor damage.

The drawings and design analysis for the tower are not available. Figures 57–60 show that the concrete walls effectively transmitted horizontal loads to the foundation.

Earthquake Damage

The concrete walls and floors sustained minor cracks. Figures 61–63 show the extent of damage.

Some interior concrete-block partitions were cracked and gypsum-board joints were loosened. The seal around the glass in the control room was loosened, and some of the glass fell out. Several light fixtures fell, but the type and quantity are not known.

Repair of Earthquake Damage

All cracks larger than 1/32 in. and all spalled areas in exposed concrete walls and floors were repaired with an epoxy grout.

Altogether 285 linear feet (lin ft) of cracks were repaired in the concrete, and 300 lin ft of recaulking was carried out on the control-room windows.

The cost of structural repairs amounted to approximately $1,693, whereas architectural (or nonstructural) repairs cost about $1,622, making the total cost of repairs about $3,315.

This structure behaved very well, in striking contrast to

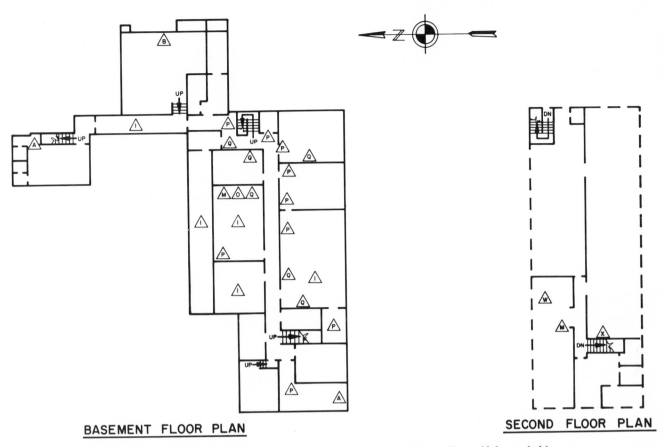

BASEMENT FLOOR PLAN

SECOND FLOOR PLAN

FIGURE 47 Plans of Public Safety Building showing damage repair (see Figure 50 for symbols).

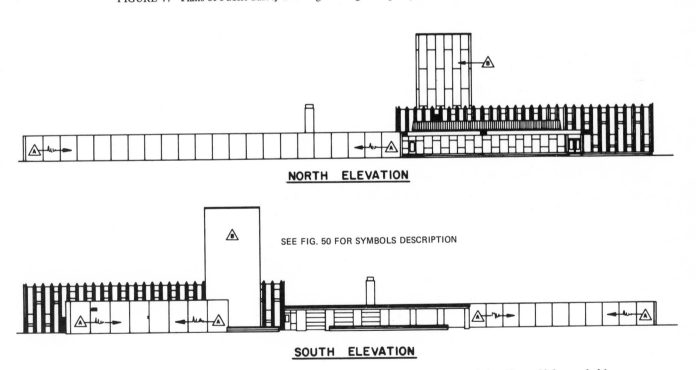

NORTH ELEVATION

SEE FIG. 50 FOR SYMBOLS DESCRIPTION

SOUTH ELEVATION

FIGURE 48 North and south elevations of Public Safety Building showing damage repair (see Figure 50 for symbols).

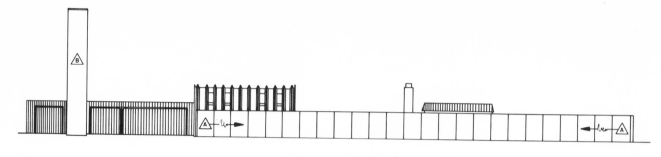

EAST ELEVATION

FIGURE 49   East elevation of Public Safety Building showing damage repair (see Figure 50 for symbols).

SYMBOL   DESCRIPTION OF WORK

Ⓐ   REPAIR CRACKS IN CONC. WALLS & CEILINGS

Ⓑ   REPAIR CRACKS IN CONC. WALLS BY EPOXY INJECTION

Ⓒ   REPAIR SPALLED AREAS OF EXT. CONC. WALLS

Ⓓ   REMOVE & REPLACE CONC. BASE SLAB AT FLAGPOLE

Ⓔ   REMOVE & REPLACE BROKEN CONC. SIDEWALKS

Ⓕ   REPAIR CRACKS IN CONC. SIDEWALKS

Ⓖ   REPAIR CRACKS IN CONC. CURBS

Ⓗ   REPAIR CRACKS IN CONC. APRON AT GARAGES

Ⓘ   REPAIR CRACKS IN CONC. SLAB WITHOUT FLOOR COVERING

Ⓙ   REPAIR CRACKS IN CONC. SLAB WITH FLOOR COVERING

Ⓚ   REMOVE & REPLACE VINYL-CORK & VINYL-ASBESTOS FL. TILES

Ⓛ   REMOVE & REPLACE QUARRY FLOOR TILES

Ⓜ   REMOVE & REPLACE CERAMIC TILES AT THRESHOLDS

Ⓝ   REMOVE & REPLACE QUARRY TILE BASE

Ⓞ   RECALK JOINTS IN CERAMIC TILE WALLS

Ⓟ   REPAIR CRACK IN CONC. MASONRY UNIT WALLS

Ⓠ   RECALK JOINTS BETWEEN CONC. MASONRY UNITS & CONC.

Ⓡ   REMOVE & REPLACE BROKEN CONC. MASONRY UNITS

Ⓢ   PATCH SPALLED AREAS OF PLASTER ON WALLS & CEILING

Ⓣ   REPAIR CRACK IN PLASTER WALLS & CEILINGS

Ⓤ   REMOVE & REPLACE CORK WALL TILES

Ⓥ   REMOVE & REPLACE CRACKED MARLITE WALL PLANKS

Ⓦ   REMOVE & REPLACE ACOUSTICAL CEILING TILES

Ⓧ   REMOVE & REPLACE METAL WALL ANGLE FOR CEILING TILES

Ⓨ   CALK JOINT BETWEEN BASE AND CONC. FL. SLAB

Ⓩ   TOUCH UP PAINTING OF REPAIRED INT. WALLS & CEILINGS

FIGURE 50   Damage-repair symbols for Public Safety Building.

FIGURE 51 City warehouse after repairs, view from southeast.

the reinforced-concrete control tower, which collapsed at Anchorage International Airport.

FIRE STATION NO. 2

Fire Station No. 2, at Hollywood and Elm Street, is a one-story building with a basement under part of it (Figure 2).

The structure, except for some interior partitions, is of reinforced concrete throughout. The roof is supported on open-web steel joists and structural-steel beams. The structural-concrete slab at the first floor is supported on reinforced-concrete beams and columns. Part of the roof was designed to carry a telephone exchange (Figures 61 and 62).

Although the seismic design criteria are not available, we know that the roof and concrete walls transmitted the lateral loads to the foundation.

Earthquake Damage

Structural damage to this building was limited to cracks in the concrete walls and floors. Minor cracks developed in wall tile, gypsum-board joints, and concrete-block partitions. The ground-floor slab separated from the foundation

walls, and parts of the sidewalks and driveway settled. The only damage to the electrical and mechanical system was a ruptured oil line.

Repair of Earthquake Damage

Cracks over 1/32 in. wide in all exposed concrete were repaired with an epoxy grout (see Figures 63 and 64 for repairs). Some of the repair quantities are listed herewith.

Replacement of Sidewalk	100 ft²
Repair of Cracks	
Concrete walls	990 lin ft
Floor slab	140 lin ft
Plaster	64 lin ft
Repair Costs	
Structural repair	$7,119
Architectural repair	1,137
TOTAL	$8,256

FIRE STATION NO. 3

Fire Station No. 3 is on Airport Heights Road, between Fifth Avenue and DeBarr Road (Figure 2).

This one-story concrete and timber building has a basement under part of it. The roof over the garage is a timber folded plate and the remainder is a flat timber-frame roof (Figure 65). The exterior walls are of reinforced concrete with insulated metal panels.

The seismic design criteria for this building are not available. The lateral loads are transmitted by the roof diaphragm to the concrete walls and then to the foundation.

Earthquake Damage

Structural damage included numerous cracks in the concrete and concrete-block walls. The concrete slab-on-grade and structural slab were also cracked, and the reinforced-concrete foundation walls and the retaining walls on the south side of the building were cracked and slightly out of plumb (Figures 66 and 67).

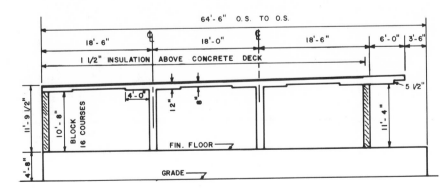

TYPICAL SECTION

FIGURE 52 City warehouse, Anchorage; typical section.

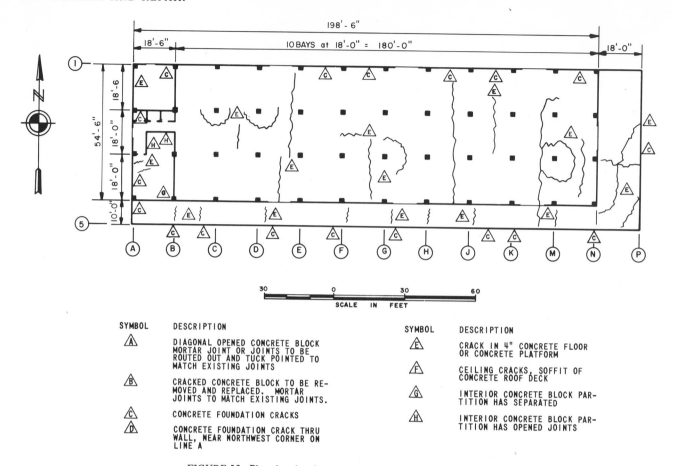

FIGURE 53 Plan showing damage to Anchorage city warehouse.

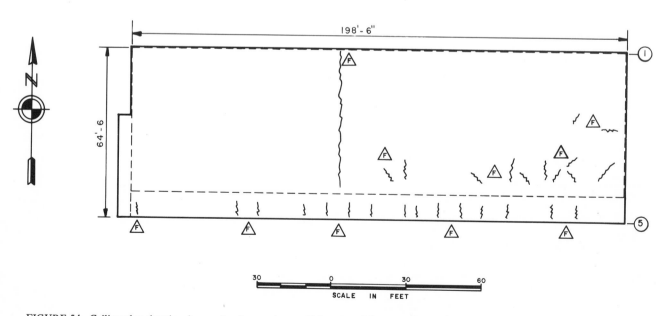

FIGURE 54 Ceiling plan showing damage to city warehouse. Columns and drop panels not shown (see Figure 53 for damage symbols).

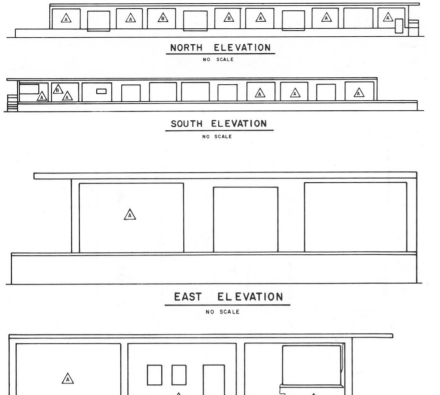

NORTH ELEVATION
NO SCALE

SOUTH ELEVATION
NO SCALE

FIGURE 55   North and south sidewall elevations of city warehouse showing typical damage (see Figure 53 for damage symbols).

EAST ELEVATION
NO SCALE

WEST ELEVATION
NO SCALE

FIGURE 56   East and west end-wall elevations of city warehouse showing typical damage (see Figure 53 for damage symbols).

FIGURE 57   Merrill Field control tower, Anchorage, viewed from south.

Nonstructural damage included damage to the pavement on the east side, which had subsided about 3 in.; the soil had moved and subsided all around the station. A hot-water heater was upset, damaging the pipes, and several unit ventilators were displaced. No damage to the electrical facilities was recorded.

Repair of Earthquake Damage

Methods of repair were the same as those used in Fire Station No. 2 and in the Merrill Field tower.

Some of the repair quantities are given in the following list.

Crack Repairs

Concrete walls and floors	390 lin ft
Slab-on-grade	400 lin ft
Masonry walls	50 lin ft
Floor tile replaced	120 ft^2
Asphalt pavement repaired	2,100 ft^2

Repair Cost

Structural repair	$ 5,940
Architectural repair	1,428
Pavement repair	4,725
TOTAL	$12,093

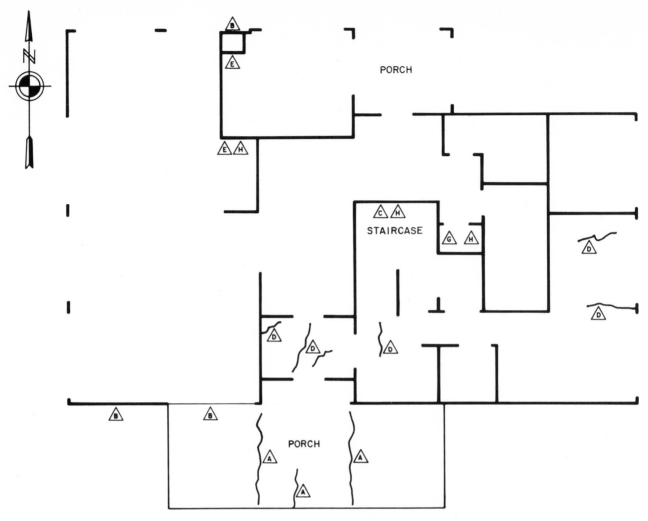

FIGURE 58   Merrill Field control tower: first-floor plan showing damage (see Figure 60 for symbols).

FAIRFAX TELEPHONE EXCHANGE

The exchange building, situated on Spenard Road south of Fireweed Lane (Figure 2), houses telephone equipment, a boiler, and a generator. This building is a one-story structure over an underground cable vault (Figures 68 and 69). The roof is constructed of metal decking on structural-steel framing, and the exterior walls are of concrete block and insulated metal panels. The interior studwall partitions are finished with plastic-coated hardboard. The foundation is of reinforced concrete, and the ground floor is a slab-on-grade and structural slab. Figure 70 shows the floor plan.

Earthquake Damage

The exchange building sustained very minor damage; some equipment was moved, some relays were destroyed when the cabinet doors fell to the floor, and an equipment race above the cabinets was pulled loose from the building.

The cost of repairs to this building was $500 (see Figure 70 for repairs). Repair to some equipment was performed by city employees.

FEDERAL TELEPHONE EXCHANGE

The Federal Telephone Exchange building, of similar construction to the Fairfax Exchange, is on DeBarr Road, west of Bragaw Street (Figure 2). It sustained little damage. A sidewalk settled 2–5 in. around the exterior of the building, and a low concrete-block wall, separate from the building, cracked and spalled slightly in the block joints.

Repairs, which cost $1,000, are shown in Figure 70.

BROADWAY TELEPHONE EXCHANGE

The Broadway Telephone Exchange building, about 65 ft square, with a 32 × 54-ft office area on the east side, is situated at E Street and Fifteenth Avenue (Figure 2).

The reinforced-concrete roof and floors are supported on

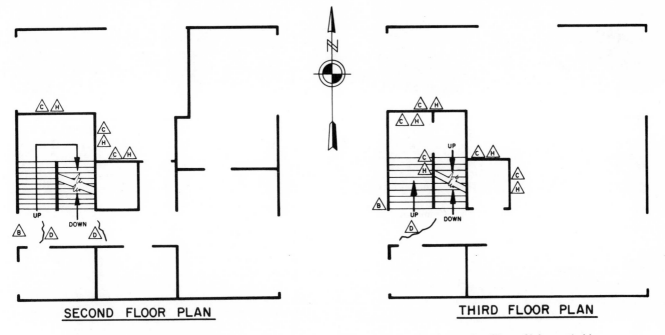

SECOND FLOOR PLAN THIRD FLOOR PLAN

FIGURE 59 Merrill Field control tower: second- and third-floor plans showing damage (see Figure 60 for symbols).

reinforced-concrete walls and columns, and on steel-pipe columns. The exterior walls are of reinforced concrete with a brick veneer. The interior walls are constructed of reinforced concrete, metal studs, wood studs, or concrete block (Figure 71).

The seismic design criteria for this building are not available. The lateral loads are transferred by the roof slab to the concrete walls and then to the foundation.

Earthquake Damage

The structural damage to this building consisted mainly of cracks in the concrete walls and floors. The basement floor had very few cracks, but the cantilever roof slab was cracked, and the roof developed leaks.

Some nonstructural damage occurred. Several interior doors were jammed and some insulation on the basement

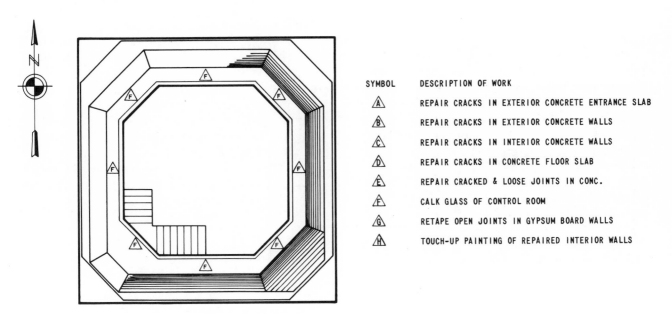

SYMBOL	DESCRIPTION OF WORK
A	REPAIR CRACKS IN EXTERIOR CONCRETE ENTRANCE SLAB
B	REPAIR CRACKS IN EXTERIOR CONCRETE WALLS
C	REPAIR CRACKS IN INTERIOR CONCRETE WALLS
D	REPAIR CRACKS IN CONCRETE FLOOR SLAB
E	REPAIR CRACKED & LOOSE JOINTS IN CONC.
F	CALK GLASS OF CONTROL ROOM
G	RETAPE OPEN JOINTS IN GYPSUM BOARD WALLS
H	TOUCH-UP PAINTING OF REPAIRED INTERIOR WALLS

FIGURE 60 Merrill Field control tower: control-room plan.

FIGURE 61   Anchorage Fire Station No. 2 (from southwest) after repair.

FIGURE 62   Anchorage Fire Station No. 2 (from north) after repair.

walls was loosened. Electrical equipment was extensively damaged. The cable-tray framing was torn loose in several places and damaged the cable insulation. Several relay panels were upset or shifted; the panels were anchored to the floor but the bolts pulled out of the concrete. About half of the lights are fluorescent, of which about one fourth fell to the floor. Several fluorescent tubes fell from the fixtures. A battery charger was damaged and was rendered inoperable.

Figures 72 and 73 describe the repairs. Cracks up to 3/32 in. wide in concrete were repaired with an epoxy adhesive injection. Cracks larger than 3/32 in. wide in concrete and any spalled areas were repaired with an epoxy grout. All other damaged items were restored to their original condition.

The following is a list of some repair quantities for the Broadway Exchange.

Crack repair in concrete	813 lin ft
Crack repair in masonry walls	100 lin ft
Roofing replacement	4,000 ft^2
Studwall installation	2,200 ft^2

Repair Cost	
Structural repair	$11,300
Architectural repair	13,300
Mechanical–electrical repair	2,600
Painting	1,700
TOTAL	$28,900

This building demonstrates the desirability of designing nonstructural components of a building to survive earthquake forces.

PUBLIC HEALTH CENTER

The Public Health Center, on E Street near Third Avenue (Figure 2), is a two-story wood-frame building with a base-

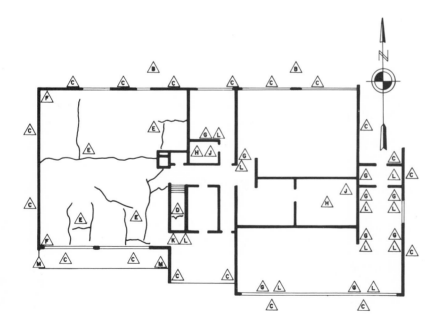

FIGURE 63   First-floor plan of Fire Station No. 2, Hollywood and Elm streets, showing damage.

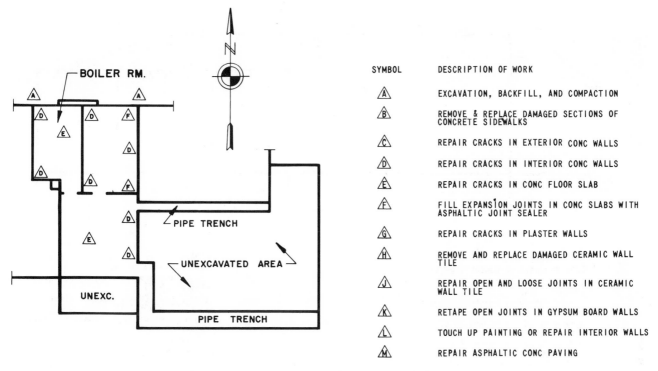

SYMBOL	DESCRIPTION OF WORK
A	EXCAVATION, BACKFILL, AND COMPACTION
B	REMOVE & REPLACE DAMAGED SECTIONS OF CONCRETE SIDEWALKS
C	REPAIR CRACKS IN EXTERIOR CONC WALLS
D	REPAIR CRACKS IN INTERIOR CONC WALLS
E	REPAIR CRACKS IN CONC FLOOR SLAB
F	FILL EXPANSION JOINTS IN CONC SLABS WITH ASPHALTIC JOINT SEALER
G	REPAIR CRACKS IN PLASTER WALLS
H	REMOVE AND REPLACE DAMAGED CERAMIC WALL TILE
J	REPAIR OPEN AND LOOSE JOINTS IN CERAMIC WALL TILE
K	RETAPE OPEN JOINTS IN GYPSUM BOARD WALLS
L	TOUCH UP PAINTING OR REPAIR INTERIOR WALLS
M	REPAIR ASPHALTIC CONC PAVING

FIGURE 64   Basement-floor plan of Fire Station No. 2, showing repairs.

ment. It has a built-up asphalt roof and asbestos-shingled walls; the interior studwalls are covered with gypsum board. The building relies on the roof and wall sheathing to transmit lateral loads to the foundation. The foundation of this structure, located near the west end of the Fourth Avenue slide, was damaged. Figure 74 shows the health center after repair.

Earthquake Damage and Repair

This building, which was displaced about 4 in. to the north, had its north foundation wall moved out of plumb and out of line. The other foundation walls sustained many cracks,

FIGURE 65   Anchorage Fire Station No. 3 (from northeast) after building repairs.

but the east wall was the most severely damaged. The basement floor was cracked and showed some settlement. Concrete sidewalks and stairs on the west side of the building were heavily damaged.

Heavy nonstructural damage was sustained by the interior studwall partitions in the basement and on the first floor. There was no indication of damage to electrical or mechanical facilities.

Figures 75–78 show earthquake repairs. The extent of some of the repairs to this building is as follows:

Repair
Cracks in foundations	60 lin ft
Cracks in floor slab	120 lin ft
Cracks in gypsum board	250 lin ft

Replace
Sidewalk	70 ft^2
Walls and windows	where damaged
Concrete stairs	where damaged
Front entrance	
North wall (Figure 76)	
Shingles	205 ft^2
Gypsum board	250 ft^2
Interior painting	800 ft^2

Repair Costs
Structural repair	$ 9,600
Architectural repair	5,900
Sidewalk repair	440
Painting	360
TOTAL	$16,300

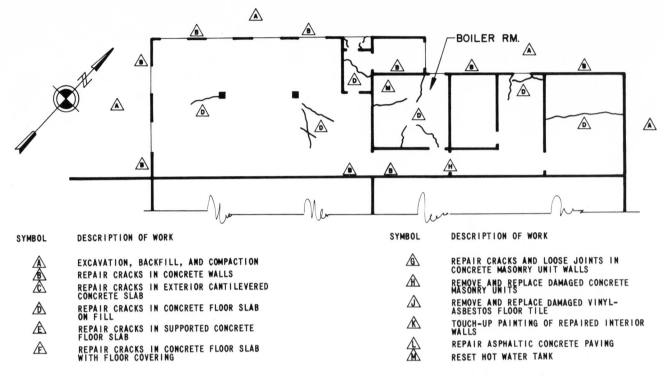

SYMBOL	DESCRIPTION OF WORK	SYMBOL	DESCRIPTION OF WORK
A	EXCAVATION, BACKFILL, AND COMPACTION	G	REPAIR CRACKS AND LOOSE JOINTS IN CONCRETE MASONRY UNIT WALLS
B	REPAIR CRACKS IN CONCRETE WALLS	H	REMOVE AND REPLACE DAMAGED CONCRETE MASONRY UNITS
C	REPAIR CRACKS IN EXTERIOR CANTILEVERED CONCRETE SLAB	J	REMOVE AND REPLACE DAMAGED VINYL-ASBESTOS FLOOR TILE
D	REPAIR CRACKS IN CONCRETE FLOOR SLAB ON FILL	K	TOUCH-UP PAINTING OF REPAIRED INTERIOR WALLS
E	REPAIR CRACKS IN SUPPORTED CONCRETE FLOOR SLAB	L	REPAIR ASPHALTIC CONCRETE PAVING
F	REPAIR CRACKS IN CONCRETE FLOOR SLAB WITH FLOOR COVERING	M	RESET HOT WATER TANK

FIGURE 66   Fire Station No. 3: Basement floor plan shows typical earthquake-damage repairs.

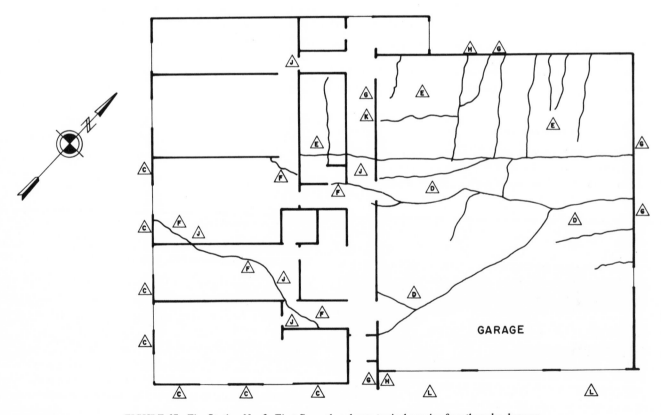

FIGURE 67   Fire Station No. 3: First-floor plan shows typical repair of earthquake damage.

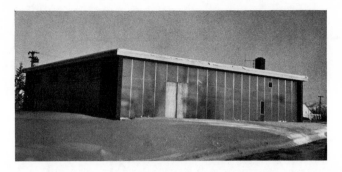

FIGURE 68   Fairfax telephone exchange, after repairs.

FIGURE 69   Federal telephone exchange (from the east).

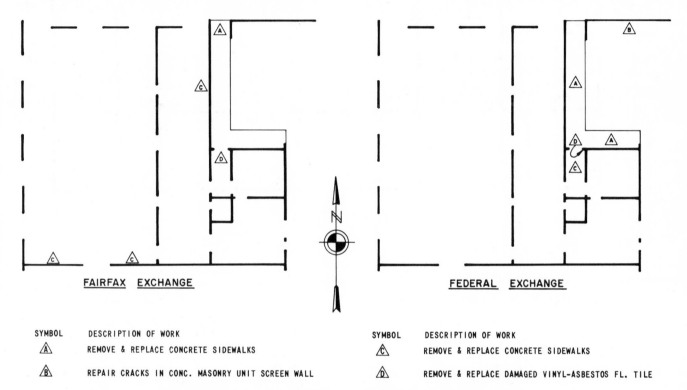

FIGURE 70   Floor plans for Fairfax and Federal telephone exchange buildings.

FIGURE 71   Broadway telephone exchange at left (from northwest) after repairs.

SCHOOLS

WEST ANCHORAGE HIGH SCHOOL

West Anchorage High School, on Hillcrest Drive just west of its junction with Minnesota Avenue (Figure 2), was built in four stages. The first stage, built in 1953, consisted of the major part of the classroom wing and included 38 classrooms, a circular library, and a cafeteria. The second stage was built in 1955 and included a large auditorium, a gymnasium, auxiliary gymnasium facilities, and a shop wing. The third stage consisted of the addition of a warehouse on the north side of the shop area in 1956. The fourth and final stage of the school was an eight-classroom extension

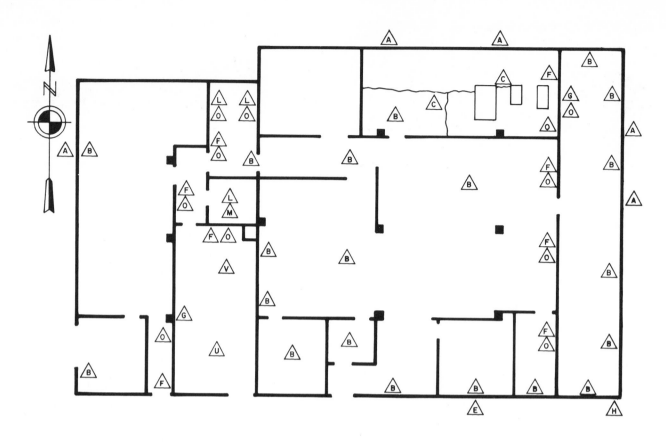

SYMBOL	DESCRIPTION OF WORK
A	EXCAVATION, BACKFILL, AND COMPACTION
B	REPAIR CRACKS IN CONC. WALLS & CEILINGS
C	REPAIR CRACKS IN CONC. SLABS WITHOUT FLOOR COVERING
D	REPAIR CRACKS IN CONC. SLABS WITH FLOOR COVERING
E	REPAIR CRACKS IN CON. CANOPIES, LINTELS & SILLS
F	REPAIR CRACKS IN CONC. MASONRY UNIT WALLS
G	REMOVE & REPLACE BROKEN CONC. MASONRY UNITS
H	REPAIR BRICK MASONRY
I	REMOVE AND REPLACE DAMAGED ROOFING & INSULATION
J	ERECTING STUDS FOR GYPSUM WALLBOARD
K	INSTALL GYPSUM WALLBOARD

SYMBOL	DESCRIPTION OF WORK
L	PATCH SPALLED AREAS OF PLASTER ON WALLS
M	REPAIR CRACKS IN PLASTER WALLS
N	REMOVE & REPLACE DAMAGED AS-PHALT FL. TILE
O	TOUCH-UP PAINTING OF REPAIRED & NEW INTERIOR WALLS
P	REMOVE & REPLACE STAINED CORK CEILING INSULATION
Q	ADJUST INTERIOR WOOD DOORS
R	RESET LOOSE RUBBER WALL BASE
S	RELOCATE WALL RADIATION IN EQUIPMENT ROOM
T	RELOCATE ELECTRICAL WALL SWITCHES & OUTLETS
U	REPAIR DAMAGED DUCT WORK
V	REMOVE & REPLACE DAMAGED IN-SULATION ON BOILER.

FIGURE 72 Repairs to Broadway exchange basement floor.

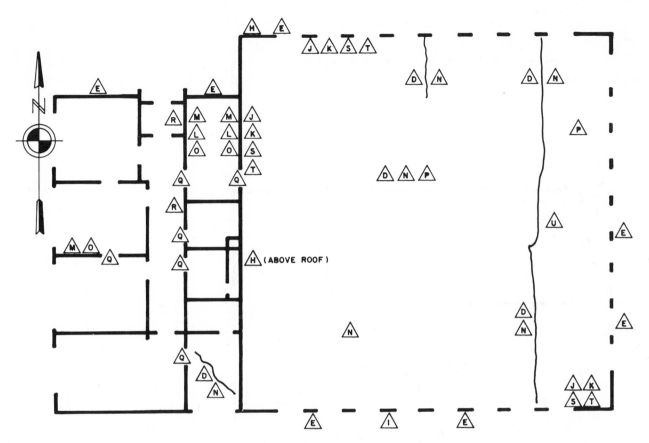

FIGURE 73   Repairs to first floor of Broadway exchange.

to the south end of the classroom wing in 1957. Figure 79 is a floor plan of the preearthquake West Anchorage High School and shows the stages in which it was built; Figure 80 shows the school after the earthquake.

First Stage: Classroom Wing, Library, and Cafeteria

The wing-shaped classroom building was a two-story reinforced-concrete structure 65 ft wide and about 520 ft long,

FIGURE 74   Public Health Center (from northwest) after repairs.

measured along the center corridor (Figures 81 and 82). Seismic zone 2 earthquake criteria were used in this initial stage.

The roof and second floors were 9-in. reinforced-concrete flat slabs, supported on concrete spandrel beams at the exterior and on concrete columns in the interior. The heads of the interior columns were provided with shear reinforcement within the body of the roof and second-floor slabs. Interior columns, 14 X 20 in. in section, with the strong axis oriented in the long direction of the building, were spaced 16 ft on centers. The exterior columns, supporting the spandrel beams, were 14 X 24 in. in section, with the strong axis oriented normal to the long axis of the building, and were spaced 32 ft on centers. In the transverse direction, the column spacing was about 25 ft between centers of exterior and interior columns and about 14 ft between interior columns. The roof slab had an overhang of about 2½ ft beyond the exterior face of the spandrel beams (Figures 81–83).

The library, attached to the east side of the classroom wing (Figure 79), is a one-story circular structure, about 25 ft in diameter, with a reinforced-concrete dome roof that is supported on 12 reinforced-concrete columns equally

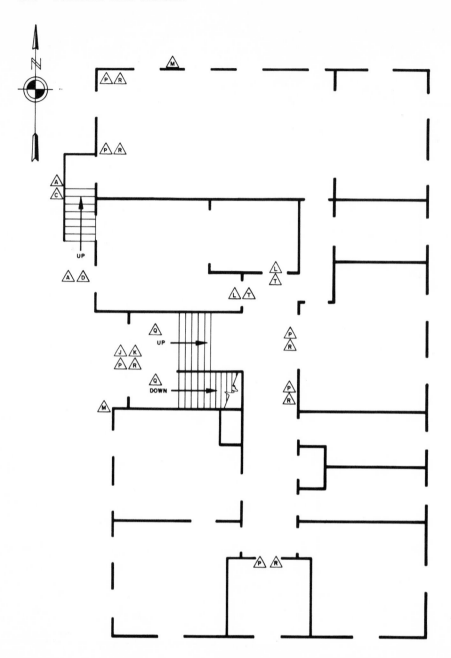

FIGURE 75 Public Health Center first-floor repair plan (see Figure 78 for symbols).

spaced around the perimeter (Figure 81). Ceiling height is about 14 ft at the eaves and 18 ft at the center of the dome.

The cafeteria is a one-story structure, lying at right angles to the north end of the main classroom wing. It has a 2½-in. concrete roof supported on steel bar joists, which are supported on and anchored to reinforced-concrete bearing walls. The exterior walls around the cafeteria extend down into the ground and form the foundation walls; they are reinforced and contain only a few openings for windows and doors.

Most exterior walls in the classroom wing were composed of Thermopane windows set in wood frames between the concrete columns and spandrel beams. Some areas, especially around the cafeteria, have exposed concrete walls. Interior partitions were generally of gypsum board on wood studs. Corridors had terrazzo floors, acoustic-tile ceilings, and gypsum-board walls above glazed-tile wainscoting. Typical second-floor classrooms had suspended acoustic-tile ceilings, whereas in the first-floor classrooms the acoustic tile was cemented directly to the underside of the second-floor slab. Typical classrooms have asphalt-tile floors and partitions finished with Marlite, wood veneer, or gypsum board.

The first floor is a 4-in. slab-on-grade reinforced with 6 × 6-in. to 10 × 10-in.-mesh welded-wire fabric. The foundations consist of reinforced-concrete walls around the exterior, with spread footings under the walls and the exterior and interior columns. The foundations are shallow, not over 5 ft deep, and bear on sand and gravel. There is a pipe trench around the outside of the building below the first floor. Similar first-floor and foundation conditions exist for the other portions of the building complex.

The classroom area had reinforced-concrete shear walls

as follows: Transversely between the first and second floors (Figure 81), there was at the north end about 100 ft of 8-in. wall along the north side of the cafeteria, 15 ft of 10-in. wall along the north side of the north stairwell, and 25 ft of 6-in. wall along the south side. About 50 ft of 8-in. wall and 25 ft of 6-in. wall were in the vicinity of the center stairwell. Longitudinally, between the first and second floors along the east side of the building, there was about 32 ft of 8-in. wall

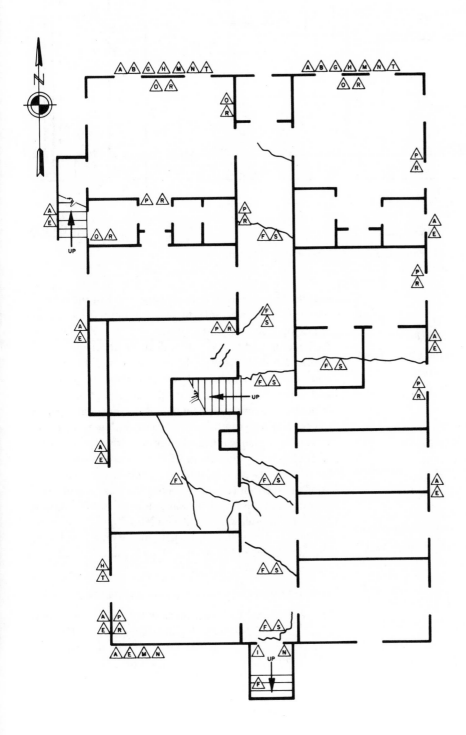

FIGURE 76   Public Health Center basement floor repair plan (see Figure 78 for symbols).

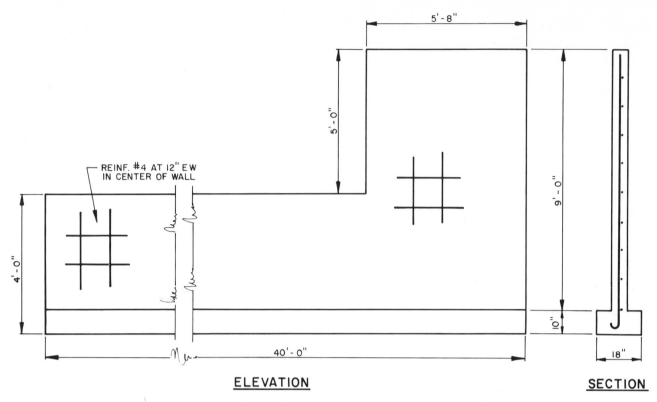

FIGURE 77 Public Health Center. Repair detail of north wall.

SYMBOL	DESCRIPTION OF WORK
A	EXCAVATION, BACKFILL & COMPACTION
B	REMOVE & REPLACE DAMAGED CONC. FOUNDATION
C	REMOVE & REPLACE DAMAGED EXTERIOR CONC. STAIRS
D	REMOVE & REPLACE DAMAGED CONC. SIDEWALK
E	REPAIR CRACKS IN CONC. FOUNDATION WALL
F	REPAIR CRACKS IN CONC. FLOOR SLAB & STEPS
G	REMOVE & REPLACE WOOD FRAMED WALL
H	REMOVE & REPLACE DAMAGED WINDOW FRAMES
I	REMOVE & REPLACE DAMAGED WOOD TRIM
J	REMOVE & RESET FRAME FOR MAIN ENTRANCE
K	REPLACE EXISTING MAIN ENTRANCE DOOR
L	ADJUST OPERATING SASH & INTERIOR DOORS
M	REMOVE & REPLACE ASBESTOS CEMENT SHINGLES
N	REPAIR CALKING BETWEEN WOOD TRIM & CONC. WALLS
O	REPLACE GYPSUM WALLBOARD
P	REPAIR CRACKS IN GYPSUM WALLBOARD
Q	REMOVE & REPLACE DAMAGED ASPHALT TILE FLOORING
R	TOUCH UP PAINTING OF REPAIRED & NEW INTERIOR WALL SURFACES
S	TOUCH UP PAINTING OF REPAIRED CONC. FLOOR SLAB
T	FINISHING OF NEW & REFITTED DOORS, WINDOWS, & WOOD TRIM

FIGURE 78 Description of repair symbols for Public Health Center.

near the library, 9 ft of 8-in. wall just south of the center stairwell; on the west side, there was about 6 ft of 8-in. wall at the south stairwell, 20 ft of 8-in. wall near the center of the building, and 8 ft of 8-in. wall at the north end near the cafeteria. A vault between the first and second floors, just north of the center stairwell, provided about 14 ft of 6-in. wall in the transverse direction and about 22 ft of 6-in. wall in the long direction of the building. As shown in Figure 82, transversely between the second floor and the roof, about 75 ft of 6-in. wall was near the north stairwell and about 62 ft of 8-in. wall and about 25 ft of 6-in. wall were near the south stairwell. Longitudinally, between the second floor and the roof (Figure 82) along the west side of the building, about 6 ft of 8-in. wall was at the south stairwell, 15 ft of 8-in. wall was near the building, and 22 ft of 8-in. wall was at the north end. Longitudinally on the east side, between the second floor and the roof, there were no reinforced-concrete shear walls.

Second Stage: Auditorium, Gymnasium, and Shop

The second-stage construction included a large auditorium about 120 × 120 ft (including the stage), a 117 × 120 ft gymnasium, auxiliary gymnasium facilities, and shop wing (Figure 79). The second stage is just north of, and adjacent to, the classroom wing and is separated from it by a 2-in. expansion joint. Zone 3 earthquake criteria were used in the design of this addition.

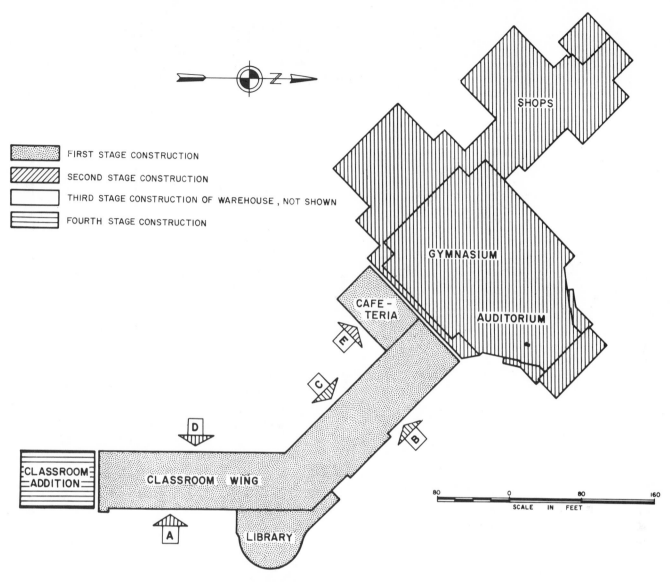

FIRST STAGE CONSTRUCTION

SECOND STAGE CONSTRUCTION

THIRD STAGE CONSTRUCTION OF WAREHOUSE, NOT SHOWN

FOURTH STAGE CONSTRUCTION

FIGURE 79   Preearthquake floor plan, West Anchorage High School.

FIGURE 80   General view of the West Anchorage High School after the earthquake and before reconstruction.

The roof consists of 3-in. tongue-and-groove wood plank supported on steel trusses, which in turn are supported on and anchored to reinforced-concrete bearing walls. The purlins over the gymnasium are supported on 36-in. wide-flange structural steel beams that span between the ends of heavy reinforced-concrete cantilever beams that project into the gymnasium area from the reinforced-concrete bearing and enclosure walls. The space between the gymnasium and the auditorium is occupied by a lobby on the first floor, a corridor with band, choral, and dressing rooms on the second floor, and a mechanical space and projection booth on the third floor. This area is of reinforced-concrete beam and slab construction.

The exterior walls around the gymnasium and auditorium are reinforced concrete with very few openings, forming a

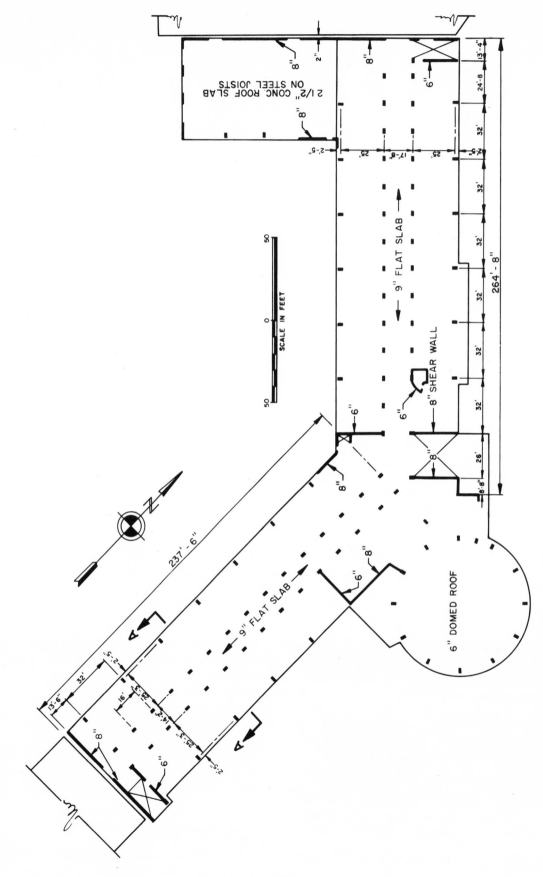

FIGURE 81 First-floor plan of preearthquake West Anchorage High School showing column spacing. Designed for seismic zone 2.

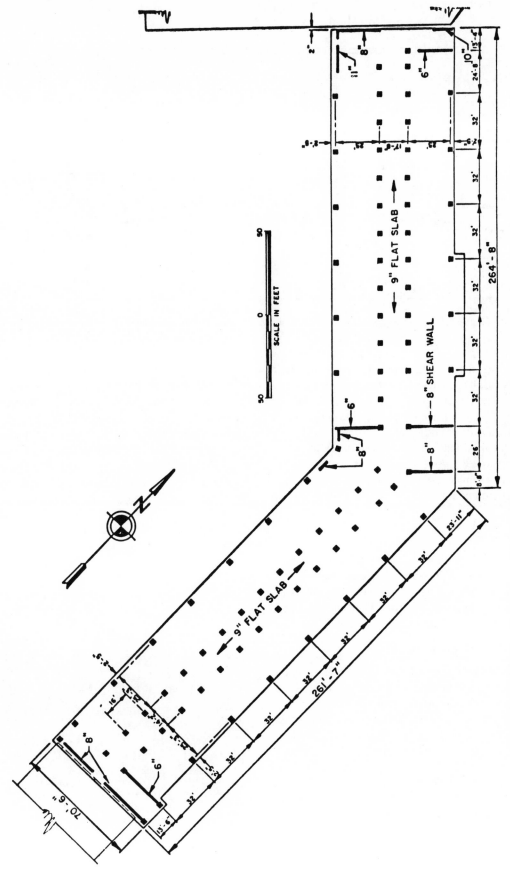

FIGURE 82 Second-floor plan of preearthquake West Anchorage High School showing column spacing. Designed for seismic zone 2.

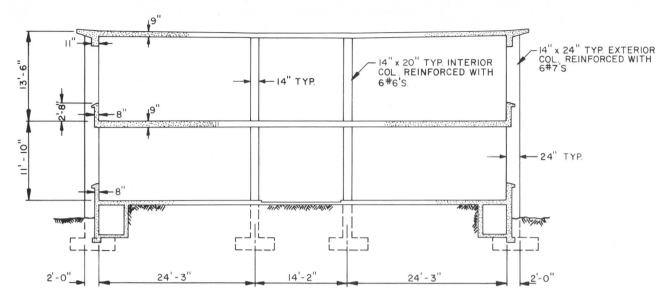

FIGURE 83   Section A-A through the classroom wing showing typical column reinforcing (West Anchorage High School).

complete box system. The walls around the shops and other one-story areas are either reinforced-concrete walls or frames with insulated glass in wood frames between. There are a few areas of Roman Brick veneer over the concrete walls in the vicinity of the entrances.

In general, the partitions are constructed of reinforced concrete; a few, however, are constructed of reinforced concrete blocks. For example, the partitions in the mechanical space and projection booth on the third floor are of concrete block.

Third Stage: Warehouse

Third-stage construction consisted of the addition of a warehouse on the north side of the shop area. This one-story reinforced-concrete building has concrete-block panel walls and spread footings on glacial till. Zone 3 earthquake criteria were used in both the third and fourth stage design.

Fourth Stage: Eight-Classroom Addition

Fourth-stage construction consisted of an eight-classroom extension added to the south end of the classroom wing. This two-story reinforced-concrete structure, separated by a 2-in. expansion joint from the remaining classroom wing, is similar in construction to the main classroom wing. Both buildings were designed for seismic zone 3 as noted in the various stages of completion, in accordance with the requirements of the *Uniform Building Code* (Pacific Coast Building Officials Conference, 1949), and with the City of Anchorage requirements for schools constructed with federal participation before 1956.

Structural damage to the building is illustrated in Figures 84-91.

Classroom Wing and Library

The classroom wing sustained extensive structural damage. Exterior columns were shattered at the roof and second-floor levels and were severely cracked and spalled at the first floor, near the top of the grade beam at windowsill level. Exterior concrete wall panels at toilets and stairwells were crisscrossed by wide cracks, and several gaping holes were left where the concrete had fallen out.

At the second-floor and roof levels, the concrete of the exterior columns had spalled off and fallen to the ground, exposing the reinforcing. The reinforcing was buckled and

FIGURE 84   West Anchorage High School: Closeup view of second-story columns and window sash, taken from the roof of the library. Failure at the top and bottom of the columns can be seen.

FIGURE 85   West Anchorage High School: Damage to elevation C of the classroom wing. Minor damage to elevation E of the cafeteria can be seen at left. Above the cafeteria roof, the battering effect of the classroom-wing roof against the gymnasium wall is visible.

FIGURE 88   West Anchorage High School: Damage to elevation B of classroom wing and undamaged wall of auditorium.

FIGURE 86   West Anchorage High School: Damage to shear walls at intersection of elevations C and D.

FIGURE 89   West Anchorage High School: Southwest elevation of classroom wing on second floor and south elevation of upper part of gymnasium (taken from roof of cafeteria). Note the shattering of the concrete in the wall to the right of the expansion joint, and the damage to the reinforced-concrete wall at the upper part of the gymnasium. This damage resulted from the pounding of the roof of the classroom wing at the expansion joint. This rammed the concrete roof at the left of the expansion joint about 4 in. into the gymnasium wall.

FIGURE 87   West Anchorage High School: Roof-slab fracture near intersection of elevations C and D.

broken and allowed vertical displacement of the columns and roof structure. In many instances, the second-story column had kicked out at the top, so that the roof and spandrel beams had dropped down nearly the full depth of the spandrel, with the roof overhang bearing on the top of the displaced column. The distortion of the wall structure at these points warped and broke some window-wall sections and caused entire window bays to collapse into some second-floor classrooms.

The grade beam at ground level sustained only minor damage except in the areas adjacent to the column at the sill line. The second floor held together and showed only small diagonal shear cracks. Roof spandrels also held to-

FIGURE 90   West Anchorage High School: Damage at a shear wall adjacent to stairs. Note the sliding action that took place in the horizontal construction joint and displacement of the upper part of the wall.

gether except at the west elevation adjacent to the change in direction of the classroom wing; at this point, roof and spandrel were ruptured and displaced about 1 ft vertically.

The south end wall had a crisscross pattern of small diagonal tension cracks and hairline cracks at horizontal construction joints.

The transverse concrete walls adjacent to the stairwells were badly damaged because of shear and shattering of concrete at the ends; most of this damage occurred at the horizontal construction joints at the second floor. Many of the vertical reinforcing bars were broken where they crossed the joint. Considerable diagonal cracking was observed in these walls above the second floor; the upper part of the walls shifted about 2 in. over the lower part at the second-floor level.

The junction of the classroom area with the gymnasium and auditorium area was damaged by the pounding that took place at the expansion joint between the two areas. The roof slab rammed inward 3–4 in. the upper part of the reinforced-concrete south walls of the gymnasium and the area between gymnasium and auditorium.

At the expansion joint adjacent to the north wall of the eight-classroom addition, the joint opened up about 2 in. on the east side of the roof. The southern portion of the addition moved south.

Interior columns in the second story were spalled and cracked at the roof and floor level; interior columns in the first story were undamaged.

The second-floor slab was only slightly damaged. Small cracks on the underside were discovered when the ceiling tile was removed. The ground-floor slab was cracked in numerous places, apparently by a settlement of ½ to 1 in. near the interior columns.

The library itself sustained very little structural damage. The peripheral columns showed hairline horizontal cracks, and the concrete walls adjoining the classroom wing and the library were badly cracked and broken.

Auditorium and Gymnasium

The principal structural damage to the auditorium was in the second story, at the southeast end where the classroom wing meets the auditorium. The wall and beam between the auditorium, the choral room, and the lobby were broken and cracked. The roof framing over the girls' rest room was shattered, and the columns and walls in the lobby were displaced laterally about 4 in. at the roof.

The upper wall of the gymnasium at the east corner was badly cracked and shattered where the roof of the classroom wing meets the gymnasium. The damage was most severe on the southeast wall, adjacent to the east corner, extending about 30 ft from the corner. The northeast corner also had numerous cracks up to ½ in. wide. The floor slabs of the locker rooms, adjoining the gymnasium were damaged by the settlement.

The damage to the auditorium and gymnasium, as we have pointed out, was caused mainly by the hammering effect of the 9-in. slab of the classroom wing.

Warehouse and Shop

The damage to this section of the building, excluding the warehouse, consisted primarily of slab settlement. The warehouse sustained extensive structural damage; several of the exterior columns were sheared off at the bottom of the roof beams.

The two-story classroom wing sustained most of the nonstructural damage in the building. The mechanical and

FIGURE 91   West Anchorage High School: Second story over classroom wings being removed during the phase II construction period. At the left, workers can be seen installing the roof on the second-floor slab; classroom wings were converted into a one-story structure.

electrical fixtures on the second floor were severely damaged, as were the interior partitions and finishes on both the first and second floors. Walls were racked and buckled, and plaster, Marlite, and glazed-tile surfaces were cracked and shattered. Only minor damage to the interior finish occurred in the library.

On the third floor between the gymnasium and the auditorium, which houses mechanical equipment and the projection booth, some concrete-block partitions failed and toppled over. Cracks were found in the floor and, to a lesser extent, in the wall finishes.

The cafeteria area of the school also sustained minor damage to architectural finishes. Some ceiling tile fell, and minor cracking occurred in some plaster and Marlite finishes.

Building Restoration

The initial restoration plan for West Anchorage High School was to repair the school in two phases. Phase I was to consist of repairing the cafeteria, auditorium, gymnasium, shops, and maintenance area, because these areas were only slightly damaged. Phase II was to consist of the repair of the classroom wing and library, which were badly damaged.

An Anchorage architectural firm was retained by the U.S. Army Corps of Engineers Alaska District to prepare contract drawings for the building restoration. In studying ways of rebuilding the second story of the classroom wing, the firm found that it would be more economical to remove this second story and build a new one-story structure that contained the same classroom space. This concept was acceptable to the Anchorage School District; a third phase was therefore added to the restoration plan, consisting of the addition of a one-story classroom wing, containing approximately 40,000 ft^2 of classroom area. Figure 92, a floor plan of West Anchorage High School as it exists today, shows the areas involved in each phase of the rehabilitation. The one-story classroom addition built in phase III is a steel-frame construction, with bar joists, steel decking, and foam concrete for the roof. Exterior walls are precast-concrete panels.

The phase II restoration contract consisted of removing the roof slab and columns from the second floor of the pre-earthquake classroom wing and converting it into a one-story structure. Repairs were made to the spandrel-beam at the first-story ceiling line, and a new roof was installed on top of the original second-floor slab.

The cost of the phase I contract was $195,633, approximately $15,000 of which was for structural repairs. The phase II contract cost approximately $800,000, of which about $150,000 was spent on structural repairs and the remainder on nonstructural repairs.

The cost of the phase III contract was $1,226,306, the cost of the new one-story classroom addition to West Anchorage High School.

Conclusions

The zone 2 requirements of the *Uniform Building Code* were obviously inadequate. If the building had been designed for zone 3 requirements, it would probably still have sustained significant damage, because of some of the design features.

The second story of the classroom wing was seriously damaged. Figures 84–91 demonstrate the results of columns and shear walls of a building with inadequate strength to resist seismic loads. Heavy roofs should be avoided in seismic areas. If a heavy roof is used, the walls and columns that support it must be strong enough to resist the resulting large lateral forces. The classroom wing of the West Anchorage High School had relatively little shear-wall area along the longitudinal axis of the building, especially between the second floor and the roof. In the southwest and west elevations, there were a few shear walls in the long direction of the building; between the second floor and roof of the east and northeast elevations of the classroom wing, there were no shear walls between two expansion joints approximately 520 ft apart.

The center of resistance of the shear walls was eccentric to the center of mass of the roof structure. Because the shear walls in the second story were both eccentric and inadequate in strength along the long axis of the building, and the mass of the roof was large, excessive stresses developed in the shear walls and they failed (Figures 85, 86, 89, and 90). As they failed, the lateral seismic loads were transferred to the columns, which also failed because they too were not strong enough to resist such great forces (Figures 84 and 85). Because the exterior columns were much stiffer than the interior columns, they failed at both top and bottom. The more flexible interior columns were only slightly damaged at the top and bottom and could deflect sufficiently to prevent the complete shattering of the concrete that occurred in the exterior columns. The roof of the classroom wing was then free to sway to and fro as a pendulum between the north and south expansion joints. If it were not for the staying properties of the eight-classroom addition on the south and the gymnasium and auditorium on the north, the roof of the classroom wing undoubtedly would have collapsed entirely. As evidenced by Figure 89, a tremendous amount of hammering took place at the two expansion joints. This structure is an outstanding example of the effects of an earthquake on a building that has an extended heavy roof without proper anchors or resisting elements, such as oversized columns or shear walls. The Ursa Major Elementary School and the Sunflower School, which were of similar construction, had more shear walls and these provided greater strength than the code required, thus preventing serious damage.

In general, shear walls must be amply strong to withstand

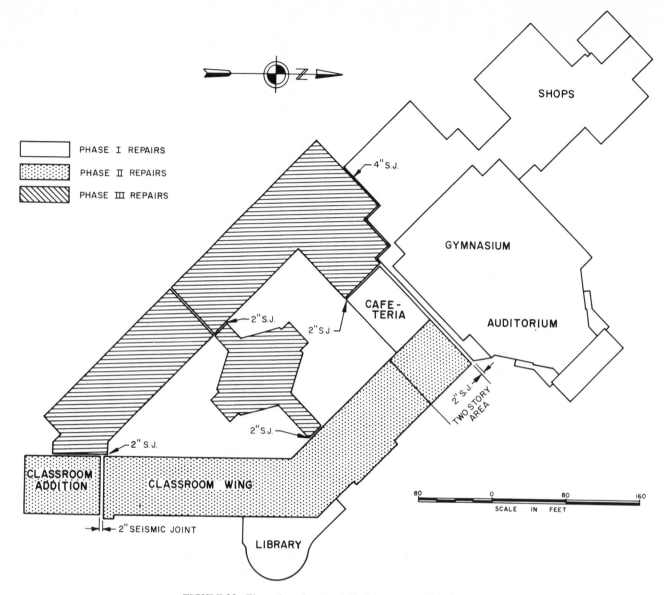

FIGURE 92   Floor plan of restored West Anchorage High School.

the loads that they may have to resist. The loads will be distributed among the shear walls and the columns according to their stiffnesses. The center of resistance of the shear walls and columns should coincide as nearly as possible with the resultant line of action of the seismic forces; if this is not the case, the design must allow for the torsional moments that will be developed.

The more flexible elements, such as slender columns, will not participate in the resistance to lateral forces until the stiffer elements fail. When the stiffer elements are not strong enough to resist the loads, and if they cannot yield to share the loads with the more flexible elements, they will fail suddenly and transfer the loads to the more flexible

walls and columns; because these are weaker in resistance to lateral forces, they will in turn fail, bringing about a progressive and rapid failure of the entire structure.

The angle where the classroom wing changes direction is another interesting feature of this structure. From the roof failure at this point (Figure 87), it appears to be a critical part of the structure and should be given special attention in the design.

The poor behavior of this building indicates that a thorough dynamic analysis should be made of its earthquake response to evaluate its true strength to resist earthquake ground motion and to examine the code requirements from this point of view.

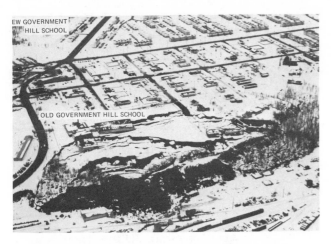

FIGURE 93   Aerial view of Government Hill slide showing the earth slide. The new school location is shown at the upper left of the photo.

OLD GOVERNMENT HILL SCHOOL

The school is located north of Ship Creek, adjacent to Loop Road on Government Hill (Figure 2). The structure was subjected not only to the forces of the earthquake, but also to the forces developed from a massive landslide (Figure 93).

This school was built in two stages. The first stage, built in 1954, included a multipurpose room, general offices, and 12 classrooms (Metcalf and Eddy, 1964). A second wing, which included eight classrooms, was added in 1958 to the east of the original buildings (Figure 94).

The roof framing over both wings was a 2-in. reinforced-concrete slab on 22-gage metal decking, welded to structural-steel frames.

The south and east wings had three-bay rigid frames, spaced 8 ft 4 in. apart. The exterior bays of the rigid frames had 12-in., 27-lb wide-flange beams welded to 6-in., 15.5-lb wide-flange columns. The interior bay had 10-in., 18-lb wide-flange beams welded to 6-in., 20-lb wide-flange columns.

The multipurpose area had open-web joists supported on steel columns, and the exterior side walls consisted of insulated glass and insulated metal panels in wood and metal frames.

The end walls were of 8-in. concrete block or 8-in. reinforced concrete. Classroom partitions were 6-in. concrete block. The walls were reinforced as follows:

Concrete-block bearing walls 8 in. thick had 5/8-in.-round reinforcing spaced at 32 in. vertically and welded wire fabric in every other horizontal joint. Concrete-block nonbearing walls 6 in. thick had ½-in.-round reinforcing,

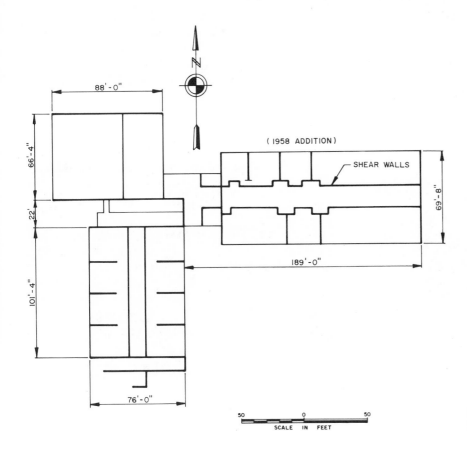

FIGURE 94   Floor plan of old Government Hill School, Anchorage.

spaced at 48 in. vertically and welded wire fabric in the horizontal joints, spaced at 32 in. Concrete walls 8 in. thick had ½-in.-round reinforcing, spaced at 10 in. each way. The foundations were either 8-in. concrete block or 8-in. concrete walls, reinforced as mentioned above. The corridor walls were of 6-in. concrete block.

This school was typical of a number of grade schools in the Anchorage area.

The design loads were 40 psf roof live load, 20 psf wind load, and fulfillment of zone 3 earthquake requirements.

The lateral forces in the east and south wings were resisted by the rigid frames and walls in the transverse direction. It is uncertain how the longitudinal forces were resisted as the translucent relights separated the roof framing from the corridor walls. The available drawings did not indicate how the lateral forces were resisted in the multipurpose room.

Earthquake Damage

The head of the Government Hill slide passed along the north wall of the east wing and through the south wing (Figures 95 and 96). The multipurpose room and office area were the only parts of the school that were not carried down with the landslide (Figure 97). The east wing separated from the rest of the building at its connection and dropped down and away. The south wing was pulled apart through the first classroom next to the multipurpose room and then moved down and away (Figures 95, 98, and 99).

Figure 100 shows the desks and furniture still upright, and evidence that the hanging lights sustained little damage indicates that the landslide occurred gradually (Meehan, 1967). The slowness of the earth movement, together with the good roof-diaphragm action and the integrity of the reinforced walls and rigid column connections, all helped to

FIGURE 96   View of old Government Hill School from the southeast showing that displaced wings remained fairly intact.

prevent the total collapse of the east and south wings. Figure 101 shows interior damage.

Although the adjacent foundation failure and building movement must have caused large lateral loads on the multipurpose room, little damage resulted, and the multipurpose room survived very well.

Repair of Earthquake Damage

Old School   The east and south wings were demolished after some furniture and mechanical equipment had been salvaged. Because of the unstable condition of the building, all salvage and demolition was performed by winching from outside the building to minimize the danger to workmen. The part of the building that was above the slide was boarded up, fenced, and left in its postearthquake condition.

FIGURE 95   View of old Government Hill School from the south showing the east wing bridging a large gap.

FIGURE 97   View of old Government Hill School from the north. The multipurpose room in the foreground sustained only minor damage.

FIGURE 98   West side of south wing of old Government Hill School, showing building separation. The head of the slide passed through the wing at approximately the point of separation.

Edwin Crittenden, Architects and Associates

FIGURE 100   Interior of old Government Hill School. Desks and equipment still remain upright, indicating a slow earth movement.

New School   At the old school site, the new bluff line is about 400 ft behind the old bluff line, and the area has been classified as a high-risk area (Eckel and Schaem, 1966, p. 56; Hansen, 1965). The only suitable site for the new school that was outside the high-risk area and was not densely populated was at the south end of the military reservation (Figure 93). This new site is about ½ mi north of the old school in an area occupied by the Bureau of Standards antenna field. It was necessary to clear the site for the new school by relocating the antenna field and related facilities. Overhead power and telephone lines and a transformer pad and enclosure also were relocated. The existing buried trunk cable between the ACS Toll Building and Elmendorf AFB had to be altered.

The site was leased to the School District, and a new 18-classroom school with related facilities was constructed. The new school is a one-story structural-steel-frame building

with precast-concrete exterior walls. The basic building is 122 × 238 ft, with a 73 × 90-ft multipurpose room on the east side. The roof consists of 1½-in., 18-gage metal deck welded on open-web joists spaced on 7-ft centers. The building was designed to resist lateral loads by the shear resistance of the tilt-up panels, 6-in. reinforced-block walls and the 8-in. poured-concrete walls around the center courts. Construction of the new school was finished in August 1965.

Repair Costs

Demolition of old Government Hill School	$ 7,500
Relocating Bureau of Standards facilities. site work, utilities	310,000
New Government Hill School	805,300
TOTAL	$1,122,800

Edwin Crittenden, Architects and Associates

FIGURE 101   Interior of old Government Hill School. There would have been small chance of survival in this area if building had been occupied.

FIGURE 99   Northeast corner of east wing of old Government Hill School. The head of the slide passed just south of this wall.

Conclusion

Basically, there were two different types of ground motion: the initial earthquake and the landslide that was triggered by the earthquake. To separate the extent of the damage caused by each would be extremely difficult. It would be impracticable, if not impossible, to design a structure to withstand landslides of this magnitude; it is therefore concluded that potential slide areas should be avoided. School sites are chosen for their functional and economic aspects, however, and potential slide sites may be difficult to recognize. Recently, the California legislature passed a law requiring that a school board have a site investigated by a competent soils engineer or geologist to evaluate the hazard of landslides and fault displacement before a school building is designed or constructed.

DENALI SCHOOL

The Denali Elementary School is located on a four-block tract of land bounded by Ninth and Tenth avenues and by Cordova and C streets (Figure 2). The building sustained severe structural and nonstructural damage. It appears that the structure did not withstand the earthquake forces be-

cause of design and construction deficiencies. The damage was so extensive that it was doubtful whether the school should be repaired or completely rebuilt. Although the decision finally was made to repair the existing building, hidden damage, uncovered in the process of repair, was so great that, had it been evident earlier, the decision to repair rather than to rebuild would probably not have been made.

The school (originally named Parkview) was a 40-room elementary school at the time of the earthquake. The main building, constructed in 1950, faces Ninth Avenue and is approximately 600 ft long and 80 ft wide, with a center corridor running the length of the building. The east classroom wing, which is used for special services, was built in 1953. This addition was approximately 246 ft long by 72 ft wide. The west wing, which included the multipurpose room, is approximately 85 ft long by 85 ft wide. The kitchen, office, and the one classroom in it were together approximately 68 ft long and 25 ft wide (Figure 102).

Initial inspection showed that the foundation wall had cracked and moved and that most of the concrete-block walls had cracked and spalled. The entrance slabs broke and the roof system was damaged.

The structure is essentially a one-story building constructed on a concrete slab with exterior walls of 8-in. con-

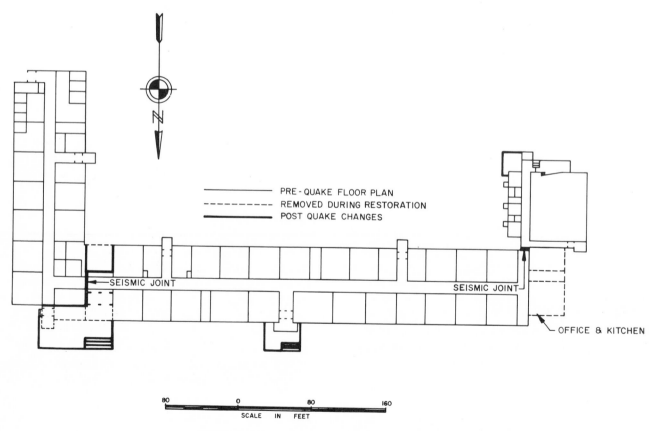

FIGURE 102   Floor plan of Denali Elementary School.

FIGURE 103   Denali Elementary School: Damage to one of the unreinforced concrete-block firewalls. At the left of the firewall is one of the typical foundation cracks that occurred around the structure.

crete block below the window heads and glass blocks above the windows to the roof (Metcalf and Eddy, 1964) (Figure 103). Glass blocks were also used in the vertical face of the monitor roof section at the midpoint of the classrooms and ran the entire length of the main building and the wing. The monitors were used to admit more natural light into the classroom areas. The interior partitions were concrete block. The roof of the main building and the east wing was supported by transverse laminated wood beams on 10-ft 8-in. centers that span the classrooms. The beams are supported by lally columns that extend into the concrete footings. The monitor roof was supported by solid, cross-braced wood beams and was supported directly on the main laminated wood roof beams.

The multipurpose room was constructed of laminated wood, three pinned arches with 8-in. concrete-block filler panels, and a concrete floor slab-on-grade. Clear height at the eaves was 17 ft.

Earthquake Damage

The foundation walls sustained cracks ranging from hairline cracks to some that were ¾ in. wide. Most of the major cracks occurred at the column lines, doors, corners, and wall intersections. In several places around the perimeter of the building, the exterior foundation wall was moved outward from the sill. The displacement generally varied from ½ to ¾ in. At the west wing, adjacent to the kitchen, the foundation wall was displaced about 1¾ in., causing severe cracking of the sill under the window.

Cracking of the entrance-platform slabs around the building was fairly extensive, and in most cases the slabs had to be replaced. The concrete masonry wall at the west end of

the building was moved noticeably outward as much as 6 in. at the sill, and the window wall above and the masonry wall below the sill were cracked and out of plumb. Portions of the long walls were moved about 2 in. in a similar manner. The lally columns apparently acted to resist further wall displacement owing to the depth of their embedment in the concrete footings and their restraint at the top plate, where they were secured to the laminated wood beams.

Most of the concrete-block parapets around the perimeter of the building failed, usually at the flashing points, because the bond of the mortar broke, and there was no vertical or horizontal reinforcing steel.

The brick boiler chimney, which had a 24-in.-square flue lining, collapsed during the earthquake and fell through the roof of the boiler room, breaking one of the main laminated-wood roof beams.

The roof supporting members had failed, damaging the roofing beyond repair.

Repair of Earthquake Damage

The structure was redesigned by Edwin Crittenden, Architects and Associates, Anchorage, Alaska, under contract to the U.S. Army Engineer District, Alaska. After the structure was determined to be repairable, the architect inspected the building and studied available copies of the original contract drawings. He concluded that the original design did not meet the lateral-force requirements of the *Uniform Building Code* and that the construction did not meet the requirements of the contract drawings. No vertical steel reinforcing bars, no bond beams, and very little horizontal joint reinforcing had been used in the exterior 8-in. concrete-block walls. The corridor walls and most of the other 4-in. concrete-block walls were not adequately supported at the top, bottom, or side. In the multipurpose room, the 8-in. concrete-block filler walls were not tied to the structure at either the top or the side. The structure contained no shear walls, and the roof system, as constructed, did not act as a diaphragm under lateral loads.

The structure was redesigned and restored in accordance with the *Uniform Building Code* for seismic zone 3.

The new design for the structure included seismic separation of the three sections of the building and removal of the section that contained the kitchen, office, and one classroom. A general plan of the restored structure is shown in Figure 102.

Repairs to the structure were extensive. The entire perimeter of the structure was excavated to expose the foundation walls. Cracks in these walls were then sealed on the surface, leaving entry ports spaced at a distance of not less than 1½ times the thickness of the cracked member. Epoxy adhesive was then forced into the crack at the first port, with sufficient pressure to advance the epoxy to the adjacent port. The original port was then sealed, and entry was shifted to the port at which the epoxy appeared until the entire crack had been treated. Some sections of the foundation were found to be beyond repair and were replaced.

All the exterior concrete-block walls, including the fire walls, were replaced with concrete-block construction meeting the requirements of the *Uniform Building Code*. The new concrete-block walls of the multipurpose room were stiffened by adding pilasters at approximately 12 ft on centers. In various locations around the building, the glass block, windows, and sills were removed to the floor level and were replaced with 8-in. reinforced-concrete-block shear walls. Figure 104 shows the repaired building.

To safeguard the school from future water damage, it was necessary to reconstruct the entire roof. This work included removing the monitors and lowering the ends of the monitor beams with the timber roof deck so that the roof would slope toward the outside walls instead of toward the center of the building. The 4-in. concrete-block interior walls were removed and replaced with incombustible stud walls with a finished surface. Broken plumbing fixtures and piping were replaced, and all piping was tested. The chimneys were replaced with reinforced-concrete block, and the entire electrical system was checked and repaired where necessary.

In the breakdown of repair costs that follows, structural costs include concrete-block repair and half the carpentry repair.

Structural repair	$ 362,500
Architectural repair	291,502
Mechanical repair, including new ventilation	183,000
Electrical repair	81,000
New roof	166,000
TOTAL	$1,084,002

Conclusions

Several major deficiencies in design and construction existed in this structure. The roof was not designed or constructed to act as a diaphragm. The building had no shear walls that were specifically designed to resist lateral loads. The concrete-block walls had no vertical reinforcing and very little horizontal joint reinforcing. In addition, no seismic joints separated the structure into approximately symmetrical units. The chimney and parapet failures are examples of the damage that can be expected to result from insufficient reinforcing or lack of proper connection between two structural elements.

CENTRAL JUNIOR HIGH SCHOOL

Most of the earthquake damage to this school was nonstructural and occurred mainly to the nonbearing concrete-block partitions. The structural damage was minor: Small cracks

FIGURE 104   Denali Elementary School. South elevation of main and east classroom wings after restoration. New shear walls can be seen at various locations between glass-block and window sections.

appeared in the masonry shear walls and some failure of lateral bracing members occurred in the gymnasium roof framing.

Central Junior High School, at Fifteenth Avenue and C Street, south of the central district, overlooks the Chester Creek Valley to the south. The one-story building has about 96,000 ft² of floor area and stands on a 14-acre tract that it shares with Chugach Elementary School (Figure 2). The architectural firm of Edwin Crittenden, Architects and Associates, Anchorage, designed the building, which was completed in the winter of 1962. The school contains a gymnasium with locker rooms, a multipurpose room with stage and kitchen, choral and band rooms, library, shop, crafts, art, and homemaking rooms, four science rooms, two special-education rooms, 28 classrooms, staff offices, toilets, and the boiler room (Figure 105). This school is similar to several other school buildings in Anchorage, and in the fall of 1966 it was generally in good condition (Figures 106–108).

The building is a steel-frame structure, with a lightweight-steel roof deck welded to steel beams or bar joists, or anchored to reinforced-concrete or concrete-block bearing and shear walls. Subsurface soil in the area of the building is sand and gravel underlain by clay. A continuous reinforced-concrete foundation wall around the perimeter of the building extends about 4 ft below grade and rests on a spread footing. Interior bearing walls and columns are supported on shallow spread footings. The roof over the classroom area is of metal T-deck units welded to steel beams or to metal anchors in bond beams over the reinforced-concrete-block bearing and shear walls. The steel beams frame into steel H-columns at the exterior of the building and onto steel-pipe columns in the interior.

The roofs over the gymnasium and the multipurpose room have a somewhat different supporting system from the rest of the building. The roof over the multipurpose

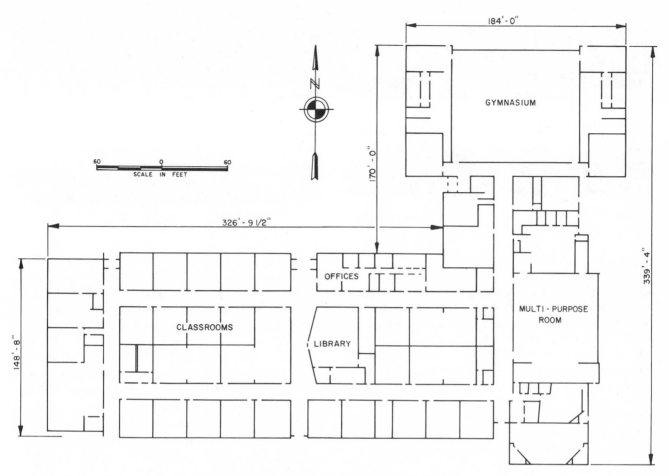

FIGURE 105   Central Junior High School floor plan.

room consists of 3-in. metal decking welded to steel purlins. The purlins, in turn, are supported by 30-in. wide-flange steel beams that frame into structural-steel columns. The framing over the gymnasium consists of metal decking supported by 6 B 12 purlins, which, in turn, are supported by

36 wide-flange 150 stringers. Cross bracing between the roof stringers consists of steel rods with turnbuckles.

The exterior walls around the classroom areas are of reinforced-concrete block with aluminum fascia or curtain walls of glass and insulating panels in aluminum frames. The

FIGURE 106   Central Junior High School, from the northeast corner of the building. The gymnasium is the section of the building with the higher roof (foreground).

FIGURE 107   Central Junior High School. This corner of the building suffered minor block damage during the earthquake.

FIGURE 108   Central Junior High School, looking northeast, from the Fifteenth Avenue side of the building.

exterior walls around the multipurpose room and the gymnasium are of insulated vertical metal siding attached to steel girts between columns, with the lower 3 ft being a reinforced-concrete block wall. Interior partitions are of concrete block, with 6-ft high concrete-block classroom partitions at the corridors with inside windows, 2-ft wire glass relights and acoustic tile above.

Earthquake Damage

This building did not sustain any significant structural damage during the earthquake. For the purposes of this report the building is divided into three areas.

Area 1 includes the general shop, crafts, art, and general science rooms, two special-education rooms, 17 classrooms, and girls' and boys' toilets. The block wall had broken at the top of the corridor wall in the shop and crafts rooms where the steel roof beam is attached to the pipe column. A few blocks were cracked at various places throughout the section, and the east–west shear wall sustained a few hairline cracks.

Area 2 consists of the multipurpose room and stage, choral and band rooms, library, three science rooms, eight classrooms, staff offices, and girls' and boys' restrooms. Damage to this section of the building was mainly to partition walls. Part of the northern half of the library wall was down, and the upper portion of the block walls at the front of the stage in the multipurpose room also fell down.

Area 3 contains the gymnasium, girls' and boys' locker, shower, and toilet rooms, homemaking room, kitchen, three classrooms, and boiler room. The main structural damage to the building occurred in the upper portion of the gymnasium, which is considerably higher than the rest of the building. The roof bracing in this area was badly bent and buckled, particularly along the east and west bays. Gusset-plate connections were twisted and torn. Figure 109 shows the framing used in the gymnasium and the damaged connections and bracing rods.

Most nonstructural damage in the building was sustained by block walls, most of which were not load-bearing walls. Other nonstructural damage consisted of minor damage to ceiling tile and cracking of floor tile in various areas.

Repair of Earthquake Damage

During the summer of 1964, a contract for about $120,000 was awarded for repairs to this building. The main structural repairs consisted of replacing damaged or buckled cross bracing and repairing the damaged connections in the gymnasium roof. Wherever necessary, concrete-block walls and ceiling tile were replaced, and isolated cracks in the floor were repaired.

Conclusions

The building sustained severe nonstructural damage. The failure of nonload-bearing interior partitions would have created a serious hazard during the earthquake if the building had been occupied. The structural failures in the gymnasium roof-bracing system could also easily have had more serious consequences than they did. Fortunately, the roof did not collapse, although all the bracing rods connecting the exterior wall were broken. Such bracing systems should be studied to determine if the building-code requirements are really adequate.

EAST ANCHORAGE HIGH SCHOOL

East Anchorage High School is located southeast of the Anchorage business district at South Bragaw and East 24th Street (Figure 2), outside the area underlain by the Bootlegger Cove Clay, but in an area underlain by a deep layer of sand and clay soil (Metcalf and Eddy, 1964). Construction records show that a layer of peat under the building had been removed. The building sustained some damage to concrete-block bearing and nonload-bearing walls, precast-concrete beams and suspended-tile ceilings and lights. In addition, an exterior brick veneer was damaged and some floor settlement was noted. In general, however, the structure did not suffer serious earthquake damage.

This building is divided into seven sections (Figures 110 and 111) separated by 2-in.-wide seismic joints. The school has 52 classrooms, gymnasium, auditorium, library, cafeteria, band room, choral room, locker rooms, shop area, laundry, office area, and boiler room.

Section 1 is 116 ft wide by 156 ft long and has a ceiling height of 13 ft. It contains the cafeteria and shop area. The roof framing is 1½-in. 20-gage steel deck on open-web joists spaced on 4-ft centers. The joists are supported at the exterior walls on a combination of reinforced-concrete beams and columns and reinforced-concrete walls. The interior joist supports are reinforced-concrete corridor walls. This section also contains the boiler room, which has reinforced-concrete walls and roof.

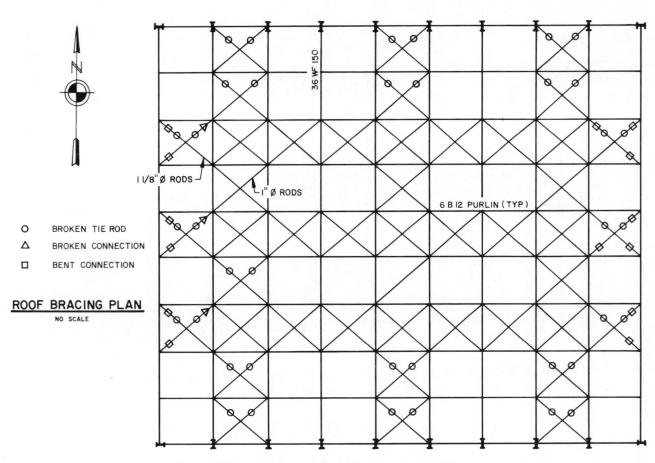

ROOF BRACING PLAN
NO SCALE

O   BROKEN TIE ROD
△   BROKEN CONNECTION
□   BENT CONNECTION

1 1/8" Ø RODS
1" Ø RODS
36 WF 150
6 B 12 PURLIN (TYP)

FIGURE 109   Roof-bracing plan, Central Junior High School.

Section 2 is 117 ft wide and 224 ft long, and the roof varies in height from 25 to 31 ft. The section contains the gymnasium, auditorium, and locker rooms. The roof framing is basically the same as in section 1, except that all joists are supported on 12-in. reinforced-concrete-block walls. The walls are reinforced with vertical 5/8-in. reinforcing bars, spaced 32 in. apart, and welded wire strips in the horizontal joints spaced 16 in. apart. In addition, there is a bond beam in the top course. The vertical reinforcing is doweled into the footings. The end walls are 8-in. concrete block reinforced with horizontal welded-wire fabric in the joints spaced 16 in. apart and vertical 3/8-in. reinforcing bars spaced 32 in. apart. The drawings, however, indicate that the nonload-bearing walls were designed to span horizontally and to permit the elimination of the vertical reinforcing when horizontal support occurred every 12 ft or less.

This section was originally designed as a slab-on-grade with spread footings under the walls and columns. Because of poor soil conditions, the foundation was changed to use piling of 25-ton capacity. Piling was driven or augered under the north and east gymnasium walls and under the entire locker room area east of the gymnasium; it was spaced a

maximum of 12 ft apart under the walls and on an 11 X 12-ft spacing under the locker room floor. The contractor was given a choice of the type and the method of placing the piling. The locker room floor was then changed to a 6-in.-thick flat slab and reinforced with 1/2-in. bars in both directions at both the top and the bottom of the slab. A second floor, with a 4½-in.-thick structural-concrete floor slab supported on 18 X 28-in. concrete beams is above the locker rooms. The concrete beams span about 25 ft, are spaced 11 ft on center, and are supported by 5-in. pipe columns encased in concrete.

Section 3 includes a 96 X 128-ft unit and a 28 X 128-ft unit. The roof framing is the same as the other sections. The interior supports for the open-web joists are 8-in. reinforced-concrete walls and 8-in. reinforced-concrete block walls. The exterior supports for the open-web joists are combinations of 8-in. concrete walls, 10 X 29-in. concrete beams, and 12 X 16-in. columns with various types of reinforcing, and 8 X 23-in. precast beams and 8 X 22-in. poured-concrete beams supported on 8-in. concrete walls and 8-in. concrete-block walls. The precast beam was pinned into the block wall with a 1½-in. pipe sleeve.

The floor is a 3½-in. reinforced slab-on-grade and the

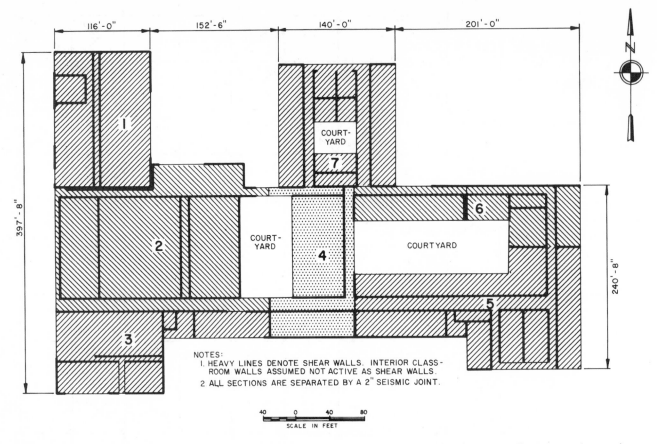

FIGURE 110   Floor plan of East Anchorage High School. Heavy lines denote shear walls, interior classroom walls are assumed not active as shear walls. All sections are separated by a 2-in. seismic joint.

drawings show that the slabs are doweled into the walls. Spread footings were used throughout this section.

Section 4, 172 × 60 ft, contains the library, offices, and classrooms. Open-web joists are supported along the east wall on 10 × 26-in. precast beams. Precast beams are fastened to 3-in. pipe columns by welding the pile cap to a 10-in. 15.3-lb channel cast into the beam. The tops of the precast beams are fastened together by welding a 1/8 × 1½-in. strap to 3/8 × 4-in. plate cast into the beams.

FIGURE 111   East Anchorage High School (from south) after repairs. This building performed well during the earthquake.

The 8-in. concrete-block corridor wall is the interior support for the open-web joists. The west exterior wall is the same as the east wall. The west wall of the corridor is part 6-in. and part 8-in. concrete block.

Section 5 is an L-shaped section containing ten classrooms, a storeroom, and a fan room. The exterior supports for the open-web joists are a combination of precast beams and prestressed beams, supported on 3-in. pipe columns.

The 10 × 18-in. prestressed beams are used for spans of about 28 ft. The design prestress force varies between 186 kips and 214 kips. All interior bearing walls are 8-in. concrete block. The column connections of the precast beams and prestressed beams are the same as previously described.

Section 6 is basically the same as section 5. Section 7 is a 140-ft square structure, framed in the same manner as sections 5 and 6.

The seismic-design loads for seismic zone 3 (1958 *Uniform Building Code*) are as follows:

Roof load	40 psf
Floor loads	up to 100 psf
Wind load	30 psf

The lateral loads were transmitted by the roof and floor diaphragm action to the shear walls and then to the foundation. The drawings specified that the decking should act as a diaphragm but did not specify the load to be resisted; the minimum geometric properties of the decking were specified.

Earthquake Damage

Section 1 Structural damage was evident in the shop and drafting rooms to the left of the corridor, where the floor slabs had settled a maximum of 2½ in. next to the corridor (Metcalf and Eddy, 1964; Meehan, 1967). In this area, several feet of fill had been required during the initial construction. The drawings indicated that the slab was to be doweled into the wall, but there was no evidence that dowels had been installed. Minor cracking occurred in the concrete walls, and some small cracks were evident in the concrete columns at the intersection with the concrete beam. Some nonstructural damage also occurred. Precast-concrete window sills were damaged, and some cracks were made in the corridor walls. The nonbearing block wall between the cafeteria and the kitchen in the northeast part of the section was badly damaged and had to be removed; the walls apparently were not reinforced as specified on the drawings.

Section 2 The 12-in. reinforced-concrete-block bearing wall on the west side of the gymnasium sustained damage at several open-web joist seats. The concrete-block walls separated at the northwest and southwest corners of the gymnasium. Field inspection indicated that the north and south 8-in. concrete-block walls bowed out 3 in. and 1 in., respectively. The drawings did not indicate that the joint reinforcement was to be continuous around the corners and at wall intersections.

The support failed for the 8 × 24-in. precast beam across the corridor at the northwest corner of this section. The beam rested on 8-in. block walls and had a 1½-in. pipe cast in the beam end. A ¾ × 3-ft dowel was then grouted in the pipe and 1 ft into the wall. The block cell was reinforced with one 5/8-in. vertical reinforcing bar.

Nonstructural damage occurred in the form of the collapse of the block wall enclosure around the ducts in the northeast and southeast corners of the gymnasium. These walls had enclosed a space approximately 2 ft deep by 18 ft wide by 30 ft high. The gymnasium floor was damaged by falling block.

Ceiling tile fell in many areas, and the ceiling suspension system was damaged. The plaster of the auditorium ceiling was cracked in many places, and damage occurred at the intersections of partitions.

Section 3 No structural damage occurred in this area, but slight nonstructural damage was observed. Some ceiling tile

fell throughout the area, and minor cracks were evident in some interior block walls.

Section 4 Structural damage was minor, but some nonstructural damage did occur. The concrete fireproofing was cracked around some pipe columns. Some damage occurred to the interior nonbearing block walls. The ceiling tile in the library received extensive damage. Some suspension systems and light fixtures failed.

Section 5 No structural damage occurred here, but in nearly every classroom the block partition was damaged at the top of the intersection with the outside wall. The damage ranged from minor cracks to broken block.

The storeroom was damaged by fire caused by acid spilling on shelves and walls. The brick veneer around the south entrance to this section was damaged.

Section 6 Structural damage was observed at the entrance to the west Corridor in section 6, where the 8 × 24-in. precast-beam support failed—the same type of failure was described in section 2.

Concrete-block walls were cracked over the doorways. Concrete fireproofing on pipe columns was cracked. Interior block walls of classrooms were damaged at the intersection with the exterior walls. The brick veneer was damaged around the firedoor at the north wall.

Section 7 One prestressed beam failed at its support in the middle of the east wall; a piece of 10-in. 15.3-lb channel was embedded in the beam. The channel was welded to the pipe-column cap and had pulled loose from the beam (Figure 112A).

The interior block partitions were damaged as described in sections 5 and 6. The brick veneer around the north entrance was also damaged.

Repair of Earthquake Damage

The damaged prestressed-concrete beam was repaired as shown in Figure 112. The damage to the support of the precast beam at the northwest corner of section 2 was repaired by placing an 8-in. reinforced-concrete wall in place of the 8-in. block wall. The beam connection was replaced according to the original drawings, except that three 5/8-in. rebars (reinforcing bars) were hooked around the dowels.

The block wall enclosing the ducts in the gymnasium was rebuilt, and the corners of the walls were repaired as shown in Figures 113–115. The corners of the gymnasium floor were replaced and the entire floor was refinished.

The floor that had settled in the shop area was replaced. The brick veneer was removed at eight locations and was replaced with vinyl-covered metal siding.

In general, all minor cracks in block or concrete were

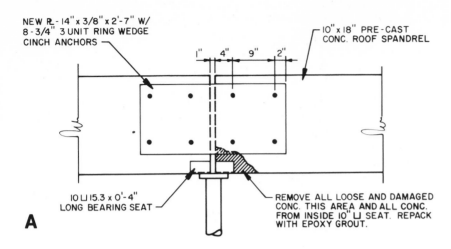

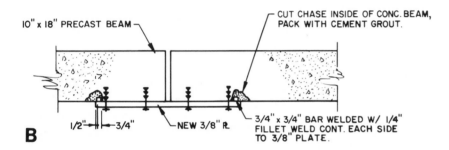

FIGURE 112 East Anchorage High School: A, Repair detail of prestressed beam connection in the east wall of section 7; B, plan view of beam connection shown. Only one failure of this type occurred in the building.

tuck-pointed with epoxy grout, and all damaged blocks were replaced to match the existing blocks. Figure 116 shows the details of some repairs.

Ceiling tiles were replaced and all plaster cracks were replastered. The 8-in. block walls that were replaced were reinforced with 5/8-in. vertical reinforcing bars spaced 32 in. apart. Bond beams were spaced at 4 ft with two 5/8-in. reinforcing bars. Walls 4 in. thick were reinforced with ½-in. vertical rebars spaced 32. in. apart; bond beams were reinforced in the same manner as the 8-in. walls.

An approximate breakdown of repair costs is as follows:

Structural repair	$ 28,400
Architectural repair	126,000
Electrical repair	23,400
Mechanical repair	4,800
Painting	15,800
TOTAL	$198,400

Conclusions

The damage to East Anchorage High School, in general, was relatively minor. The damage to concrete-block bearing and nonbearing walls was typical of buildings throughout the area. The cracked or spalled concrete-block nonbearing

walls would not be considered serious damage but it was relatively costly to repair. The damage to the precast-concrete beam connections points out the difficulty of obtaining connections that will resist lateral loads in this type of construction.

The damage to the concrete-block bearing walls indicates that the reinforcing and connections in this type of construction must have special attention during design and construction. There are many instances where this material behaved very well.

The omission during construction of reinforcing bars specified in the drawings points out the desirability of careful inspection during construction.

PRIVATE STRUCTURES

FOUR SEASONS APARTMENT BUILDING

The construction of the Four Seasons apartment building, a luxury apartment house at the corner of Ninth and M streets (Figure 2), had begun during the summer of 1963. At the time of the earthquake, the building was structurally complete, with work proceeding rapidly on the interior finish. This structure collapsed completely but fortunately there were no tenants in the building and no workmen on the site at the time of failure.

This was the first building in Anchorage in which the lift-slab construction technique was used. It was a six-story reinforced-concrete building; the dimensions of a typical floor were 75 ft 8 in. × 130 ft 8 in. (Figure 117). Figure 118 shows a typical floor plan of the building. Lateral forces were resisted by two poured-in-place concrete shafts, one for a stairwell and one for an elevator. The floor slabs

were made of 8-in. concrete, posttensioned, and supported on 10-in. wide-flange steel columns; these flat slabs were cast in two sections, posttensioned on the ground, and then jacked to vertical position. The two shafts and the strip connecting the sections of the floor slab were poured after the slabs had been jacked into position. After this, steel shear heads were embedded in the slabs and welded to the steel columns. The slabs were keyed and doweled into the poured-in-place concrete shafts.

The building was designed for *Uniform Building Code*

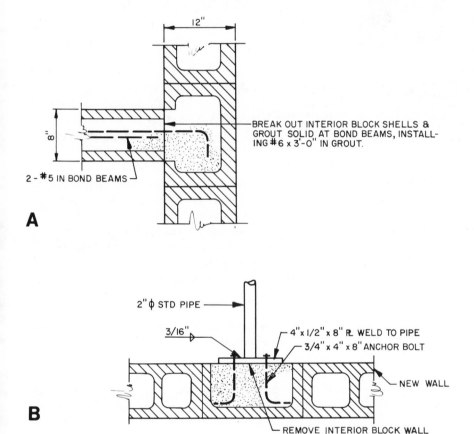

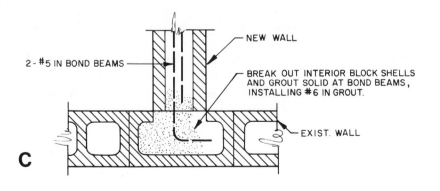

FIGURE 113 East Anchorage High School: A, Detail showing intersection of new block walls as restored. B, Detail showing lateral bracing, installed during repair, for block wall enclosing ducts in the gymnasium. C, Detail showing intersection of new and existing block walls as repaired.

FIGURE 114 East Anchorage High School gymnasium after repairs. Duct enclosure in the left corner was heavily reinforced and laterally supported at 8-ft intervals when rebuilt. The 12-in. block-bearing wall, which is about 31 ft high, suffered minor cracking under some joist seats. The 12- and 18-in. walls separated at the corners.

zone 3 earthquake requirements. The design and construction appeared to have been in agreement with these requirements.

The Four Seasons apartment building collapsed during the earthquake, leaving only a heap of rubble (Figures 119 and 120). Pictures taken after the rubble was cleared show the ground floor slab that still remained in 1967 (Figures 121 and 122).

A thorough and more detailed description and an analysis of this building are given by Berg and Stratta (1964) and by Clough and Benuska (1966), whose works were used as source material for this report.

The collapse of the Four Seasons apartment building has been attributed to inadequate length of lapping of the reinforcing bars at the bases of the two towers. Bond failure effectively disconnected the towers from their foundations and left them free to rock and break the connections of the floor slabs to the towers. The code requirements on overlapping of bars were not adequate to prevent failure.

HILLSIDE APARTMENT BUILDING

The Hillside apartment building, on the south side of Sixteenth Avenue opposite H Street (Figure 2), was constructed during the spring and summer of 1951 and completed in September of that year. This building sustained severe damage during the earthquake.

Soon afterward, by direction of the City of Anchorage Building Inspection Division, a small portion of the roof and third-floor slab of the northwest corner of the building was leveled to the second-floor slab. This partial demolition,

which was ordered to eliminate a hazard has mistakenly been attributed by some persons to earthquake action.

The following description of earthquake damage to the Hillside apartment building is based on the reports of inspection teams composed of engineers from the Alaska District U.S. Army Corps of Engineers, the engineering firm of Metcalf and Eddy, and on a formal report making recommendations for repair or disposal of the building. No plans for the building were available.

This apartment building was constructed on a steep natural slope that dropped off toward the south at a grade of about 5 ft in 10 ft. After construction, the slope toward the south along the east and west sides was regraded to approximately 1¼ ft in 10 ft. The subsoil in the vicinity is gravelly sand to a depth of approximately 39 ft below the present street level, as indicated by a test-boring hole taken near the intersection of Sixteenth Avenue and G Street.

The building was rectangular; the north side (208 ft long) faced Sixteenth Avenue, and the east and west walls (40 ft 8 in. long), with two single-bay projections and two double-bay projections, extended another 4 ft from the south side of the building. The building had three stairway systems, each with a north entrance from Sixteenth Avenue. Each stairway served 16 apartments that were arranged around the stairway on three levels in the north half of the building and on five levels in the south half of the building. The north-side apartments were a half story lower than the corresponding apartments on the south side. The building contained a total of 48 apartments, including 12 efficiency units, 26 one-bedroom, and 10 two-bedroom units (Figure 123).

The foundation walls of the building were of reinforced concrete with concrete spread footings. The interior columns rested on reinforced-concrete piers with spread footings. All footings were placed on firm soil, and all exterior footings extended at least 4 ft below the finished grade around the building. The top of the concrete foundation walls was stepped with the finished grades so that only the concrete-masonry units were exposed above the ground.

The superstructure of the building had a steel frame with steel pipe columns along the exterior walls and structural-steel H columns down the center line between the north-side and south-side apartments. The connections of beams to columns were not moment resisting. The spandrel beams—framing to the pipe columns along the north and south sides, to the corner pipe columns, and to the center H columns along the east and west sides—were 10-in.-deep structural-steel I beams. On either side of the center H columns were 10-in.-deep structural-steel channels attached to the columns; the channel on the north side was a half story lower than the corresponding one on the south side. Framing members running between the spandrel beams on the north and south sides of the building and the center chan-

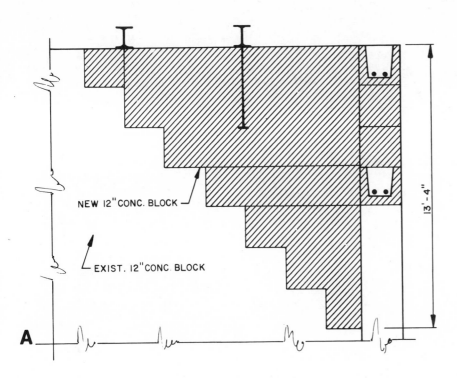

NEW 12"CONC. BLOCK

EXIST. 12"CONC. BLOCK

13'-4"

A

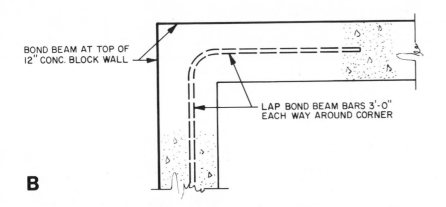

BOND BEAM AT TOP OF
12" CONC. BLOCK WALL

LAP BOND BEAM BARS 3'-0"
EACH WAY AROUND CORNER

B

FIGURE 115 East Anchorage High School:
A, Elevation of wall repair at northwest
corner of gymnasium; B, plan of wall repair
at northwest corner of gymnasium. Failure
to continue reinforcing past corners and
intersections was a common deficiency
found in many buildings.

nels were 10-in.-deep structural-steel I beams. Supporting the floor and roof slabs were 9-in.-deep bar joists spaced 12 in. and 16 in. on centers, depending on spans, and attached to the main framing beams. The steel-pipe columns on the north side of the building ranged in size from 3 in. in diameter at the top floor to 5 in. in diameter at street level. The pipe columns on the south side varied in size from 3-in. diameters at the top floor to 6-in. diameters at the basement level. The interior columns along the center line between the north and south apartments varied from 6-in. lighter H columns at the top floor to 6-in. H columns at the basement level.

The basement level on the north side and the lower basement level on the south side of the building had 4-in.-thick concrete slabs placed on grade and reinforced with 6 X 6-in. No. 10 welded-wire mesh. All other floor and roof slabs were 2½-in.-thick Pumicrete reinforced with 6 X 6-in. No. 10 welded-wire mesh. The roof slabs had 1½-in. rigid insulation beneath built-up roofing.

The stairs were of steel-pan construction with nonskid cement-filled treads. The wall stringers were structural-steel channels, and the stairwell stringers were continuous boxes made of welded steel plates.

The exterior of all spandrel beams was encased in Pumi-

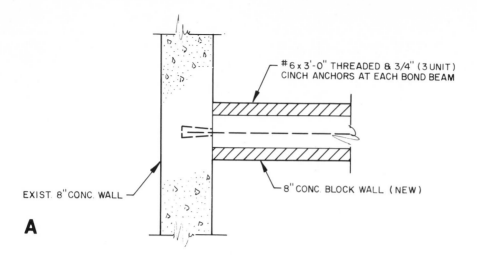

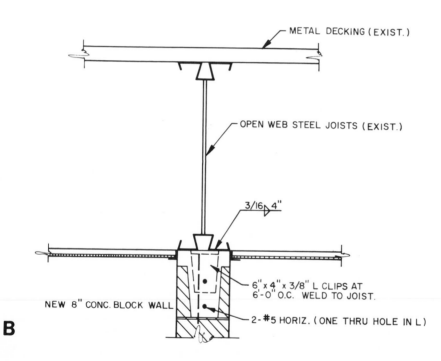

FIGURE 116   East Anchorage High School:
A, Connection detail of new block wall and
existing concrete wall; B, detail showing
connection of new block wall to existing
open web joists.

crete. Copings and canopies were constructed of the same
material. The exterior walls between the encased spandrel
beams and the window sills on the north and south sides of
the building were 9-in.-thick cavity-type walls made up of
two layers of 4-in.-thick pumice-concrete masonry units
separated by 1 in. of fiber glass insulation. The two layers
of block were reinforced and tied together with K web
Dur-o-wal joint reinforcement.

The entrances to the three stairways were narrow-stile
aluminum doors with tubular aluminum frames and 12-in.-
square glass-block sidelights. These glass-block sidelights
extended the entire height of the stairways, forming two
vertical glass-block panels in each stairway tower.

All interior partitions were unreinforced pumice-concrete
masonry units. The partitions within individual apartments
were 4 in. thick. The party walls running north and south
between units and around stairways were 8 in. thick. The
party wall running east and west between the north and
south apartments was made up of two 4-in. masonry units,
separated by an 8-in. pipe space. All rooms within the apart-

Anchorage Daily Times

FIGURE 117   Picture taken during construction of Four Seasons apartment building shows prestressed floor slabs being jacked into position. The two concrete towers have not yet been constructed.

FIGURE 119   Four Seasons apartment building taken from east side. Concrete shafts toppled toward the north (summer 1964).

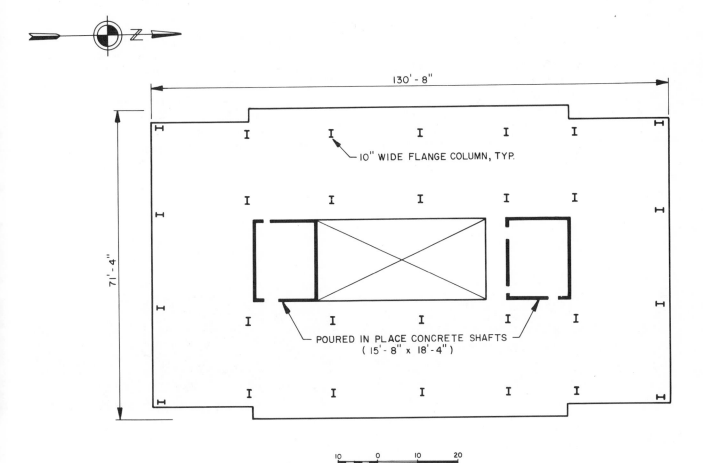

FIGURE 118   Typical floor plan of Four Seasons apartment building.

FIGURE 120   Four Seasons apartment building just before cleanup operations during summer 1964. Broken concrete floor slabs and large number of 1/2-in.-diameter posttensioning cables used in floor slabs.

FIGURE 122   Four Seasons apartment building, from northeast corner of building, shows remains of poured-in-place concrete shaft in the foreground (fall 1966).

ment units had plaster walls and ceilings. The ceilings were suspended from the bar joists.

Earthquake Damage

The rest of this report is based on observation and estimates of damage made on June 6, 1964. The Hillside apartment building has since been razed.

Many of the exterior cavity walls had fallen or had been seriously shattered. The vertical glass-block panels in the three stairways fell out or were broken. Most of the aluminum sashes on the lower floors were seriously racked, and a large percentage of the glass was broken. A great many of the interior block partitions were toppled or seriously shattered.

The entire building was racked about 4 in. toward the west between the first and second floors on the north side and 10 in., more or less, on the south side. The building appeared to be plumb in the north and south direction. Some of the connections between the north and south spandrels to the center steel H columns had failed at the second floor on both the east and west ends of the building.

Except for one large crack in the second floor running north and south just inside the entrance to the apartment on the northeast side of the center stairway, the roof, floors, and ceilings were not noticeably damaged. The stairs appeared to be reasonably intact. The foundations were apparently in satisfactory condition. The plumbing and heating systems had suffered some damage. The electrical systems were subjected to considerable damage.

Exterior Damage

North Elevation.   A large percentage of the block walls had collapsed, especially on the first and second floors near the

FIGURE 121   Four Seasons apartment building, looking northeast. Far side of building shows ramp leading to underground parking garage (fall 1966).

FIGURE 123   The south side of the Hillside apartment building in May 1964.

northeast and northwest corners, at the returns into the stairway towers, and around the entrances. The outer 4-in. block had fallen off the upper part of the stairway towers between the vertical glass-block panels. The two layers of blocks forming the 9-in. wall were not tied together. The block walls on the third floor had several large cracks. The vertical glass-block panels in each stairway tower had fallen out almost completely. The north wall was racked toward the west from the first-floor level to the third-floor level. The top of the pipe column on the northwest corner of the first floor was approximately 4 in. out of plumb toward the west. The columns on the northwest corner between the second floor and the third floor and between the third floor and roof had collapsed, letting an entire bay of the third floor and roof down onto the second-floor slab. This corner of the building had been razed under direction of the City of Anchorage Building Inspection Department to protect the adjacent property. The columns along the center of the building were racked approximately 3 in. toward the west at each floor level. At the northeast corner, both the first- and second-floor columns were approximately 3–4 in. out of plumb toward the west. The same columns were plumb in the north and south directions on the first floor and 1 in. out of plumb toward the south on the second floor. The column on the third floor at the northeast corner was plumb. The extent of the damage of the north elevation may be seen by examining Figures 124 and 125; Figure 123 shows damage to the south elevation.

East Elevation. The block walls at the first- and second-floor levels of the north-side apartment and at the first- and upper-basement-floor level of the south-side apartment fell down. About 75 percent of the outer row of the 9-in. hollow-block walls fell at the second-floor level of the

FIGURE 125 Hillside apartment building, during demolition: A, North side; B, northwest corner.

FIGURE 124 Typical damage to interior block partitions in the Hillside apartment building.

south-side apartment; there was no evidence that wall ties had been used to join the two layers of 4-in. block that formed this wall. The connections of the spandrel beams to the center column at the second-floor level on the north side and the first-floor level on the south side failed and dropped the floors.

South Elevation. Most of the block walls had collapsed down to window sill level on the first floor. All the blocks forming the three sides of the single-bay-window projection facing west and the single-bay-window projection facing east completely collapsed. All the blocks on the three sides of the double bays in the center also fell. All the blocks up to the window sills in the center bays between the two double bays and in the first bay west of the eastern double-bay projection had completely collapsed. At the upper-basement level, most of the blocks forming the three sides of the single west-bay projection and the front portion of the single east-bay projection fell off. The two side portions of the east double-bay projection and the east side of the west double-bay projection lost most of their blocks. The west side of the west double-bay projection was seriously cracked and ready to collapse. The outer row of blocks fell off the west side of the east-bay projection on both the upper-basement and the second-floor levels. Also, on the second-floor level of the west side of the east double-bay projections, the outer row of blocks fell.

At the southeast corner the two upper floors were displaced approximately 6 in. toward the west, whereas from about the center of the building to the southwest corner this deflection was about 10 in. The southwest corner was out of plumb approximately 4 in. in a westerly direction at the second-floor level and was approximately plumb in the north–south direction.

West Elevation. The entire block walls from the first floor to the roof on the south side collapsed. The connection of the first-floor spandrel beam to the center column on the north side was seriously damaged.

Interior Damage

All interior block partitions were badly shattered, and some of the 4-in. block partitions within the apartment units had completely or partly collapsed. Except for some ceiling damage in the vicinity of damaged interior partitions and exterior walls, there was no noticeable damage to ceilings and floors. The floors were reasonably level and intact. There was one major floor crack, in a north–south direction, on the second-floor level on the north side of the building near the entrance to the apartment east of the center stairway.

Repair of Earthquake Damage

The Hillside apartment building, as observed on June 6, 1964, was neither safe nor fit for occupancy and was in a condition extremely hazardous to the general public. It was recommended at that time that the property be immediately fenced off to prevent unauthorized access until the building was razed or rehabilitated.

Because the floors, roof, and stairs had not suffered serious damage, and the plumbing and heating systems had some salvage value, it was reasonable to investigate the cost of rehabilitating the structure to meet the requirements of the present building code, compared to the cost of demolishing the existing structure and constructing an entirely new building on the existing foundation. Rehabilitation would require replumbing the steel frame and providing additional framing, bracing, and shear walls.

The estimated cost of demolition of the existing building and construction of a new building was $1,100,000, whereas the estimated cost of the rehabilitation of the existing building was $870,000. These figures were, in themselves, inconclusive and were not the sole basis for determining the disposition of this building. A completely new building, embodying contemporary design standards and modern materials, is obviously a more valuable asset than is a building, constructed to meet 1950 design standards, that has been partly restored. The value of such a new building was thought to be approximately 15 percent greater than that of the restored 1950 building.

From the standpoint of finance, a completely new building may reasonably be expected to have a useful life (and a corresponding amortization period) of 40 years. The rehabilitated building, on the other hand, would still contain many features and appurtenances dating back to the year 1950. Hence, a considerable portion (14 years) of the building's useful life had already been expended, leaving a remaining useful life (and amortization period) of 26 years.

The apparently low ($870,000) rehabilitation cost, considered in the light of the two factors derived above, amounts to $1,540,000 when computed as follows:

Rehabilitation cost	×	ratio of amortization	×	increased worth of entirely new building	= comparative cost of rehabilitation
$870,000	×	$\frac{40}{26}$	×	1.15	= $1,540,000

It was, therefore, a cost of $1,540,000 that was compared with the estimated construction cost of $1,100,000 for an entirely new building.

On the basis of the foregoing cost comparison, rehabilitation of the Hillside apartment building was considered to be not economically feasible, and the building was therefore completely demolished during the summer of 1964 at a contract cost of $34,670.

Conclusions

This building was not designed and constructed according to the earthquake requirements of the *Uniform Building Code*; indeed it appeared to be very weak in this respect. Although extensive damage was to be expected, this weak building surprisingly survived strong ground shaking without collapsing and without loss of life. This is particularly striking when compared to the behavior of the Four Seasons apartment building, which was designed according to the *Uniform Building Code*, but collapsed completely. Studies should be made to clarify the ability of structures to withstand earthquakes without collapsing.

MT. McKINLEY BUILDING

The Mt. McKinley apartment building, at Denali and Fourth Avenue (Figure 2), is about four blocks east of the east boundary of the Fourth Avenue landslide (Berg and Stratta,

FIGURE 126 Aerial view of the Mt. McKinley building showing undamaged penthouse and television antenna. Note gap in the end-wall pier at the third story.

1964; Clough and Benuska, 1966). The building is similar to the 1200 L Street apartment building except that the two buildings stand at an angle of 180 degrees to one another. The Mt. McKinley building had some shops on the first floor and a television tower and penthouse on the roof; the main entrance faces east (Figure 126).

Figure 127 shows the general plan and part of the structural framing. The exterior walls are 8 in. thick from the roof to the eighth floor, 10 in. thick from the eighth to the second floor, and 12 in. thick below the second floor. The walls between window openings were designed as columns and, together with the spandrels between the windows, act as continuous frames. The 12-in. walls around the stairs and elevator core were also designed to act as columns and function as part of the interior framing. On the exterior, some of the spandrels were recessed about 1½ in. from the face of the vertical walls and apparently were not designed to resist other than vertical loads.

The central core consists of elevator shafts, stairwalls, and a chimney. The central core and exterior vertical walls or piers transmitted the lateral loads to the foundation. The frame action of the exterior vertical walls or piers and the exterior spandrels is also a part of the resistance for lateral loads. The building was originally designed for *Uniform Building Code* zone 2 requirements. Unverified reports state that after construction was begun the FHA required additional earthquake resistance.

Earthquake Damage

Figures 128–131 show that the spandrels in all the exterior walls suffered damage from overstress in shear and were badly cracked and fractured. The spandrels at the corners of the building also sustained similar damage. The vertical

FIGURE 128 East view of Mt. McKinley building showing beam failure over the first-story window, column failure at left, and vertical pier failure over the entrance. Spandrel-beam failure shown at second and third stories is typical of failure that occurred throughout the building.

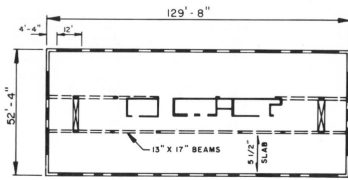

FIGURE 127 Plan of Mt. McKinley building.

Anchorage Daily Times

FIGURE 129   Mt. McKinley building (from west). The top five stories sustained increasingly lighter damage.

exterior walls or columns had large diagonal cracks over the entrance on the east side at the second floor and smaller cracks at the floors above the second. The east vertical pier on the north end wall failed about half way up the third story at a construction joint. In the south end wall, similar failures seemed to be imminent in both piers at the second-story level.

The walls around the core area had light diagonal cracks and had horizontal cracks at the construction joints. These cracks were most severe at the third, fourth, fifth, and sixth floors. The floors received some damage around the core area. Figure 132 shows a damaged column at the ground level in the south end wall.

Repair of Earthquake Damage

A private engineering firm designed and supervised the repair of these buildings for the new owner.

Repairs consisted of removing loose material and patching the cracks with gunite. Bent or broken reinforcing had to be removed, and new reinforcing was welded into place.

The smaller cracks in the exterior walls were grouted and sealed with mastic. The east pier in the north end wall was

jacked up and repaired as stated in the previous paragraph.

The spalled areas in the stairwell and elevator core were repaired with Gunite, and the smaller cracks were repaired with an epoxy compound.

Conclusions

The proportions of the spandrels and columns that made up the exterior walls were such that a very unfavorable distribution of shears and moments in the spandrels resulted. There was no loss of life in the building, so in this sense the earthquake design was satisfactory. However, a different way of laying out and reinforcing the walls would have avoided extensive and costly damage. In this sense the building is an object lesson for thorough earthquake design.

1200 L STREET BUILDING

The 1200 L Street apartment building stands between Twelfth and Thirteenth avenues on L Street (Figure 2), about four blocks southeast of the L Street landslide and seven blocks south of downtown Anchorage. The main entrance faces west. This building suffered extensive and severe structural damage.

Anchorage Daily Times

FIGURE 130   North part of west side of Mt. McKinley building.

FIGURE 131 South part of west side of Mt. McKinley building.

As shown in Figure 133, this structure is almost identical to the Mt. McKinley building.

Earthquake Damage

The damage to this building was similar to but less severe than that sustained by the Mt. McKinley building (Berg and Stratta, 1964; Clough and Benuska, 1966).

As shown in Figures 134 and 135, the west pier of the south end wall failed; this damage has been attributed to flexure failure. The other end-wall piers showed evidence of incipient failure (Figure 134).

The spandrels had diagonal cracks, and the construction joints all showed movement (Figures 136 and 137). The spandrels at the building corners were damaged more than the corners of the Mt. McKinley building (Figure 138).

Repair of Earthquake Damage

The 1200 L Street apartment building was rehabilitated by the new owner by methods similar to those used on the Mt. McKinley building. Figures 133 and 139 show some of the many cracks in the building.

The building originally cost about $1,200,000. After the earthquake the FHA repossessed the building and sold it to

the highest bidder for approximately $500,000. The cost of repairing the building is estimated to have been in the range from $300,000 to $500,000.

The piers and spandrels forming the walls of the Mt. McKinley and the 1200 L Street buildings were proportioned in such a way that very unfavorable distributions of shears and moments were developed in the spandrel beams. Because no lives were lost, however, the building can be considered to have behaved satisfactorily, although the economic loss was excessive.

THE J.C. PENNEY BUILDING

The J. C. Penney Building stood on the south side of Fifth Avenue between D and E streets (Figure 2). This building is of particular interest because it was one of the relatively new structures in Anchorage that was damaged beyond repair. The structure was built during 1962 and 1963. At that time, the city of Anchorage required that buildings be designed for zone 3 requirements of the *Uniform Building Code.*

The building was a five-story reinforced-concrete flat-slab structure, measuring 130 × 150 ft in plan, six bays wide

FIGURE 132 Column at south end wall of Mt. McKinley building.

FIGURE 133   1200 L Street apartment building, during repair (from southeast). The area at right has been repaired but not yet painted.

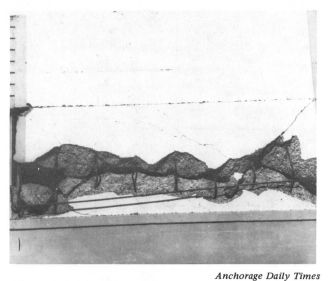

Anchorage Daily Times

FIGURE 135   West pier of south end wall in 1200 L Street apartment building. Failure occurred in the second story but not at a construction joint.

FIGURE 134   1200 L Street apartment building (from the south) showing damaged spandrel beams and vertical wall failure.

FIGURE 136   1200 L Street apartment building (from the west) was not as severely damaged as the Mt. McKinley building.

Anchorage Daily Times

FIGURE 137   Spandrel failure in south end wall of 1200 L Street apartment building. These spandrels are at the third and fourth floor. Diagonal cracks that existed in vertical pier did not reproduce clearly in this photo.

Anchorage Daily Times

FIGURE 138   The cantilever spandrels sustained heavy damage in the 1200 L Street apartment building.

in each direction, and 66 ft high. The long axis lay in an east–west direction, parallel to Fifth Avenue. The stories were 14 ft high for the first floor and 13 ft high for the other floors.

The foundation for the structure consisted of reinforced-concrete spread footings for the interior columns and a continuous spread footing around the perimeter. The first floor was a 4-in. concrete slab-on-grade. The roof and remaining floor slabs were 10-in.-thick reinforced-concrete flat slabs, designed without drop panels or column capitals with shear heads of reinforcing steel at all interior columns. Design live loads were 40 psf for the roof, 125 psf for the fourth floor, and 75 psf for the second and third floors.

The south and west exterior walls were poured-in-place reinforced-concrete shear walls that extended the full height of the structure and had openings only in the first story. The north and east walls were covered with 4-in.-thick precast nonstructural panels extending from the second floor to the roof. In the east elevation, a shear wall extended the full five-story height in the two north bays, and in the two south bays there was a shear wall in the bottom three sto-

ries. Figure 140, a first-story plan of the building, indicates the column spacing and shear-wall locations.

Earthquake Damage

The J. C. Penney Building sustained a severe failure as a result of the forces developed by the earthquake. The west

FIGURE 139   1200 L Street apartment building during repair.

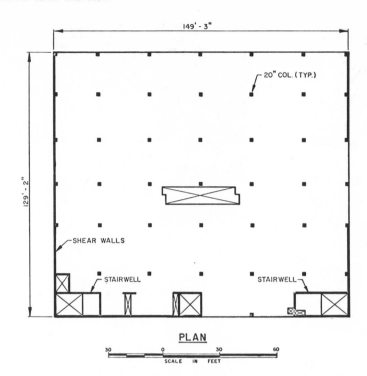

PLAN

SCALE IN FEET

FIGURE 140   Floor plan of the J.C. Penney Building.

wall failed in shear at the north, and a portion fell several feet to the ground. Most of the precast panels on the north and east sides of the building were also badly cracked and displaced. A woman in front of the store was killed when one of these panels fell from the building; however, no lives were lost within the store.

The east shear wall at the northeast corner failed, and this corner of the building collapsed. Figures 141–145 show the extent of earthquake damages. The building, which was determined to be damaged beyond repair, was removed and replaced by a new structure.

Conclusions

Many lessons on design and construction procedure may be learned from the behavior of this building. It is essential that the elements connecting precast-concrete panels to the building frame be strong enough to withstand earthquake forces. Highly unsymmetrical arrangements of shear walls that induce torsional oscillations should be avoided; if they are used, a very thorough analysis should be made, and the design should provide adequate resistance against the true earthquake forces. Construction joints in concrete walls should be well made, so that they do not provide planes of weakness.

SUMMARY AND CONCLUSIONS

Many buildings in Anchorage sustained structural damage. Some of these buildings such as the Four Seasons apartment building, the Government Hill School, and the J. C. Penney Building, collapsed partly or completely, constituting hazards to the life and limb of occupants during the earthquake. Most of the damaged buildings, however, did not partly collapse and were not directly hazardous to the occupants in this respect; the Mt. McKinley apartment building,

FIGURE 141   The northeast corner of the J. C. Penney Building, where the failure of the roof, floor slabs, and column pulled the east-elevation shear wall inward. Damage to the cast-in-place concrete wall at the south end of the east elevation resulted from inserts that fastened the precast panels to the wall being torn from their original positions. There was no shear wall at the east end of the north elevation. The exterior shear wall on the south elevation at the second-floor level shifted outward several inches at the east end.

FIGURE 142 South and east elevations of J. C. Penney Building show failure of the south wall at the first-story level. East elevation shows that the precast-concrete exterior panels dropped vertically to the ground. The picture also shows failure of the cast-in-place reinforced-concrete wall, where the inserts for the fastening of precast panels were originally attached. This failure required temporary shoring until the wall was demolished.

FIGURE 144 Precast panels, 5 in. thick, from the J. C. Penney Building lay where they fell after being torn loose during the earthquake. Shear wall failed at second-floor level. Panels that fell on the car in front of the building killed one person.

the 1200 L Street apartment building, and the Hillside apartment building are striking examples of such structures. The cost of repairing these buildings, however, was relatively large, emphasizing that, on the whole, it is not sufficient merely to design structures so that they are safe during earthquakes; the cost of repairing damage should be held to an acceptable level. For example, if a large metropolitan area, such as Los Angeles, were to experience earthquake damage to multistory buildings comparable to that experienced in Anchorage, an economic loss, estimated at several billion dollars, would result; this would not be acceptable. From the studies of the damage to buildings in Anchorage, it is concluded that most of the damage could have been avoided by better earthquake-resistant design,

FIGURE 143 Northeast corner of the J. C. Penney Building, where column and floors failed. Shear wall was pulled inward and broken into three sections. Picture shows army guards who were used to supplement the Anchorage Police downtown and in other areas of severe destruction.

FIGURE 145 North and west elevations of the J. C. Penney Building, showing the north wall after the precast panels were removed. Note failures of floor slabs and west wall, allowing the northwest corner of the structure to drop.

which could have been achieved with little extra cost. Engineering designers can profit by studying the damage incurred by Anchorage buildings and creating concept designs that would avoid the damage.

A comparison of the behavior of the Hillside apartment building with that of the Four Seasons apartment building is especially thought-provoking. The Four Seasons apartment building, which was designed in accordance with the 1963 *Uniform Building Code* requirements for seismic zone 3, collapsed completely. On the other hand, the Hillside building, which was not constructed in accordance with the *Uniform Building Code* and, in many respects, was at variance with standard earthquake-engineering practice, did not collapse. It can be concluded that in the seismic regions of the United States there are structures that, like the Four Seasons building, will collapse if shaken with similar intensity. Such buildings should be identified and strengthened. The nature of the dynamic properties of the Hillside apartment building that enabled it to survive prolonged and intense shaking without collapse should be studied, and the information should be incorporated in engineering design practice.

ACKNOWLEDGMENTS

Except as otherwise noted, figures are credited to the U.S. Army Corps of Engineers.

REFERENCES

Berg, Glen V., and James L. Stratta, 1964. Anchorage and the Alaska earthquake of March 27, 1964. Report of the American Iron and Steel Institute. New York: American Iron and Steel Institute. 63 p.

Blume, John A., and Associates, 1966. Report on structural damage in Anchorage, Alaska, caused by the earthquake of March 27, 1964. Report prepared for Structural Response Program, Operational Safety Division, Nevada Operations Office, U.S. Atomic Energy Commission. San Francisco: John A. Blume and Associates Research Division. 91 p.

Clough, Ray W., and K. Lee Benuska, 1966. FHA study of seismic design criteria for high-rise buildings. A Report for Federal Housing Administration, Technical Studies Program (HUD TS-3). Los Angeles: T. Y. Lin and Associates. 347 p.

Committee on the Alaskan Earthquake, 1965. The Alaskan earthquake. California Department of Water Resources Bulletin No. 116-5. Sacramento: California Department of Water Resources. 94 p.

Eckel, Edwin B., and William E. Schaem, 1966. The work of the Scientific and Engineering Task Force—Earth science applied to policy decisions in early relief and reconstruction *in* The Alaska earthquake, March 27, 1964: Field investigations and reconstruction effort. U.S. Geological Survey Professional Paper 541. Washington: Government Printing Office. p. 46-69.

Hansen, Wallace R., 1965. Effects of the earthquake of March 27, 1964, at Anchorage, Alaska. U.S. Geological Survey Professional Paper 542-A. Washington: Government Printing Office. 68 p. Also, *in* The Great Alaska Earthquake of 1964: Geology. NAS Pub. 1601. Washington: National Academy of Sciences, 1971. p. 289-357.

Meehan, John F., 1967. The response of several public school buildings in Anchorage, Alaska, to the March 27, 1964, earthquake, *in* Volume II-A: The Prince William Sound, Alaska, earthquake of 1964 and aftershocks. Environmental Science Services Administration, U.S. Coast and Geodetic Survey. Washington: Government Printing Office. p. 219-243.

Metcalf and Eddy, [1964]. Informal report to the U.S. Army Corps of Engineers. Boston: Metcalf and Eddy, Consulting Engineers.

Pacific Coast Building Officials Conference, 1949. Uniform Building Code (1949 edition). Los Angeles: Pacific Coast Building Officials Conference.

U.S. Army Engineering Division, 1964. Report on analysis of earthquake damage to military construction in Alaska, 27 March 1964. Washington: U.S. Army, Office of Chief of Engineers, Directorate of Military Construction. 113 p.

WARREN GEORGE   JAMES F. SIZEMORE
PAUL KNOWLES   DUANE E. CARSON
JOHN K. ALLENDER
U.S. ARMY CORPS OF ENGINEERS DISTRICT,
ALASKA

Structures in Small Communities

The city of Anchorage was the largest community to experience severe shaking. Because Anchorage had the most as well as the biggest structures, the earthquake damage there was the most impressive. The smaller communities, such as Seward, Valdez, Homer, Palmer, Moose Pass, Kenai, Hope, and Girdwood, with populations of a few thousand or a few hundred persons, had correspondingly less to be damaged. Usually earthquake damage to modest structures in small communities is not described in engineering reports; attention is focused on large buildings and large communities even though the inhabitants of the small towns suffer as much from the damage as those in large cities. The Corps of Engineers' office in Anchorage was responsible for the repair and rehabilitation of buildings in small communities after the Alaska earthquake; it therefore developed information on the damage, repair measures, and costs. In some of the small communities, the average earthquake loss per capita was found to be as great as, or greater than, that in Anchorage.

The description of damage and repair in these small communities illustrates the effect of an earthquake on small towns and villages. A significant portion of the cost of the earthquake was spread out over the sparsely populated region, but the damage received relatively little attention compared to the damage in the larger city.

ABSTRACT: Many small communities were affected by strong ground shaking. Those damaged significantly ranged from about 40 to 125 mi from the causative fault and contained buildings of various structural types and a variety of functions. The buildings were mostly modest in size and value, and some were relatively old. They sustained differing degrees of damage and required repair, sometimes at considerable cost. Many of them had structural weaknesses that made them susceptible to damage that could have been avoided by better earthquake-resistant design and construction at little extra cost. Some wood-frame buildings showed excellent resistance to ground shaking. We conclude that buildings critical to the functioning of a community should be designed to be functional after a strong earthquake.

SEWARD

STATE-OWNED STATE COURT AND CITY HALL BUILDING

The old Seward State Court and City Hall building stood on the southeast corner of the block facing Fifth Avenue and Adams Street (Figure 1). The main entrance was on the Fifth Avenue side. At the time of the earthquake, the building was approximately 60 years old and was being used as a city hall, with jail facilities in the basement. In Figure 2, a

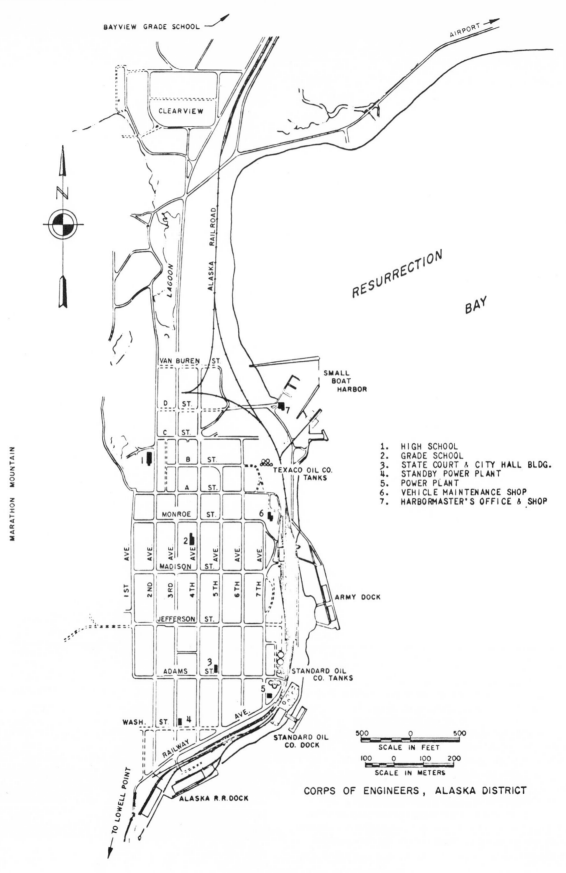

FIGURE 1   Preearthquake Seward, Alaska, and vicinity.

FIGURE 2   Seward City Hall, from northeast. Although the exterior walls appear to be in good condition, they actually were not.

picture taken after the earthquake, the building appears to be in fair condition, although its condition was actually very poor; earthquake damage was so extensive that the building was demolished and replaced by a new one.

Information on this building was taken from a report prepared for the Alaska District Engineers by Peter H. Hostmark and Associates, consulting engineers, Seattle, Washington, and submitted in April 1964. No plans of the original structure are available.

The building measured about 42 × 140 ft and actually consisted of three separate structures, approximately equal in size, separated by two 12-in.-thick brick walls parallel to the side wall of the structures. The rear wall between these two dividing walls was also constructed of brick, whereas the front wall, facing Fifth Avenue, was wood frame. The area enclosed by the three brick walls was three stories high; the two end portions of the building were two stories high. The outside walls were wood frame, and the entire building was covered on the outside with stucco plaster. The interior partitions were wood frame covered with wood-lath and plaster. The floors and roofs were constructed of wood joists supported on wood beams and columns. The building contained no elevator, and the upper floors of the structure could only be reached by two steep stairways.

Description of Building and Earthquake Damage

This detailed description of the building and the earthquake damage was made during an inspection performed in April 1964.

Originally, only the middle third of the building had a basement. The two end portions of the building had been constructed with a 3- to 4-ft crawl space below the first floor. Later, efforts had been made to extend the basement into both these sections of the building. At the south end of the building, the soil had been excavated right up to the face of the foundation walls, but no effort had been made

to support the nearly vertical gravel faces to prevent them from sliding out and undermining the foundation walls.

Similar excavations had been made at the north end of the building. In the northeast corner, the foundation walls had been underpinned by pouring new concrete walls and slabs inside and below the old walls. In the northwest corner, the excavation extended to within 3–4 ft of the original foundations, but no retaining walls had been constructed to contain the vertical faces of the excavation. The interior foundation wall, parallel to the north basement wall, was the only one that had been properly underpinned with a new concrete wall. The earthquake caused the gravel to slough away from the foundations and sometimes to expose the underside of the footings. The concrete in the original basement walls was of very poor quality. The surfaces of the walls were full of large rock pockets or honeycomb concrete and cavities. The concrete mixture used for their construction had too much coarse aggregate and too little sand and cement.

Jail cells, a solitary-confinement cell, a storage room, and a boiler room, were contained in the middle portion of the basement. The walls were constructed of 2 × 4-in. wood studs spaced 2 in. apart; the doors were of similar construction. The solitary-confinement cell had brick walls, steel-barred inside gate, and a steel vault outside door. None of these cells received any daylight.

The three brick walls of the building were in very poor condition after the earthquake. In many places shear cracks extended from floor to ceiling. In other places, the walls were completely shattered (Figure 3). Diagonal cracks were evident above many of the doors and windows. The brick parapet wall on the south side of the three-story portion of the building was completely shattered. The stucco facing

FIGURE 3   Seward City Hall: Broken west wall under window in third story of the middle portion of building.

had been forced out and the open crack was full of loose brick. Only the stucco-lath and plaster had prevented these bricks from cascading down onto the lower roof of the south portion of the building. The mortar between the bricks had very poor bonding qualities. In several places, it was found that there was no bond at all; some bricks could be pried out of the walls, which were damaged so badly that it was necessary to remove them immediately.

With the exception of the three brick walls already mentioned, the walls and partitions in the building were constructed of wood studs covered with wood-lath and plaster. The plaster facing was found to be badly cracked and damaged on a large number of the walls. In this type of construction, the plaster provides the strength to resist earthquake forces; the badly cracked walls therefore represented structural damage. Large cracks or separations were also found where the stud walls abutted the brick walls.

The extent of the earthquake damage to the plaster in the building was so great that ordinary patching of cracks would not have been satisfactory. All existing lath and plaster would have had to be removed before new lath and plaster could be applied.

The wood-joist floors were severely damaged in only two places. In one small area along the south wall of the building, the joist ends were crushed against the foundation wall. In part of the building, the roof and floors were crushed and broken under the weight of the collapsed brick chimney and wall. Otherwise the floors appeared to be in good condition and structurally sound.

With the exception of the large hole made by the falling chimney in the north part of the building, no water leaks could be found in the roof. The roofing, however, appeared to be old and in need of replacement.

The nonstructural damage was influential in the decision to rebuild this structure.

The original electrical wiring of the building was done with the "knob and tube" system. This wiring was later augmented and partly replaced with a surface-mounted system. The old system was in very poor condition, and only about half the circuits were in use.

In some places, the earthquake vibrations tore the light fixtures off the ceilings, shattering some on the floors. Others were left hanging from the ceiling supported only by their electrical wires. Concealed wiring must also have been damaged, making the entire wiring system a dangerous fire hazard.

The building was heated by steam generated in an oil-fired boiler in the basement; old-fashioned radiators along the outside walls were used to heat the rooms. No provisions were made for ventilation or air conditioning.

The heating system, which was not in operation, had been drained at the time of inspection; consequently, no actual leaks could be found. In some places, however, evidence was found that the pipes had been subject to violent movements and stresses during the earthquake. Broken pipes and leaks probably would have been found if pressure had been restored.

Although the fixtures had remained in place during the earthquake, a number of the joints in the stacks and piping had worked loose and showed evidence of leaks. The entire plumbing system would have had to be taken apart and reassembled with new jointing material before it could safely be used again.

Building Repairs

Because the building was old and had sustained extensive earthquake damage, it was decided that repairs would be too costly. The old structure was demolished during the summer of 1964. The Anchorage architectural firm of Manley & Mayer was retained by the Alaska District Corps of Engineers to design a new structure. A two-story building with basement, 131 × 55 ft in plan, was designed and constructed to replace the old structure; construction of the new office building was completed in January 1966 (Figure 4). Total contract cost of this new building was $600,895.

This old building was in poor condition and obviously had not been designed to resist earthquakes. The earthquake caused more deterioration, and left it in a very hazardous condition. If the community had lacked funds, this old damaged structure might have been patched, plastered, painted, and continued in service despite its hazardous condition. It may be inferred that many small communities in seismic regions are continuing to use very hazardous buildings.

CITY-OWNED BUILDINGS

The Seward standby power plant, the vehicle maintenance shop, and the harbor master's office and shop (separate

FIGURE 4 New State Court and office building, built to replace old Seward City Hall building, which was damaged beyond repair in 1964 earthquake (summer 1966).

structures) were destroyed completely either by fire, or by the tsunami, or by a combination thereof.

Standby Power Plant

The old Seward standby power plant building at the southern end of Seward (Figure 1) had been extended to make additional room for the diesel-powered generators. The older part of the structure was separated from the newer part by an earthquake-caused fissure that opened in the earth at the junction of the new and old portions of the structure. An 8-in. separation at this joint indicated considerable earth displacement. The building had concrete floors, reinforced-concrete walls, and a wooden roof supported on steel beams. This structure was completely gutted by fire immediately after the earthquake, and only the concrete walls remained standing. The building and the enclosed generating equipment was replaced with a prepackaged unit (Figure 5). The cost of the prepackaged units, including installation, was $96,476.

Because the major damage by fire had destroyed all evidence of structural damage, other than the parting of the building, it would be difficult to draw any meaningful conclusions as to the structure.

Vehicle Maintenance Shop

The old city vehicle maintenance shop at Seventh and Madison streets (Figure 1) was a wood-frame structure with a gasoline tank and a filler pump. This structure was completely destroyed by the earthquake and subsequent tsunamis.

Before the earthquake, the city of Seward had engaged an architectural firm to design a new public works building. A contract for construction of the new building was

FIGURE 6   The new prefabricated metal structure that houses Seward's vehicle maintenance and electrical-repair shops.

awarded late in 1963, with the idea of using the equipment from their old building in the new structure. Because of inclement weather, the city instructed the contractor to stop the work, and no work had been done on the new building when the earthquake hit.

Seward also lost its electrical-repair building in the earthquake; the city therefore requested that both facilities be combined in a common building, which would be easier to maintain. After determining that these structures were eligible for emergency restoration money, the Corps of Engineers proceeded to design a new structure. A new prefabricated metal building, 52 × 114 ft in plan, was built at an approximate cost of $160,000 (Figure 6).

Because the buildings were destroyed by the earthquake, they were eligible to be replaced with emergency restoration funds. Structural damage caused directly by earthquake forces was difficult to distinguish from damage caused by the tsunami.

Harbor Master's Office and Shop

The original harbor master's office and shop building (Figure 1) consisted of two structures that contained the living quarters and working area. The first floor of the office was constructed of concrete blocks and the second floor was wood frame. The shop was a small shed that housed marine facilities. Both structures were completely washed away by the tsunami that followed the earthquake. They were replaced with one prefabricated metal building at a total cost of $123,700 (Figure 7).

SCHOOLS

William H. Seward Grade School

The William H. Seward Grade School (Figure 1) was erected in the 1920's. The school is a two-story building

FIGURE 5   Standby power plant units used to replace Seward's old standby power plant, which was completely destroyed in the 1964 earthquake.

FIGURE 7 Seward: The harbor master's office and shop building during construction. The prefabricated metal structure replaced two smaller buildings that were swept away by the tsunami.

whose central basic structure measures 105 X 60 ft. A 91 X 40-ft gymnasium had been added on the north end, and a two-story 60 X 55-ft classroom addition had been added on the south end (Figure 8). The central portion of the structure has a full basement with concrete foundation walls and floors. The gymnasium on the north and the classroom addition on the south have concrete foundation walls but no full basement. Above the foundation the walls, floors, and roof are of wood with a stucco exterior finish and a plaster interior finish.

Earthquake Damage Damage to this building was minor and mostly nonstructural. The main structural damage was to the boiler-room chimney that was located in the basement of the central building. This unreinforced brick stack sheared off at the roof line. Minor cracking occurred in the stucco exterior and plaster interior finishes. Some light fix-

tures fell and minor damage occurred to boiler-pipe connections and to several radiators that tipped over. Later, the boiler was found to have settled to such an extent that it interfered with the operation of the heating system. It was presumed that the earthquake caused this settlement.

Building Repairs Because the city wanted to resume classes as soon as possible after the earthquake, emergency repairs were made to the building. The fallen brick chimney was replaced above the roof line with a temporary metal stack. Loose plaster was removed; the heating system was checked and the radiators repaired; and light fixtures were replaced as required and the wiring thoroughly checked. Since the building was considered to be structurally sound, classes resumed within 3 weeks.

The Alaska District Office of the Corps of Engineers engaged M. W. Wallenstein, an Anchorage architect, to prepare plans and specifications for permanent repairs to the building. These repairs, consisting of patching the stucco exterior finish and the plaster interior finish, repairing roof leaks, and painting where necessary, were made during the summer of 1964.

During the winter of 1964–1965, the school district had trouble with the heating system. The building was again inspected, and the trouble was traced to a slight settlement of the boiler. The boiler therefore was replaced, a new fire-rated metal stack was installed between the floor and roof to replace the old brick stack, and a fire-rated enclosure was built around the new boiler. The cost of these repairs was about $8,900.

The total amount spent on repairing earthquake damages to the William H. Seward Grade School was approxi-

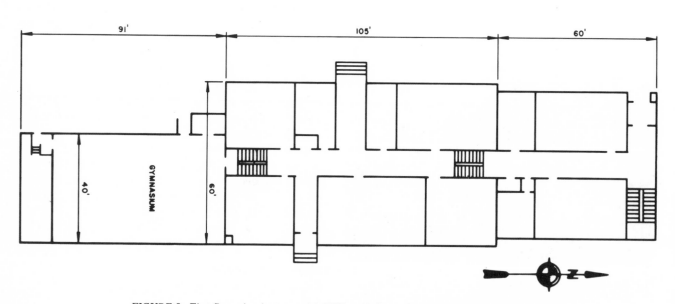

FIGURE 8 First-floor plan (not to scale), William H. Seward Elementary School, Seward.

mately $38,900. The building was about 40 years old so the amount spent on repairs was not large.

This wood-frame and plaster building survived the earthquake with relatively little damage. The building was not specifically designed to resist earthquakes, but it demonstrates that this type of construction is much more resistant to earthquakes than is the unreinforced-brick building.

Bayview Grade School

The Bayview Grade School stood at the north end of Seward (Figure 1). Visible surface cracks in the ground surrounding the school indicated gross movement of the ground.

The school was a 94 X 58 ft single-story wood-frame building with a stucco exterior finish and plaster interior finish. The foundations were concrete. The boiler room was in the basement (Figure 9). The roof structure was wood joists spanning between two interior bearing walls and the exterior bearing walls.

Earthquake Damage   The concrete foundation walls, which were of very poor quality concrete, were badly cracked. The interior cross walls were not adequately tied to the roof structure, but were spiked to the roof deck with large nails spaced 2–3 ft on centers and were also fastened to the exterior walls with nails. The lateral forces were not transferred from the roof diaphragm to the interior walls, and the building racked considerably, causing the exterior wall to separate from the interior walls.

The interior finish was damaged, as was the exterior stucco finish. Because the plaster and stucco provide much of the strength to resist the earthquake forces, this might be called structural damage.

Building Repairs   During the summer of 1964, the Alaska District contracted for the school to be repaired. The interior shear walls were securely spiked to the roof-framing

structure, and the exterior walls were connected to the interior shear walls. Damaged plaster on the interior and stucco on the exterior were replaced and painted. The concrete foundation walls were epoxy-grouted. The cost of these repairs was about $2,500.

During the winter of 1964–1965, trouble developed in the heating system that was ascribed to damages caused by the earthquake. The boiler was therefore replaced, and a fire-rated room was built around it. The chimney was replaced with a new fire-rated metal stack. The cost of this repair was approximately $2,800.

The total amount spent on repairs to the building was $5,300, which is a modest amount for a school that was built as a temporary structure during World War II.

In this building, the majority of the structural damage could again be traced to improper connection details. Not all the damage was apparent after the earthquake and, as in the case of the William H. Seward School, some of the damage was not noticed until the following winter.

Seward High School

The Seward High School, within the Seward city limits (Figure 1), was specially important to the residents of Seward, because for the first week after the earthquake, the school was used as their emergency sleeping quarters and food dispensary. The building sustained only minor damage.

The school is a two-story steel-frame structure with concrete shear walls that was designed and constructed during the 1950's (Figures 10 and 11). Just behind the school, bedrock is exposed on the steeply sloping hillside, indicating that the footings of the building rest very close to solid rock. The main floor is of concrete; the second floor and roof are of metal decking with concrete filler. Exterior walls are constructed of concrete, steel frame, and glass. Mechanical equipment is kept in a small basement beneath the main floor.

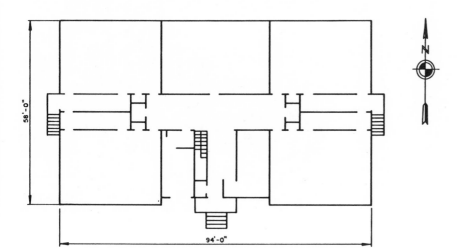

FIGURE 9   First-floor plan (not to scale), Bayview Elementary School, Seward.

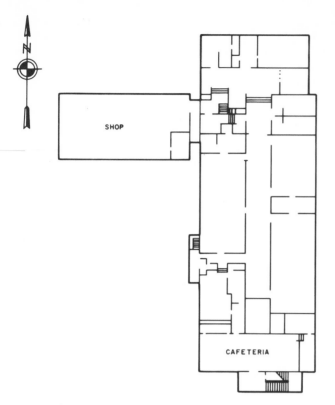

FIGURE 10   First-floor plan (not to scale), Seward High School.

Earthquake Damage   Only two instances of structural damage occurred. A brick incinerator stack behind the school building, which had only minimum reinforcing, collapsed, and a concrete stack, which extended from the boiler room in the basement through and above the roof, cracked at the second-floor line and at the roof line.

The extent of the nonstructural damage was some minor cracks in the concrete walls and some ceiling tiles dislodged from the ceiling of the second-story rooms.

Building Repairs   No major repairs were required for the structure. Fallen ceiling tiles were replaced. The concrete stack for the boiler caused the most concern; it was uncertain whether there was reinforcing steel in the stack. As an emergency measure to allow classes to resume, a steel angle frame was built around the stack, with slip-joint connections at the roof and second floor. During summer 1964, after a more complete investigation had determined that the stack contained adequate reinforcing steel, the angles were removed and the cracks in the concrete stack were epoxy-grouted. The total cost of the repairs for the high school was $10,925.

This school is a good example of a well-designed and well-constructed building resisting earthquake forces without serious damage. It is also an example of how important

it is that certain critical structures in a community have adequate strength to be functional after the earthquake. Schools, hospitals, police and fire stations, and public utilities should be designed to be stronger than the minimum requirements of the building code specify.

VALDEZ

STATE-OWNED BUILDINGS

State Mental Hospital

The old mental hospital at Sixth and Nizina streets in Valdez (Figure 12) consisted of a complex of buildings originally built to be a motel. The State of Alaska purchased the complex and remodeled it for use as a mental hospital. All the buildings in the complex (Figure 13), except buildings 1, 2, 3, and 4, had been remodeled and were occupied by patients at the time of the earthquake. The earthquake damage ranged from minor cracking in walls and slabs to complete failure.

Buildings 1, 2, 3, and 4 measured about 29 × 140 ft and had concrete slabs-on-grade, concrete walls with interior furring, insulation, and dry wall, wood joists and sheathing, mopped-on roofing, tile ceiling, and a dry-wall interior finish. Building 5 was used as the food-service wing. The 29 × 140-ft building had a 14 × 48-ft attached refrigeration wing that had wood-frame walls and roof, wood siding, and concrete slab-on-grade. Building 6, the administration wing, was 29 × 95 ft. Buildings 7 and 8 were wards, each measuring 29 × 142 ft. Building 9 was used for housing and storage and was 29 × 95 ft. Buildings 5, 6, 7, 8, and 9 were similar in construction to Building 1.

FIGURE 11   Front view of Seward High School. The building sustained only minor earthquake damage.

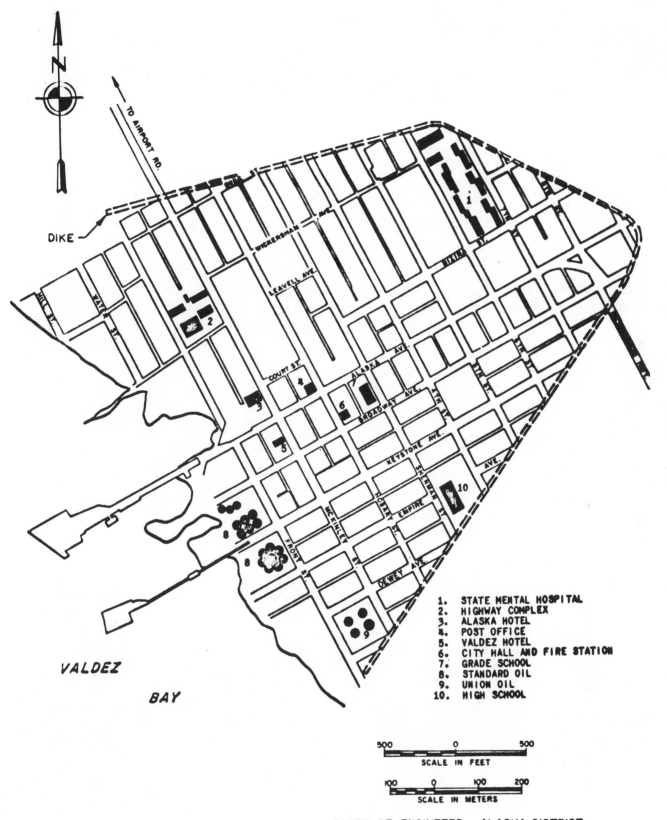

1. STATE MENTAL HOSPITAL
2. HIGHWAY COMPLEX
3. ALASKA HOTEL
4. POST OFFICE
5. VALDEZ HOTEL
6. CITY HALL AND FIRE STATION
7. GRADE SCHOOL
8. STANDARD OIL
9. UNION OIL
10. HIGH SCHOOL

SCALE IN FEET

SCALE IN METERS

CORPS OF ENGINEERS, ALASKA DISTRICT

FIGURE 12   Preearthquake Valdez.

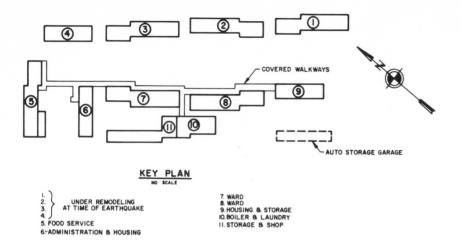

KEY PLAN
NO SCALE

1.
2. } UNDER REMODELING
3. } AT TIME OF EARTHQUAKE
4.
5. FOOD SERVICE
6. ADMINISTRATION & HOUSING

7. WARD
8. WARD
9. HOUSING & STORAGE
10. BOILER & LAUNDRY
11. STORAGE & SHOP

FIGURE 13   Building layout (not to scale), Valdez mental hospital.

Building 10 housed the boiler room and laundry. The one-story boiler room had a concrete floor slab-on-grade, concrete-block walls, steel-joist roof purlins, and a wooden roof deck with mopped-on roofing. The laundry room was similarly constructed and measured 36 × 48 ft in plan. Building 11 was the storage and shop building. The storage part of the building was 20 × 108 ft in plan, and the shop portion was 28 × 42 ft. Construction was concrete slab-on-grade, concrete-block walls, and a wooden roof. The un-numbered garage building had wood-frame walls, a roof with mopped-on roofing, plywood and shiplap exterior finish, and an overhead door at each car space.

Earthquake Damage   Valdez stood on sloping ground at the mouth of a glacial valley. During the earthquake, a submarine landslide just offshore caused the soil under Valdez to move seaward so that it was stretched and cracked. The concrete floor slabs of buildings 1–5 were cracked by this soil movement (Figures 14–17).

The west side of Building 6 settled about 1 in. The floor slabs sloped slightly and the wall was therefore proportionately out of plumb. The walls and floor slabs were badly cracked (Figures 18 and 19).

Differential settlement of 6–7 in. occurred between the east and west walls of Building 7, causing large cracks in the floor and walls. Damage to Building 8 was similar to that sustained by Building 7, but the damage was more severe (Figures 20 and 21).

A block wall near the northwest corner of Building 9 was severely damaged, and ground settlement also caused the walls to tilt out of plumb (Figures 22 and 23). Building 10 sustained little damage other than the ground settlement.

In Building 11 the walls were out of plumb because of ground settlement. The unnumbered garage building collapsed during the earthquake, which resulted partly from the heavy snowload on the roof (Figure 24).

There was some cracking of interior finishes in the buildings and some damage to electrical mechanical systems.

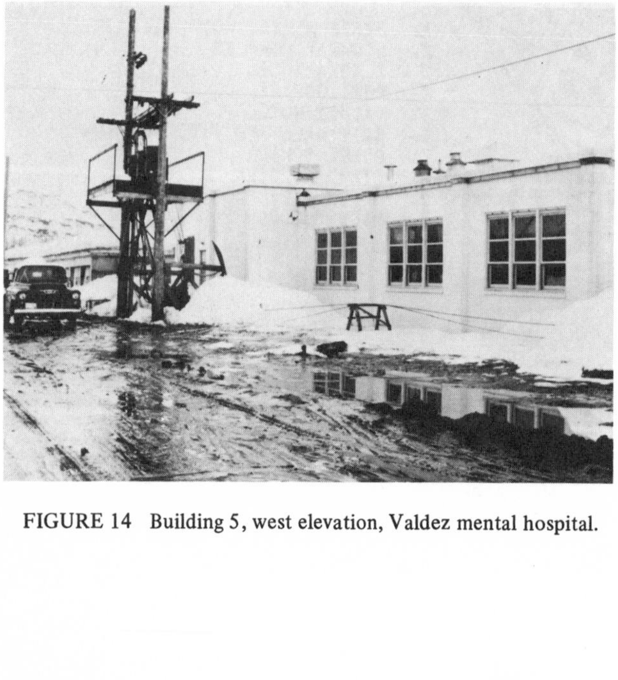

FIGURE 14   Building 5, west elevation, Valdez mental hospital.

FIGURE 15   Valdez mental hospital: Refrigeration wings of Building 5.

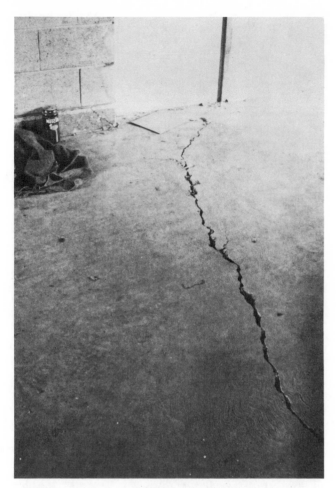

FIGURE 16   Valdez mental hospital: Crack in floor slab at the entry to the dining room in Building 5. This crack did not extend into the dining room.

Shortly after the earthquake, the patients and hospital staff were moved to Anchorage. The buildings had been damaged beyond economical repair for use as hospital facilities, and a new state mental hospital was authorized.

Because of the shortage of usable structures in Valdez, the State Highway Department used sections of the old hospital as an office building until the new Highway Department complex was completed.

The damage to the buildings can be attributed to the general seaward movement of the land on which the buildings were constructed. It would be difficult to design any structure to withstand the foundation movement to which these buildings were subjected. In a mountainous country, the most attractive and convenient site for a town is on an outwash plain at the mouth of a canyon, but such a site can be very damaging and hazardous when an earthquake occurs. Convenience must not be permitted to outweigh excessive hazard.

State Highway Complex

The State Highway Department Complex in Valdez consisted of a garage and maintenance shop, a dry-storage warehouse, a steel-storage warehouse, a shop and laboratory building, a miscellaneous-storage warehouse, and two fuel pumps (Figure 25). During the earthquake, the complex moved seaward and settled so that the floors of the structure were close to the water level during high tide. The buildings were determined to be beyond repair and were abandoned; a new complex was built to replace them.

The warehouse (Building 485-140-402) was 40 ft wide and 80 ft long. It was a timber-frame building with corrugated metal siding and roofing. Four timber trusses with intermediate rafters supported the roof and tied the walls together. The floor was heavy wood planking, and the entire building was supported on wood blocking. There was no insulation, plumbing, heating, ventilation, telephone,

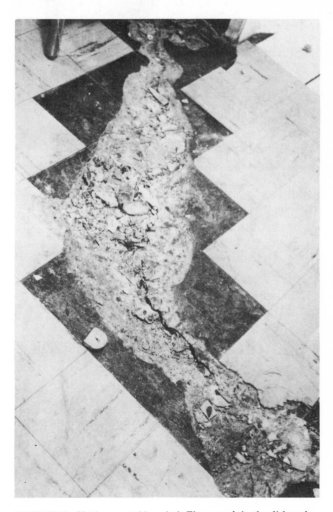

FIGURE 17   Valdez mental hospital: Floor crack in the dishwashing room of Building 5.

FIGURE 18   Valdez mental hospital: Crack in the concrete floor at the south entry of Building 6.

FIGURE 20   Valdez mental hospital: Crack in corridor slab and crack in the concrete-block wall of building.

FIGURE 19   Valdez mental hospital: Building 6, west elevation.

FIGURE 21   Valdez mental hospital: Damage at corridor intersection between buildings 7 and 8.

FIGURE 22   Valdez mental hospital: Damage to interior wall at the northwest corner of building.

FIGURE 23   Valdez mental hospital: Damage at northwest corner of Building 9.

FIGURE 24   Valdez mental hospital: Collapsed auto storage garage.

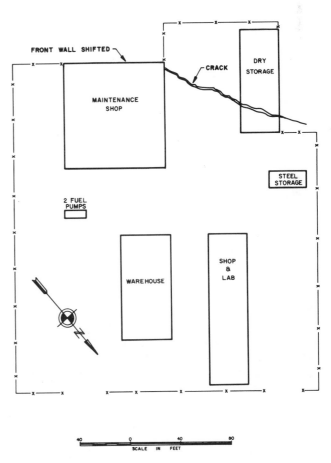

FIGURE 25   Plot plan, State Highway Complex, Valdez.

or equipment-handling machinery. The building was used for miscellaneous storage. There was no apparent structural damage caused by ground shaking.

The shop and materials laboratory building (Building 485-140-403) was 30 ft wide and 120 ft long and was constructed of timber frame with insulated walls and ceilings and corrugated-metal siding and roofing. The floor was a concrete slab on grade. The northern half (1,800 ft²) of this building was used as a soils and materials laboratory and was finished with floor tile and painted plywood or Celotex-board ceilings and walls. The laboratory was well lighted and was equipped with a heating system, plumbing, and an overhead monorail hoist for handling sample barrels. Concrete-block rooms had been built for grinding or crushing samples and for the 100 percent humidity room for curing concrete test samples. The remaining half of the building was used as an equipment-repair shop. The earthquake caused no apparent structural damage to the building.

The steel-storage warehouse (Building 485-140-404) was 12 ft wide and 28 ft long and was constructed of timber frame with corrugated-metal siding and roofing. The floor was heavy wood planking, and the entire building was supported on timber skids. An overhead monorail with a hand-operated chain hoist was provided for handling steel rods and shapes that were stored in the building. This building sustained no apparent structural damage as a result of the earthquake.

The sand storage building (Building 485-140-405) was 30 X 80 ft and had a timber frame with corrugated-metal siding and roofing. The floor at the south end was wood and at the north end there was a dirt floor. The entire building was set on timber blocking, and had no heating system, plumbing, ventilating, fire alarm, or material-handling equipment. As a result of the earthquake, one fissure opened under the north half of this building and one under the south end, causing the building to displace permanently in a lateral direction and making the main doors difficult to operate.

The garage and maintenance shop (Building 485-140-701) was an 80 X 80 ft structural steel building with corrugated-metal roofing, plywood siding, and a concrete floor slab; the walls and ceiling were insulated (Figure 26). A 5-ton Whiting traveling crane was housed in this building, about three fourths of which was used for maintenance and parts storage, and the remainder for warm storage. A 2- to 3-in. horizontal movement of column footings and a concrete threshold slab on the south side of the building resulted from the earthquake, leaving the south side of the building about 2 in. out of plumb (Figures 27 and 28).

These buildings were found to be not worth moving because of the ground settlement, lateral movement, and resulting questionable stability of the foundations. The old structures were used until the new highway complex was

FIGURE 26   Garage and maintenance building, State Highway Complex, Valdez.

FIGURE 27   Separation between the concrete floor slab and the perimeter wall footing in the maintenance shop, State Highway Complex, Valdez.

FIGURE 28 South exterior wall and an interior wall of the main-tenance shop, State Highway Complex, Valdez, showing foundation failure caused by horizontal movement of the perimeter wall footing. This movement left the south wall 2–3 in. out of plumb.

contained six classrooms, a multipurpose room, a stage, and a partial basement. Part of this basement was finished and had a concrete floor; the unfinished portion had a dirt floor. The building had a continuous concrete exterior-wall footing, and posts with isolated footings carried the interior loads. The building was wood frame with wood exterior siding. Interior walls were finished with plaster or drywall.

Damage to the building was caused principally by move-ment of the foundation. After the earthquake, the perime-ter wall footings were approximately 1 ft lower than the interior footings, causing an upward bow in the floor (Fig-ure 30). In the basement, plaster was cracked and there was damage from mud and water (Figures 31 and 32).

Some engineers were of the opinion that the remarkable differential movement of the footings was caused by settle-ment of the exterior wall footings; others thought it was the result of an upwelling of soft soil under the building, where the ground was not frozen. Possibly both movements were involved, emphasizing the importance of giving special con-sideration to potential earthquake effects when building on this type of soil.

Valdez Junior–Senior High School

The Valdez Junior–Senior High School at Empire and Sherman streets was designed by Manley and Mayer, archi-tects, Anchorage; construction was completed in 1956 (Fig-ure 33). This building was in the area affected by the Valdez slide, which influenced the decision on the disposi-tion of the school. The building was temporarily repaired, and classes were held in it until a school could be built at the new townsite.

The old Junior–Senior High School building was divided

completed, at which time they were demolished. The build-ings withstood the earthquake without serious structural damage other than the foundation damage. In some cases, it was difficult to distinguish between the earthquake dam-age and natural deterioration because of the age of the buildings.

CITY-OWNED BUILDINGS

Valdez Elementary School

The Valdez Elementary School, at the corner of Broadway and Hobart streets (Figure 29), was 40–50 years old and sustained heavy damage during the earthquake. It was judged to be damaged beyond repair, and a new grade school was built at the new Valdez townsite (Tanaka, 1973, this volume).

The main part of the old building (Figure 29) was 78 × 118 ft in plan, with an 11 × 48-ft addition at the front. It

FIGURE 29 Exterior of the old Valdez Elementary School. The vertical line between the one- and two-story sections indicates a differential movement.

FIGURE 30 Valdez Elementary School: The multipurpose room shows evidence of the foundation settlement. The floor bowed upward about 12 in.

FIGURE 32 Damage to plaster finish in a classroom of the Valdez Elementary School.

into two sections (Figure 34). The main section was 61 × 95 ft and was 24 ft high at the eaves. The second section contained the shop and boiler room and was 28 × 41 ft. The long axis of the building ran nearly north to south.

Constructed with continuous reinforced-concrete perimeter-wall footings, the building had a 4-in.-thick reinforced-concrete slab floor placed on fill, which made the finished floor elevation approximately 4 ft higher than the elevation of the ground outside the footings. The floor slab was reinforced with wire mesh, but no provisions were made to tie the slab into the wall footings. The exterior walls were steel frame, with plywood sheathing on both surfaces to form

diaphragms; they were covered on the exterior with metal siding. The classroom section had a corridor running the full length of the section. The 6-in. concrete block walls of the corridor were load bearing and supported one end of the steel joists used in the roof system. In the exterior walls, the steel joists were supported by 2-in. rectangular steel-tube columns, spaced 4 ft on centers.

The shop and boiler room addition was constructed in a similar manner to the classroom section, as was the multipurpose room except that its roof was about 21 ft high. Steel joists spanned the 61-ft width and supported 1½-in. steel roof decking.

Earthquake Damage Most of the damage to this building was caused by foundation movements. The continuous wall footings moved outward (Figure 35). The foundation walls along the long sides of the building moved 6–12 in. outward

FIGURE 31 Mud and water damage in the basement of the Valdez Elementary School.

FIGURE 33 Exterior of old Junior–Senior High School at the old townsite of Valdez.

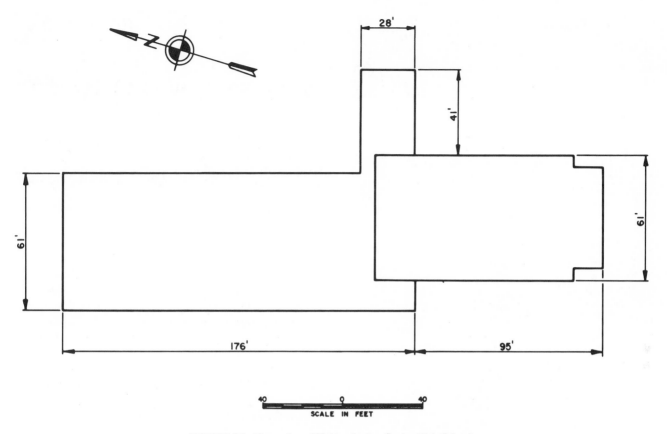

FIGURE 34   Floor plan of Valdez Junior–Senior High School.

from their original positions. The roof system remained well connected to the walls and sustained only minor damage. The concrete floor slab of the building was cracked.

Building Repairs   Because of the unstable foundation conditions, no permanent repairs were made to this building. Temporary repairs were made, however, so that it could be used until another school building could be constructed at the new townsite; the brick chimney was guyed, and the cracks in the concrete floor slab were patched. Fill material was placed and compacted around the perimeter foundation wall (Figure 36). The cost of the temporary repairs was about $10,100.

SMALL TOWNS AND SCHOOL DISTRICTS

PALMER HIGH SCHOOL

The city of Palmer is 45 mi northeast of Anchorage in the Matanuska Valley. The high school, about 1 mi south of town, was built in 1952; an addition was built in 1958. After the earthquake, a gymnasium and some classrooms were added (Figure 37). Information on design and analysis was not available, but some information on the type of construction was obtained from the maintenance personnel and by inspection of the building.

The main classroom area has two stories, but the shop, multipurpose room, and classroom wings have only one story (Figures 38 and 39).

This structure received light damage, which included some damage to the interior lightweight block partitions and several fallen light fixtures.

The roof had a 3-in. timber deck, supported on open-web steel joists and laminated beams. The ground and first floors were of 2½-in. concrete fill on metal decking, supported by open-web steel joists, which in turn were supported by reinforced-concrete bearing walls.

The design criteria for the original building and for the 1958 addition were not available. The 1964 addition was designed for zone 3 seismic requirements of the *Uniform Building Code*.

Earthquake Damage

Except for some minor cracks in concrete walls, no structural damage was observed in this building. Interior 4-in. lightweight concrete-block classroom partitions, however, had many minor cracks, and about five of these partitions

FIGURE 35   Separation between the concrete walk and the entry slab at the main entrance to the Valdez Junior–Senior High School.

FIGURE 37   Palmer High School (front view), built in 1952, sustained little damage.

failed to some extent. The partitions were anchored at the sides with dovetailed anchors and were bolted to a wood plate at the top. The 4-in. blocks were reinforced horizontally with K web at every other course and had no vertical reinforcing. On the ground floor, these walls were 12 ft high and 28 ft long. Minor damage such as cracks in walls, broken and damaged floor and wall tile, and loosened caulking around glass blocks occurred in the first floor. One 8-ft fluorescent-light fixture fell in the chemistry laboratory and 12 4-ft fixtures fell in the study hall.

Repair of Earthquake Damage

Six free-standing wall partitions on the ground floor and three on the first floor were repaired (Figure 40). All the fluorescent-light fixtures were checked and repaired or replaced. The cracks in the block or concrete walls were re-

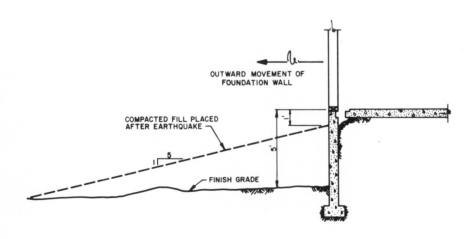

OUTWARD MOVEMENT OF
FOUNDATION WALL

COMPACTED FILL PLACED
AFTER EARTHQUAKE

FINISH GRADE

SCALE IN FEET

FIGURE 36   Temporary foundation stabilization, Valdez High School.

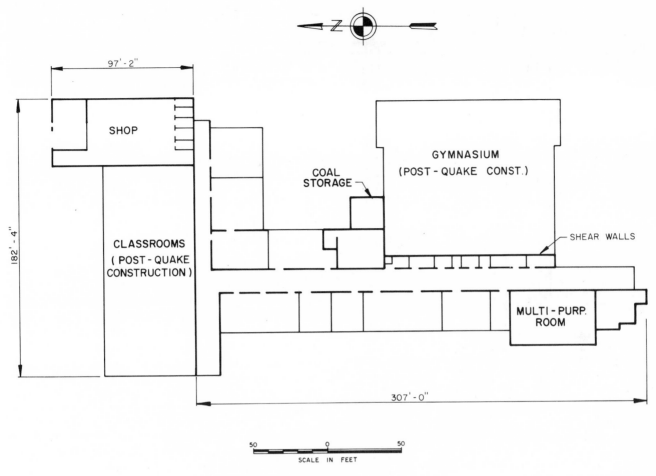

FIGURE 38   Palmer High School, ground-floor plan.

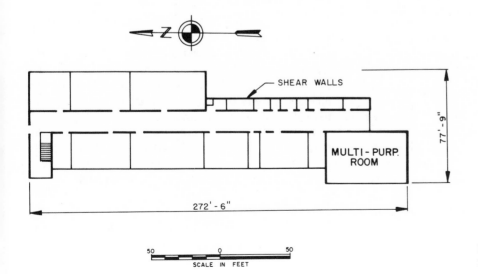

FIGURE 39   Palmer High School, second-floor plan.

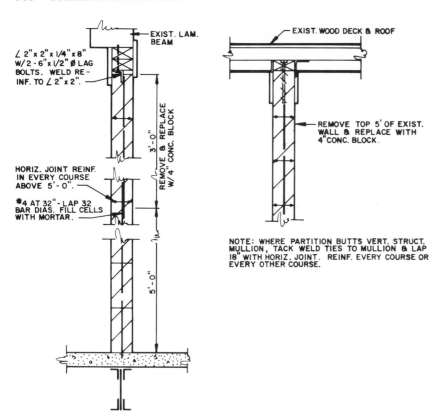

∠ 2" x 2" x 1/4" x 8"
W/ 2 - 6" x 1/2" ⌀ LAG
BOLTS. WELD RE-
INF. TO ∠ 2" x 2".

EXIST. LAM.
BEAM

HORIZ. JOINT REINF.
IN EVERY COURSE
ABOVE 5'-0".

#4 AT 32" - LAP 32
BAR DIAS. FILL CELLS
WITH MORTAR.

REMOVE & REPLACE
W/ 4" CONC. BLOCK

3'-0"

5'-0"

EXIST. WOOD DECK & ROOF

REMOVE TOP 5' OF EXIST.
WALL & REPLACE WITH
4" CONC. BLOCK.

NOTE: WHERE PARTITION BUTTS VERT. STRUCT.
MULLION, TACK WELD TIES TO MULLION & LAP
18" WITH HORIZ. JOINT. REINF. EVERY COURSE OR
EVERY OTHER COURSE.

FIGURE 40 Typical concrete-block partition repair, Palmer High School.

paired, all floor and wall tile was repaired, one handrail was replaced, and 3 handrails were repaired.

Approximately 300 blocks were removed and replaced, 200 ft of cracks were repaired in blocks, and 400 ft of cracks were repaired in concrete walls.

The total cost of the repairs was $10,200.

This school withstood the earthquake well, and the structural design conformed to seismic-code requirements. The nonstructural elements of the building had not, however, been designed for a seismic area. The long partitions, for example, should have been designed to span vertically instead of horizontally. For this reason, the building sustained considerable nonstructural damage.

KENAI ELEMENTARY AND JUNIOR HIGH SCHOOL

Kenai is about 75 mi southwest of Anchorage on the west side of the Kenai Peninsula. The Kenai Elementary and Junior High School, whose construction dates are not known, is an L-shaped two-story structure 195 × 240 ft in size (Figure 41). It sustained a small amount of structural damage.

The original school building had structural-steel framing and reinforced-concrete floors, roof, and exterior walls (Figure 42). The gymnasium had timber decking on open-web joists, structural-steel framing, and a concrete foundation; the exterior walls were metal siding. The newer wings had timber decking on glue-lam beams supported by timber columns; the exterior walls were metal siding (Figure 43). Most of the interior partitions were wood-stud walls with gypsum sheathing.

The newer parts of the building were designed and constructed in accordance with the seismic zone 3 criteria of the 1958 *Uniform Building Code*. The design criteria for the original building were not available.

Earthquake Damage

One of the concrete-block chimneys was extensively damaged. The chimney, which was reinforced, was 54 in. square, about 50 ft high, and extended 22 ft above the roof. Field reports indicated that the reinforcement failed in bond at the roof line. The chimney did not collapse but had to be braced as a safety precaution; the firebrick inside the chimney collapsed below the roof line.

In three classrooms, about 72 pendant fluorescent-light fixtures swung violently, and their bases damaged the ceiling tile. In another classroom, the two-tube 48-in. fluorescent fixtures tore loose and about 20 of them fell.

Repair of Earthquake Damage

The damaged chimney was shored up, so that classes could be resumed, and was later rebuilt from the roof up. The second chimney was undamaged.

All light fixtures were checked for damage and repaired

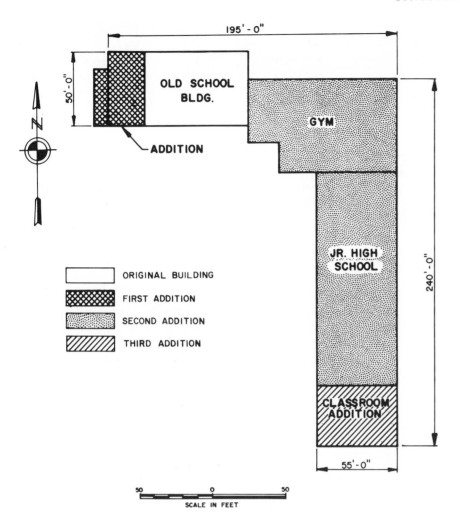

ORIGINAL BUILDING

FIRST ADDITION

SECOND ADDITION

THIRD ADDITION

SCALE IN FEET

FIGURE 41   Plan of Kenai Elementary and Junior High School. All additions were constructed before the earthquake.

wherever necessary, the entire roof was checked for leaks and repaired, and the broken windows were replaced.

A breakdown of costs is not available, but the total repair cost was $8,000.

If the school had been occupied at the time of the earthquake, the light fixtures that fell would have been a serious hazard. Falling light fixtures, toppling interior walls, bookcases, filing cabinets, and other nonstructural items can cause injury and loss of life and did so in Anchorage. Earthquake effects should be considered in the design and construction of these items.

FIGURE 42   Kenai Elementary School: One reinforced block chimney failed because of inadequate splice in reinforcement. The chimney (arrow) that did not fail was unused and filled with concrete.

FIGURE 43   Kenai Elementary and Junior High School (from rear) after repairs. Wing at right is new addition.

FIGURE 44   Kenai Central High School, which sustained no structural damage.

KENAI CENTRAL HIGH SCHOOL

The Kenai High School was a new one-story structural-steel building (Figures 44 and 45) close to the older school. The building had been completed just before the earthquake and was not yet occupied. The major earthquake damage was nonstructural.

The roof was metal decking on open web joists supported on structural-steel columns and reinforced-concrete bearing walls. The exterior walls were insulated metal panels and reinforced-concrete tilt-up panels. The floor was a concrete slab-on-grade. The interior partitions were 4-in. precast-concrete panels, concrete-block walls, or stud walls.

The building was designed for seismic zone 3 criteria, in accordance with the 1961 *Uniform Building Code*. Other design loads or stresses used are as follows:

Structural steel	ASTM A-36
Concrete precast walls	$F'c$ = 3,000 psi (28-day ultimate strength)
Concrete general	$f'c$ = 2,000 psi (28-day ultimate strength)
Snow load	40 psf
Wind load	25 psf

Earthquake Damage

This well-designed building sustained no apparent structural damage. The insulated metal panels on the west wall of the commercial room and on the east wall of the shop, however, were pulled free from the foundation wall (the fasteners were spaced at 5-ft centers).

The ceiling tile along the sidewalls of the library sus-

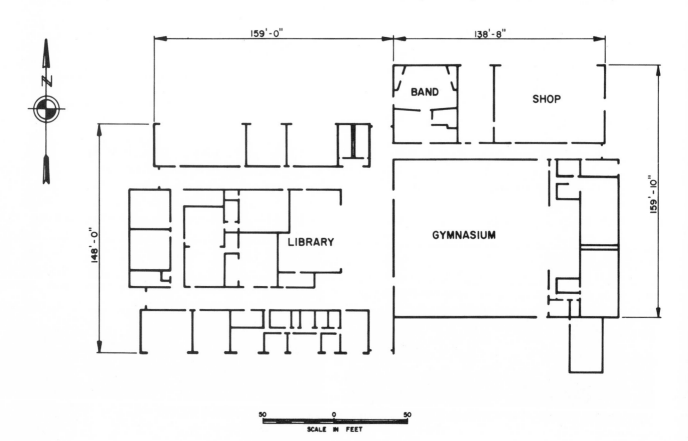

FIGURE 45   Floor plan, Kenai High School.

tained considerable damage (Figures 46–49). The tee hangars next to the wall were bent and twisted, and permitted the tile to fall. Three fluorescent-light fixtures fell, again illustrating the potential hazard of nonstructural damage. Other light fixtures showed signs of movement but did not fail.

Repair of Earthquake Damage

The ceiling tile and runners and the light fixtures were replaced or repositioned wherever necessary. The metal panels were reconnected with ¼-in. studs.

The total repair cost was approximately $4,000.

HOMER ELEMENTARY SCHOOL

Homer, on the southwest tip of the Kenai Peninsula, is about 125 mi southwest of Anchorage. The old elementary school, a two- and three-story building with about 18,000 ft² of floor space, sustained only minor earthquake damage.

FIGURE 47 Displaced ceiling tile and bent runner tees in the library of Kenai Central High School.

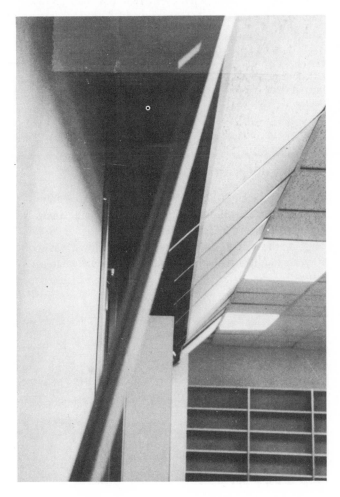

FIGURE 46 Bent runner tees and fallen ceiling tile in library of Kenai Central High School.

FIGURE 48 Damaged runners and fallen ceiling tile in corridor of Kenai Central High School.

FIGURE 49 Bent runner tees, displaced ceiling tile, and displaced lights in Kenai Central High School.

FIGURE 50 Old Homer Elementary School and addition. This building sustained little damage except for two badly cracked masonry chimneys.

Repair of Earthquake Damage

The concrete-block chimneys were removed, and the roof, interior walls, and ceilings were repaired. Repair quantities were as follows:

Painting	3,000 ft^2
Exterior crack repairs	60 lin ft
Interior crack repairs	120 lin ft
Ceiling tile replaced	100

The total repair cost was $4,300.

HOMER HIGH SCHOOL

Homer High School (Figure 51) is a one-story steel-frame building with concrete-block partitions and metal siding. The main building measured 68 × 222 ft and had a 27 × 48-ft wing. At the time of the earthquake, the building was about 10 years old; it sustained no apparent earthquake damage.

The original structure was a wood-frame building 44 ft wide and 54 ft long. A two-story steel-frame and concrete-block-wall building 58 ft wide and 64 ft long was later added (Figure 50). No design analyses are available for either building.

Earthquake Damage

A concrete-block chimney in the teacherage was badly cracked. The chimney was not adequately fastened to the building structure and pounded against the roof; it damaged the interior walls and interior finish and was in danger of collapsing. A second block chimney in the teachers' lounge was similarly damaged. The only other structural damage was minor cracking in the block walls of the addition.

A kitchen exhaust fan was shaken loose and the ceiling plasterboard in the kitchen was badly cracked in one area. A total of 96 4-ft-long fluorescent-light fixtures swung against the ceiling, damaging the tile.

FIGURE 51 Homer High School received no apparent earthquake damage.

GIRDWOOD COMMUNITY HALL

The town of Girdwood, 35 mi southeast of Anchorage, faces the Turnagain Arm of Cook Inlet. The ground surface in this area subsided several feet during the earthquake, causing maximum high tides to flood the area occupied by the Girdwood Community Hall. The community hall was therefore moved to higher ground.

The cost of building a new foundation and of moving the structure was $2,140. A new well was drilled at a cost of $6,700.

HOPE SCHOOL AND QUARTERS

Hope, Alaska, with a population of 50 people, is about 30 mi south of Anchorage across the Turnagain Arm of Cook Inlet. The village received little direct damage from the earthquake, but the land did settle about 5 ft, resulting in damage to some houses by high tides.

The school and living quarters were in a wood-frame structure 1½ stories high and 25 × 30 ft in plan. The upper half-story serves as living quarters for the teacher.

Earthquake Damage

The building sustained little damage. A concrete-block chimney in the teacher's living quarters was cracked and broken. Two window panes were broken and some light fixtures were loosened. Some minor cracks were made in the walls, and an oil heater was damaged.

Repair of Earthquake Damage

The block chimney was replaced by a prefabricated insulated chimney, and a new oil heater was installed. The broken windows were replaced, the entire interior repainted, and all lighting fixtures tightened. Because of saltwater contamination of the old well, a new well was drilled.

The repair costs for this building amounted to $2,300. The new well and its equipment cost $5,000.

MOOSE PASS ELEMENTARY SCHOOL

Moose Pass is situated about 60 mi southeast of Anchorage, on the Kenai Peninsula. The Moose Pass School is an L-shaped wood-frame building (Figure 52) one and two stories high, covering a total area of about 4,130 ft².

Earthquake Damage

Two chimneys constructed of 8 × 16-in. unreinforced-concrete block collapsed. The built-up roofing developed many leaks after the earthquake, some of which were caused by the collapsing chimneys. Minor damage occurred to the windows, the front entry, and the furnace room and its equipment.

The school water supply was from a private source; a new source had to be found when the earthquake disrupted the supply.

Repair of Earthquake Damage

The two chimneys were reconstructed with reinforced concrete block, the old built-up roofing was removed and replaced, and all broken windows were replaced. The rear concrete stairs were repaired with epoxy cement. About 1,200 ft² of interior walls were painted. The furnace was resited, the hot-water radiators were repaired, and a new hot-water tank was installed. A new well was driven to furnish 10 gallons of water per minute.

The approximate repair cost was $10,000.

SUMMARY AND CONCLUSIONS

Ground movements caused damage to structures in small communities, but there was no easily perceived relation between degree of damage and distance from causative fault. Because the causative fault made a relatively small angle with the horizontal plane, it is not possible to determine precisely the shortest distance from a community to the plane. Estimated distances in miles are as follows: Seward, 20; Cordova, 20; Whittier, 30; Moose Pass, 30; Valdez, 30; Homer, 40; Girdwood, 40; Hope, 50; Anchorage, 60; Palmer, 60; Kenai, 60. Ground shaking did not cause great destruction in any of the small communities, even in those within 30 mi of the fault; in Cordova, which was within 20 mi of the fault, shaking caused only minor damage. The earthquake ground motions were not recorded; consequently, it is not known how the intensity of shaking differed in the various communities.

The small communities had buildings that were smaller, older, and of lesser quality than those in Anchorage. The approximate populations at the time of the earthquake were 1,900 in Seward, 1,200 in Homer, 1,100 in Palmer, 900 in Kenai, and 700 in Valdez. Moose Pass, Hope, and Girdwood were smaller communities. The damage and loss of life sustained by a small community during an earthquake tend to be overshadowed by those sustained by a large community. Although the small community might sustain the same *per capita* damage loss and the same percentage of injuries and loss of life, that community would receive less attention because of the greater total value of loss and the larger total number of deaths in the large community.

The building damage described in this paper shows that many buildings in small communities were deficient in earthquake resistance and sustained damage. In many cases, the damage was not spectacular but required costly repairs. In some of the small communities the average *per capita*

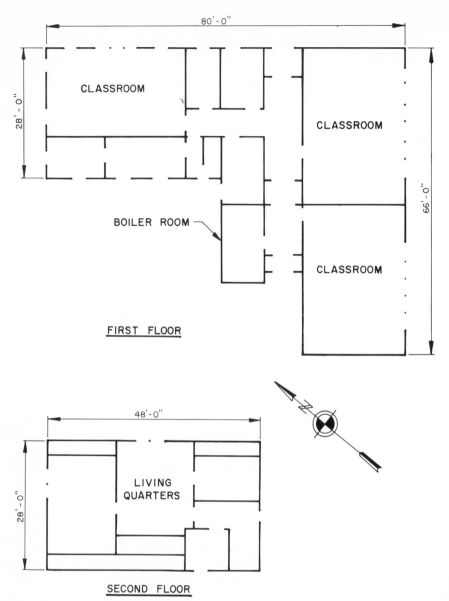

FIGURE 52   Plan of Moose Pass Elementary School.

loss from the earthquake is estimated to have been equal to or greater than that in Anchorage.

In the small communities relatively close to the causative fault, some buildings, mostly one- and two-story wood-frame buildings, received little damage. This shows that buildings can be constructed close to the causative fault of a very large earthquake so as to withstand the ground shaking without appreciable damage, even if special earthquake design is not incorporated and no extra cost is incurred.

Critical buildings in small communities, as well as those in large communities, should be designed so as to be functional after an earthquake. Hospitals, schools, housing for agencies that must cope with the disaster, and public utilities should be designed to have greater strength than is spec-ified by the building code, because it is after an earthquake that their functioning is most necessary.

ACKNOWLEDGMENT

All the illustrations in this paper are credited to the U.S. Army Corps of Engineers.

REFERENCE

Tanaka, James M., 1973. Relocation of Valdez *in* The Great Alaska Earthquake of 1964: Engineering. NAS Pub. 1606. Washington: National Academy of Sciences.

WARREN GEORGE   JAMES F. SIZEMORE
PAUL KNOWLES   DUANE E. CARSON
JOHN K. ALLENDER
U.S. ARMY CORPS OF ENGINEERS DISTRICT,
ALASKA

Structures on Military Installations

Earthquake damage, repair of damage, and cost of repairs are described for selected buildings at Fort Richardson, an Army base, and at Elmendorf Air Force Base (AFB), both large military installations on the outskirts of Anchorage. These buildings, which differ in form and function from the civil buildings in Anchorage, behaved somewhat better under earthquake conditions than comparable buildings not on military bases. Much of the damage that they did sustain could have been avoided at little extra cost by better earthquake engineering. The relatively long duration of strong shaking increased the severity of the damage.

FORT RICHARDSON

BUILDING 600, 500-ENLISTED MAN (EM) BARRACKS

This barracks (Figure 1) was completed in 1950 at an original cost of $3,213,000. The building received minor structural damage, such as spalled and cracked concrete; nonstructural damage consisted of the collapsed concrete-block partition walls.

The structure was 463 X 44 ft and 35 ft high, with two short wings and a one-story mess hall separated from the main structure by 8-in. seismic joints (Figures 2 and 3). The building was constructed with 5-in. reinforced-concrete slabs supported on moment-resisting structural-steel frames (Figures 4–6). The roof consisted of pitched-wood trusses over a 4–in. concrete ceiling. All structural steel was encased in concrete for fire protection (Figure 7). The three-story wings and one-story mess hall were constructed in the same manner as the main building; the exterior walls, stair walls, and fire walls were of reinforced concrete, and the interior partitions were 4–in. unreinforced-concrete block.

The original design analysis for this structure is not available, but the Alaska District during that period was designing for *Uniform Building Code* zone 2 requirements. The construction drawings specified concrete with a 28-day ultimate strength of 3,000 psi and reinforcing steel with a working strength of 20,000 psi.

ABSTRACT: Close examination and analysis of the earthquake damage, the repair of damaged installations, and the cost of the repairs on two large military installations in the Anchorage area lead to certain interesting conclusions. Much of the damage could have been avoided by better earthquake design and improved construction at little extra cost. In most cases, the cost of repairing architectural damage exceeded the cost of repairing structural damage.

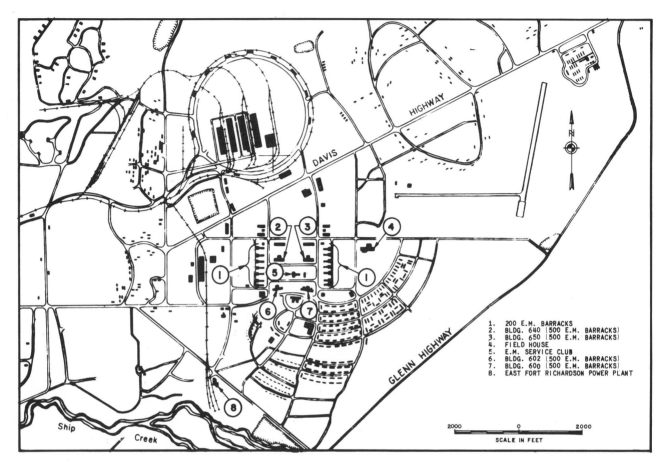

1. 200 E.M. BARRACKS
2. BLDG. 640 (500 E.M. BARRACKS)
3. BLDG. 650 (500 E.M. BARRACKS)
4. FIELD HOUSE
5. E.M. SERVICE CLUB
6. BLDG. 602 (500 E.M. BARRACKS)
7. BLDG. 600 (500 E.M. BARRACKS)
8. EAST FORT RICHARDSON POWER PLANT

2000   0   2000
SCALE IN FEET

FIGURE 1   Vicinity map, Fort Richardson, Alaska.

FIGURE 2   Building 600, 500-EM barracks, Fort Richardson. Front view after repairs.

FIGURE 3   Building 600, 500-EM barracks, Fort Richardson. Rear view after repairs.

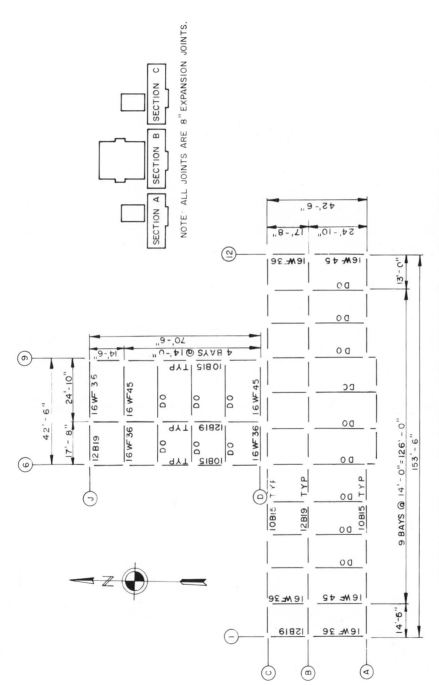

FIGURE 4 Building 600, 500-EM barracks. Fort Richardson. Section A, second-floor framing plan.

875

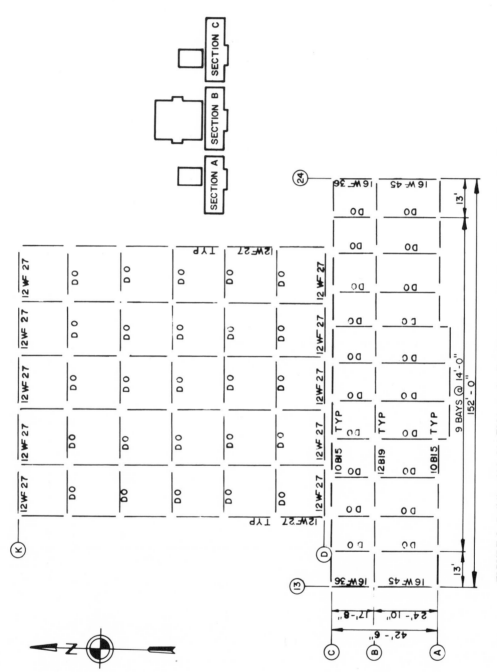

FIGURE 5 Building 600, 500-EM barracks, Fort Richardson. Section B, second-floor framing plan.

876

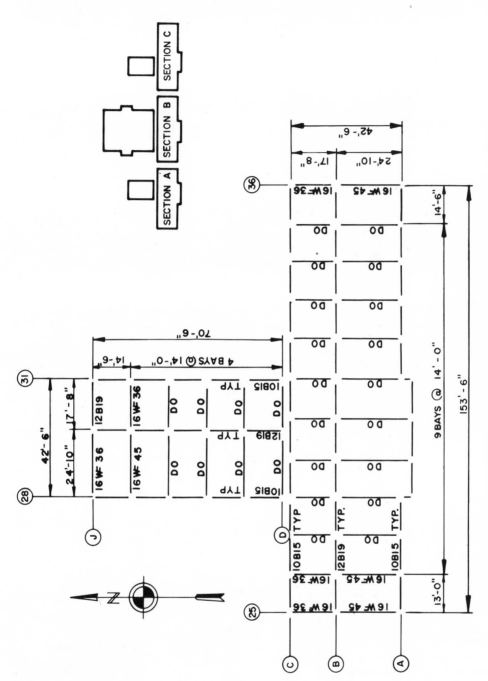

FIGURE 6   Building 600, 500-EM barracks, Fort Richardson. Section C, second-floor framing plan.

877

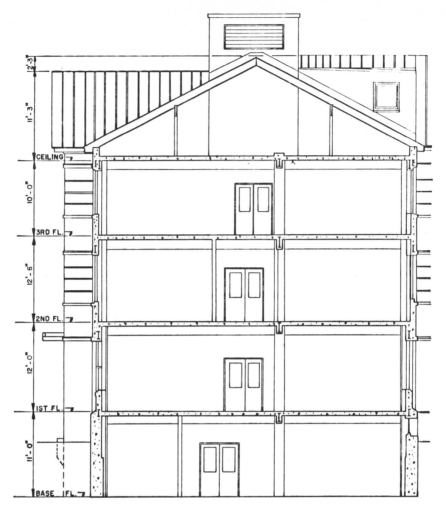

FIGURE 7 Building 600, 500-EM barracks, Fort Richardson. Typical section.

Earthquake Damage

The structural frame and concrete floor slab received minor damage. The roof beams carrying the concrete penthouse showed signs of high stress and large deflection (Figure 8). The concrete stair walls, fire walls, and exterior walls sustained horizontal and diagonal cracking (Figures 9–12). Some of the horizontal cracks were at construction joints. The concrete cover for the structural-steel beams and columns had minor cracks and some spalling. The ceiling over the third floor was cracked, but how much of this was caused by the earthquake is not known.

The major effect of the earthquake on this building was to damage or knock down 4-in. concrete-block interior partitions. Although these walls were pinned with dove-

FIGURE 8 Building 600, 500-EM barracks, Fort Richardson. Structural-steel beam encased in concrete over the third floor in west wing of the main section. This beam carried a concrete penthouse and was strengthened by welding a structural tee to the bottom flange.

FIGURE 9 Building 600, 500-EM barracks, Fort Richardson. Reinforced-concrete shear wall and fire wall at the first floor in the east wing. Extensive cracks around openings and penetrations are typical damage.

tailed anchors, an analysis indicated that the block walls without reinforcing did not have adequate strength to withstand the horizontal forces. Figure 13 shows a typical office area after debris had been removed.

Some damage occurred to the interior finish, light fixtures, and plumbing fixtures. Figure 14 shows damage at a seismic joint.

Repair of Earthquake Damage

After the earthquake, the lateral resistance of the building was analyzed by Andersen, Bjornstad, and Kane, consulting engineers for the Corps of Engineers. The assumption was made that the shear walls would take the earthquake loads, unless the relative stiffnesses indicated that the frame would participate in the action.

The lateral resistance of section B (Figure 15) was provided by exterior concrete walls and interior fire walls and stair walls. The analysis found that section B was weakest in the east–west direction and that the wall on column line C was the weakest element. If an allowable shear of 125 psi on the concrete is assumed, this wall would resist an acceleration force of 4.8 percent of the weight of the supported structure.

Section C consisted of two separate structures denoted as C-1 and C-2 (Figure 16). The south wall of unit C-2, between column lines 25 and 28, was found to be capable of resisting an acceleration force of 7.5 percent of the total weight of the supported structure. Unit C-1 had walls on three sides only. The resulting large eccentricity between the center of resistance and the center of gravity imposed forces on the north–south walls from the east–west earthquake motion. Analysis indicated that the wall on column line 28 would resist an acceleration force of 8 percent of gravity. However, the analysis showed that a typical struc-

tural steel frame would resist 10.2 percent of gravity on each frame. Figures 17–20 show the shear walls in sections B and C.

The existing 4-in. unreinforced-concrete-block partitions were analyzed, and it was found that for an 11-ft 4-in. span, the block wall would resist only half of the normal *Uniform Building Code* design loads.

To make the necessary structural repairs, the cracks in the concrete stair walls and shear walls were repaired with an epoxy sealant, installed under pressure. Areas of spalled concrete or wide cracks were repaired with an epoxy grout.

The roof beams supporting the penthouse were strengthened by welding a tee section to the bottom flange of the beam.

Nonstructural repairs included the replacement of some 4-in. block walls with reinforced 6-in. concrete block. Other walls were removed down to the wainscot or completely removed and replaced with metal studs and gypsum board. Some 4-in. block walls were left in place and repaired with Gunite either on one or on both sides. All other block walls were repainted and left in place.

Some light fixtures and the shower fixtures in the latrines were replaced. Some new floor drains were installed. The entire exterior of the building was sandblasted and repainted. The interior walls and ceiling were repainted. Figures 21–24 itemize structural and nonstructural damage.

Approximate repair costs were as follows:

Concrete-block walls repaired or replaced	$ 150,000
Architectural repair	22,000
Mechanical repair	4,000
Electrical repair	17,000
Pressure epoxy	21,000
Epoxy grout (1,670 lin ft)	35,000
Structural repair	6,000
Painting	95,000
Total repair cost	$ 350,000
Original cost	$3,213,000

Conclusions

This structure is an example of extensive nonstructural damage in a building that sustained little structural damage. Even the painting of a building after repairs is costly. The cost of structural repair was only a small fraction of either the combined repair cost or the original cost.

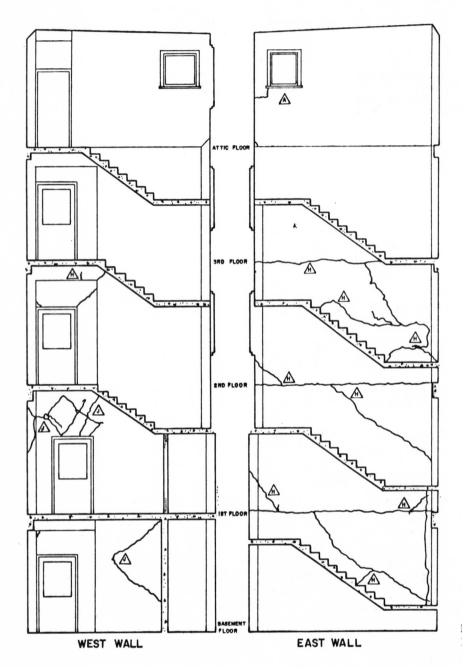

FIGURE 10   Building 600, Fort Richardson. Repair details of stair A.

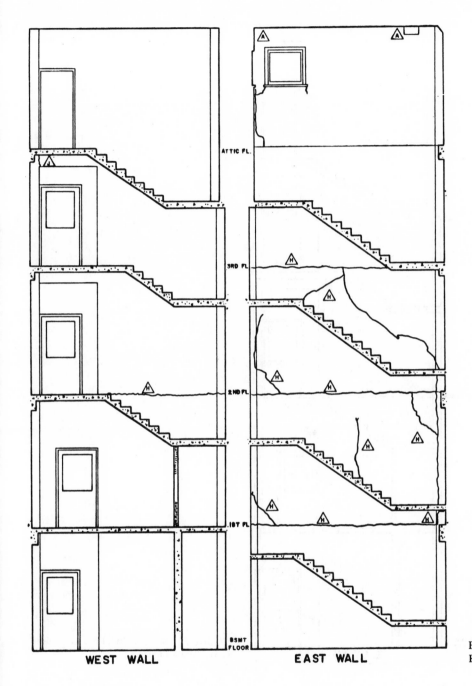

WEST WALL   EAST WALL

FIGURE 11 Building 600, Fort Richardson.
Repair details of stair B.

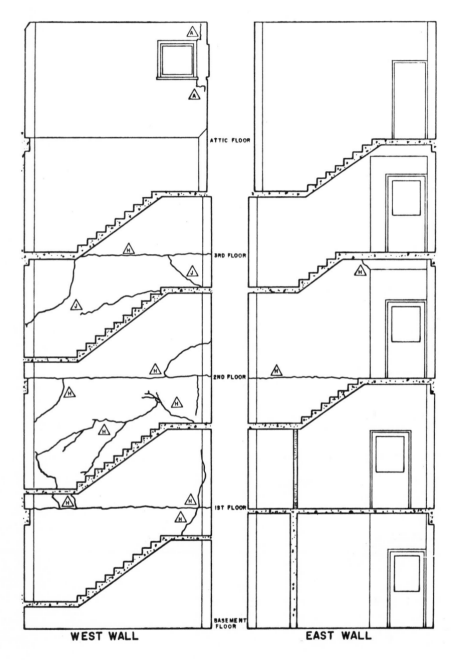

FIGURE 12   Building 600, Fort Richardson.
Repair details of stair C.

FIGURE 13 Building 600, 500-EM barracks, Fort Richardson. Office on the second floor of the middle section after a 4-in. unreinforced-concrete-block partition collapsed.

FIGURE 14 Building 600, 500-EM barracks, Fort Richardson. Damage to coverplate at seismic joint at the first floor in the east wing.

NOTE: Heavy lines denote shear walls.

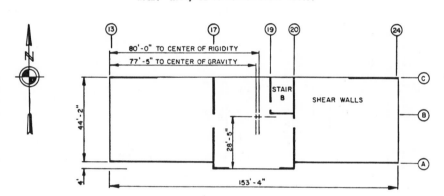

FIGURE 15 Building 600, 500-EM barracks, Fort Richardson. Section B, first-floor plan.

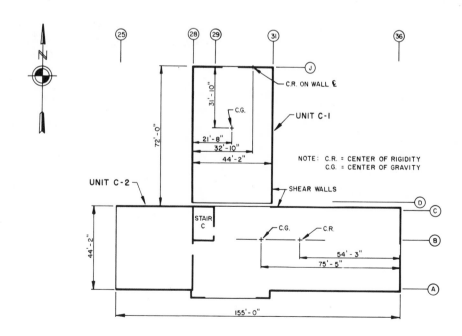

FIGURE 16 Building 600, 500-EM barracks, Fort Richardson. Plan showing shear walls, section C, first-floor plan.

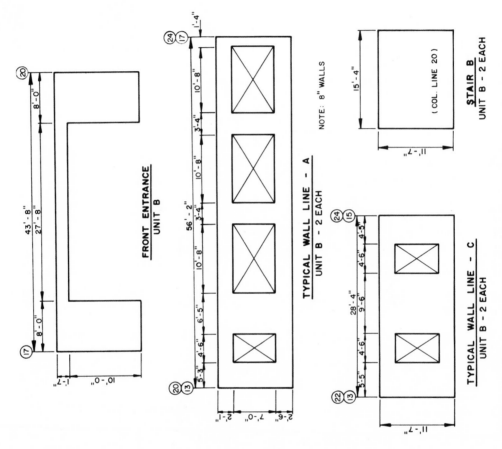

FIGURE 17 Shear-wall elevations of Building 600, Fort Richardson. Front entrance, typical wall lines A and C, and stair B, unit B.

884

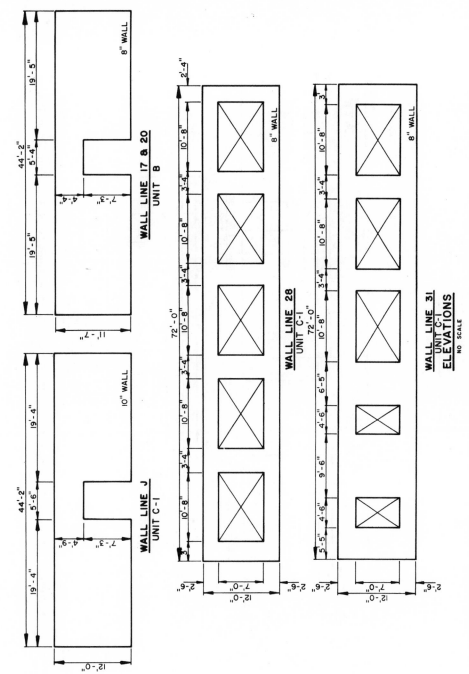

FIGURE 18 Shear-wall elevations in Building 600, Fort Richardson. Wall lines J, 28, and 31, unit C-1; wall lines 17 and 20, unit B.

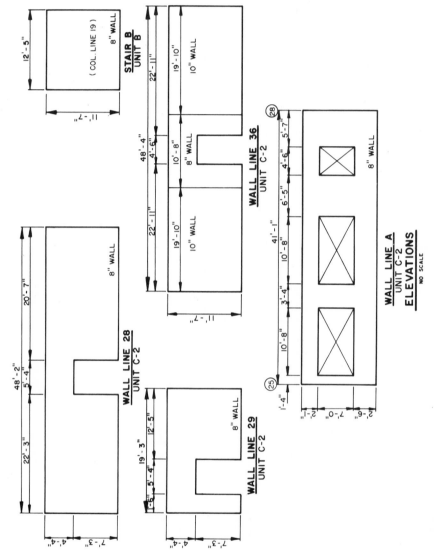

FIGURE 19 Shear-wall elevations in Building 600, Fort Richardson. Wall lines 28, 29, 36, A, unit C-2; and stair B, unit B.

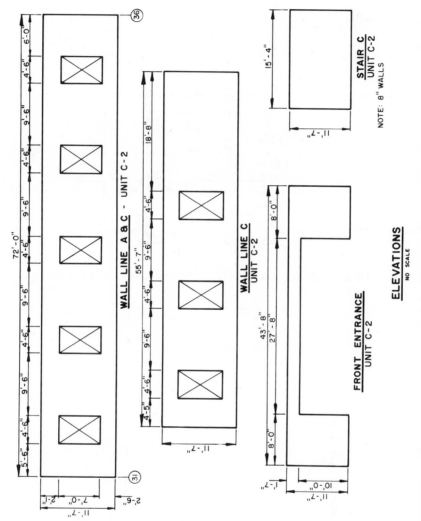

FIGURE 20 Shear-wall elevations in Building 600, Fort Richardson. Wall lines A and C, front entrance, and stair C, unit C-2.

887

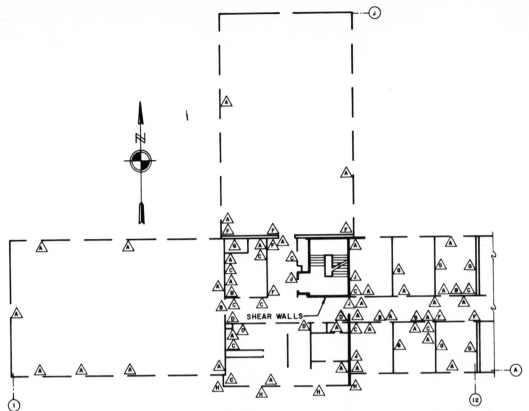

FIGURE 21   Repair plan, 500-EM barracks, Building 600, Fort Richardson. Section A, first-floor plan.

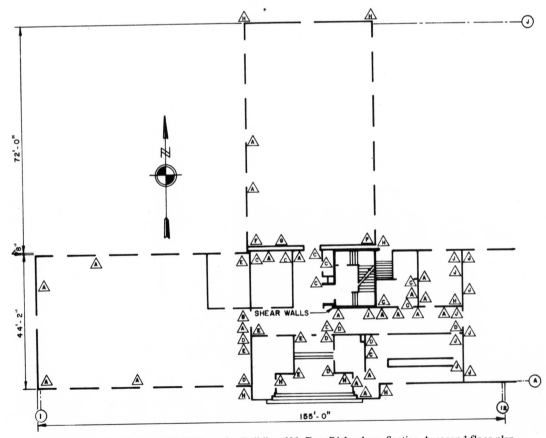

FIGURE 22   Repair plan, 500-EM barracks, Building 600, Fort Richardson. Section A, second-floor plan.

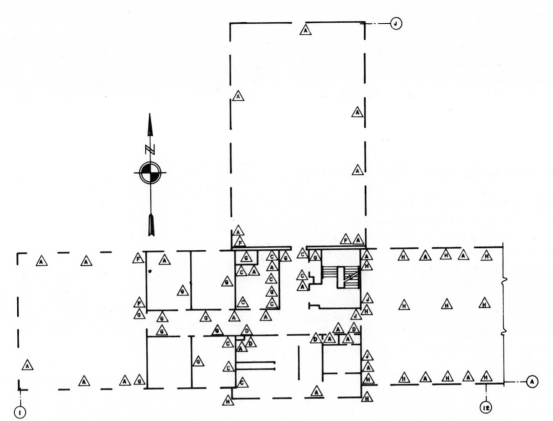

FIGURE 23 Repair plan, 500-EM barracks, Building 600, Fort Richardson. Section A, third-floor plan.

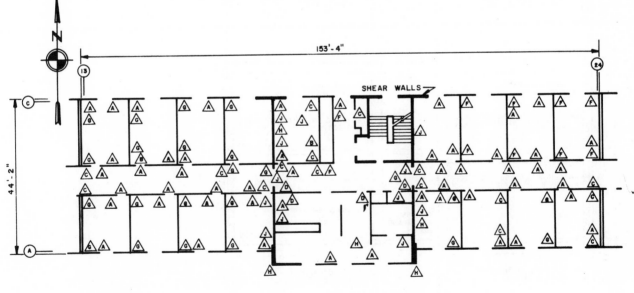

SYMBOL	DESCRIPTION
A	REPAIR CRACKS IN CONCRETE BLOCK, CHIP OUT GROUT AND REPOINT WITH NEW MORTAR
B	REPLACE CONCRETE BLOCKS
C	FASTEN WALL WITH CLIP ANGLE
D	GUNITE ONE SIDE OF BLOCK WALL
E	GUNITE BOTH SIDES OF BLOCK WALL
F	REMOVE 4" CONC. BLK. WALL AND REPLACE WITH NEW 6" CONC. BLK. WALL
G	NEW 6" CONC. BLK. WALL
H	EPOXY GROUT
I	PRESSURE EPOXY
J	REMOVE 4" CONC. BLK. WALL ABOVE WAINSCOT AND REPLACE WITH STL. STUDS AND 1/2" GYP. BD.
K	REMOVE 4" CONC. BLK. WALL AND REPLACE WITH STEEL STUDS AND 2 LAYERS 1/3" GYP. BD. EA. SIDE
L	NEW STEEL STUDS AND 2 LAYERS 1/2" GYP. BD. EA. SIDE

FIGURE 24 Repair plan 500-EM barracks, Building 600, Fort Richardson. Section B, second-floor plan.

BUILDINGS 602, 640, AND 650, 500-EM BARRACKS

These 500-EM (enlisted men's) barracks on Fort Richardson, all of the same design (Figure 1), were completed in 1952 at a total cost of $3,200,000. The concrete-block nonstructural partitions in the buildings sustained considerable damage. The structural reinforced-concrete walls and floors showed numerous small cracks but relatively small damage.

Each building consists of three stories above a full basement. The main buildings (Figure 25) measure 47 × 459 × 44 ft.

The buildings were constructed with reinforced-concrete slabs, beams, and columns (Figure 26). The top two stories are used as squad rooms and NCO (non-commissioned officers') quarters, the first story houses storage rooms, classrooms, a laundry, and a mechanical room. Figures 27–29 show typical wall sections and beam details.

The 500-EM barracks were designed to resist lateral forces by moment-resisting concrete frames. The original analysis ignored the stiffness of the concrete stair walls, fire walls, and block-filler panels, as well as the large eccentricity

FIGURE 25   Building 640, 500-EM barracks, Fort Richardson, after repair. The main structure is separated into three units by crumple joints.

resulting from this stiffness. The original analysis and construction drawings did not specify the criteria used in design, but the following lateral-force C-factors, apparently for zone 2, were used in computing column and beam moments from seismic loads:

Roof to third floor	$C = 0.132$
Third to second floor	$C = 0.108$
Second to first floor	$C = 0.092$
First floor to basement	$C = 0.080$

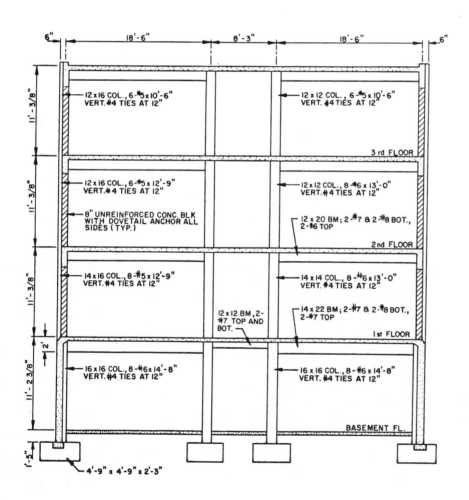

FIGURE 26   Typical section through buildings 602, 640, and 650, Fort Richardson.

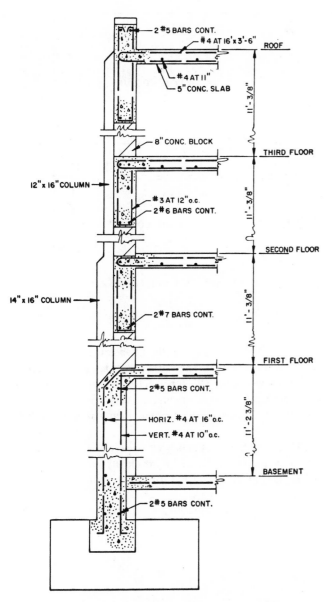

FIGURE 27 Typical wall section through three-story portion of 500-EM barracks, buildings 602, 640, and 650, Fort Richardson.

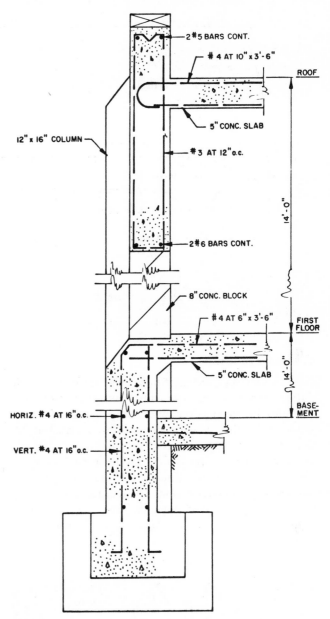

FIGURE 28 Section through mess hall of 500-EM barracks, buildings 602, 640, and 650, Fort Richardson.

Although no comparison was found in the analysis between the wind and earthquake loads, earthquake loads were used in the analysis. The following design data were obtained from the drawings and design analysis:

Concrete	f'_c = 2,500 psi @ 28 days
Reinforcing steel	f_s = 20,000 psi

Snow load	40 psf
Wind load	40 psf
Living quarters	40 psf
Storage	100 psf
Mess hall	100 psf
Kitchen	40 psf
Corridors	60 psf
Lobby and stairs	100 psf
Offices	50 psf

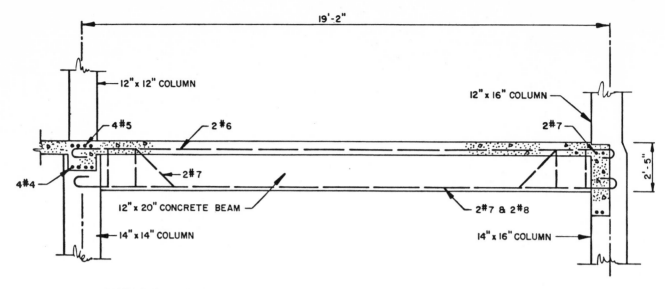

FIGURE 29 Typical beam detail of 500-EM barracks, buildings 602, 640, and 650, Fort Richardson.

Earthquake Damage

The structural components of these buildings withstood the earthquake without major structural damage. As shown in Figure 30, the concrete stair walls received diagonal cracks and the cold joints showed evidence of movement. Most of the exterior concrete columns received horizontal cracks and occasional severe fractures below the spandrel beams. The cracks probably were cold joints (Figures 31 and 32).

Some of the interior columns showed cracks both below and above the beams and column intersection (Figure 33).

The greatest nonstructural damage to these buildings in-volved collapse or damage to the nonbearing concrete-block walls (Figures 34–37). The room partitions and corridor partitions were generally constructed of 4-in. unreinforced-concrete block, and the original drawings showed the walls pinned to the surrounding concrete member with dovetail anchors.

The exact extent of collapsed walls is not known, be-cause the military personnel immediately removed all the walls that looked unsafe and sometimes removed walls that could have been repaired.

Figure 38 shows typical damage at the seismic joints.

FIGURE 30 Building 640, 500-EM barracks, Fort Richardson. Concrete wall in first-floor stairwell has horizontal and diagonal cracks.

FIGURE 31 Building 640, 500-EM barracks, Fort Richardson. View of west end of building; both corner columns have severe fracture.

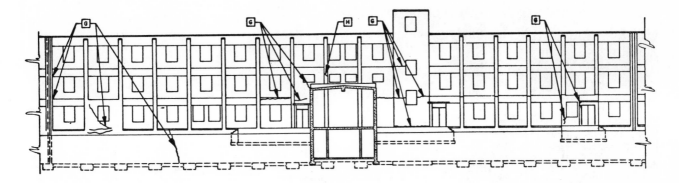

FIGURE 32   Typical exterior elevation of 500-EM barracks, Fort Richardson, showing damage location. See Figure 44 for damage symbols.

FIGURE 33   Building 640, 500-EM barracks, Fort Richardson. Typical column on first floor showing cracking near beam connection.

FIGURE 35   Building 640, administrative office, 500-EM barracks, Fort Richardson. Collapsed 4-in. unreinforced wall at crumple joint.

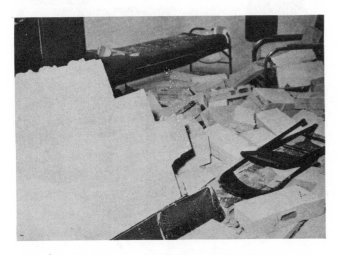

FIGURE 34   Building 640, 500-EM barracks, Fort Richardson, where 4-in. unreinforced-concrete-block partitions collapsed on the third floor.

FIGURE 36   Building 640, 500-EM barracks, Fort Richardson; 4-in. unreinforced-concrete-block partition collapsed above the ceramic-tile wainscot.

FIGURE 37   Building 640, 500-EM barracks, Fort Richardson; 4-in. unreinforced-concrete-block partition in first-floor latrine in the east wing.

FIGURE 38   Seismic joint in 500-EM barracks, Fort Richardson.

Repair of Earthquake Damage

After the earthquake, the Alaska District Corps of Engineers entered into contract with Anderson, Bjorstad, and Kane, consulting engineers, to analyze the 500-man barracks for lateral resistance. Sections 2 and 3 (Figures 39–42) only were analyzed, because inspection showed these sections had less shear resistance and greater eccentricity than section 1.

The exterior 8-in. block filler panels were assumed to provide no lateral resistance. The following figures indicate the relative stiffnesses of the members in section 3 in the north–south direction:

Bent on column line 38	0.017
16 interior bents	0.099
Wall on column line 32	0.504
Wall on column line 31	0.380

The wall on column line 32 and the frames on column lines 37 and 38 were found to resist 0.10 and 0.044, respectively, of the mass tributary to each column line.

The block panels on column line 38 were assumed to resist lateral loads, and the following relative stiffnesses were calculated for the transverse direction:

Bent on column line 38	0.288
Interior bents—16 total	0.071
Wall on column line 32	0.365
Wall on column line 31	0.276

It was found that with the end wall effective on column line 38, the eccentricity was reduced to a small value. The decision was made to reinforce and Gunite the two end walls to take the entire earthquake load.

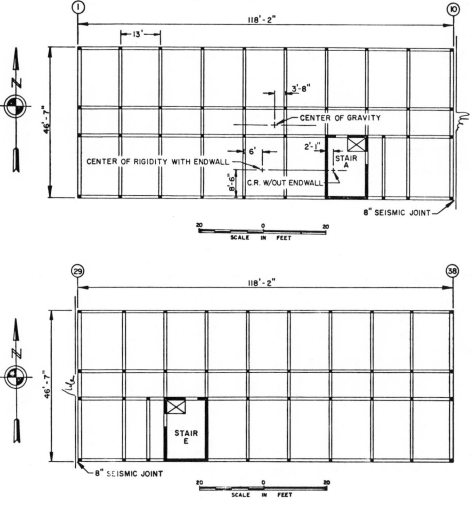

FIGURE 39   First-floor framing plan, buildings 602, 640, and 650, Fort Richardson. A, Section 2. B, Section 3.

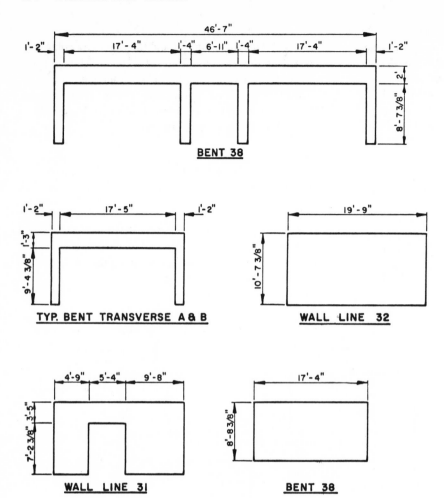

FIGURE 40 Fort Richardson. Typical building elements that contribute to the shear.

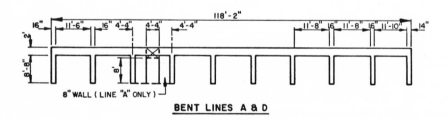

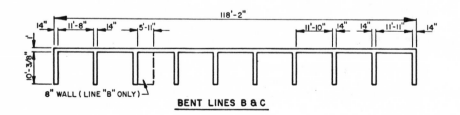

FIGURE 41 Fort Richardson. Buildings 602 and 650, section 3.

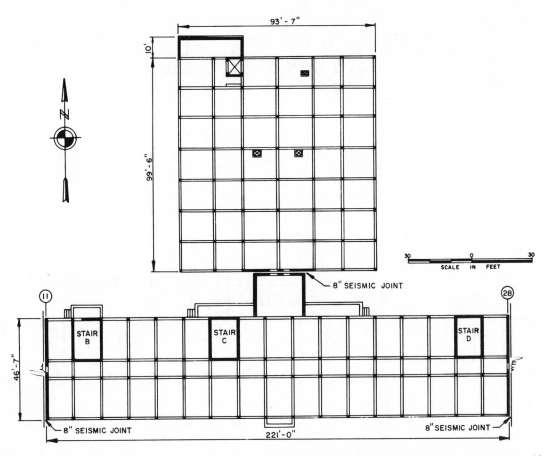

FIGURE 42   Fort Richardson, first-floor framing plan, section 1, of buildings 602, 640, and 650, 500-EM barracks. See Figure 43 for key plan.

The concrete frames were found to be capable of resisting 0.095 of the weight in the longitudinal, or east–west, direction. The resistance of the stair walls in this direction was disregarded as each wall had a door or window opening and had little area to provide resistance.

All cracks and spalled areas in the structural concrete were repaired with epoxy grout. The specific areas are shown in Figures 43–46.

The end walls at column line 1 and 38 were Gunited (Figures 47 and 48). The Gunite was anchored to the existing wall and frame with expansion anchors.

All 4-in. concrete-block walls were removed and replaced with metal-stud walls and gypsum board, except around the latrine walls. Damaged latrine walls were replaced with new concrete-block walls. The exterior and interior of the buildings were painted, and electrical and mechanical facilities were repaired.

Buildings 602 and 650 were repaired under one contract for $512,000. Building 640 was repaired under another contract for about $374,000.

An approximate breakdown of repair costs for buildings 602 and 650 follows:

Building 602

Block wall, repair or replacement	$ 87,300
Miscellaneous architectural repair	14,300
Painting and sand blasting	132,100
Electrical repair	3,500
Mechanical repair	2,700
Epoxy grouting	16,100

Building 650

Block wall, repair or replace	$ 62,700
Miscellaneous architectural repair	36,400
Painting and sand blasting	132,100
Electrical repair	5,700
Mechanical repair	3,000
Epoxy-grout structural repair	16,100
Total repair, buildings 602 and 650	$512,000

An approximate breakdown of repair costs for Building 640 follows:

Structural repair	$ 61,500
Block wall repair	100,500
Architectural repair	124,200
Painting	71,200
Mechanical repair	14,200
Electrical repair	2,400
TOTAL	$374,000

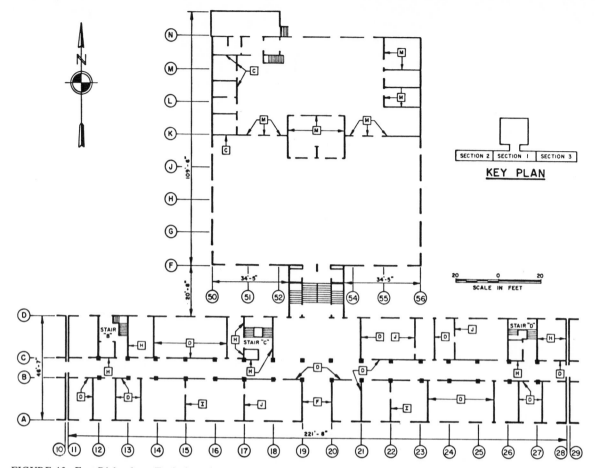

FIGURE 43   Fort Richardson. Typical repair plan for 500-EM barracks, buildings 602, 640, and 650. Section 1, first-floor plan.

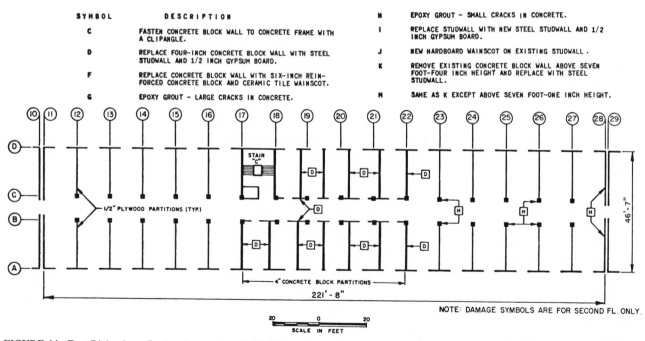

SYMBOL	DESCRIPTION
C	FASTEN CONCRETE BLOCK WALL TO CONCRETE FRAME WITH A CLIP ANGLE.
D	REPLACE FOUR-INCH CONCRETE BLOCK WALL WITH STEEL STUDWALL AND 1/2 INCH GYPSUM BOARD.
F	REPLACE CONCRETE BLOCK WALL WITH SIX-INCH REINFORCED CONCRETE BLOCK AND CERAMIC TILE WAINSCOT.
G	EPOXY GROUT - LARGE CRACKS IN CONCRETE.
H	EPOXY GROUT - SMALL CRACKS IN CONCRETE.
I	REPLACE STUDWALL WITH NEW STEEL STUDWALL AND 1/2 INCH GYPSUM BOARD.
J	NEW HARDBOARD WAINSCOT ON EXISTING STUDWALL.
K	REMOVE EXISTING CONCRETE BLOCK WALL ABOVE SEVEN FOOT-FOUR INCH HEIGHT AND REPLACE WITH STEEL STUDWALL.
M	SAME AS K EXCEPT ABOVE SEVEN FOOT-ONE INCH HEIGHT.

NOTE: DAMAGE SYMBOLS ARE FOR SECOND FL. ONLY.

FIGURE 44   Fort Richardson. Section 1, second- and third-floor plan. Typical repair plan for 500-EM barracks, buildings 602, 640, and 650.

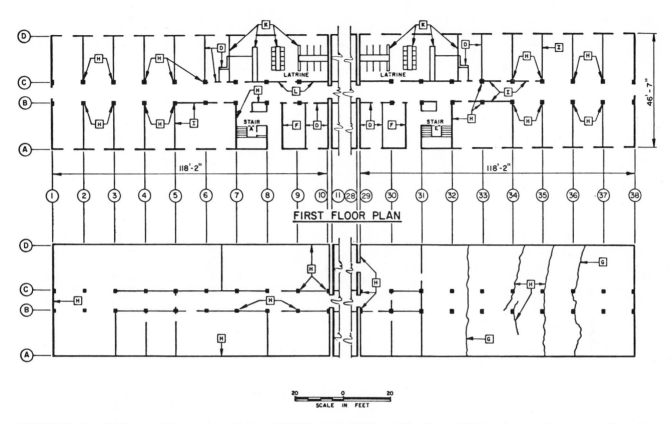

FIGURE 45   Fort Richardson. Typical repair plan for 500-EM barracks, buildings 602, 640, and 650. Sections 2 and 3, basement-floor plan (see key plan, Figure 43, for location).

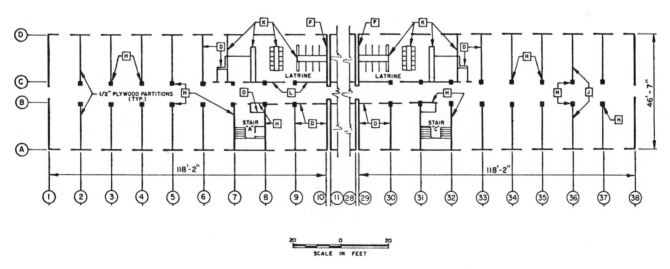

FIGURE 46   Fort Richardson. Typical repair plan for 500-EM barracks, buildings 602, 640, and 650. Sections 2 and 3, second- and third-floor plan (see key plan, Figure 43, for location. Damage symbols are for second floor only).

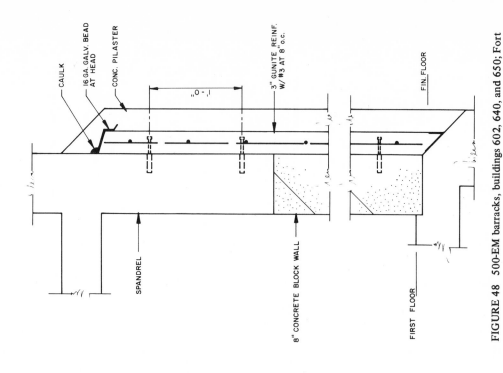

CAULK

16 GA GALV. BEAD AT HEAD

CONC. PILASTER

1'-0"

3" GUNITE REINF. W/ #3 AT 8" o.c.

SPANDREL

8" CONCRETE BLOCK WALL

FIN. FLOOR

FIRST FLOOR

FIGURE 48   500-EM barracks, buildings 602, 640, and 650; Fort Richardson. Typical section through exterior end wall, showing method of repair.

EXIST. CONC. COLUMNS

D

C

B

A

3" GUNITE WITH #3 AT 8" o.c.

FIGURE 47   500-EM barracks, buildings 602, 640, and 650, Fort Richardson. Endwall repair in which Gunite was added to strengthen the end wall and reduce the eccentricity of sections 2 and 3. (Figure 48 gives details.)

The total repair costs for the three buildings was $886,000. The original cost in 1950 was $2,889,000.

Conclusions

The damage sustained by these buildings demonstrates the need for adequate reinforcing and anchorage of all concrete-block walls, regardless of their function. The construction joints in walls and columns should be designed so that they are not planes of weakness. The cost of repairing the non-structural damage was one third of the original cost of the building. Repairs were, therefore, costly, although structural damage was small.

SERVICE BUILDINGS

The service buildings include many structures on Fort Richardson that furnish support facilities. This report covers two of these units, the Fieldhouse and the Enlisted Men's Service Club; the other service buildings received somewhat less damage. The damage to these two buildings consisted of spalled concrete, ruptured connections, and collapsed concrete-block walls. Structural damage was minor.

Fort Richardson Fieldhouse

The Fieldhouse, designed in 1951 by Pietro Belluschi for the Alaska District Corps of Engineers, cost $2,022,000 to build (Figure 1 shows location on Fort Richardson).

Earthquake damage to the building was minor and consisted of spalled concrete, damaged roof purlins, and damaged tile, gypsum board, concrete block, and flooring.

The Fieldhouse had a main unit (Sector 1), a second (Sector 2), and three smaller units. All the units were separated by 8-in. seismic joints. Figure 49 gives the basic dimensions. Sector 1 had an eave height of 36 ft; it housed a gymnasium, exercise room, offices, and other rooms. The roof was constructed of metal deck on purlins supported on structural-steel rigid frames spanning 155 ft in the east–west direction and spaced at 28-ft 10-in. centers. The sidewalls were 8-in. reinforced-concrete walls. A reinforced-concrete beam and slab balcony and second floor were along the east side of the gymnasium. The first floor was a reinforced-concrete beam and slab over a full basement.

Sector 2, which housed a swimming pool or natatorium, handball courts, and other rooms, had a maximum height of 34 ft. The high part of the roof was constructed of metal decking and purlins supported on structural-steel trusses spanning 92 ft and spaced at 20-ft centers. The trusses were connected to structural-steel columns. The other units varied in height from 11 to 22 ft and were constructed of reinforced-concrete beams and slabs. The walls and floor were constructed in the same way as the main unit (Figures 50 and 51).

The design analysis for the Fieldhouse is not available, but the following criteria were found on the drawings, which complied with seismic zone 3 criteria.

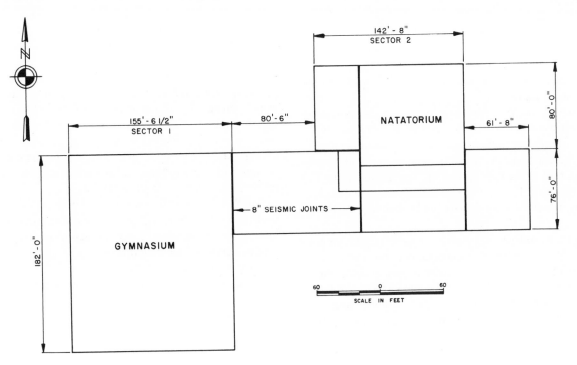

FIGURE 49   Plan of Fieldhouse, Fort Richardson.

FIGURE 50 Fort Richardson Fieldhouse, from the southeast. This complex was separated into five units by crumple joints and received little damage.

FIGURE 51 Fort Richardson Fieldhouse, from the west. Structure on the near side is the gymnasium, and the high structure on the far side is the natatorium.

Ultimate concrete stress	2,500 psi @ 28 days
Structural-steel stress	20,000 psi
Reinforcing-steel stress	20,000 psi
Allowable soil pressure	5,000 psf
Design wind pressure	30 psf

In the main unit, the lateral loads were transferred to the foundation by rigid frames in the east–west direction and to the exterior walls and foundation by cross bracing in the north–south direction.

In the second unit, the lateral loads were transferred to the foundation in the high roof area by moment-resisting connections between the trusses and columns in the north–south direction and to the exterior walls and foundation by cross bracing in the roof in the east–west direction. In the low roof areas, the concrete roof transferred lateral loads through the walls to the foundation by diaphragm action.

Earthquake Damage Structural damage to this building was minor. At the north wall of the main unit, the purlins were too short to span the distance and had been extended during construction by welding a short piece of web and lower flange to the end of the purlin. Because of the misalignment of the bolt holes, several of the purlins were welded to the clip angles and seat angles (Figure 52). At most of these connections along the north wall, either the weld failed or the connection was severely distorted. At a few locations,

FIGURE 52 Building 690, Fort Richardson Fieldhouse. Purlin connection failed at northwest corner of gymnasium. Because of misalignment of bolt holes, the connection was field-welded.

the concrete had cracked or spalled around the 3/4-in. anchor bolts in the end wall.

The second unit also received little damage. At the east wall of the swimming pool, two 3/4-in. anchor bolts that connected the bracing to the lower chord of the truss failed and let the bracing drop down.

Around the exterior of the building, some concrete cracked or spalled at various locations (Figures 53–54).

Some ceramic tile in the latrines was damaged, and some gypsum board and cement asbestos board was damaged. A 4-in. unreinforced-concrete-block wall between the balcony and handball court on the second floor of the second unit received severe damage. Some roof damage occurred next to the parapet, and some copper flashing was damaged. No electrical or mechanical damage was noted.

Repair of Earthquake Damage The roof purlins were repaired as shown in Figure 55. Also, all bolted connections were tightened or repaired as necessary. All cracks in the exterior walls were repaired and areas of spalled concrete were cleaned and repaired. Figure 56 indicates the truss-bracing repair. Additional reinforcing was installed at the column and spandrel-beam connections at six places on the north and south walls of the main unit.

The 4-in. block walls were replaced with metal-stud walls, and other block walls were repaired as required. All interior finish was repaired where necessary and repainted. Exterior door and window frames were recaulked, and the exterior walls were repainted.

An approximate breakdown of repair costs follows:

Structural repair	$ 45,500
Floor repair	64,000
Architectural repair	49,500
Total repair costs	$ 159,000
Original cost	$2,022,000

FIGURE 53   Building 690, Fort Richardson Fieldhouse. Cracks and spalled area in concrete column at northwest corner of gymnasium.

FIGURE 54   Building 690, Fort Richardson Field-house. Concrete spalled at southwest corner of gymnasium.

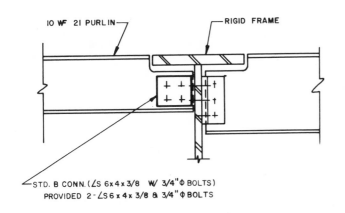

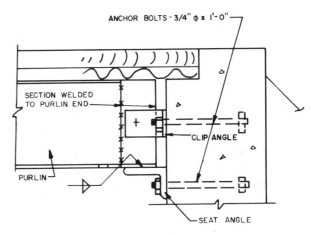

FIGURE 55   Typical purlin repair details, Fort Richardson Fieldhouse.

Building 636, Enlisted Men's Service Club

The location of the Enlisted Men's Service Club is shown on Figure 1. The building was designed and constructed between 1950 and 1952 at a cost of $560,000. Damage was substantial and consisted of collapsed 4-in. block walls, cracked and spalled concrete, and damaged light fixtures. Structural damage, again, was only a small fraction of the original cost.

The building consisted of two structures: a one-story club area and a two-story guest house, each over a full basement; the two structures were connected by a two-story passageway. Figures 57 and 58 give a general view of the club.

The club area is framed with two-span reinforced-concrete rigid frames spaced at 18-ft centers. Figure 59 indicates the details of the concrete frames. The roof was constructed of reinforced-concrete pan joists spaced on 25-in. centers with a 2½-in. concrete slab. The end walls were of 8-in. unreinforced-concrete block, and the sidewalls consisted of insulated metal panels and 8-in. concrete block. The first floor was also pan-joist construction.

The guest house was a two-story concrete-frame building, 22 ft high, with a daylight basement. The roof and floors

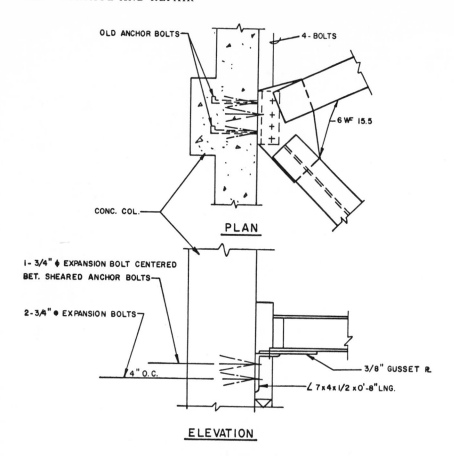

FIGURE 56 Repair detail of truss-bracing connection, Fort Richardson Fieldhouse.

FIGURE 57 EM Service Club, Fort Richardson. View from the northeast shows the guest wing on the left and the club area on the right. The club area received the most damage.

FIGURE 58 EM Service Club, Fort Richardson. View from the southwest shows the club area, which had little lateral resistance in the longitudinal direction.

were pan-joist construction supported on reinforced-concrete beams and columns. The exterior walls were unreinforced-concrete block.

The club area building was designed as a moment-resisting frame in the transverse axis. A seismic factor of 0.108 was used for the frame design above the first floor in the transverse direction. The original design analysis did not specify the basic criteria used to establish seismic factors. The analysis did not include a seismic design in the longi-tudinal axis or a seismic design of the guest house. The design loads and design stresses were as follows:

Snow load	40 psf
First floor, club area	100 psf
Concrete	2,500 psi
Reinforcing steel	20,000 psi

Earthquake Damage The concrete rigid frames received hairline cracks at the haunches, and the concrete spandrels

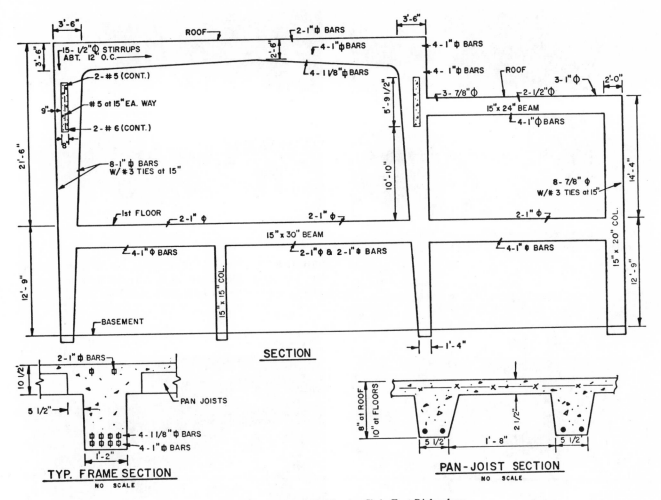

FIGURE 59 Detail of EM Service Club, Fort Richardson.

between the rigid frames were deeply cracked (Figure 60); the pan joists were also cracked. No serious damage was evident at the column bases, but some spalled concrete had to be repaired. The guest house sustained no structural damage.

Figures 61–64 show the nonstructural damage that occurred. The 4-in. unreinforced-concrete-block partitions either collapsed or were heavily damaged throughout the club. The collapse of a 4-in. wall into a stairwell resulted in one fatality.

Some damage to mechanical fixtures and piping resulted from partition failures. The suspended light fixtures received damage from hammering against the ceiling, and some fell.

Repair of Earthquake Damage It was necessary to chip and patch 50 ft² of concrete on exterior walls and columns and 8 ft² at the base of interior first-floor rigid-frame columns.

At the interior spandrel beam and haunches of first-floor rigid frames, 190 lin ft of cracks had to be chipped and

FIGURE 60 EM Service Club, Fort Richardson. Rigid concrete frame cracked through and below the haunch. Reinforced-concrete spandrel shows both horizontal and vertical cracking.

FIGURE 61   EM Service Club, Fort Richardson. Collapse of this 4-in. reinforced-concrete-block wall resulted in the death of one man.

FIGURE 63   EM Service Club, Fort Richardson. First-floor latrines after 4-in. concrete-block walls partly collapsed. Walls were not reinforced but were fastened with dovetail anchors.

FIGURE 62   EM Service Club, Fort Richardson. 8-in. unreinforced-concrete-block wall collapsed above the quarry-tile wainscot.

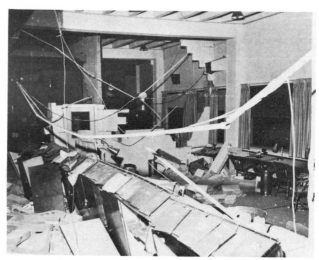

FIGURE 64   EM Service Club, Fort Richardson. Nonstructural damage in writing room of guest house.

found to meet code requirements; 100 ft of cracks were patched in the floor. The roof slab over stair A was replaced.

A total of 7,800 ft² of 6-in. reinforced-concrete block and 225 ft² of new 8-in. reinforced-concrete block was installed in the club (Figure 65). All the block partitions in the guest house were replaced with metal studs. Other repairs included exterior and interior painting, installation of new venetian blinds, replacement of tile, installation of vibration dampers on the air-handling unit, installation of new pipe supports, restoration of electrical circuits, and installation of 25 new lighting fixtures.

An approximate breakdown of repair costs follows:

patched. In the interior concrete walls and in the underside of the floors, 70 ft of cracks had to be filled. The pan-joist concrete floor was load-tested in accordance with the *American Concrete Institute* (ACI) *Building Code* and was

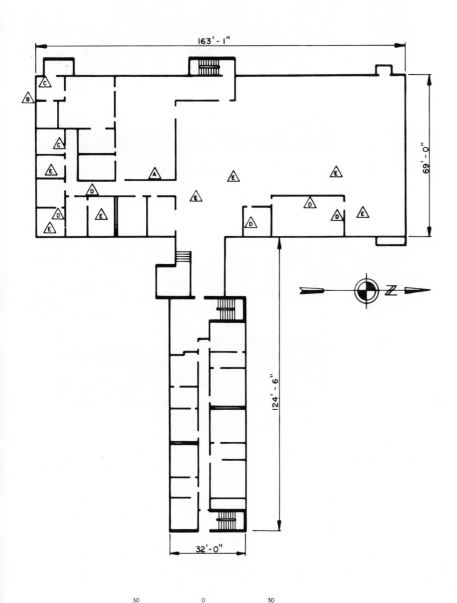

SYMBOL	DESCRIPTION
A	INSTALLED 2"x4" STUD WALLS AT 16" O.C. 8'-0" HIGH, BOARDED EACH SIDE OF WALLS 1/2" GYP. BD.
B	REMOVED TOP FIVE COURSES OF 4" C.M.U. ABOVE C.T. AND REPLACED WITH 4" C.M.U.
C	REMOVED 4" C.M.U. (APPROX. 6'-10" HIGH ABOVE WAINSCOT) AND REPLACED WITH 2"x4" WOOD STUDS AT 16" O.C. AND 1/2" GYP. BD. EACH SIDE
D	INSTALLED 2"x6" STUD WALL AT 16" O.C. WITH 1/2" GYP. BD. EACH SIDE
E	REMOVED ALL DAMAGED ASPHALT FLOOR TILE AND REPLACED WITH ASPHALT TILE TO MATCH

FIGURE 65   Plan of EM Service Club, Fort Richardson.

Repair or replace walls	$ 27,000
Structural repair	33,000
Architectural repair	86,000
Painting	44,000
Mechanical repair	3,000
Electrical repair	2,000
Total repair cost	$195,000
Original cost	$560,000

Although the total cost of repair was 35 percent of the original cost, the structural repair was only 16 percent of the total repair cost. This building is another of the many buildings for which nonstructural damage was much more costly than structural damage.

200-EM BARRACKS, FORT RICHARDSON

The 200-man barracks are near the 500-man barracks on Fort Richardson (Figure 1). A group of 14 barracks was designed and constructed from the same plans during the period 1950–1952 at a contract cost of $6,430,000. Typical damage includes spalled concrete, cracked concrete or block walls, collapsed block, and damaged light fixtures.

Each barracks was 46 ft wide and 174 ft long, with a mess facility 37 × 110 ft at one end of the barracks. The barracks were three stories high; the mess hall was one story high. Both structures had a daylight basement. Figures 66–68 show typical building elevations. Each build-

FIGURE 66   Front of the 200-man barracks, Fort Richardson. The structural frames performed well during the earthquake, but exterior columns were cracked at construction joints at each floor.

FIGURE 67   Rear of the 200-EM barracks, Fort Richardson.

SOUTH ELEVATION

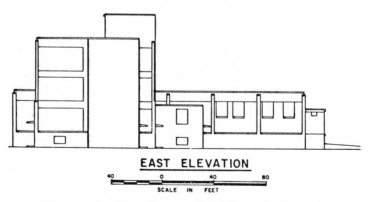

EAST ELEVATION

SCALE IN FEET

FIGURE 68   South and east elevations, 200-EM barracks, Fort Richardson.

ing contained sleeping quarters and mess and recreation facilities.

The structural framing consisted of 5-in. reinforced-concrete slabs, supported on reinforced-concrete beams and columns. The roof and floors were designed as one-way slabs spanning the short direction. Figures 69–71 show typical framing details.

The exterior walls were 8-in. concrete-block filler panels. The unreinforced filler panels were connected to the frame with dovetail anchors.

The interior partitions around the latrines and around some individual sleeping rooms were 4-in. unreinforced-concrete block with provisions for the walls to be pinned with dovetail anchors. At the time of construction, this type of construction conformed to the existing standard specifications, which are no longer permissible.

The concrete stair walls were 8 in. thick and were reinforced with 5/8-in. bar reinforcing spaced at 18 in. each way.

These buildings were designed to resist lateral loads along both axes by moment-resisting concrete frames. The rigidity of the stairwells and end walls in the three-story units were not considered in shear distribution, and the frames were de-signed to resist the total horizontal loads. The original criteria for lateral-force design specified a shear factor of 0.108, which was used in the beam and column design.

The design loads and allowable stresses are as follows:

Roof live load	40 psf
Floor live load	40 psf
Dining-room floor and corridor	100 psf
Concrete stress	$f_c' = 2,500$ psi
Reinforced steel	$f_s' = 20,000$ psi

Earthquake Damage

The barracks suffered little structural damage. Most of the exterior concrete columns received horizontal cracks at each construction joint at the floor level. The construction joints in the exterior and interior stairs also showed slight movement. Some concrete spalling at column and beam intersections and in the stair walls was evident.

The collapse and cracking of the 4-in. unreinforced interior block walls was the major nonstructural damage. The latrine cavity walls collapsed down to the top of the tile wainscot, damaging latrine fixtures and floor tile.

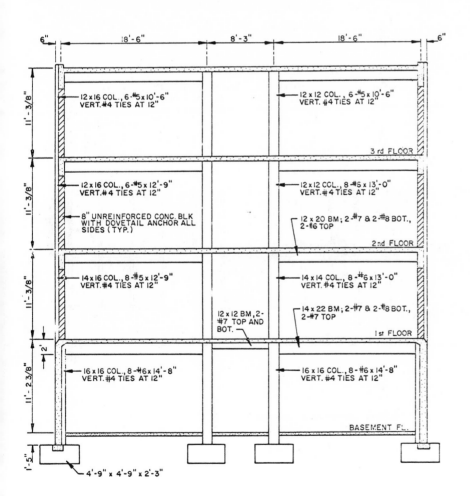

FIGURE 69 Typical section, 200-EM barracks, Fort Richardson.

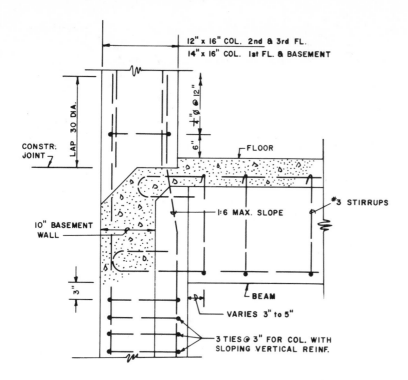

FIGURE 70   Typical exterior column details, 200-EM barracks, Fort Richardson.

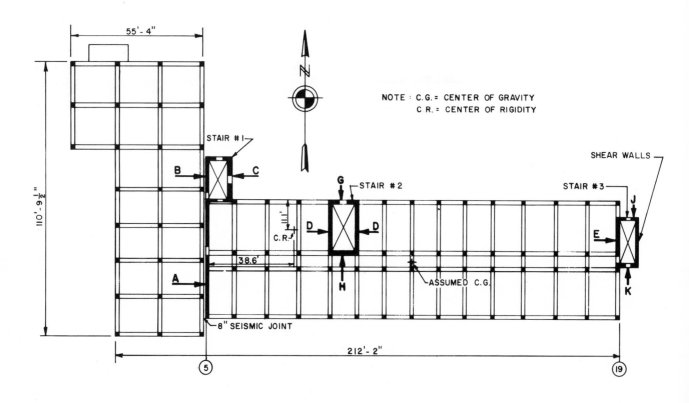

FIGURE 71   First-floor plan, 200-EM barracks, Fort Richardson.

The 4-in. block partitions separating the noncommissioned officers' rooms and lining the corridor partitions also received damage at intersections with other walls and columns and along the top of the walls.

The exterior 8-in. concrete-block filler walls received some diagonal cracking. Joints of these walls also showed movement. The concrete blocks adjacent to the concrete frame fractured at a few locations.

Repair of Earthquake Damage

After the earthquake, the buildings were anlyzed for seismic loads under the 1964 *Uniform Building Code*. The following data were calculated:

Fundamental period of vibration (T)
    Transverse axis   0.24 sec.
    Longitudinal axis   0.12 sec.
Coefficients for base shear (C)
    Transverse axis   0.081
    Longitudinal axis   0.10
Minimum total lateral force $V = ZKCW$
(Assume frame take 100 percent of the load $K = 0.67$)
Transverse axis $V = (1.0)(0.67)(0.081)(W) = 0.054 W$
Longitudinal axis $V = (1.0)(0.67)(0.10)(W) = 0.067 W$

The factor of $0.108W$ used in the original design was thus substantially greater than required by the 1964 *UBC* seismic criteria.

The building was also analyzed assuming the concrete walls would resist all the seismic shear (Figures 71 and 72 give shear-wall details). The analysis indicated that the building had the least resistance in the longitudinal direction, and the reinforcing in walls K and J would be much over-stressed by the code-specified forces. These walls sustained only minor damage, indicating that the concrete frames, the exterior concrete-block panels, and the other elements were actually resisting some of the forces.

In one of the more seriously damaged barracks, the following repairs were made:

• 2,050 ft² of 4-in. block walls were replaced by 6-in. reinforced block walls.
• 470 lin ft of 4-in. block walls were replaced to the door heads with metal studs and gypsum board.
• All interior latrine walls that formed pipe chases were replaced down to the wainscot with metal studs and gypsum board.
• 205 lin ft of the tile joints and 330 lin ft interior block joints were repointed.
• Cracks in 45 ft² of concrete walls were repaired with epoxy grout.
• 11,290 lin ft of exterior block joints were repointed.
• All exterior surfaces were sandblasted and painted.
• Some light fixtures were replaced.

Figures 73–75 give details of interior-wall repair.

The repair cost could not be itemized because the 14 buildings were repaired under a single contract. The average repair cost, however, was $73,000 per building, the major portion of which was for nonstructural damage.

EAST FORT RICHARDSON HEATING AND POWER PLANT

The Fort Richardson Power Plant is located north of the Glenn Highway and southwest of the central post area, about 6 mi northeast of downtown Anchorage (Figure 1). A cooling pond lies to the south of the plant.

The soil under the building foundation consisted of a 30-ft layer of sand and gravel overlying a 7-ft layer of silty clay.

The plant had a generating capacity of 18,000 kW and a heating capacity of 1,080,000 lb/hr of steam; it had five turbine generators and eight coal-fed boilers (Figures 76 and 77). Designed in 1951, the plant was completed in 1953

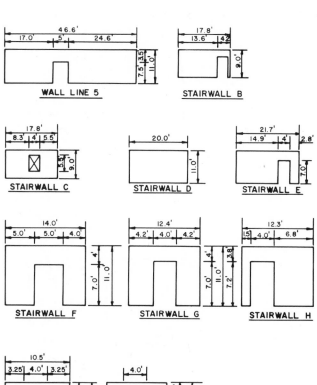

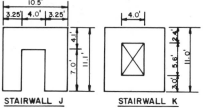

FIGURE 72 Stair wall elevations, 200-EM barracks, Fort Richardson.

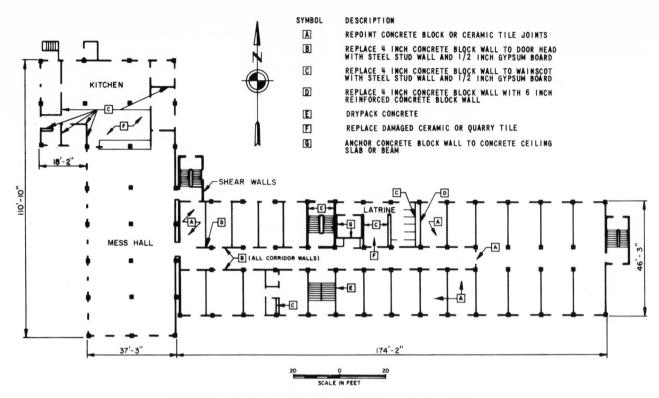

SYMBOL   DESCRIPTION

A   REPOINT CONCRETE BLOCK OR CERAMIC TILE JOINTS

B   REPLACE 4 INCH CONCRETE BLOCK WALL TO DOOR HEAD
WITH STEEL STUD WALL AND 1/2 INCH GYPSUM BOARD

C   REPLACE 4 INCH CONCRETE BLOCK WALL TO WAINSCOT
WITH STEEL STUD WALL AND 1/2 INCH GYPSUM BOARD

D   REPLACE 4 INCH CONCRETE BLOCK WALL WITH 6 INCH
REINFORCED CONCRETE BLOCK WALL

E   DRYPACK CONCRETE

F   REPLACE DAMAGED CERAMIC OR QUARRY TILE

G   ANCHOR CONCRETE BLOCK WALL TO CONCRETE CEILING
SLAB OR BEAM

FIGURE 73   Repair plan of first floor, 200-EM barracks, Fort Richardson.

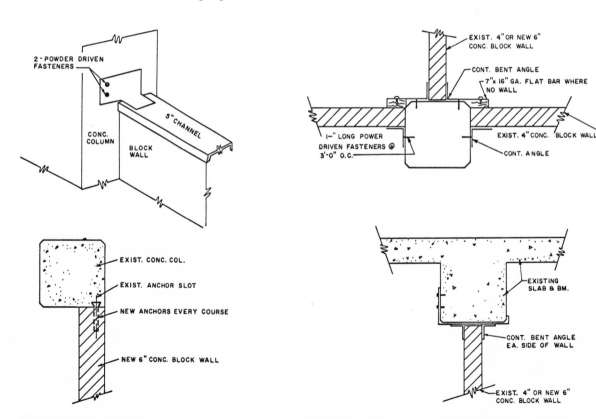

FIGURE 74   Repair details of interior partitions, 200-EM barracks, Fort Richardson.

FIGURE 75   Partition repair details, 200-EM barracks, Fort
Richardson.

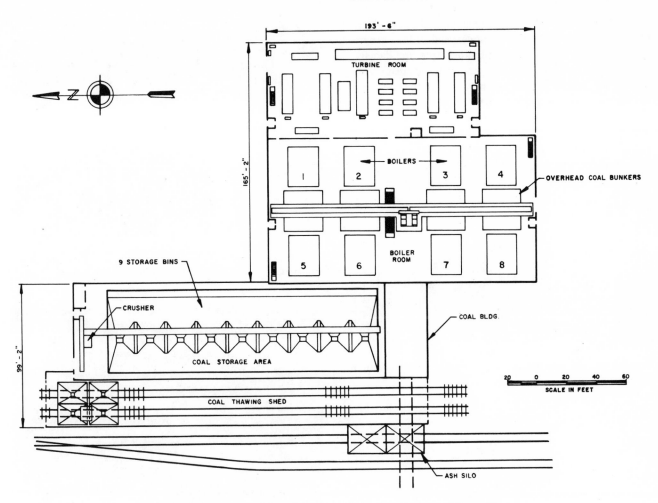

FIGURE 76 First-floor plan of East Fort Richardson Heating and Power Plant.

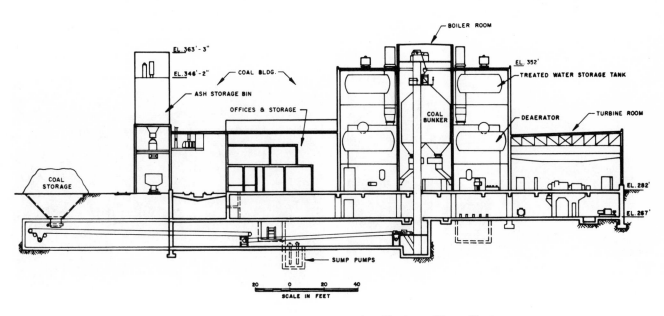

FIGURE 77 Section, East Fort Richardson Heating and Power Plant.

at a cost of $11,235,000. It served as a prototype for the Elmendorf plant, which had six boilers and turbine generators. The plant, which sustained limited structural damage but extensive nonstructural damage, produced steam without interruption; it had the capability to produce power, but the receiving stations were not functioning.

The boiler-room area in this plant was 40 ft longer than that at the Elmendorf plant. The remainder of the plant was almost identical in size and construction to the Elmendorf installation (Figures 78–89).

FIGURE 78   East Fort Richardson Heating and Power Plant, from southeast.

FIGURE 79   Ash silo and coal-thawing shed of East Fort Richardson Power Plant.

FIGURE 80   Main floor of boiler room in East Fort Richardson Power Plant. Vertical cross bracing in this area was bowed.

FIGURE 81   Second-floor framing in boiler room area of the East Fort Richardson Power Plant. The power building suffered only minor structural damage in the earthquake.

FIGURE 82   Roof framing over turbine room sustained no structural damage. East Fort Richardson Power Plant.

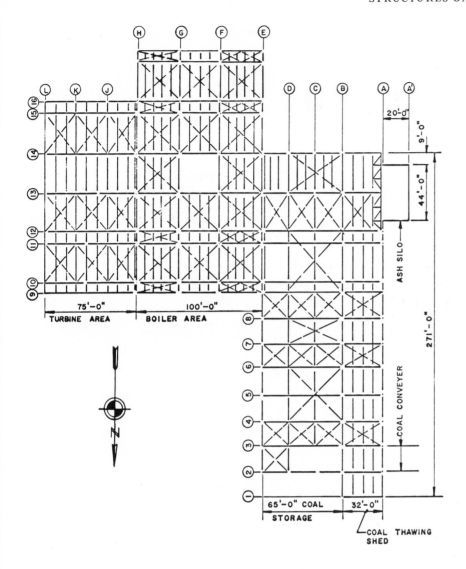

FIGURE 83 Roof-framing plan, East Fort Richardson Power Plant.

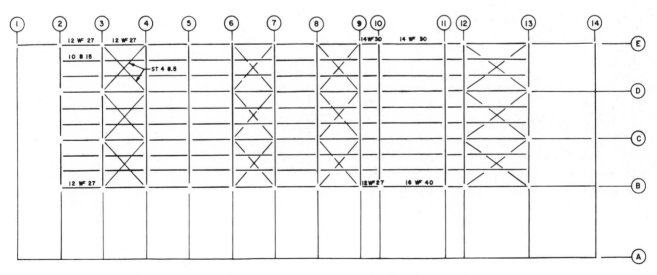

FIGURE 84 Top chord framing, coal-building roof framing, East Fort Richardson Power Plant.

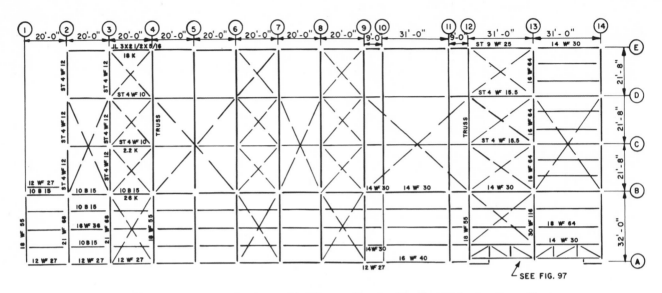

FIGURE 85   Bottom chord framing, coal-building roof framing, East Fort Richardson Power Plant.

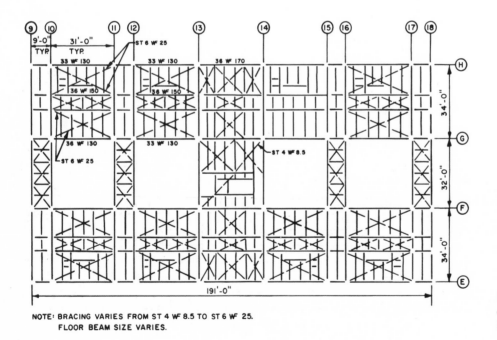

NOTE: BRACING VARIES FROM ST 4 WF 8.5 TO ST 6 WF 25.
FLOOR BEAM SIZE VARIES.

FIGURE 86   Fan-floor framing at elevation 329 ft 10¾ in., East Fort Richardson Power Plant.

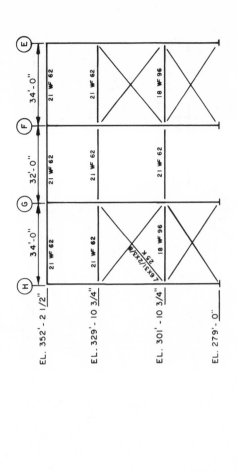

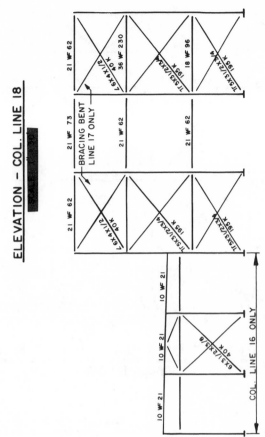

ELEVATION – COL. LINE 18

ELEVATION – COL. LINES 16&17

NOTE: DIAGONALS IN COL. LINE 17 ARE 2 ∠'S 6"x4"x1/2".

FIGURE 88 Framing elevations, East Fort Richardson Power Plant.

FIGURE 87 Typical floor-framing plan at elevation 301 ft 10¾ in., East Fort Richardson Power Plant.

917

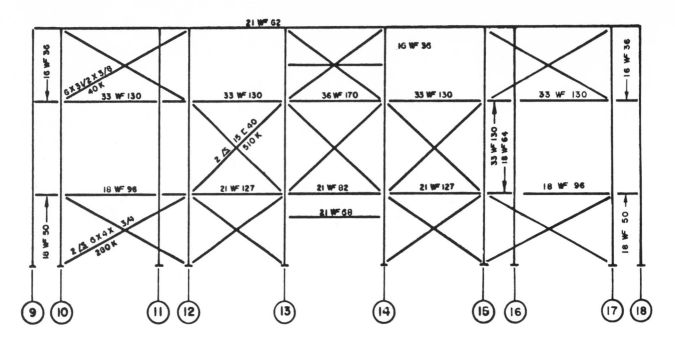

ELEVATION - COL. LINE E & H

SCALE: 1" = 30'

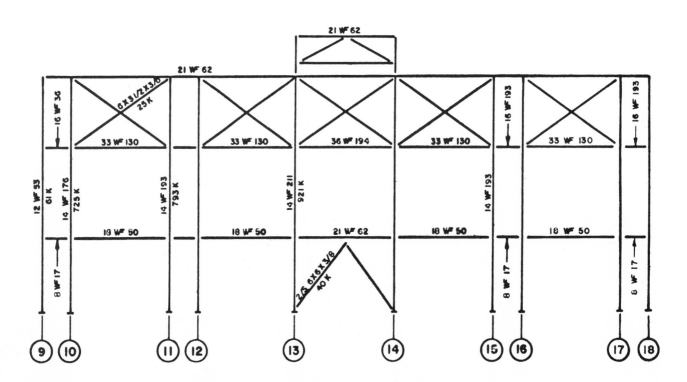

ELEVATION - COL. LINE F & G

FIGURE 89   Framing elevations, East Fort Richardson Power Plant.

The turbine-room and boiler-room areas were designed in accordance with the 1949 *Uniform Building Code.* The following horizontal shear factors (*C*) were used at the respective story heights (*N*).

$N = 0$	$C = 0.133$
$N = 1$	$C = 0.109$
$N = 2$	$C = 0.092$
$N = 3$	$C = 0.080$
$N = 4$	$C = 0.071$

A *C* factor of 0.133 was used throughout the coal building. The factors used in the design of the ash silo are not known.

Earthquake Damage

The Fort Richardson Power Plant received only minor structural damage; however, the structure was highly stressed. Similar areas were more severely damaged in the Elmendorf plant.

No structural damage occurred in the turbine-room area. In the boiler room, however, the main vertical bracing in both directions on the main floor was bent. One vertical diagonal on the second floor was bent, and other cross bracing showed distress (Figures 90 and 91). The horizontal bracing for the treated-water tanks on the third floor was

FIGURE 91 Cross bracing in column line E on second floor. Gusset plate shows distress, but connection was not repaired. This bracing was designed to resist an ultimate tensile force of 510 kips. East Fort Richardson Power Plant.

slightly bent (Figure 92). Some vertical diagonals in the west wall of the boiler-room area above the third floor were bent, as was one horizontal bracing member under the third floor.

In the coal building the connection of a 21-in., 73-lb beam to column B-13 was overstressed and yielded without failing. The corresponding connection in the Elmendorf plant failed completely. Column B-13 was twisted about its vertical axis (Figures 93–96). The horizontal truss along column line A, between columns 12 and 14, was damaged; the connections yielded, and one tension member failed (Figure 97). Some roof bracing over the coal-thawing shed was bent, and a few connections showed distress. The coal-storage area sustained little or no damage. Figure 98 shows spalled concrete at columns in the coal-thawing shed.

FIGURE 90 Bowed diagonal in main floor of boiler room, East Fort Richardson Power Plant.

FIGURE 92 Platform framing for treated-water tanks where some horizontal bracing in platform was bowed and later repaired. East Fort Richardson Power Plant.

FIGURE 93 Column B-13 showing damaged strut and lateral bracing. East Fort Richardson Power Plant.

FIGURE 94 Column B-13 in place showing distress. East Fort Richardson Power Plant.

FIGURE 95 Column B-13 showing localized yield. East Fort Richardson Power Plant.

Failure of pipe hangers, damage to the superheater tubes, and damage to the tile brick composed the major nonstructural damage in this plant. The semirigid pipe hangers did not permit either free lateral movement or prevent all movement; when the piping moved horizontally, many hangers were therefore bent or failed completely. In some cases, the pipe hanger was welded rigidly to the support beam. Failure and damage of hangers occurred throughout the boiler-room area.

In Figure 99, damage to the grating is shown to have obviously been caused by the excessive lateral displacements of the valve, indicating that the piping network moved considerably in relation to the structure. Figure 100 shows the results of a piping system not being restrained against movement. Here the soot-line hangers failed and the pipe and fitting fell, which damaged the grating.

The superheater tubes, waterwall tubes, and tile brick

FIGURE 96 Column B-13 after removal from building. East Fort Richardson Power Plant.

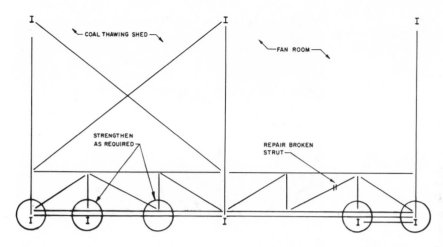

FIGURE 97   East Fort Richardson Power Plant. Repair plan, fan-room roof.

FIGURE 98   Movement of column A-12 in coal-thawing shed caused concrete to spall from wall about 5 ft above ground. East Fort Richardson Power Plant.

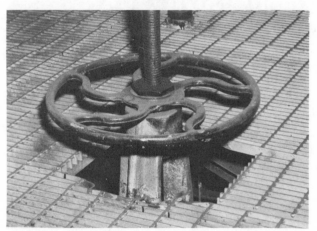

FIGURE 99   Movement of the valve damaged the grating; pipeline hangers provided no horizontal support. East Fort Richardson Power Plant.

were all damaged because of the movement and battering of the angle spacer (Figure 101).

The floor slab in the coal-thawing shed settled, and this, together with pressure of coal cars in the shed, caused the rails to shear.

A sewer line at the northwest corner of the building sheared as the result of a vertical displacement of about 3 in.—the only indication of soil subsidence around this plant.

Repair of Earthquake Damage

Some structural repair was needed in the boiler room. Two east–west diagonals were replaced; one diagonal, between boiler rooms 2 and 4 on the main floor, was repaired; and one diagonal was straightened on the second floor. The horizontal bracing for one treated-water tank on each side of the building was straightened, and three vertical diago-

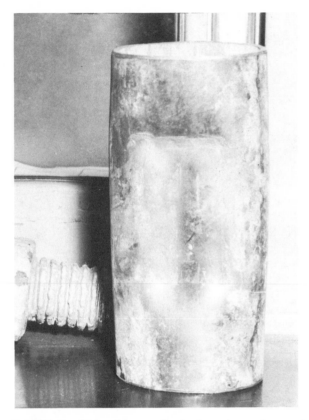

FIGURE 100   Grating was damaged when pipe hangers failed, and soot line slipped out of dresser couplings and fell. East Fort Richardson Power Plant.

FIGURE 101   Piece of water-wall tube shows damage from angle spacers. East Fort Richardson Power Plant.

nals in the west wall and five diagonals in the east wall above the third floor were straightened or replaced as necessary. One 5-in. structural tee in the third-floor bracing was replaced.

In the coal building, the horizontal truss on column line A was repaired (Figure 98). The 15-in. channel was stiffened with welded plates (Figures 102–105), and one double-angle web member was replaced.

About 15 ft of column B-13 was replaced with a 10-in., 72-lb section (Figure 106). The 21-in., 73-lb beam on column line 13 was repaired and reconnected (Figures 107 and 108). Figure 109 shows the original connection. One horizontal diagonal between column lines 12 and 13 was repaired and one diagonal over the coal-thawing shed was straightened.

Nonstructural repair in the power plant included the repair or replacement of loose waterwall tubes, crown circular tubes, baffles, fire brick, and refractory in boilers 1 and 8. The superheater tubes were replaced in boilers 4 and 6 and were either repaired or replaced in boilers 1, 2, 3, 5, and 7.

Critical pipe hangers and supports were repaired throughout the plant.

The total cost of repair was $164,000, of which $15,000 was for structural repairs—a very small sum compared to the $11,235,000 original cost.

This structure again demonstrates the necessity of designing all elements in a building for earthquake forces. If the failure of the pipe hangers had caused the high-pressure steam lines to rupture, severe injury or death could have resulted to any nearby occupants of the building.

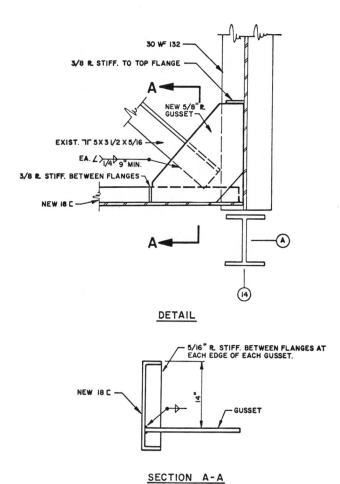

FIGURE 102 Repair of horizontal truss shown in Figure 97. East Fort Richardson Power Plant.

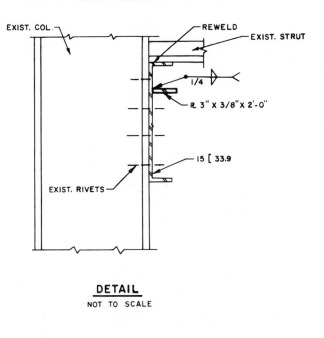

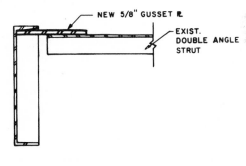

FIGURE 103 Repair detail for channel. The locations are circled in Figure 97. East Fort Richardson Power Plant.

FIGURE 104 Repair to gusset at column A-14, East Fort Richardson Power Plant.

FIGURE 105 Repair to channel on column line A. Channel acts as one chord of horizontal truss. East Fort Richardson Power Plant.

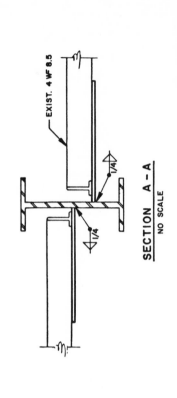

EXIST. 24 WF

EXIST. TEE'S 4 WF 8.5

NEW WEB ℞

1/4" FILLET WELD (14 INCHES TOTAL)

A

NEW 10" x 1/2" ℞ GUSSETS

14 WF 30

NEW COLUMN

13

PLAN

NEW 3/8" ℞ STIFF. TOP OR BOTTOM OF NEW GUSSETS

14 WF 30

B

A

EXIST. 4 WF 8.5

1/4

1/4

SECTION A - A
NO SCALE

FIGURE 108   Repair detail at column B-13. East Fort Richardson Power Plant.

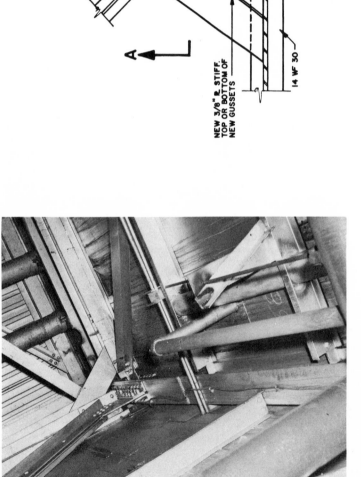

FIGURE 106   Column B-13 after repair; about 15 ft of column had to be replaced. East Fort Richardson Power Plant.

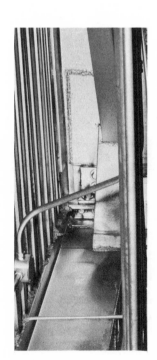

FIGURE 107   View of 21-in. beam repair and cross-bracing repair at column B-13. East Fort Richardson Power Plant.

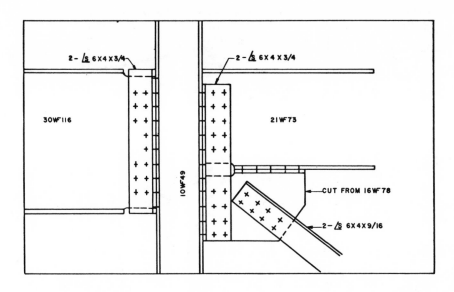

FIGURE 109   Detail of original connection at column B-13. East Fort Richardson Power Plant.

ELMENDORF AIR FORCE BASE

5040TH AIR FORCE HOSPITAL

The Air Force Hospital, halfway between Elmendorf AFB and Fort Richardson (Figure 110), was one of the largest structures in the area. The hospital provides complete medical facilities for the large number of Army and Air Force men and their dependents. Within 3 days of the earthquake, a command inspection had determined that the damage sustained by the hospital could seriously affect the military mission in Alaska; an order was therefore issued to repair the hospital immediately. The need for quick action increased the cost of repairs.

The hospital was designed in 1952 by the firm of Skidmore, Owings, and Merrill, and the structural design was done by Isadore Thompson of San Francisco, California. The seismic design followed the 1949 *Uniform Building Code* requirements, and the concrete design and details were in accordance with the 1951 *American Concrete Institute Code*.

The Elmendorf AFB Hospital basically consisted of three wings (Figures 111 and 112). Wing A was a seven-story wing, 44 ft wide and 366 ft long, with a stairwell core at each end. The wing was designed to carry four additional floors, making it an eleven-story structure. Near the intersection point with wing B, wing A widens and joins a 43 X 110-ft 11-story elevator and stair core. The stairwell cores at the ends of the wing and the elevator shaft near the center of the wing were designed to provide the main lateral-force resistance for the wing. Forces were to be transmitted to these elements by the floors, which acted as diaphragms; some resistance was to be furnished by the columns in the exterior walls. A first-floor plan of the elevator shaft is shown in Figure 113. Figures 114 and 115 show details of the thickness of the reinforced-concrete shear walls in the elevator core. The floors were beam and slab construction. The bearing walls were of reinforced concrete, and the window walls had spandrel beams of reinforced concrete, concrete columns, and concrete-block filler walls. An 8-in. seismic joint separated the wings along their intersection.

Wing B was a three-story, 173-ft square concrete structure with full basement. Construction was similar to that of wing A.

Wing C was a two-story structure, 88 ft wide and 109 ft long, consisting of basement and first floor and separated from wing A by an 8-in. seismic joint. Construction was similar to that of wing A.

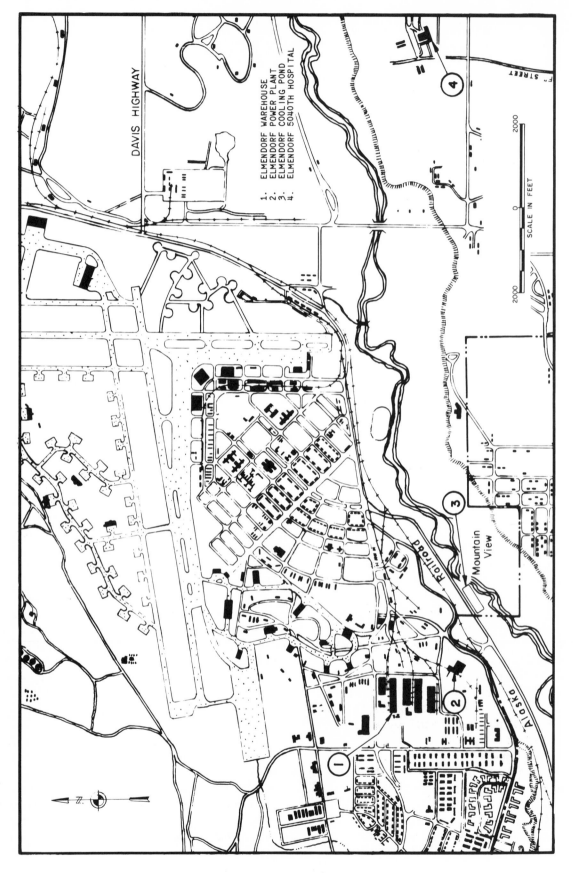

FIGURE 110 Vicinity map of Elmendorf Air Force Base (AFB).

1. ELMENDORF WAREHOUSE
2. ELMENDORF POWER PLANT
3. ELMENDORF COOLING POND
4. ELMENDORF 5040TH HOSPITAL

DAVIS HIGHWAY

Mountain View

Railroad

ALASKA

"F" STREET

SCALE IN FEET

926

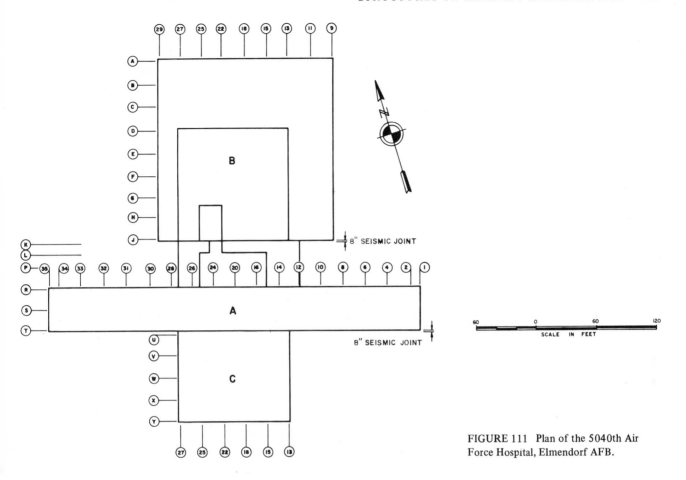

FIGURE 111   Plan of the 5040th Air Force Hospital, Elmendorf AFB.

FIGURE 112   Exterior view of 5040th Air Force Hospital, Elmendorf AFB.

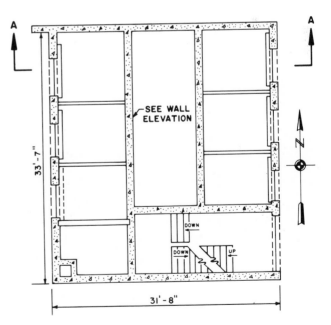

FIGURE 113   First-floor plan of elevator shaft near midpoint of wing A, 5040th Air Force Hospital, Elmendorf AFB.

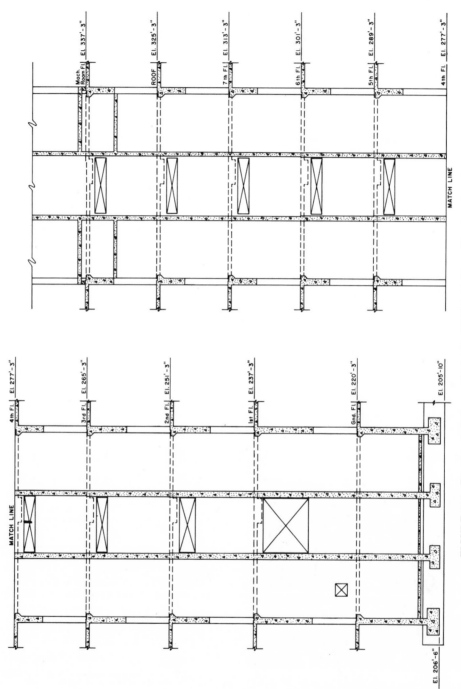

FIGURE 114 Elevator-shaft shear-wall details, 5040th Air Force Hospital, Elmendorf AFB.

928

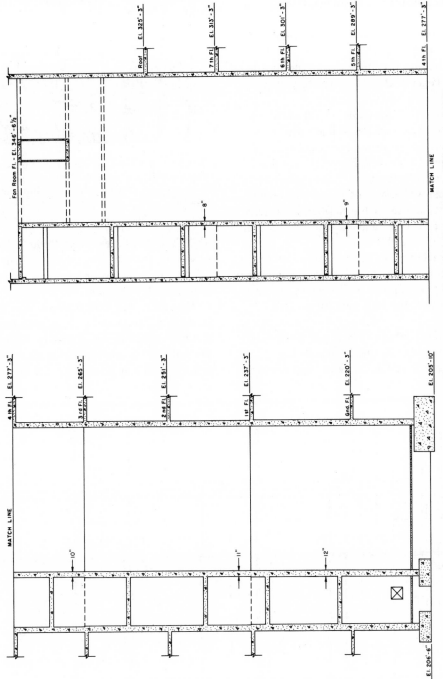

FIGURE 115 Wall elevation, elevator-shaft shear-wall details, 5040th Air Force Hospital, Elmendorf AFB.

929

Earthquake Damage

Information about damage was gained mainly from contract drawings used in the repair and from a damage report on USAF Hospital, Elmendorf AFB, Alaska, by Isadore Thompson, consulting engineer to Skidmore, Owings, and Merrill, Architects.

All shear walls in the building showed diagonal hairline cracking. The cracks varied from barely perceptible above the fourth story to hairline size in the second and fourth stories. One or two larger cracks in the first story were about 1/64 in. wide.

At wall column row 19 in the elevator well, above the fourth floor, there were diagonal cracks that varied from hairline to barely perceptible. Figure 116 is a photograph taken during the repair of this wall. Figure 117 is a detail taken from the contract drawings and shows the reinforcing steel used in this shear wall between the fourth and fifth floors. From the first floor to the fourth floor, the cracks varied from hairline to 1/32 in., and one crack in each story was approximately 1/16 in. wide.

Generally, construction joints appeared tight, but on investigation many joints proved not to have been completely cleaned and showed signs of sawdust, dirt, wood, and so forth, that were left when the walls were constructed (Figure 118).

Most of the concrete appeared to be sound, but some void pockets were found in columns. Numerous large pockets of bad concrete were found at wall 19 of the eleva-

FIGURE 116 Closeup of elevator core between fouth- and fifth-floor levels. Repairs were made by routing and sealing the cracks and injecting epoxy 24 hours later. 5040th Air Force Hospital, Elmendorf AFB.

tor well; some of it extended through the wall (Figure 119). At wall 19, between the fourth and fifth floors, an opening 5 ft 4 in. wide by 6 ft high and not shown on the original plans was left in the wall.

The second and third stories of wing B showed minor cracks at the north and south end of the eastern shear walls that were more horizontal than the typical shear-wall cracks. The wall did not continue below the second floor at these points, which may be the reason it was overstressed. The

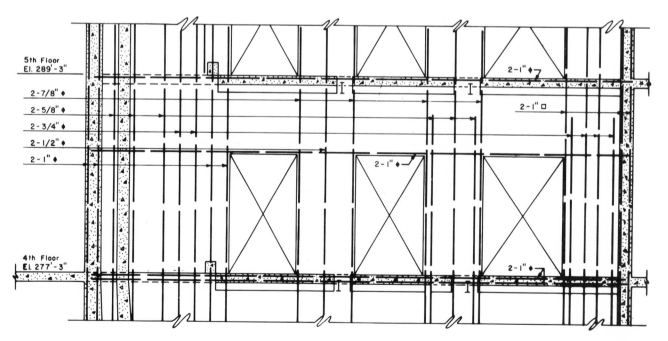

FIGURE 117 Shear-wall reinforcing in elevator shaft between fourth and fifth floor. 5040th Air Force Hospital, Elmendorf AFB.

FIGURE 118 Improper construction along cold joint in one of the shear walls; exposed reinforcing steel and holes in concrete can be seen. Above the joint is the tile cement used to apply the interior finish. 5040th Air Force Hospital, Elmendorf AFB.

FIGURE 119 Holes left in elevator-shaft wall during original construction. At the right can be seen the hoisting cables for the elevator. Above the large opening on the right is a cold joint running down to the left to a void that was left in the wall during construction. The aluminum nipple used to inject the epoxy can be seen at top of photo. 5040th Air Force Hospital, Elmendorf AFB.

construction joints in the shear walls did not show signs of horizontal movement.

The main longitudinal shear wall for the building was on column row R. At each floor were two large openings in the wall; a deep beam above each opening was designed to make wall R act as a unit during an earthquake. These beams, which showed heavy cracking and damage, proved to have been poured in two parts with a longitudinal construction joint one third to one half of the way up the height of the beam. This joint ran the entire length of the beam so that, in effect, there were two shallow beams, each of which was reinforced on one side only, instead of one deep beam reinforced on both sides. These beams were also reduced in size because space was needed for air conditioning ducts and piping. The beams failed on floors 1 to 5 with large chunks of concrete spalling (Figure 120).

The exterior spandrel wall (window wall) showed numerous, very faint hairline cracks that may not have been caused by the earthquake. Three or four vertical cracks adjacent to the columns in the spandrel beams were probably old expansion-contraction cracks working under seismic stresses.

At the rear of the elevator core of wing A on column line K of the first story, column K-15 was shattered at the top, and the beam at columns R-15 and R-25 on the third floor was badly cracked.

The corbels holding up the concrete-slab parking area over the basement drive-in garage were damaged. These corbels on column line R were all severely shattered. The concrete beams were placed with no corbel-to-beam connections.

The spandrel beams connecting the outer walls to the elevator core were severely damaged, and the damage increased with height.

The only physical evidence of the relative motion of the different wings was scratches left on the floors by cover plates over the seismic joints on the third floor between wings A and B. The scratches indicated a maximum relative movement of 3¾ in. between wings A and B and close

FIGURE 120 Large duct and electrical conduit passing through one of the beams on column row R. Missing concrete at the bottom of the beam leaves the tension steel exposed. The small channel is for the support of the suspended ceiling. 5040th Air Force Hospital, Elmendorf AFB.

to 4 in. at the fourth floor. Unused conduit stubs at the fourth floor had a 4-in. gap, and the ends had banged together. These must be considered large displacements.

Block filler walls on the first to the fifth floors showed large X cracks between windows (Figure 121). The plaster walls in the rooms were all badly cracked, and in some cases entire wall sections were loosened from their backing. This cracking was usually not related directly to structural cracking except in cases where plaster-wall backing was fastened to a structural wall. In most cases, the relative displacement between floors cracked the plaster walls. In some cases, the racking of the plaster wall left it tipped with a crack between the floor and bottom of the wall.

Tile was cracked on the floors and walls of operating rooms, and some had fallen to the floor. The tiles directly over cracks in concrete walls were split through, and in most cases tile was loosened some distance on each side of the crack; there was evidence of movement between the concrete wall and the floor slab.

The wall inserts holding the marble slabs in the main entry were loosened, and some of the slabs broke. The mechanical system was severely damaged. Elevator guide rails were knocked out of plumb, and the motors on the elevator head house were shifted out of alignment. Fan motors in the top floor of the elevator shaft were moved around or tipped over, mostly because they were not tied down. Steam, water, and sewer lines were damaged because some pipe-support inserts pulled out. There was little damage to the electrical system.

Building Repairs

Repairs to the hospital consisted of immediate emergency repairs to make the hospital operational, and long-term per-

FIGURE 122   Voids left in a concrete shear wall at the construction joint. Vertical members are furring strips for attaching the interior finish. 5040th Air Force Hospital, Elmendorf AFB.

manent repairs to put the hospital back in preearthquake condition.

Emergency Repairs   The first letter-type contract was awarded 24 hours after the earthquake. On Sunday, March 29, the contractor had 20 men at work in the hospital. The contract provided for the immediate repair of column K-15 on the first floor by adding steel ties and enclosing the entire column and column head with 6 in. of high early-strength concrete. Columns R-15 and R-20 in the third story were repaired with concrete jackets. Parts of the elevator-shaft core walls at the first floor were removed with jackhammers. These shattered portions occurred mainly between doors where the control-box opening caused an additional weakening of the concrete wall.

The damage in the operating rooms, emergency rooms, and so forth, was repaired as part of a crash program. The exterior beams, damaged where they joined the elevator core on column line R, were repaired by removing the beams and replacing them with new poured-concrete beams. The Air Force moved back into this part of the hospital on April 6, 1964.

Permanent Repairs   The second category of repair was carried out in two phases. Two contracts were used to give the Alaska District Engineers time to check the design and construction procedures. The Air Force was using half of wing A before it was repaired, while the contractor was working on the other half of the wing. As soon as the contractor had finished the first portion of the wing, the hospital crew moved into it and the contractor then repaired the vacated portion. Much of the damage was not immediately visible until the suspended ceiling, wall plaster, floor tile, and other interior finish had been removed. Figure 122 shows some of the damage that became visible when the interior finish was removed.

FIGURE 121   Cross cracks between windows in the block filler walls on wing A. 5040th Air Force Hospital, Elmendorf AFB.

The first contract called for epoxy-injection grouting of the cracks in shear walls and in column–beam junctions. The prime contractor subcontracted the epoxy work to an experienced epoxy repair firm. Crack grouting was performed by inserting aluminum nipples into the cracks and injecting pot-mixed epoxy through a quick-connecting nozzle. The cracks were grouted 24 hours after the aluminum nipples were installed. Setting time for the grout mix was 3 hours. This method of crack grouting had a tendency to clog the cracks with dust, and the epoxy mix tended to drain from the cracks, especially where the opposite side of the wall could not be sealed. Test cores and sonic testing showed incomplete penetration of the grout. It was then decided that epoxy would have to be injected from both sides, working from the bottom up on each panel, if full sealing was to be obtained. The process, however, would have involved the removal of interior finish and of insulation that had not previously been contemplated, and the cost would have been prohibitive. It was finally decided that the grouting was to be finished, after first cleaning out and replacing with Gunite all the badly spalled areas and rock pockets in the shear walls, and reinforcing them by Guniting the sides of beams.

Another epoxy subcontractor was obtained for the rest of the work. His method involved painting the crack with a beeswax–epoxy mixture and placing toothpicks or nails, depending on the size of the crack, into the crack in lieu of aluminum nipples; the 24-hour waiting period was not necessary with this method. A contact, pressure-type nozzle was then used over the hole that was left after the toothpick or nail had been removed. The epoxy ingredients were pumped to the nozzle by two separate pumps and mixed there; the mixture had a gel time of 7 minutes and would be self-sealing as it emerged from the far side of the wall. This system was satisfactory for grouting the cracks and was used to complete the scheduled work. Figures 123 and 124 show some of the epoxy repairs. One problem with this method is that if one of the pumps gets out of adjustment the precise ratio of resin to catalyst is unbalanced, resulting in a nonhardening mix. The balance is easily checked by pumping a small amount into a paper cup every 15 minutes. Because the gel time was only 7 minutes, the operator could check the mixture visually.

Approximately 70 percent of the exterior block filler walls were removed to the sill line of the windows. In a few cases, the entire wall was removed. This work had to be done with some care since the block walls were attached to insulation, to interior plaster finish, or to ceramic-tile walls that had to be left in place. Nearly total replacement of the block walls was required on the first five floors. Figure 125 shows damage to a column at the fourth-floor level.

The plaster walls were badly cracked in almost every room, requiring either patching or replacement.

FIGURE 123 Elevator core after epoxy repairs had been made. Cross cracking between the windows in concrete-block filler panels can be seen. 5040th Air Force Hospital, Elmendorf AFB.

FIGURE 124 Repairs made to concrete shear wall. The three round holes in center of photo show where core samples were taken to check the penetration and bonding of the epoxy. 5040th Air Force Hospital, Elmendorf AFB.

FIGURE 125   Damage to column R-27 at fourth-floor level caused by improper splicing of reinforcing steel. 5040th Air Force Hospital, Elmendorf AFB.

The total cost of repairs was $2.4 million. The original cost of the structure was $8.9 million, but replacement cost in 1964 would have been considerably more. Of the $2.4 million total, approximately $400,000 was for structural repair and $2 million for nonstructural repair.

The importance of nonstructural damage, both in curtailing the operational capabilities of the hospital and in the cost of repair was very evident. For the hospital, the nonstructural-repair cost of $2 million was 22 percent of the original cost of the building, whereas the structural-repair cost was a mere 4.5 percent of the original building cost. The high cost of the nonstructural repair was no doubt partly attributable to the need for quick repair of this important building. The hospital's inability to function after the earthquake emphasizes the need to give special attention to the earthquake-resistant design of hospitals that are urgently needed after a disaster.

WEST ELMENDORF HEATING AND POWER PLANT

The Elmendorf Power Plant is situated on a bluff at the south boundary of the air base (Figure 111). A pump house furnishing condenser-cooling water is at the base of the bluff. A cooling pond is about 1,200 ft southeast of the plant, south of The Alaska Railroad yards and north of Ship Creek. The plant was located on gravel, underlain by clay that was about 45 ft below the surface and about 10 ft below the building foundations.

The plant, which has three 7,500-kW generators and six coal-fed boilers, with a generating capacity of 22,500 kW and a heating capacity of 950,000 lb/hr of steam, is the prime source of heat and power for the air base. Designed in 1953 and modeled on the Fort Richardson Power Plant, the plant was constructed in 1956 at a cost of $11,961,000. Figures 126–128 show the general plans, and Figures 129–131 show the equipment layout for each floor. Figures 132–136 give interior and exterior views of the plant.

The plant is divided into a turbine area, boiler area, and coal-handling area as indicated on Figures 127 and 130. The turbine area is on the east side of the building and is 38 ft high, 75 ft wide, and 151 ft long. The superstructure in this area is a structural-steel frame consisting of roof purlins on trusses and steel columns. The first floor is a reinforced-concrete slab with beams supported on concrete columns. The three turbine generators are mounted on separate concrete foundations. A 25-ton traveling crane is mounted overhead.

The boiler-room area is a three-story structural-steel-frame building with a penthouse (Figure 134). This area has a total height of 69 ft, and is 151 ft long, and 100 ft wide. The six boilers and miscellaneous piping are on the first floor. Along with other equipment, the third floor carries four treated-water tanks with a total capacity of 60,000 gallons.

Three coal bunker (Figures 130 and 131) extend from the second floor to the roof. Each full bunker weighs 550 tons and is supported directly on columns. Floor bracing and vertical cross bracing provide lateral resistance.

The coal-handling area is 271 ✕ 97 ft, the height of which varies between 36 and 41 ft. The coal-thawing shed and coal-storage area are one-story high, and the remainder of the area is two-stories high (Figures 129 and 137). This area is constructed much the same as the boiler and turbine areas, except that the second floor is a concrete slab on steel beams. The area also has a partial subbasement. The coal bunkers in the storage area are precast concrete; an overhead conveyer is used to transport the coal.

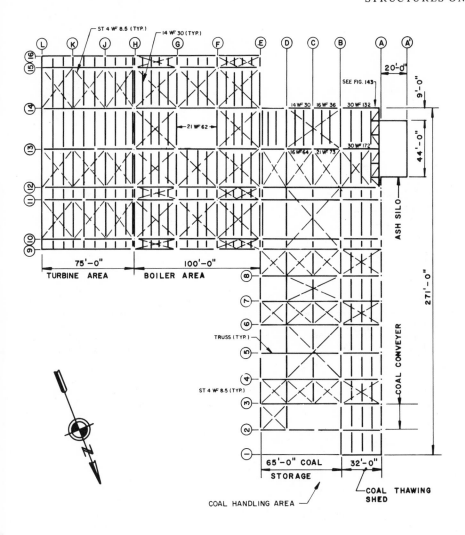

FIGURE 126 Roof-framing plan, West Elmendorf Power Plant.

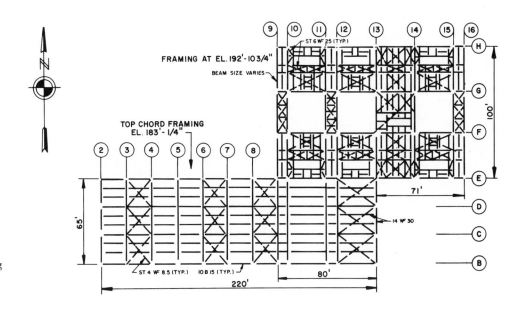

FIGURE 127 General framing plan, West Elmendorf Power Plant.

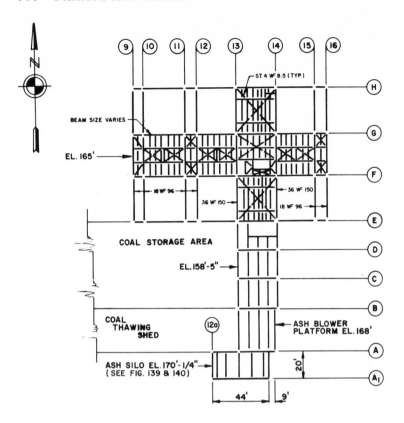

FIGURE 128 Framing plan, coal-handling area, West Elmendorf Power Plant.

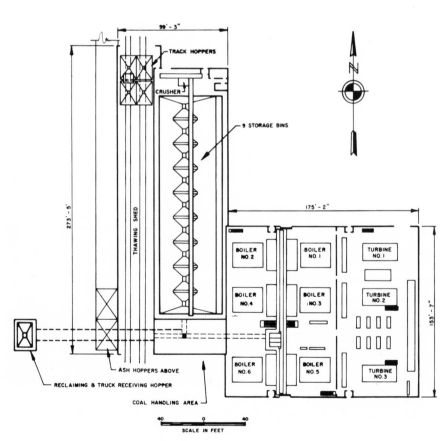

FIGURE 129 Main floor plan, West Elmendorf Power Plant.

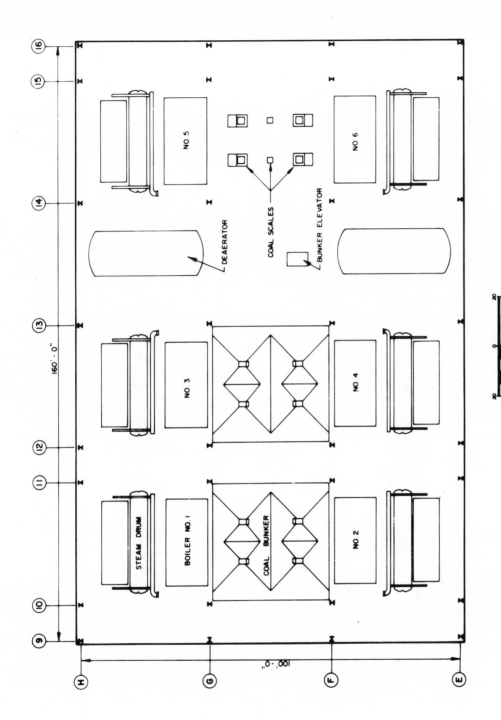

FIGURE 130 Plan below fan platform, second floor, West Elmendorf Power Plant.

937

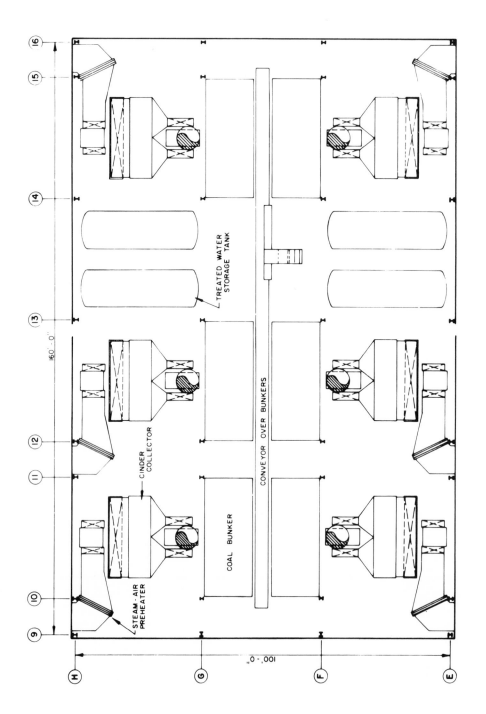

FIGURE 131 Plan below roof, West Elmendorf Power Plant.

FIGURE 132   West Elmendorf Heating and Power Plant, from south.

FIGURE 135   Operating floor in boiler room, West Elmendorf Power Plant.

FIGURE 133   View of northeast end of West Elmendorf Power Plant after repairs of earthquake damage. Coal-stocking conveyor was not damaged.

FIGURE 134   West Elmendorf Power Plant, from southeast.

U. S. Air Force

FIGURE 136   Turbine room in West Elmendorf Power Plant.

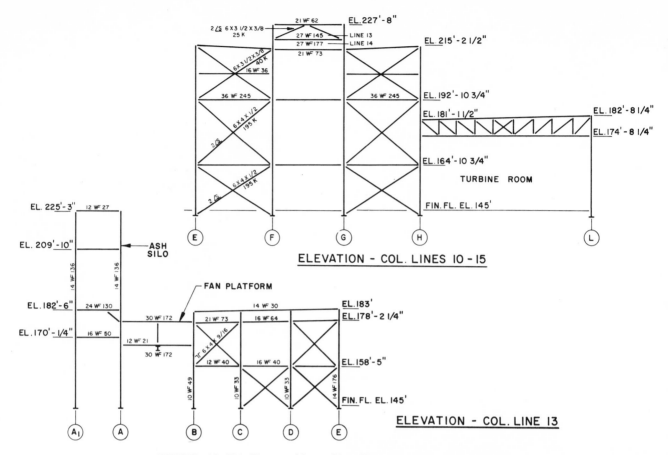

FIGURE 137 West Elmendorf Power Plant. Elevation of column lines 10–15.

An ash silo (Figures 138–140) at the northwest corner of the coal building is 20 × 44 ft and its top is 83 ft above the ground; the bottom clearance is 28 ft 6 in. The top 16 ft is a structural-steel separator room, the middle 26 ft is a reinforced-concrete hopper, and the lower 13 ft is a structural-steel unloader room.

The following list indicates design loads, allowable stresses, and building codes used in the building:

Roof

Live load	40 psf permanent
Snow load	40 psf
Wind load	20 psf
All piping considered as deadloads	

Fan Floor

Live load	300 psf
Impact	100% of fan equipment
Maximum steel stress	12,000 psi
Minimum beam depth	1/12 span

Main Floor

Live load	400 psf
Office floor	100 psf

U. S. Air Force

FIGURE 138 East view of ash silo. Line on the coal-shed roof indicates the approximate roof separation caused by the connection failure at column B-13. The silo is now leaning away from the building and is about 5 in. out of plumb. West Elmendorf Power Plant.

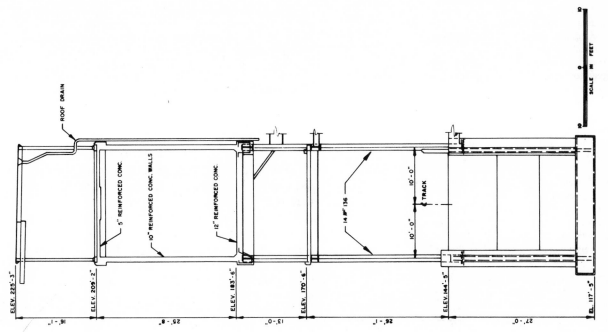

FIGURE 140 Elevation of column line 13a, ash-silo tower. West Elmendorf Power Plant.

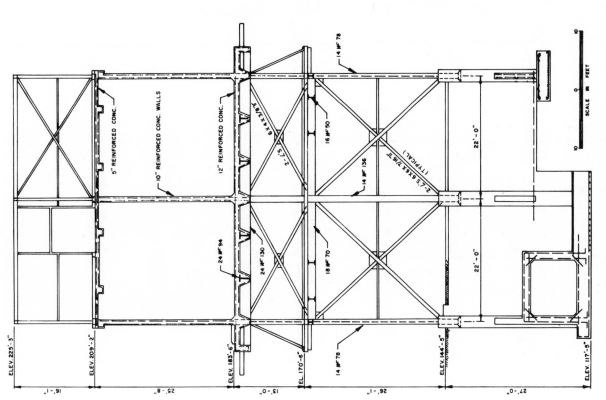

FIGURE 139 Elevation of column line A₁ ash-silo tower. West Elmendorf Power Plant.

941

Ash-Blower Platform
  Equipment + 100% + 100 psf
  Reinforcing steel stress   12,000 psi
Turbine Foundations
  Reinforcing steel stress   12,000 psi
  Designed for General Electric and Westinghouse specifications
Lateral Loads
  Wind   30 psf on stacks
                                      20 psf on vertical surface
  Seismic zone 3, *Uniform Building Code*
  (Design analysis indicates 1949 code, and drawings show 1952 code)
  $F = CW$
  C = Coefficient in Table 23-C of *Uniform Building Code*
  $W = D.L.$ + perm $L.L.$
Soil Pressure
  Dead load   7,000 psf
  Dead + live load   8,500 psf
  Dead + seismic load   10,000 psf

(Fort Richardson design analysis allowed 4,000 psf, 5,000 psf, and 6,000 psf, respectively. The design analysis did not clearly indicate that footings had been redesigned for the higher pressures.)
Concrete Stresses
  Footings   2,500 psi
  Other   3,000 psi
Reinforcing Steel Stresses
  f_s = 20,000 psi, except as noted
Structural Steel Stress
  f_s = 20,000 psi tension on net section, except as noted

All cross bracing was designed for tension only, with connections to resist 15 kips, unless otherwise noted on the drawings.

The bracing on column lines F and G was designed to carry 10 percent of the fan-platform load to the roof (Figure 141). The roof bracing carried this load to column

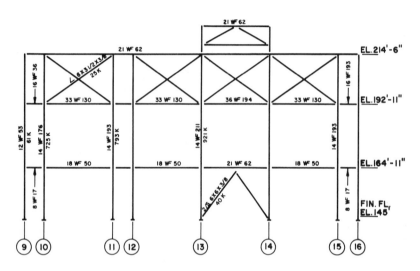

ELEVATION - COL. LINE F & G

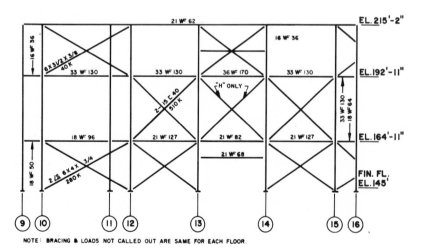

NOTE: BRACING & LOADS NOT CALLED OUT ARE SAME FOR EACH FLOOR.

ELEVATION - COL. LINE E & H

FIGURE 141 West Elmendorf Power Plant. Elevation of column lines E–H.

lines E and H. The remainder was carried by platform bracing to column lines E and H.

The turbine room bracing in walls at column lines 9 and 16 was for local stiffening only, because the boiler room bracing took the turbine room loads. The top-story loads in the boiler room were distributed to column lines 10, 13, and 14 by roof bracing (Figure 138).

Lateral forces in the coal building were taken by diagonal members extending to the foundation. The coal-shed framing was designed to resist transverse loads by moment-resisting column connections and had cross bracing to resist the longitudinal loads (Figure 142). The ash silo relied on the coal building to resist lateral loads in the east–west direction and had cross bracing to take the north–south loads (Figure 139). The horizontal truss at the fan-room elevation (Figure 143) transmitted the east–west silo loads to column lines 12, 13, and 14. A system of struts then carries the seismic loads to diagonal-tension bracing in column lines 13 and 14. The available design analysis did not cover the

ash silo, nor was there an analysis of the bracing to resist the silo loads. Lateral loads were shown on the horizontal truss at column line A in the construction drawings (Figure 144). In the analysis of columns E-13 and E-14, each had a horizontal load from the silo of dead load + ½ live load = 86 kips × 0.109 = 9.4 kips. The bracing between columns A and E in column line 13 that appeared in the design analysis, however, does not agree with that shown in the contract drawings. This indicates that the bracing was probably redesigned at a later date to include the lateral loads from the ash silo.

Earthquake Damage

The coal building was the only area that received heavy damage. The bracing and struts that resisted the lateral loads from the ash silo were damaged.

A 21-in. beam at column B-13 failed at the connection (Figures 144 and 145). This beam acted as a strut to carry the silo seismic loads to diagonal-tension bracing, and the

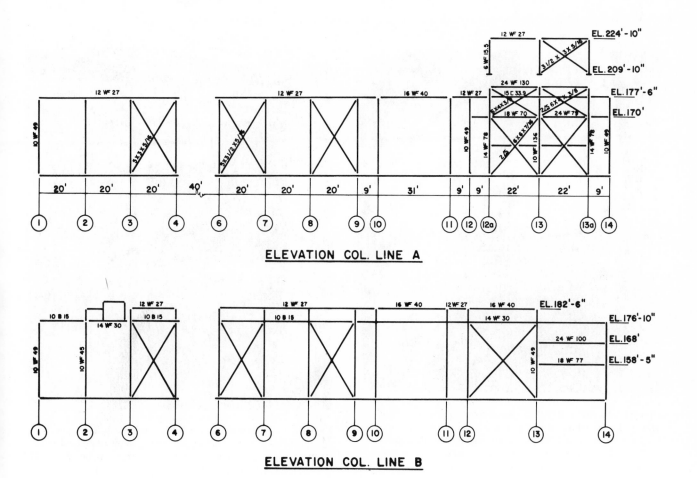

FIGURE 142 West Elmendorf Power Plant. Detail of column lines A and B.

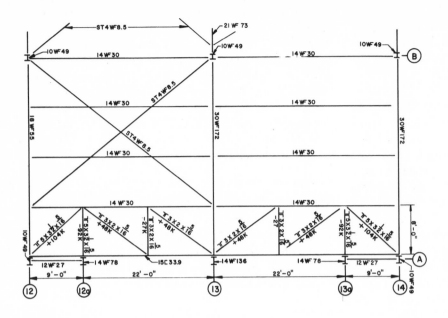

FIGURE 143 West Elmendorf Power Plant. Original plan, fan-room roof (forces shown were taken from the contract drawings).

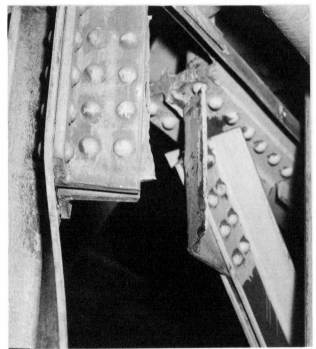

U. S. Air Force

FIGURE 144 View of 21WF73 beam connection to 10WF49 column. This is column B-13 on Figures 126 and 144. The 6 × 4 × 9/16 diagonal angles, tee gusset, and bottom flange of the 21-in. beam are shown. This was the only total connection failure in the West Elmendorf Power Plant.

FIGURE 145 View of column B-13 before removal showing rotation of near flange. Clip angles connected tee gusset and 21WF73 beam. Webs of gusset and beam completely failed. Pipe at left is a temporary support. West Elmendorf Power Plant.

roof bracing also framed into each side of the beam (Figure 146). The roof braces on each side were in different horizontal planes and were connected to the beam approximately 1½ ft from the column, which may have contributed to the beam failure; the preceding analysis, however, indicates that, even without this, the beam was overstressed by 73 percent. Column B-13, a 10-in. section, was twisted about its vertical axis for 20 ft.

A horizontal truss between columns 14 and 12 along column line A, designed to transfer the silo seismic load to column lines 14, 13, and 12, was twisted for a distance of 18 ft (Figure 147). The web members framed into the bottom flange of this beam and the top flange of the other chord. Some web connections failed, and a 15-in. channel forming the other truss chord was twisted and bent (Figure 148).

The roof bracing over the coal-storage area was bowed and some connections showed permanent deformation.

The framing supporting the fan-room floor consisted of 12-in. beams of various weights. A 21-lb beam over the thawing-shed door failed at its connection to a 24-in. beam. Figure 149 shows repair.

Postearthquake Analysis

Calculations indicate that the ash silo would have a dead weight of 1,072 kips and a full live load of 868 kips, using an ash weight of 45 pcf. The total lateral loads from the silo would be 400 kips. Column line 12a and 13a would each receive 200 kips. If we assume the horizontal truss to act as two simple trusses, column line 13 would receive a total of 258 kips. This load would stress the 21-in., 73-lb strut to 12.0 kips per in.[2]. If we analyze the strut as a secondary member with an unsupported length of 33 ft, the allowable stress is 6.6 kips per in.[2]. This results in an overstress of 81 percent, which is more than the allowable overstress of 33 percent. It should be stated that the lateral

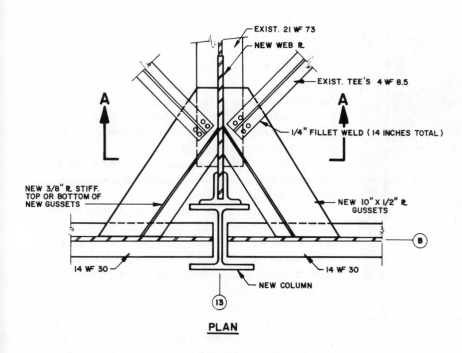

PLAN

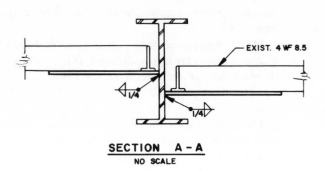

SECTION A - A
NO SCALE

FIGURE 146 Repair detail at column B-13. Note eccentricity of S+4WF in section A–A. West Elmendorf Power Plant.

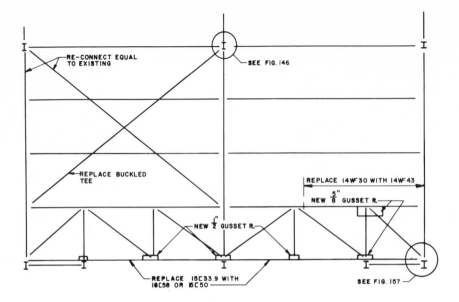

FIGURE 147 Repair plan, fan-room roof. West Elmendorf Power Plant.

U. S. Air Force

FIGURE 148 Column A-14. This bracing resisted lateral loads from the ash silo (Figure 147 shows repairs). West Elmendorf Power Plant.

loads assigned to column line 13 according to the code may have had little relation to the actual loads during the quake. The lateral bracing connected to this strut would produce a load perpendicular to the strut and may have contributed to the failure.

The ash silo itself received little damage. Figure 150 indicates the relative movement between the silo columns and a concrete wall at column line A. When the 21-in. beam failed, the silo moved and began to hammer the building. A resulting gap between some members indicated the silo

to be leaning 3 in. toward the west at the coal-building roof and about 5 in. at the top of the silo.

The cross bracing on the main floor of the boiler room area was bowed. This was typical of bracing in each direction near the middle of the area and was probably caused by the angles elongating under a tension load and then bowing under compression when the building returned to, or past, its original position (Figure 151).

The Elmendorf Power Plant was out of operation about 5 hours because of nonstructural damage to the plant, pump house, and water lines.

The 24-in. supply lines and 18-in. return lines for the turbine condenser were ruptured between the plant and the pump house because of a localized slide. The 36-in. line between the pump house and the cooling pond was broken in about five places; the cooling pond required minor repairs to cracks and joints.

A break in the instrument air-control line was another factor in the plant shutdown. Also, an 8-in. domestic water line for fire control broke in the main floor, allowing 60,000 gallons of treated water stored on the fan-room floor to enter the lines and run into the basement sump, submerging the sump pumps. The sump had to be pumped out immediately.

High-pressure-steam loop lines and electrical control and supply circuits were lightly damaged. One control panel in the main floor of the boiler room upset (Figure 152); this panel had been anchored with one 1/2-in. bolt in each corner.

Chemicals upset in the laboratory, and some testing equipment was damaged. The superheating coils and brick tiles in the boilers were damaged.

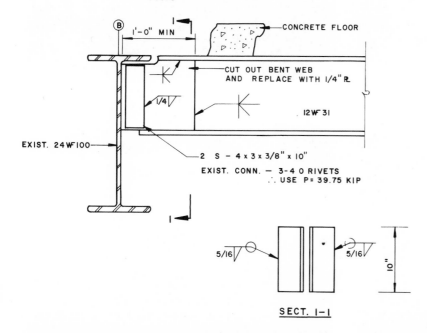

NOTE: 12WF 31 UNDER CONCRETE FLOOR
PARALLEL TO AND ABOVE ROLL-UP
DOORS

CONCRETE FLOOR

1'-0" MIN

CUT OUT BENT WEB
AND REPLACE WITH 1/4" PL.

12WF 31

EXIST. 24WF 100

2 S - 4 x 3 x 3/8" x 10"

EXIST. CONN. — 3-4 ⌀ RIVETS
∴ USE P = 39.75 KIP

SECT. 1-1

FIGURE 149   Repair detail, fan-room floor.
West Elmendorf Power Plant.

FIGURE 150   Column in coal-thawing shed showing independent
movement of column. West Elmendorf Power Plant.

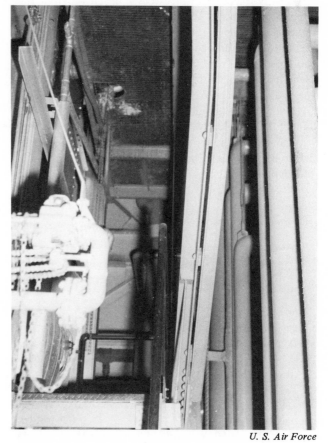

U. S. Air Force

FIGURE 151   Cross bracing in boiler-room area showing bow,
which is typical of damage to the cross bracing in the boiler room.
West Elmendorf Power Plant.

FIGURE 152 Damaged control panel that had not been adequately anchored in the boiler-room area of West Elmendorf AFB Power Plant. Panel had one ½-in.-diameter anchor bolt in each corner.

U. S. Air Force

U. S. Air Force

FIGURE 154 Measuring device between turbine foundation and operating floor shows no differential settlement. West Elmendorf Power Plant.

Many of the coal cars that were in the coal-thawing shed slipped off the track. The track was damaged, and the slab-on-grade subsided about 2 in. Figure 153 shows the settlement of the soil around the plant. A transformer pad on the southeast side of the building tilted because of soil settlement and the transformers had to be shimmed up. Part of the ceiling of the latrine collapsed when the 24-in., 100-lb beam supporting the ceiling deck moved west with the silo and let the deck drop down.

Figure 154 indicates that no differential settlement occurred between the turbine foundations and the building foundation.

U. S. Air Force

FIGURE 153 Outside wall of West Elmendorf Power Plant shows ground consolidation or settlement. Transformer pad on east side of plant was tilted away from the building.

Repair of Earthquake Damage

Column B-13 was replaced down to elevation 155 ft with a 12-in. column. A new web was welded in the 21-in. beam and the beam was reconnected (Figure 155). All diagonal cross-bracing connections were checked, and loose or sheared rivets were replaced with high-strength bolts; bowed diagonals were straightened by heat treatment or were replaced.

The ash silo was left out of plumb and braced as shown in Figure 156.

The horizontal truss was repaired (Figures 147 and 157–159) by replacing the original channel with a heavier channel and replacing the damaged 14-in. beam with a 43-lb beam.

All new connections were welded (Figures 149 and 159) because the existing rivet holes were difficult to match.

The support-beam connections under the fan-room floor were removed and replaced with welded connections, permitting the framing in column line B to be plumbed. Figures 160 and 161 show other welded connections.

The cooling-water lines were repaired immediately. The 24-in., 18-in., and 10-in. lines between the plant and pump house were replaced with steel pipe, making it possible to run overhead lines to the pump house and keep the lines away from the unstable ground. The electrical lines also were placed overhead (Figure 162). The 36-in. line between the pump house and cooling line was inspected internally by camera and was repaired in at least five places.

The latrine ceiling was restored to its original condition.

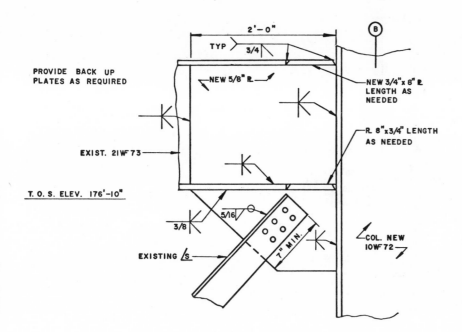

FIGURE 155   Repair detail for 21WF73 at column B-13. West Elmendorf Power Plant.

Most of the remaining nonstructural damage in the plant was repaired by plant personnel.

A breakdown of the repair costs follows:

36-in. water line and cooling pond	$ 50,000
Water and electrical lines between pump house and plant	86,000
Building—structural repair (approximately)	90,000
Building—miscellaneous (approximately)	20,000
TOTAL	$246,000

The original cost of the plant was $11,961,000, based on 1956 prices, so that the repair cost of $246,000 is 2 percent of the original cost.

The damage to the Elmendorf Power Plant calls attention to the importance of maintaining utilities in a functioning condition. Such facilities are of great importance in a disaster and should be designed so as to be capable of functioning after a severe earthquake.

FIGURE 156   New bracing on ash silo of West Elmendorf Power Plant, which was added to meet criteria of the 1964 *Uniform Building Code.*

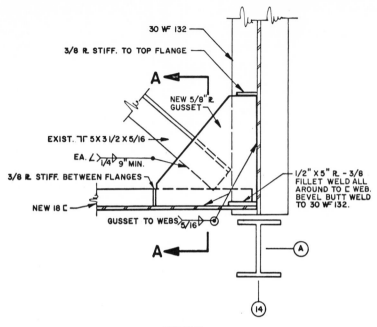

30 WF 132

3/8 ℞ STIFF. TO TOP FLANGE

A

NEW 5/8" ℞ GUSSET

EXIST. ℡ 5 X 3 1/2 X 5/16

EA. ∠ 1/4 9" MIN.

3/8 ℞ STIFF. BETWEEN FLANGES

NEW 18 ℂ

GUSSET TO WEBS 5/16

1/2" X 5" ℞ - 3/8 FILLET WELD ALL AROUND TO ℂ WEB. BEVEL BUTT WELD TO 30 WF 132.

A

A

14

DETAIL

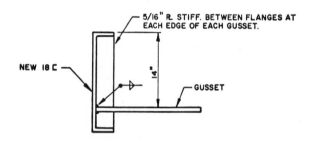

5/16" ℞ STIFF. BETWEEN FLANGES AT EACH EDGE OF EACH GUSSET.

NEW 18 ℂ

14"

GUSSET

SECTION A-A
NO SCALE

FIGURE 157 Repair detail of horizontal truss, West Elmendorf Power Plant.

U. S. Air Force

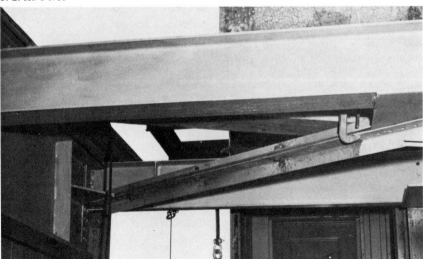

FIGURE 158 South end of horizontal truss along column line A during repair. Twisted beam at top was replaced. Door leads to ash silo on far side of wall. West Elmendorf Power Plant.

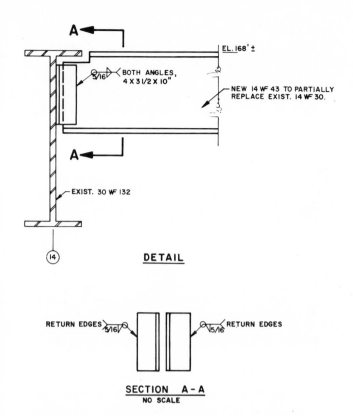

FIGURE 159 Purlin-repair detail of fan roof, West Elmendorf Power Plant (chord of horizontal truss between column lines A and B).

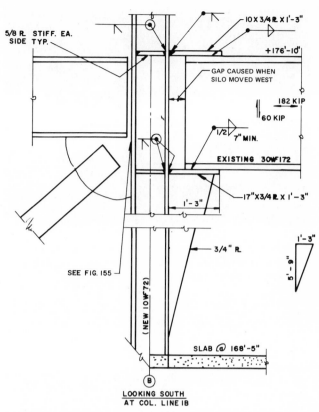

FIGURE 160 Repair detail of 30WF172 at column B-13, West Elmendorf Power Plant.

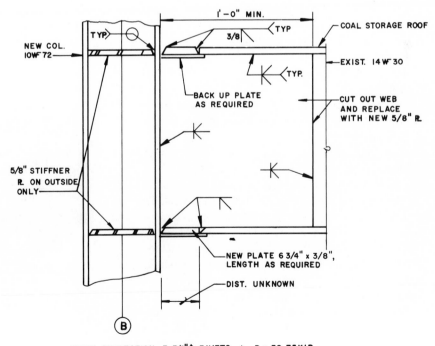

FIGURE 161 Repair details of 14WF30 at West Elmendorf Power Plant, column B-13.

EXIST. CONNECTION 3-3/4"∅ RIVETS ∴ P = 39.75 KIP

Section elevation of column line 13 on Figure 137 for location

FIGURE 162 Pump house for West Elmendorf Power Plant. Conduits and water lines were relaid overhead after a small landslide broke the water lines.

ELMENDORF WAREHOUSE

The one-story Elmendorf Warehouse 21-884, with an area of 226,000 ft² (Figures 110 and 163), was designed in 1951 and constructed in 1952 for a contract price of $3.82 million. The collapse of three of the five sections was the most dramatic structural failure on the base. Several adjacent warehouses of slightly different construction received only minor damage.

The warehouse, 225 ft wide and 1,004 ft long, ran in an east–west direction and was divided into five sections by concrete firewalls and seismic joints. An enclosed railroad siding and unloading ramp was run along the north wall. Figure 163 shows the warehouse as it appeared after the earthquake.

The roof system consisted of 2-in. tongue and groove decking nailed to wood blocking. The roofing was supported on structural-steel purlins, beams, and interior columns. The exterior walls and firewalls were of reinforced concrete with columns.

This warehouse was originally designed with structural-steel framing and cross bracing in the exterior walls. The contractor, however, chose to construct the building of reinforced-concrete tilt-up panels and reinforced-concrete columns. The remainder of the structure was constructed as originally designed. The 5-in. tilt-up panels were reinforced with wire mesh and 1/2-in. bars at 4-ft centers, and the columns had four 3/4-in. bars and 3/8-in. ties at 16-in. centers.

The fire walls were used as bearing walls for the framing from one side, and a structural-steel frame supported the roof on the other side. The structural-steel frame had light cross bracing in the outside bays; 1-in. anchor bolts embedded about 12-in. in the concrete provided the beam connections in the concrete. The beam connection had two bolts at the fire walls and four bolts at the sidewall. Figures 164 and 165 give general framing details.

Each section in this structure relied on diagonal bracing in the roof to transmit lateral loads through the steel beams to the tilt-up walls and to the foundation parallel to the length of the building and through the cross bracing and fire walls to the foundation in the transverse direction.

The design stresses and loads were as follows:

Concrete—footings	f_c' = 2,500 psi
—all other	3,000 psi
Reinforcing	f_s = 20,000 psi
Structural steel—1946 *American Institute of Steel Construction specifications*	
Soil bearing	5,000 psf
Snow load	50 psf
Floor loads	250 psf
Wind	40 psf
Seismic	8% gravity

Earthquake Damage

Sections 2, 3, and 4 completely collapsed; the contents of section 3 partly supported the roof. Sections 1 and 5 collapsed partly at the end walls. Many of the anchor bolts connecting the roof framing to the concrete columns pulled loose from the concrete. In general, there were no ties at the top of the concrete columns and the concrete failed with little damage to the anchor bolts (Figure 166).

The cross bracing in the column lines that supported the roof at the fire walls pulled free; in most cases the welds broke before the members deformed.

FIGURE 163 Elmendorf Warehouse 21-884, north elevation, showing the collapsed sections 2 and 4, and section 3, which collapsed but was supported by the material stored within. Roof failures are evident at the exterior walls of sections 1 and 5.

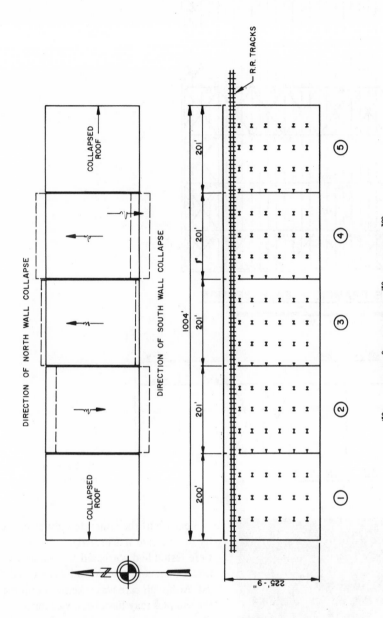

FIGURE 164 Floor plan and schematic plan of building collapse, Elmendorf Warehouse.

953

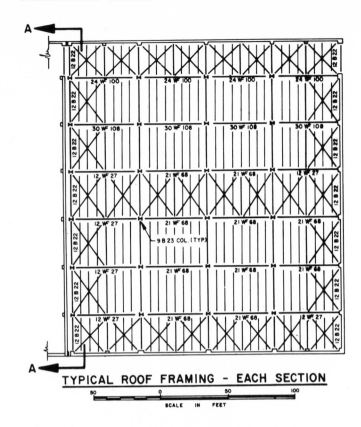

TYPICAL ROOF FRAMING - EACH SECTION

SCALE IN FEET

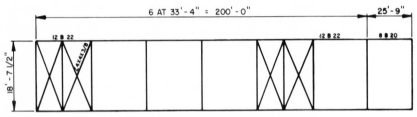

SECTION A - A

FIGURE 165   Typical framing details, Elmendorf Warehouse.

FIGURE 166   Failure at the tip of an exterior column. Anchor bolts showed only minor signs of stress in bending and shear. Elmendorf Warehouse.

Because of the concrete failures in the columns the quality of concrete was investigated. Two square samples that were tested had corrected test values of 2,075 psi and 2,927 psi. A 6-in. core sample had a corrected test value of 4,100 psi. Although care was taken in sampling, the concrete in the samples may have been weakened. Figures 167 and 168 show damage at two columns. Figures 169–175 give general views of the warehouse.

FIGURE 167 Exterior beams and purlin with nailing strip and roof of collapsed section. Lower part of photo shows the anchor bolts that were only slightly bent when the concrete column failed. Elmendorf Warehouse.

FIGURE 169 Exterior column base after the wall fell. The reinforcing broke with little sign of distortion. The arrow points to the reinforcing in place at the fracture zone. Elmendorf Warehouse.

FIGURE 168 Failure of interior concrete columns built into one of the transverse fire walls, Elmendorf Warehouse.

FIGURE 170 Damaged wall being removed. Roof section is supported by 6 × 6-in cribbing on exterior and new pipe columns on the interior. Elmendorf Warehouse.

FIGURE 171   South elevation looking west from section 4. In the foreground is the south wall of section 4 and roof, which collapsed to the north. Elmendorf Warehouse.

FIGURE 172   View of section 2, which collapsed to the south, showing total separation of anchor bolts from the columns. Elmendorf Warehouse.

FIGURE 173   Collapse of sections 2 and 3. Section 3 was supported by material stored within, which did not allow it to collapse as section 2 did. After the earthquake, section 3 was leaning to the north and it is assumed that it would have collapsed in that direction. Elmendorf Warehouse.

FIGURE 174   Fire wall between sections 3 and 4. The side wall of section 4 is lying in the foreground. Elmendorf Warehouse.

FIGURE 175   South elevation, showing collapsed sections 2 and 3. Section 3 collapsed but was supported by the materials stored inside. Sections 1 and 5 (not in the photo) remained fairly plumb. Elmendorf Warehouse.

Repair of Earthquake Damage

Sections 4 and 5 were demolished completely, and the roof systems of sections 1, 2, and 3 were jacked up. The exact cause of the collapse of this structure is difficult to determine. It seems likely, from the information available, that the anchor bolts and cross-bracing connections failed and started the collapse. There were no connections between the roof system and the cross walls except for the diagonal bracing, and, as the cross bracing in the roof system was halfway down the beams, an eccentric load was exerted on the anchor bolts. It is, of course, possible that the actual earthquake forces were sufficiently in excess of the 8 percent of gravity design loads to produce failure.

The demolition and salvage cost approximately $200,000. The rebuilding of the three units cost about $1,300,000.

SUMMARY AND CONCLUSIONS

Some structures at Fort Richardson and at Elmendorf AFB were damaged by the ground shaking. In general, however, the behavior of the structures on the military bases was judged to have been somewhat better than that of comparable structures elsewhere in Anchorage. Most of the damage that was sustained by military structures could have been avoided by more careful and more detailed engineering design. The extra cost of this additional effort in creating the designs and in construction would have been relatively small.

One of the most important lessons learned from the earthquake is that the seismic design should prevent any damage that might interfere significantly with the operation of the base. There should be no collapse of structures, no interference with the functioning of a structure because of nonstructural damage, and no damage to equipment required for operation of the base. On the basis of the Alaska experience, we conclude that such earthquake-resistant design and construction can be achieved with little extra cost by giving careful attention to the design requirements.

Most of the damage sustained by the two military bases was not severe enough to interfere with the effective operation of the bases, but it did involve significant expenditures for repair. It would probably not be economically justifiable to require a military base to be designed so that there would be no damage in the event of very strong ground shaking; if the cost of repairing the damage does not exceed the overall cost required to prevent it, that amount of possible damage would be acceptable. Much of the damage at Fort Richardson and at Elmendorf AFB could have been prevented by changes in the original designs that would have involved little, if any, extra cost. Designers of structures for military bases can learn how to avoid such damage by studying the damage caused by the Alaska earthquake.

ACKNOWLEDGMENT

Except as otherwise noted, the figures in this paper are credited to the U.S. Army Corps of Engineers.

GARY G. STURMAN
U.S. ARMY CORPS OF ENGINEERS DISTRICT,
ALASKA

The Alaska Railroad

ABSTRACT: The 1964 earthquake severely damaged The Alaska Railroad. Landslides, embankment failures, subsidence of ground, tsunami action, and soil movements that distorted or destroyed bridges were the main causes of damage. Reconstruction of the railroad facilities was completed in 2½ years at a cost of $22 million.

The Alaska earthquake of March 27, 1964, severely damaged The Alaska Railroad, a government-owned transportation enterprise. The railroad—extending from Seward, the southernmost terminus, about 420 mi through the south central Alaska "rail belt" to Fairbanks—is the key transportation link between these two cities. Severe to moderate damage was inflicted on 112 mi of track from Seward to Anchorage, on the 12.4-mi branch line from Whittier to Portage, and on about 100 mi of track north of Anchorage. (See Figure 1 for the extent of the railroad within the zone of greatest earthquake activity.) Within this area, bridges, shops, docks, communications facilities, and rolling stock either suffered major damage or were totally destroyed.

Immediately after the earthquake, Alaska Railroad personnel, assisted by Clair A. Hill & Associates (consulting engineers from Redding, California) and Earl and Wright (a firm of consulting engineers from San Francisco, California), attacked the big problem of assessing the damage to the facilities. The Alaska Railroad staff, having completed a survey of damage, had opened the track to traffic between Palmer and Anchorage by April 7, 1964, 11 days after the earthquake. With Alaska Railroad personnel and equipment, supplemented by equipment hired from contractors, the track between Anchorage and Whittier was open to traffic by April 20, 1964.

The railroad contracted with Clair A. Hill & Associates to make the necessary engineering studies, including soils analyses for recommendations on preparation of contracts for permanent restoration of the roadbed from Anchorage to the Portage area. The railroad authorities assigned to the U.S. Army Engineer District, Alaska, the task of designing and supervising construction of the new dock, marshaling yard, transit shed, and enginehouse at Seward. The Alaska Railroad and Earl and Wright undertook all other design work, with Earl and Wright personnel working in the Anchorage railroad design office to expedite plans.

By September 1966, the railroad had reconstructed all essential bridges, roadbed, track, shops, transit sheds, and

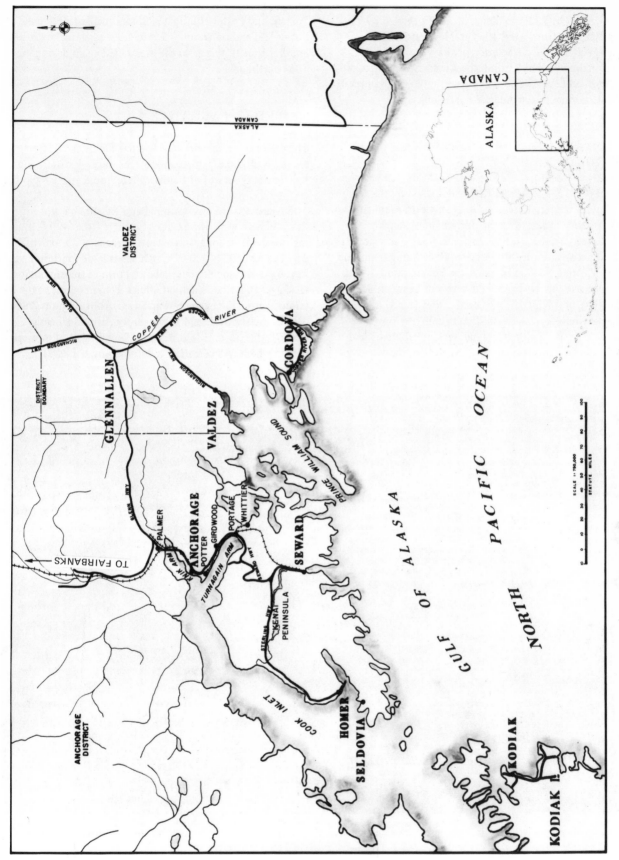

FIGURE 1 Route map of southern portion of The Alaska Railroad.

dock, at a cost of $22.1 million. All freight carried by The Alaska Railroad from April 1964 to May 1966 came through Whittier. On completion of the $11 million dock and marshaling yard at Seward, the Alaska Steamship Company resumed deliveries to that port, and the railroad resumed its normal preearthquake operations.

RECENT HISTORY OF THE ALASKA RAILROAD

Until May 1962, The Alaska Railroad, owned by the federal government, operated independently of all other railroads in North America in regard to the normal interchanging of cars between carriers. At that time, a rail-barge service was initiated between Prince Rupert, British Columbia, and the port of Whittier, Alaska. In 1963, the Puget Sound–Alaska Van Lines also initiated a rail-barge service between Seattle, Washington, and Whittier, thus connecting The Alaska Railroad with what many Alaskans like to call "the lower 48."

In the past, the railroad had had serious problems with snowslides and landslides south of Anchorage, between Portage and Potter Hill. In 1929, rains caused sliding at Potter Hill and on October 3, 1954, an earthquake caused another slide in this area; the area failed again during the 1964 earthquake.

RAILROAD FACILITIES

The major terminal and maintenance facilities of The Alaska Railroad are at Anchorage, Seward, Whittier, and Fairbanks; those at Fairbanks suffered no damage from the earthquake.

Seward was the key terminal and was the hardest hit. Located here were two marginal wharves, one 490 ft long, the other 680 ft long; three gantry cranes; a 70-ton stiffleg derrick; two 100 × 400-ft transit sheds; a depot building; heating plant; enginehouse; about 11 mi of marshaling-yard trackage; and other small buildings. These facilities extended across the entire Seward waterfront (Figures 2 and 3). The Alaska Steamship Company delivered all cargo through this port, except that for Anchorage and interior Alaska which was delivered to Whittier by barge.

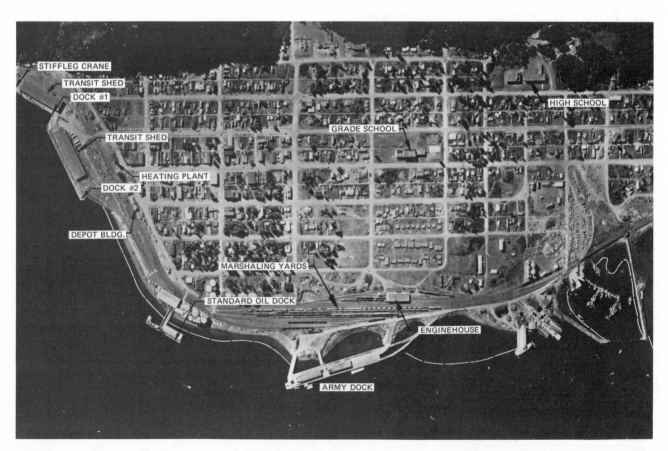

FIGURE 2 Preearthquake photograph of the Seward waterfront showing The Alaska Railroad facilities that extend across the entire waterfront.

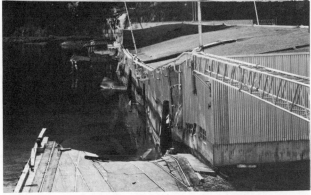

FIGURE 3   A, Vertical photograph of Seward waterfront after the earthquake showing destroyed docks, marshaling yards, warehouses, and damaged or destroyed rolling stock. B, View looking south of Dock 2.

The railroad facilities located in Anchorage, adjacent to Ship Creek, include the railroad's main office and depot building, office annex, car shop, general repair shop, paint shop, diesel and heavy equipment shop, wheel shop, wood warehouses, a metal-storage shed, about 35 mi of marshaling-yard trackage, and other small buildings. These facilities (Figure 4) constitute the heart of The Alaska Railroad.

Whittier, a port of limited use before the earthquake, is located on Prince William Sound and connected to the Seward–Anchorage mainline track by a spur line 12.4 mi long. Whittier railroad facilities include a marginal dock, depot building, transit shed, rail-barge slip, communications building, fire station, about 4 mi of marshaling-yard trackage, and other smaller structures (Figure 5). After the earthquake, this port was the only one where cargo for An-

chorage and interior Alaska could be unloaded from ships. The Canadian National Railway from British Columbia, the Puget Sound–Alaska Van Lines from Seattle, both rail-barge shippers, and the Alaska Steamship Company all began calling at the port of Whittier after the earthquake.

The railroad continues north from Anchorage to the coalfields near Palmer and on to Fairbanks, the railroad's northern terminus.

At the time of the earthquake, The Alaska Railroad had about 2,000 railcars of various types and 37 diesel–electric engines. The main-line track from Seward to Fairbanks is 470.3 mi long; additional branch lines increase this total to 543.7 mi of track. About 200 mi of the total trackage was in the zone of the earthquake damage.

Before the earthquake, the average traffic hauled by the railroad between the major cities was as shown in Table 1.

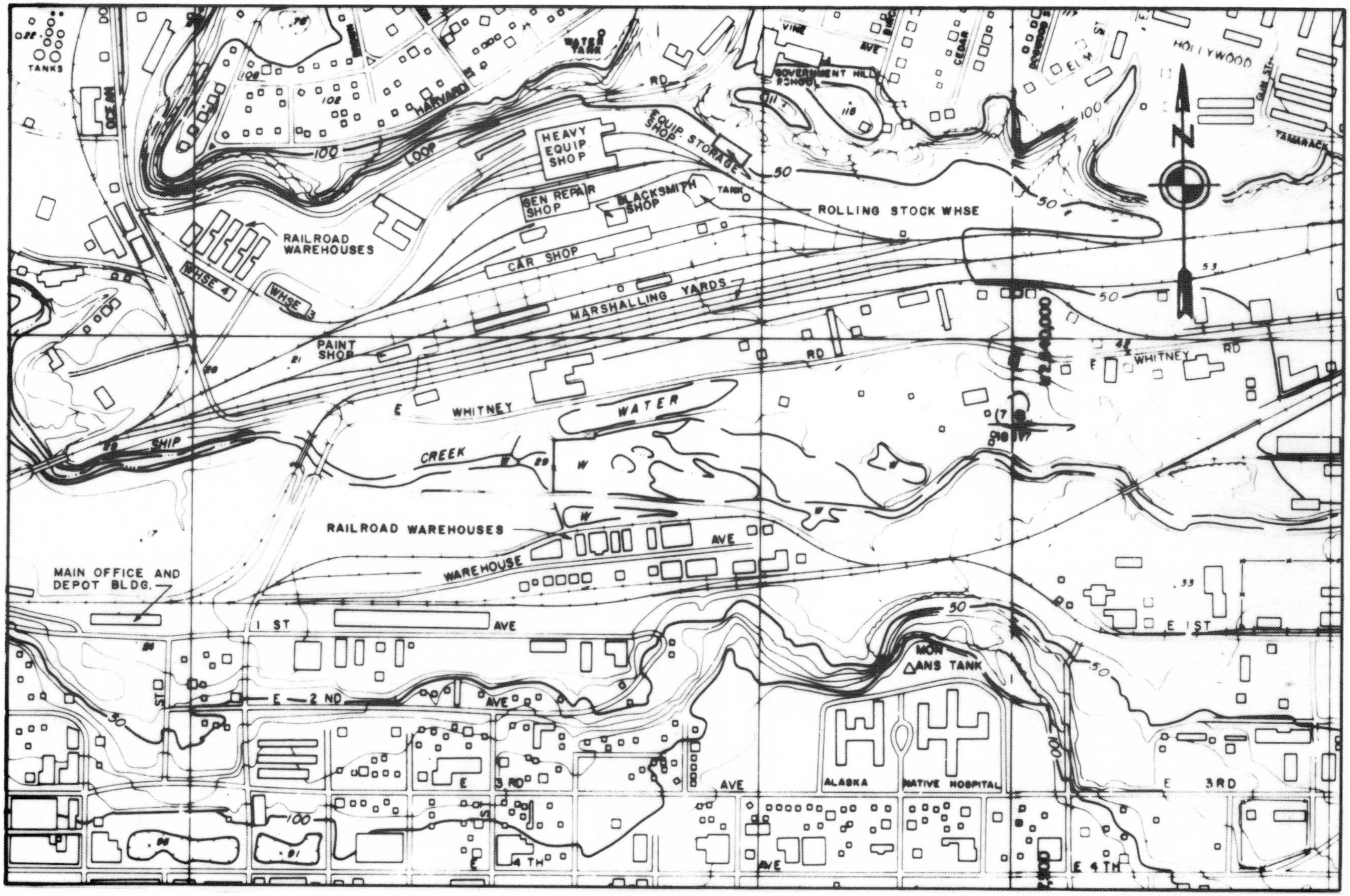

FIGURE 4 Alaska Railroad facilities in Anchorage.

FIGURE 5   Whittier waterfront showing major Alaska Railroad facilities after the earthquake.

There was a noticeable change in the distribution of freight carried by the railroad after the earthquake. Ships began to deliver freight directly to Anchorage on a year-round basis; this decreased the quantity of freight from Seward to Anchorage. Reduced docking facilities at Valdez resulted in the delivery of more freight to Anchorage, thereby increasing the amount of freight from Anchorage to Fairbanks.

LOCATION OF THE RAILROAD

The section of railroad affected by the earthquake of March 27, 1964, lies in south central Alaska. Seward, the railroad's most southerly point, lies at the head of the deep fiord, Resurrection Bay, an arm of the North Pacific Ocean. The town is situated on an alluvial outwash delta formed by a small steep-gradient stream. This stream, Lowell Creek, is now diverted through a tunnel to a point south of the town. Steep mountains, to an elevation of 5,000 ft mean sea level (MSL), surround the Seward area. Resurrection River, a large glacier-fed stream enters the bay north of Seward.

From Seward, the railroad and highway enter the Chugach National Forest and proceed north up the Snow River Valley toward Placer Pass and Portage. The railroad leaves the route of the highway at Trail Lake to cross the 1,060-ft-high pass through the rugged Chugach Mountains. From the pass, the railroad proceeds down the Placer River Valley over a steep, winding grade that goes through six short tunnels to rejoin the highway. This junction, at the head of Turnagain Arm, a branch of Cook Inlet, is the site of the town of Portage. A spur track from the port of Whittier connects with the main-line track at this point.

From Portage the railroad and highway proceed west along the north side of Turnagain Arm to Anchorage (Figure 6). Here the railroad is constructed alternately on side-hill benches through bedrock and glacial till and on the mud flats, from Portage to Potter, a section point about 12 mi southeast of Anchorage. From Potter to Anchorage, the track passes over a relatively flat coastal plain, dotted with numerous small lakes and swamps; the transition from the mud flats to the plain is made at Potter Hill, where the track bed is cut into the side of a sandy silt cliff.

Whittier, The Alaska Railroad's port of entry for railcars carried by barge, lies on the south shore of Passage Canal, a

TABLE 1   Average Traffic Hauled by The Alaska Railroad

Route	Cars/Trip[a]	Trips/Week	Type of Cargo
Seward to Anchorage	73 (42)	5 (2)	Cargo vans, groceries, fresh vegetables, petroleum products, automobiles, lumber, and beer
Anchorage to Seward	43 (25)	5 (2)	Vans of household goods, automobiles, scrap iron, personal effects, contractor equipment, and construction materials
Whittier to Anchorage	37 (29)	3 (4)	Same as from Seward
Anchorage to Whittier	23 (29)	3 (4)	Army equipment, scrap, contractor equipment, household goods, and automobiles
Anchorage to Fairbanks	51 (75)	4 (4)	Essentially the same as from Seward to Anchorage
Fairbanks to Anchorage	23 (23)	4 (4)	Essentially the same as from Anchorage to Seward

[a] Numbers in parentheses represent postearthquake traffic (October 1966).

fiord of Prince William Sound, about 62 mi southeast of Anchorage by road. The port of Whittier, which, like that of Seward, has year-round ice-free navigation and high rugged mountains, was originally developed by the Corps of Engineers in 1942–1943 to provide a secondary year-round port through which supplies could be transported to military bases at Anchorage and Fairbanks. The 12.4-mi-long spur track from Whittier to Portage passes under the Chugach Mountains through two unlined tunnels, 2.5 mi and 1 mi long, respectively, and continues to Portage across gravel alluvium.

The railroad from Anchorage north to Palmer and the Matanuska Valley crosses a coastal plain crisscrossed by many glacial rivers and streams.

SEWARD

Of the terminal areas belonging to The Alaska Railroad, Seward sustained the most severe damage (Figures 7–9). The material on which The Alaska Railroad constructed its docks and marshaling yard is slate debris deposited as a large delta of Lowell Creek to a depth of 150 ft on the floor of Resurrection Bay. The slate debris ranges in size

from minute particles to boulders of several cubic feet in volume.

Before the earthquake, the two Alaska Railroad piers perched on about a 1:2 underwater ground slope. The failure of the railroad's docks and warehouses in this area was caused by the collapse of the underwater slope.

The subsequent tsunami further damaged partly collapsed buildings, the marshaling yard, boxcars, and engines.

Unpublished U.S. Army Corps of Engineers reports on inspections of the structures early in April 1964 briefly describe the damage to railroad structures. An assessment of the possibility of repair follows:

Dock 1.   This structure consists of a concrete pier and a steel-frame warehouse building with metal walls. Most of the building was destroyed and washed away. The remaining portion is unsafe and must eventually be removed. It may be used for temporary unloading if care is used. Complete area is structurally unsound.

Dock 2.   This structure consists of a concrete pier and a steel-frame warehouse building with metal walls. The building has lost its foundation because the outer side of the pier has collapsed. The building and pier are unusable, unsafe, and must be considered a complete loss.

Alaska Railroad Roundhouse (Enginehouse).   The building is a steel-frame, mill-type building with concrete-block walls. The building twisted and bent with failure in walls and frame; it is unsafe and should be removed.

Depot.   The depot is a one-story frame building with concrete basement. The building is sound and apparently undamaged.

The docks were severely damaged, but portions were

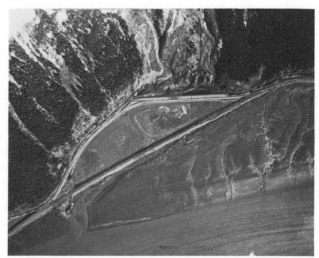

Park Aerial Surveys, Inc.

FIGURE 6   Vertical photograph showing typical relation between mountains, mud flats, railroad, and highway between Portage and Potter.

found to be usable. Of the three gantry cranes and one stiffleg crane in use on the docks before the earthquake, only one remained standing (Figure 10). After the earthquake, the railroad provided new rails for the remaining gantry crane and constructed a dolphin at the north end of Dock 2 so that cargo could be loaded or unloaded from ships at that dock. Minor repairs were made to Dock 1 to make it usable for barge loadings and unloadings. Docks 1 and 2 were the only facilities at Seward for receiving deep-draft vessels bringing supplies to Seward.

The railroad marshaling yard, spread across the Seward waterfront, was very badly damaged. Of the 2,000 cars owned by the railroad, about 250 were in Seward at the time of the earthquake. The following buildings and equipment at Seward were destroyed or so badly damaged that their repair was considered uneconomical:

1 Army dock (owned by the railroad)	70 flatcars
2 railroad docks	3 locomotive cranes
1 depot building	1 outfit car
1 dock heating system	1 hopper car
2 gantry cranes	24 boxcars
1 stiffleg crane	11 heater and refrigerator cars
2 transit sheds	21 gondolas
1 enginehouse	4 diesel carrier vans
1 10-ton bridge crane	1 gas-powered loader
6 unit rail boxes	3 tank cars
2 cranes	25 push cars
2 power cars	1 tie tamper
1 GP-7 locomotive	

An unknown number of oil-tank cars, belonging to the Standard Oil Company, were damaged or destroyed.

The 11 mi of marshaling-yard trackage were damaged or destroyed by a combination of slides, tsunami waves, and petroleum fires. Many of the railcars, battered by the tsunamis, would have suffered only minor damage if the earthquake had not caused petroleum products (from ruptured fuel tanks and tank cars) to be spread over the area and ignited (Figures 11-14).

The original cost to The Alaska Railroad of major facilities destroyed at Seward totaled about $8.5 million. Early in May 1964, the decision was made to rebuild The Alaska Railroad facilities at Seward. President Johnson made available about $19 million for rebuilding destroyed track and bridges between Anchorage and Seward and another $7.8 million for rebuilding The Alaska Railroad facilities at Seward. The railroad authorities decided to relocate their new facilities at the north end of Resurrection Bay rather than to rebuild at the old site along the Seward waterfront. The earthquake had proved the entire Seward waterfront to be unstable, and it would be virtually impossible to design a structure any safer from failure than the two original docks had been.

On June 1, 1964, The Alaska Railroad allocated $100,000 to the Corps of Engineers for advance design work on the railroad dock and backup facilities. The first step was to establish a suitable site. Three locations (Figure 15) were considered: one on the northwest, one on the northeast, and one on the east side of Resurrection Bay. The Alaska Railroad decided that the northwest location was definitely preferable from an operational viewpoint because of restrictions imposed by the labor unions concerning overtime and portal-to-portal pay and because of more accessibility to restaurants and housing. The railroad manager estimated that the choice of the northwest site would result in an annual operating costs savings of $100,000.

Initially, neither the northeast nor the northwest site was thought to have a satisfactory foundation. Investigations by Shannon & Wilson, Inc. (1964), soils mechanics and foundation engineers, later indicated that the foundation at the northwest site would be adequate. Maintenance dredging, however, would increase the annual costs of operating the site because of material carried by Resurrection River during floods. The east site was unsatisfactory from the operational standpoint because of the long circuitous railroad track required between the dock and marshaling yard. None of the possible locations satisfied everyone, but because the railroad preferred it, the northwest site was finally selected for detailed study and design. In selecting a new dock location, the effect of the tsunami was not seriously considered, because it would be impossible to locate the dock so as to avoid this danger.

NEW ALASKA RAILROAD DOCK

On July 2, 1964, The Alaska Railroad arranged for the Corps of Engineers to design, supervise, and inspect the construction of The Alaska Railroad facilities at Seward. The total expenditure was not to exceed $7.8 million. The Alaska Railroad facilities were to be completed by December 31, 1964. On July 23 and 24, 1964, the preliminary design was reviewed to ensure that the Seattle District of the Corps of Engineers, where the detailed design was being made, had received all the criteria.

After this review, the engineers concluded that the project, as designed, could not be constructed for the amount allotted. In establishing the original estimate of $7.8 million, a marginal wharf at the old townsite, without an enginehouse and without gantry cranes, had been envisioned, a normal construction schedule had been hoped for, and no auxiliary refinements to attract shippers to the terminal had been planned. In an attempt to reduce the overall costs, it was decided to salvage as much material as possible from the damaged railroad facilities at Seward and to supply these materials to the construction contractor as

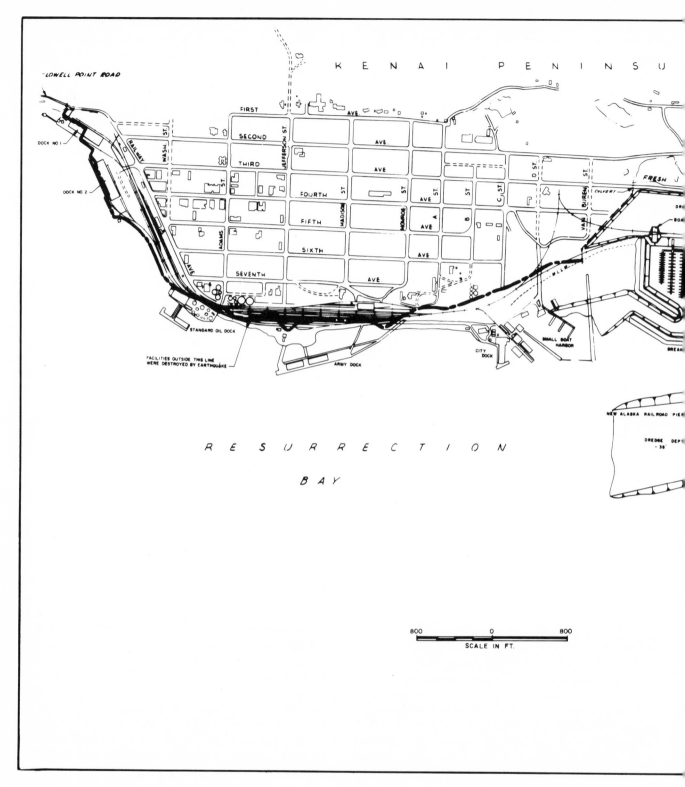

FIGURE 7   The old and new railroad facilities at Seward.

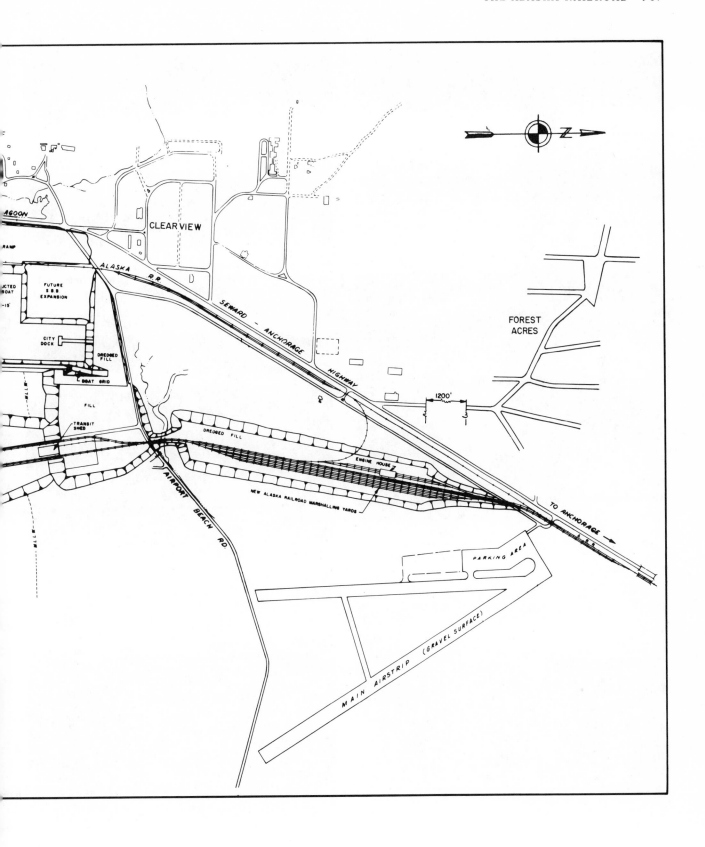

The Alaska Railroad

FIGURE 8   View of railroad dock, warehouse, and cranes at Seward before the earthquake, looking northeast.

FIGURE 9   View of docks, damaged warehouses, single remaining crane, and portion of marshaling yard at Seward after the earthquake, looking southwest.

FIGURE 10   Northeast view of Docks 1 and 2; only the north portion of Dock 1 remains. A gantry and stiffleg crane were lost when this structure collapsed.

FIGURE 11   Postearthquake view of Seward marshaling yard showing damaged freight cars and twisted track. The new railroad dock is located on the north end of Resurrection Bay, which is behind the damaged bus in this photograph.

FIGURE 12   Postearthquake view of Seward marshaling yard and burned oil tank cars. This area is visible on Figure 3.

FIGURE 13   Locomotive at Seward, overturned by the force of the tsunami.

FIGURE 14   View of track about 1 mi north of Seward showing fishing boats and debris on tracks.

government-furnished materials. The engineers planned several economizing measures, such as the use of lagging (Figure 16) on the piles to increase skin friction and to reduce overall length of piling required, the use of larger precast deck panels to save labor, reduction of Cooper's E60 loading to E50, and consideration of building a shorter dock. The use of a center sheet pile with earth-filled core was considered. In addition, separate schedules were to be incorporated in the bidding documents for a shorter dock, with two additive items to extend the dock an additional

96 ft and an extra 72 ft. The basic dock length was to be 432 ft in order to allow cranes to boom directly opposite vans aft of number 5 hatch on a converted liberty ship. The bid documents had two completion schedules, one for December 20, 1964, and the other for September 15, 1965. To decrease costs, the engineers considered moving the dock seaward to reduce the amount of dredging required, but they feared that a dock nearer deep water would be more susceptible to submarine landslides that might occur during another major earthquake.

While preliminary design was progressing, consultants to the Corps of Engineers (R. B. Peck, T. F. Thompson, L. Bjerrum, and S. Wilson) were working to determine the feasibility of constructing the dock at the northwest site. The overall stability of the northwest site from slide failure was adequate, but the ability of the soils at the site to support the H-piling was questionable.

Typical sections of the solid-core dock that was eventually abandoned and of the all-pile dock that was constructed are shown in Figure 17. Cost estimates showed that the solid-core dock would decrease the cost of the structure by about $500,000.

To expedite the construction schedule, as requested by The Alaska Railroad, the piling for the dock was purchased in advance so that it would be available when the contractor was ready to start construction. To meet the requested completion date of December 20, 1964, the order

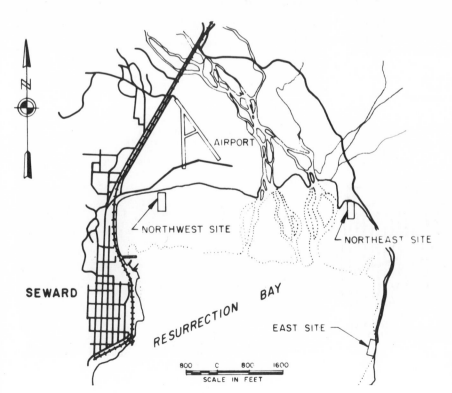

FIGURE 15   Three sites considered for The Alaska Railroad's new Seward dock facilities.

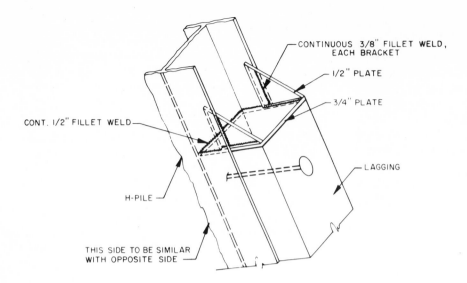

FIGURE 16   Isometric drawing of H-pile lagging.

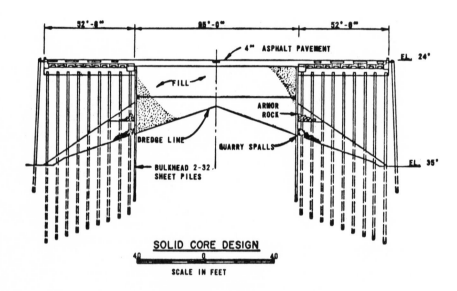

FIGURE 17   Typical sections of all-pile and solid-core dock.

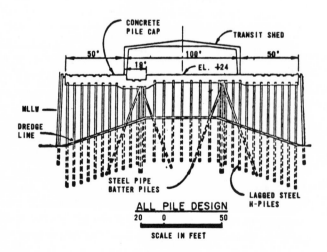

for piling was given in advance of a decision as to which type of dock was to be built. Based on the solid-core dock concept, a contract for $906,000 worth of steel was awarded on August 10, 1964. On August 11, the consultants and Corps of Engineers personnel agreed that the H-pile design was preferable; the supply contract was accordingly modified to delete the sheet pile necessary for the design with a solid core and to add the necessary H-piles. Proposals for construction were received in August 1964, and contract negotiations were completed in September of that year. It had become obvious by this time, that the work could not be completed by December 20, 1964. The contract was awarded on September 18, 1964, to William A. Smith Construction Company; completion was scheduled for September 15, 1965.

Before dock construction could proceed, it was necessary to dredge the area on which the dock was to be constructed and to provide shoreward landfill for access to the dock. A contract for dredging on an hourly basis was awarded on August 12, 1964. Work actually started August 28, 1964; a hydraulic pipeline dredge with a 20-in. diameter discharge started work in the railroad dock area in preparation for dock construction. By October 28, 1964, sufficient progress had been made by the dredge to allow the actual construction of the railroad dock to begin (Figure 18). To achieve design load-bearing capacities, piles had to be driven deeper than originally planned, and more piles had to be ordered. In addition, initial welding procedures used by the contractor did not conform to the specifications, and some piles had to be pulled out and redriven.

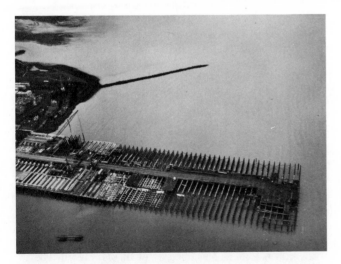

FIGURE 18 Construction of Alaska Railroad Dock, October 1965. The promotory (upper center) is rock-protected outfall sewer construction by Corps of Engineers for City of Seward. This barrier acts as a jetty to prevent material from being carried into dredged area adjacent to dock.

TRANSIT SHED

A new two-story transit shed (100 × 240 ft) was constructed on the new Alaska Railroad dock at Seward. This building replaced the two transit sheds that were located on the old railroad docks destroyed by the earthquake. The new transit shed is a prefabricated storage structure for goods in transit to other areas. The building has offices for the dock superintendent, yardmaster, agent, stevedoring firms, and steamship company. A mechanized ventilation system exhausts fumes from fork lifts operating in the warehouse portion of the building.

The basic building foundation and shell were constructed under the dock-construction contract awarded in August 1964 (Figure 19). The remainder of the building was completed under a separate contract, awarded in November 1965. The structure, costing $260,000, was completed in July 1966.

ENGINEHOUSE

A new enginehouse, in which to repair engines, was constructed in the new marshaling yard to replace the severely damaged one abandoned in the old railroad yard. The enginehouse foundation is visible at the right of the marshaling yard shown in Figure 20. The new enginehouse is a metal building 70 ft wide and 180 ft long. Because this was the last construction contract advertised for The Alaska Railroad at Seward, and the availability of sufficient funds to construct the desired length was uncertain, the building was bid as a basic structure 126 ft long, with two additive items—a single 18-ft-long bay and two 36-ft-long bays. The basic bid item of seven bays was planned to accommodate two locomotives, end to end. While the design was being prepared, however, The Alaska Railroad decided to purchase larger new locomotives. The railroad authorities preferred an eight-bay basic-bid item but agreed to the shorter structure, pending availability of additional funds. The railroad was able to finance the eight-bay structure by bid-opening time, and the construction contract was amended May 17, 1966. The design of the structure was almost identical to the original enginehouse that had been badly damaged by the earthquake. It included a small office, storage space, and lavatory.

Three tracks run through the enginehouse. The center track is the locomotive and equipment storage track; the two outside tracks are repair tracks, one with a pit and the other with a traveling overhead 15-ton crane. To use a preengineered building and still provide adequate clearances for the traveling crane, it was necessary to construct a 4-ft-high reinforced-concrete wall on which the building was set. The building was completed in July 1966 at a cost of

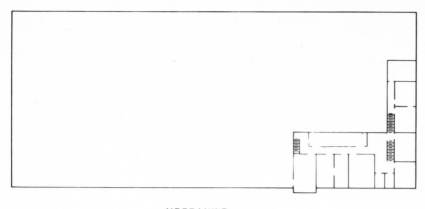

MEZZANINE

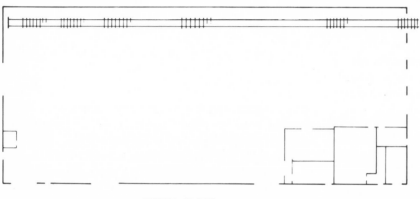

FIRST FLOOR

SCALE IN FEET

FIGURE 19   Seward transit shed.

FIGURE 20   Laying rail in new railroad marshaling yard at Seward in October 1965.

$304,000. Figure 21 shows the enginehouse location before construction.

NEW MARSHALING YARD

The new railroad marshaling yard at Seward was built on sandy gravel fill dredged from the approach and berthing area around The Alaska Railroad dock. The plan had been to pump the dredged material as close as possible to the location where it was to be used as fill, but the dredge could not pump the fill the required distances. The material was eventually placed by dredging it to the south end of the marshaling-yard area and then hauling it by truck to the north end. A total of 660,000 yd³ of fill was placed. The yard layout (Figure 21) has a total of 5.5 mi of track, compared to about 11 mi of track in the old yard. About 400 cars can efficiently utilize the new yard. The cost of this part of the dock-construction contract, including clearing, fill, and track construction, amounted to $970,000.

FIGURE 21   Looking south at The Alaska Railroad's reconstructed marshaling yard at Seward. Small-boat basin and City of Seward are visible in upper right portion of photograph.

ANCHORAGE

Anchorage, Alaska's largest city, is the administrative, logistical, and maintenance center for The Alaska Railroad (Figure 22). Although Anchorage as a whole sustained the bulk of the property damage in Alaska, The Alaska Railroad suffered less damage there than at Seward. Steam lines sustained major damage in addition to the following railroad property, which was eventually dropped from accounting rolls: three dormitories (30 X 80 ft), a wheel shop, one general office annex, and one car shop. The main office and depot building (Figure 23) was about 56 X 300 ft in area and three stories high; because of poor foundation conditions, it was built on a wood-pile foundation. The building was undamaged except for some cracked plaster, which was repaired under a contract administered by the railroad. The equipment-storage building, a new pre-engineered steel structure (Figure 24), was damaged

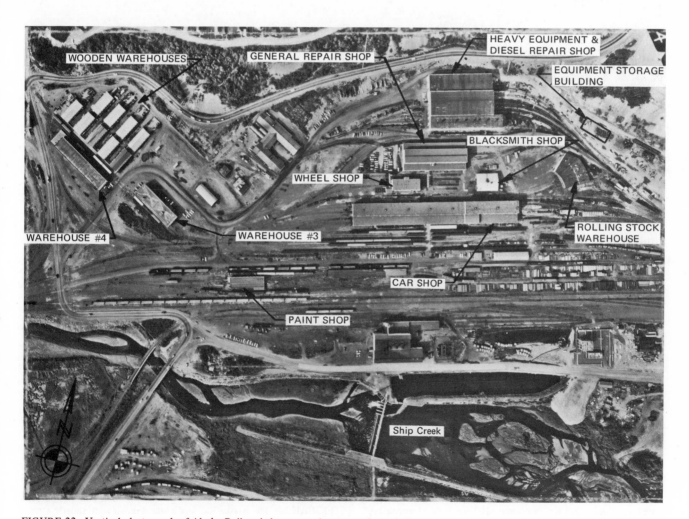

FIGURE 22   Vertical photograph of Alaska Railroad shops, warehouses, and marshaling yard. Downtown Anchorage is just south of this area.

FIGURE 23   The main office and depot building for The Alaska Railroad in Anchorage. Gravel fill in the foreground is part of the buttress being built in July 1966 to stabilize the Fourth Avenue area. Gantry crane (upper center) was knocked over by the earthquake.

The Alaska Railroad

FIGURE 25   Interior of The Alaska Railroad's slide-damaged equipment-storage building. This building was not repaired.

beyond economical repair by the Government Hill slide. The buckled rigid frames can be seen in upper left of Figure 25. This building was razed and not replaced.

The office annex building was a two-story concrete-block building on integral reinforced-concrete ground slab and footings, with wood-frame partitions and steel-joist second-floor and roof construction. Block walls in this structure were cracked at corners and leaned outward. Concrete-block parapet walls were dislodged. This building was demolished and replaced with a preengineered steel building costing $300,000.

The wheel-repair shop was a two-story concrete-block structure with steel frame, concrete second floor, and heavy

timber roof deck (Figure 26). Damage to the shop included collapsed block walls, bent columns, and diagonal ties. The Alaska Railroad constructed a new building on the existing foundation at a replacement cost of $297,000.

The car shop is a two-bay single-story steel-frame structure, 90 × 600 ft, with insulated metal-panel walls and heavy timber roof deck. Damage to this building was major, including elongated anchor bolts, stretched and broken sway bracing, loosened siding, and torn roofing. The Alaska Railroad had the building repaired at a cost of $622,000.

The railroad's general-repair shop is a three-bay one-story

FIGURE 24   The Alaska Railroad's equipment-storage building in Anchorage, destroyed by Government Hill landslide. Government Hill Elementary School stands in scarp at top of slide.

The Alaska Railroad

FIGURE 26   The Alaska Railroad's wheel-repair shop shortly after the earthquake showing steel-frame and concrete-block construction.

building, 100 × 350 ft, with steel frame, insulated metal-panel walls, heavy timber roof deck, two 60-ton bridge cranes in the center bay, and a 7½-ton bridge crane in the side bay. The building sustained heavy damage; column anchor bolts in this building were elongated, diagonal-rod sway bracing was stretched and broken, some siding was loosened, and some roofing torn. Repair of bracing and damaged foundation cost $191,000.

The heavy equipment and diesel repair shop is a four-bay one-story steel-frame structure with insulated metal-panel walls and a steel deck roof. The building was a 220 × 320-ft structure, with heavy-laced structural sway bracing, overhead cranes in three bays, and some concrete-block partitions. Damage included elongated column anchor bolts, cracked concrete-block partitions, and concrete service-platform columns broken at the floor line. The building actually sustained very minor damage and was repaired by The Alaska Railroad at a cost of $47,800.

Wooden warehouses and the rolling-stock warehouse (Figure 22) sustained little damage. About 2 mi of the 35 mi of marshaling-yard tracks in Anchorage were damaged. Most of the damage was caused by minor settlement or cracks that bent rails and sheared bolts. Repairs to track in the marshaling yard were made by The Alaska Railroad's own work force and by National Mechanical Contractors at a cost of $279,500. Three wooden dormitories, 30 × 80 ft, no longer in use and badly damaged by foundation failure, were torn down. The Alaska Railroad facilities in Anchorage were repaired at a total cost of $1,923,300.

WHITTIER

Railroad facilities in Whittier, although only about 45 mi from the earthquake epicenter, sustained relatively minor damage because the railroad had only a limited rail-barge and petroleum transportation operation in Whittier at the time of the earthquake. Also, foundation conditions are

FIGURE 28   Closeup view of rail-barge slip at Whittier.

generally better at Whittier than at Seward, where comparable docking facilities were destroyed.

The Alaska Railroad facilities damaged or destroyed in Whittier included the marginal wharf, transit shed, rail-barge slip, depot building, and marshaling yard.

The rail-barge slip (Figure 27), at the north end of the marginal wharf, was used to load railroad cars onto barges and then to unload them. The wooden towers used to lift and lower the slip were knocked down by the earthquake. Plate girders supporting ties and rails were bent and could not be reused (Figure 28).

The replacement facility designed by The Alaska Railroad was essentially the same as the original, except that the new towers were made of steel (Figure 29). The abutments used for the original structure were repaired and raised about 6 ft. Because this unloading facility was so urgently needed, fabrication was accelerated by assembling as much as possible at the plant in Seattle. Replacement of the rail-barge slip cost about $550,000 with an expedited schedule. The cost of the original slip, towers, and abutment, constructed in 1962, was $254,299.

Until completion of the new slip, The Alaska Railroad used a 250-ton floating crane obtained from the U.S. Army in California to provide almost uninterrupted rail-barge service to Anchorage by unloading onto the marginal wharf. Cost of repairing this facility was $399,000.

The Whittier depot, a wooden two-story structure not in use at the time of the earthquake, had one end knocked off by the tsunami (Figure 30). The railroad made minimal repairs to this building.

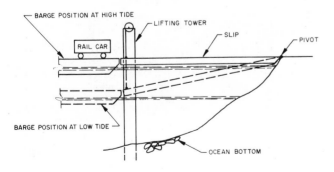

SCHEMATIC OF RAIL - BARGE SLIP AT WHITTIER

FIGURE 27   Schematic of rail-barge slip at Whittier.

The Alaska Railroad

FIGURE 29   New towers that operate The Alaska Railroad's rail-barge slip at Whittier.

The 4 mi of marshaling-yard track at Whittier were severely damaged. Track was buckled and pulled apart, debris was scattered over the tracks, and minor cracks and differential settlement occurred throughout the area. Track was repaired and debris cleared by The Alaska Railroad, but the cost figures are not available for this damage.

Steam, water, and sewer lines were damaged by ground cracks and differential settlement, but there was little or no damage to the railroad's communications building and fire station. The total cost of repairing and replacing Alaska Railroad facilities in Whittier was about $1,213,000.

PORTAGE

The railroad's depot at Portage, its only building of any importance in the area, was a one- and two-story combination post-and-beam concrete-block and timber-frame structure (Figure 31) with a café and apartment in the lower portion of the building. The depot was deflected out of shape by ground fissures and differential settlement, because the material under the building was a deep, sandy silt formation. Except for the apartment on the west end, the structure was torn down and never rebuilt. A communications building, which suffered some damage, was repaired for $21,000.

BRIDGES

The bridges between Seward, Mile 0, and the Portage area (about Mile 64) were the most severely damaged. In all, 109 bridges on The Alaska Railroad were damaged by the earth-

quake; 71 of the bridges were totally unserviceable for train operation until repairs could be made.

In general, the railroad used three types of bridge. The large steel-truss structures were used for large-stream and river crossings (Figure 32); the plate-girder and treated-timber structures were used for small-stream crossings (Figures 33 and 34). The only consistency about the bridge failures between Seward and Portage was that there tended to be shortening or longitudinal compression that dislodged superstructures from substructures (Figures 35 and 36). This bridge shortening was indicated for either a lateral or an upward movement.

The following is a general summary of earthquake damage to bridges and trestles:

1.   Trestle bents were crowded to the center of the structure, dislodging caps from piles and stringers. The compression of stringers and decks frequently broke stringer chords, with some relieving in vertical ruptures and others (more common) relieving with lateral breaks. At other locations, the stringers and decks overrode the bulkhead at the approach grade.

2.   Lateral distortion up to 8 ft developed where water crossed diagonally under the bridges. These thawed water channels may have acted as shear zones.

3.   Vertical distortion in trestles was as much as 5 ft, with the general pattern of approach grade subsiding as much as 4 ft and with a general vertical movement of pile bents at the centers of structures. Where the diagonal lurching passed through structures, piles were displaced as much as 12 ft, and a racking of the pile bents frequently broke off

The Alaska Railroad

FIGURE 30   Tsunami-damaged Alaska Railroad depot at Whittier.

U.S. Army

FIGURE 31   Alaska Railroad depot at Portage after the earthquake. The most apparent damage was in the right portion of building.

U.S. Army

FIGURE 32   The Alaska Railroad's Twentymile River Bridge (Mile 64.7). Destroyed highway bridge is at left of railroad bridge, and pilings of older railroad bridge are to the right.

U.S. Army

FIGURE 34   Typical small wooden railroad bridge.

U.S. Army

FIGURE 33   Typical plate-girder railroad bridge. Cribbed foundations shown were replaced after the earthquake.

The Alaska Railroad

FIGURE 35   Typical wooden bridge showing lateral movement of bridge superstructure.

The Alaska Railroad

FIGURE 36 Wooden bridge with vertical separation of substructure and superstructure.

the piling at the groundline or moved piles out from under the caps.

4. The longitudinal compression of the steel structures punched girders and trusses through the back walls of the abutments, sheared anchor and other connecting bolts, racked roller nests, and rotated pedestals where anchor bolts failed in tension. Intermediate piers were displaced with the same type of damage.

5. Piers were displaced as much as 20 in., requiring the resetting of 75 percent of the bearings on the damaged bridges. One stream pier was broken off at a cold joint, displaced 4 in. on the base, and tipped 8 in. Complete replacement of the shaft was necessary.

The Twentymile River Bridge (Mile 64.7) was a steel-truss structure with seven spans, each 70 ft 1 in. long. The Twentymile River has a drainage area of 160 mi². The de-

sign flow is 8,600 ft³/sec. Each span rested on a concrete pier supported on 11 steel piles, each of which consisted of three railroad rails welded together. This bridge sustained relatively minor damage, such as broken head walls at end abutments and one shifted pier. The land subsidence in the area caused the greatest problem: Six piers and two abutments had to be raised 4½ ft to keep the bridge above high tides. The piers and abutments were raised without interrupting service by jacking up each bridge span and cribbing with old railroad rails. Concrete was eventually poured around the cribbing, and new base plates were set. The girders over the pier that moved were welded together, and a common bearing was provided because of the shift (Figures 37 and 38).

The foundation material in the area of the Twentymile River Bridge varies from compact silty sandy gravel near the river bottom to very dense silty sand at 35 ft below the bottom. All bridges in the Portage area are constructed on this type of foundation material. Repair to the Twentymile River Bridge cost $160,000, primarily for raising the piers and abutments.

One important design modification made by the railroad was the installation of safety links at viaducts and at other structures with a series of spans; this linkage was made by bolting one span to another (Figure 39).

The timber trestle bridges were rebuilt to the same basic design except that steel piles replaced wood piles, and concrete headwalls replaced wood headwalls at abutments. The previous type of construction with an all-wood structure is shown in Figures 40 and 41 (Mile 63.4) and Figures 42 and 43 (Mile 34.5). The cost of repairing one bridge was from $300 to $160,000; the total repair cost for all bridges on the railroad amounted to $1,567,000 by December 1966. As of August 1968, some minor bridge repairs remain to be completed.

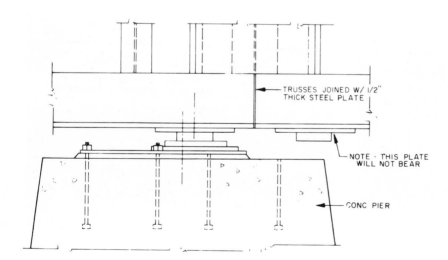

FIGURE 37 Detail of repaired truss on Twentymile River Bridge. Note that the bridge pier shifted to the left, leaving the right truss with no bearing.

The Alaska Railroad

FIGURE 38   View of raised concrete pier on railroad bridge crossing Twentymile River near Portage.

U.S. Army

FIGURE 41   Postearthquake view of bridge at Mile 63.4.

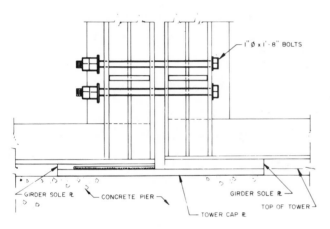

FIGURE 39   Elevation detail at expansion bearing.

U.S. Army

FIGURE 42   Preearthquake view of bridge at Mile 34.5.

U.S. Army

FIGURE 40   Preearthquake view of bridge at Mile 63.4.

The Alaska Railroad

FIGURE 43   Postearthquake view of bridge at Mile 34.5 shows extreme vertical displacement of this bridge.

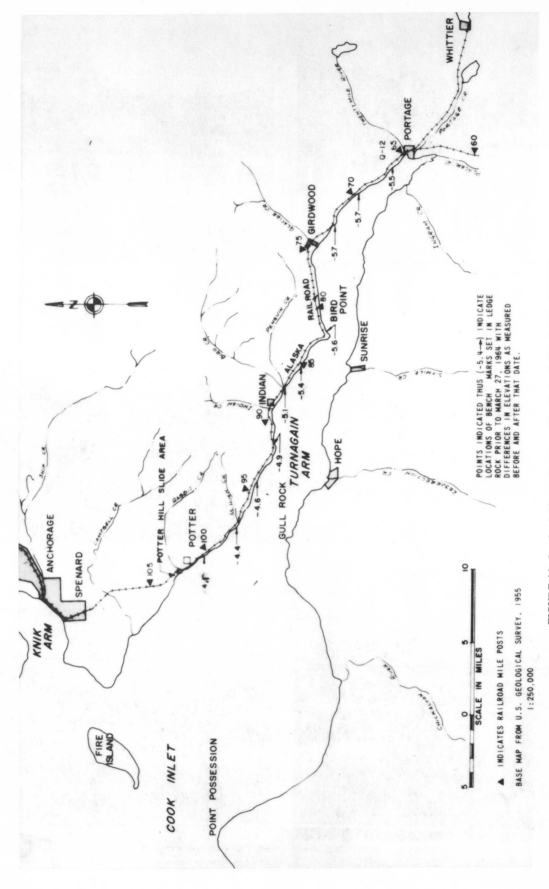

FIGURE 44 Land subsidence elevations, The Alaska Railroad, Mile 61.5–103.

ROADBED AND TRACK DAMAGE

The damage to the roadbed and track extended from Seward (Mile 0) to Pittman (Mile 167) and included the Whittier and Palmer branch lines; 3 mi of main line and 8 mi of yard and dock tracks were totally destroyed at Seward, because of the submarine slide, and at Potter Hill, because of the landslide. Because of local subsidence of the embankment, 47 mi of main line and 5 mi of siding, most of which was in the Portage area, were damaged. In the Portage and Potter Flats areas, the subsidence varied from 4 to 6 ft (Figure 44). In addition, 37 mi of main-line track and 7 mi of siding and yard track were subject to tidal erosion owing to the subsidence of the entire Turnagain Arm area. This section of track, extending from the vicinity of Portage (Mile 62) along Turnagain Arm to Potter Flats (Mile 102.8), included 10 mi of the track previously mentioned.

Sections of track, totaling about 4 mi, were damaged by bending and kinking (Figures 45 and 46). In some areas (Figure 46), repair was limited to resetting ties and laying new rail. Figure 47 depicts settlement of fill. Major snowslides covered the track at numerous locations but did little damage to the railroad.

IMMEDIATE REPAIRS MADE TO ROADBED AND TRACK

On March 29, 1964, after assessment of the damage by Alaska Railroad personnel, priority was given to opening the main line from Anchorage to the Matanuska coalfields. Next, private contractors were given the task of rebuilding the grade that had been destroyed south of Anchorage at Potter Hill and Mile 112. Increased section crews at Potter and Whittier and an extra crew began general track repairs,

U.S. Army

FIGURE 46   Postearthquake view showing kinked rail and local subsidence. Crack in fill side slope can be seen in lower center of photograph.

while section crews at Tunnel and Moose Pass, both between Seward and Portage, were flown in to assist with work between Anchorage and Whittier. Heavy-equipment operators brought crawler-tractors (D-7's) from Tunnel to Portage to begin removal of snowslides.

These first efforts at track repair were hampered because the ground was frozen several feet deep. The track surface could be raised only by the slow process of shimming. Where the distortion was too great for shimming, crawler-tractors (D-9's) with hydraulic rippers had to be used to rip the frozen ties, to grade, and then to build a uniform grade line. Contractors on Potter Hill also had to resort to ripping

U.S. Army

FIGURE 45   Preearthquake view down railroad track.

U.S. Army

FIGURE 47   Postearthquake view of track in Portage area showing undulating effect on the railroad left by the earthquake.

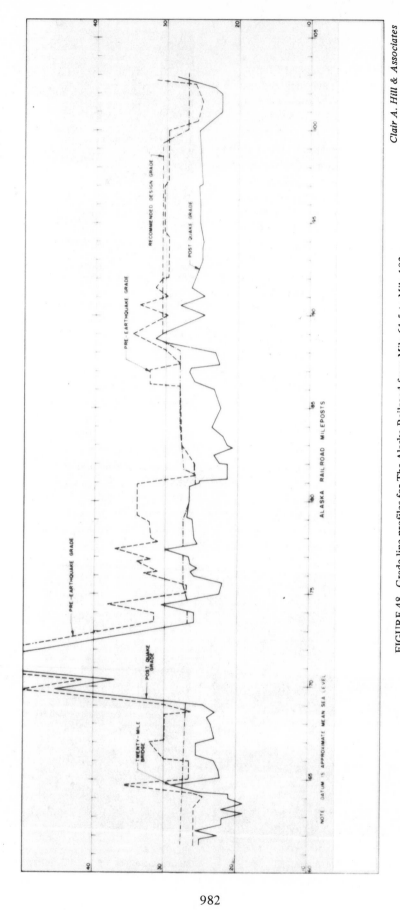

FIGURE 48   Grade-line profiles for The Alaska Railroad from Mile 61.5 to Mile 103.

Clair A. Hill & Associates

982

through the frost to begin borrow excavation.

The first borrow pit for train haul was opened at Mile 131 on April 3, 1964. Within 7 days, the contractors had completed their grade work south of Anchorage; this involved the moving of 175,000 yd^3 of material. Tracklaying was done as soon as the grade was completed. It was estimated that limited service might be restored to Whittier by April 13 or 14; however, on April 12, high tides began to overtop the grade from Bird Flat to Portage, thereby confirming the suspicion that the entire area had subsided as much as 6 ft. Portage was abandoned and some track was further damaged. By April 20, after the subsidence of the high tides, an extra crew and work trains were moved to the new yard at Portage and a nearby borrow pit was opened. A grade line of 29 ft, based on the preearthquake datum, was established as the goal to be reached before the high tides of May 14 and 15.

Because of the head differential that occurred at high tides, it became necessary to seal the exposed railroad grade with impervious material. Accordingly, a pit with fine-grain material was established at Milepost 71, which could be reached by a work train. The high tides in late April caused enough damage between Bird Creek and Indian to show an immediate need for rock riprap in that area. A contract was consequently awarded to produce and load riprap at Bird Point (Mile 81). The first trainload of rock was dumped on May 1. The combination of rock riprap, impervious fill, and gravel succeeded in holding the railroad grade from Anchorage to the Portage depot during the high May tides.

From the Portage depot to the siding on the Whittier branch, it was necessary, because of tide damage, to repair the track twice daily for several months after the track was reopened. During May, June, and July, the main line from Girdwood to Portage and the Whittier branch line were raised to a minimum elevation of 31 ft, on the basis of the preearthquake datum, and the work of raising the Seward main line south of Portage began. Railroad grades throughout this area were being raised before the engineers had determined the final grade.

A contract was awarded to produce riprap at Mile 91.3 for the protection of the railroad grade along Turnagain Arm between Girdwood and Potter Hill. A work train near Seward progressed north with its crew repairing roadbed and tracks en route. By the end of August 1964, the main line to Seward was open to rail traffic. At the end of the work season in October 1964, the main line from Potter to Portage and the branch line had been raised to a minimum elevation of 31 ft, on the basis of preearthquake datum. Except for placing ballast and replacing worn and kinked rail, the line had been brought substantially to preearthquake standards. With the completion of the riprap, a grand total of 3,083,000 yd^3 of material had been hauled to rebuild the railroad. The breakdown of the total follows:

	1964 (in yd^3)	1965 (in yd^3)
Common material train-hauled off-track	886,000	528,000
equipment	225,000	575,000
SUBTOTAL	1,111,000	1,103,000
Rock riprap	459,000	410,000
TOTALS	1,570,000	1,513,000
GRAND TOTAL		3,083,000

PERMANENT REPAIRS TO ROADBED AND TRACK

Final raising to recommended grade line and riprap protection of the railroad along Turnagain Arm were begun in the spring of 1965 and essentially completed by late fall. The railroad added a final 2 to 3 in. of pit-run ballast in the summer of 1966 to complete the raising of the grade line.

The firm of Clair A. Hill & Associates studied the problem of land subsidence between Mile 61.5 and 103 to determine what new grade line should be established and what new railroad cross section should be used in the design of rock-protected slopes. The firm recommended that 1:2 side slopes be used for all fill sections on the slope exposed to wave attack. After beginning construction, the railroad decided against this because of additional expense involved in larger fill quantities and the difficulty involved in placing fill on 1:2 slopes with on-track equipment.

In their second study, Clair A. Hill & Associates analyzed the anticipated effects of waves and tides on the railroad fill and recommended the size of the stones necessary for various sections of embankment fill exposed to wave attack. Because of differing water depths at fill sections, degree of exposure of fill to wave attack, and wave heights, rock riprap was designed for various reaches along the railroad (Table 2).

TABLE 2   Design Rock Sizes for Embankment Slopes for a 1:2 Side Slope

Mile	Minimum Rock Size (in lb)
61.5–75.5	Highway protects railroad from wave action
75.5–79.4	500–600
79.4–81.8	600–800
89–97	3,000–3,300
97–103	400–500[a]

[a] Potter Flats reach required heavier rock.

In constructing the rock-protected slopes, the railroad personnel found that it was difficult to maintain these minimum sizes economically, and they finally reduced the size criteria to allow for some small rock (Figures 48 and 49).

Damage to embankment and rail north of Anchorage

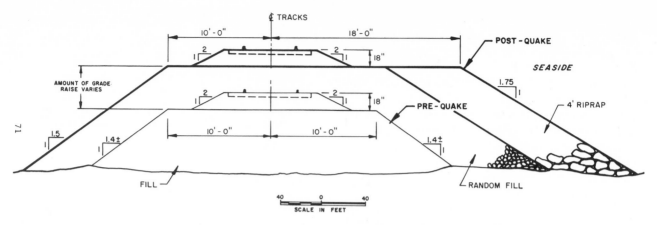

FIGURE 49   Mile 61.5 to 103, typical preearthquake and postearthquake sections.

was relatively minor. Land subsidence did not create a problem along the Knik Arm as it did along the Turnagain Arm.

The total cost to repair damaged embankment, raise embankments, protect slopes from wave damage, rebuild the grade at the two major slides (discussed in the following paragraph), and straightening and relaying track for the various sections of line is estimated by The Alaska Railroad (1967) as follows:

Palmer branch line	$ 16,000
Anchorage to Matanuska River	370,000
North of Matanuska River	140,000
Anchorage to Portage	5,168,000
Whittier branch line	303,000
Portage to Seward	820,000
TOTAL	$6,817,000

SLIDES

Two major slides occurred on The Alaska Railroad: one at Mile 21.4 adjacent to Kenai Lake, and the other in the Potter Hill area between Mile 103 and 104. A less significant slide occurred between Anchorage and Palmer.

At Kenai Lake, the earthquake caused an underwater landslide that removed about 261 ft of track and roadbed from the alluvial fan at Boulder Creek (Figure 50). Several other smaller landslides occurred at the margin of this fan, which was severely fractured. At the preearthquake center line of the track, the track was about 12 ft above the average water surface. It was recommended that, to avoid deep fractures, the new alignment should be as close to the highway as practicable. It was further suggested that, be-

U.S. Army

FIGURE 50   Kenai Lake slide, Mile 21.4, The Alaska Railroad. The state highway from Anchorage to Seward, just out of view at right of photograph, sustained no damage in this area.

cause of the unstable condition of the roadbed adjacent to the slide, any temporary use of the present alignment should be avoided. It was considered that to run rolling stock over this portion of the roadbed might produce additional landslides and that a lake landslide would be a rapid failure. In rebuilding this section, The Alaska Railroad moved the alignment in an easterly direction toward the highway.

The second major landslide occurred almost continuously from Mile 103 to Mile 104 (Figure 51). Slides in the Potter Hill area are not new; this section of track has been destroyed several times by slides within a period of about 35 years.

Immediately after the earthquake, the railroad embankment and track through this area had been rebuilt to provide access to Whittier. Shortly thereafter, U.S. Geological Survey personnel suggested that, to avoid future failures in this section of track, the railroad should adopt a new alignment well east of the present line or should retain the present alignment only if it were economically feasible to stabilize the embankment in this area. In the permanent repair of this section of track, the railroad selected a combination of these alternatives. The track was moved landward as much as 100 ft, and a subdrain system was installed.

Although other smaller slides occurred, the two mentioned above were the most significant.

TUNNELS

The Alaska Railroad's six unlined tunnels on the main line between Seward and Portage and the two unlined tunnels

The Alaska Railroad

FIGURE 52   Preearthquake view of one of the unlined Whittier branch tunnels on The Alaska Railroad. The tunnel, over 15,000 ft long, is constructed through a graywacke formation that requires very little shoring.

on the Whittier branch sustained very little damage. Figure 52 gives a preearthquake view of the longest of the two Whittier tunnels. The Whittier branch tunnels have large wooden doors to reduce freezing near the tunnel portals. These doors and the wooden shoring at each end of the tunnels were undamaged (Figures 53–55). The only problem caused by the earthquake within the tunnels was an overhead raveling of material, which fell on the track. Dam-

FIGURE 51   Potter Hill slide (Rabbit Creek) on Alaska Railroad between Mile 103 and 104.

The Alaska Railroad

FIGURE 53   View in longest of the two Whittier branch tunnels showing both an unlined section of the tunnel and a section, near the end of the tunnel, with shoring.

U.S. Army

FIGURE 54   Alaska Railroad tunnel near Whittier. There was no damage to the doors, on each end of the tunnel, that prevent cold air from Bear Valley from passing through the tunnel to cause freezing.

age to the tunnels was considered insignificant, compared to the severe damage to railroad facilities in other areas.

CONCLUSIONS

The Alaska Railroad sustained extensive damage from landslides, embankment failures, subsidence of ground, tsunami action, and soil movements that damaged bridges. In approximately 2½ years, the railroad reconstructed its facilities at a cost of $22 million.

The earthquake produced a change in the pattern of transportation. Before the earthquake, Seward had been the only year-round open port, and cargo was delivered by railroad to Anchorage and to the interior of Alaska; after the

U.S. Army

FIGURE 55   Closeup view of shoring in Alaska Railroad tunnel near Whittier. This structure was not damaged by the earthquake.

earthquake, the use of icebreakers made possible the delivery of freight by ship directly to Anchorage throughout the year.

The facilities of The Alaska Railroad could be constructed so as to withstand very strong earthquake shaking without significant damage, but the cost of such construction would be prohibitive. The economically correct approach is to construct the facilities so that the cost of earthquake repairs does not exceed the amount required to prevent the damages.

ACKNOWLEDGMENTS

We should like to express appreciation for the time and assistance given by The Alaska Railroad staff, in particular for that given by Irvin D. Cook, Chief Engineer; Charles L. Griffith, Assistant Chief Engineer; Bruce Cannon, Engineer of Structure; and Cliff Fugelstad, Assistant Chief Engineer, Maintenance of Way.

Except as otherwise noted, the figures in this paper are credited to the U.S. Army Corps of Engineers.

REFERENCES

Alaska Railroad, 1967. Summary of damage costs to The Alaska Railroad. Report by the Engineering and Accounting Staff. Anchorage: The Alaska Railroad, March.

Shannon & Wilson, Inc., 1964. Report on subsurface investigation for city of Seward, Alaska, and vicinity, to U.S. Army Engineer District, Anchorage, Alaska. Seattle: Shannon & Wilson, Inc. 77 p.

GARY G. STURMAN
U.S. ARMY CORPS OF ENGINEERS DISTRICT,
ALASKA

The Alaska Highway System

Alaska's road system, like its other transportation systems, was severely damaged by the earthquake of March 27, 1964. The area of major damage was confined to south central Alaska and Kodiak Island, except for a single damaged bridge at Klawock, in the southeastern Alaska panhandle. The highways within Alaska are generally referred to by name, rather than by route number (Figure 1), and are sometimes named for their builders after being constructed over many types of difficult terrain and soil conditions. The Richardson Highway from Valdez to Fairbanks, constructed across glacial outwash and river flood plains, through the rugged Chugach Mountains, and over tundra and permafrost, is a prominent example. The Copper River Highway leading from Cordova is built over swamps, a multitude of braided glacial streams emanating from Sheridan and Scott glaciers, and the forbidding Copper River Delta. The Seward Highway, the only one between Seward and Anchorage, rims the north shore and east-shore tidal flats of Turnagain Arm, and passes through the Chugach Mountains of the Kenai Peninsula. The progress in road construction in Alaska, from trails to modern highways, is shown in Figure 2. Of the 1,373 mi of paved roads in existence at the time of the earthquake, more than 50 percent were in the zone of damage.

ADMINISTRATION OF ROAD DEVELOPMENT IN ALASKA

Roads in Alaska increased from almost none in 1900 to about 4,400 mi of paved and unpaved highways in 1964. During most of the territorial period and up to 1959, road development in Alaska was administered by the Alaska Road Commission, which was controlled by the War Department from 1905 to 1932. In 1932, the Alaska Road Commission was transferred to the Department of the Interior where it remained until 1956, when it was transferred to the Department of Commerce. With the advent of state-

ABSTRACT: The highway system in the region of strong shaking was severely damaged. Roads on soft ground or on embankments suffered extensive cracking, settlement, and sloughing. Subsidence of some areas subjected roads to damage from high tides. Many bridges were severely damaged because of movement of soils on the stream embankments.

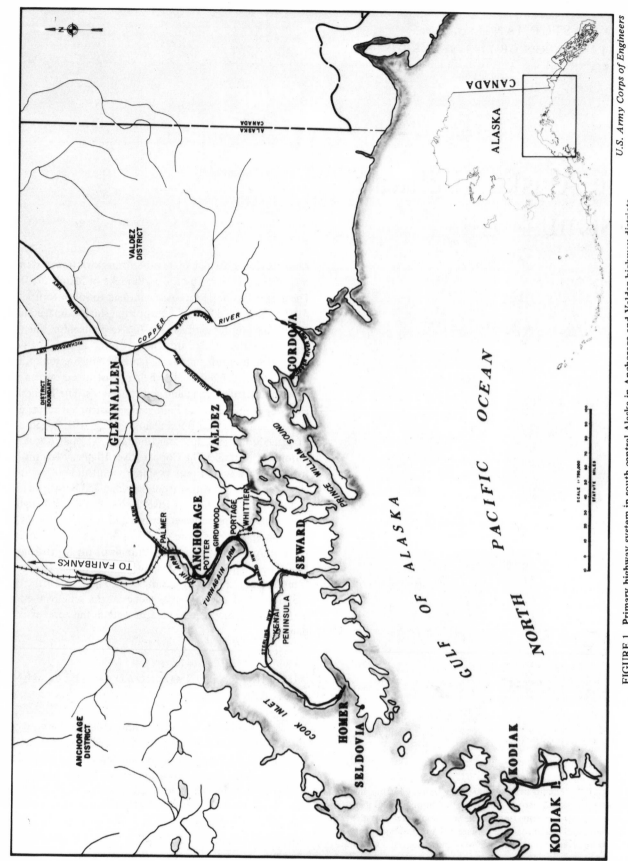

FIGURE 1 Primary highway system in south central Alaska in Anchorage and Valdez highway districts.

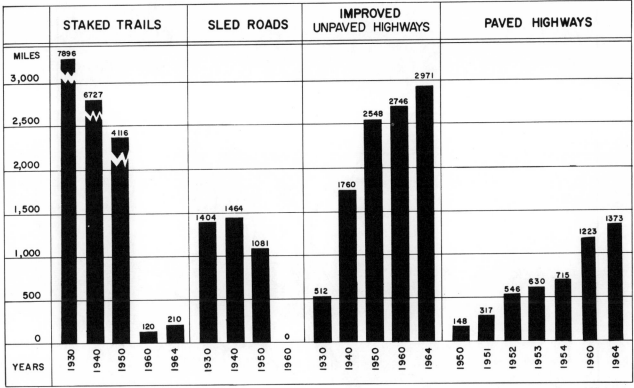

Harvey Golub, Alaska Department of Highways

FIGURE 2   Progress of road construction in Alaska.

hood in 1959, road development became the responsibility of the Department of Highways, which is now responsible for the construction of all roads, except those in national forests and parks. The present Department of Highways has its central headquarters in Douglas, Alaska, near Juneau, the state capital. Five district offices, located in Anchorage, Fairbanks, Nome, Juneau, and Valdez, generally design all roadways and administer contracts within their own districts. All bridges are designed at the central headquarters in Douglas. Damage caused by the earthquake was limited to the Anchorage and Valdez districts whose boundaries are shown in Figure 1. In the Anchorage district, the major highways dealt with in this report are the Seward–Anchorage, the Sterling, and the Glenn highways and roads on Kodiak Island. The important highways in the Valdez district are the Richardson and Copper River highways.

ANCHORAGE HIGHWAY DISTRICT AREA

The earthquake caused severe damage to the majority of roads in the southeastern part of the Anchorage district; the most spectacular and most severe damage was on the Seward–Anchorage Highway along a 17-mi section that parallels Turnagain Arm (Figure 3). This paved road, completed in 1953, is the only road that connects Anchorage with Seward and the remainder of the oil-rich Kenai Peninsula. Damage along this portion of road consisted of cracks and fissures, snow slides, and destruction of a total of 4,567 ft of bridge roadways (Figures 4–6). General subsidence over the entire area lowered roads below tide levels (Figure 7). On the Kenai Peninsula, roads over marshy or unstable areas were damaged more than those constructed on or very near bedrock. A timber trestle bridge over the Snow River near Seward and a precast-concrete bridge, built in 1952, over the Kenai River at the western end of Kenai Lake were both destroyed. Elsewhere along the roads on the peninsula, the earthquake triggered slides and caused cracks in the pavement. North of Anchorage the damage was not as great as it was to the south; transverse and longitudinal fissures in the roadways and numerous side-hill failures and slumps occurred at various locations between Anchorage and Glennallen. Damage to the bridges was small compared to the damage to bridges in the rest of the system, although some permanent displacement was found on the partly completed piers and abutments of a bridge complex over the Knik and Matanuska rivers.

DAMAGE TO HIGHWAYS

The roadbed from Anchorage south to Bird Flats sustained severe damage. Settlements and fissures occurred on many

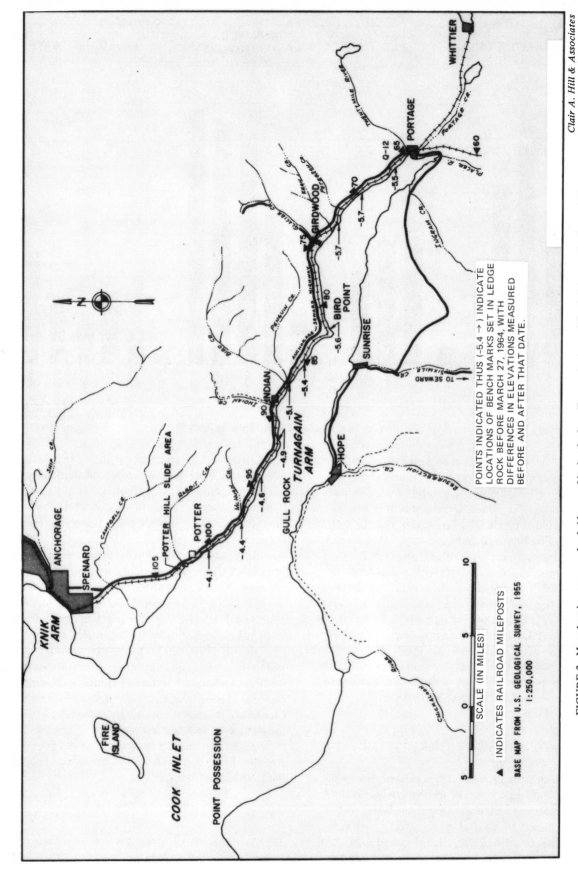

POINTS INDICATED THUS (-5.4 →) INDICATE
LOCATIONS OF BENCH MARKS SET IN LEDGE
ROCK BEFORE MARCH 27, 1964, WITH
DIFFERENCES IN ELEVATIONS MEASURED
BEFORE AND AFTER THAT DATE.

▲ INDICATES RAILROAD MILEPOSTS

BASE MAP FROM U.S. GEOLOGICAL SURVEY, 1955
1:250,000

SCALE (IN MILES)

5   0   5   10

Clair A. Hill & Associates

FIGURE 3   Map showing measured subsidence of bedrock along Turnagain Arm of Cook Inlet on the Seward Highway.

U.S. Army

FIGURE 4   Anchorage–Seward Highway. Portage area showing broken embankment and pavement.

of the high fills, especially on O'Malley Road and in the Sand Lake area near Anchorage. A large failure of a fill also occurred at the crossing of Rabbit Creek. Heavy shear and settlement caused one part of the road to drop 4 ft. All major cracks and patches were reopened by the temblor, and considerable splitting and heaving of the embankment occurred. The road from Anchorage to Potter is constructed over glacial alluvium, whereas the one from Potter to the west end of Bird Flats is built on bedrock, except for transverse crossings of major stream valleys.

U.S. Army Corps of Engineers

FIGURE 6   Anchorage–Seward Highway. Effects of land subsidence at Peterson Creek on Turnagain Arm.

The most severely damaged road section in the Anchorage district was along Turnagain Arm from Bird Flats to Ingram Creek (Figure 3). Most of the road in this area is constructed over unconsolidated material, underlaid by undetermined depths of silt. Turnagain Arm is essentially a submerged glaciated valley in the form of a tidal fiord.

Differential settlement of the road caused many large transverse and longitudinal fissures. A damage report, submitted by 1LT James W. Dunmeyer (1964), U.S. Army (Alaska), on Sunday, March 29, 1964, described the roadbed damage as follows:

Fifty yards south of Twenty Mile Creek Bridge a fissure begins that runs for approximately 500 yards down the center of the road. It varies in width from 6 inches to 3 feet and goes to a depth of 10–12

U.S. Army

FIGURE 5   Anchorage–Seward Highway. Snowslides near Kern Creek between Girdwood and Portage.

U.S. Army Corps of Engineers

FIGURE 7   Anchorage–Seward Highway between Portage and Girdwood showing severe erosion of landward side of highway embankment caused by land subsidence.

feet. This fissure makes the road unusable for vehicles (Figure 4). Between Portage River Bridge and Placer River Bridge there is a fissure that runs down the center of the road for 1,000 yards, approximately. It ends at the abutment of the Placer River Bridge. It varies in width from 6 inches to 6 feet and in depth from 10–12 feet.

Two weeks after the earthquake, seasonal high tides, which before the earthquake did not reach the highway embankment, caused further damage (Figure 7). The Turnagain Arm area had subsided some 4–5 ft as a result of the earthquake. Because of the subsidence, the tidal flow passed through the drainage openings in the roadway embankment on rising tides and returned on the falling tides. Much of the roadway was under water during the extreme high tides. Some of the cross fissures were enlarged by tidal action to openings in the embankment 20–75 ft wide. A Bureau of Public Roads report (May 1964) on the emergency reconstruction of the Seward–Anchorage Highway around Turnagain Arm stated that the rapid change in the tide level caused a large differential in water surface on Turnagain Arm. This differential produced high flow velocities, particularly on falling tides. The result was severe erosion of the roadway embankment by the action of the tides; the erosion was much worse on the landward side than on the seaward side (Figure 7). Where the roadway was behind the railroad fill, the embankment suffered little damage from inundation by tidal action. The tidal range near the mouth of Portage River was 42 ft.

Between Ingram Creek and Seward and Kenai, the highway leaves the tidal flats and runs into the mountains. Throughout this length of road, longitudinal and transverse

U.S. Army Corps of Engineers

FIGURE 8   Highway on the 5-mi-long Homer Spit in October 1966 after the new small-boat harbor and highway had been reconstructed.

cracking and differential settlement occurred; snowslides blocked the road in one area. Streets and roads in Seward sustained differential settlement and cracking of the pavement.

A 5-mi stretch of gravel road, extending the length of Homer Spit (Figure 8), experienced little damage from cracking and fissuring. The general landmass around Homer, however, subsided about 3 ft, and the local subsidence was about 3½ ft at the end of the spit. The total subsidence of 3 ft at the landward end and 6½ ft at the seaward end of the spit caused the road to be inundated by the daily high tides.

The Cape Chiniak Road on Kodiak Island (Figure 9) sustained considerable damage, first from the action of the earthquake and later from inundation by high tides. Most of the earthquake damage consisted of cracks, slides, and differential settlement; a tsunami compounded this damage.

Many longitudinal and transverse fissures occurred on the Glenn Highway north of Anchorage. The Alaska Department of Highways (1964) describes some of the side-hill failures and side-hill slumps:

There is approximately 2,500 feet that slipped downhill near Mile 58. At Mile 68.5 there is a 1,000-foot-long side-hill fracture. At Caribou Hill, Mile 105 and Mile 107, two 2,000-foot side-hill slumps have occurred.

In most of the district, the ground was frozen down to the water table at the time of the earthquake.

DAMAGE TO BRIDGES

In the southeastern section of the Anchorage district, many bridges were damaged and some were destroyed. Some bridges were essentially unharmed in areas where the earthquake had caused much other destruction. One of the earlier inspections revealed the following damage (Smith, 1965, p. 4):

The basic damage was to substructure elements, and superstructure failures followed substructure failures. It is evident that damage was the direct consequence of severe, repetitive, horizontal earth movements.

Types of bridge damage in the Anchorage district included sheared and bent anchor bolts, concrete piers broken at groundline, roadway slabs torn loose from stringers, and broken soleplate welds. Displaced piers and split piles, broken abutment backwalls, settlement of fills behind abutments, and tilted rockers were also found.

Spectacular failures occurred on the Turnagain Arm portion of the Anchorage–Seward Highway. All bridges sustained shortening, closure of expansion devices, crowding of abutments up to 6 ft, and as much as 3 ft of settlement of approach fills. Heavy rigid concrete spans were displaced

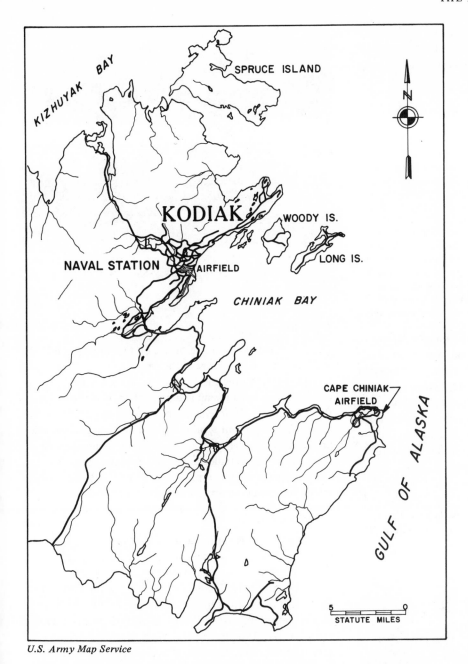

U.S. Army Map Service

FIGURE 9   Kodiak Island road system.

horizontally; some were parted at the joints over pile caps and dropped to the ground; others had their slabs punctured by the timber piles when they fell. Conventional structures and concrete slabs on steel stringers resting on concrete piers with three-rail piles experienced different types of failure: Anchor bolts were sheared, rockers were tilted, and soleplates were torn loose; despite these failures, all remained in service.

On the Kenai Peninsula, most of the bridges sustained some type of damage. The Kenai River Bridge at the west end of Kenai Lake and the bridges spanning the Snow River north of Seward were most severely damaged and were rendered unusable by the earthquake.

On Kodiak Island, the earthquake generated sea waves that destroyed 9 of the 14 timber bridges on the Cape Chiniak Road. Because of changes in drainage patterns and topography, 12 new timber trestle bridges had to be constructed.

North of Anchorage, bridge damage diminished; some decks were displaced and anchor bolts sheared. The existing

Knik River Bridge suffered minor damage, and the Knik River Bridge complex, under construction at the time of the earthquake, experienced some pier displacement.

Snow River Bridges

Engineers observing the Snow River bridges made the following comments (Smith, 1965, p. 3):

We continued to Snow River where a contractor was building three new bridges for the State. Here too, the earthquake had wreaked havoc. The existing bridges had toppled into the mud. The old roadway fill, once 10 feet high, had disappeared for a mile, and the waters on the Snow River wandered as they chose across the now level muck. New concrete piers, with footings 10 feet below the ground and resting on 30 piles each (each driven 80 feet into the ground and tested to support 100 tons) now tilted 15 degrees upstream. Wooden forms atop the shafts were broken and twisted and looked like jaunty caps. At one abutment where 11 piles had been driven into the ground and cut off at the proper elevation, some were now seven feet higher than others, and nobody could guess if the earth had pulled some of the piles down or pushed others up.

The Snow River Overhead, a 1,500-ft timber trestle with one concrete rigid frame over the railroad, was virtually destroyed (Figure 10); however, the abutments remained in good condition. The west side of the bridge was 6 in. to 2 ft lower than the east side. Snow River Bridge 2, a timber trestle 95 ft long, was bowed up in the center but was passable after the earthquake. Bridge 3, also a timber trestle 209 ft long, was destroyed by the earthquake. The abutments and all bents (except those at Bridge 3) appeared to have settled about 12 ft. In 1949, drillers had penetrated 110 feet, but had found no bottom for the piling (Figure 11). Bridge 1, a steel stringer on timber pile bents with a laminated timber deck, was under contract for replacement. The abutment settled on one side.

U.S. Army Corps of Engineers
FIGURE 10   Seward Highway–Snow River Overhead.

U.S. Army
FIGURE 11   Seward Highway–Snow River Bridge.

Kenai River Bridge

The 400-ft precast-concrete bridge on timber piling, built in 1952 over the Kenai River at the western end of Kenai Lake, was destroyed by the earthquake. All the spans dropped onto the river bottom and acted as a dam, backing up ice flows and water. Maintenance men had to dynamite the ice and rubble to prevent serious flood damage to communities upstream. When the spans collapsed, they jammed piling through the concrete deck. All the bents and piling failed, and the concrete spans separated (Figure 12). Fill was observed to have come toward the river from each side.

Twentymile River Bridge

The Twentymile River originates from glaciers of the Chugach Mountains. Upstream from the highway and railroad-bridge crossings, a marshlike area of several square miles is periodically flooded during extreme high tides. The movement of the tides in and out of this area is restricted by the Twentymile River Bridge. Observations made during 5 days in May 1964 by the U.S. Geological Survey indicated very high velocities, the highest being 5.27 fps on an incoming tide.

The material in the area is generally gravel above an elevation of approximately –10 ft. Below this elevation, the strata are essentially silts and sands and, apparently, do not become more dense with depth. Relatively loose lenses or layers of silts exist 75 ft below the surface. The gravel stratum at the site was only 5 percent medium and coarse gravel.

The 825-ft concrete-girder bridge over the Twentymile River was destroyed by the earthquake (Figure 13). The earthquake displaced all the timber pile bents supporting the concrete superstructure, causing the roadway to drop into the water and the spans to separate. The concrete deck

U.S. Army

FIGURE 12   Sterling Highway–Kenai River Bridge. Piling has punched through concrete deck at right.

was pierced by the timber piles, the east abutment was destroyed by fissuring of the embankment (Figure 14), and the bridge was shortened.

Knik River Bridge

At the time of the earthquake, a major bridge complex, crossing the Knik and Matanuska rivers (Figure 15) 20 mi north of Anchorage, was under construction. This $6 million project, Alaska's largest single highway contract up to that time (March 1964), included the construction of four continuous welded-plate girder bridges and 2½ mi of access road. Because both of these rivers originate in the glaciers of the Chugach Mountains, the material at the bridge sites consists mainly of granular glacial deposits. The gravel stratum is composed of medium and coarse gravel.

Piers and abutments had been completed for the first of the four bridges. This first structure was composed of six central spans of 202 ft and two end spans of 156 ft. Piers and abutments were founded on cast-in-place piling driven approximately 60 ft below the ground surface to a minimum bearing of 60 tons each. All piers and both abutments were displaced both laterally and longitudinally, but they remained essentially plumb. Minor alterations to the structural steel were made to correct for the shifting. One span was shortened by 2 ft, and two spans were lengthened by

U.S. Army

FIGURE 13   Anchorage–Seward Highway. Aerial view of Twenty-mile River bridges. Structures, from left to right, are highway bridge, Alaska Railroad bridge, and remains of piling of old railroad bridge.

U.S. Army

FIGURE 14   Anchorage–Seward Highway, Twentymile River Bridge. Structure in upper right corner of photograph is Alaska Railroad bridge.

Alaska Department of Highways

FIGURE 15 Knik River Bridge complex under construction at the time of the earthquake is located on the Glenn Highway between Anchorage and Palmer.

Alaska Department of Highways

FIGURE 16 Seward Highway, Resurrection River Bridge 596. View shows tipped piers and rocker and bent anchor bolts. Pier is on timber piles.

1 ft; the bearings were moved laterally a maximum of 8 in.

The older bridge, located approximately 8 mi upstream, was 1,992 ft long and consisted of steel through trusses on concrete piers and steel-stringer approach spans on timber pile bents. The earthquake displaced all the piers and cracked one at the water line, tipped the rockers and turned them over on one pier. Traffic, however, was able to use this bridge at reduced speeds after maintenance forces had repaired the damage.

The other bridges in the district received similar damage, but to a lesser degree (Figures 16–18).

VALDEZ HIGHWAY DISTRICT AREA

DAMAGE TO HIGHWAYS

The Richardson and Copper River highways were the two most severely damaged routes in the Valdez district. The Richardson Highway extends northward from the seaport of Valdez on Prince William Sound to Fairbanks, a distance of 364 mi. The highway, formerly a military wagon road, was named after General W. P. Richardson, U.S. Army, President of the Alaska Road Commission from 1905 to 1917. It is completely paved, and improvements are continually being made. At present, this is the only highway that breaches the rugged Chugach Mountains to connect Valdez with the interior highway system. Most of the damage on this highway occurred near Valdez, where the highway and bridges are constructed over alluvial material. The section of the road that runs through the Chugach Mountains received no apparent damage, but damage was heavy in the section of highway beyond the mountains. The

severity of damage to the road decreased with the distance from the earthquake epicenter.

The Copper River Highway (Figure 19), an unpaved road, extends from the coastal town of Cordova to a point on the west shore of Miles Lake, about 50 mi northeast of Cordova. After crossing braided glacial streams, swamps, and the Copper River Delta, it follows the east side of the Copper River. At Mile 49, the road again crosses the Copper River over the Million Dollar Bridge, which was constructed in 1910 by engineers of the Copper River and Northwestern Railroad. The present road from Cordova uses the old rail-

Alaska Department of Highways

FIGURE 17 Anchorage–Seward Highway, Ingram Creek Bridge 620. Tipped rockers and bent anchor bolts are visible. Pier is concrete.

Alaska Department of Highways

FIGURE 18 Anchorage–Seward Highway, Peterson Creek Bridge 636. Broken abutment backwall can be seen.

road alignment and most of the railroad bridges (the railroad was abandoned before World War II). Damage along the highway was severe but not as disastrous as the bridge damage. Longitudinal and transverse ground cracks, in addition to settlement, were apparent on the road. The roads most severely damaged were those constructed over alluvial material; those constructed on or very near bedrock received little or no damage. The degree of damage was, in fact, a direct reflection of the geologic environment of the highway. Table 1 lists the damage to the highways during the March 1964 earthquake, and Figure 20 shows damage on the highways.

DAMAGE TO BRIDGES

Damage to bridges on the Richardson Highway from Valdez to the district boundary was minor compared to damage to the bridges on the Copper River Highway from Cordova. Except for culverts, the bridges on the Richardson Highway were either timber trestles on timber piling or steel stringers on three-rail pile bents. The light damage sustained by the timber bridges located a few miles from Valdez consisted mostly of split piles. Near Valdez, two steel-stringer bridges with concrete abutments sustained heavier damage, such as fractured abutments and piling clusters, broken soleplate welds, and a general shifting of all piers. A timber bridge near milepost 65 from Valdez was so severely damaged (decking splintered and stringers failed because they collapsed or lost bearing) that it was replaced with a culvert (Figure 21).

Damage to bridges on the Copper River Highway was severe. Of 52 bridges, 34 were destroyed or so severely damaged as to require replacement. Most of these bridges were steel or timber superstructures on timber piling or steel

stringers on three-rail pile bents; the existing Copper River and Northwestern steel-truss railroad bridges were on concrete piers. These bridges were constructed across the Scott and Sheridan glacier outwash plains and the Copper River Delta. Sediments in these areas vary from clay to gravel, and all material is deposited by the many meandering glacial streams. The bridges that were located on or very near bedrock received little or no damage compared to the damage sustained by those constructed on the sedimentary deposits.

Damage to the bridges on the Copper River Highway consisted of broken three-rail pile bents (Figure 22), bent and sheared anchor bolts (Figures 23 and 24), sheared diaphragm bolts, broken soleplate welds, expansion rollers flat or at full travel, and tipped or bent piling. It also included split-timber piling, displaced or settled abutments, spalled and fractured abutment backwalls, and broken and split pile caps. The most apparent bridge damage was the numerous broken and tipped three-rail pile bents that had been made with ASCE 70-lb railroad rails from the abandoned Copper River and Northwestern Railroad. Before they were driven, the rails had been welded into clusters of three and lengthened with splice welds. Records indicated that considerable difficulty had been experienced during driving because the rail cluster kept breaking at random points (Migliaccio, 1965):

From the evidence gathered in the field, it appears that most of these structures were subjected to large horizontal accelerations which resulted in almost every case in failure of the superstructure to substructure connections. It would appear that if these connections had not failed, total destruction of the substructure unit would have resulted. Aside from settlement or uplift of individual substructure units, acceleration appears to have been confined to the horizontal direction, since all bolt and weld failures appear to be shear failures with no evidence of tensile strain, even in bolts which did not shear.

The Scott Glacier bridges are located on the Copper River Highway from Mile 7 to about Mile 13. The Scott Glacier stream is a braided glacial stream (Figure 19) that is constantly cutting laterally and changing channels. The delta is flat and swampy. The stream flows south and empties into the Gulf of Alaska. Materials encountered during foundation investigations (May 4–20, 1964) ranged from clayey silts to sandy gravels. Silts and sands are interlayered and generally stratified throughout the flood plain. No material larger than 2 in. in diameter was encountered; however, there were indications that erratic boulders might be present. Organic matter was present in all strata, and organic lenses were common in the clayey silt strata. A very dense, silty sand deposit was encountered at elevations ranging from –35 to –60 ft in all borings. A total of 11 bridges (with an aggregate length of 1,877 ft) cross the numerous streams that emanate from the Scott Glacier. Five of the bridges were constructed of steel stringers with a reinforced-

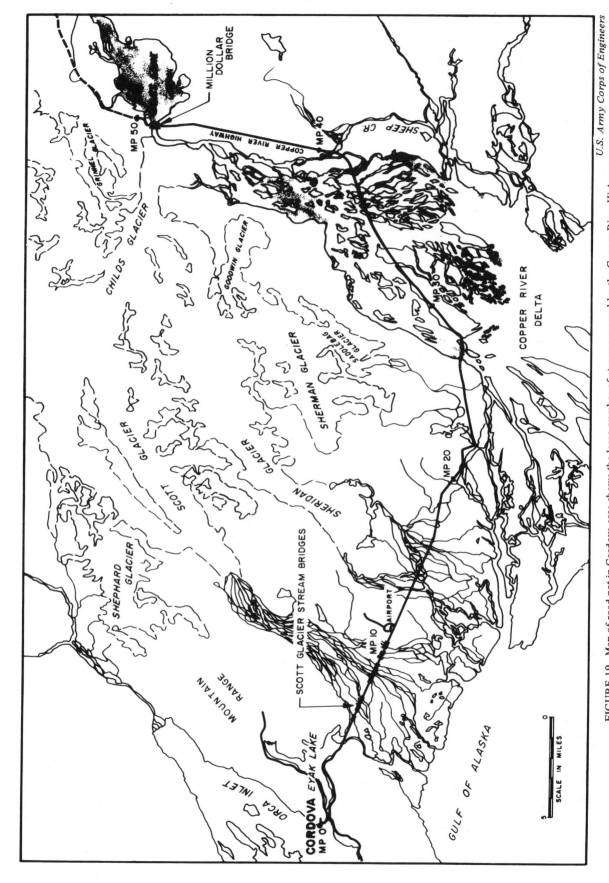

FIGURE 19 Map of road net in Cordova area shows the large number of streams crossed by the Copper River Highway.

U.S. Army Corps of Engineers

TABLE 1   Earthquake Damage to Highways in the Valdez District

Mileposts (MP)	Area Traversed	Types of Soil	Damage Sustained	Other Data
Richardson Highway				
Valdez to MP 6	Valdez glacier outwash plain and Lowe River flood plain	Sand, gravel, silt, and possibly clay	Transverse and longitudinal roadway cracks. Slumps similar to circular arc failure. Displacements: vertical, 1 ft; horizontal, 3–6 in. Heavy damage, severe settlement and distortion.	Groundwater level, 4–5 ft below surface. Area frozen to 4–5 ft below surface at time of earthquake. Fine sand and water ejected. Entire section moved seaward 5 ft. Undulation of roadway preserved. Dips in road apparent after quake.
MP 6–65	Chugach Mountains	Bedrock	Minor transverse roadway cracks. Light damage, local settlement.	Between MP 12 and 17, rock well jointed and set parallel to roadway. Same condition in tunnel at MP 15.8. Only effect of earthquake on tunnel was increase in water seepage.
MP 65–75	Little Tonsina River Valley	Glacial lacustrine deposits with ice lenses	Transverse roadway cracks at intervals of 100 ft or less. Horizontal and vertical displacements. Heavy damage (see Figure 21).	Permafrost occurs sporadically. All soil frozen to a depth of 10 ft or more. Large quantities of mud and water ejected.
MP 75–82	Tonsina River flood plain and southwest side of Copper River Valley	Lacustrine clay and silt covered by a veneer of sandy gravels	Minor roadway cracks; negligible damage.	Soil frozen. Slumping of roadway at MP 80 aggravated by earthquake. Road fill dropped 3–5 ft during earthquake in an arc-shaped fracture. (Note: slumping has been a maintenance problem since construction of highway.)
MP 82–147	Copper River Valley	Lacustrine deposits	Minor transverse roadway cracks less than 2 in. wide and differential settlement; light damage.	Permafrost present.
Copper River Highway				
Cordova to MP 7	Portion of Chugach Mountains	Bedrock	Negligible damage.	Follows old Copper River and Northwestern Railroad alignment.
MP 7–50	Copper River flood plain, glacial outwash plains, and Copper River Delta	Variable from gravel to clay; glacial alluvium to river silt	Ground cracking, shoulder slumping, transverse cracking. Subsidence as much as 6 ft (see Figure 20).	Many meandering streams and rivers. Little damage to roadway prism, constructed on or near bedrock.

FIGURE 20   Copper River Highway, near Mile 27, showing ground cracks.

FIGURE 22   Copper River Highway, Scott Glacier Bridge 7, showing three-rail piling failures, split rails, and weld failure.

one of the richest copper lodes in history. The engineers who constructed the bridge were immortalized in Rex Beach's novel, *The Iron Trail*. Before World War II, mining was suspended and the railroad was abandoned. After the war, the Alaska Road Commission, utilizing for the most

concrete deck supported on timber substructures. The rest of the bridges were constructed of steel stringers and a reinforced-concrete deck supported on three-rail bents (Table 2).

In April 1909, construction of a bridge over the Copper River was begun by the Copper River and Northwestern Railroad. This bridge, completed in 1910, gave access to

FIGURE 21   Richardson Highway, Little Tonsina River Bridge, Mile 65.

FIGURE 23   Copper River Highway Bridge 331. Upstream bearing at abutment 1 with rollers lying flat.

Alaska Department of Highways

FIGURE 24 Copper River Highway Bridge 331. Upstream fixed bearing of span 2. Displacement 19 in. northward, 5 in. downstream.

Alaska Department of Highways

FIGURE 25 Preearthquake view of Copper River Highway Bridge 206—Million Dollar Bridge.

part the existing railroad bridges, started to construct a motor road over the old railroad bed. After statehood was granted, the Alaska Department of Highways continued the work and reopened the Million Dollar Bridge in 1961 (Figure 25).

Plans were drawn and contracts awarded for the extension of the Copper River Highway into the interior to connect with the Edgerton cutoff. Construction was under way when the earthquake struck. When the damage was assessed

by aerial reconnaissance soon thereafter, bridge engineers found that the north span of the historic Million Dollar Bridge, which had withstood the ravages of glacial ice, cyclonic winds, and numerous earthquakes for 50 years, had fallen into the Copper River (Figure 26). Detailed inspection in July 1964 revealed the following serious damage (Golub, 1964):

Abutment #1 relatively undamaged–no sign of movement of abutment itself. Top of backwall and wings are cracked and chipped

TABLE 2 Summary of Findings on the Copper River Highway[a]

Bridge	Name	Spans	Damage Report
348–352	Scott Glacier	Streams 1–5	These steel-stringer bridges on timber substructures all show similar damage with various degrees of severity. Examples of damage include piles pulled away from caps on upstream side, downstream piles split, and general displacement of substructure.
348	Scott Glacier 1	6 at 25 ft	Severely damaged; slab separated from stringers.
349	Scott Glacier 2	8 at 25 ft	Moderate damage.
350	Scott Glacier 3	6 at 25 ft	Severely damaged.
351	Scott Glacier 4	3 at 25 ft	Severely damaged.
352	Scott Glacier 5	3 at 25 ft	Minor damage.
406	Scott Glacier 6[b]	12 at 25 ft ± 3 at 34 ft ±	Many caps and piles broken; badly damaged.
407	Scott Glacier 7[b]	7 at 25 ft	Piles broken or missing caps broken; badly damaged.
408	Scott Glacier 8[b]	6 at 25 ft ±	Relatively minor damage. Caps broken, anchor bolts sheared.
409	Scott Glacier 9[b]	3 at 25 ft	Abutment backwall sheared; minor damage.
410	Scott Glacier 10[b]	3 at 25 ft	No damage.
411	Scott Glacier 11[b]	14 at 25 ft	Severe damage. Most caps and many piles broken.

[a] Source: Alaska Department of Highways (1964).
[b] Steel stringers on three-rail pile bents.

U.S. Army

FIGURE 26 Copper River Highway Bridge 206 (Million Dollar Bridge); span 4, at right center.

from pounding of deck. Backwall is pockmarked from rivets at end of truss [Figure 27]. Span #1 is displaced. Anchor bolts are sheared. [See Figure 25 for preearthquake view of piers and spans.]

At pier #2, rollers are lying flat and anchor bolts are bent. Span #1 moved south and Span #2 moved north. The spans are jammed tight on the upstream side, separated by two inches downstream, jamming together pulverized sliding beam between spans [Figure 28] as well as the ends of the concrete deck and bent the finger joint and its connections.

Spans #2 and #3 were displaced on pier #3. Ends of trusses jammed together; all anchor bolts sheared. Sliding beam between spans pulverized. Joint angles and ends of concrete slab badly damaged. Piers #2 and #3 seem to have suffered no structural damage.

Pier #4 [Figure 29] is virtually destroyed. The upper portion has split into three parts, with each of the end pieces separated from the middle by a crack up to two feet wide. Middle portion has a vertical crack running completely through it. Upper half of pier has also sheared horizontally and has moved about 2 feet south in respect to the lower half. The entire pier has a list toward the south. There is no evidence of reinforcement in upper pier and failure seems to be along construction joints. The bearings of span #3 are displaced 9 feet 3 inches from their former position on pier #4 in a northward direction and approximately 6 feet transversely. Bottom lateral bracing is mutilated and rivets have popped. Span #4 has dropped off pier #4 and is in the river, probably resting on the bottom [Figures 26 and 30]. The truss and concrete deck appear undamaged from L_0 to L_2 where the deck is broken, and the bottom chords apparently bent or broke from the fall. Verticals L_1U_1 are bent completely out of shape in compression [Figure 31]. End posts (chord) show no damage above water.

Abutment #5 does not show signs of any major damage. There is some spalling and breaking of the concrete at the bridge seats caused by the fall of span #4 and all anchor bolts are either broken or bent [Figure 32].

The State Highway Department considered that the raising, relocation, and rehabilitation of these spans would be a difficult and expensive operation.

DAMAGE TO BUILDINGS

The State Highway Department's office building and garage complex, although not seriously damaged, was reconstructed

Alaska Department of Highways

FIGURE 27 Copper River Highway Bridge 206 (Million Dollar Bridge). Downstream end abutment 1 shows concrete pocked by rivets.

Alaska Department of Highways

FIGURE 28 Copper River Highway Bridge 206 (Million Dollar Bridge). Sliding beam between spans 1 and 2.

FIGURE 29 Copper River Highway Bridge 206 (Million Dollar Bridge). Downstream end of pier 4 looking southward.

FIGURE 31 Copper River Highway Bridge 206 (Million Dollar Bridge). Vertical L_1U_1 on downstream truss span 4.

FIGURE 30 Copper River Highway Bridge 206 (Million Dollar Bridge). Looking upstream at pier 4.

on the new Valdez townsite. In Valdez, its buildings were old wood-frame structures, previously used by the Bureau of Public Roads.

ALASKA HIGHWAY DEPARTMENT'S RESPONSE TO THE EARTHQUAKE

Immediately after the earthquake, the Alaska Highway Department mobilized on an emergency basis. The most urgent need was to give aid to personnel stranded on the highways or surging onto the roads in fleeing from the damaged cities. Highway-maintenance camps found themselves caring for stranded, homeless, and hungry persons. Above Valdez, 27-Mile Camp sheltered more than 300 homeless and hungry Valdezians. Silvertip, a camp on the Seward Highway, housed motorists stranded because of destruction

Alaska Department of Highways

FIGURE 32   Copper River Highway Bridge 206 (Million Dollar Bridge). Upstream bearing, abutment 5.

from Anchorage, the highway fill across the stream had settled. Bulldozers were used to provide a temporary ramp over the damaged portion. A severe landslide 10 mi from Girdwood, a small town on Turnagain Arm near Portage, was breached by bulldozers of the highway department and of the Army engineers. Bailey bridges were installed across Glacier and Virgin creeks. Light traffic was restored between Seward and the rest of the Kenai Peninsula less than 2 weeks after the earthquake. A portion of the collapsed Snow River crossing was rehabilitated by the Juneau contractors who were engaged in construction there at the time of the earthquake. Highway maintenance crews, contracting company personnel, and the U.S. Army combined forces to replace the collapsed bridge over the Kenai River with a Bailey bridge.

While temporary access to isolated areas was being established, a thorough inspection of all damage to roads and bridges was initiated so that a detailed assessment of the required work and its cost could be prepared. Emergency repairs (Figure 34) were begun at once, and initial estimates of damage were forwarded to the Department of Highways Headquarters.

A crash program of temporary road and bridge repair by normal contract methods with an abbreviated advertising period was instituted. A contract was awarded for $1.35 million.

In Valdez, maintenance crews filled in cracks and made temporary repairs to bridges until normal contracts could be let. A construction company was awarded a $105,000 contract to repair cracks on the Richardson Highway, for repairs to the Upper Lowe River Bridge, and to replace the damaged Little Tonsina River Bridge with twin culverts.

of highway bridges. Maintenance men and engineering personnel were mobilized immediately after the earthquake to assess damage and report by radio to Alaska State Civil Defense Headquarters in Anchorage. They also set out warning flares and markers at the most severely damaged sections of the roadway and placed barricades where roads were impassable.

The next objective was to restore traffic service to communities isolated by the earthquake. The reestablishment of traffic service between Seward and Kenai, which was given priority, was to be accomplished by immediate temporary road repairs and construction of temporary bridges with the use of only local material and available equipment. The U.S. Army installed the bridge shown in Figure 33. Authorized contractors performed urgent work with their own equipment. Forces of the Alaskan Command assisted the highway department in clearing slides, erecting temporary Bailey bridges, and evacuating the homeless. At Rabbit Creek, 8 mi

U.S. Army

FIGURE 33   Seward–Anchorage Highway. Bailey bridge across Virgin Creek on Turnagain Arm installed by Army combat engineers 3 days after the earthquake.

Alaska Department of Highways

FIGURE 34   Seward–Anchorage Highway, near Ingram Creek. Temporary timber trestle bridge under construction.

At Cordova, maintenance crews made spot repairs to the damaged portion of the Copper River Highway from the city to the airport. Five temporary timber bridges were constructed across the Scott Glacier streams at a cost of $130,000.

PERMANENT RESTORATION IN THE ANCHORAGE HIGHWAY DISTRICT

Permanent reconstruction of earthquake-damaged structures and roadbed in the Anchorage district was delayed for about a year. The inconvenience and discomfort caused by the delay were well justified by the additional time afforded for study of latent effects from frozen surface conditions, effects of general land subsidence on stream-flow characteristics, and effects of land movement on previous survey data. Final damage assessments also had to wait until the surrounding soil had thawed and the drifted snow had melted. Broken or damaged foundation piling were not apparent as long as they remained locked in frozen material. Subsidence in the Turnagain Arm area had an immediate influence on tidal sloughs, increasing dramatically the amount of flood flows. The changes in the water-table elevations also materially affected the general drainage pattern. Side-hill road sections that developed crevices as a result of the earthquake sustained additional failures during and after spring runoff.

ROAD REPAIR

Approximately $7 million was spent for grading, drainage, and paving of 18.23 mi of the Anchorage–Seward Highway between Girdwood and Ingram Creek and for the construction of nine composite steel and concrete bridges, with a total length of 2,355 ft. Construction also included repairs to the existing Ingram Creek Bridge. Plans called for the construction of a 40-ft-wide roadway consisting of a bituminous concrete pavement 24 ft wide and 2 in. thick and shoulders 8 ft wide with a bituminous surface treatment, the replacing and extending of about 44 metal culverts, and the furnishing and placing of about 125,000 yd^3 of stone riprap for embankment protection. The elevation of the road, as designed, is about 4 ft above the estimated maximum high tide. The remainder of the repairs to the damaged sections of highway from Anchorage to Seward consisted of spot repairs, resurfacing, and crack repairing.

The Homer Spit Road was repaired with material dredged from Kachemak Bay and taken from about 400 yd offshore. Repairs to the roadbed on Kodiak Island consisted of raising the existing gravel road above maximum high tides. The total cost of these repairs was $325,000. North of Anchorage, repairs amounting to about $500,000 consisted mainly of the reconstruction of sections of road damaged by side-hill failures, crack patching, sealing, and minor repaving.

BRIDGE REPAIR

Permanent restoration of damaged or destroyed bridges began only after the results of foundation investigations and site surveys had been properly analyzed and incorporated into the designs. In the Anchorage Highway District, individual bridges that needed either major repairs or replacement were those over the Snow, Kenai, Twentymile, and Knik rivers.

Snow River Bridges

A bridge-construction contract was being carried out in the Snow River area at the time of the earthquake. The contract, for $485,000, was for the construction of two bridges, an overpass at The Alaska Railroad, and approach grading. The Foundation Study Report (Sherman and Shumway, 1962) stated, in part that, "The natural foundation material at the proposed bridge site is unique. From the surface to a depth greater than 100 feet the material is composed of a fine to medium sand with scattered stringers of pea gravel and silt." The outstanding characteristic was the looseness of the predominantly silt and sand strata. On the basis of penetrometer tests in the summer of 1964 in the Snow River bridges area, it was concluded that the granular sediments below the river were more compact than they were before the earthquake (Lemke, 1967). The partly constructed substructure of one of the bridges was removed and a new substructure was built. The contract was completed October 1, 1965, with the preearthquake design. Figure 35 shows the postearthquake Snow River Overhead.

Kenai River Bridge

A contract was awarded on October 13, 1964, for the construction of a permanent bridge over the Kenai River to

FIGURE 35 Snow River Overhead, completed after the earthquake.

replace the U.S. Army's Bailey bridge. The new bridge is a State Department of Highways standard composite girder bridge on piles. The cost of the bridge was around $390,000. An abbreviated plan and profile of the structure is shown in Figure 36.

Twentymile River Bridge

The contract for the Girdwood to Ingram Creek grading and drainage project also included reconstruction of the Twentymile River Bridge. This is a 570-ft standard composite steel-girder bridge, consisting of a reinforced-concrete deck with a 30-ft clear roadway width supported on five composite

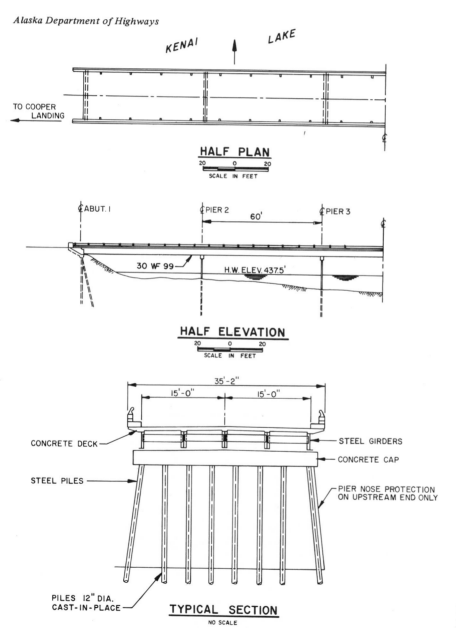

FIGURE 36 Postearthquake Kenai River Bridge, Anchorage Highway District.

welded-steel girders. Six reinforced-concrete piers over cast-in-place concrete piles support the superstructure (Figure 37). The foundation-investigation report recommended displacement piles. A desirable penetration to an elevation 30 ft below low channel for pier piles and 20 ft below natural ground for abutment piles was also recommended. The bridge was completed in 1967.

Knik River Bridge

Damage and subsequent repairs to the Knik River Bridge complex have already been described. Minor modifications were made in the structural steel to take care of the pier shifting. Repair, which cost about $16,000, took about 2 weeks. No permanent repairs were made on the old Knik

Alaska Department of Highways

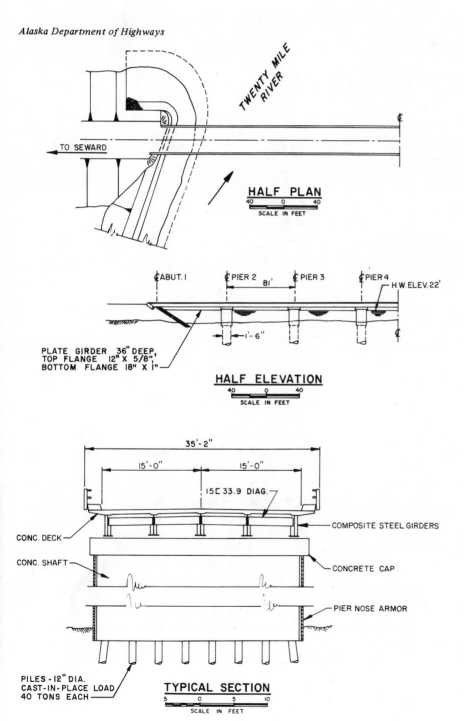

FIGURE 37   Postearthquake Twentymile River Bridge, Anchorage Highway District.

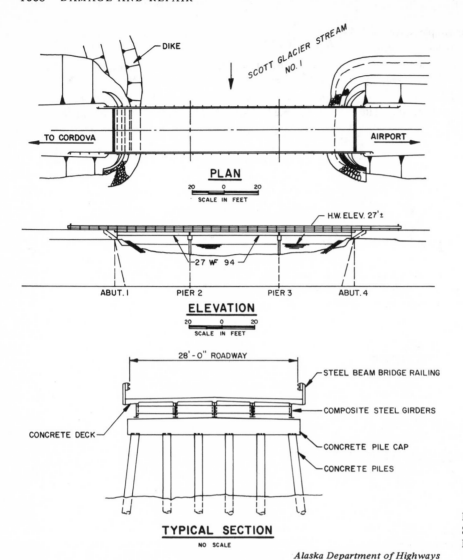

PLAN

SCALE IN FEET

ELEVATION

SCALE IN FEET

TYPICAL SECTION

NO SCALE

FIGURE 38   Typical bridge over one of the Scott Glacier streams in the Valdez Highway District.

Alaska Department of Highways

River Bridge, other than removal of the damaged rockers and fixing of the ends at the broken pier; these repairs were made for about $10,000. Light traffic continues to use this bridge.

PERMANENT RESTORATION IN VALDEZ HIGHWAY DISTRICT

ROADWAY REPAIR

To restore the Richardson Highway, a contract for $160,000 to repair cracks at various locations from Mile 5 to Mile 66 was awarded. The portion of the highway from Valdez to Mile 5 required complete rebuilding; to accomplish this and to apply a bituminous surface treatment, a contract for $1.5 million was awarded.

Restoration costs for the Copper River Highway from Mile 5.8 to the Cordova Airport (Mile 13) were $2.3 million. This contract required construction of a 28-ft-wide road in the same location as the existing road. Rock-slope protection was required on the seaward side of the road at all bridge approaches. A major amount of the total cost was for permanent bridges.

BRIDGE REPAIR

C. P. Smith, chief bridge engineer for the Alaska Department of Highways at the time of the earthquake, made the following statement on permanent replacement of bridges in the Valdez district (Smith, 1965, p. 8).

The design for permanent replacement bridges envisioned a series of simple composite steel-beam-concrete-slab spans on pile bent piers and abutments, incorporating every practicable device to insure a simplicity of detail and modular application to various sites. Twenty-five standard drawings were developed covering 50, 60, and 80-foot spans for 28, 30, and 41-foot roadway widths, using either H-pile or cast-in-place concrete pile bents, elastomeric bearings, standard rolled beams, and bolted field connections. The details received favorable comment from contractors and fabricators. Because these simple, economical structures will be applicable to the continuing normal Alaska Highway program, it is contemplated that the designs will later be refined to incorporate welded girder sections. Aside from modification of some detail to prevent minor damage, . . . it becomes increasingly evident that design against the type of forces experienced in an earthquake of this magnitude is uneconomical and falls in the calculated risk category, . . . the elimination of damage entirely is impractical.

On most of the bridges along the Copper River Highway, the ends of the concrete curbs were doweled into the top of the abutment backwall with several number 4 bars. The curbs were continuous with the superstructure curbs in fixed ends or had an expansion joint in them at expansion ends. Relative movement of the superstructure caused considerable damage to these curb ends and, in almost all cases, resulted in spalling and fracturing of the abutment backwalls in the vicinity of the curbs.

Eleven bridges were constructed to replace those damaged by the earthquake (Figure 38). These are standard highway composite girder bridges, consisting of a reinforced-concrete deck on top of 27WF94 and 36WF135 structural steel stringers with 15U33.9 structural-steel cross beams. Abutments and piers are of reinforced concrete on reinforced-concrete piles. The total length of all the bridges amounts to about 1,900 ft, the longest bridge being 402 ft.

The matter of replacement of the Million Dollar Bridge is still under study. From the description of the damage, the bridge apparently will not be economically salvageable. The raising, relocation, and rehabilitation of these massive spans will be a difficult and expensive operation.

The damaged bridges from Cordova to the airport have been replaced at a cost of approximately $2 million. The decision to reconstruct the road and bridges on the Copper River Highway east of the Cordova Airport was recently made. Because the old town of Valdez was found to be on unstable ground, the decision was made to relocate the town a few miles west of the existing site. The Alaska Department of Highways also decided to build a new highway complex at the new townsite of Valdez. The total cost of this move was $765,000.

CONCLUSIONS

The highway system in the region of strong shaking was severely damaged. Roads on soft ground or on embankments sustained extensive cracking, settlement, and sloughing. Subsidence of some areas lowered the roads so that they were damaged by high tides. Landslides and snowslides blocked the highways. Many bridges were severely damaged or collapsed; a common cause of damage was the movement of soils in the bridge abutments into the channel, which compressed the bridge. The highway system crossed many areas of very soft soils, and these were responsible for most of the damage. It therefore appears that earthquake-resistant construction of the highway system to enable it to survive a large earthquake without significant damage is not economically justifiable. The system should instead be constructed so that the cost of the damage caused by earthquakes does not exceed the cost of construction needed to avoid the damage. Improved designs could have avoided or greatly reduced some of the damage with only moderate cost.

REFERENCES

Alaska Department of Highways, 1964. Report of damage caused by March 27, 1964, earthquake to Alaska's federal-aid highway system. Juneau: Alaska Department of Highways. p. 9–10.

Dunmeyer, James W., 1964. Earthquake damage March 27, 1964, Seward Highway and Sterling Highway to Kenai (unpublished report). USARAL #4626-2. Ft. Richardson: U.S. Army, Alaska, March 29.

Golub, Harvey [1964]. Bridge damage report, March 27 earthquake. Anchorage: Alaska Department of Highways, April 24. p. 1–43.

Lemke, Richard W., 1967. Effects of the earthquake of March 27, 1964, at Seward, Alaska. U.S. Geological Survey Professional Paper 542-E. Washington: Government Printing Office. 43 p. Also in The Great Alaska Earthquake of 1964: Geology. NAS Pub. 1601. Washington: National Academy of Sciences, 1971. p. 395–437.

Migliaccio, Ralph, 1965. Earthquake damage to highways in the Valdez District, Alaska. Anchorage: Alaska Department of Highways, January. p. 1–9.

Sherman, R. G., and R. D. Shumway, 1962. Foundation study report, Snow River Bridge No. 605, center channel. Project No. F-031-(6). Anchorage: Alaska Department of Highways, May. p. 2.

Smith, Charles P., 1965. Highway destruction in Alaska: Part I, Alaska bridges experience an earthquake. Transport-Communications Monthly Review (August), 3–8.

JAMES M. TANAKA*
U.S. ARMY CORPS OF ENGINEERS DISTRICT,
ALASKA

Airports and Air Traffic Control Facilities

ABSTRACT: The earthquake temporarily disrupted the vital air-transportation systems of Alaska in the strongly shaken region. Bryant Army Airfield on Fort Richardson was the only major airfield in the Anchorage area that was fully operational immediately after the earthquake. Although the runways, taxiways, and aprons at all major airfields were in satisfactory condition to have handled air traffic after the earthquake, immediate service was not available because of the failure of the control towers at Anchorage International Airport and at Elmendorf Air Force Base. The loss of electrical power at Merrill Field and Kodiak and the failure of land-communication lines further delayed the resumption of regular air-transportation services.

The earthquake emphasized the importance of the air-transportation system to the disaster-relief operations and its relatively low vulnerability compared to highway and rail systems.

*Now with the Federal Aviation Administration, Anchorage.

Air transportation provides Alaskans with a vital link between the communities within Alaska and the outside. For many communities, air transportation is the only direct means of travel. The reliance on air transportation within Alaska is amplified significantly over that of other states by the lack of interconnecting highways and railroads and by the vast area covered by this state. Only south central and interior Alaska have an interconnected highway system linked to the rest of the United States. The railroad system within the state is limited to service from the seaports at Seward, Whittier, and Anchorage to the interior city of Fairbanks (Figure 1). The remainder of the state depends on air or sea transportation for the necessities of life.

Air transportation became even more vital to Alaska immediately after the great earthquake. Many of the communities within the earthquake-affected areas were isolated because of the damaged railroads, highways, and communications. The status and needs of these communities were not known until contact was made by aircraft. Transportation to provide immediate relief to the stricken communities and to assess the damages was confined almost entirely to aircraft. The Civil Air Patrol, which is equipped primarily with single-engine light aircraft, flew mileage equivalent to 3½ trips around the world in rescue and supply missions to the stricken and isolated communities during the first 10 days after the earthquake. The military airlift effort was even greater (U.S. Alaskan Command, 1964).

In addition to the local dependence on airport facilities, domestic and transoceanic flights between the United States, Europe, and Asia are dependent on control and advisory facilities in Anchorage and on the en route services at various points in the earthquake-affected area.

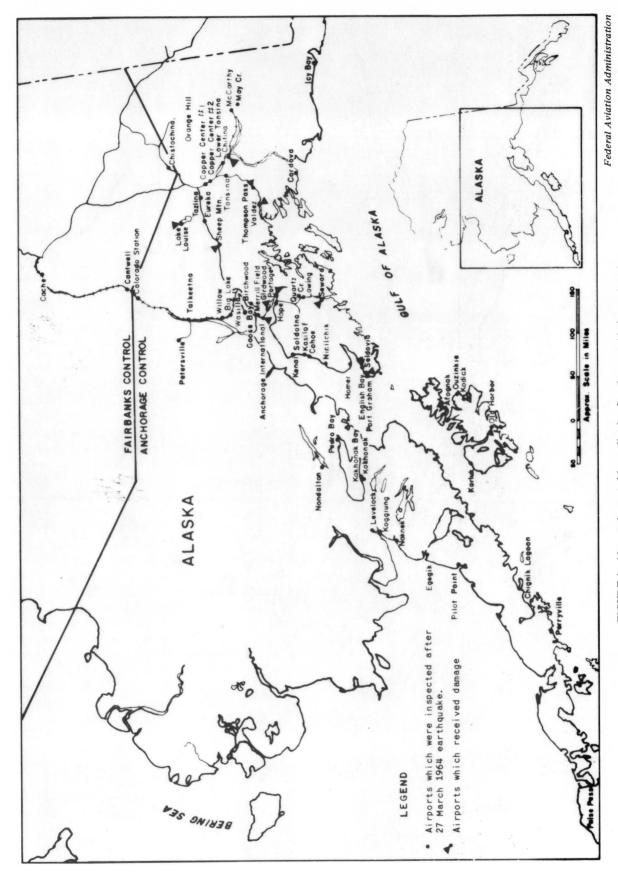

FIGURE 1 Airports inspected immediately after the great Alaska earthquake.

Federal Aviation Administration

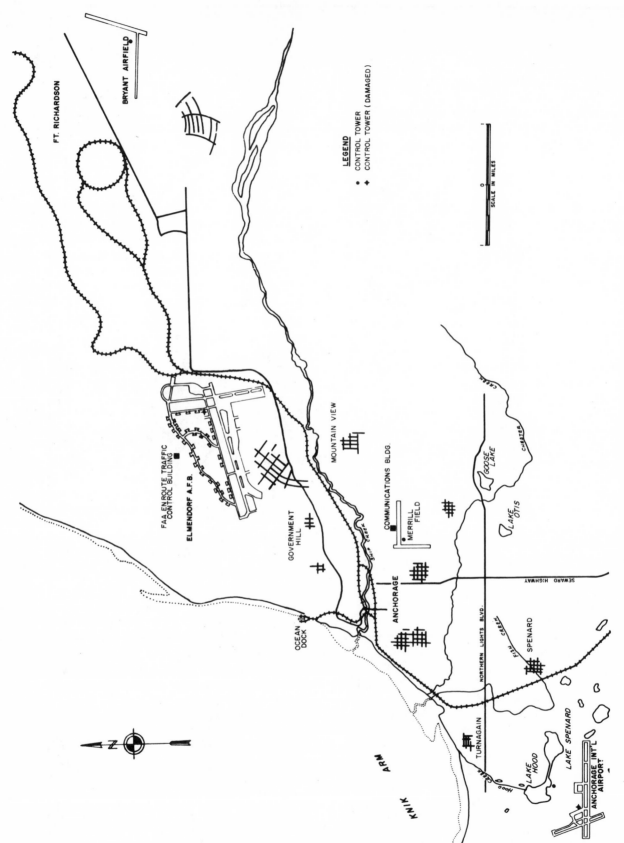

FIGURE 2   Airfields and control facilities, greater Anchorage area, Alaska.

EARTHQUAKE EFFECTS ON AIR TRAFFIC CONTROL FACILITIES AND RELATED SERVICES

CONTROL, ADVISORY, AND SPECIAL SERVICES

All control and advisory services were temporarily disrupted within the boundaries of the Anchorage advisory and control area (Figure 1). The interruption in services was attributable mainly to the failure of communications in the Anchorage area, the center of communications for Alaska. The loss of service resulted from the failure of land lines (telephone, interphone, and teletypewriter). The Anchorage International Airport control tower collapsed, killing one person and injuring a second, but other air traffic control facilities incurred only minor damage, and services were not disrupted by physical damage to buildings or to installed equipment.

EN ROUTE TRAFFIC CONTROL SERVICES

The en route traffic control service operates from a control building on Elmendorf Air Force Base (AFB), immediately north and east of the city of Anchorage (Figure 2). The facility controls en route international and domestic air traffic within the Anchorage flight advisory and control area; its services were halted immediately after the earthquake because of the loss of communication lines. The Fairbanks air-route traffic-control center radar approach control and the King Salmon approach control facilities assumed control of the en route traffic normally directed from Anchorage as soon as these stations were aware that the Anchorage facilities were inoperable. Air traffic control services within the Anchorage Control area were discontinued and only advisory services were provided until limited communications facilities were restored, approximately 8½ hours after the earthquake. Aircraft under Anchorage control at the time of the earthquake either proceeded to their flight-plan destination or were diverted to alternate airports.

ANCHORAGE INTERNATIONAL AND DOMESTIC FLIGHT SERVICE STATION

The Anchorage International and Domestic Flight Service station, located at Merrill Field in Anchorage, Alaska, disseminates information to aircraft on weather and runway conditions (Figure 2). The facility became inoperative because of the loss of communication circuits. Approximately 5–10 minutes after the earthquake, two long-distance circuits and ground-to-air circuits were found to be operational; however, all local telephone, interphone, and teletype services within the facility were inoperable. Although the local circuits were individually restored piece-meal to provide increased communication capabilities, the quality of the service was not up to standard until the communications cables were permanently repaired.

ANCHORAGE INTERNATIONAL AIRPORT CONTROL TOWER

The Anchorage airport, approximately 4 mi southwest of the city of Anchorage (Figure 2), is one of Alaska's major airports, serving both intrastate and transoceanic flights. The Anchorage International Airport control tower was the only civilian air-traffic facility that sustained severe structural damage from the earthquake. The tower collapsed (Figures 3–6) killing one employee and injuring a second. A brief description of the structural failure is included in this report.

The loss of the control tower eliminated the controlled use of Anchorage International Airport after the earthquake. The Federal Aviation Administration (FAA) immediately initiated the installation of temporary services to compensate for the loss of the control tower. The radio equipment installed in an FAA flight-check aircraft parked on the ramp at the airport was employed to provide limited communications with aircraft operating on the surface of Anchorage International Airport and in the traffic pattern. By midnight (about 6½ hours after the earthquake), one of the Anchorage International Airport traffic-control-tower frequencies was installed in the adjacent Lake Hood seaplane-base control tower, approximately 3,500 ft from the destroyed Anchorage International Airport control tower (Figure 2). All air traffic was notified that the Lake Hood control service was providing service to both the Lake Hood seaplane base and the Anchorage International Airport. Within about a week after the earthquake, additional air-to-ground frequencies were installed in the Lake Hood control tower. The Lake Hood tower was able to satisfactorily control aircraft in the traffic pattern; however, the tower operators were unable to observe aircraft movement and ramp activity on all parts of the Anchorage International Airport. Lake Hood tower continued to control Anchorage International Airport traffic until a new tower was commissioned in April 1965.

CONCLUSIONS

The most vulnerable item in the air traffic control service was the land communication system (cables, telephone exchanges, and so forth) within the Anchorage area. Portable radio-communication units of the Gonset type proved to be the most useful instruments in reestablishing some semblance of essential communication between the control facilities in the greater Anchorage area. Without even limited coordination between facilities, air traffic control services within the Anchorage area would have literally come to a halt.

FIGURE 3   Anchorage International Airport, May 23, 1964. The aircraft near the intersection of the runways are parked adjacent to the airport terminal. The control tower, which was totally destroyed, was attached to the terminal building. Lake Hood seaplane base is north of the airport; Lake Hood tower controlled Anchorage International Airport traffic until a new tower was constructed. The west portion of the Turnagain slide area is visible at the top of the photograph.

EFFECTS OF THE EARTHQUAKE ON AIRCRAFT

Vibration damage to the air carrier and civil fleet was very light, although many aircraft were parked and tied down within 10 ft of each other. Most aircraft were available for use immediately after the earthquake. Very little damage was done to the FAA fleet of seven aircraft. A Fairchild C-123 aircraft sustained aileron and wing-tip damage while parked in the hangar at the Anchorage International Air-

State of Alaska, Division of Buildings

FIGURE 4 The upper four stories of the Anchorage International Airport control tower collapsed onto the west parking apron, fatally injuring one controller and severely injuring a second.

port; a metal workstand had shifted into the aircraft during the earthquake. This damage was repaired and the aircraft was back in service less than 2 days after the earthquake.

Although the Anchorage International Airport serves a large number of domestic and international jet aircraft, damage to the air-carrier fleet was slight. Kodiak Airways, based at Kodiak, Alaska, lost two aircraft as a result of tsunamis. One aircraft, a Grumman G-21 amphibian, was parked in a hangar that was destroyed by a tsunami, and a Cessna-180 aircraft on floats was lost when it broke its mooring. One aircraft belonging to Reeve Aleutian Airways

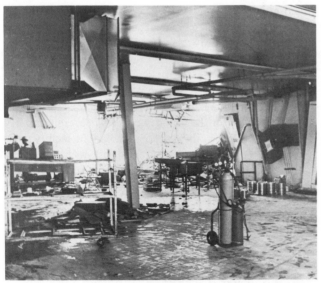

State of Alaska, Division of Buildings

FIGURE 5 The Anchorage International Airport flight kitchen, which was extensively damaged by the collapsing control tower.

State of Alaska, Division of Buildings

FIGURE 6 Anchorage International Airport control-tower debris removal.

was damaged while it was raised on jacks for repairs in a hangar at the Anchorage International Airport; the violence of the earthquake shook the aircraft from the jacks.

The general-aviation fleet sustained little damage from the earth tremors. Small aircraft at locations such as Seward were destroyed by tsunami action, and a few small aircraft were damaged or destroyed when several hangars in the Anchorage area were damaged.

EFFECTS OF THE EARTHQUAKE ON CIVIL AIRPORTS

Immediately after the earthquake, the FAA began to investigate the condition of civil and municipal airfields that were thought to have received substantial earthquake damage. Several local engineering firms assisted the FAA staff in its investigations. The Corps of Engineers also inspected several airfields and made repairs sufficient to permit immediate emergency use. Figure 1 shows the location of all the airfields inspected by the FAA and of those that sustained damage. Subsequent routine inspection of all airfields in Alaska did not disclose any additional earthquake damage at other locations.

ANCHORAGE INTERNATIONAL AIRPORT

The Anchorage International Airport (Figure 2) is the largest and busiest civil airfield in Alaska. Since the advent of international polar flights, Anchorage International has become the primary refueling station for many American and foreign jet aircraft en route to and from the Orient and northern Europe. This airport is also the originating point of flights throughout the interior and western portions of Alaska and to the rest of the United States.

The airfield facility consists of two asphaltic concrete-surfaced runways with associated taxiways, and service- and passenger-access parking aprons. The main east–west runway is 10,600 ft long and is capable of handling any commercial jet aircraft currently in operation. The north–south runway is 5,000 ft long. A modern airport passenger terminal stands near the intersection of the runways. The terminal is a two-story building constructed at the edge of an apron embankment with two stories above ground facing the airport access road (east) and the finished floor elevation of the west side of the second floor at apron level to permit passenger access to the aircraft parking apron. The control tower (six floor levels and control cab) projected through the terminal building.

Several maintenance hangars and service parking aprons are located on the north side of the east–west runway, east of the terminal building, and an Alaskan Air National Guard complex stands on the opposite side of the runway (Figure 3).

The restrictions placed on the use of the airport immediately after the earthquake were not necessarily related to a lack of air traffic control services. Misinformation on the condition of runways and taxiways and nonavailability of airport-lighting aids, the instrument landing system, airport weather observations, and other factors were critical elements in restricting the use of the airport.

Control Tower and Passenger Terminal

The most significant damage caused by the earthquake was the destruction of the Anchorage International Airport control tower. The lower two floors of the control tower were integrally connected to the terminal structure; the upper four stories and control cab projected above the roof of the terminal. The control tower failed at the second-story level (ground level at the apron side) and collapsed to the west (Figure 4). The failure caused considerable damage to the air-terminal kitchens, adjacent to the control tower (Figures 5 and 6). The terminal facility sustained considerable additional damage from failures of concrete-block interior walls, lighting fixtures, and acoustical ceiling tiles. Many windows were shattered and displaced. The entire structural frame was subjected to severe horizontal strain and was permanently displaced to the east 1/2 to 1½ in. per floor (Manley and Mayer Architects, 1964).

Runways, Taxiways, Parking Aprons, Pavements

The earthquake damage to the runways, taxiways, parking areas, roads, and drainage systems of the Anchorage International Airport was equivalent to several years of deteri-

oration by normal wear and weathering. At least 6 ft of frost penetration existed at the time of the seismic disturbance. During the passage of the waves, the brittle pavements and frozen base materials were subjected to tensile stresses in excess of their strength that caused narrow cracks. Immediately after the earthquake, fine fissures were observed throughout the area, including the unpaved surfaces. The fissures were not large and appeared similar to shrinkage cracks. Aerial photographs, taken before and after the earthquake, were compared in an effort to measure the earthquake-induced crack frequency, but this method proved ineffective because many of the earthquake-induced cracks were small and not visible. Direct observation of other pavements during the earthquake revealed the development of many fissures that were later difficult to see without close scrutiny. The fractures are assumed to be the result of excessive flexure rather than permanent horizontal displacement (Adams, Corthell, Lee, Wince, and Associates, 1964).

Drainage Systems

The subgrade drainage-collection system for the east–west runway was apparently not damaged; however, the asphalt surface-sealing material placed near the surface of the ground to exclude surface drainage was cracked over approximately 95 percent of its length. This cracking permitted erosion and subsequent subsidence of the seal material. One underdrain outfall line was misaligned and required realignment. The remaining outfalls were nearly half full of silt (Adams and others, 1964). Two catch basins and 16 headwalls of the storm drainage system were displaced and required realignment. Many lengths of drainpipes were broken and misaligned, permitting the entry of the overlying soil (Figure 7). A vertical displacement also occurred between the pavement surface and catch basins in isolated areas (Figure 8; Adams and others, 1964).

MERRILL FIELD

Within the city limits of Anchorage (Figure 2), Merrill Field provides service for the majority of the wheel-equipped small-aircraft fleet in the Anchorage area. The facility consists of an asphaltic concrete-surfaced east–west runway, 4,000 ft long, and a gravel-surfaced north–south runway, 2,460 ft long. Several aircraft hangars stand next to the aircraft parking aprons.

The FAA's Communications Center for the Anchorage complex is in the Merrill Field Communications Building. The FAA also occupies part of the building and part of a maintenance-shop hangar, both of which are north of the east–west runway (Figure 9).

The structures related to airport activity sustained only slight damage from the earthquake. The FAA's Anchorage

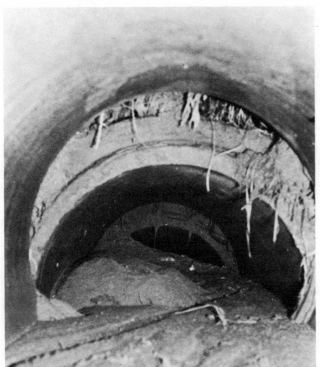

FIGURE 7 Vertical displacement of storm-drain line, Anchorage International Airport.

Communications Center became inoperable because of power and control-cable failures in the greater Anchorage area and not because of damage to the installed equipment.

The only detrimental effect of the earthquake on the runways appeared in the form of fine cracks that were probably caused by the flexural stresses induced by the passage of the earthquake waves. No noticeable permanent displacement of the pavement surface was detected.

SEWARD MUNICIPAL AIRPORT

The Seward Municipal Airport is about 1 mi northeast of Seward, a seaport city located on the Kenai Peninsula (Figure 1). The airport is constructed on an alluvial fan that forms the beach at the north end of Resurrection Bay; its facilities consist of two gravel-surfaced runways that extend northward from the upper reaches of the tidal flats, and a gravel-surfaced parking apron (Figure 10). Several private-aircraft shelters were located adjacent to the runway and parking apron.

The airport sustained only slight damage from the seismic ground motion. No extensive fissuring occurred. Only a few cracks were more than 6 in. wide; the majority of the fissures were limited to the north end of the airfield. The tsunamis are generally credited with being the most destruc-

tive force, destroying all but one hangar building and the Cordova Airlines office building. The tsunamis washed off all the gravel surface material, which had been applied the year before the earthquake, and deposited silt and debris. The general land subsidence caused by the earthquake permitted the inundation of the south end of both runways during the high-tide periods.

Air transportation was the only means of rapid transportation to the city of Seward immediately after the earthquake. Both the railroad and highway routes from Anchorage were impassable because of bridge damage, subgrade damage, and landslides. The Corps of Engineers, by local contract procedures, immediately began to clear the debris and repaired the runways sufficiently to permit aircraft operations. Because of flooding during the high-tide periods, the use of the total length of the runways was limited to the low-tide periods until the permanent restoration was completed.

The FAA considered the possibility of moving the runways from the area adjacent to the tidal flats; however, suitable space that met approach and airfield requirements was limited near the city. The FAA therefore recommended that the airport be reconstructed at its original location. Because the Corps of Engineers was engaged in the general restoration of the area, including the municipal, state, and Alaska Railroad facilities at Seward, the restoration of the airport also became its responsibility.

The restoration included the reestablishment of the runway, apron, and taxiway grades above the high-tide elevation, with modifications to the drainage system to accommodate the change caused by the general land subsidence (Figure 11).

VALDEZ MUNICIPAL AIRPORT

Before the earthquake, both the city of Valdez and the airport were situated on the unconsolidated outwash delta that formed the east shore of the port of Valdez (Figure 1).

FIGURE 8 Vertical displacement of pavement surface and catch basins, Anchorage International Airport.

MERRILL FIELD
COMMUNICATIONS
BUILDING

CONTROL TOWER

Air Photo Tech, Inc.

FIGURE 9 Merrill Field, Anchorage, services the wheel- and ski-equipped small-aircraft fleet. The Merrill Field communications building serves as the hub for FAA traffic-control communications. The airport sustained negligible damage in the earthquake.

The airport was about 3 mi northeast of the city. The airport facilities consisted of a gravel-surfaced runway, 3,530 ft long, and a gravel-surfaced parking apron. Several privately owned hangars stood next to the apron (Figure 12).

The earthquake induced general subsidence and horizontal movement of the delta toward the port of Valdez. The amount of horizontal and vertical movement increased toward the shoreline. Catastrophic submarine slides and tsunamis totally destroyed the Valdez waterfront facilities.

The west (seaward) end of the runway and the parking apron were fissured extensively. The fissures were up to 48 in. wide and ran north to south and paralleled the shore-

FIGURE 10 The City of Seward is situated on an extensive delta at the north end of Resurrection Bay. The waterfront facilities were destroyed by submarine slides, tsunamis, and fire. The municipal airport is visible in the lower right corner of the photograph. Reconstruction of the small-boat basin and The Alaska Railroad dock, between the airport and city, was in progress when the photograph was taken. The erosion caused by the tidal action created by land subsidence can be seen at the ends of the runway.

line. The frequency and width of the fissures decreased toward the east end of the runway.

Before the earthquake, the runway had a gradient of 1.2 percent down toward the west end. Postearthquake surveys revealed that the gradient had gradually increased to 2.1 percent.

Immediately after the earthquake, the west 500 ft of the runway was unusable because of the fissures. Temporary repairs were made by filling the fissures with pit-run gravelly material, and the field was totally operational within 2 days. The fill material was placed in the fissures without compaction because of the urgency of repairing the runways for emergency use. Permanent restoration necessitated the removal of the uncompacted fill that had been placed in the larger fissures. The excavations were backfilled and compacted in lifts to eliminate any soft areas. The material used to fill the fissures immediately after the earthquake contained numerous cobbles that were unsuitable for a runway surface; the entire area of the runway and parking apron was therefore resurfaced.

MINOR INTERIOR AIRFIELDS

These minor airfields, most of them north and east of Anchorage, serve areas that are also accessible by road. The effects of the earthquake on these airfields is interesting because their locations roughly outline the northern limit of ground fissuring.

Chitina Airport, about 100 mi northeast of Valdez

(Figure 1), consists of a 3,550-ft runway and a parking apron, both with gravel surfaces (Figure 13). The airport stands on a moraional deposit adjacent to the Copper River. Both ends of the runway are embankment sections constructed of material obtained from the center of the runway. The north 300 ft of the runway was extensively fissured (Figure 14). The embankment was approximately 10–12 ft deep here. Four large fissures, about 12 in. wide, crossed the field, and the north end subsided slightly.

Thompson Pass Field, often referred to as "Thirty Mile Strip," serves primarily as an emergency landing strip for light aircraft flying through Thompson Pass between Valdez and the interior of Alaska. The Richardson Highway also goes through the pass, which is about 30 highway miles northeast of Valdez. The runway is on a terminal moraine of the Worthington Glacier, adjacent to the Richardson Highway (Figure 1). The 1,800-ft landing strip is the prod-

FIGURE 11 The Seward reconstruction effort was essentially completed when this photograph was taken. The highway and Alaska Railroad enter the city from the canyon in the upper right and pass by the reconstructed airport, Alaska Railroad freight dock, and small-boat basin before entering the downtown area of the city.

FIGURE 12   The city of Valdez (lower center) and the municipal airport (center right) stand on an extensive delta formed by the Robe, Lowe, and Valdez Glacier rivers. The waterfront facilities were totally destroyed by submarine slides and tsunamis. Subsidence of the delta subjected the remnants of the waterfront to tidal flooding, as can be seen here. The seaward portion of the delta was designated a high-risk area, and the entire community was relocated at the Mineral Creek townsite (upper left); the townsite was being prepared for occupancy in 1966, when this photograph was taken. The airport was not relocated.

uct of grading the local materials to a relatively smooth surface and gradient, with side ditches to provide drainage. The east 500 ft of the runway was crossed with fissures up to 2 in. wide that crossed randomly, although the general direction was north and south.

Lake Louise Airport, in the Copper River lowlands about 125 mi northeast of Anchorage (Figure 1), has a 2,450-ft landing strip constructed from local materials that are predominantly silt and silty sand. The field lies on a peninsula of the lake; the finished grade of the field is about 20 ft above the level of the lake (Figure 15). Three small fissures appeared in a fill section on the north edge of the field. These fissures were up to 2 in. wide at the shoulder and diminished rapidly in size, so that 15 ft from the shoulder none exceeded 1/4 in. The damage did not constitute a threat to air traffic or ground operation and was left to be repaired by normal maintenance operations.

MINOR SEACOAST AIRFIELDS

Most of the minor seacoast airfields damaged by the earthquake were on the east side of Kodiak Island and along the

Federal Aviation Administration

FIGURE 13   Chitina Airport is built on an end moraine that forms the bank of the Copper River. Both ends of the runway were constructed of material obtained from the center. The north 300 ft (near end) of the airstrip was fissured extensively (Figure 14).

Federal Aviation Administration

FIGURE 14   A fissure that occurred in the north end of the Chitina Airport. The man demonstrates the relative size of the crack.

Bureau of Land Management

FIGURE 15 Lake Louise Airport is on a peninsula of the lake that is used primarily as a recreational area. The earthquake caused minor fissuring along the north end (top) of the airstrip.

Bureau of Land Management, 1962

FIGURE 16 The beach airstrip served the village of Afognak on Afognak Island (Figure 1). Both village and airstrip were inundated by tsunamis, and the village was destroyed. After the earthquake, it was relocated at Port Lions, on Kodiak Island, and a new airstrip was constructed to serve the new community.

east shore of Cook Inlet. These airfields generally serve fishing villages and are minimal facilities capable of accommodating only light aircraft. Although the facilities are minimal, they are of great importance nonetheless to the communities because boats and float-equipped aircraft are the only other means of transportation.

The village of Afognak, with its adjacent 1,800-ft gravel-surfaced runway, was situated on a beach along the south shore of Afognak Island just north of Kodiak Island (Figures 1 and 16). Immediately after the earthquake, tsunamis almost totally destroyed the village and severely damaged the airstrip. The village was relocated at Port Lions, on Kodiak Island, and a new airstrip was constructed nearby (Figure 17).

The village of Old Harbor is on the northeast shore of Sitkalidak Strait on Kodiak Island (Figure 1). This fishing village and its adjacent airstrip were also destroyed by the tsunamis that followed the earthquake. The fishing village was reconstructed at its original location, but the airstrip was moved parallel to the beachline (Figures 18 and 19).

English Bay, on the south end of the Kenai Peninsula (Figure 1), has its 2,000-ft-long gravel airstrip on a narrow spit at the head of the bay in lower Cook Inlet. When the airstrip was constructed, the spit was known to be threatened by wind-driven seas, but this was the only location possible for an airstrip that could service the nearby village (Figure 20). After the earthquake, general land subsidence along Cook Inlet caused the south end of the airfield to

Bureau of Land Management

FIGURE 17 The new airstrip constructed at Port Lions to serve the village that was moved there from Afognak Island. The road leading from the lower end of the airstrip connects it with the new village.

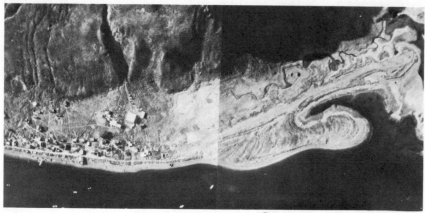

Bureau of Land Management, 1962

FIGURE 18   Preearthquake view of the village of Old Harbor and its airstrip.

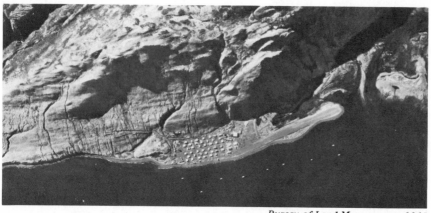

Bureau of Land Management, 1965

FIGURE 19   The village of Old Harbor and its airstrip were destroyed by the tsunamis that followed the earthquake. The only structures not destroyed can be seen at the upper right edge of the village. The village was reconstructed at its original location, but the airstrip was moved to the seaward edge of the beach.

Bureau of Land Management, 1964

FIGURE 20   Postearthquake view of the village of English Bay and its airstrip.

flood during high tides. The airstrip was reconstructed by raising the runway grade above the high-tide elevations (Figure 21).

Seldovia, one of the larger fishing villages on the southeast shore of lower Cook Inlet, is the processing center for the King Crab fishery in the area (Figure 1). The 2,100-ft airstrip serving the community is at the foot of a mountain immediately west of the village. Both ends of the runway were constructed near a slough that is subject to the tidal fluctuations in Cook Inlet. Superficial inspection indicated that the airstrip sustained no damage attributable to the earthquake, but the general land subsidence subjected both ends of the airfield to flooding during high tides (Figure 22). Runway grades had to be reestablished above the high-tide elevations (Figure 23).

EFFECTS OF THE EARTHQUAKE ON MILITARY AIRFIELDS

Three major military establishments with airfield facilities are located in the area that experienced major damage from the Alaska earthquake. Two of the facilities, Elmendorf AFB and Fort Richardson, are in the greater Anchorage area. The third, Kodiak Naval Station, is on the east side of Kodiak Island (Figure 1). The discussion in this report will be limited to the effects of the earthquake on the airfields and support facilities directly related to aircraft operations.

ELMENDORF AFB

Elmendorf AFB, immediately north of Anchorage, borders the city (Figure 2). Its neighbor to the east is Fort Richardson, a U.S. Army installation. Elmendorf is an air-defense base that also serves as a logistic base for military

organizations throughout Alaska and for military flights to the Far East. It is also the headquarters of the Alaskan Command, the joint command for all military services in Alaska.

The airfield facilities at Elmendorf AFB consist of two paved runways with associated taxiways, aprons, control tower, and hangars (Figure 24). The east–west runway is equipped with instrument-landing equipment and can accommodate aircraft under all weather conditions. The north–south runway is used primarily during adverse crosswind conditions and is equipped with runway lights but not with instrument-landing facilities. The airfield facilities are surfaced with either portland-cement concrete or asphaltic cement concrete.

General Geology

Most of the airfield facilities are situated on an extensive glacial outwash terrace, composed of a clean sandy gravel that provides an excellent airfield subgrade. An extensive morainal pattern exists immediately north of the facility where the topography is the irregular terrain associated with ground moraines. Underlying the moraines and terrace is a deposit of blue-gray clay and silt (Bootlegger Cove Clay) that underlies much of the Anchorage area. This blue-gray clay occurs near the surface at the west end of the east–west taxiway and runway.

Airfield and Control Facilities

The airfield pavements, lighting, and landing aids sustained no damage directly attributable to the earthquake, presumably because of the excellent *in situ* subgrade materials. The airfield lighting and landing aids were temporarily inoperative because of the failure of the power source and not because of failure within the systems. All airfield lighting and landing aids were operational by 1:00 a.m. on the day after the earthquake.

FIGURE 21 The general land subsidence of the west shore of Cook Inlet subjected the airfield to tidal flooding. The finished grade of the airstrip was consequently raised sufficiently to prevent flooding.

FIGURE 22   The village of Seldovia. The structures along the shoreline and the ends of the runway were inundated during high tides. The picture shows the effect of the flooding of the runway.

The Elmendorf AFB control tower, separated by expansion joints from an adjacent two-story reinforced-concrete communications building, sustained considerable damage. The control tower was 19 ft square and seven stories high above ground level. A steel balcony extended beyond the walls and above the seventh floor. The eighth floor was a steel observation cupola that served as the traffic-control center. A reinforced-concrete elevator shaft was in the northwest corner. The first three floors of the control-tower were subjected to severe stresses, which resulted in cracks 12–24 in. apart (Figures 25 and 26). No apparent damage was visible between the third floor and the observation

FIGURE 23   Seldovia, October 1966; the results of the restoration effort. The shoreline was reestablished by a massive earth fill that permitted the sea-oriented industries to relocate along the water. The airstrip was also filled to prevent tidal flooding.

cupola, but the cupola was extensively damaged (Figures 27 and 28) (Fisher and Merkle, 1965).

The loss of the control tower temporarily limited the incoming and outgoing traffic. The radio equipment in a parked C-123 aircraft was used as a temporary control tower until a mobile unit arrived from Tinker Air Force Base, Oklahoma; the mobile unit was totally operational on Easter Sunday, 2 days after the earthquake. Because Elmendorf AFB was the only fully operational facility in the Anchorage area capable of accommodating jet aircraft, both commercial and military aircraft used that airfield until Anchorage International Airport was able to provide partial service. The mobile control unit effectively controlled traffic until communication equipment was installed in an old tower on the roof of a hangar at the intersection of the north–south/east–west parking apron. The old tower controlled traffic until June 28, 1967, when a new reinforced-concrete tower was commissioned.

Support Facilities

Two maintenance hangars that had been constructed during World War II sustained structural damage. The vertical bracing and their connections were damaged in both hangars because of their inability to withstand the lateral loads induced by the earthquake (Figure 29) (Fisher and Merkle, 1965).

The Elmendorf AFB air terminal is occupied by the Base Operations Office, the control center for air traffic using the airfield facilities, and by the passenger terminal for military flights. The ceiling and light fixtures collapsed leaving the passenger terminal in a shambles. A reinforced-concrete chimney also collapsed, causing additional roof damage

(Figures 30 and 31). Although the structure was damaged, the defense mission of the airfield and the massive airlift after the earthquake precluded any interruption of the base operation facilities; emergency lighting, including candles, was used on the night of March 28, 1964, to keep the facilities operating.

FORT RICHARDSON

Fort Richardson is about 8 mi northeast of the city of Anchorage, in the greater Anchorage area. The west boundary of the installation adjoins the boundary of Elmendorf AFB; the east boundary extends into the Chugach Mountains. Fort Richardson, the largest Army post in Alaska, is the headquarters of the U.S. Army Alaska (USARAL).

Bryant Army Airfield, the Fort Richardson aviation facility (Figure 2), is the operating station for a portion of the USARAL Aviation Battalion. The airfield facilities at the time of the earthquake consisted of one fixed-wing-aircraft runway and one helicopter runway, and helicopter and fixed-wing parking aprons with connecting taxiways. All the facilities were paved with asphaltic concrete. The primary structures were two maintenance hangars, a control tower, and an operations building (Figures 32 and 33).

Fort Richardson occupies the eastern end of the glacial outwash terrace on which Elmendorf AFB is situated. The subsurface material is composed mainly of a clean sandy gravel that provides an excellent subgrade.

Bryant Field facilities withstood the earthquake without significant damage. Immediately after the earthquake, the control tower, which was equipped with a standby genera-

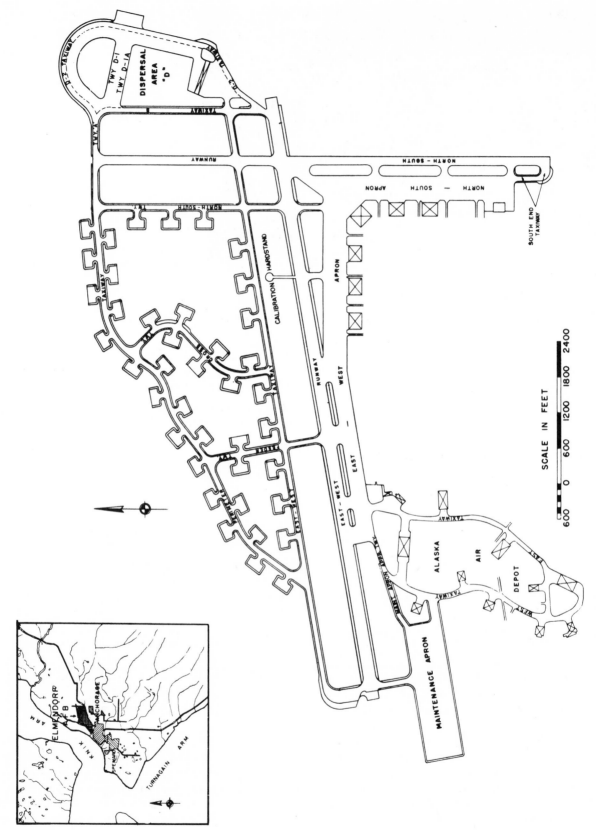

FIGURE 24 Elmendorf AFB, Anchorage, Alaska. Layout of airfield pavement facilities.

1026

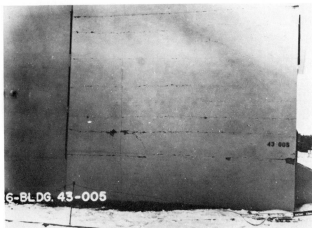

U.S. Air Force

FIGURE 25   Horizontal cracks in the reinforced-concrete walls of the Elmendorf AFB Control Tower are an indication of the severity of the stresses induced by the earthquake. The structure adjacent to the tower (left) is the two-story reinforced-concrete communications building. The pattern of the cracks indicates that failure occurred along the lift joints formed while the concrete was being placed.

tor that started automatically when the primary power system failed, was the only operable tower in the greater Anchorage area. The control tower also had a direct line with the Anchorage Control Center at Elmendorf AFB; the telephones in the tower became the relay point between USARAL Operations Center at Fort Richardson and the Anchorage Center on Elmendorf AFB.

Very little aircraft damage had occurred, although one Mohawk (OV-1A) sustained some damage to its outer skin and bulkhead. Once the weather cleared, the battalion sent aloft practically 100 percent of its aircraft on damage-assessment and mercy missions.

U.S. Air Force

FIGURE 27   The observation cupola of the Elmendorf AFB Control Tower was damaged beyond use.

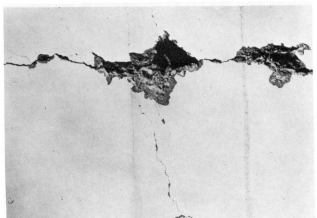

U.S. Air Force

FIGURE 26   This closeup view of a horizontal crack in the wall of the Elmendorf AFB Control Tower reveals the damaged vertical reinforcing steel.

U.S. Air Force

FIGURE 28   Elmendorf AFB Control Tower. Steel platform was constructed around the seventh floor and the observation cupola occupies the eighth floor.

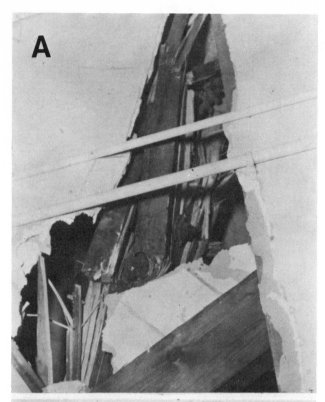

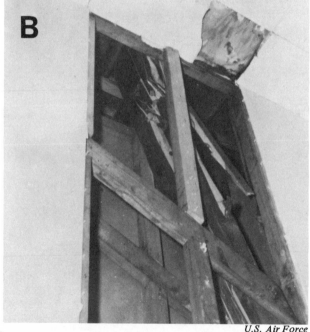

FIGURE 29   Timber structural members in Elmendorf AFB Hangar D-25 were shattered by the earthquake.

FIGURE 30   The reinforced-concrete chimney of the Elmendorf AFB Air Terminal collapsed, damaging the roof and interior of the building.

Two Mohawks, equipped to take aerial photographs, provided the first concrete information on the overall damage in the Anchorage area on March 28, 1964. The photographic coverage was extended to include Homer, Seldovia, Kodiak, and major land-transportation links in the earthquake-affected areas. These photographs made possible the rapid assessment of the damage and have been of considerable scientific and engineering value.

The Army helicopters played an important role in flying mercy and logistic missions in areas not accessible by any other means of transportation. The fixed-wing fleet performed a valuable service in flying Army troops and supplies to the outlying areas to aid the stricken communities.

The structures at Bryant Field also withstood the forces of the earthquake with little damage other than some cracks in the nonstructural concrete-block walls of both the hangar and the Unit Operations building.

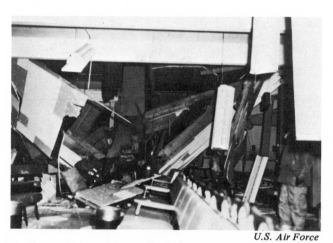

FIGURE 31   The interior damage to the waiting room of the Elmendorf AFB Terminal was caused mainly by the chimney failure.

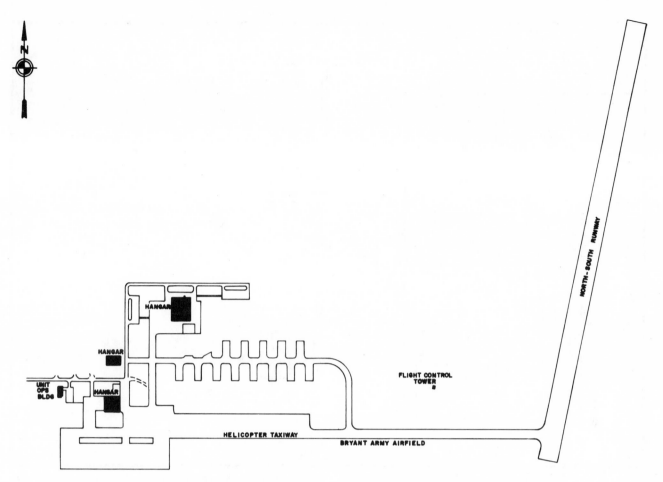

FIGURE 32   Airfield facilities, Bryant Army Airfield, Fort Richardson, Alaska.

FIGURE 33   Bryant Army Airfield, on Fort Richardson, serves as the operating station for a portion of the USARAL Aviation Battalion. The Bryant Field Control Tower, near the intersection of the runway, was the only one that was fully operational in the Anchorage area immediately after the earthquake.

U.S. NAVAL STATION, KODIAK

Kodiak Naval Station is on Kodiak Island (Figure 1), about 250 air mi southwest of Anchorage and 670 mi west of Juneau. The airfield at the station provides facilities for military air transportation and for the commercial air carriers that serve the city of Kodiak and outlying villages.

The present mission of the Naval Station is to provide services and material to support the naval and air operations of units and operating forces of the Navy. The mission includes aircraft maintenance, all-weather landing facilities, and logistic support for the Naval District and tenant organizations.

The airfield facilities at the Naval Station consist of three paved runways, parking aprons, seaplane facilities, and associated maintenance hangars. The main east–west runway, which is 7,500 ft long, is instrumented and provides all-weather service.

The damage caused by the motion of the earthquake was limited, for the most part, to the cracking and settlement of

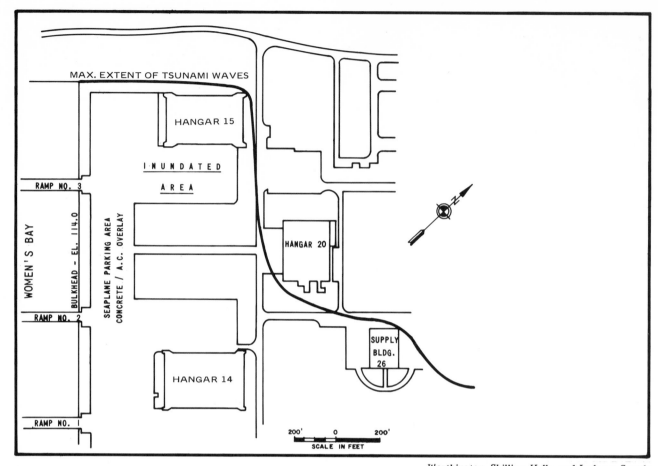

Worthington, Skilling, Helle, and Jackson, Seattle

FIGURE 34   Maximum depth of tsunami in Hangars 14 and 15 at the U.S. Naval Station, Kodiak, was about 4 ft. Tsunami waters did not enter Hangar 20.

pavements and floor slabs, structural damage to the hangars, and breaks in the utility lines. The major damage was caused by the series of tsunamis that inundated portions of the station (Figures 34–36), and by the flood damage caused by the 5½-ft general land subsidence (Hill, 1965) (Figure 37).

Airfield Damage

The tsunamis caused erosion along the runway shoulders and approaches and deposited ice and debris on the airfield (Figure 38). Riprap and fill at the seaward end of all three runways were washed away, and the runway threshold lights were damaged by the tsunamis and subsequent flooding. Two runway ends had to be raised 3½ ft to provide sufficient freeboard above the high tides.

A considerable amount of localized settlement, in addition to the general land subsidence, occurred under the apron and hangar floor slabs (Figure 39). Portions of the apron and hangars were constructed on hydraulic fill that was dredged from the bay, and the localized settlement was attributable to the further consolidation of this fill. The

U.S. Navy

FIGURE 35   The parking aprons and structures at the U.S. Naval Station, Kodiak, flooded by the tsunamis.

U.S. Navy

FIGURE 36 The black oil marks on the walls of the Kodiak Naval Station's primary power plant show the maximum height of the tsunamis that flooded the station.

U.S. Navy

FIGURE 38 The tsunamis deposited this mooring buoy and ice on the airfield at Kodiak Naval Station, along with other debris.

areas of localized settlement were raised by mud jacking, and the joints and cracks were sealed. The apron, formerly used as a seaplane ramp, was constructed only a few feet above high tide and because of the general land subsidence, it fell below the higher tide elevations (Figure 39). An earth dike, approximately 2,000 ft long, was constructed around the lower portion of the apron and was faced with riprap

U.S. Navy

FIGURE 37 The 5½-ft general land subsidence of Kodiak Naval Station permitted flooding of the aprons during high tides. Womens Bay is left of the small white structure. A dike was constructed across the apron to prevent flooding. Hangar 14 is in the foreground; Hangar 15 is in the background (Figure 34).

U.S. Navy

FIGURE 39 The seismic forces consolidated the dredge fill, creating differential settlement of apron slabs and floors. The tsunamis also eroded unprotected soil around the structures.

for protection against waves, and a pumping station was constructed inside the dike to remove runoff and seepage water. The bulkhead retaining the dredge fill at the seaward side was also damaged (Hill, 1965).

Damage to Structures

Three hangars, Buildings 14, 15, and 20, were damaged to different extents by both the earthquake and subsequent tsunamis. Each hangar has a structural-steel frame supported on piling; the hangar floors are supported on dredged fill. Buildings 14 and 15 each measure 320 × 240 ft and have attached two-story lean-tos measuring 26 × 240 ft. The structures are identical in design and construction. Building 20 measures 175 × 160 ft, with attached lean-tos on two sides (Worthington and others, 1964).

Building 14 was constructed on approximately 19 ft of dredge fill and sustained more earthquake damage than the other two hangars. The tsunamis that flooded the hangar floor with 4 ft of water eroded the soil around the structure. The floor slab and underlying fill settled as much as 18 in. at the northerly corner of the building. The hangar door sills were supported on piling; thus, the settlement of the apron created a step at the juncture of the door and apron (Figure 39). The structure was subjected to severe lateral stresses that buckled a gusset plate in a diagonal brace (Figure 40) and bowed some of the braces (Worthington and others, 1964).

Building 15 is almost identical to Building 14, except that a control tower is located in its southerly corner (Figure 37). The structure was inundated with 3 ft of water by the tsunamis. The only significant difference in construction between Buildings 14 and 15, when considering the effects of the earthquake, is the depth of dredged fill under the hangars. Except for the southerly corner, which was constructed on 17 ft of dredged fill, Building 15 was constructed on natural ground. The southerly corner settled slightly; however, the magnitude of settlement and floor-slab damage was significantly less than that experienced in Building 14. The steel frame of the structure also suffered minor damage to the bracing. The difference in the performance of the two identical structures is attributable to the depth of uncompacted fill placed during construction.

Building 20 was constructed on 17–18 ft of dredged fill. Although the tsunami did not flood this structure (Figure 34), the consolidation of the dredged fill caused the floor slabs and approach apron to settle. The structural members sustained more permanent lateral displacement (2½ in.) than those in the other hangars, and the bracing at the door pockets was badly bowed.

A supply building, Building 26, located adjacent to Buildings 14 and 20 (Figure 34) is a three-story reinforced-concrete structure with a basement. The building, which is of flat slab construction with the exterior walls acting as

U.S. Navy

FIGURE 40   The gusset plates for diagonal bracing of Hangars 14 and 15 were buckled by the seismic forces.

the principal shear walls, is approximately 141 ft wide by 181 ft long, with columns spaced at 20-ft intervals in each direction. The main structure is supported on piling and the basement floor is supported on fill. The tsunamis submerged the first floor with 9–10 ft of water. Portions of the basement floor slab floated because of hydrostatic pressure under the slab.

CONCLUSIONS

The importance of maintaining operational air-transportation facilities in the event of a natural disaster was emphasized by the Alaska earthquake. In Alaska, air transportation is used more widely than in other states. The facilities required to provide air transportation are consolidated within small areas compared to those of land transportation, such as highways and railroads; this situation makes air-transportation facilities less vulnerable to incapacitating damage and therefore more reliable. The city of Seward was served by rail and highway transportation, but extensive damage to both facilities rendered them inoperative for a long time; the airfield was made operational under emergency conditions within a matter of hours by a relatively simple maintenance operation that is within the capability of almost any community. Although several runways were damaged by tsunamis, air transportation was available to all communities within a few hours. The first physical contact with the city of Valdez was made by aircraft. Emergency supplies and specialized personnel to satisfy immediate needs were airlifted to Alaska from other parts of the country.

An analysis of the earthquake damage reveals that the airfield facilities, runways, taxiways, and aprons at all the major airports could have accommodated aircraft immediately after the earthquake. The primary reason for the interruption of immediate service was the lack of communication caused by the failure of control towers at Elmendorf AFB and Anchorage International Airport, by the loss of electrical power at Anchorage (Merrill Field), Elmendorf, and Kodiak, and by the failure of land-communication lines. The structures and equipment required by the en route traffic control facilities at Anchorage were not damaged; their inability to operate was caused mainly by the failure of communication lines and electrical generating plants.

The reliability of air service could have been greatly increased at little or no increase in cost by adhering to the structural requirements of earthquake-resistant design, by consolidation of control facilities, and by the installation of emergency generating equipment. The use of radios and microwave communications between control facilities, rather than full reliance on land communications, would also have increased the reliability of the air-transportation systems.

ACKNOWLEDGMENT

Except as otherwise noted, the illustrations are credited to the U.S. Army Corps of Engineers.

REFERENCES

Adams, Corthell, Lee, Wince, and Associates, 1964. Earthquake damage survey, Anchorage International Airport. Anchorage: Federal Aviation Agency, Alaskan Region. 10 p.

Fisher, Walter E., and Douglas H. Merkle, 1965. The great Alaska earthquake, Volume I. Air Force Weapons Laboratory Technical Report No. AFWL-TR-65-92. Kirtland Air Force Base: Air Force Systems Command. 100 p.

Hill, Millard M., 1965. Alaskan earthquake report for U.S. Naval Station, city of Kodiak and Kitoi Bay Research Station, Kodiak, Alaska. Kodiak: Bureau of Yards and Docks. 10 p.

Manley and Mayer Architects, 1964. Anchorage International Airport—Post earthquake analysis of terminal building. Report prepared for the Department of Public Works. Anchorage: State of Alaska, Department of Public Works. 17 p.

U.S. Alaskan Command [1964]. Operation helping hand: The armed forces react to earthquake disaster. Seattle: Headquarters Alaskan Command. 83 p.

Worthington, Skilling, Helle, and Jackson, 1964. Report on seismic damage to the Naval Station at Kodiak, Alaska. Kodiak: Bureau of Yards and Docks.

CLAUDE B. RICHARDSON
U.S. ARMY CORPS OF ENGINEERS DISTRICT,
ALASKA

Damage to Utilities

ABSTRACT: Utilities owned by the state or by municipalities
that were damaged by the earthquake were repaired with federal
funds. The utilities restored included water-supply and sewage-
disposal systems, electrical and telephone systems, and public
streets.

The major damage to utilities occurred in Anchorage, where the
many earth slides set in motion by the earthquake caused extensive
damage to all utility systems.

The utilities examined in this chapter are those common to
populated areas—water supply, sewage disposal, electrical
and telephone systems, and public streets. Only those utilities owned by the State of Alaska, or by municipalities, and
eligible for restoration with federal funds under Public Law
875 are discussed in this report. Privately owned gas, electric, and telephone systems and other privately or federally
owned utilities not restored with federal funds are not examined. Related studies on highways, railroads, ports, airfields, and utilities at military installations are found elsewhere in this volume. Earthquake effects on utilities in
Whittier and Valdez are treated in the papers devoted to
those communities. For the purposes of this report, utilities
are grouped by population centers. The description of each
utility generally includes preearthquake condition, earthquake damage, temporary and emergency repairs, results of
damage surveys, and details of permanent restoration of the
utility to preearthquake condition.

In the emergency immediately after the earthquake,
everyone with and without equipment, as well as contractors with crews and heavy equipment, helped to remove
hazards, clear roadways, and restore electricity, water, and
sewer systems by any means available. Where it was possible
to provide organized assistance, federal help was provided;
this assistance, performed by contractors under supervision
of the Corps of Engineers, fell into two categories: emergency work and restoration work.

Emergency work was performed under verbal contracts
on a time, material, and equipment basis. This work began
as quickly as possible as a service needed to ensure public
health, welfare, and safety. The contractor worked under
verbal instructions from the Corps of Engineers in response
to requests from the person or agency for whom the work
was done.

Restoration work was performed under competitive-bid
fixed-price contracts with the scope of the work delineated
by plans and specifications. The winter conditions existing
at the time of the earthquake and the time required to

make damage surveys and to prepare plans and specifications governed the sequence of restoration operations.

"Earthquake damage" was a term used to typify damage to be repaired that in no way indicated the exact cause of damage. Most damage repair, such as cleanup of the Turnagain Slide area, was obviously necessitated by the earthquake. Some work, however, could not be associated directly without background knowledge of the particular situation. For example, installation of a sewage pump at an Anchorage lift station was repair of earthquake damage, because the pump was needed to prevent damage from flooding basements as a result of the general subsidence of the Anchorage area during the earthquake.

There were three principal sources of earthquake damage to utilities. The first was damage by seismic action. Facilities not constructed to withstand strong ground motion were broken, damaged, or put out of operation. Heavy equipment, not properly anchored, broke loose and moved on its foundations or toppled over. Generators driven by turbines tripped safety circuits and shut down. Aerial facilities, such as power lines that are tensioned and guyed for static stability, became unbalanced from the ground shaking. Contrary to popular opinion, seismic action alone was not a major cause of damage to buried utilities. In the Mountain View section of Anchorage, for example, photographic inspection of sewers was discontinued because insufficient damage was located to warrant the cost of the survey.

Destructive forces caused or triggered by the seismic action were the second source of earthquake damage to utilities. These forces included fissures, slides, ground settlement and associated phenomena, tsunamis, damaging local waves, and fires. Earthquake damage from these secondary effects was the most serious. Surface, aerial, and buried utilities were broken and destroyed where there were grabens, severe fissures, differential ground settlements, pressure ridges, and slides. In the Turnagain Heights slide area, for instance, large extensional cracks formed in the ground in areas bordering slides and grabens and extended as far as 200 ft back from the edges of the slides. Buried utilities, paving, sidewalks, curbs, and gutters were broken by these cracks.

Tectonic uplift and subsidence made up the third source of earthquake damage to utilities. At several locations the earth's surface was raised or lowered as a result of the earthquake and remained at the new elevation. The Girdwood-Portage area sank about 6 ft whereas the Cordova area rose 6 ft and significant changes in elevation occurred over an area of approximately 20,000 mi². In areas of subsidence, high tides about a month after the earthquake flooded buildings, drowned wells, and damaged highways. Because of uplift, sewer outfalls at Cordova no longer extended to a sufficient depth in tidewater for the flushing action of

tides to carry sewage away from docks and harbors. Utilities may not have been damaged as the ground rose or sank, but they were now no longer functional as a result of the change in elevation. These examples illustrate some of the indirect effects that legitimately have been termed earthquake damage.

Many of the utilities encountered during emergency and restoration work were originally constructed to standards and codes in use before Alaska attained statehood. The codes developed in Alaska since 1959 are more restrictive. Some utilities developed by private interests in areas later annexed by a city contained materials and construction work that did not conform to state and city codes in effect at the time of the earthquake. Utilities, however, were repaired and renewed by contractors under the supervision of the Corps of Engineers to standards that met current state and local codes. Corps of Engineers' code grade of materials and construction standards generally complied with existing State of Alaska and local codes. Where a local code varied considerably from that of the Corps, but was still standard to the industry or was an acceptable local means of accomplishing the work, the local code was followed, providing the finished job was acceptable. No significant problems arose over these situations. In some cases, the agency requesting the repairs desired restoration of a facility or portion of a utility with better material or construction than had formerly been used, and they paid the increase in cost.

The term "grant-in-lieu" is one of the facets of Public Law 875 that entitles an eligible recipient to be paid, in cash, the cost of restoring a damaged facility. Use of the "grant-in-lieu" was very limited, and the local representative of the Office of Emergency Planning ruled on cases individually. Amounts of the grants were determined by estimates prepared by the Corps of Engineers. As an example, sidewalks in the downtown Seward area were damaged and broken up, and some were washed away as a result of the tsunami that followed the earthquake. The city had planned to construct new sidewalks, curbs, and gutters. The new sidewalks were to be wider and not in the same location or elevation as the old ones. Repair of the old sidewalks would have been pointless if the concrete would have to be broken up again in the city's betterment program. The city was consequently paid in cash from federal funds the amount that repair of the old sidewalks would have cost, and this constituted a "grant-in-lieu."

ANCHORAGE AREA

The Anchorage area (Figure 1) has an average annual precipitation of 14 in., including both rain and snow. Temperatures range from a low of −39 °F to a high of about +80 °F. Hard freezing and snowfall can be expected any time

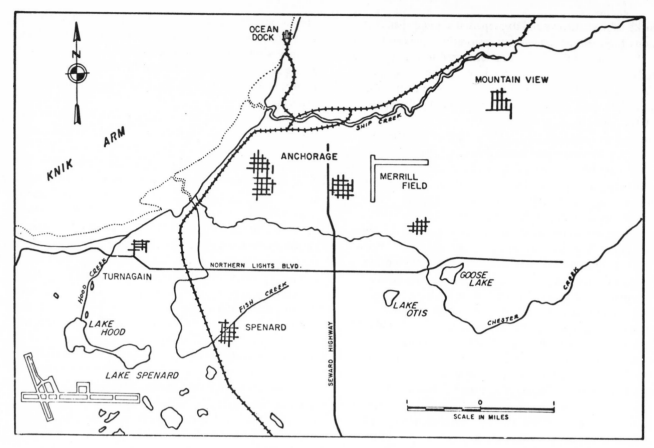

FIGURE 1   Anchorage and vicinity.

after the middle of October; spring breakup usually occurs after the end of March. Sometimes, summers are cooler and frost stays in the ground longer than normal. *In situ* soil consists largely of outwash sand and gravel, with some deposits of glacial till and clay. Installation of water and sewer lines is normally started in May. Because of the extreme cold, buried utility lines, particularly water systems, are installed a minimum of 10 ft below grade to protect them from freezing.

The elevation of most of the Anchorage area ranges from 110 to 140 ft above mean sea level (MSL), but some areas, at watercourse valleys, lie at a lower level. The city dock and facilities around the mouth of Ship Creek are a few feet above tidewater. The ground conditions in these areas required wide trenching and low slope angles on embankments when repairs were made to buried utilities. Powerline poles were often braced to prevent them from sliding into excavations. Tides in the Anchorage area are uncommonly high, averaging about 29 ft between normal highs and lows. Spring and fall equinox tides are frequently 36 ft. Sometimes a strong wind up the inlet boosts these tides even higher; on occasion, bore tides have been observed as far in-

land as Anchorage. The design, construction, and restoration of sewer lines and outfalls were geared to tide action in the Anchorage area.

Water, sewer, telephone, light and power, and street utilities are owned and operated or maintained by the City of Anchorage. The gas utility in Anchorage is privately owned and has a grid of lines throughout the city, buried about 30 in. below grade in alleys, where these existed, or in streets. Contractors repairing earthquake damage and restoring other buried utilities had to work in and around gas mains and laterals, and to coordinate with the gas company for line locations, schedule outages, cutoff breaks, and so forth, which added to the complexity of the work.

WATER UTILITY

The City of Anchorage Water Utility supplies fluoridated potable water in adequate supply for fire protection to all sections of Anchorage (including the city dock area and the industrial area near the mouth of Ship Creek), parts of Spenard, and several housing developments near the city. The system is supplied from the water-treatment plant on

Ship Creek and from wells throughout the city and area (Figure 2). In 1952, the Corps of Engineers constructed a dam in Ship Creek to impound water for military and civilian use. Intake water flows through a 30-in.-diameter cast-iron pipe to a valve pit, from which lines run to Fort Richardson and to Elmendorf AFB and a 20-in.-diameter welded steel line continues to the municipal treatment plant, built by the city in 1962. The plant has a gravity-type operation with electrically operated valves. A standby diesel-driven generator provides power for emergency operation. Water from the treatment plant flowed 14,000 ft west in a 24-in.-diameter wood-stave pipeline, with no valves or taps, to a valve and distribution box in the Mountain View area. The wood-stave line continued another 16,000 ft in decreasing diameters between valve boxes and distribution feeders and terminated at Fifth Avenue and Gambell Street in a 10-in.-diameter line that fed the distribution system.

Seven wells with electric deep-well pumps inject fluoridated and chlorinated water into the distribution system. During winter months the well water is about 38 °F and is used to minimize freezing in the distribution system. Freezing is a potential problem because the temperature of the water from the treatment plant is about 32 °F during winter months. Utility personnel attempt to keep positive flow in the distribution system to prevent freezing.

At the time of the earthquake, the distribution system totaled 140 mi of line, ranging from 20- to 2-in.-diameter lines buried a minimum of 10 ft. Lines were about equally divided between cast iron and asbestos cement. The distribution system had high- and low-pressure areas with pressure-reducing valves at interconnections. Water generally flowed east to west in downtown Anchorage, gridded between mains. About 8,000,000 gallons of water per day, half from the treatment plant and half from wells, were being supplied at the time of the earthquake, the normal rate of supply for the time of year.

Effects of the Earthquake

Because of electrical-system failures, the treatment plant and deep-well pumps shut down immediately. The wood-stave pipeline from the treatment plant (elevation 252 ft) soon drained through leaks. No water was available for household use or for fire fighting. Fortunately, the fire hazard was considerably lessened by the failure of the electrical

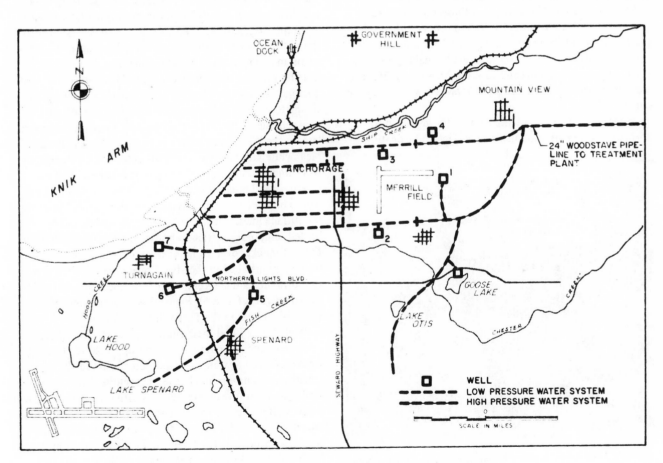

FIGURE 2 Principal wells and water-distribution mains in the Anchorage area.

system and Anchorage escaped any major fires. After a hasty inspection, the treatment plant was declared to be usable. The standby generator was started, and the plant resumed operation at 6:45 p.m. on the day of the earthquake. The structural damage to the treatment plant is described in the paper by George and others (1973), Structures in Anchorage (p. 774, this volume). Water-utility crews in radio-equipped trucks surveyed the distribution system and informed the central office of known breaks, slide areas, grabens, and so forth. Buried lines were obviously sheared in areas, such as those in Figures 3 and 4. The distribution system was valved to fill usable portions and to prevent infiltration of groundwater and sewage. The damaged, but partly usable, system was made to exfiltrate for sanitary purposes and to prevent freezing. Wells 1, 6, and 7 were inoperable, but when electric power was restored, the other four wells were put back in operation to supply as much water to the system as possible.

Emergency Measures

Large quantities of potable water were required immediately. National Guard and Civil Defense facilities and disaster provisions could not meet the requirements. The military from Fort Richardson and Elmendorf AFB supplied truckloads of water in hardboard drums with sterile plastic liners and covers. These lister-bag stations were set up as directed by disaster coordinators to enable people to obtain water for drinking and cooking purposes. This service continued in some areas for as long as 2 weeks after the earthquake.

Plans were made for a temporary water service in the form of a system of 4-in.-diameter surface-laid irrigation

FIGURE 4   Maintenance crews closed off lines that were obviously broken or sheared (Anchorage, March 1964).

pipe and fittings. Lines were to be fed from fire hydrants through short lengths of fire hose, and houses were to be fed through ordinary 1/2-in.-diameter garden hose tapped from the irrigation pipe, with the garden hose fastened to the outside faucet of the house. These were normal-stock items and were ordered by telephone from firms in the Seattle–Tacoma area and delivered to McChord Field, near Tacoma. Military Air Transport Service (MATS) airlifted the materials to Elmendorf AFB for surface transportation to Anchorage. The first surface-laid pipe was put in service late on the Wednesday after the Good Friday earthquake. Meanwhile, utility crews and contractors doing emergency work under direction of the Corps of Engineers had repaired several breaks in main distribution lines so that water would be available at fire hydrants in damaged areas to supply surface lines. Contractors laid surface lines and connected temporary service to houses for several weeks after the earthquake; over 14 mi of temporary surface lines were ultimately installed in the area. Consumers were warned that drinking and cooking water from these lines should be boiled (Figures 5 and 6). Figure 7 is an aerial view of surface-laid lines in the Turnagain section.

Wells 6 and 7 and their pump houses were completely destroyed, and the pump house and upper 20 ft of casing were destroyed at well 1. A contractor restored the casing, constructed a new pump house, redeveloped and tested well 1, and put it back in service. Another contractor drilled a new well to replace wells 6 and 7. Although the first site ended in a dry hole, another site (near Goose Lake) was successfully drilled, developed, and tested. The completed facility fed 1,080 gallons per minute of fluoridated and chlorinated water into the distribution system.

FIGURE 3   Ground subsidence in graben areas sheared buried water lines (Anchorage, March 1964).

FIGURE 5 Temporary water-distribution system used fire hoses and aluminum irrigation pipe (Anchorage, June 1964).

City of Anchorage

FIGURE 6 Garden hoses tapped aluminum pipe to furnish water to houses (Anchorage, May 1964).

Damage Survey

Climatic conditions at the time of the earthquake and normal breakup thereafter made it impossible to assess damage accurately until about June 1. As the ground thawed, new leaks showed up. Some lines had been holding pressure but bled off as frost melted from the ground. Additional surface lines were laid as underground lines failed. The entire distribution system was studied and divided into areas to delineate the scope of work on plans and specifications. The water system was restored under competitive-bid, fixed-price contracts.

Fears that the 14,000-ft 24-in.-diameter wood-stave

pipeline between the treatment plant and Mountain View had been damaged beyond repair by the earthquake were proved to be unjustified when leakage tests and exploratory excavations were made on this line; insufficient earthquake damage was found to warrant replacement or repair. A project was developed to install a bypass on more stable ground around the wood-stave line between the valve box in Mountain View and its termination in the distribution system at Fifth Avenue and Gambell Street. Further earthquake mo-

FIGURE 7 Surface-laid irrigation pipe distributed water in Turnagain section of Anchorage (June 1964).

tion could have triggered slides and destroyed sections of the wood-stave line that provided water for firefighting in the dock and industrial area. This section of the city could not be supplied by wells because of pressure-reducing valves in the system.

To ensure that the work of correcting the system could stand subsequent inspection, the whole distribution system was pressure-tested and repaired where necessary. Locations of known breaks were determined from surface observation of slides, grabens, differential settlement, ground cracks, and so forth, but a complete survey could be made only by pressure-testing closed lines section by section. Water service in the Fourth Avenue graben was not replaced because an urban-renewal project was being developed that would include new buried utilities. Tie lines had to be installed across this area, however, to provide water for fire fighting to the warehouse area and The Alaska Railroad depot on the north and to the Anchorage-Westward Hotel area to the west.

Restoration Projects

As a public health and sanitation measure, the Corps of Engineers awarded a contract to test the water systems of residences connected to temporary, surface-laid water lines. These houses were in areas of damaged and broken buried utilities, and there was danger that broken water lines could fill with groundwater that had been contaminated by sewage. To test whether a house service line or water system was broken, a pressure pump was attached to the outside faucet and the system was pumped up to 50-psi gage pressure; the buried service line was shut off in the house. The test was then made with the service-line valve opened in the

house and the curb cock closed, to determine the condition of the buried line from the distribution system to the house. Water systems were tested in 415 homes, and 40 breaks were found at street valves. These breaks were repaired when the city distribution line was dug up and repaired or replaced. Leaks found inside the house were pointed out as a service to the occupant.

The Turnagain Heights area (Figure 8) extends north from Northern Lights Boulevard. In the slide area in the northwest portion, about 75 homes were destroyed by the earth movements. No emergency or restoration work was attempted in the slide area because utilities over the bluff were a total loss in a now uninhabitable area. Debris of wrecked homes was cleared from this area, and houses that could be salvaged were moved to staging areas for later relocation; the slide area was then graded and sloped to tidewater.

Restoration work was undertaken in the area that did not slide. This area elongated more than 3 ft from Northern Lights Boulevard north, so that a home near the new bluff line was now perhaps 3 ft further north of the boulevard. This elongation was caused by a series of ground cracks about every 50 ft in progressively longer intervals toward Northern Lights Boulevard, which are indicated by the repairs to the cracked asphalt streets (Figure 9). Buried water lines throughout this area were asbestos cement mains that extended north from Northern Lights Boulevard with connecting grid lines. The type of breaks in the pipes was unknown, but breaks were assumed to have occurred where ground cracks were noticeable on the surface. The extent of breakage between ground cracks was unknown; the asbestos cement pipe may have crushed or slivered for some distance

FIGURE 8   Buried water lines were lost where homes slid over the bluff in the Turnagain Heights section of Anchorage (April 1964).

FIGURE 9 The Turnagain section that did not slide stretched north to south through a series of ground cracks about every 50 ft as indicated by the repairs to the asphalt street (Anchorage, July 1964).

on either side of a break, or it may have broken cleanly. A clean break could be repaired by installation of a splicing sleeve sealed with neoprene "O" rings in a manner similar to that used in an initial installation. If breaks were too close together, the cost of repeated excavation, repair, and backfilling would soon approach that of installing a new line. Early restoration was necessary so that contractors would not concurrently be working on other utilities in the same areas. The Corps of Engineers advance-ordered enough pipe to renew 25 percent of the pipe for this section and a large number of repair sleeves; excesses could be used elsewhere on similar work. As it turned out, the asbestos cement pipe had comparatively clean breaks where ground cracks were noticeable on the surface and very few breaks between. Most line repairs were made by installing splicing sleeves over pipe breaks. A new cast-iron water-supply main was installed across Fish Creek parallel to Northern Lights Boulevard and connected to existing asbestos cement branch lines.

Asbestos cement lines were pressure-tested for leaks at 150 psi, then tested at 60 psi for joint leaks before backfilling was completed. Lines were thoroughly flushed and chlorinated and turned back to the City of Anchorage Water Utility. The chlorination left strong unpleasant residual taste and odor for a long time; less chlorination was used after subsequent repairs.

In one instance, an existing facility was improved in the restoration work. The Susitna View Corporation was a nonprofit privately owned company formed to distribute water through buried lines to some 16 homes in Turnagain that would not otherwise have service. When Turnagain was annexed by the city of Anchorage, the corporation remained

in operation. Its system consisted of 1,200 ft of 2½-in.-diameter buried wrought-iron pipe, now damaged or destroyed. The Office of Emergency Planning (OEP) considered replacement of this line justifiable, but the city objected to installation of wrought-iron pipe, or of any pipe less durable than asbestos cement or cast iron or smaller than 6-in. in diameter. A line able to supply sufficient water for normal needs and for fire fighting was needed for this area. Public funds, however, would apply only to equivalent restoration of the wrought-iron pipe. The resident-owners already had extensive financial losses from earthquake damage to their homes and were not willing or able to finance the improvement of the system. The Susitna View Corporation dissolved and handed over the utility to the city of Anchorage. OEP adjudged it as still replaceable with public funds, and the city paid the difference in cost between 2½-in. wrought-iron pipe and 6-in. asbestos cement pipe.

The water-utility restoration in areas of the K–L street and Fourth Avenue grabens was accomplished in much the same manner as that in Turnagain Heights. Repairs were made to known breaks. The K–L street graben (Figure 10) from Third to Eighth avenues was directly across east–west laterals in downtown Anchorage. Figure 11 shows the graben area between Fourth and Sixth avenues; the banks of which are outlined by snow on the ground. In this section, streets were backfilled to grade, old water lines in the sunken area were abandoned, and new lines were installed to match the grade of existing lines on either side of the graben. The graben turned to the southwest near Presbyterian Hospital and Providence Nursing Home and angled across Eighth Avenue, generally disrupting buried utilities along Eighth Avenue between L and O streets.

FIGURE 10 The K-L street graben extended south toward Presbyterian Hospital (PH) and then turned southwest and sheared through an apartment house (Anchorage, April 1964). The shaded part was later removed and the remainder was repaired and occupied.

Utilities were completely broken in the Fourth Avenue graben, but interconnecting mains were installed across the area to serve the warehouse area to the north and the Anchorage-Westward Hotel area to the west. Water lines across the Fourth Avenue graben area were installed as interim service, because the area was to be buttressed (stabilized) and utilities added in an urban-renewal contract.

The Corps of Engineers negotiated an architect–engineer contract for the design of a cast-iron pipeline to bypass the wood-stave line from Pine Street, in Mountain View, to downtown Anchorage. This work involved route survey and preparation of plans, profiles, and specifications for the contract. The City of Anchorage and Corps of Engineers obtained construction easements and utility rights-of-way from property owners along the proposed route. The developer of a private tract in the Mountain View area did not

want the line installed across his property; this portion of the line was therefore temporarily deleted so that the rest of the work could be started.

The construction contractor on this job brought in a new 4-yd^3-capacity backhoe right after the earthquake; the extensive excavating and backfilling task was completed in near-record time. A new route was selected, across Mountain View to the valve box at Pine Street, that crossed the Glenn Highway farther east than originally planned. This section of highway, however, was newly paved and the Alaska State Highway Department would not permit it to be broken for a water-line crossing, so the contractor was obliged to jack the line through below grade.

The utility department insisted that their specially trained and qualified personnel do the work of tapping the wood-stave line, and the contract included this stipulation.

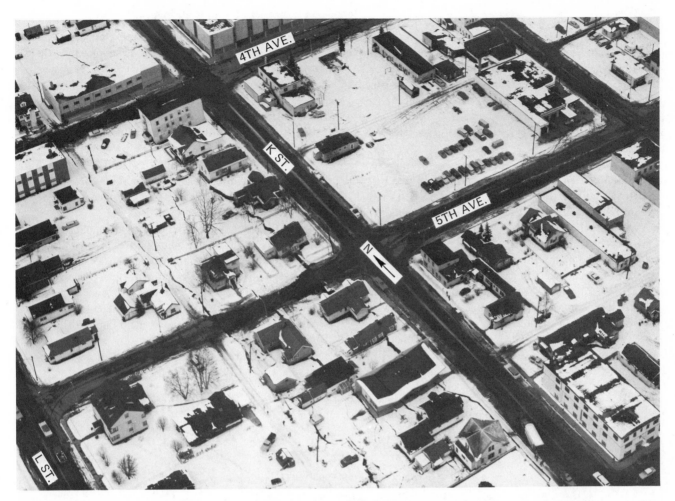

FIGURE 11 The K–L street graben extended from the State Court House on Fourth Avenue. Utility lines were severed (Anchorage, April 1964).

When the water lines had been repaired, a pitometer test was performed to locate undetected leaks and to determine the direction and magnitude of flow-in lines for comparison with calculated or estimated flows and direction of flow. The area from Chester Creek to Ship Creek west of Gambell Street was selected for initial testing, because it combined typical industrial, hotel, apartment, and residential customers. Testing could be extended to other areas if warranted by these findings.

Excavations were made at 15 selected locations in the distribution system, and corporation cocks were installed at water mains. Pitometer tubing was inserted and the excavations were then backfilled with gage lines terminated above ground for connecting test equipment. Tests were made by recording gage readings with different valving arrangements in the distribution system and at various hours during the day and night. Six leaks of nominal loss were located, mainly in abandoned services; one was caused by a leaking fire hydrant. No damage was found that could be attributed to the earthquake, such as pulled pipe joints, shifted valve boxes, cracked valves, canted thrust blocks, or broken service lines. Because of the small amount of damage in this area, further testing in other areas was not considered. Valves throughout the system were difficult to operate and an annual valve-turning program was recommended.

Summary

The restoration of the water utility was speeded up by ordering new pipe and fittings in advance of contract awards; thus, the material was made immediately available for installation and assuring completion of the water-utility restoration before freezeup, which occurred in the middle of October 1964. Line repairs were required at breaks that were located by pressure testing, usually in the close vicinity of surface cracks, grabens, and perceptible evidence of differential settlement. Buried lines were completely destroyed in slide areas. Numerous house services were broken off near distribution mains. No explanation has been found for this situation, but it is thought that the earthquake shaking caused the sand bedding around mains and house services to compact and settle. The water main may have settled further than the house-service line, causing the two to break apart. With this exception, water lines were generally undamaged in areas that experienced only seismic action.

SEWER SYSTEMS

The composite sewer system for the Anchorage area is shown in Figure 12. Raw, untreated sewage flowed through five outfalls into Knik Arm and into water deep enough for the washing action of tides to carry the sewage away from the area. The trunk lines emanating from these outfalls were controlled by numerous joint-use agreements between the City of Anchorage, Spenard Public Utility District, the State of Alaska, and the federal government (through the military installations). The five outfalls were as follows:

• The Army dock outfall, a 24-in.-diameter concrete pipe for sewage from the Government Hill section of

Anchorage and from Elmendorf AFB. This line was originally installed by military personnel and terminated on the tideflat. During the later growth and development of the area, the line was turned over to the city of Anchorage, except for the portion on the military reservation. The city later extended the outfall into deep water and now owns and maintains the system.

• The Air Force outfall, a 30-in.-diameter concrete pipe located just north of the mouth of Ship Creek, in the dock area. Sewage from the Mountain View section of Anchorage and from the 5040th Air Force Hospital flowed through this outfall, which was owned and maintained by the military.

• The Chester Creek outfall, a 42-in.-diameter corrugated-iron pipe, the principal outfall in the area. The city of Anchorage owned and maintained this outfall, which handled sewage flowing from Anchorage proper, from several outlying districts to the south and east of Anchorage, and from the Fish Creek trunk at manhole 0. The Fish Creek trunk contains sewage from the Spenard Public Utility District.

• The Hood Creek outfall, which handled sewage from

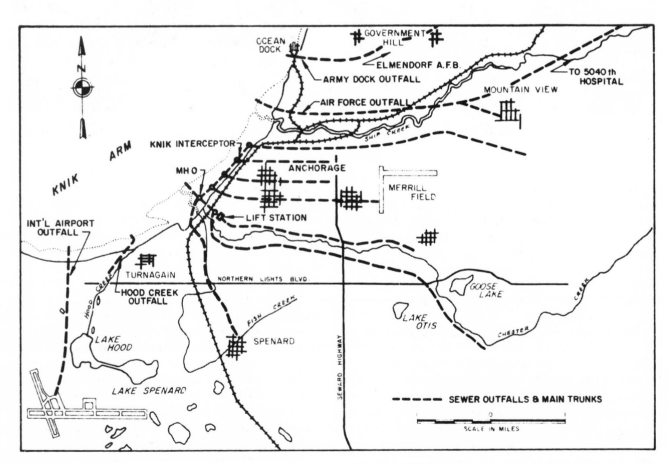

FIGURE 12 Anchorage area showing sewer mains and outfalls.

the Turnagain section of Anchorage and was owned and maintained by the city. The Turnagain sewage system and this outfall were installed by private interests and were purchased by the city when it annexed this section.

• The International Airport outfall, a 10-in.-diameter concrete pipe, which handled sewage from the International Airport complex. This outfall and collector system was installed by the Federal Aviation Agency and was turned over to the state when Alaska attained statehood in 1959.

Various types of sewer pipe were used in these installations: concrete pipe (CP), asbestos-cement (AC), wood-stave, vitrified-clay, and asphalt-coated corrugated-metal pipe (CMP). Pipe joints were mortar, tongue and groove, neoprene O-rings, and connector bands (for CMP).

The sewer systems for the City of Anchorage Sewer Utility, including Spenard Public Utility District, consisted of an arrangement of laterals emptying into collectors and outfalls in a manner normal to cities of comparable size and dispersion. Sanitary and storm sewers in downtown Anchorage flowed through east–west laterals, crossing The Alaska Railroad grade to flow into the Knik interceptor, a 30-in.-diameter CMP installed in the tideflat running south to the Chester Creek outfall. This interceptor was below high-tide level and was pressurized with bolted manhole covers. Areas north of Chester Creek flowed into the north Chester Creek trunk, and the areas south flowed into the south Chester Creek trunk. A lift station elevated sewage from the Chester Creek trunks and storm sewers so that it flowed out into manhole 0 and the outfall, unaffected by tides.

The city owned and maintained about 33.5 mi of storm sewers and 116.4 mi of sanitary sewers at the time of the earthquake. The Spenard Public Utility District owned and maintained some 45 mi of line that flowed into the Fish Creek trunk.

Effects of the Earthquake

The electricity failed, causing the lift station to stop operating; the water system failed, so very little sewage was flowing. The K–L street graben cut off collector lines between Third and Twelfth avenues and blocked sewage flow from all the area to the east. The Fourth Avenue graben interrupted lines between Fourth and First avenues. The Hood Creek outfall in Turnagain was carried away in the slide. Other damage would be apparent as soon as water and electrical services were restored, and damage continued to show up during the following weeks and months. The system would probably leak at numerous locations, contaminating broken water mains and groundwater.

Emergency Measures

The experienced utility personnel were able to anticipate trouble spots and to plan work in advance. Bolted manhole

covers in the Knik interceptor were terminated below the silt level, so that ice cakes would not break off manhole risers. The bolted cover was removed immediately from the manhole below Third Avenue so that sewage from the line along the south side of Ship Creek would not back up and flood. Covers along the north and south Chester Creek trunks were removed from manholes where laterals came in. The ability of all these lines to pass sewage was unknown, but it was assumed that there would be blockages, and there were.

The K–L street graben blocked the flow of important laterals. Trucks with open-top oil drums were assembled, and sewage pumping began as soon as the level began to rise in the manholes. Utility workers excavated and shunted one sanitary-sewer lateral into a nearby storm sewer. The lateral down Eighth Avenue, west of L Street, was broken up for several blocks where the graben angled across Eighth Avenue, and the line was replaced by a contractor engaged by the Corps of Engineers. When this line was completed, sewage flowed down the bluff, through a culvert in the railroad grade, and onto the tideflats. This was not a desirable situation, but work on this line could not be resumed until spring breakup.

In Turnagain Heights, another contractor was engaged to make emergency repairs on electrical, sewer, and water utilities. Broken sewer lines were extended to the new bluff line. Trenching and ditching enabled open ditch sewage to flow to tidewater without ponding; open sewage runs were heavily chlorinated. With frozen ground and winter conditions still prevalent, little additional work was attempted. About all that could be done until spring breakup was to keep sewage flowing in any manner possible. A portion of the Fish Creek trunk in the bed of Fish Creek had several breaks at undetermined locations. Manhole covers were removed so that sewage could overflow into the creek rather than back up in the line, and the creek was heavily chlorinated.

Damage Survey

The Anchorage and Spenard sewers were considered jointly in planning damage surveys and performing the restoration work. Sewer systems had been kept operational by emergency work since the earthquake. Many unsanitary conditions existed, and now the full extent of damage and how it should be fixed had to be determined. Many surface conditions indicated obvious sewer-line breakage, but where surface conditions provided no clues, condition of lines was unknown.

Because sewer lines were all oriented for gravity flow, any elevation changes would critically affect restoration work. The needed topographic surveys were in progress but no information had yet been made public. Sewer lines would have to be thoroughly inspected in and around areas of noticeable surface damage and the inspection carried into undisturbed areas if warranted by the damage found. Photographic inspection of sewer lines was used to survey the damage in lines less than 24 in. in diameter and to make permanent film record of sewer conditions. About 300,000 lin ft of sewer lines in Anchorage and Spenard were in and around areas of major earthquake damage. Detailed plans of sewer systems were obtained from the city and from the Spenard Utility District, and the areas were divided for convenient photographic inspection. The photography was reviewed, damage assessed, repairs indicated on drawings, construction contracts negotiated, and repairs made. Activities were scheduled so that photography would progress from one area to another, and construction contractors would follow to make repairs.

Contracts were negotiated with two architect–engineers for photographic inspection of sewer lines. One started in Turnagain and the other in Spenard, and they ran elevations on inverts at manholes to verify line gradient. Some sewer lines had to be flushed before they were photographed. With hoses from the nearest fire hydrant, the crews washed down manholes to establish a flow of flushing water in the line. Under normal conditions, work was performed on the surface of the ground and personnel did not need to enter a manhole. One method was to wash a plastic balloon on a restraining line through the sewer. The flow around the restrained balloon set up velocities with good washing and flushing action. Following is a typical procedure for flushing and photographing a sewer line:

Flushers upstream at the manhole at the beginning of the sewer line washed a balloon attached to a line through to the downstream manhole, where it was retrieved with a hook, the balloon was removed, and the cable for pulling the camera was attached. The line was pulled out at the starting manhole to thread the cable to pull the camera. The camera was attached to the control cable and lowered in the manhole, established on its runners, and pulled through the line, trailing its control cable. A distance-calibrated device triggered the camera at maximum intervals of 2½ pipe diameters, or every 30 in., taking a picture and advancing the film. The camera operated with open lens and photographed at the flash of a strobe light. When the photography was completed, the camera was removed from the manhole and its control cable was pulled out again. This procedure was then repeated throughout the length of the sewer. Manholes were normally about 300 ft apart. If equipment passed through the line satisfactorily, up to 900 ft of line could be photographed in one sequence, requiring about 3 hours.

One architect–engineer used a single-lens 16-mm camera that used both monochromatic and color film. The other architect–engineer used a twin-lens camera with 35-mm monochromatic film that provided a good three-dimensional picture through a stereoscopic viewer. Where sewer lines were too dirty to determine the condition of the pipe, it was necessary to clean them and repeat the photography. Figures 13–17 are enlarged monochromatic renditions of 16-mm color photographs of dirty and earthquake damaged sewer lines.

During the sewer photography, an Anchorage newspaper reporter interviewed crews on their work for a news item. When the reporter asked for a sample of the photography, the foreman explained that no prints were available on the present work, but he provided a print of a photograph taken in a sewer in another state. The picture showed a rat in the service line, observing the photography, and the high resolution of the photography was stressed by pointing out that the whiskers on the rat could be seen (Figure 18). The complete explanation was not printed in the published article, and some citizens, alarmed at the thought that Anchorage sewers were infested with rodents, demanded that immediate corrective measures be taken. The mistake was pointed out and the work continued as before. Figure 19 is a print from one of the twin negatives of sewer-line photo-

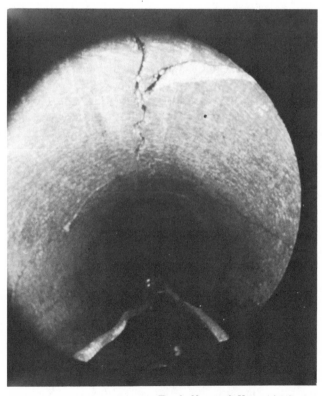

Tryck, Nyman & Hayes, Anchorage
FIGURE 13   Cracks in 8-in. asbestos-cement sewer line. This line was in area of other earthquake damage and was dug up and replaced (Anchorage, September 1964).

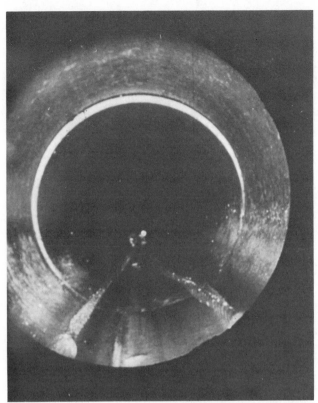

FIGURE 14   A 10-in. concrete sewer. Joint was offset and was dug up and relaid. Several adjacent lengths of pipe had similar joint offsets (Anchorage, September 1964).

FIGURE 15   This 8-in. concrete sewer line has a badly offset joint and deposits of grease. Water is leaking from the line, which was dug up and reset (Anchorage, September 1964).

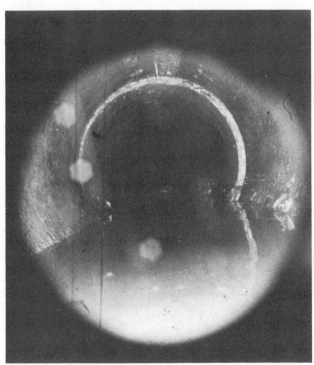

FIGURE 16   10-in. asbestos cement sewer line. The joint is bad and the line is not draining properly. This pipe was dug up and reset (Anchorage, September 1964).

graphs taken by the twin-lens camera, showing earthquake damage and foreign objects found in the sewer lines.

An architect–engineer contract was negotiated to have sewer lines 24 in. in diameter and larger physically inspected and to have damage lists made up for repair contractors. All architect-engineer personnel working on the photography and physical inspection of sewers were required to have up-to-date tetanus shots. Lifelines and attendants on the surface were required for workers in manholes. More elaborate safety procedures and equipment were required for physical inspection of sewers. The architect–engineer obtained sewer plugs and demonstrated methods of bracing and blocking plugs. Wet suits, waterproof gloves and flashlights, two-way radios, 30-minutes supply of oxygen, goggles, distance-calibrated body lines, and safety belts were all part of the required equipment. An air compressor was used at all times for positive airflow in the line being inspected. A standby backhoe, bulldozer, and four-wheel-drive truck with operators were available while the sewer inspector was working. An assistant was in the manhole at either end of a line during inspection; one man paid out body line and recorded distances on signal from the inspector. The inspector would not enter a line more than one-

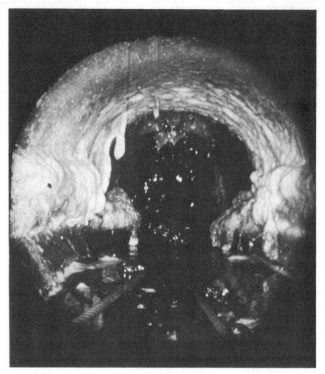

Tryck, Nyman & Hayes, Anchorage

FIGURE 17   This 12-in. concrete sewer line was so dirty that it had to be cleaned to determine condition of the pipe and joints (Anchorage, September 1964).

fourth full of standing or running water or effluent and would take an air hose into a line when entering to examine line blockage.

Two-way radio communication was used, even when in-

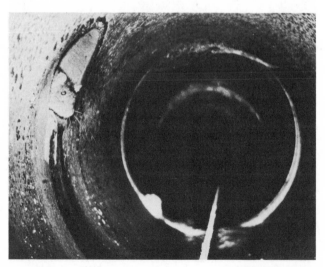

Anchorage Daily Times

FIGURE 18   A sample of sewer photography taken in another state. The whiskers on the rat demonstrate the fine detail picked up by the camera.

Harold Galliett & Associates, Anchorage

FIGURE 19   A 12-in. concrete pipe with badly offset joint (Anchorage, August 1964).

specting corrugated metal pipe, and an assistant on the surface made notes on damage descriptions given by the inspector.

About 500,000 lin ft of sewer lines were photographed, and 60,000 ft of lines were inspected physically. Earthquake damage was shown on plans for use in construction contracts. A standard set of specifications was used to make up a variety of construction-plan packages. The sewer photography was beset with pitfalls that interfered with time-footage schedules. Some lines could not be photographed until repair work had progressed sufficiently to drain away sewage. Some manholes had to be pumped to lower sewage levels. Some line breaks in sandy areas continually filled with sand that prevented good photography, and continued cleaning did not alleviate this condition. The north Chester Creek trunk could not be inspected physically. A deposit of mud and pea gravel similar to poor concrete had accumulated to a depth of nearly one fourth of the diameter of the pipe. The line was cleaned with a bucket machine, but the deposit at some locations could not be removed and left water traps in between the deposit. The line could not be inspected or photographed, but it passed sewage adequately.

Restoration

Eleven contracts were awarded for repair of earthquake damage of sewer lines. The work consisted of repair to joint separations, relaying of certain portions of lines to grade, realignment of pipe, repair of broken joints, manhole repairs (these manholes nearly all consisted of precast-concrete sections, although some in Turnagain were concrete-block construction), cleaning some sewers, and photographing some lines that could not previously be photographed. Essential repairs were completed before freezeup in the fall of 1964, so that the systems would function during the winter. A final contract was let in 1965 for repair of all sewer damage not repaired in 1964 or of damage that showed up in the 1965 spring breakup. Repairs of some parts of the sewer systems became separate projects because of unusual circumstances of climate, tides, or other environmental conditions, which are discussed in the following paragraphs.

Knik Interceptor This line was 30-in.-diameter corrugated-metal pipe, 6,000 ft long from manhole 0 to the south bank of Ship Creek; manholes were from 300–500 ft apart. The line carried sewage from key laterals in Anchorage and in the industrial area on the south bank of Ship Creek. Manhole risers and bolted covers were located below the level of the silt cover, so that ice cakes would not damage them. The line was buried from 12 to 20 ft below the silt, which was generally covered with 2–3 ft of water at high tide. Personnel familiar with the system walked around on the tide-flat with rods, searching for the manhole covers. The architect–engineer physically inspected about 2,000 ft of this line at the Chester Creek end.

The Corps of Engineers ordered 800 ft of replacement pipe and negotiated a contract for installation (Figure 20) near the midpoint of the line where known blockage was found. This was probably the most difficult sewer-repair work encountered. The contractor had to dike around excavations to prevent flooding, which sometimes occurred in spite of precautions. Attempts were made to inspect the north end of the line visually, but this proved too hazardous. After cameras were run through this portion, laterals were again tied into the collector. Flow in the line was poor in the spring of 1965, and it was found that the south end

FIGURE 20 Repairing the Knik Interceptor, a 30-in. corrugated-metal sewer pipe in the tideflat (Anchorage, June 1965).

of the pipe was partly crushed, and rocks had become trapped in it. After repairs had been made to this line, sewage passed through satisfactorily.

Army Dock Outfall This outfall was damaged by the earthquake, and sewage floated to the surface near the dock. Complaints came from oceangoing vessels that cooling water lines in the ships were becoming plugged with sewage. The outfall was under water, and the extent of the damage could not be determined; in addition, one of the ramps to the dock had been constructed astride the outfall line. Relaying the line could not be attempted because the handling of freight passing through the port had first priority. Several open joints were observed in the line between the two ramps during a seasonally low tide in October 1964, but no repairs could be attempted at that time. The city utility installed a new outfall through the rock-filled portion of the ramp in 1965 (Figure 21), and the old outfall was abandoned.

Sewage Lift Station From a new set of high-water marks on the lift-station fill embankment, it was estimated that the area around the mouth of Chester Creek sank about 3 ft during the earthquake. A dike 3 ft high was placed around the fill to prevent the high tides of the fall equinox, which are generally higher than spring tides, from covering the graded area at the station. The dike served its purpose, but the basements of a number of homes in low areas were flooded with sewage during the fall-equinox high tides. Apparently, abnormally high tides, failure of electric power to lower the sewage level in the lift station, and failure of the flapper-type bypass valve to spill sewage into tidewater when the level rose dangerously high caused this situation. The electrical service and installation were examined, but no improvements were recommended. A project, however, was initiated to install an automatically operated diesel-driven pump that would be actuated by a float switch at high sewage levels.

Government Hill Utilities The slide in this area (Figure 22) demolished the Government Hill School, three residences, and several facilities of The Alaska Railroad at the toe of the hill. Water and sewer lines serving the south portion of Government Hill were also destroyed in this slide, and service was restored by the installation of new lines laid in undisturbed ground in a street farther north.

Fish Creek Trunk The Fish Creek trunk, a 36-in. corrugated metal pipe north of Northern Lights Boulevard, followed the creek through the Turnagain section, in and along the creekbed, and then along the south bank to the tideflat and across to manhole 0. Bands pulled off at several joints in the line because of seismic action in the clay of the creekbed. Manhole covers were removed so that sewage

FIGURE 21   The old City Dock sewer outfall was abandoned and a new one installed through the earth-fill portion of the ramp (Anchorage, January 1965). Note ice on piling in harbor.

would not back up into Spenard, and all flow in the trunk poured into Fish Creek, which was heavily chlorinated. In the course of the emergency repairs, this trunk was repaired from the tideflat to the site where the trunk left the creekbed. The trunk upstream was renewed during the restoration work, and various repairs were made in the diminishing diameters that led back into Spenard.

Late in 1964, a silt blow was noticed a short distance out on the tideflat, which terminated in a hole in the sewer line—several hundred cubic yards of silt had washed down

FIGURE 22   Sewer and water lines were lost in the Government Hill slide. New lines were laid in undisturbed ground north of the new bluff line (Anchorage, April 1964).

into the line. About 20 ft of silt covered the line at this place. The broken line was dug up and repaired in the hope that flow in the line would wash away the silt that had entered it. In the spring and summer of 1965, numerous complaints were made about sewage washing into the mouth of Chester Creek at high tide. After close surveillance, it was noticed that sewage was rising and bubbling into tidewater along the route of this trunk across the tideflat to manhole 0. At low tide, an excavation was made to uncover the line and a cut was made in the pipe with a cutting torch. A sanitary engineer observed that the interior of the line was over half full of silt and gravel that would not wash away. A contract was awarded to clean and repair 850 ft of this line, and subsequent operation has been satisfactory.

International Airport Outfall   Runway, taxiway, and apron runoff, and sanitary sewage from the airport-complex collector system ran 9,000 ft north to the outfall in a 10-in.-diameter concrete-pipe sewer line. Earthquake damage to the outfall was suspected, and blue dye added at the last manhole was observed, through binoculars, to bubble out of several joints in the outfall; the outfall was consequently repaired during the restoration work.

The line from the airport to the outfall was inspected photographically, and several breaks and offset joints were repaired. Considerable debris was found in the line. Tracks at several manholes indicated that vehicles had backed in to throw oil and beer cans and rags down the manhole.

Summary   Photographic inspection of sewer lines proved to be an adequate means of locating earthquake damage.

Sewer lines in and near graben areas and slide areas sustained greatest damage. The Knik Interceptor sewer line in the tide-flat was broken and crushed by pressure ridges. In the Turn-again Heights slide area, buried utility lines were completely destroyed. The area behind the new bluff required the great-est number of repairs; when the area was elongated, utility lines were pulled apart in the process. In the Fourth Avenue graben, buried utilities were completely destroyed.

Sporadic sewer and water-line breakage occurred in areas bordering grabens. The damage included crushed pipe, bro-ken bells, and so forth. Repairs throughout the city of Anchorage proper were required in an inexplicably irregular pattern. Some house services protruded into the sewer mains, seemingly because of differential ground movement; some of the damage may have been caused by errors in con-struction.

The program of flushing or cleaning and then photo-graphing the sewers for damage inspection had a beneficial effect on the sewer system. About 140 tons of street-sanding material is spread throughout the city each winter, and none is removed. Because a large percentage of this sand washes into storm sewers, it was necessary to clean the pipes to make photographic and visual inspection. It is not known how much additional earthquake damage may show up later.

In areas further back from Turnagain Arm, where no differential ground movement occurrred, the earthquake caused relatively little damage. In Mountain View, the amount of damage was not sufficient to warrant the cost of making a photographic inspection. Some lines were photo-graphed as random samples, and further work was then can-celed. Selected lines were photographed in builtup areas south and east of Anchorage with the same result.

Some low spots in sewer lines were found by photogra-phy. If water in the line was deeper than one third of the pipe diameter, the line was relaid to grade. Some of these low spots might have been errors in the original construction. Lines do plug, however, if the gradient is not sufficient to create a washing and scouring action. Because of the severe winter season in this area, the depth of frozen ground, and the burial of sewer lines, maximal emphasis was given to in-spection and restoration of buried utilities. They were re-stored more completely than other utilities because it was not possible, as it was with electrical and telephone-utility restoration, to limit the work to fit more nearly the letter of Public Law 875.

CITY OF ANCHORAGE TELEPHONE UTILITY

The Telephone Utility operated and maintained the city-owned telephone system that served 25,863 subscribers in the Anchorage area. It was a dial system with relay-type crossbar switching equipment at four exchanges. The Broad-way exchange was the largest and was attended at all times. Federal, Dimond, and Fairfax (Spenard) exchanges operated automatically and were unattended. Several PABX's (pri-vate automatic branch exchanges), in downtown Anchorage office buildings, were also utility-owned. In the downtown area, telephone cables were installed in underground duct runs; elsewhere, aerial cables were supported on power line poles and on some telephone utility poles. About 10 per-cent of the poles used for supporting telephone cables were owned by the utility.

The Broadway exchange at Fifteenth Avenue and C Street was the principal center of operations. An under-ground building next door had just been completed for the installation of a new high-speed switching system. At the time of the earthquake, part of the new equipment had ar-rived but was not yet uncrated. The city telephone system had long-distance service to parts of Alaska and to places outside Alaska through facilities of the Alaska Communica-tions System (ACS), located on Government Hill. A 600-pair and a 200-pair cable connected the city system with ACS and the military bases. The 600-pair cable was owned by the utility and was used for priority teletype and data cir-cuits. This cable was installed underground in ducts from the Broadway exchange to the south bank of Ship Creek below the Native Hospital, as well as aerially across Ship Creek, the railroad yard, and up Government Hill to the ACS Building. The 200-pair cable, whose ownership was established later, ran from a utility communications man-hole at Third Avenue and E Street, in underground conduit to the C Street bridge over Ship Creek, crossed in buried conduit under the creek, and continued across the railroad switchyard up Government Hill to the ACS Building. This cable had 176 pairs of circuits obligated for federal govern-ment use; the rest were long-distance toll circuits for the use of the utility.

Effect of Earthquake

All the exchanges lost electrical power and switched to emergency batteries. Relay racks and panels at the Broadway exchange were tipped over by the shaking. The Fairfax ex-change, in Spenard, was slightly damaged and was operating on standby power with about half of its 2,000 lines func-tional. Federal and Dimond exchanges were only slightly damaged. The 600-pair cable traversed ground that had several slides. The aerial cable was still intact, but poles whipped and guys were broken; further slides at the toe of Government Hill would knock down several aerial spans. The 200-pair cable was stretched tight at the manhole splice at Third Avenue and E Street because of slides and ground cracks (Figure 23) along the route of the buried conduit. Nearly all overhead cables throughout the area remained un-damaged, except in slide areas. Underground communica-tion cables were destroyed in the Fourth Avenue graben,

FIGURE 23   There were several large ground cracks along the route of the duct run containing the 200-pair cable to Government Hill (Anchorage, April 1964).

and about 300 ft of cable was destroyed in the K–L street graben.

Emergency Measures

The telephone utility had available some additional cable splicers and wiremen who had been engaged for the installation of the new high-speed relay telephone system. With this additional help, the internal repairs progressed rapidly. Although the building was damaged, repairs to the switching equipment were not delayed because a large supply of repair materials was available among the materials ready for the installation of new equipment. By midnight, utility repairmen repaired sufficient equipment to enable the Broadway exchange to resume operation.

Splicers worked all night splicing in a shoofly cable around the broken splice in the 200-pair cable. Service to ACS was not reestablished, however, and another break was

found on Government Hill. Another section of cable was spliced in around this break and service was restored on Monday, March 30 reestablishing long-distance toll service to parts of Alaska, Canada, and the Lower 48. The Corps of Engineers had contractors working on restoration of telephone lines in Turnagain and along the K–L street graben in connection with debris removal and electrical repairs.

Restoration Work

The 200-pair cable, which was thought to belong to the city, had been given to the city to maintain by the local ACS. In return, the city had been allowed to use unobligated circuits for long-distance toll service. The ownership became an issue when the city planned a microwave facility from the Broadway exchange to the ACS Building across Ship Creek. Because the "grant-in-lieu" benefit from OEP was only about 8 percent of the total cost, the plan was abandoned and renewal of the cable was requested. It was determined that, although the local ACS had given the cable to the city of Anchorage, the national ACS headquarters had not transferred the title to the city, which therefore had to purchase and install a new cable with their own funds.

Overhead and underground telephone cables and facilities were repaired in conjunction with the overhead and underground electrical-utility repair work described in the following section.

CITY OF ANCHORAGE MUNICIPAL LIGHT AND POWER UTILITY

The Anchorage Municipal Light and Power Utility (MLP) operated and maintained the city-owned electrical generating station and the transmission and distribution systems. The generating station, along the south bank of Ship Creek north of the Native Hospital, consisted of two 15,000 kW natural-gas-fired turbine-driven generators. The dual-fuel turbines could be switched over to diesel oil in the event of gas-system outage. A 235,000-gallon storage tank was located at the generating station. The power was generated at 4,160 V and transformed to 33,000 V to feed the transmission system. Transmission lines were of single wooden-pole angle-arm construction and fed 9 outdoor package-style substations that contained a switchrack, transformer, and cubicles with 4,160-V distribution-feeder breakers. The aerial distribution feeders fed pole-line transformers that stepped the voltage down for the customer service lines.

In the downtown area, electricity was distributed through a system of underground transformer vaults and buried duct runs. Customers were supplied with 120- and 208-V power through underground service ducts. Underground telephone and electrical-power ducts were installed in parallel runs with a common concrete envelope, but each system had separate manholes. Figure 24 shows underground duct runs and manholes.

The MLP also received power at 33,000 V from the Bureau of Reclamation's Anchorage substation. The utility was serving about 9,000 customers at the time of the earthquake. Turnagain was served by Chugach Electric Association before the section was annexed by the City of Anchorage and did not transfer to city electrical service after annexation. The MLP served some customers outside the city limits, including International Airport.

Effect of the Earthquake

The MLP was supplying a load of 24,000 kW—16,000 kW from one of its own turbine generators, and 8,000 kW from the Anchorage Substation. Electrical systems tripped and shut down during the earthquake motions. The control cabinet beside unit 1 at the generating station tore loose its

floor anchors and fell over. The whole plant was shaken, supplies were thrown around, and the natural-gas fuel system failed.

Transmission-line poles whipped and pulled up guy-line anchors or broke guy cables, but conductors remained intact though sagging was uneven. Immediately after the earthquake, the overhead system was estimated to be 75 percent operational with risk. Some poles were not vertical, but all were standing although some ground in the area was unstable and had shifted several feet. Figure 25 shows a pavement break in the pressure ridge that destroyed a warehouse on C Street, although the power poles remained intact. Figure 26 shows power poles in the K–L street graben; an old table had been placed in the ground crack to prevent people from falling in.

Underground duct runs along the Third–Fourth avenue alley were destroyed for six blocks between Cordova and E streets. Other damage to duct runs and manholes was not determined immediately but would show up later.

The MLP lost 317 customers in the evacuation of the L Street and McKinley apartment buildings (two identical 14-story buildings) and in businesses lost in the Fourth Avenue graben. In addition, 20 light standards were destroyed, half in Turnagain and half in the Fourth Avenue graben.

Emergency Measures

A standby diesel-driven generator at the generating station was started to provide station power. Generator 1 was out of operation until the control cabinet was remounted and repaired. Unit 2 was inspected and was considered safe to operate; it was consequently switched over to diesel-oil operation.

Crews that were dispatched in line trucks reported damage by two-way radio to the central office. They checked transmission lines and switched damaged sections out of the system. Substation 3 at the Third–Fourth avenue alley on C Street was unusable. Because fuel oil was ponding in the dock storage-tank area, the transmission-line switch to the substation serving the dock area was opened; it would not then be energized when power was restored.

A usable system remained, and unit 2 was started to supply power. Other utility workers had checked substations and distribution-feeder circuits. Houses were inspected to ensure safe wiring and restoration of power. Damaged facilities were cut out of the system, allowing repairs to be made later, and power was restored to operational systems without delay.

Service was restored to some areas at 8 p.m. on March 27. At this time, however, the generator shut down because of low fuel. A concrete retaining wall near the 235,000-gallon storage tank had been tipped over by slide material from above, and a large hole was cut in the base of the tank

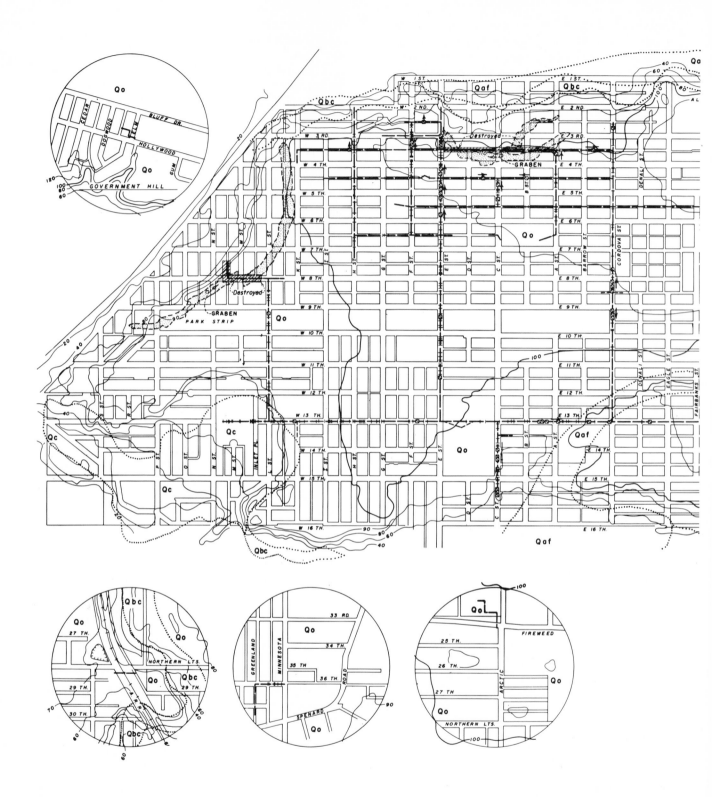

FIGURE 24   Topography, surface geology, and location of fractures in underground communication and electrical systems of Anchorage.

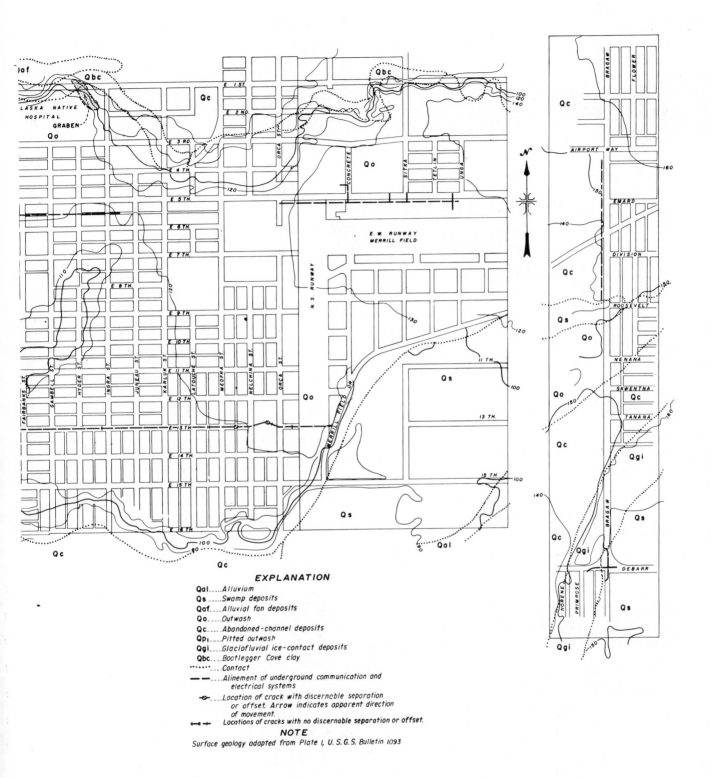

EXPLANATION

Qal.....Alluvium
Qs.....Swamp deposits
Qaf.....Alluvial fan deposits
Qo.....Outwash
Qc.....Abandoned-channel deposits
Qpi.....Pitted outwash
Qgi.....Glaciofluvial ice-contact deposits
Qbc.....Bootlegger Cove clay
·······.....Contact
— · —.....Alinement of underground communication and
          electrical systems
⊶.....Location of crack with discernable separation
          or offset. Arrow indicates apparent direction
          of movement.
⊢—+.....Locations of cracks with no discernable separation or offset.

NOTE

Surface geology adapted from Plate I, U.S.G.S. Bulletin 1093

SCALE OF FEET

U.S. Geological Survey

FIGURE 25   Looking south on C Street from First Avenue; nearly all power-line poles are intact (Anchorage, March 1964). A pressure ridge buckled the pavement and wrecked the warehouse.

through which the oil was draining. At this point, the station's standby capability had been exhausted. Furthermore, oil could not be obtained from the dock area because it was sealed off to all traffic to prevent fires. Diesel fuel, borrowed from the military, was delivered in truckloads of 55-gallon drums. This operation continued until natural gas was restored on Sunday morning, March 29.

The underground portion of the electrical system was inspected carefully and tested between manholes and vaults. Only MLP electricians were permitted to enter vaults and to make circuit connections. Electrical service was restored to usable parts of the system; temporary overhead and surface-laid lines were installed to supply customers with damaged underground service facilities.

Meanwhile, the control cabinet at unit 1 was repaired and reinstalled, and the unit was made serviceable. This was

FIGURE 26   View looking west on Eighth Avenue from L Street. Utility lines were shaken in the graben (Anchorage, April 1964).

fortunate because unit 2 was damaged in the aftershock that occurred on the Friday after the earthquake. Unit 2, which had just been shut down, was rotating slowly on cool-down to prevent warping of the turbine rotor, driven by a small electric motor from station power. Station power was shut down in the aftershock, unit 2 stopped rotating, and the rotor warped; it was out of service for several months until a new rotor could be installed.

A Corps of Engineers contractor began work in Turnagain to restore service in the remaining area. Another contractor, on emergency work in the Fourth Avenue graben area, removed substation 3 and stored it at Third Avenue and Cordova Street. Contractors also inspected aerial and underground electrical and telephone facilities and reported on the damage found. These contractors assisted the MLP for several weeks by improving temporary service and making repairs to keep the facilities operating.

Restoration Projects

Overhead Electrical and Telephone Systems The systems were inspected from the ground during the emergency work, and lists of damage were submitted. Further inspections were made with hydraulic "sky buckets" and additional damage lists were compiled. These additional damaged items included cracked insulators, pulled splices in conductors, broken or partly failed pole-line-transformer mounting brackets, and several broken ground wires. The repair of these important damaged items by contractors probably prevented intermittent failures during inclement weather.

The extent of the repairs exceeded authorizations for expenditures of federal funds specified by Public Law 875. A sample area of Anchorage, with representative damage, facility intensity, and dispersion, and containing one third of the city's surface and overhead facilities was selected. Overhead telephone and power lines, and other equipment within this area were repaired and restored to preearthquake condition. The repairs necessary exceeded the authorization and intent for the particular area, but because some earthquake damage in other areas was not repaired, these repairs were completed.

Transmission-Line Crossing at Ship Creek A 33,000-V line spanned the tideflat and Ship Creek to supply the substation that served the dock area. A twin-pole H-frame deadend tower on the south end of the crossing span stood on a silt ridge formed by tide action and creek runoff (Figure 27). Since the earthquake, the silt ridge had been eroding around the crossing tower and continued action would wash it away. The cause of this situation was studied to see what remedial action should be taken. The basic cause was thought to be the subsidence of the area around the mouth of Ship Creek. No data were available from topographic surveys still in progress, but tides were leaving new high-water marks on railroad and other embankments, which indicated about 3 ft of subsidence.

It was determined that tide-runoff characteristics had changed on the silt ridge. Before the earthquake, the top of the ridge was about +20 ft elevation and normal high tide was +27 ft measured from mean low water at low tide. As the water level receded with the outgoing tide, the flow over the ridge was even and gentle until about elevation 20 ft (MLLW); after that, the water level receded more rapidly and runoff was more rapid. But the higher-velocity runoff was confined within the banks and meanderings of the creek

FIGURE 27 After the earthquake, the power-line-crossing tower (arrow) was endangered by the erosion of outgoing tides (Anchorage, August 1965).

bed. Since the earthquake, the subsidence had caused the tide basin north of The Alaska Railroad depot to hold about twice the volume of water it had formerly held at normal high tide. The water level still receded in the same manner as before, but the relative ground and water-surface elevations were different.

Higher runoff velocities now occurred while water was still 3 or 4 ft deep over the silt ridge and eroded it until the water level dropped to the elevation where it was contained within the creek banks. Although the equilibrium configuration is unknown, the silt ridge will probably adapt, in time, to postearthquake flow characteristics. Line poles across the tideflat would be subject to damage from floating ice during winter months. To prevent this damage, the line could either be moved to a less hazardous area, or poles could be protected with rock-filled cribs. Attempts to coordinate a new crossing site were abandoned in favor of protecting the line then in place.

Substation 1   This substation on the Eighth to Ninth Avenue alley on Fairbanks Street, had a 1,500-kilovolt-ampere (kVA) transformer, 33,000-V switchrack, and 5,000-V feeder breakers in outdoor cubicles, all in a fenced enclosure. The earthquake resulted in loads changing in areas served by substations when a number of customers from the area served by substation 3 moved to the area served by substation 1. This substation therefore would be overloaded during the coming winter. Removal of equipment at substation 1 and installation of equipment from substation 3 would increase the capacity from 1,500 kVA to 5,000 kVA. A contract was awarded for this work; also, the increased capacity of the new substation 1 required addition of several new underground and overhead feeders.

Underground Duct Systems   Duct runs were inspected during the emergency work in winter weather, but after breakup, new damage became evident and another inspection was necessary. Because these facilities were given priority, second only to buried water and sewer utilities, it was mid-August before attention was focused on restoration of duct runs. The history of the ductworks and maintenance problems of the underground systems were accumulated throughout the summer. Before the earthquake, telephone cables in duct runs had been failing too quickly after installation. Water traps in the duct runs were suspected; several freeze–thaw cycles could split sheaths and jackets on cables and cause early failure. It was decided that duct runs should be inspected by closed-circuit television to ascertain whether there was earthquake damage that needed to be repaired.

From the Bureau of Reclamation at Denver, Colorado, the Corps of Engineers obtained closed-circuit television equipment, which their geologists used to inspect deep well casings and screens. The unit was mounted on a truck for

FIGURE 28   Truck-mounted television equipment being loaded aboard a MATS Air Force C-124 at Denver for flight to Anchorage, Alaska, in September 1964.

independent remote-site operation and was furnished with an experienced geologist operator. It was airlifted from Lowry AFB, Denver, by MATS to Elmendorf AFB, Anchorage, and was used in Anchorage to inspect underground duct runs (Figure 28). The spare duct in each run was representative of all the ducts because the system consisted of asbestos-cement ducts in a concrete envelope.

The 2½-in.-diameter probe with side-viewing capability was 55 in. long (Figure 29) and would not pass through the curves in some ducts. An adaptor bridle was used for axial

FIGURE 29   The 55 × 2½-in.-diameter television-camera probe did not negotiate all curves in duct runs (Anchorage, September 1964).

M. H. Logan, U.S. Bureau of Reclamation

FIGURE 30 The adapter bridle on the television-camera probe enabled it to photograph objects straight ahead (Anchorage, September 1964).

M. H. Logan

FIGURE 32 Truck-mounted unit with television-camera probe, control cable, and monitoring set (Anchorage, September 1964).

viewing and this also helped the probe to negotiate the sharper line curvatures (Figure 30).

The probe, trailing its control cable, was pulled by an electrically driven winch (Figure 31). The truck-mounted unit is shown in operation in Figure 32. The operator watched a monitoring screen in the truck van and directed the operation by sound-powered telephone to the assisting electricians. One operated the winch, another fed the distance-calibrated cable into the duct run after the probe and gave distance readings to the operator. The operator inspected the interior of the ducts and logged damage by type and location. An MLP or telephone-utility engineer watched the monitoring screen with the operator to help determine the extent or type of damage.

The duct systems consisted of four to twelve ducts in a bank. The 3½-in.-diameter asbestos cement ducts, in con-

crete envelopes, were buried 4–6 ft below grade, usually in alleys, with 180–540 ft between manholes. Where communication and electrical ducts were in one common envelope, only one duct in the envelope was examined with the TV probe, after it had been cleaned by mandrel and brush. During September and early October 1964, 23,594 lin ft of communication ducts and 10,510 ft of electrical ducts were examined. The condition of the spare duct was considered representative of all ducts in an envelope. Communication ducts from A to E streets in the Third–Fourth avenue alley were destroyed by the Fourth Avenue graben. A section along Eighth Avenue west of L Street was destroyed by the K–L street graben.

The following comments on analysis of damage to the underground systems are quoted from a report on the underground survey by Lynn R. Burton, U.S. Bureau of Reclamation (1967).

DAMAGE TO SYSTEMS

Cracks in the ducts were clearly visible on the monitor screen, and the amount of separation and offset was accurately determined. Approximately 90 percent of the cracks exhibited no measurable displacement and were not considered indicative of serious damage to concrete envelopes. Lateral, vertical, and longititudinal displacements along fractures were observed at 52 locations [Figure 33]. . . . The maximum displacement noted was 1 inch, although most were in the 1/16- to 1/4-inch range. Soil and water had entered the ducts through many such openings, and water was found in some areas where only hairline cracks were present.

INTERPRETATION OF DATA

Although their plotted locations exhibit no well-defined pattern, the cracks are concentrated in the vicinity of the Fourth Avenue slide and in areas near the slopes of stream valleys and local drainage channels. The concentrations of fractures north of Sixth Avenue between Barrow and F Streets are clearly the result of ground adjustments related to the Fourth Avenue slide. Others, such as those located on Thirteenth Avenue and along C Street south of Thirteenth Avenue, probably reflect local subsidence resulting from incipient failure of outwash and alluvial materials on valley slopes.

FIGURE 31 Electric-drive motor and variable-speed transmission for pulling television probe and control cable through duct (Anchorage, September 1964).

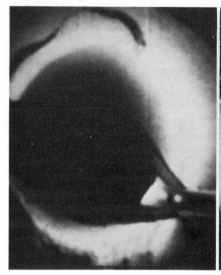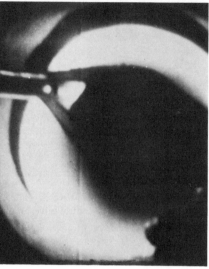

FIGURE 33   Axial views of breaks in the transite ducts. The semicircular dark zones within the brightly illuminated areas are fractures along which offset has occurred. One rod of the pulling bridle and the back of the auxiliary lighting unit extend toward the camera (Anchorage, September 1964).

U.S. Bureau of Reclamation

As a result of the television inspection, very few duct repairs were necessary. The original $1.25 million that had been programmed for repairs to the combined underground systems was reduced to $150,000, and the actual restoration cost was only about one third of this amount.

One damaged manhole was completely replaced in the fall of 1965, and another was repaired by pouring a second manhole around the existing one and drawing the two walls together with bolts; it was not necessary to remove conductors from the manhole and duct runs to do this work.

Known duct breaks or offsets, seen on the television monitoring set, were repaired during the construction season of 1965. At 25 locations, the damage consisted of a break in the duct with an estimated separation of less than ¼ in., or of visible damage that could not be assessed. To investigate the damage carefully and to determine the repair work necessary, excavation and uncovering the concrete envelope was planned around the ducts. An offset of less than ¼ in. was to be jacked back in place, braced, circumferentially routed, filled with epoxy, and backfilled. Smaller cracks in the envelope were to be routed, filled with epoxy, and backfilled. After five such excavations, the damage found was so slight that only one crack was routed and filled with epoxy, the rest were backfilled, and work on the balance of the 20 work items was canceled.

Utilities for Government Hill School and National Bureau of Standards Annex

Reconstruction of the school on the old site was not possible because the ground was unstable. The only suitable alternate site on Government Hill was on the military reservation and had been allocated to the National Bureau of Standards for reconstruction and enlargement of their antenna fields. To make the site available for the new school, the Bureau of

Standards had to move further west and a ravine had to be filled to provide proper ground configuration for the antenna field. Also, a transmission line and a buried communication cable that crossed the area and the ravine would have to be moved.

With the cooperation of all agencies, new facilities were established and utilities were installed for both the Bureau of Standards and the new Government Hill School. A half mile of 36-in.-diameter corrugated-steel pipe was installed in the ravine and covered with from 10 to 20 ft of backfill. The power line was relocated. It was not necessary to move the buried communication cable, but it required protection where it was exposed and suspended in a catenary for about 30 ft across the ravine. On the first day of construction, the contractor's digging equipment cut into this cable near the Bureau of Standards building. About half of the 200 cable pairs, including important data circuits, were severed or damaged. Air Force wiremen and cable splicers made the repairs as a training exercise. Many of the pairs were spliced and cut over with no circuit interruption.

Sewer, water, and power lines to the Government Hill School were installed, in addition to storm sewers and catch basins for the access road. A system of traffic lights was provided to control traffic on the access roads to the new school.

Summary

The overhead electrical and telephone-utility facilities were about 75 percent operational immediately after the earthquake. Underground systems were perhaps 80 percent operational, excluding the totally destroyed portions. Light emergency repairs, with temporary surface and aerial lines, quickly made these systems about 90 percent operational. Some emergency repairs constituted full restoration, others were temporary and hasty and required additional work. Intermittent power and telephone service was restored within a few hours in some areas, but took several days to a week in others. Contractors on emergency work assisted in the initial restoration of service and continued to improve hastily installed facilities for several weeks. Telephone and electrical duct-system damage surveys and restoration work were inseparable and were carried out jointly. The television camera probe identified earthquake damage, and equally important, verified the lack of it, thus preventing unecessary expenditures. These utilities were given secondary priority because they were less vital than water and sewer utilities and could be bypassed with temporary overhead facilities at almost any time during the winter.

CITY OF ANCHORAGE STREET UTILITY AND CONSTRUCTION RIGHTS-OF-WAY

About 90 percent of all streets in residential areas were paved with asphalt. Concrete curbs and sidewalks existed in downtown areas and in about half of the older residential areas of Anchorage. Mountain View and Government Hill sections had numerous paved streets but few curbs, gutters,

or sidewalks. In Turnagain Heights, streets were nearly all paved and had concrete curbs but no sidewalks, and nearly all homes had concrete driveways. Very few downtown alleys were paved; most had gravel surfaces.

Earthquake Damage

Street paving, sidewalks, and curbs were broken in areas affected by earthslides. Figure 34 shows Fourth and Fifth avenues intersected by the K–L street graben. Streets, houses, and buried utilities sank by the amount of ground movement. Immediately after the earthquake, these streets were impassable to vehicular traffic. The Fourth Avenue and K–L street grabens broke up all surface-installed facilities and blocked traffic. The slide area in Turnagain did not impede traffic because it was on the edge of the area and access to the slide area was necessary only for evacuation and salvage operations that required off-highway equipment.

Emergency Work

Contractors, under instructions from the Corps of Engineers, began to clear debris and repair streets to make them passable for police, ambulance, fire engines, and utility trucks on missions concerning public health and safety and for the

FIGURE 34 Filling and grading was required to restore traffic through the K–L street graben (Anchorage, April 1964).

repair of other utilities. It was necessary to clear fallen lines and broken utility poles that blocked streets near slide areas. Grading made streets passable across grabens.

Restoration Work

Streets, curbs, gutters, sidewalks, and driveways were broken up in many places during the repair of buried utilities. Restoration of these surface facilities was not included in individual repair contracts for buried utilities because more than one buried utility could require repair in a damaged area: A sewer line might require repair on one side of a street and a water line on the other. To repair paving after repair of each buried utility could require double restoration in overlapping areas, whereas the paving could be restored only once under provisions of Public Law 875. For this reason, a separate paving contractor, with adequate equipment, was engaged. The same applied to concrete work on gutters, sidewalks, and driveways. In Turnagain Heights, water lines were inside the curbing, and numerous driveways were broken to make repairs.

All concrete repair and paving necessitated by repairs to buried utilities were handled in one contract. This work included patchwork and new curbs, gutters, and asphalt paving (Figure 35). A small amount of concrete work was necessary to repair breakage caused by the earthquake. Some street development was paid for with federal-assistance funds from the Bureau of Public Roads. Repairs to these streets, Fifth and Sixth avenues, and C and L streets, were made with funds from the State of Alaska Highway Department, with federal assistance.

SEWARD

Seward was subjected to strong ground motion in the earthquake and facilities that were not constructed to withstand strong seismic action were damaged, shifted, or destroyed. Power and telephone lines whipped violently and broke or stretched guy cables, but shaking did not cause extensive damage to buried utilities. These, however, were damaged by ground subsidence, differential settlement, and sliding, cracking, and fracturing of frozen ground. Underwater landslides in Resurrection Bay generated huge waves that swept over builtup areas near sea level and wrecked or washed away waterfront buildings and utilities.

When the shaking had subsided, tsunamis started to come in, and for several hours they continued to damage facilities as high as 31 ft above mean lower low water (MLLW). The waves washed mud and silt into sewers and broken water lines, and the hydraulic pumping effect of the continuous wave action packed mud into the lines.

The original townsite of Seward is a tract of gently rolling land near sea level. The town is nestled against Mt.

Marathon and Resurrection Bay with a freshwater lagoon on the northeast. The city had to expand and develop north across the lagoon. Settlement of Forest Acres began shortly after World War II, and development of Clearview began around the middle 1950's. The Army built Fort Raymond during World War II, abandoned it shortly thereafter, and gave it to the City of Seward, at which time it was renamed Forest Acres. The fort contained three pumped wells, buried water and sewer lines, and overhead electrical-power lines when it was annexed by the city. The military had installed utilities to serve dispersed facilities, and the location of buried lines was poor for residential connections; a number of homes were constructed near or even directly over buried utility lines.

ELECTRIC UTILITY

There were privately owned and city-owned generating and distribution systems in Seward at the beginning of World War II. The city acquired the privately owned system after the war, combined the two systems, and enlarged the utility service to serve more customers in the area; it also planned a hydroelectric project at Crescent Lake, about 30 mi north of Seward. A 69-kV transmission line from Crescent Lake to Seward was constructed in 1954, and the project was then discontinued.

The Chugach Electric Association (CEA) completed construction of the Cooper Lake hydroelectric plant and transmission system in 1962. With the purchase of the Moose Pass private utility-distribution system, CEA could furnish Cooper Lake power to the city of Seward at a metering station at Mile 25 (from Seward) over the city's 69-kV transmission line. The line was constructed for 69-kV and used to transmit 24-kV power. A power-interchange agreement was made whereby the Cooper Lake plant supplied nearly all the city's requirements. Under terms of this agreement, the city kept its own standby generators operational at all times. These were two 1,400-kVA steam-turbine-driven units located in the old townsite near the Standard Oil Company storage tanks. CEA installed a 3,000 kVA substation at Mile 7 in the transmission line to supply 12.5-kV power to CEA customers and to the city substation, where voltage was transformed to 2,400 V to feed the city distribution system.

Earthquake Damage

Some storage tanks at the Standard Oil tank farm broke open during the earthquake and the oil ignited. The nearby building, housing the standby generators, burned, and all the equipment was destroyed. The 69-kV transmission line across the freshwater lagoon was demolished. Power poles and spans of conductors were destroyed in the old townsite by slides, destruction of the dock, movement or destruction

FIGURE 35 Example of street repair necessitated by repair to underground utilities (Anchorage, June 1965).

of buildings, and by waves. The only electrical service available after the earthquake was from an emergency generator that provided a limited amount of power at the hospital.

Emergency Work

The Army at Fort Richardson supplied portable generators, which the Alaska State Air National Guard flew to Seward. These units were immediately put in service at the hospital and at the water wells. The Corps of Engineers contracted with City Electric of Anchorage to perform emergency work on the distribution system to restore electrical power as quickly as possible. Journeymen electricians, supplies, equipment, and line trucks were flown to Seward by the Air National Guard on Easter Sunday, March 29, 1964. The first task was construction of a temporary line around the lagoon to bypass the destroyed portion of the 69-kV line. This was done by hanging 15-kV insulated cable from stub poles, thereby energizing the substation and restoring service expeditiously.

Buildings were inspected to ensure that interior wiring was safe; if it was not, the house service was cut off at the distribution transformer so that the greatest number of customers could be served immediately and repairs made later. No water was available for fire protection, and every precaution was taken to prevent fires caused by faulty wiring. The 2,400-V distribution system was repaired and made operational in near-record time by electricians working around the clock. As soon as power had been initially restored, the contractor converted the temporary connections and facilities into permanent, code-grade installations. A new line was constructed around the lagoon to replace the temporary line. To relieve heavily loaded 2,400-V lines, 7.2-kV circuits were installed and fed from the substation.

Some customers moved to other parts of Seward, overloading the circuits and necessitating several new ones. A new feeder was installed to serve the cannery.

The postearthquake condition of outdoor lights and utility poles in the warehouse area is shown in Figure 36.

FIGURE 36 Electrical facilities at the dock and warehouse were damaged (Seward, April 1964).

WATER UTILITY

Seward obtained surface-water from two sources: Mt. Marathon and Jap Creek. The latter source, developed by the Army and turned over to the city with Fort Raymond, was a good source during winter months, but because of glacial runoff, was turbid and roily in late spring, summer, and early fall. The Marathon intake was a good source in late spring, summer, and early fall when mountain springs were not frozen. The three pumped wells served as a reserve supply for fire protection and supplemented requirements while surface sources were being changed. The cost of electricity was high, and wells were pumped only when necessary, which in a normal year was for about 30 days during the spring and fall. A saltwater fire-protection system was installed at the dock and extended into the downtown business area. It was supplied by four electrically driven pumps that provided 3,250 gallons of water per minute.

Expansion of the cannery in the late 1950's increased the town's freshwater requirement. In 1960, a 14-in. cast-iron line was installed from Forest Acres to the downtown area, where a water-storage tank was added in 1962. System-grid-distribution improvements were made at this time, and electrical remote water-level controls were added to the pumps. At the time of the earthquake, Seward's water supply was coming from Jap Creek and was supplemented by automatic operation of wells in Forest Acres.

Earthquake Damage

The water system was inoperative immediately after the earthquake because electrical failure stopped the pumps and lateral movement, differential settlement, and cracks in the frozen ground broke water lines at numerous locations. Ground movement, varying from a few inches to

several feet broke buried lines. The flow of water from Jap Creek was low and leaks from breaks in the supply line further decreased the flow. Water for firefighting was inadequate. The saltwater fire-protection system, including pumps, intake, and delivery lines, was damaged when the dock and warehouse slid into the bay and was further damaged by tsunamis. As a result, fires in Seward burned uncontrolled because no fire-fighting equipment was operational.

Emergency Work

During the emergency period immediately after the earthquake, an immediate and organized effort was made to restore the utilities. The Corps of Engineers rented off-highway vehicles (weasels) and assisted the utility personnel in inspecting the Jap Creek water-supply line and intake. They found several line repairs were needed and that floating ice had blocked the intake, nearly stopping the flow. Chunks of ice were shifted around, and the flow, although still limited, was improved. Men and materials were dispatched to make temporary line repairs.

The portable generators from Fort Richardson were used to pump wells, which benefited nearby residents, although the line breaks cut off the flow to other areas. When the 4-in.-diameter aluminum irrigation pipe and fittings arrived by air from Anchorage, temporary surface lines were installed to restore water service in the manner previously described in this report.

The Corps of Engineers negotiated a contract for emergency work to clean up debris, clear streets, wreck and remove damaged buildings, install surface water lines, and perform other tasks associated with cleanup after the disaster. Figure 37 shows wreckage to be cleared from the road and railroad between the old townsite and Clearview.

FIGURE 37   Power lines had to be restored after tsunamis washed boats and debris across the area (Seward, April 1964).

FIGURE 38 Street debris was cleared away and power lines rebuilt in south end of Seward (July 1964).

Tidal waves had completely destroyed the small-boat basin and had deposited debris several hundred feet inland. Figure 38 shows the south end of the Seward townsite after considerable debris had been removed. Wrecked boats and damaged buildings had been removed and streets cleared for public access and police and fire protection.

SEWER UTILITY

Sewer lines were of vitreous clay and concrete pipe, installed with solid mortar joints. There were no lift stations, and all lines operated by gravity flow. Untreated raw sewage flowed into Resurrection Bay through two outfalls. One outfall served the old townsite collector system. Sewage from Forest Acres flowed into a collector from Clearview and on into the bay through the Clearview outfall. Installation of lines and facilities was normal to the industry. Manholes were assembled from precast sections and were about 300 ft apart in the city-block areas.

Earthquake Damage

Along the bay side of the old townsite, large areas of ground slid into the bay, carrying away buried utilities, including the sewer outfall. The remaining ground cracked 100–200 ft inland in places, breaking sewer lines. Tsunamis and waves from slides and seiches pumped mud and silt into sewer lines and manholes; some manholes overflowed and mud rose above the inverts in others. The Clearview outfall traversed part of the lagoon area that sank several feet during the earthquake, and the bay end of the outfall was washed away by the waves.

Emergency Work

Sewer lines were blocked from the bay inland and some manholes overflowed with sewage. Covers were removed to permit the sewage to drain away on the surface, and ditch-

ing and drainage improvements were made to permit flow of open-ditch sewage into the bay. The open-ditch sewage was heavily chlorinated. The contractor who was removing debris, clearing streets, and repairing the water-utility also made emergency sewer repairs. Vehicle and walkway crossings were installed over drain ditches. Sewage was pumped from a number of manholes onto the ground to keep the level low enough to prevent flooding inside buildings.

STREET UTILITY

The old townsite had asphalt paving on several well-traveled streets; other streets had a gravel surface. Tsunamis and underwater slides caused by the earthquake generated waves that washed concrete sidewalks around, shifted blocks of concrete askew, and washed away asphalt paving and surface gravel. Streets were first cleared of debris, and gravel fill was then used to make streets passable for vehicular traffic. Broken sidewalks were hauled away and replaced with gravel fill to make temporary walkways.

DAMAGE SURVEY

The Corps of Engineers contracted with an Anchorage consulting engineer to make a damage survey and to submit recommendations for restoration of the water, sewer, electrical, and street utilities owned by the City of Seward.

Sewer Utility

The architect–engineer made a photographic inspection of the city sewers with a single-lens 16-mm camera in the same manner that the Anchorage sewers had been inspected. It was necessary to clean a number of sewer lines with a water jet to wash out silt and mud deposits before a camera could be pulled through. This time-consuming method was the only means of determining line conditions. Because of the rigidity of mortar joints in the sewer line, the architect–engineer used a ½-in.-joint offset as a basis for recommending pipe replacement or resetting. Repairs were recommended for about 85 percent of the lines of 8-in. diameter or larger; new outfalls were recommended for Clearview and the old townsite. New sections of line at accessible locations were recommended in Forest Acres, so that repair of existing lines would not disturb house foundations. To prevent procurement delays after the award of a contract, the Corps of Engineers ordered asbestos-cement pipe for replacements on the basis of the architect–engineer's recommended renewal requirements.

Water Utility

After the emergency repairs had been made, an inspection of the Jap Creek and Marathon intake water supplies indicated that only minor repairs were still necessary. It was recommended that the three wells in Forest Acres be rehabilitated. Pressure and leakage tests were made on buried water lines, and repairs or renewals were recommended according to location, grouping of breaks, and type of damage. The architect–engineer studied water requirements for the business area, cannery, dock, small-boat basin, and so forth and also considered the requirements of facilities not yet reconstructed. Changes in looped lines and grid connections were developed to provide a water system that would be capable of serving all facilities when restored. Locations and types of repairs, as well as new lines, were listed so that contract drawings could be prepared. The Corps of Engineers ordered cast-iron water pipe according to the size and footage recommendations of the architect–engineer so that materials would be available when a contract was awarded.

Electrical Utility

The electrical system, including the 2,400-V distribution network, was surveyed, and repaired. Lists were made of work not already done. Before the earthquake the city substation was overloaded and did not have the flexibility needed to handle the load from facilities destroyed by fires, tsunamis and waterfront slides. Restoration of the system as it existed before the earthquake was not attempted because of the redistribution of load. Feeder loading would be improved by the addition of distribution circuits from the 7,200-V line feeding the substation and replacement of the 2,400-V transformer by 7,200-V pole-mounted distribution transformers. Part of this was included in the emergency repairs, and recommendations were made for several more circuits.

Streets

The inspecting engineers recommended backfilling the low spots remaining in the streets and grading streets in areas not covered during the emergency work. The city elected to receive "grant-in-lieu" funds instead of having the sidewalks replaced. By this plan, they could relocate, delete, or add walks as desired. The architect–engineer documented areas eligible for replacement so that the claim could be processed.

RESTORATION

A contract was awarded for the work of restoring utility facilities usually as recommended by the architect–engineer. Advance orders for materials saved valuable construction time; replacement sewer and water pipe had already been delivered to Seward when the contract was awarded.

As had happened in other areas, all the earthquake damage was not evident at the time of the damage survey; other damage showed up later. Two of the three wells in Forest Acres were rehabilitated, but the third was abandoned. A new well was drilled, using the pump and controls from the abandoned well.

The standby well at the City Hospital was operating satisfactorily at time of the damage survey, but it required rehabilitation shortly thereafter, and this repair was included in the work of restoration. Water-line repairs were made throughout the system, and temporary aboveground irrigation pipe was removed from service as buried water lines were restored.

During the time that the city had no standby power-generating capability, its power-interchange agreement with the Chugach Electric Association was not being honored. The Corps of Engineers obtained two 600-kW diesel-driven generators from the Army at Fort Richardson and had them installed at the site of the old standby generating plant that had burned down in the oil fires after the earthquake. This installation included a temporary building to house the generating units, fuel-storage tanks, and a transformer to tie into the city's 2,400-V distribution system. This provided temporary standby generating power while two new 1,500-kW diesel-driven outdoor generators were purchased and tied into the system.

The Clearview sewer outfall was extended into deeper water. Ground across the lagoon had subsided, and 4-ft high extensions had to be added to manholes across this area; the grade later proved to be inadequate and sewage did not flow satisfactorily. The outfall was relaid in 1965. After reconstruction of the small-boat basin and The Alaska Railroad dock, a new saltwater fire-fighting system was installed. Potable water lines and sewer lines were added at the new small-boat basin and at the railroad dock.

CORDOVA

Shaking affected utilities in this area in much the same way as in other areas near the epicenter. Surface facilities were severely shaken and aerial lines were whipped by the ground motion. Power conductors stretched or broke and pole guys were loosened or broken. Tsunamis damaged the harbor facilities, but because the whole Cordova area was uplifted about 6 ft and had remained at this new elevation, tsunamis did not damage the dock or reach into the builtup area of the city.

The city (Figure 39) owned, operated, or maintained water, sewer, electrical, and telephone utilities. The water-supply system was badly damaged and is discussed separately. The water and sewer systems were not severely damaged and were made functional by limited repairs.

The sewer system sustained major passive damage from the tectonic uplift. The outfall no longer extended into tidewater at low tide, interrupting the washing action of the tide that was needed to carry sewage away from the harbor area. A new sewer outfall was installed as part of a contract for dredging and restoration of harbor facilities.

The diesel engine-generator plant and telephone switchboard required little repair beyond general cleanup. One small contract was awarded to clear debris and to repair the aerial telephone and power-distribution systems.

A number of homes around Odiak Slough had privately installed buried sewer lines that had extended out into tidewater, and these were now exposed at low tide, with open-

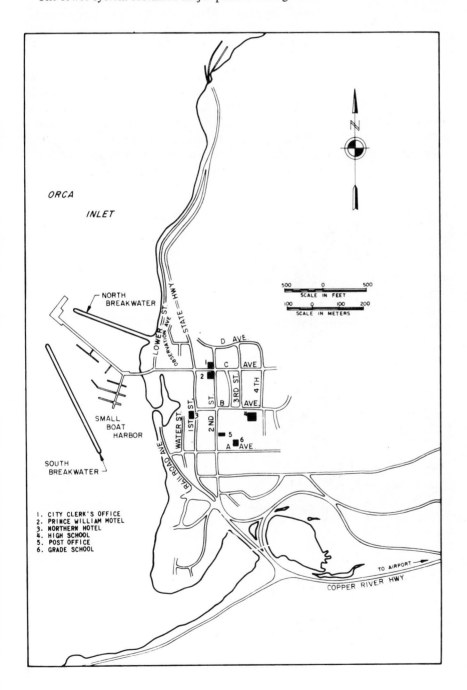

FIGURE 39 Cordova and vicinity.

ditch sewage running to tidewater. To remove this health hazard, an attempt was made to develop a project to install collectors and a sewer outfall. The attempt, however, failed and individuals were left responsible for their own sewer and septic-tank installations.

WATER UTILITY

The distribution system was a network of buried lines that supplied potable water to residences and business firms. The supply was adequate for normal requirements and for fire fighting in the city and dock areas. The water-supply system for the city dated back to the copper-mining days, shortly after the turn of the century. It had been maintained and additions had been made over the years.

A suitable source of water had been difficult to develop. Eyak Lake, a large body of water to the east of the town, was contaminated by human waste and was difficult to treat because of the presence of finely dissolved silt from glacial streams. A suitable supply was found in Meals Lake, which lay to the south at an elevation of 360 ft above mean sea level, about 1 mi from the city across Odiak Slough up about 1,800 ft of bluff terrain and across 3,000 ft of muskeg and undergrowth. Meals Lake was dammed to increase its storage capacity, and a 10-in.-diameter wood-stave pipeline was installed from Meals Lake to the bluff and continued down with an 8-in.-diameter line to a chlorinator building located on the south bank of the slough.

A cast-iron line was laid across the slough to feed the city distribution system. Because the water supply from Meals Lake was inadequate and had to be augmented, Haney Creek, further south, with a good year-round flow was chosen as the additional source. The creek was dammed, and a 10-in.-diameter wood-stave line was installed from the intake 3,000 ft down the canyon and then 4,000 ft north across the muskeg to Meals Lake. According to the best available records (Figure 40), this system was installed in about 1907.

In about 1955, APW Lake, near Meals Lake, was dammed and developed as an auxiliary source, probably for storage of excess water from Meals Lake. An 8-in.-diameter wood-stave line was installed from APW Lake to the bluff and parallel to the line from Meals Lake down to the chlorinator building. Valves inside the building made possible the shunting of water from Meals Lake back to APW Lake. APW Lake was dammed at an elevation of 375 ft, or about 15 ft higher

FIGURE 40   Aerial view of Cordova in 1959 showing chlorinator building, Alaska Public Works Lake, Meals Lake, and Haney Creek Canyon. Route of pipelines is indicated.

than Meals Lake, and the water was brackish. This was there-fore held for standby firefighting capability.

Shortly after the earthquake, the supply of city water in Cordova diminished until it did not meet the requirements for normal use. The city began to pump water from Eyak Lake, but the State of Alaska Public Health Department prevented it from continuing this practice because of im-purities, pollution, and overchlorination.

A project was developed to restore the water system in Cordova. The Corps of Engineers contracted for a survey and a report on the damage to the system, with recommen-dations on renewal or restoration and comparative costs. An on-site inspection of the line was made. The wood-stave pipe down Haney Creek Canyon had shifted, buckled, and moved laterally during the earthquake and had several leaks (Figure 41). At the log bridge, the line had shifted and part of the bank had collapsed (Figure 42). The line had buckled and was leaking badly (Figure 43) at another location. Over the years, new sections of pipe had been installed where sections had been worn thin from transporting gravel. Gravel cleanout piles were observed at numerous locations, and steel banding around the wood-stave line was broken at frequent intervals. Most of the 4,000-ft section across the muskeg flat had shallow cover. About 85 leaks, presumably caused by ground shaking, were counted in this portion of the line.

The level of Meals Lake was very low because of the many leaks in the Haney Creek supply line (Figure 44), and the line from Meals Lake to the bluff was in about the same condition as the line from Haney Creek. The two wood-stave lines down to the chlorinator building were in much better condition and, while covered, showed no leaks.

FIGURE 42   Pipeline from Haney Creek to Meals Lake. Log bridge was endangered by bank sloughing (Cordova, July 1964).

The architect–engineer recommended renewal of the line from the intake at the Haney Creek dam to Meals Lake and from the intake at Meals Lake dam to the bluff, with contingencies to "find and fix" any damage in the wood-stave lines down to the chlorinator building. The Corps of Engineers ordered polyvinylchloride (PVC) replacement

FIGURE 41   Lateral shift caused leaks in 10-in. wood-stave pipeline, installed in 1907. Note anchor lines to fallen tree to prevent snow slides from moving the pipeline (Cordova, July 1964).

FIGURE 43   Wood-stave pipeline buckled from ground movement in Haney Creek Canyon (Cordova, July 1964).

FIGURE 44   Water level in Meals Lake was drawn down because the water from the Haney Creek line was leaking away (Cordova, July 1964).

pipe, valves, and fittings, so that the material would be available when a construction contract was awarded. A contractor speeded up the installation of the PVC replacement pipe by using helicopter service to transport men and material over the difficult terrain.

SUMMARY

Shaking caused the greatest single damage to utilities, namely that incurred by the wood-stave pipelines, but it caused very little damage to other utilities in the area. There were no problems from differential ground settlements or slides such as caused extensive damage in other areas. The approximately 6 ft of tectonic uplift caused indirect damage to the sewage system. This gravity-flow system, which was coordinated with tidewater, became a sanitation hazard and required a new outfall below water level at low tide.

KODIAK ISLAND

Kodiak is the only city of any size in the area; it combines with urban fringes to make up a population of about 2,600, excluding military installations. The city owned, operated, or maintained water, sewer, and street utilities; the telephone and electrical utilities were privately owned and operated. Damage from shaking was not as severe as in other areas nearer to the epicenter. The primary source of damage was the several very destructive tsunamis that swept over port and harbor facilities and inundated about 40 percent of the downtown area. These waves caused extensive damage to all facilities in the waterfront area. To compound the damage, the area subsided about 6 ft as a result of the earthquake.

WATER UTILITY

Water was supplied from two reservoirs of different elevation in the same watershed. The lower reservoir supplied water to part of the area; in addition, some of the water from the lower reservoir was pumped to the upper reservoir, which supplied water to the rest of the city. Supply lines to the city were buried wood-stave pipe. The water-distribution system consisted of buried asbestos cement pipe. Lines were looped and gridded to provide an adequate supply of water, including water for fire-fighting purposes.

SEWER UTILITY

A system of laterals and collectors carried untreated sewage into the bay through seven outfalls that ranged in size from 8- to 12-in. in diameter. Sewer lines were of concrete and asbestos cement pipe and were all gravity-flow lines with no lift stations.

STREET UTILITY

Concrete curbs, gutters, and sidewalks existed in the downtown area, and streets were paved with asphaltic concrete.

EARTHQUAKE DAMAGE

Utilities were not materially affected by ground shaking, but they were damaged by the tsunamis. A number of power-line poles and fire hydrants were broken off in the waterfront area, and sewer outfalls were washed away. Devastating structural and harbor damage resulted from the tsunamis. The 5 or 6 ft of tectonic subsidence caused slower sewer drainage as tidewater rose to higher elevations in the outfalls.

EMERGENCY AND RESTORATION WORK

Emergency work was performed by contractors under the supervision of the Navy. Fishing boats were removed from the streets and the debris was cleared away so that traffic could pass. Electrical and water-utility repairs were made to restore facilities. The Corps of Engineers restored the sewer outfalls in the course of their other work on harbor facilities.

HOMER

The city is small, but it has a moderate residential area and a total area population of about 1,200. No public utilities existed at the time of the earthquake; homes and business firms had individual wells and sewer systems that consisted either of septic tanks or of direct drainage into the bay, according to their location. One private water system supplied the school and a dozen or so residences. The Homer Electric Association [REA (Rural Electrification Administration) facility] supplied electric power.

Utility damage was slight because there were few utilities. These were privately owned, and they were not restored with federal funds. The principal damage in the area resulted from the sinking of the Homer Spit, but this subsidence did not involve any publicly owned utilities other than the access road.

SELDOVIA

The city is small, with a total area population estimated at about 500. Electric power and telephone services were supplied by private firms, individual sewer lines drained into the bay, and the only city utility was the water system.

The water supply was through a 10-in.-diameter steel and wood-stave pipeline from an inland creek beyond the airstrip. The pipeline had shallow cover and was laid near the road from the airstrip that ran around the lagoon. The road and pipeline followed a dike along tidewater to the city and the main water line supplied businesses from pipelines supported on the underside of the boardwalk. Most of the business district of Seldovia was on a boardwalk supported by piling.

The city was in the process of rehabilitating the water system at the time of the earthquake. Insulated steel pipe in culvert was being installed under the boardwalk, and steel pipe had been procured for renewal of the supply line. The land in the Seldovia area sank 3–4 ft as a result of the earthquake; tidewater now lapped away at fill along the dike, which began to erode rapidly. Within a month after the earthquake, the road to the airport and the pipeline along it began to cave away because of this erosion, and high tides now covered the boardwalk in the city and would have floated it away if sandbags had not been used to hold it down.

Contractors, under supervision of the Corps of Engineers, made emergency repairs along the dike, raised buildings on the boardwalk to reduce water damage, and sandbagged the boardwalk to hold it in place. In 1965, an urban-renewal contract, partly funded by Public Law 875, was awarded for improvement of the Seldovia boardwalk business complex. Several portions of the boardwalk were filled with rock and surfaced; new water-distribution pipe was buried in this fill. At other locations, the boardwalk was raised. The dike around the lagoon was raised, and banks were protected from tidewater erosion. The road was raised, and a new water line was installed along the stabilized dike.

GIRDWOOD AND PORTAGE

The area around the upper reaches of Turnagain Arm consisted largely of deep silt formations that extended from bases of mountains across the flood plains of glacier-fed rivers to tidewater and the arm. A combination of compaction and tectonic subsidence caused these silt plains to settle 9–12 ft for about 25 mi, according to measurements along transportation routes around the arm. The village of Portage was located along The Alaska Railroad and the highway where the track to Whittier branched off from the Seward–Anchorage line (Figure 45).

Before the earthquake, high tides came near the highway embankment at some locations. Now, high tides washed over the highway and railroad tracks. Equinoctial high tides, heightened by winds up the Arm, carried anchor ice inland across the highway and railroad track and deposited it in places not previously covered by tidewater.

Anchor ice is a wintertime ice formation peculiar to this climate and region. Mixtures of ocean water and freshwater in Cook Inlet and in Turnagain and Knik arms would probably freeze solid on the surface except for tide action, which breaks up the ice. Blocks of ice form in random shapes and sizes from 4 ft to many feet across; ice cakes 1,500 ft long and 2 to 5 ft thick have been noted; if they formed on the mud flats, they have been known to be as much as 20 ft thick. These blocks float around in slack water, run in and out with the tide, group into flotillas from wind action, and are deposited along shorelines. Outgoing tides deposit chunks of this ice on silt flats—hence the name.

All the residents moved out of Portage, with the exception of one filling-station operator and his family whose station, being on higher ground, was not inundated. Portage had no publicly owned utilities; all losses were sustained by individuals.

The city of Girdwood was about 12 mi from Portage in the direction of Anchorage along Turnagain Arm. This area subsided about the same amount as Portage did, but it was originally at a slightly higher elevation. High tides now covered the floors in the homes and businesses of some of

FIGURE 45 Portage–Girdwood area, around the head of Turnagain Arm, which subsided about 9 ft. High tides carried anchor ice over tracks and highway. Turnagain Arm lies to the left (Portage, April 1964).

the approximately 100 inhabitants. Several wells were drowned with salty tidewater.

The city was incorporated and had an elected mayor and councilmen. There were no city-owned utilities, and the only city-owned facility was a community meeting hall and a well. The hall was a wooden-frame building with a community library in one corner. The well was no longer productive. After the earthquake, the city ambitiously embarked on a relocation program and acquired a site about 1½ mi further inland on the floodplain between Glacier and California creeks, astride the site of a new state highway into the Mount Alyeska ski resort. Some future utility planning was done for the city, but construction with use of public funds had to be limited to a restoration project to move the community hall to the new townsite and to drill a well there. It was pointed out to the city officials that the whole area between the two creeks had been inundated by several feet of water from floods in the past. The townspeople, however, were anticipating future business development in the area of the new highway to cater to off-highway business and some new construction at the elevation of the highway.

MUNICIPALITY OF KENAI

The only publicly owned and operated facility in this area was a small electric-power distribution system. About 400 residences and small businesses were supplied with electric power along a 10-mi stretch, turning generally east–west. A Chugach Electric Association (CEA) substation fed the system with three-phase 2,400-V three-wire service. The system was developed by a private individual who procured a small natural-gas well and a war-surplus diesel-engine-driven generator; a spark-fired ignition system was added for operation on natural gas. This equipment was put in operation near the center of the present system, and a substation was constructed to transform the three-phase 120/208-V generated power to 4,160-V four-wire distribution service with three single-phase transformers. This system served customers to the west.

After the municipality of Kenai was organized, it purchased the generating facility and distribution system. The CEA completed its substation in 1962 and offered power to the Kenai area at a reasonable rate. The municipality constructed a three-wire delta 2,400-V line from the CEA substation to the old substation at the generating facility; customers on the east were supplied from the new line. The 2,400-V and 4,160-V systems were tied together at the substation by stepping the 2,400-V power down to the 120/208-V substation bus voltage. The generating facility was retired shortly afterward. At the time of the earthquake, this distribution system consisted of the 2,400-V line on the east that fed through two voltage regulators and three single-phase transformers feeding the 120/208-V substation bus, then through three single-phase transformers to feed the 4,160-V line. System development and improvements were planned for the coming construction season. At the old substation, transformers and regulators were skid mounted on the ground. Lines in and out, fuses, disconnects, lightning arrestors, equipment connections, and bus risers were mounted on an aerial structure between twin poles.

EARTHQUAKE DAMAGE

Transformers and regulators at the old substation shifted around, and some tipped over from the shaking. Buses, tanks, neutrals, and grounds short-circuited and caused fuses to blow. The system was deenergized while emergency repairs were made to restore service.

RESTORATION

The system was eligible for restoration with public funds, but several problems were encountered in determining what this would comprise. Facilities at the old substation were not code grade, and any restoration work would constitute a betterment that the municipality could not afford. On the other hand, the Corps of Engineers could not accept the responsibility of constructing a facility that would not meet *National Electric Safety Code Standards.*

Planning sketches and cost comparisons were made of several substation restoration schemes. A project was developed, for $2,500 less than the most economical restoration scheme, to convert the 2,400-V line to 4,160-V four-wire service, to tie together the two parts of the distribution system, and to exclude the old substation from the system. A construction contract was awarded to add the fourth wire to the 2,400-V line and to change distribution-transformer connections from line-to-line to line-to-neutral. Service at the CEA substation was changed to 4,160-V and the distribution system was changed over; the old substation was cut out of the system and retired.

STATE OF ALASKA

DEPARTMENT OF PUBLIC WORKS

The Glennallen sewer line, a 10-in.-diameter corrugated-metal-pipe from the school and highway complex, extended about 2,500 ft to an outfall in Moose Creek. The line was only partly functional after the earthquake, and a damage survey indicated that the flow was partly blocked and the line had several leaks. A contract was awarded to relay several sections of pipe, and the flow was reestablished.

DEPARTMENT OF AVIATION

Anchorage International Airport complex was supplied with potable water in sufficient quantity for fire fighting from a 480-ft-deep well. The well, drilled in 1959 under contract from the Federal Aeronautics Administration, was turned over to the State of Alaska along with other airport facilities when statehood was attained in the same year. This well was drilled with a 36-in.-diameter bit, backfilled to a depth of 370 ft, cased with 16-in.-diameter casing, and backfilled to the surface. It was surged, bailed, and developed for pumping rates of 440–590 gallons per minute. The completed well operated daily and supplied water in satisfactory quantities up to the time of the earthquake. Shortly thereafter, operation of the pump became increasingly rough, and water production declined until use of the well was discontinued in September 1965.

Because local operating and maintenance personnel were unable to handle the repairs, the state engaged a private drilling company. When the pump and column were pulled from the well, shaft-bearing wear indicated that the casing was crooked and that one guide bearing had failed. Impression tests and slope tests were made in the casing. Material was removed to lower the bottom of the well about 7 ft, and 12-in.-diameter casing and screens were installed within the 16-in. original casing. After this installation, the well was surged, bailed, and tested for 18 hours and was returned to operation after a 300-gallon per minute pump had been installed. The well operated satisfactorily, but the output was substantially less than the original installation and did not supply enough water to meet minimum fire-fighting requirements for the airport complex.

In November 1965, the state applied for a new facility because of the failure of the attempted restoration. The Corps of Engineers studied and evaluated the problem and determined that misalignment of the casing was not so great that a new bearing and lube line would not have sufficed to restore the original shaft and column. Lowering of the well and installation of the new 12-in.-diameter casing had irreparably damaged the original screens; the well was beyond restoration, and the application for a new facility was denied.

ACKNOWLEDGMENT

Except as otherwise noted, figures are credited to the U.S. Army Corps of Engineers.

REFERENCES

Burton, Lynn R., 1967. Television examination of earthquake damage to underground communication and electrical systems in Anchorage *in* Effect of the earthquake of March 27, 1964, on the Eklutna Hydroelectric Project, Anchorage, Alaska. U.S. Geological Survey Professional Paper 545-A. Washington: Government Printing Office, 1967. p. 25–30.

George, Warren, Paul Knowles, John K. Allender, James F. Sizemore, and Duane E. Carson, 1973. Structures in Anchorage *in* The Great Alaska Earthquake of 1964: Engineering. NAS Pub. 1606. Washington: National Academy of Sciences.

DAVID P. BELANGER
U.S. ARMY CORPS OF ENGINEERS DISTRICT,
ALASKA

Port of Whittier

ABSTRACT: The port of Whittier, although close to the epicenter of the earthquake, did not sustain severe structural damage from the shaking of the ground. Submarine landslides and large water waves generated by them extensively damaged waterfront facilities and caused 13 deaths. Other damage was caused by consolidation and settlement of ground. Oil-storage tanks were badly damaged and their contents caught fire. The port was repaired and resumed its operations.

The port of Whittier was the closest developed community to the epicenter of the earthquake. In this community were the 14-story Hodge Building containing apartments and the 6-story Buckner Building. The latter building housed a variety of community facilities, including the chapel, the radio and TV stations with studios, hobby shops, large kitchens, bakeries and dining rooms, three clubs, the jail, two rifle ranges, a four-lane bowling alley, bachelor and family quarters, a theater, complete hospital facilities with surgical operating rooms, and various other welfare facilities. On the Whittier townsite, there also were a considerable number of buildings of various sizes and constructed of a variety of materials, including reinforced concrete, concrete block, tilt-up concrete, wood frame, and structural steel; some were founded on rock and others on alluvium.

Other facilities of the town included railroad yards, petroleum, oil, and lubricant (POL) storage tanks, railcar loading docks and piping, spacious waterfront docks and warehouses, a small-boat harbor, a 6500-kW high-pressure steam power plant with associated electrical generators and switchgear, and a unique 1.5 million-gallon underground water storage tank (Figures 1–6).

Submarine landslides occurred during the earthquake, and the waterfront was hit by three tsunamis, one of which was the largest observed anywhere during the earthquake. The whole area subsided 5.3 ft. The structures in Whittier were not severely damaged by the shaking of the ground. The main power plant was off the line for only 6 hours until a small break in the condensate return lines could be bypassed. The generating equipment, boilers, turbines, and other auxiliary equipment continued to operate and the utility distribution systems for steam, water, and electricity remained generally intact.

Whittier is located at lat. 60°47′N, long. 148°41′W, at the west end of Passage Canal, 40 air mi southeast of Anchorage, and approximately 33 mi southwest of the reported epicenter of the earthquake. The port of Whittier can be reached by ship, by airplane, and by a railroad that

FIGURE 1 Preearthquake photo of Whittier showing major facilities and glacial delta of townsite: (1) DeLong Dock, (2) small-boat harbor, (3) power plant, (4) Sportsman's Inn, (5) Buckner Building, (6) railroad depot, (7) transit warehouse, (8) marginal wharf, (9) car-barge slip, (10) U.S. Army POL tank farm, (11) U.S. Army POL Dock, (12) Union Oil Co. Dock, (13) Union Oil Co. complex, (14) Columbia Lumber Co., (15) Koppers Co., Inc., (16) school, (17) Hodge Building, (18) gymnasium, (19) underground water reservoir, (20) fire station, (21) Alaska Communications Building, (22) Headquarters Building, (23) cold-storage warehouse, (24) composite shop.

travels through the mountains in tunnels under Portage Pass. It cannot be reached by road.

The port of Whittier is well protected from the open sea, because Passage Canal is a relatively narrow estuary extending from Prince William Sound. Most of the townsite of Whittier is on an outwash delta from Whittier Creek on the south side of the bay. This site, sheltered from the high winds that blow down from the glacier at Portage Pass, was selected to serve as a winter port for the city of Anchorage, because the Passage Canal is not icebound during the winter.

High winds blow down from the Portage Glacier at the western end of the passage; winds at 80 mph are common throughout the year, with velocities reaching 100 mph during the winter months.

Tides have an extreme range of 20 ft, from an extreme low of –4 ft to a high of +16 ft. The mean tidal range is 9.6 ft, from a mean low tide of 1.5 ft to a mean high of 11.1 ft, all with respect to mean lower low water (MLLW). The weather on the day of the earthquake was calm, with a light snow falling and a glassy surface on the water in the bay. At the time of the earthquake, the tide was only 1 ft above MLLW, so that the runup of the tsunamis was not as great as it might have been if the earthquake had occurred at high tide.

The area of the townsite is underlain by slate and graywacke, covered with relatively shallow glacial deposits and moraine, reworked outwash and stream gravel, and artificial fill of varying depth (Kachadoorian, 1965). Unconsolidated deposits are at least 44 ft thick beneath the Hodge Building, whereas the large Buckner Building, railroad depot, and power plant rest mainly on or close to bedrock. The other railroad and Army buildings rest on greater depths of unconsolidated deposits and fill material.

While the Army was operating the port of Whittier, approximately 90 percent of the town's income came from the Army port facilities; a few people worked for The Alaska Railroad, Union Oil Company, Columbia Lumber Company, Two Brothers Lumber Company, and the U.S. Post Office. The Army port operation was closed down in 1959, because the port facilities were no longer needed for

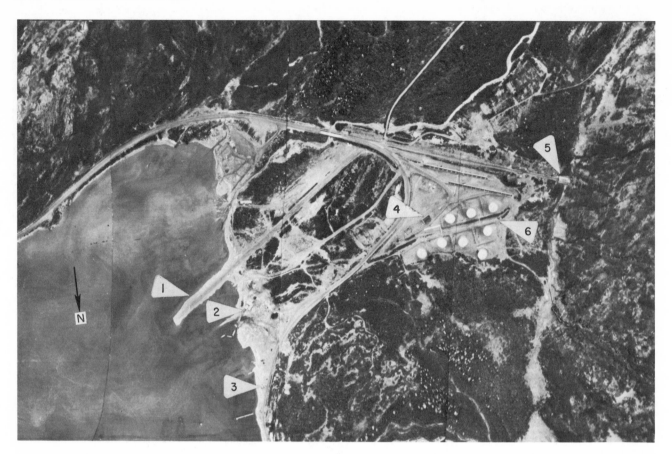

FIGURE 2   Preearthquake photo of Whittier (West Camp) showing remote facilities at the west end of Passage Canal. (1) airstrip, (2) Two Brothers Lumber Co., (3) pump house, (4) U.S. Army petroleum distribution pumping station, (5) railroad tunnel portal, (6) U.S. Army POL tank farm.

shipment of military supplies into Alaska. The population was then reduced to about 70 people, the approximate number of residents in March 1964. Since 1959, the economy has been largely supported by The Alaska Railroad through its continued operation of the rail barge. There are also a few permanent residents who are engaged principally in hunting, fishing, and catering to tourists.

Before 1941, the single southern terminus of The Alaska Railroad was at Seward. In 1941, the Department of Defense undertook to relocate some of its facilities, for strategic reasons, at the head of Passage Canal at Whittier. Services of the Army Corps of Engineers, Alaska District, were used in the design and administration of the construction of the port and related support facilities. To join Portage and Whittier by railroad, 3½ mi of tunnels were constructed. The railroad connection was completed in 1943. Concurrently with the tunnel construction, the West Camp, the railroad yards, the first section of the timber dock, the railroad depot, the engine-terminal facilities, the coach and engine shed, the cold storage building, the dam and water supply, and the power house were constructed. In 1945, the

Columbia Lumber Company and Union Oil Company leased property at Whittier and began operations there.

From 1943 to 1949, general cargo-handling facilities, including the second section of the timber dock, additional warehousing, and an equipment shop were constructed on the waterfront. On June 17, 1953, all the dock facilities were lost in a disastrous fire. Because most of the military supplies for Alaska had been coming through Whittier, immediate measures were taken to restore the operation of the port. A DeLong prefabricated dock was installed with the necessary approach, railroad trackage, and unloading facilities. This provided a one-berth temporary unloading facility until the permanent main dock could be reconstructed.

Construction of permanent dock facilities was started immediately. These consisted of a 60 × 1,000-ft steel and concrete wharf and a 130 × 900-ft transient-storage warehouse. These waterfront facilities were completed on November 15, 1957. The Buckner Building, Hodge Building, warehouses, gymnasium, ammunition-storage igloos, and other support facilities were under construction at the same time.

FIGURE 3   Postearthquake photo (July 1964) of Whittier townsite. Comparison to Figure 1 reveals the differences in shoreline and waterfront facilities.

In 1959, Congress declared the military transportation facilities to be in excess of Army needs, and the Army withdrew its operations during the following year. The maintenance and heating of the vacated buildings were taken over by The Alaska Railroad. All utility systems, the railroad and hydrotrain slip, the lumber companies, the Union Oil Company, and the Army petroleum distribution system facilities, and commercial tourist facilities were in operation in March 1964. Except for partial occupancy of the first four floors of the Hodge Building, most buildings were vacant.

THE EARTHQUAKE EXPERIENCE

Interviews with Whittier residents were the most important sources of information on the 1964 earthquake. The accounts of their experiences may be summarized as follows: At first the earth shook in a slight, predominantly north–south rolling motion. The shaking reached its maximum intensity in about 1½ minutes and then gradually subsided

during the next 2½ minutes (Kachadoorian, 1965). The total duration, according to witnesses and meter recording charts, was about 4 minutes. Those people who were located on bedrock described the earthquake movements as jarring, whereas those on consolidated deposits reported more of a rolling or "round-and-round" motion (Kachadoorian, 1965).

At least three seawaves were observed during and immediately after the earthquake. A fire started in the area of the Union Oil Company and U.S. Army tank farms and burned until March 31, completely destroying the storage tanks (Kachadoorian, 1965).

EFFECT OF THE EARTHQUAKE ON STRUCTURES

WATERFRONT AREA

Along the waterfront, shaking of the ground and subsequent land subsidence severely damaged one of the towers of the

FIGURE 4   Postearthquake photograph (July 1964) of Whittier (West Camp) at west end of Passage Canal. Compare to Figure 2 for differences in shoreline.

FIGURE 5   Newly erected DeLong Dock (1954) with approach at left. Note burnt piling of old timber dock at right of new dock.

FIGURE 6   A preearthquake view of some of the waterfront facilities, later damaged by the tsunami, including the towers of the carbarge slip, the Union Oil Co., and U.S. Army tank farms and POL unloading pier.

rail-barge slip (Figure 6), the marginal wharf, and the high-way and railroad bridges crossing Whittier Creek. The sea-waves contributed greatly to this damage.

In the area further away from the waterfront, the damage was caused by shaking of the ground. Relatively minor dam-age was done to the reinforced-concrete Buckner Building, the steel-frame power plant, the underground water tank (Figure 7), and the wood-frame railroad depot.

BUCKNER BUILDING

The composite Buckner Building was planned in 1950 and 1951, and construction was completed in 1953. This build-ing is unique in that it is a complete city in itself. It was designed to provide mess, sleeping, recreational, medical, and administration facilities for 1,250 men.

The major portion of the building consists of six stories. The main hallway measures 525 ft from end to end. This structure is probably the largest, and from the standpoint of facilities, undoubtedly the most complete building in Alaska.

The long dimension of the structure lies in a north-easterly–southwesterly direction. The lower two floors are each 12 ft high; the remaining stories are each 10 ft high. The contract drawings designated the floors as follows: a basement floor, ground floor, first, second, third, and fourth floors, and the roof and penthouses. Therefore, the fourth floor is actually six floors above the foundation (Figure 8).

On the floor plan of the Buckner Building (Figure 9), although no attempt was made to show all rooms or all the structural frames, the plan does indicate all earthquake joints. This building was constructed with concrete floor

FIGURE 8   North side of the Buckner Building, showing entire side of structure with penthouse on top for ventilating equipment. Col-umns in exterior walls indicate spacing of frames. Six-story framed-glass fire-escape walls in each unit were not broken.

and concrete exterior walls. Lateral resistance was furnished by the structural frames, with the floor slabs acting as struc-tural diaphragms. Footings for the columns were extended to solid bedrock. Lateral forces, in part, were resisted by the stairwells and elevator shafts located throughout the building. Walls for these shafts are poured 8-in. reinforced concrete.

Interior partitions in the building are of two types: con-crete block (both 4 and 6 in.) and wood stud with gypsum board. Because of the multipurpose use of the building, it contained many items of specialized equipment for example, the bowling alley, located on the ground floor (Figure 10); an x-ray machine, in the hospital on the third floor, section A (Figure 11); the light for the operating room table, in the hospital building, section A, third floor (Figure 12); and a large oven, located in the kitchen on the first floor.

Structural damage to the Buckner Building was almost negligible; the majority of the damage was to nonstructural items. At one stairwell at the east end of the building, a cold joint worked considerably. The construction joints in ex-terior walls showed evidence of movement; each joint was clearly visible and had fresh mortar spalls.

HEATING AND POWER PLANT

The heating and power plant building is 110 × 96½ ft × 47 ft high, with the 96½ ft lying in a north–south direction (Fig-ure 13). Although the building has only two stories, a ground floor and a second floor (called the operating floor), it is as high as a four- or five-story building. The finished elevation of the ground floor is +34 ft; elevation of the operating floor is +49 ft. The latter is divided into two almost-equal parts;

FIGURE 7   The unique underground 1-million-gallon water-storage reservoir during initial construction phases in 1954. Structure, in bedrock, later received a concrete cap and was buried.

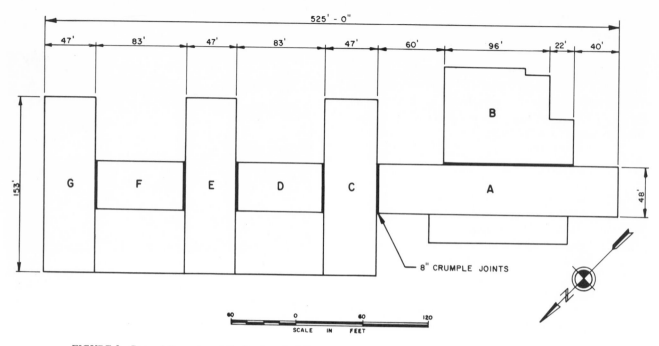

FIGURE 9 General floor plan of the Buckner Building showing major dimensions and earthquake crumple joints.

FIGURE 10 Four-lane bowling alley (section A) suffered no damage. Overhead suspended electrical bus duct was free to move through openings in the walls.

FIGURE 11 X-ray machine in hospital area (section A). Leveling bubble at base of machine returned to perfect level after earthquake.

FIGURE 12 Operating-room light (section A), although heavy and suspended, caused no chipping at ceiling mount.

FIGURE 13 West side of power plant. Exposed bedrock indicates type of building foundation. Transformer bank in the foreground and overhead distribution is typical for incoming commercial power. Note good condition of foundation and absence of glass breakage.

the north half is called the turbine room, the south half the boiler room. On one half of the operating floor are three large steam-turbine generators—two of 2,000-kW capacity and one of 2,500-kW capacity—in addition to all the switchgear and control panels to control electric power for the buildings in the port (Figure 14). Special foundations were provided for the generators, isolating them from the operating floor.

Concrete footings for the turbine-generator units extend below the ground floor, and a structural-steel and concrete frame was built to raise the units to the same level as the operating floor. An earthquake joint separates the generator foundations from the operating-floor slab (Figure 14). Crane rails support a large mobile crane above the generators (Figure 15). The other half of the operating floor contains the boilers that provide steam for the turbine generators and for the space-heating needs of the port (Figure 16). Many catwalks and galleries provide access to the valves and pipes above the boilers on the floor (Figure 17). These items account for the relatively great height of the operating floor that makes the building appear to be taller.

All footings for the building are concrete and rest on solid bedrock. A 1-ft-thick concrete wall is built up to 7.5 ft above the ground floor. Column footings are located inside these walls. Exterior wall framing is of structural steel with metal siding. The operating floor is constructed with structural-steel beams supporting a 6-in. concrete slab. The half of the roof directly over the generators is constructed

FIGURE 14 Earthquake joint around turbine-generator pedestal, separating it from the building foundation. Large gap along right edge of joint cover shows where displacement took place.

FIGURE 15   Overhead crane and roof structure above generator room.

FIGURE 17   Catwalks, piping, and large tanks withstood movement by earthquake.

with structural-steel trusses supporting steel purlins, and the other half has structural-steel stringers supporting steel purlins. Lateral forces are resisted by diagonal structural-steel cross bracing between columns in the wall framing and between trusses on stringers in the roof framing. All connections are riveted, rather than bolted or welded. Figure 15 shows typical roof framing used in the building. For structural design of the power plant, there was a roof load of 100 psf with 50 psf considered permanent for seismic design. A 300-psf loading was used for the operating floor. The equipment load, or one half of the floor load where the equipment load was not known, was added to the floor live load when seismic forces were figured. For seismic design, earthquake zone 3 was used. Seismic forces were computed as outlined in the 1951 *Uniform Building Code*.

FIGURE 16   Boilers that provided heat for the port and steam for the generators.

As a result of the earthquake, there was no apparent structural damage to this building. All beam-to-column and cross-bracing connections that were inspected were found to be in excellent condition. The cover over the earthquake joint around the 2,000-kW generators on the operating floor indicated strong motion during the earthquake. Steel cover plates over the joint were displaced (Figure 14).

A conversation with Mr. John Ireland, a power plant operator at the time of the earthquake, revealed that damage to the power plant building was very minor. After a thorough inspection, he found that only one condensate-return line had been broken during the earthquake. Two 10-in. water lines that supplied freshwater to the power plant and to the buildings in the port of Whittier from a million-gallon reservoir on the hillside above Whittier were ruptured. The power plant therefore had to obtain its water supply from an emergency source before it could resume operations; water was pumped through a fire hose from the saltwater pumphouse. The power plant continued to operate until June 1966, when it was shut down because the port of Whittier was turned over to Government Services Administration for disposal.

HODGE BUILDING

The Hodge Building, designed in 1954, was completed in 1957. The architects were Foss, Malcolm, and Olsen of Juneau, Alaska; the structural design was planned by the engineering firm of Stevens and Rubens of Seattle, Washington. The U.S. Army Engineer District, Alaska, provided information on the nature of the foundation and supervised the construction of the building (Figures 18 and 19).

This apartment house is a 14-story structure with penthouses and a basement. It is divided into three monolithic units separated by 8-in. crumple (or earthquake) joints: The

FIGURE 18 Northeast side of Hodge Building a few days after the earthquake. Displaced earthquake-joint covers are protruding from central section.

central or middle unit is rectangular, approximately 47 × 83 ft; and the two end units are basically L-shaped, with an overall dimension of 96 × 91 ft. The basement of the building contains storage rooms for occupants and mechanical rooms. The main floor consists of a large lobby, a playroom, and more than 30 single-room bachelors' quarters. On the second floor are both single quarters and apartments and two lounges. The remainder of the floors consist of one-, two-, and three-bedroom apartments. Each of the end L-shaped units has one stair tower and two elevator shafts. The story height for the basement and main story is 10 ft 7½ in.; for the remainder of the building, the height is 8 ft 8 in.

The Hodge Building is a reinforced-concrete structure (Figure 20). Exterior walls of the east, west, and central portion of the building were designed as shear walls. The basement is a 4-in. nonstructural slab on grade. The remainder of the floors are one-way slabs, most of which are 6½ in. thick. The majority of the beams used in the building are 14 × 20 in. The columns were designed for a maximum thickness of 14 in. and the width was varied with the load. Exterior walls are exposed, unpainted concrete.

The structural design of the building was planned in accordance with the *American Concrete Institute Bulletin* (ACI 318-51). As recommended by the *Engineering Manual for War Department Construction*, floor loadings were as follows: roof live load, 100 psf; stairs, lobby, and main corridors, 100 psf; interior corridors, 60 psf; and bachelor officers' quarters, 40 psf.

All structural concrete used in the building had an ultimate strength of 2,500 psi with a 28-day compressive strength of 1,125 psi. All reinforcing steel used was of intermediate grade, with deformations conforming to *American Standards for Testing Materials Specification A-305*.

The structural engineers based the soil pressures used in their foundation design on values obtained by the Corps of Engineers, Alaska District, through extensive field exploration in the area of the building site.

The building is constructed on Whittier Delta, formed by a glacier that is only a short distance up the canyon from the building; the existing material at the site is a silty sandy gravel. The maximum depth of drill holes beneath the building was 44 ft. Exposed bedrock is visible approximately 200 ft east of the building, and the exact amount of glacial deposits immediately beneath the building is unknown. Based on the aforementioned soil conditions, the footings were designed for an allowable soil-bearing pressure of 10,000 psf with an allowable one-third increase of this value when stresses produced by wind or seismic forces are included.

The seismic design of the building, planned for zone 3 earthquake forces, conformed to the *Pacific Coast Uniform Building Code* (1952 edition). The lateral force (F), or shear, was determined by the formula $F = CW$,

where C = seismic coefficient = $\dfrac{0.15 \ (4)}{(N) + (4.5)}$,

N = number of stories above the story under consideration,

and

W = dead load

The shear and the overturning effect produced by the shear were transmitted to shear walls (Figure 21) in proportion to their relative rigidity. The floors were assumed to be infinitely stiff in transmitting the shear to the walls. The

FIGURE 19 Exterior view of the rear of the Hodge Building, showing two L-shaped end units.

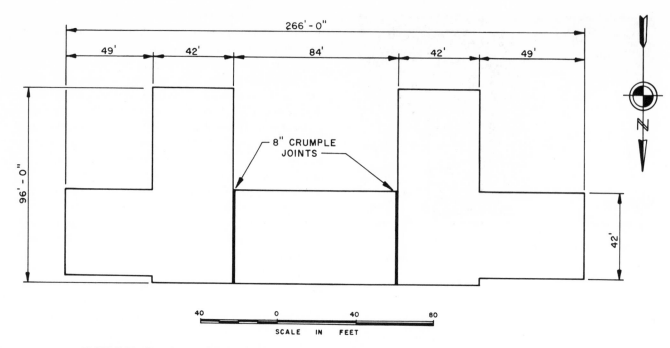

FIGURE 20   Plan sketch of Hodge Building, showing principal dimensions and the location of earthquake joints.

wall piers and spandrels were designed to develop the wall as a cantilever beam above the foundations.

The lintel beam above the doorway where the corridor (Figure 21) penetrates the shear wall is the principal point of structural damage in the building. It was reinforced as shown in Figure 22 (f), which is a direct copy of the contract drawing. This beam in the east end of the middle unit is shown in Figure 22 (a–e). The lintel was 8 in. thick on the ninth through the fourteenth floors; on the fourth through the ninth floors it was 10 in. thick; and on the main through the fourth floors it was 11 in. thick (Figure 21).

Other structural damage throughout the building was minor. Although interior nonbearing block partitions are not direct structural items, it is worthwhile to mention them here. On the thirteenth and fourteenth floors, most of the interior block partitions had been knocked down. On the twelfth floor, there was a noticeable reduction in the amount of damage to partitions. Pictures taken inside the building immediately after the earthquake are not available, so that it is impossible to ascertain the exact number of blocks on the floor. For the steel plate to have bent in the manner shown in Figure 23, the central portion of the building must have moved in a north–south direction.

Figure 24 shows the junction of the floor slab and the exterior walls. All exterior pictures of the building indicate that the outside walls were poured up to the bottom of the floor slab of the story above. The floor slab was then poured, adding another cold joint that moved during the

earthquake. The spandrel beams beneath the windows worked sufficiently to enable water to penetrate the building through the cracks in these cold joints during a blowing rainstorm (Figure 25).

MARGINAL WHARF AND IN-TRANSIT STORAGE WAREHOUSE

The marginal wharf is a very expansive structure, designed to handle all freight shipped into Alaska by the Army. The dock, located on the south shore of Passage Canal, is more than 1,000 ft long and runs in a northeasterly–southwesterly direction. It has a deck width of 60 ft, with two railroad tracks on the north half and a traffic lane or storage area on the south half (Figure 26).

The dock (Figure 27) was designed for railroad loads of Cooper E-60, a deck load of 600 psf, snow loads of 100 psf, a ballard pull of 200,000 lb, and earthquake requirements for zone 3. All concrete used had a 28-day compressive strength of 4,000 psi. Reinforcing steel was of intermediate grade with deformation conforming to ASTM 305-50T, and an allowable tensile stress of 20,000 psi was used. All structural steel was designed with an allowable working stress of 20,000 psi. The foundation for the dock consisted of steel H-piles that formed bents spaced 12 ft on centers. Batter piling size was either 12BP53 or 14BP73. The 14BP73 piles forming the north side of each bent and located beneath the railroad tracks were spaced 5 ft 6 in. on centers. The south side of each bent was formed with the 12BP53 piling,

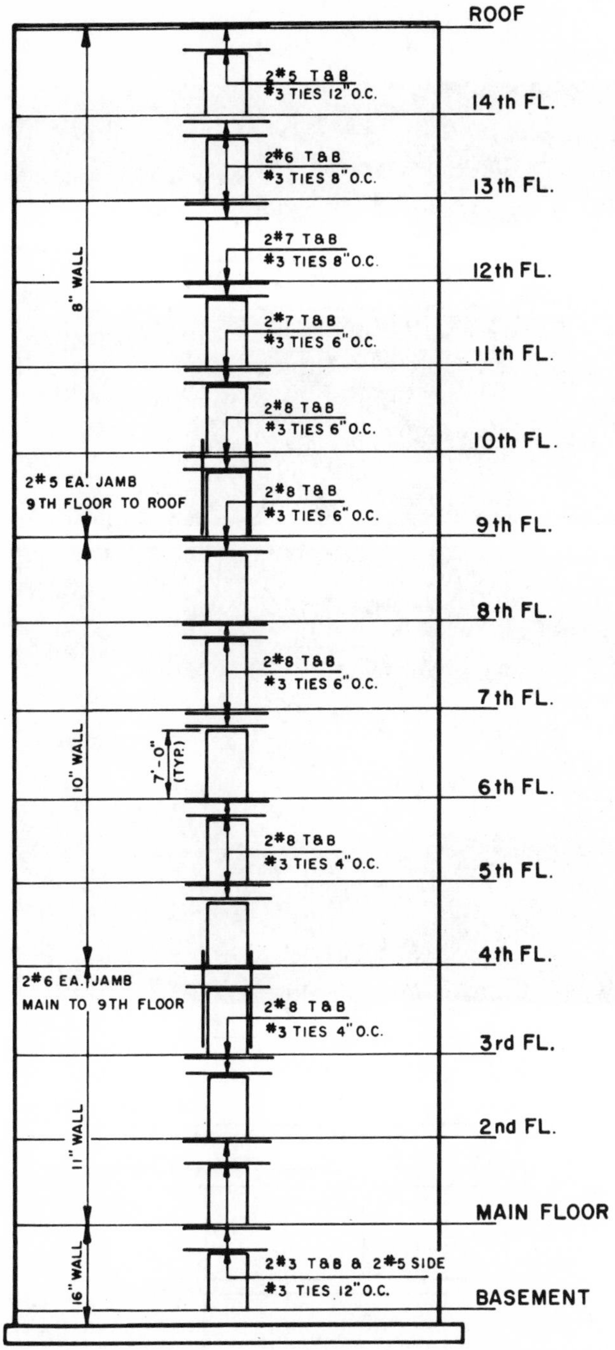
ROOF
14th FL.
13th FL.
12th FL.
11th FL.
10th FL.
9th FL.
8th FL.
7th FL.
6th FL.
5th FL.
4th FL.
3rd FL.
2nd FL.
MAIN FLOOR
BASEMENT
2#5 T&B
#3 TIES 12" O.C.
2#6 T&B
#3 TIES 8" O.C.
2#7 T&B
#3 TIES 8" O.C.
2#7 T&B
#3 TIES 6" O.C.
2#8 T&B
#3 TIES 6" O.C.
2#8 T&B
#3 TIES 6" O.C.
2#8 T&B
#3 TIES 6" O.C.
2#8 T&B
#3 TIES 4" O.C.
2#8 T&B
#3 TIES 4" O.C.
2#3 T&B & 2#5 SIDE
#3 TIES 12" O.C.
2#5 EA. JAMB
9TH FLOOR TO ROOF
2#6 EA. JAMB
MAIN TO 9TH FLOOR
8" WALL
10" WALL
11" WALL
16" WALL
7'-0" (TYP.)

FIGURE 21 Elevation sketch of Hodge Building showing shear-wall dimensions and reinforcing detail.

spaced 7 ft 6 in. on centers. On the south side of the dock, a continuous steel-sheet-piling bulkhead wall was driven. Fill from the dredging in front of the dock was pumped behind this bulkhead to form the foundation pad for the in-transit warehouse. The sheet-pile bulkhead was capped with a large, reinforced-concrete beam that was also supported by the last row of piling in the dock. This large beam was tied to a 24 X 36-in. concrete deadman anchor, 64 ft south of the bulkhead, by anchor ties 2¾ in. in diameter. The steel bulkhead was tied to the same anchor by horizontal ties (Figure 28).

Pile caps for each of the bents were of reinforced concrete, and the dock surface was formed with precast-concrete panels. The panels on the south half of the dock were removable because there was no railroad track on them.

A structural inspection of the Whittier Dock was made on April 6, 1964, by C. K. Balhiser (1964), Assistant Chief of Design Branch, Alaska District, Corps of Engineers. The damage descriptions given here were taken from his report. About 50 percent of the 12BP53 piling adjacent to the warehouse side of the wharf had their inside flanges buckled about 4 ft below the cap (Figure 29).

These two rows were the shortest and, therefore, the stiffest piling used in the wharf. The eastern 260 ft of the wharf showed more horizontal movement than any other portion. Both flanges of the short innermost piling buckled and showed evidence of torsional movement. The seaward piles were bent outward, and expansion joints on the deck also showed the outward movement of this portion of the wharf.

The reinforced-concrete-pile caps on the western 750 ft of the wharf showed little or no damage, but the pattern of the cracks indicated a strong north–south movement. The concrete caps topping the eastern 270 ft of piling showed this same cracking pattern, but the caps had been more distorted and, in a few cases, had failed (Figures 30 and 31).

The steel-sheet piling beneath the face of the warehouse shows a definite outward bulge between the upper longitudinal concrete cap and the rod ties 10 ft below. There was, however, no sign of failure.

The in-transit storage warehouse stands parallel to the marginal wharf, with its long axis in a northeasterly–southwesterly direction. The building, 830 ft long and 100 ft wide, is a one-story structure except for the eastern 50 ft, which is a three-story section containing office space for port activities.

The warehouse was designed for the following loads: roof live load, 100 psf; windload, 20 psf; office floors, 50 psf; warehouse floors, 600 psf; and earthquake zone 3, with earthquake forces computed in accordance with the *Uniform Building Code* (1952 edition). All concrete had a 28-day compressive strength of 3,000 psi. The reinforcing steel was of intermediate grade with deformation conforming to ASTM-A-305-50T and an allowable tensile stress of 20,000 psi. Structural steel was designed with an allowable stress of 20,000 psi. An allowable soil-bearing pressure of 6,000 psf was used for footing design.

Figure 32 shows typical framing in the western 230 ft of the building and also framing that was used up to the

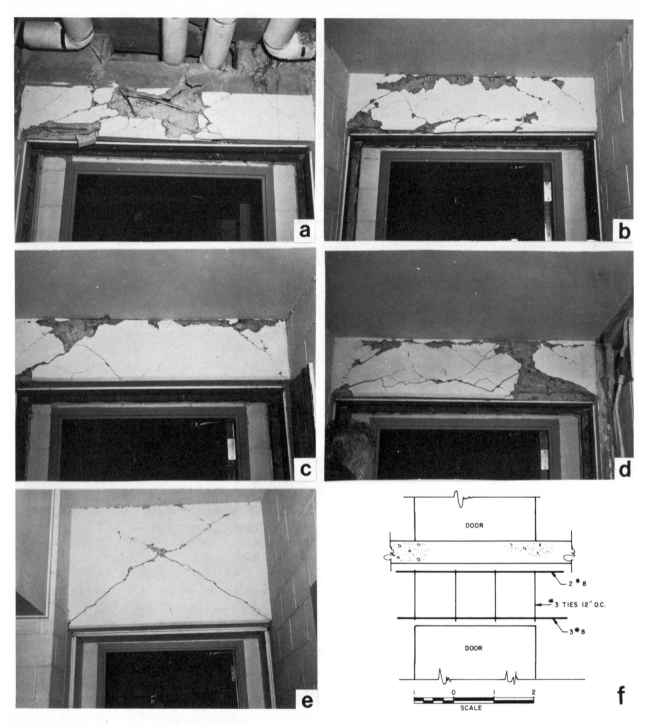

FIGURE 22   Lintel beam over corridor doorways in Hodge Building at penetration through shear wall. (a) Fourteenth floor; note position of top reinforcing steel and absence of properly placed ties. (b) Thirteenth floor; note bottom reinforcing and visible ties. (c) Seventh floor; note decreasing damage. (d) Ninth floor; shows in detail how partition walls were connected to shear walls, columns, and floor slabs above with dovetail anchors. (e) First floor; deep lintel beam with characteristic cross crack. (f) Reinforcing plan as designed.

FIGURE 23 Cover plate over 8-in. earthquake joint at east end of center portion of the thirteenth floor of the Hodge Building. Plate is of 1/4 in. steel and is attached to the central portion of the building. The corridor runs in an east–west direction; this shows that the plate was damaged by north–south movement of the two building units.

eastern 50 ft (the three-story reinforced-concrete portion of the building). These sections are of typical bents spaced at 20 ft on centers for the length of the building. The southern portion of the floor slab is depressed 3 ft 9 in. to provide an area for a railroad track.

In the western 230 ft of the building, 18WF50 (18-in. wide-flange 50 lb/ft) girders support ten B 11-5 roof purlins. These girders are supported at four points, on the north and south ends by concrete columns and at interior points by pipe columns. Both the concrete and the steel columns are supported by spread concrete footings. The bents in the remaining 530 ft of the building, except for the eastern-most 50 ft, are formed as follows: 21WF62 girders are supported at the north and south end by concrete columns and at two interior points by wide-flange steel columns. The north wall in the eastern 720 ft of the building is supported by the steel-sheet piling bulkhead and its concrete cap. The remainder of the columns are supported by spread-concrete footings. The structural frame of the eastern 50 ft of the building consists of concrete columns and beams with concrete exterior walls. Interior partitions and walls are of concrete block.

The concrete floor slab on grade inside the building cracked in a line parallel to the north wall and to the row of steel-sheet piling. The crack was caused by consolidation of the fill south of the bulkhead wall, causing the floor slab to settle as much as 2 ft in some places. A photograph (Figure 33) taken shortly after the earthquake illustrates the fill settlement inside the building. In the reinforced-

concrete three-story office portion of the building, this settlement carried through the structure, cracking the beams, concrete-block walls, stairwells, walls, and structural floor slabs (Figures 34 and 35). The damage to this part of the structure is not unusual, in view of the amount of settlement that took place.

COMPOSITE SHOP BUILDING

Construction of the composite shop building was completed in 1954 (Figure 1). This one-story structure, 100 ft wide by 660 ft long, had three different roof heights, necessitated by the multipurpose use of the building. The roof

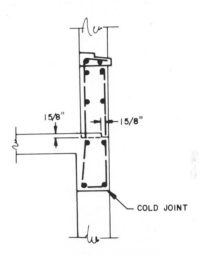

TYP. SPANDREL SECTION

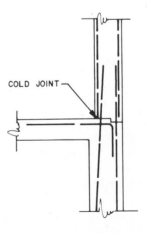

TYP. SPLICE FOR VERT. WALL REINFORCEMENT

NO SCALE

FIGURE 24 Typical wall and floor sections of the Hodge Building showing the method of construction taken from contract drawings.

FIGURE 25   View of exterior of Hodge Building illustrates movement of cold joints in wall construction. Note spandrel beams beneath windows. Joints had actually worked enough to allow water to enter the building during a windblown rainstorm.

height for the eastern 520 ft is 17 ft 5 in.; the height is 23 ft 10 in. for the next 80 ft, and 28 ft 3 in. for the westernmost 60 ft (Figure 36). Structural bents, spaced at 20 ft on centers for the length of the shop, form the frames of the building. Typical bents are formed with exterior concrete columns and two interior steel-pipe columns, supporting wide-flange steel girders (Figure 37). The roof was constructed of steel roof decking supported by steel purlins. Lateral forces in the roof are resisted by diagonal steel bracing, either steel rods or angle iron.

The composite shop was designed for the following loadings: roof live, 100 psf; wind, 20 psf; and earthquake zone 3. Lateral forces were computed in accordance with the *Pacific Coast Uniform Building Code*. The equation

$$F = \frac{(0.60)\,W}{(N) + (4.5)}$$ was used in calculating the lateral forces,

with W = dead load + 1/4 snow load and N = 0. Lateral forces were resisted by diagonal bracing in the roof and by the exterior concrete columns and walls.

In the western end of the building (the high bay containing the 25-ton overhead crane), most of the 7/8-in. diagonal bracing rods were broken loose. Either the rods tore loose from their mounting saddles or the welds of the gusset plate were broken loose (Figures 38–40). The roof deck and walls in this area moved and buckled extensively (Figures 38–46), shearing purlin ends and in some cases causing them to twist and lay over. Bolts had become loosened at various connection points throughout the roof structure. One large beam showed evidence of extreme torsional forces by re-

maining severely twisted (Figures 38 and 39). The exterior transition wall between the low and high bays and the walls of the fresh-air-ventilator penthouse on the roof of the high-bay area sustained extensive superficial cracking (Figures 45 and 46). The crumple joint experienced severe movement and sheared a reinforced-concrete column adjacent to the joint (Figure 46). The structural support along one edge of the penthouse failed, letting the edge fall through the roof deck. The fresh-air ventilator fan inside was almost completely broken loose as mounting bolts were sheared (Figure 43).

The Alaska Railroad contracted for repair of this shop building. The contractor was required to inspect all cross-bracing connections and to replace damaged cross bracing throughout the roof. All sheared bolts were replaced and loose bolts tightened. The turnbuckles on the diagonal bracing were then tightened and gusset plates were welded to the flanges of the girders to which they were attached. Roof purlin connections to concrete fire walls were also repaired. In the westernmost 60 ft of the building, tongue-and-groove wood decking (2 × 6 in.) was used to replace the damaged metal roof decking.

GYMNASIUM, HEADQUARTERS BUILDING, COLD-STORAGE WAREHOUSE, SCHOOL, FIRE STATION

The damage to these buildings, all located on the fan formed by the Whittier Glacier (Figure 1), was almost negligible.

The gymnasium (Figure 47) is basically a one-story structure with a basement under the southern half. The building is 108 × 80 ft, with the 108-ft dimension in an east–west direction. The building, completed in 1955, has an overall height of 29 ft 3 in. Its framework consists of structural frames spaced at 14 ft 10 in. on centers along the east–west

FIGURE 26   Front view (preearthquake) of in-transit warehouse and west portion of marginal wharf.

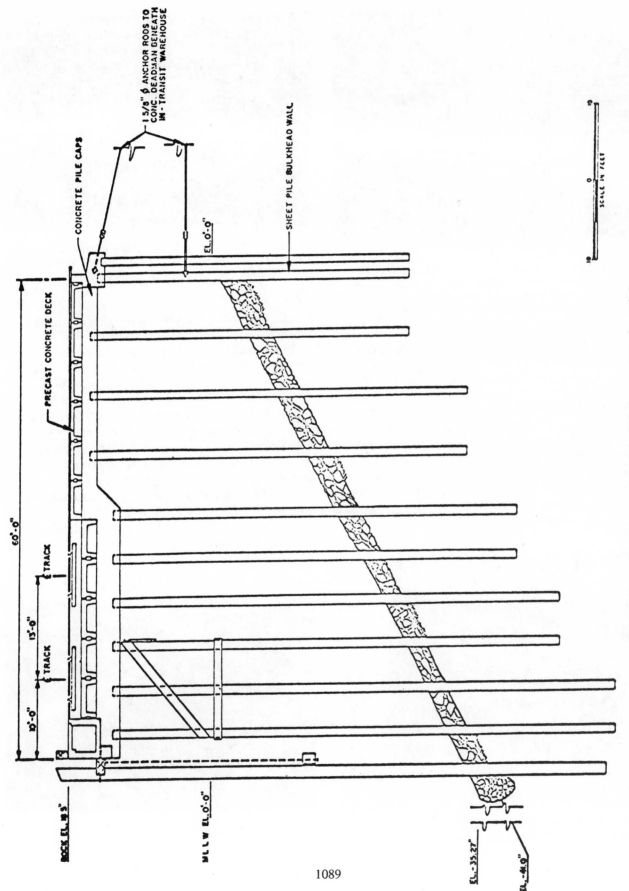

FIGURE 27 Typical cross section of the dock shows construction technique.

FIGURE 28   Construction of marginal wharf in 1953 showing anchor tie rods and concrete anchor. Note the overhead dredge pump line that transported spoil from the dredge to the fill area behind the bulkhead wall (extreme upper left).

FIGURE 30   Postearthquake view (beneath dock) of concrete cap resting on top of bulkhead wall at south side of wharf. Note cracking in cap (arrow).

dimension (Figure 48). The frames are formed with concrete columns in the exterior walls, and structural-steel roof trusses supporting steel purlins and metal roof decking span the 80-ft dimension. Lateral forces are resisted in the plane by steel rods 3/4 in. in diameter. The north and south exterior walls are formed with precast concrete panels, whereas the east and west walls are cast-in-place concrete panels. The floor-framing system under the northern 60 ft of gym floor consists of laminated timber beams supported by concrete columns (Figure 49). The southern portion of the building has a basement in which the dressing rooms are located. The floor slab for the main floor is of structural concrete.

The headquarters building (Figure 50) is a two-story structure, 181 × 41 ft, with an eave height of 22 ft above the finished first floor and with the long axis lying in an east–west direction. It is situated on the outwash fan formed by the Whittier Glacier (Figure 1). The structural system is formed with reinforced concrete block. The only noticeable earthquake damage to this building was to nonstructural members, mainly the concrete-block partitions around the stairwell and the light fixtures.

The cold-storage warehouse (Figure 51) is a one-story structure, 245 ft long by 100 ft wide, with the 245-ft dimension in an east–west direction. A concrete roof slab is supported by concrete columns that form bays spaced at 23 ft 4 in. on centers (Figure 52). The columns are supported by

FIGURE 29   Buckled flanges on piling beneath dock. Channel strut shown below was added as part of dock repairs.

FIGURE 31   North edge of wharf showing damaged fender piling (arrows).

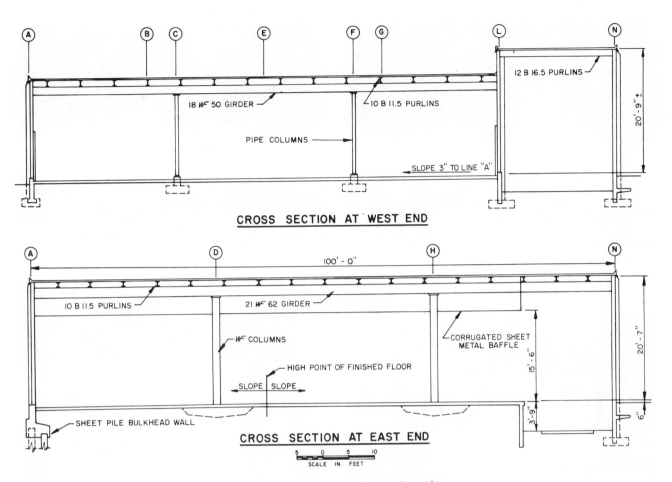

FIGURE 32   Cross sections of the in-transit warehouse.

FIGURE 33   Consolidation of fill in the in-transit warehouse caused floors to buckle and separate from partition walls.

FIGURE 34   Base of interior steel column in the in-transit warehouse. Note cracks in floor slab around column.

FIGURE 35   Floor separation from partition walls because of fill consolidation in in-transit warehouse.

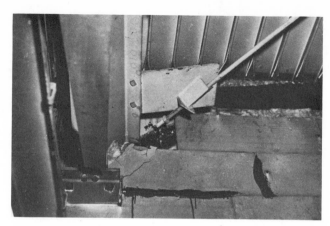

FIGURE 38   Note pronounced twist in large beam spanning bay.

FIGURE 36   Exterior view of northeast side of composite shop in September 1966.

FIGURE 39   Metal siding was sheared from exterior wall on high bay area. Arrow shows pronounced twist in large beam spanning bay. Large rail in lower-right corner is one of those that carried the 25-ton overhead crane, which remained on its rails in the shop building.

FIGURE 37   Interior view of eastern end of shop building in September 1966 showing columns, girders, purlins, and decking.

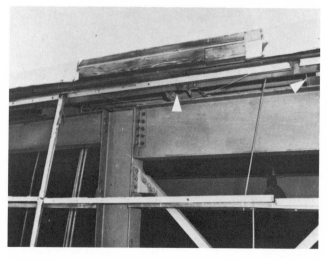

FIGURE 40   Closeup of sheared purlins in shop building (arrow).

FIGURE 41   Interior view of ceiling in shop building above 25-ton crane showing roof deck torn away from exterior wall. Note diagonal tension rod broken loose from mounting.

FIGURE 43   Interior view of shop building roof showing twisted purlins. Note dangling fresh-air vent that was nearly shaken loose (arrow).

spread-concrete footings. The building is situated on an area of stream gravel and unreworked outwash deposits. Bedrock is located about 60 ft below grade level. Exterior walls are of tilt-up concrete that, together with the concrete columns, resist seismic forces.

No structural damage was found in the building, but some light fixtures were broken in an upstairs office area in the southwest corner of the building. Large, complex refrigeration equipment, housed in a room at the southeast corner of the building, was anchored to the floor slab and equipment pads, and no fractures or spalling were noticeable, nor was any of the complex equipment damaged.

FIGURE 44   Cupola on fresh-air ventilator broke through roof at high-bay end of composite shop.

FIGURE 42   Multibolt gusset plates in shop building held joints firm, causing X-type wall bracing to buckle in midspan.

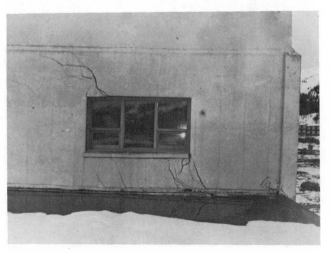

FIGURE 45   Fracturing in exterior wall transition from low to high bay in shop building.

FIGURE 46   Crumple joint in composite shop.

FIGURE 47   Exterior view of gymnasium (September 1966).

FIGURE 48   Interior view of gymnasium ceiling showing typical framework.

FIGURE 49   Floor framing system used under main gymnasium floor. No shifting was detectable here.

Jerry Takes, U.S. Army
FIGURE 50   Headquarters building.

FIGURE 51   South side of cold-storage warehouse showing tilt-up concrete wall construction.

FIGURE 52   Main storage area with division of bays and concrete slab roof. No structural damage was found in this structure.

NONSTRUCTURAL DAMAGE IN VARIOUS BUILDINGS

Nonstructural damage consisted mainly of disruption of electrical circuits, breaking of walls and partitions, and moving of heavy mechanical and electrical equipment and machinery.

Throughout the various buildings, suspended lighting fixtures showed evidence of violent movement. Hangers rigidly affixed to the ceilings were snapped off, and heavy louvered fixtures fell. Even fixtures with swivel joints at their ceiling mounting and with rigid attachment were often broken off at the rigid connection (Figure 53). Generally, chain-hung fixtures and fixtures that were not pendant-mounted were undamaged, except for broken globes and lamps.

A flexible electrical conduit and conductors spanning the 8-in. earthquake joint between the upper floors of the Hodge Building were pulled apart by the displacement of the three monolithic units of the building. During construction, insufficient slack was left to allow for this extreme differential movement (Figure 54). On lower floors of the building, the breaking of conduit and wires lessened as the joint apparently moved less at the base. On the bottom floors, the electrical system was undamaged.

Superficial fractures of plaster and collapse of concrete-block curtain walls and partitions were observed throughout the various buildings, with more serious damage appearing on the upper floors (Figures 55–61). Throughout all buildings, heavy equipment and machinery that was not firmly anchored was displaced, and, in some cases, the electrical service to the equipment was broken (Figure 60). Ceiling-suspended mechanical piping and electrical conduit caused spalling of plaster at wall penetrations by the transverse movement from their hangers. Most utility-equipment hangers were suspended from cast-in-place inserts from the floor deck above and showed no evidence of pulling away from the ceiling. In the Buckner Building, evidence indicated that hangers supporting heavy equipment had swung in an east–west direction. The continuous overhead ventilation duct became separated and dislocated in its hangers because of this swinging (Figure 61).

In the school, chalkboards fell from the walls, and acoustical-tile panels fell from the ceilings. Where suspended ceilings were used, usually at least the outside row of ceiling panels was battered out as the movement of the building separated tee supports (Figure 54). No glass was broken in the six-story framed-glass fire-escape walls in the Buckner Building, however. Very few cracks were observed in the ceramic-tile wainscot in kitchens, bakery, latrines, and surgical areas. Very little window glass was broken in the 14-story Hodge Building (Figure 18) or in the Buckner Building (Figure 8).

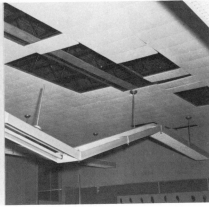

FIGURE 53   Lighting fixtures rigidly attached to the ceiling in the Hodge Building frequently sheared at the ceiling (left). Light fixtures with swivel ceiling attachment (right), but with rigid fixture attachment, frequently sheared at the fixture. Note fallen chalkboard below lights and fallen ceiling-tile panels.

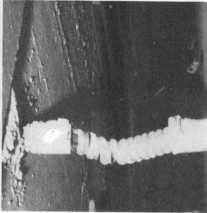

FIGURE 54 Flexible electric conduit and conductors spanning an 8-in. earthquake joint on the fourteenth floor of the Hodge Building were broken because of insufficient slack. Damage was less on lower floors (right).

FIGURE 55 Collapsed 4-in. concrete-block curtain wall on the fourteenth floor of the Hodge Building.

THE UNION OIL COMPANY COMPLEX

In 1946, the Union Oil Co. leased a plot of Whittier waterfront and developed it into a petroleum-receiving facility for the distribution of fuels to interior Alaska. The facility was constructed on fill taken from both the delta and the harbor floor in front of the dock. A 14 × 810-ft timber approach was constructed from the shore to a 59 × 268-ft offshore wharf. Eight large fuel-unloading lines ran parallel to the approach to valves on the wharf. All facilities were supported on wooden piles (Figures 5 and 62).

In 1964, the tank-storage yard contained 13 tanks with a total storage capacity of 9.5 million gallons of aircraft fuel, diesel oil, gasoline, and kerosene. A 3.5-ft-high dike surrounded the storage area to contain spillage from any ruptured tank. Other shore facilities included a fuel-pumping station (with a capacity of 500 barrels per hour) in a 20 ×

FIGURE 56 Collapsed 6-in. concrete-block wall in the composite shop building.

FIGURE 57   Spalled plaster indicating lateral movement of pipes in Buckner Building.

44-ft building, a 20 × 24-ft building containing a 40-boiler plant that supplied heat and steam for a 40 × 120-ft warehouse and a 20 × 38-ft barrel-reconditioning plant, a 30 × 30-ft auto repair garage, and a three-story wood-frame

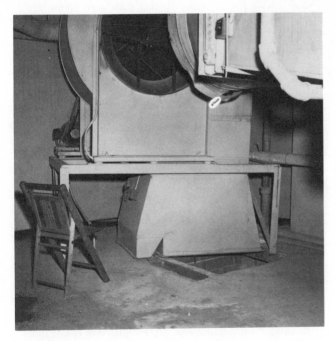

FIGURE 58   Fresh-air unit in penthouse of Hodge Building moved from its original position. Stand was not secured to floor.

FIGURE 59   Surge tank in penthouse of Hodge Building. Note slit in tank insulation, indicating movement of tank in its saddle supports. Tank was installed in north–south direction.

office and apartment building (28 × 80 ft). All the work buildings mentioned were wood-frame structures with sheet-metal siding (Figure 62). The barrel plant refilled the reconditioned barrels with refined products for shipment by rail car (the Union Oil Co. owned a railroad spur, which made possible the simultaneous loading of three railroad tank cars). At the peak of its operation, the company transported about 500,000 gallons of fuel per week by railroad to Anchorage; at the time of the earthquake, most of the tanks were filled with a recent shipment.

On March 27, 1964, there were two families of Union Oil Co. personnel in Whittier; three other company families who normally resided there were spending their weekend in Anchorage.

Mr. Richard Osburn, an employee of the Union Oil Co., reported that he and his family were preparing for supper in their apartment in the main apartment building when the shaking started. About 1 minute after the start of the earthquake, they decided to leave the building; they started to drive east in their pickup truck along the public road toward the warehouse and wharf. As they passed the four Army storage tanks, they saw one large tank tear open from the top and begin spilling fuel. Aware of probable fire, Osburn and his wife abandoned the truck and, carrying their three young children, started to run across the railroad yard toward the Hodge Building. As he crossed the yard, Mr. Osburn looked out at the bay near the ferry slip and saw a high wave, about 40 ft high, breaking just offshore and approaching in a southwest direction. The edge of this wave contained churning timbers and debris. He had proceeded toward the Hodge Building when he heard the first big explosion behind him and saw the whole Union Oil storage

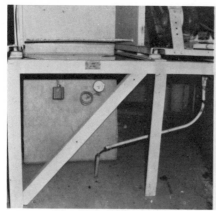 

FIGURE 60 Heavy equipment not firmly mounted moved considerably, breaking electrical connections. (Left) A fresh-air unit; (right) a heavy lathe.

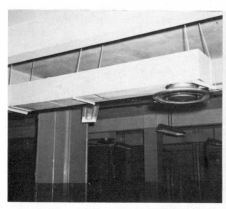 

FIGURE 61 Two views of overhead ventilation ducts and pipe hangers (Buckner Building) showing lateral movement. Greatest movement was shown by hangers.

FIGURE 62 Preearthquake aerial view showing operating facilities of the Union Oil Co. and the Columbia Lumber Co. Small storage tanks and buildings directly behind the Columbia Lumber Co. belong to the Koppers Co., Inc.

yard burst into flames. Throughout that evening he heard seven or eight explosions as various tanks ignited. The wave lost momentum rapidly when it proceeded overland and did not reach his parked truck. Mr. Osburn reported that, although he did not see it, apparently a second wave hit the Union Oil Co. and Columbia Lumber Co. areas and moved debris in a southeasterly direction (Figures 63–65). He returned to his apartment twice during the evening to get clothing and supplies for his family and noted that the fire was very close to the building.

In the course of an investigation of the damage to Whit-

tier, after it had burned for 3 days, Mr. Richard Grocock, Union Oil Co. engineer, noticed that fuel tanks that were almost full had been moved as much as 190 ft. The water from the wave rose to chest height on the first floor of the main apartment building, but the building had not been moved on its foundation (Figure 66). The fire had burned to within 4 ft of the building, and diesel oil flooded the basement, but the building was not even scorched by the heat. In all, over 5 million gallons of various types of fuel were destroyed, along with 472 barrels of refined products. All 11 tanks were ruptured, and only 3 tanks remained

FIGURE 63 Aerial view of destruction at Union Oil Co. and Columbia Lumber Co. Note easterly pattern of debris and outline where the seawave melted the snow.

standing. Those remaining were a mass of twisted steel (Figure 67). The dike surrounding the tank farm was leveled by the wave.

For approximately $60,000, the Union Oil Co. contracted for the salvage and removal of all debris from Whittier. In the spring of 1966, the company terminated its lease at Whittier after it had transferred its operations to Anchorage.

U.S. ARMY PETROLEUM DISTRIBUTION FACILITIES

In 1949, the Whittier Petroleum Distribution Facility was able to expand its storage of fuel, which had previously been only diesel, to include automotive and aviation gasoline. The storage tanks in West Camp, erected on moraine (Figure 68), were specially reinforced for seismic zone 3 construction and for the extremely heavy snow loads encountered in Whittier. Each tank was surrounded by a dike to withhold spillage in case of rupture. Two 15-point tank-car loading platforms were constructed, together with integral piping and railroad trackage (Figure 69). A steel-frame pump house with purlin and concrete-slab roof was built to house the pumping equipment for transferring fuels from storage tanks to the tank-car and truck-loading racks. The storage tanks were filled by using the pumps aboard the ship. A concrete-block combination building with concrete-slab roof housed general office and shop facilities. In 1962, the 700-ft Army pier was declared a fire hazard and condemned. Two alternate pipelines to the marginal wharf were therefore constructed across the tidal flats close to shore, providing two points for unloading tankers at the wharf. The Army pier was not in use when the earthquake occurred.

At the time of the earthquake, all tanks were nearly full, including 77,700 barrels of diesel fuel and 191,000 barrels

of jet fuel. Approximately 56,000 barrels of diesel fuel were lost at the townsite from tank rupture and fire and from the draining of the four 12-in. lines leading to West Camp; about 3,000 barrels of jet fuel were lost from a leak at a broken pressure-relief pipe on tank 802 at West Camp. At the small tank farm at the townsite, one of the 27,240-barrel tanks ruptured near the top during the initial seismic shaking. A fire that started at the Union Oil Co. site when spilled fuel flooded the boiler room soon flashed over to the spilled fuel in the U.S. Army tank farm. The major fire was extinguished after 3 days; however, a small fire burned for 7 days as fuel drained from the four main 12-in. lines leading to the West Camp area. Both the power plant and transfer-pump buildings were demolished by the tsunami. The pier was completely destroyed and washed away. Geological investigation revealed that the end of the pier was on the edge of one of the major submarine landslides, which possibly caused its destruction.

FIGURE 64 Union Oil Co. tank farm and refilling area after the earthquake.

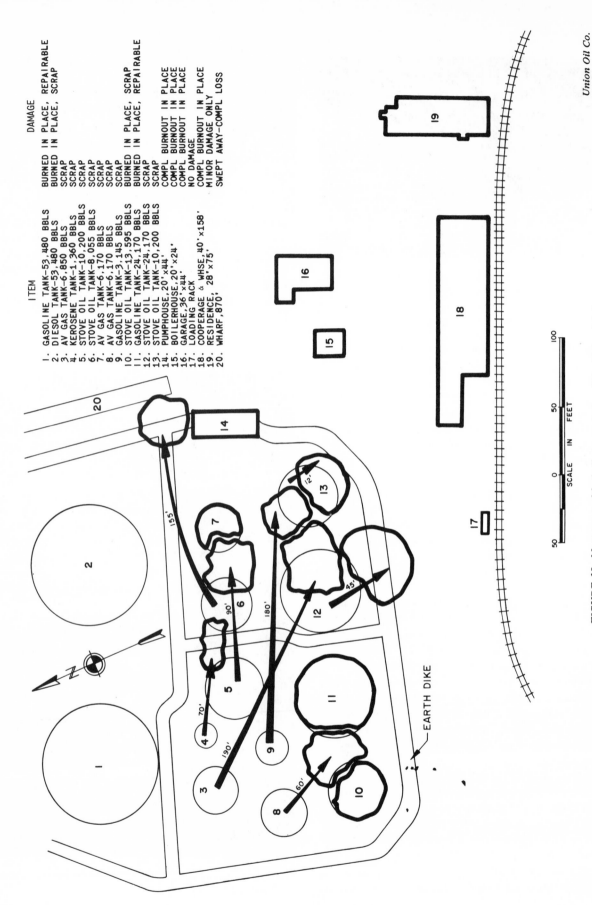

	ITEM	DAMAGE
1.	GASOLINE TANK—53,480 BBLS	BURNED IN PLACE, REPAIRABLE
2.	DIESOL TANK—53,480 BBLS	BURNED IN PLACE, SCRAP
3.	AV GAS TANK—6,850 BBLS	SCRAP
4.	KEROSENE TANK—1,360 BBLS	SCRAP
5.	STOVE OIL TANK—10,200 BBLS	SCRAP
6.	STOVE OIL TANK—8,055 BBLS	SCRAP
7.	AV GAS TANK—6,170 BBLS	SCRAP
8.	AV GAS TANK—6,170 BBLS	SCRAP
9.	GASOLINE TANK—3,145 BBLS	BURNED IN PLACE, SCRAP
10.	STOVE OIL TANK—13,595 BBLS	BURNED IN PLACE, REPAIRABLE
11.	GASOLINE TANK—24,170 BBLS	SCRAP
12.	STOVE OIL TANK—24,170 BBLS	SCRAP
13.	STOVE OIL TANK—10,200 BBLS	COMPL BURNOUT IN PLACE
14.	PUMPHOUSE, 20'×44'	COMPL BURNOUT IN PLACE
15.	BOILERHOUSE, 20'×24'	COMPL BURNOUT IN PLACE
16.	GARAGE, 36'×44'	NO DAMAGE
17.	LOADING RACK	COMPL BURNOUT IN PLACE
18.	COOPERAGE & WHSE, 40'×158'	MINOR DAMAGE ONLY
19.	RESIDENCE, 28'×75'	SWEPT AWAY—COMPL LOSS
20.	WHARF, 870'	

FIGURE 65 Movement of fuel-oil storage tanks of the Union Oil Co.

Union Oil Co.

1100

FIGURE 66 Easterly view of destruction at the Union Oil Co. Drum-storage area and sheet-metal debris in foreground indicate location of processing plant and warehouse. In background is the main apartment building, relatively undamaged by fire or water, although its basement was flooded with fuel. Tanks to the left of the building are those of the U.S. Petroleum Distribution Office.

FIGURE 68 View of part of U.S. Army Petroleum Distribution tank farm at West Camp. In right foreground is the combination building; in upper right, the receding glacier from which much of this delta was formed.

The two 12-in. lines that connected the transfer-pump house to the marginal-wharf unloading terminals were broken near the car-barge slip (see Figure 70). These lines, bent back in a large U by the wave traveling in a south-westerly direction, were deposited near the tank farm. The piping that had been on the Union Oil Co. pier was bent back in a large U toward the U.S. Army tank farm, apparently hit and destroyed by the same wave (from a south-easterly direction) that demolished the Columbia Lumber Co.

Damage in the West Camp area was not apparent until

detailed investigations were made. There was no fire, and no tanks were ruptured. Several 3/4-in. pressure-relief lines broke away from the main lines at the base of the tanks (Figure 71). One valve was shaken slightly open and approximately 3,000 barrels of leakage seeped through the broken pressure-relief line before the leak was located beneath the snow cover. Stairways welded to the sides of the tanks broke their welds at the base-support brackets (Figure 72). Nearly all the tank-level gages were broken off their mountings on the side of the tank (Figure 70). Distinct evidence of fuel actually splashing out of one tank was indicated by the spillage on the side of the tank and on

FIGURE 67 Twisted wreckage that remained in the Union Oil Co. area after the fire and tsunami. The building in the center foreground was the boiler house where the fire started.

FIGURE 69 Two 15-station railroad tank-car loading racks. Transfer piping runs underground to pumphouse.

FIGURE 70   Remains of the pumphouse and twisted fuel piping that led from the pier after fire and tsunami. Tank at rear was a full 8,000-barrel oil tank that was skidded 155 ft by the force of the tsunami.

the snow adjacent to the tank. Many tanks developed a circumferential bulge around the base (Figures 73 and 74). This pronounced bulge occurred only in tanks not completely full, presumably because of the sloshing of the fluid. Investigation showed that the floor plates also bulged and rippled. At first, the bulging was considered serious, but further investigation of the tank interiors by Alaska District

FIGURE 72   Typical mounting details at base of ladders on tanks. Welding scars show where bottom bracket was rewelded to tank. Note the small ripple or outward bulge extending around the perimeter of the tank 6 in. above base.

FIGURE 71   Typical facilities at each tank include a 12-in. drain line with a 3/4-in. pressure-relief line that spills into the top of the tank and a liquid level gage. Welding scars are evident where tank gage was rewelded to side of tank. Pressure-relief lines were broken off the 12-in. line, which was below snow level at the time of the earthquake.

Engineers revealed that structural damage was not serious and that the tank shell was completely secure. The I-beam and channel-beam structural members supporting the roof were shaken out of plumb but were structurally sound enough to support the snow loads.

There was evidence that the tank bottoms actually lifted off their concrete pads. Snow around the base of the tank had been sucked in 3–4 ft underneath the tank and compressed to ice. When this ice melted late in the spring, the tanks resettled level on their foundations. Paint markings around the bases of the tanks indicated that the tanks had assumed a new set after the earthquake. When tank walls were checked for plumb, slight misalignment was noted in most cases. Paint was scraped for about 18 in. along the vertical linkage pipe that extends through loops from the tank gage to the top of the tank; this indicates extensive vertical movement. Scraping was found along other vertical rising pipes in the area, as well as on horizontal piping at penetrations, clamps, and brackets on the tank-car filling stand; however, no piping was broken in the West Camp complex.

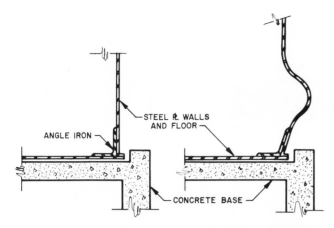

FIGURE 73   Reinforcing plate at bulge in base of tank.

In the composite building, joints cracked in the concrete-block walls; the chimney cap broke off and was tumbled across the roof, damaging the roofing. The transfer pump house received no structural damage or damage to piping or machinery.

A saltwater pumping station (for protection from fire) near the shore was completely destroyed by a combination of compaction and seismic shock. Compaction of unconsolidated deltaic deposits around two 16-in. well casings caused these casings to protrude 6 in. higher above ground level than they did before the earthquake. Inspection of the inside of the casing showed it to be broken in several places. The top section was tipped approximately 7 degrees from vertical. It was almost impossible to remove some sections of the 12-in.-diameter turbine pump from the casing. The reinforced-concrete pump building received little damage. Machinery was damaged by the shifting casing, and mountings were torn loose when the pipe casing lifted the pumps off the floor. Because this whole area subsided 5.3 ft, the pump house, which was previously above the high-tide mark, is now frequently several feet under water at high tide. A new pump house and wells that replaced the damaged facility are now capable of protecting the tank farm area from fire.

After the earthquake, the Petroleum Distribution Office installed two new 12-in. lines from the old tank-farm area to the DeLong dock to enable the West Camp tank farm to unload tankers.

THE COLUMBIA LUMBER CO.

In 1945, the Columbia Lumber Co. of Alaska, with main offices in Juneau, leased a portion of waterfront acreage on both sides of the mouth of Whittier Creek. Initially, the company employed nearly 60 people and managed logging operations from the mountains around Passage Canal. When this area was depleted, they continued their operations by barging logs in from the Yakutat area, over 300 mi east. The first large mill building, which burned in 1955, was replaced by a small wood-frame building with sheet-steel siding. The operation was somewhat reduced with the new mill. Numerous single- and two-family wood-frame buildings were constructed east of the mill area. The new mill operations included one large circular head saw, two 2-ton planers, several large electric motors, a small boiler and heating plant that furnished steam for heating the various buildings, and numerous conveyors, ball chains, kilns, and jump rolls salvaged from the old mill. In the early 1950's, a wet pond was dug near the shore to hold barged logs for processing. The mill at Whittier was operated only during the summer, because extremely deep snows and high winds made operating conditions highly inefficient in the winter. The lumber company employed about 27 men in 1963, but only two families and a bachelor were living in the company buildings in March 1964 because normal operations had not resumed.

The account of what happened to the company facilities during the earthquake has to be pieced together from fragmentary reports from nearby residents and from investigations made immediately after the earthquake. No eyewitness accounts are available because all the occupants of the area were missing and presumed dead.

The pattern of debris indicates that a strong tidal wave approached the Columbia Lumber Co. site in an east–

FIGURE 74   Pronounced bulge at base of one large storage tank at the West Camp tank farm.

FIGURE 75   View east across the Columbia Lumber Co. site. Debris pattern and high-water mark are indicated by melted snow. Sites of the Union Oil Co. and U.S. Army POL facilities can be seen beyond.

southeast direction (Figure 75). All buildings and structures, machinery and vehicles, and stacks of lumber were moved. A large 200-hp motor had been winterized by wrapping a sheet of polystyrene (4 mils thick) around the motor to keep it dry. Although this motor was torn from its concrete base mount and moved more than 200 ft inland, the plastic wrapping was still in place. A large 2-ton lumber planer was broken in half when it was similarly moved by the wave. All residences were leveled; one 2-story residence lost the entire first floor when the wave hit and the second story fell upright in place onto some other demolished buildings (Figure 62). A railroad bridge across Whittier Creek near the burning tower was completely washed away. The gate to the wet pond and the pond itself were washed away, and the pond area was filled with equipment and debris left from the backwash. The Alaska Railroad awarded a $13,133 contract for the cleanup of debris and the search for bodies.

Some salvageable equipment and machinery was returned to Anchorage and later sold. The lumber company terminated its lease in 1964 and later moved its operation to Haines, Alaska.

To the south of the Columbia Lumber Co., the facilities and storage tanks of the Koppers Co., Inc., can be seen (Figures 62–64). This plant had processed railroad ties with a pressure creosote treatment but had closed its Whittier operation in 1962. The tanks shown are riveted-plate creosote and Wolman salt storage tanks. No seismic damage was noted here, and the tsunami did not reach this plant because it was on higher ground.

TSUNAMIS

Several tsunamis were generated during the earthquake, presumably by submarine landslides of unconsolidated deposits. These waves caused extensive damage to waterfront facilities. The runup of the second wave reached an altitude of 104 ft along the shore northwest of the townsite; at the head of Passage Canal, it was measured at 82 ft; when it hit the railroad station, it was 26 ft high. In Passage Canal, at least three different waves were generated and recorded as traveling in different directions. The force of the water drove a 2×6-in. plank through a six-ply tire. Three vacant homes and the Columbia Lumber Co. were completely destroyed, and the wave action was blamed for all 13 deaths at Whittier.

SUBSIDENCE

Total subsidence as a result of the earthquake, including tectonic subsidence and compaction, was determined to be 5.3 ft at Whittier. High tides now cover additional acreage at the head of Passage Canal that was previously above the high-tide level. Much of the land leased by the Two Brothers Lumber Co. and about 350 ft of the eastern end of the airstrip are now regularly under water at high tide. Windswept waves and high tides now are attacking areas above the level where riprap protected the steep banks (compare Figures 1 and 2 to Figures 3 and 4). In such areas, roads and bridge embankments are eroding. A combination of subsidence and submarine landslides caused major damage to the hydro-train slip towers. The ramp at this slip is pivoted at the shore end, and two steel towers support machinery and counter-weights to adjust the movable end of the ramp so that it will fluctuate with the tides.

CONSOLIDATION OF SOILS

Consolidation of loose sediments was most evident at the marginal wharf and in-transit warehouse. Fill was provided under these structures by pumping dredged spoil from the bottom of the bay in front of the dock. Settlement as much as 18 in. was measured inside the warehouse where the slab floors fractured longitudinally and parallel to the bulkhead wall. A submarine landslide undermined one of the com-pany slip towers and tipped it seaward at an angle of about 30 degrees. As a result of the general land subsidence in the area, the shore-end assembly was under water and had to be raised.

The head of Passage Canal also was compacted about 6 in.; in a concrete pumphouse that enclosed two 40-ft wells, the well casings protruded 6 in. more than they had before the earthquake. The surface materials became com-pacted, and consolidated deposits at greater depths kept the well casing from sinking. Compaction may have caused an estimated subsidence of 2–3 ft in parts of the delta area at the head of Passage Canal. A few ground cracks appeared west of the townsite, near Whittier Creek, and ran a few hundred feet inland parallel to the water. They were prob-ably caused by the shifting of the sediments toward the scarp of an offshore submarine landslide near this point.

Consolidation was also evident along the railroad track just outside Whittier. The track was separated and a stair-step effect could be seen as the track proceeded from the tunnel. The greater depths of unconsolidated deposits be-tween bedrock and the track bed allowed more compaction to occur.

DEATHS AND INJURIES

At Whittier, 13 persons were dead or missing as a result of the earthquake. All deaths were attributed to the wave ac-tion. One small baby, swept from her mother's arms near the railroad depot and found alive again within the hour, later died of multiple injuries and exposure. The death toll was relatively low because of the small population of Whit-tier. Two people were seriously injured by splinters from the damaged railroad station that were driven through their arms by the force of the wave. An emergency first-aid cen-ter was set up in the fire station; the next day, the injured were evacuated by helicopter to hospitals in Anchorage.

EMERGENCY RELIEF

Poor flying weather delayed relief at Whittier. Because of the short runway, part of which was washed away by the tsunami, only helicopters and light fixed-wing aircraft could reach the town. The single railroad spur to Whittier was so badly damaged that it was rendered useless, and all wire communications were dead. The morning after the earth-quake, a Coast Guard plane flying over the port reported the oil tanks burning, and a commercial pilot later said that Whittier was aflame. During the early afternoon of the same day, an Alaska highway patrolman reported that the tun-nels were open and listed the casualties in the community.

An Army helicopter landed at Whittier late on Saturday afternoon, picked up an injured couple and their dead baby, and returned to a hospital in Anchorage. Additional flights were made into Whittier during the next few days to trans-port passengers and emergency supplies. Electricity for the community was restored within 6 hours; running water, within 10 hours. The women of the community set up a community dining room in the school cafeteria because their individual homes had been badly damaged. Except for this situation, normal community life was restored within 3 days (U.S. Alaskan Command, 1964).

RESTORATION EFFORT OF VARIOUS FACILITIES

The immediate restoration effort was concentrated on re-habilitating the car-barge slip for emergency use, cleaning up the debris at the Columbia Lumber Co. site in a search for missing persons, repairing the marginal wharf and in-transit warehouse, and reestablishing the railroad link with Portage. Within the week after the earthquake, military per-sonnel arrived to help the railroad crews clear debris from the tunnel and to establish radio communication with Fort Richardson. A telephone link through the tunnel to Portage soon followed. On April 6, a platoon of soldiers arrived by helicopter to begin the heavy cleanup work, including re-moval of interior and exterior debris and repairs to bridges, roads, and utilities. A kitchen crew arrived to relieve the ladies of their chores in the community kitchen, which re-mained in operation until early in May when the general cleanup was completed (U.S. Alaskan Command, 1964).

Railroad crews, starting immediately to clean up the yards at Whittier, removed approximately 5 tons of loose rock that had fallen from the ceiling inside the tunnel. The track bed between the tunnels and from the eastern tunnel to Portage had to be regraded before service could be restored.

The total cost of the rehabilitation of the Hodge Build-ing, composite shop, and railroad depot amounted to

$130,000. The Alaska Railroad began a rehabilitation of the Hodge Building to provide living quarters for personnel stationed there. Many of the damaged 4-in. partition walls were replaced by wood-stud and gypsum-board partitions, which had withstood the effects of the earthquake much better than block walls. All damaged earthquake-joint covers were replaced. Partial repairs of the first through the seventh floors were made; however, railroad activity was severely reduced at Whittier during 1966 and no further repairs have been made to the Hodge Building.

The Alaska Railroad awarded a contract for all miscellaneous repairs in the shop, including the complete removal of the sheet-steel roof deck over the high-bay crane area and the entire rebuilding of the structural framework of the roof. A new wood roof deck was installed and finished with built-up roofing. All damaged earthquake-joint covers were replaced, wall fractures were grouted, torn gusset plates were replaced, and diagonal tension rods were replaced with angle-iron cross braces (Figure 76).

Only the eastern end of the railroad depot, containing the waiting room, was extensively damaged by the tsunami. The Alaska Railroad decided to eliminate that part of the building, adding exterior siding and entrance doors for weather protection.

STRUCTURAL REPAIR OF THE IN-TRANSIT WAREHOUSE AND MARGINAL WHARF

The Alaska Railroad contracted for the repair of the in-transit warehouse. About 50 percent of the floor slab in the

FIGURE 76 Postearthquake view of the western end of the shop building in the high-bay crane area. Wood decking was used to replace damaged metal decking. New angle-iron cross bracing replaces tension-rod cross bracing.

FIGURE 77 Taken beneath the dock, almost in the center, this view shows channels that were added to each side of pile bent to form horizontal strut.

eastern 600 ft of the building was replaced, and ramps were added at the doorways to provide an entrance for vehicles.

To prepare plans and specifications for immediate repair of the wharf (Figures 77 and 78), The Alaska Railroad engaged a firm of consulting engineers. Principally the east end of the wharf was repaired; only four fender piles were replaced on the west end. The precast panels on the south side of the wharf were removed, and two 14BP73 fender piles were driven between every other row of pile bents on the eastern 470 ft of dock. These fender piles were connected with an H section used as a cap, and this section is

FIGURE 78 View of new channel strut and new angle bracing between channel strut and top of piles.

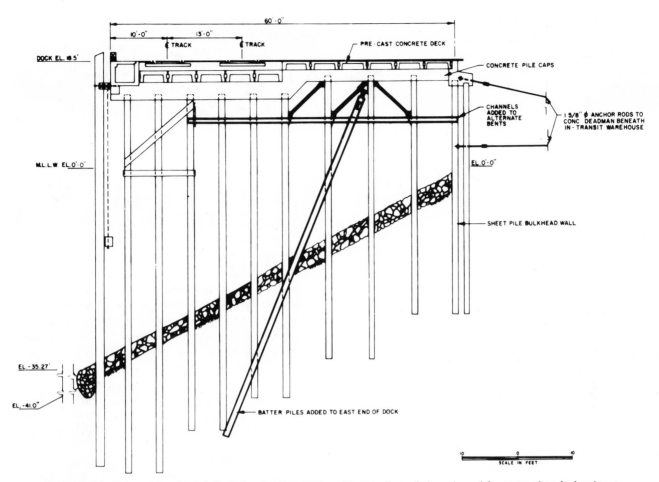

FIGURE 79 Cross section through dock showing the addition of batter piles and channels used for postearthquake bracing.

long enough to be connected to a pile in adjacent bent rows (Figure 79). A horizontal strut, placed at elevation +7.83, was also added to each row of bents in the eastern 500 ft. This strut consisted of two channels that were added, one on each side of the row of piling, and it extended from the bulkhead wall to the third row of piling from the outside edge (Figure 26). Between rows 2, 3, and 4, out from the bulkhead wall, cross bracing (Figures 73 and 74) was added between this horizontal strut and the point at which the pile frames into the concrete cap. Cost of repairs to both the wharf and the warehouse amounted to $498,000.

ACKNOWLEDGMENT

Except as otherwise noted, illustrations are credited to the U.S. Army Corps of Engineers.

REFERENCES

Balhiser, C. K., 1964. Report to Alaska District, Corps of Engineers, from the Assistant Chief of Design Branch, April 6.

Kachadoorian, Reuben, 1965. Effects of the earthquake of March 27, 1964, at Whittier, Alaska. U.S. Geological Survey Professional Paper 542-B. Washington: Government Printing Office. 21 p. Also in The Great Alaska Earthquake of 1964: Geology. NAS Pub. 1601. Washington: National Academy of Sciences, 1971. p. 439–459.

U.S. Alaskan Command [1964]. Operation helping hand: The Armed Forces react to earthquake disaster. Seattle: Headquarters Alaskan Command. 83 p.

JAMES M. TANAKA*
U.S. ARMY CORPS OF ENGINEERS DISTRICT,
ALASKA

Relocation of Valdez

To reduce future earthquake hazard, proposals are often made to rebuild a city severely damaged by an earthquake on a different site. Some cities have been relocated; for example, in A.D. 518, the city of Scupi in Yugoslavia was severely damaged by an earthquake and was abandoned. The new city, renamed Skopje, was built a few kilometers to the southeast. The city of Guatemala Antigua was abandoned after an earthquake, and the new Guatemala City was built. The decisions to relocate these cities were made without benefit of technical knowledge about earthquakes or structures, so that no advantage was gained. For example, the city of Skopje was again severely damaged by earthquakes in 1555 and in 1963. The relocation of a city is a serious matter for the community, involving not only technical considerations but also political, economic, and social problems. The relocation of Valdez is of special interest because, for the first time, information is available on the technical, political, economic, and social considerations that prompted the decision to move the city. In addition, reliable data are available on the engineering and on the costs of the move. These data will help to assess the merit of relocating the city after some time has passed, and they should also be of value to other cities that may consider relocating after earthquakes.

Valdez, located at lat. 61°07′N and long. 146°16′W, at the eastern end of Port Valdez, an estuary of Prince William Sound (Figure 1), is Alaska's northernmost ice-free port and serves as a major highway-transportation link with the interior of Alaska. The fiord shoreline of Valdez Arm and Port Valdez terminates at an outwash plain at the east end, which is supplied by material carried by the Lowe and Robe rivers and the stream from Valdez Glacier. The delta slopes westward from an elevation of about 300 ft at the toe of the glacier to sea level in a distance of approximately 4 mi. The town of Valdez stands on the seaward edge of the outwash delta (Figure 2). Subsurface investigations conducted by the Alaska Department of Highways show the delta to be composed of poorly consolidated silt, fine sand,

ABSTRACT: The town of Valdez, situated on the seaward edge of an outwash delta, was severely damaged by the earthquake of March 27, 1964. A large submarine landslide and the resulting waves destroyed the waterfront facilities. The ground beneath the town was deformed during the earthquake, producing numerous cracks that damaged the foundations of structures. On the basis of the results of postearthquake investigations, a repetition of the disaster was considered probable in the event of another earthquake, and the decision was made to abandon the old site of Valdez and to reconstruct the town on the nearby less-hazardous Mineral Creek site. The new community of Valdez was conceived, planned, designed, and constructed between March 1964 and February 1967. The estimated cost of relocating the city of about 750 persons was approximately $50,000 per capita.

*Now with the Federal Aviation Administration, Anchorage.

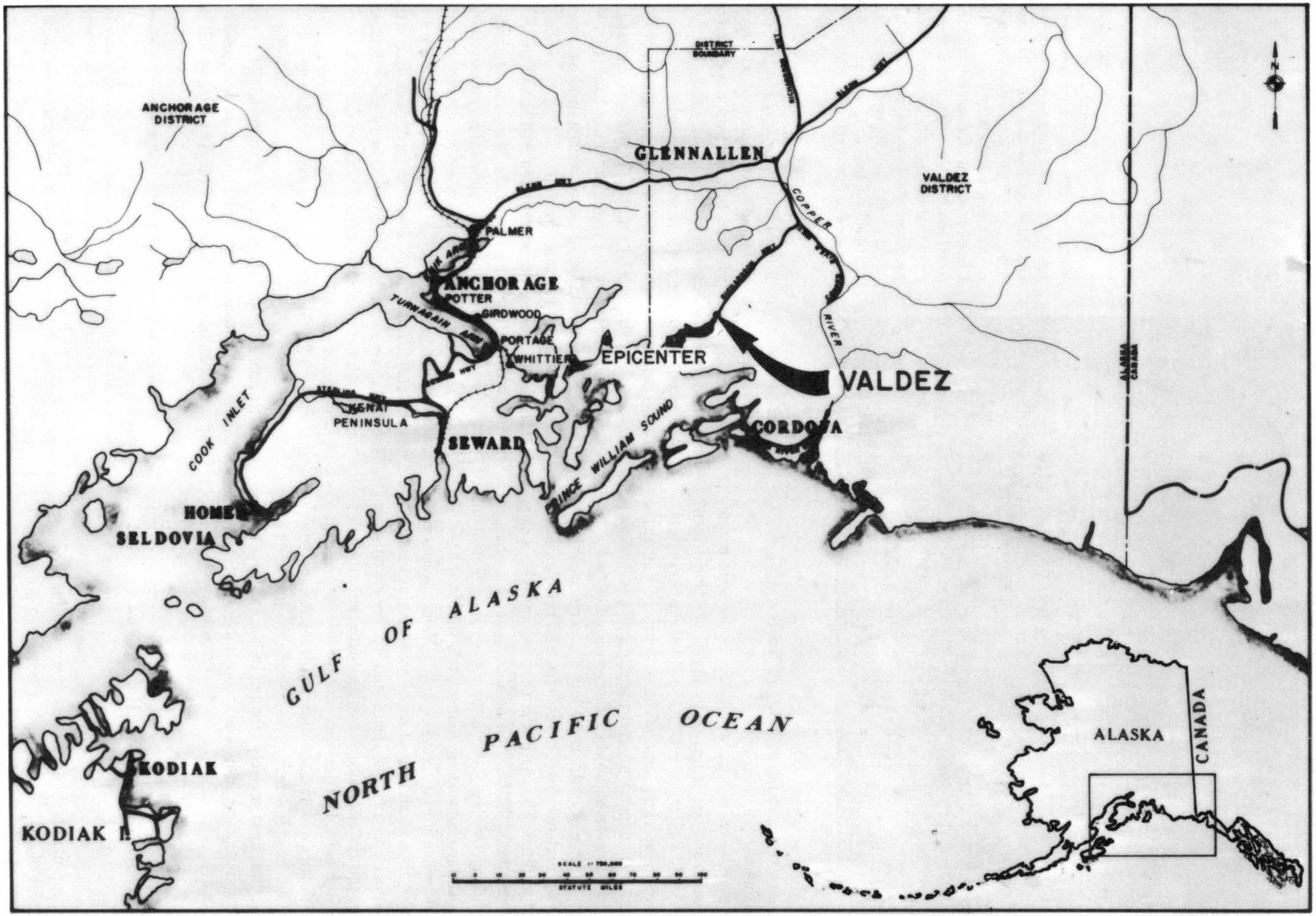

FIGURE 1 Location map of Valdez area.

FIGURE 2   Northeast end of Port Valdez, 1965. The southern terminus of the Richardson Highway can be seen emerging from Lowe River Canyon (upper center) and entering preearthquake Valdez on the upper delta. The Valdez airport is on left of the preearthquake townsite. The Mineral Creek townsite is on the alluvial fan at the lower left. The reconstruction of the water-front facilities and the townsite was in progress at the time the picture was taken. The rock ribs contributing to the stability of the alluvial fan can be seen immediately landward of Port Valdez.

and gravel. The water table is within a few feet of the sur-face throughout the delta.

The population of Valdez was 555 at the time of the 1960 Census and was estimated by the Alaska Department of Health and Welfare in 1964 to be 1,000 during the peak periods of the working season. The economy of Valdez is almost entirely dependent on the sea; shipping is its major industry. The main harbor facilities consisted of two wharves, capable of berthing the largest steamers serving Alaska, with related cargo, dry-storage, and petroleum-product facilities. The south wharf was occupied by a can-nery. A small-boat basin, covering about 3 acres, and a ferry-landing dock lay between the two wharves. Petroleum-product storage tanks stood immediately shoreward and south of the harbor facilities (Figure 3). Valdez was also a home port for a small fleet of commercial fishing vessels. The Alaska Department of Health and Welfare Psychiatric Hospital and the Headquarters of the State Department of Highways, Valdez District, were also in Valdez. The com-mercial district was near the shore, with the residential area farther inland. A map of Valdez and the locations of the structures most severely affected by the earthquake that were considered during the reconstruction are shown in Figure 4.

EFFECTS OF THE MARCH 27, 1964, EARTHQUAKE

Valdez, approximately 45 mi east of the earthquake epi-center, was the civilian community nearest to the epicenter. The first tremors were felt at approximately 5:36 p.m. and

lasted for about 5 minutes. Fissures appeared in the frozen crust throughout the delta and were observed to open and close, ejecting large quantities of water and suspended silt and sand in the areas that were cleared of snow. The fis-sures extended to zones of weakness, such as the unfrozen ground beneath structures, disturbing foundations and cracking floor slabs. Cracks up to 3 ft wide crisscrossed the entire town, rupturing the water and sewer lines (Figure 5). The delta elongated toward the waterfront and became per-manently displaced in this direction.

The earthquake-induced submarine slide and the re-sulting waves virtually destroyed the town's waterfront structures (Figure 6). In some communities, the earthquake resulted in relatively small loss of life because of the time of day at which it occurred; most people were in transit from their jobs or schools. The dock at Valdez, in contrast, was in a state of maximum activity when the earthquake and the submarine slide occurred. The SS *Chena*, a con-verted liberty ship about 400 ft long, had arrived in Valdez an hour and 20 minutes before the earthquake and was dis-charging cargo (Figure 7). Thirty lives were lost in the catastrophic slide and the waves that followed. The events at the waterfront during the earthquake are described by Captain M. D. Stewart, Master of the SS *Chena* as follows:

The *Chena* arrived at Valdez at 1612 hours, March 27. About 1731 o'clock, while discharging cargo, we felt a severe earthquake— followed almost immediately by tidal waves. There were very heavy shocks about every half a minute. Mounds of water were hitting at us from all directions. I was in the dining room. I made it to the bridge (three decks up) by climbing a vertical ladder. God knows how I got there.

The Valdez piers started to collapse right away. There was a

FIGURE 3 Preearthquake aerial photograph of the Valdez waterfront, September 1963.

Bureau of Land Management

tremendous noise. The ship was laying over to port. I had been in earthquakes before, but I knew right away that this was the worst one yet. The *Chena* raised about 30 feet on an incoming wave. The whole ship lifted and heeled to port about 50°. Then it was slammed down heavily on the spot where the docks had disintegrated moments before. I saw people running—with no place to run to. It was just ghastly. They were just engulfed by buildings, water, mud, and everything. The *Chena* dropped where the people had been. That is what has kept me awake for days. There was no sight of them. The ship stayed there momentarily. Then there was an ungodly backroll to starboard. Then she came upright. Then we took another heavy roll to port.

I could see the land (at Valdez) jumping and leaping in a terrible turmoil. We were inside of where the dock had been. We had been washed into where the small-boat harbor used to be. There was no water under the *Chena* for a brief interval. I realized we had to get out quickly if we were ever going to get out at all. There was water under us again. The stern was sitting in broken piling, rocks, and mud.

I signaled to the engine room for power and got it very rapidly. I called for "slow ahead," then "half ahead," and finally for "full." In about four minutes, I would guess, we were moving appreciably, scraping on and off the mud (bottom) as the waves went up and down. People ashore said they saw us slide sideways off a mat of willow trees (placed as part of the fill material in the harbor), which helped put our bow out. We couldn't turn. We were moving along

the shore, with the stern in the mud. Big mounds of water came up and flattened out. Water inshore was rushing out. A big gush of water came off of the beach, hit the bow, and swung her out about 10°. If that hadn't happened, we would have stayed there with the bow jammed in a mud bank and provided a new dock for the town of Valdez!! We broke free. The bow pushed through the wreckage of a cannery. We went out into the bay and had to stop. The condensers were plugged with mud and pieces of the dock. The chief mate, Neal L. Larsen, checked to see then if we were taking water. We were taking none. It was unbelievable after what the ship had been through. We had the lifeboats all manned and ready. I didn't think she would float in deep water. Maybe the soft mud bottom made the difference.

The submarine landslide carried away the docks, and a series of waves destroyed the waterfront structures and advanced into the town damaging other property (Figure 8). Property damage was confined to the area of the business district, immediately shoreward of the waterfront structures. The first wave that struck Valdez was generated by the movement of the mass of soil during the submarine slide. This wave, estimated to be about 30 ft high, surged onto the beaches causing additional damage to the already devastated waterfront. Although eyewitness accounts of

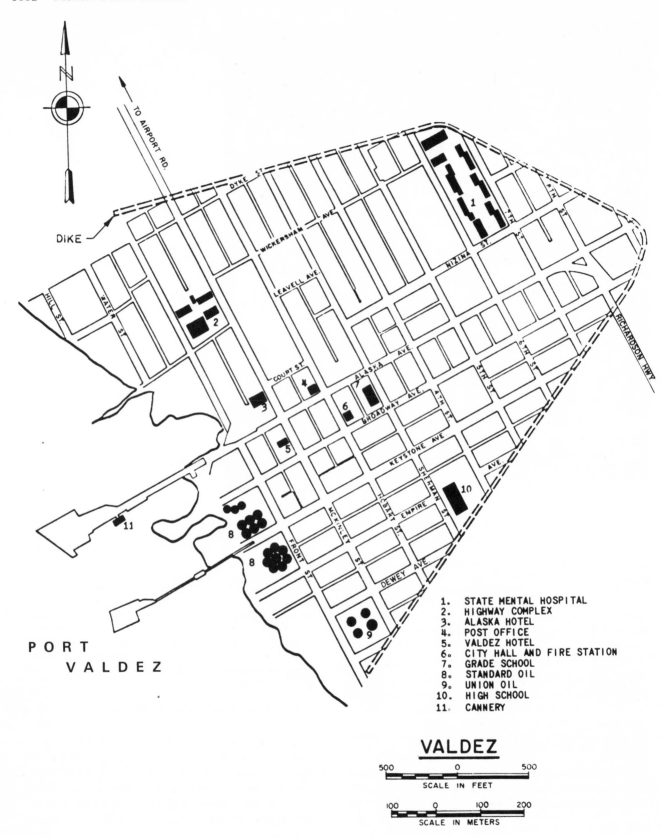

FIGURE 4   Preearthquake plan of Valdez.

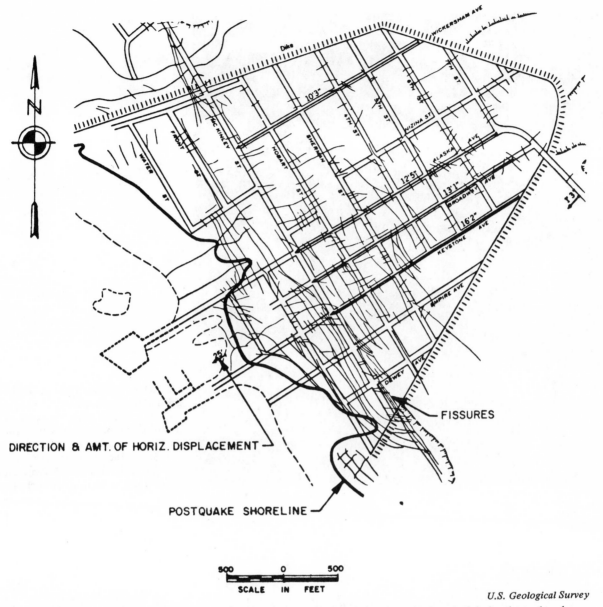

DIRECTION & AMT. OF HORIZ. DISPLACEMENT

FISSURES

POSTQUAKE SHORELINE

500 0 500
SCALE IN FEET

U.S. Geological Survey

FIGURE 5 Plan of Valdez showing the fissuring pattern and horizontal displacement that occurred during the earthquake.

the number and timing of the waves vary, it seems that three or possibly four waves struck Valdez; the first during the movement of the submarine slide, and the last at approximately 2:20 a.m. on March 28, after the high tide.

After the earthquake, remnants of the dock approaches were the only remaining indications of the waterfront structures that had been there (Figure 9). Debris and boats were deposited on the beach, intermingled with the damaged structures. The Union Oil Co. petroleum-products storage tanks and several commercial structures were destroyed by fire (Figure 10). Almost every structure in Valdez suffered some damage. Concrete-block structures, such as the

Alaskan Hotel (Figure 11), the State of Alaska Psychiatric Hospital (Figures 12–14), and various other commercial structures were extensively damaged. Although wood-frame structures were generally flexible enough to withstand the strains of the earthquake, differential foundation settlement occurred under the majority of the structures in the town. The buildings and the equipment of the power and telephone company, a privately owned utility, were not extensively damaged, and the company was in operation immediately after the earthquake, although the distribution system had suffered extensive damage (Figure 15). In the city-owned hospital, floor cracks up to 3 in. wide, cracked

FIGURE 6   Postearthquake aerial photograph of the Valdez waterfront taken during low tide in August 1964. The extent of the waterfront damage caused by the earthquake can be seen by comparing this photograph to Figure 3. The temporary dock constructed after the earthquake is located adjacent to the remnants of the right approach ramp.

T. Valkenburg

FIGURE 7   The vessel SS *Chena* resting in Port Valdez after riding through the submarine slide and tsunamis, March 1964. The Valdez High School (lower left) is four city blocks landward of the pre-earthquake shoreline. The landward extent of the tsunamis can be seen on the road between the waterfront and school. The distance the waves advanced can be calculated by locating the high school on Figure 4.

U.S. Army

FIGURE 8   The distance that the tsunamis advanced into Valdez is shown by the variation in the snow cover and debris. The Standard Oil tank farm is in the foreground (March 1964).

FIGURE 9 The remnants of the approach fill are the only visible traces of the waterfront facilities after the earthquake. The small-boat basin, which lay between the dock approaches, virtually disappeared. Ground fissures can be seen across the road leading to the waterfront.

FIGURE 10 The waterfront debris left by the tsunamis. Union Oil tank farm caught fire during the earthquake and can be seen burning in the background.

FIGURE 11 Failure of concrete-block structure was caused by the earthquake ground motion. The buildings on the west side of McKinley Avenue were also damaged by the tsunamis.

FIGURE 12 Preearthquake view of a typical State of Alaska Psychiatric Hospital building. The structures were predominantly constructed of concrete block.

FIGURE 13 View of concrete-block corner failure, State of Alaska Psychiatric Hospital.

FIGURE 14 View of the garage failure at State of Alaska Psychiatric Hospital.

walls, and chimney damage resulted; most dishes, medicine bottles, and the like, however, escaped damage.

The earthquake extensively damaged the water and sewer systems. The sewer outfalls were completely destroyed by the submarine slide, and the distribution and collection systems were ruptured by numerous fissures and by the horizontal displacement of the delta toward the port of Valdez (Figure 5). The 200,000-gallon water-storage tank, a wooden tank supported on a timber tower, was not damaged; the cross braces of the supporting tower, however, were slightly damaged. The main water-supply well was operative after the earthquake, but subsequent tremors and land movement necessitated its abandonment in September 1964. Aid came to Valdez on the day after the earthquake in the form of a detachment of soldiers from Fort Wainwright, near Fairbanks, about 365 mi away. Arrangements were made for the evacuation of the women and children to Glennallen, where the Alaska State Civil Defense and the U.S. Army had established a refugee center. The Corps of Engineers dispatched a disaster team to give immediate emergency aid and to assess the damage. A resident engineer from the Corps of Engineers followed to supervise the immediate measures required to ensure the public safety according to the provisions of Public Law 81–875. These emergency measures for the protection of the public included debris clearance, roping off of unsafe areas, and reestablishment, by means of temporary repairs, of the water-supply and sewage-disposal systems. This work was carried out locally by means of contracts negotiated on the spot. Fairbanks had used the port of Valdez extensively and extended considerable aid at this time by lending equipment and by providing technical assistance.

RECONSTRUCTION PLAN

Under the sponsorship of the Alaska Housing Authority, the State of Alaska Highway Department and the U.S. Geological Survey initiated a subsurface exploration immediately after the earthquake. The U.S. Army Corps of Engineers engaged Shannon & Wilson, Inc., consultants from Seattle, Washington, to complete the subsurface investigations (Shannon & Wilson, 1964). Initial investigations substantiated the fact that the delta on which Valdez was situated consisted of saturated fine outwash soil, which was subject to liquefaction and sliding under seismic conditions. Further research by the U.S. Geological Survey revealed that similar slides had occurred in the Valdez area at least five times during the past 70 years (Coulter and Migliaccio, 1966, and Geology volume).

In contrast to the geologic conditions at the preearthquake location of Valdez, an alluvial fan known as the Mineral Creek site, located on the north shore of the port of

FIGURE 15 Typical powerline and telephone-wire failure along Alaska Avenue. Debris was being cleared while the photograph was taken.

Valdez, about 4 mi from the old town, is underlain by dense cobbles and gravel in a matrix of medium-to-fine sand (Coulter and Migliaccio, 1966) (Figure 16). A series of bedrock ridges and islands located seaward of the fan forms a natural buttress against sliding or horizontal soil movement during earthquakes (Figure 2). Although the ground surface was frozen to depths of as much as 6 ft at the time of the earthquake, there were no fissures. The U.S. Geological Survey (Coulter and Migliaccio, 1966) summarized the subsurface conditions at each location as follows:

In summary, Valdez is unsuitable as a habitation site or port facility in the following respects: Poor foundation conditions on saturated fine-grained materials which are unstable under seismic conditions; exposure to slide or seismically generated sea waves; exposure to serious floods.

In contrast with the unfavorable geologic conditions at the present site of Valdez, the conditions at the new Mineral Creek townsite are very suitable for habitation and port facilities. The Mineral Creek site is situated on an alluvial fan confined on the seaward side by a series of bedrock ridges and islands. It is underlain by coarse tabular cobble gravel having an interlocking bedded texture which will provide excellent foundation conditions. The bedrock configuration at the mouth of Mineral Creek effectively prevents the stream from swinging eastward into or near the townsite.

In summary, the Mineral Creek townsite has the following advantages: A series of bedrock ridges and islands which act as a resistant buttress retaining and protecting the toe of the alluvial fan from danger of sliding or slumping. This bedrock buttress plus the higher elevation of the Mineral Creek site also provides protection from slide or seismically generated sea waves; a stable foundation anchor on bedrock for a major dock facility, favorable offshore conditions, and a protected locality for a small-boat harbor; good foundation conditions on the basis of the absence of ground breakage and fissures, and of vibration damage to the single-dwelling there, the coarse alluvium of the Mineral Creek site appears to be relatively stable under seismic conditions and excellent natural protection from floods.

On the basis of the investigations, the Scientific and Engineering Task Force recommended to the Federal Reconstruction and Development Planning Commission that the

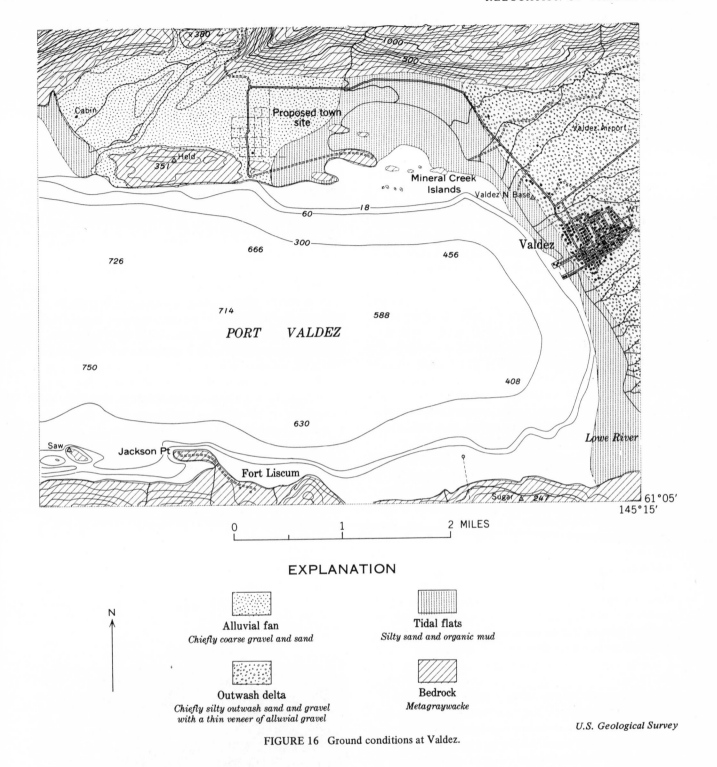

EXPLANATION

Alluvial fan
Chiefly coarse gravel and sand

Tidal flats
Silty sand and organic mud

Outwash delta
*Chiefly silty outwash sand and gravel
with a thin veneer of alluvial gravel*

Bedrock
Metagraywacke

U.S. Geological Survey

FIGURE 16 Ground conditions at Valdez.

town of Valdez be relocated at the Mineral Creek site. The recommendation was endorsed by the federal and state commissions, and a plan for relocation was presented to the city officials for consideration. The relation between the Mineral Creek townsite and Valdez is shown in Figures 2 and 16.

The adoption of the City of Valdez Resolution Number 5, dated April 27, 1964, for relocation of the city to the Mineral Creek site set in motion a unique coordinated and cooperative effort of various federal, state, and local agencies. The Corps of Engineers, under the sponsorship of the

Office of Emergency Planning (OEP), began the task of repairing (commonly referred to as "winterizing") utility systems and essential public facilities such as the schools, the hospital, and the docking facilities in the existing townsite to the minimum extent required to provide the essential facilities until the Mineral Creek site was prepared for occupancy.

Concurrently with the "winterization" effort, the Alaska State Housing Authority, under the sponsorship of the Urban Renewal Administration, began planning the Mineral Creek townsite and for the acquisition of the property in the existing townsite. The Alaska State Highway Department began to design the extension of the Richardson Highway into the Mineral Creek site, and the Corps of Engineers began to design a deep-draft vessel dock with warehouses and a small-boat basin with ferry-landing facilities at the shore of the Mineral Creek site.

EMERGENCY MEASURES AND WINTERIZATION AT THE OLD VALDEZ TOWNSITE

The emergency measures for the protection of public health and safety officially began with the award of a contract to a Valdez contractor for debris removal on March 29, 1964. The contractor was to perform the following tasks:

1. Provide messing facilities to operate until April 30, 1964.
2. Perform temporary repair of the sewage collection and outfall system, where possible, and install septic tanks where sewers were damaged to the extent that repairs could not be easily made.
3. Perform temporary repair of the water-supply line from the water-storage tank to the power plant. As an emergency measure, approximately 8,000 ft of surface-laid aluminum irrigation pipe was used as a supply line, and garden hoses were used as service connections.
4. Remove debris and demolish unsafe structures.
5. Repair power and telephone services.

While the emergency measures were being taken, the Corps of Engineers dispatched a damage-survey team, composed of civil, structural, electrical, and mechanical engineers and an estimator, to assess the damage to the utilities and structures and to outline the scope of the work necessary to effect the repairs. Because of the decision to relocate the city of Valdez, an agreement between the local officials and federal and state commissions was necessary to determine the extent of temporary winterization required and to establish schedules and priorities. The majority of the policy decisions were reached at meetings of representatives of the participating agencies. The general plan and schedule for the temporary restoration at the old townsite was as follows:

1. *Temporary docking facilities.* A minimal docking facility, capable of berthing one liberty-class vessel, was needed as soon as possible for unloading the material required for reconstruction and to stimulate the economy. A portion of the ramp approach to the east dock that survived the earthquake was used as an access ramp, and the construction of a timber pile and deck dock and mooring dolphins (Figure 17) was completed on August 15, 1964.

2. *Temporary warehouse.* A temporary warehouse, measuring about 45 × 165 ft, was constructed near the temporary dock facility as a dry storage area. Timber piling was driven into the ground, both as a foundation and a post support for the roof beams. Three sides and the roof beams were covered with corrugated metal (Figure 18).

3. *Temporary ferry landing.* A temporary ferry-landing terminal was constructed to ensure continuous surface transportation between Cordova and Valdez. The ferry in service has a bow ramp capable of accommodating a tidal fluctuation of about 6 ft. A three-ramp docking facility is usually needed to service ships at all tide stages. To provide minimal facilities pending completion of the permanent installation at the Mineral Creek townsite, a single ramp, deep enough only at high tide, was constructed by dredging the remnants of the northwest dock approach, and dolphins were installed for safe mooring.

4. *Repair of water and sewage-disposal systems.* A contract was awarded June 18, 1964, for the minimum repair of the water and sewer systems to provide utility service until relocation to the Mineral Creek site. The existing

FIGURE 17   The temporary dock, constructed at the damaged townsite, for unloading material required for reconstruction and freight destined for the interior of Alaska.

FIGURE 18 The temporary warehouse, constructed near the temporary dock as a minimal dry-cargo storage facility.

water-supply system was constructed mainly of cast-iron pipe with mechanical joints. The sewer system was constructed primarily of wood-stave pipe, buried 5–10 ft underground. During emergency repair immediately after the earthquake, most of the damage to the water-supply and sewage-collection systems was found to be caused by the separation of the pipes at the joints. The hydrostatic pressure created by the earthquake also forced sand and silt into the ruptures, filling the pipes, valves, and fire hydrants. In many cases, manholes were also filled with sand and silt. Ruptured pipes usually were found wherever a ground fracture appeared.

The bid schedule in the contract documents was established on a unit-cost basis for each type of repair anticipated. The type of repair was established from the experience gained during the emergency repairs, and the number of repairs was based on a systematic condition survey. The contract covered only the lines and appurtenances required to serve the habitable structures.

Under the contract, sanitary sewer manholes were to be cleaned and the sewer pipe inspected to determine the areas requiring repair. The water-distribution system was to be isolated between valves and pressure-tested to locate the leaks; all fire hydrants and valves were to be checked and repaired if necessary.

The damaged pipe and appurtenances found during the inspection were repaired sufficiently to last 1–2 years. On August 14, 1964, the contract for winterization was completed.

REHABILITATION OF SCHOOLS

The rehabilitation of the schools presented an unusual problem. At the time of the earthquake, Valdez had only one high school and one grade school. The wood-frame grade school, constructed in the 1930's, was supported on a concrete foundation with a partial basement; the interior was mainly finished with wood-lath and plaster. During the earthquake, the center of the building settled about 1 ft less than the perimeter footings of the building. The interior walls were extensively cracked, the plumbing and wiring were damaged, and water and mud from the tidal waves had wrought havoc in the basement. The high school was a modern wood and steel-frame structure containing eight classrooms, a library, manual-training room, gymnasium, and kitchen. The interior partitions in the classroom area were predominantly of concrete block, with a wood-frame partition separating the gymnasium from the classroom area. Most of the damage sustained by the structure was caused by horizontal strain in the soil, which spread the foundation outward from the roof and parallel to the long axis of the building. This spreading caused the floor slab to settle and crack and forced all the walls out of plumb. Much of the damage was attributed to the height of filled ground under the floor. The concrete-slab floor, resting on the ground, was as much as 3 ft above the exterior finished grade.

The federal and state agencies and the local authorities, in an effort to improve morale, agreed that all efforts should be made to rehabilitate the schools so that classes could resume on the normal opening date in September. They feared that families would be reluctant to return permanently if schools were not available for the whole school term.

The high school was to be repaired only to the minimum extent required to provide safe classroom space. Because the period of occupancy was to be only 1 year, the people of Valdez realized that it would not be economical to repair the gymnasium, and it would have to be posted as an unsafe area. On August 6, 1964, a contract was awarded for inspection and repair of the heating, electrical, and utility systems, for the filling of floor-slab cracks, and for epoxy grouting of cracks in the concrete-block walls. The contract was completed on August 17, 1964.

Estimated costs for repair of the grade school were $85,000, and the condition of the school was such that it would be a fire hazard even after repairs; consequently, the decision was made to construct a new six-classroom grade school. The length of time required for the procurement of construction materials and the impaired docking facilities at Valdez made it obvious that a school could not be constructed in time if normal contracting procedures were followed. A steel, rigid-frame prefabricated insulated-panel structure, similar to that used in many other localities for school facilities, was therefore procured by government purchase. The design of the foundation and interior of the structure was formulated while the exterior of the structure was being fabricated at the stateside factory. The building for the new grade school was originally planned to be next to the Valdez High School, to minimize the cost of installing utilities and to reduce operating costs. The foundation and floor-framing system were to be designed to permit the structure to be moved, without being dismantled, to the Mineral Creek site after it had been prepared. Because a feeling of apprehension about the potential move developed among the citizens of Valdez, the Federal Reconstruction and Development Planning Commission for Alaska recommended that the grade school be constructed at the new Mineral Creek site, despite the additional expense and inconvenience of transporting the children to school. This move would be a visible proof of the determination of all agencies involved to provide new homesites for the citizens as soon as possible, and it would stimulate the citizens' desire to move. The city council agreed to this recommendation, and the final decision to move was made on July 30, 1964.

The construction of the school at the Mineral Creek site posed many engineering and construction problems. The townsite planning had so far progressed only to the plotting stage, and no utilities were available within 4 mi. The design of streets and utilities had not begun. The foundation for the grade school was therefore designed to permit future raising if the finished floor grade was not compatible with the drainage pattern of the developed townsite. A temporary septic tank and a cesspool were provided, a domestic-water-supply well with a chlorinator was installed in the mechanical room of the building, and a 30-kW diesel generator was borrowed from the U.S. Air Force "Helping Hand" stock. On August 17, 1964, a contract was awarded for site preparation and construction. The prefabricated structure purchased by the government arrived at Valdez about August 22, 1964, and the facility was ready for occupancy on September 21 (Figures 19 and 20).

TEMPORARY REHABILITATION OF HOSPITAL

The temporary rehabilitation of the city-owned hospital was necessary to meet the medical needs of the area. The next closest hospital to Valdez is at Glennallen, which is approximately 120 mi northeast by road. The Valdez Hospital is a one-story concrete-block structure with a concrete slab on grade and a roof system of steel joists and decking. The building is about 37 X 160 ft, with a 38 X 53-ft service and boiler room attached. The long axis of the building lies in a north–south direction. The fissures in this area developed in this direction, spreading the floor of the structure in the direction of the short axis. The overall change in width was approximately 1/2 in. The walls of the structure, other than those of the boiler room and the ambulance entrance, were not structurally damaged and were only slightly cracked. The ambulance entry wall was extensively

FIGURE 19   New elementary school ready for occupancy in 1964. The children were the first citizens of the Mineral Creek townsite.

damaged above the overhead door frame, and the frame was torn from the wall; the exterior wall of the furnace and service room also was extensively damaged.

To make the facility operable, the cracks in the floor slab and in the walls that were not structurally damaged were filled and refinished. The structurally damaged walls of the ambulance entrance and boiler room were replaced. The heating, plumbing, and electrical systems were tested and repaired. The windows and doors were checked for operation and adjusted where necessary.

To further stimulate the economy, interior partitions of the hospital were rearranged to accommodate the 35 mental patients who had been evacuated immediately after the earthquake to the Alaska State Psychiatric Institute at Anchorage. Part of the hospital was used for emergency treatment of acutely ill patients.

REHABILITATION OF THE AIRPORT

The state-operated airport facilities east of the city consisted of a gravel-surfaced runway, 150 ft wide and 4,400 ft long, and a 225 X 600-ft gravel-surfaced apron northeast of the city. One wood-frame hangar stood next to the apron. The airport was on the northern part of the delta on which the city was constructed (Figure 2). Damage was attributed solely to the fissuring induced by the earthquake, which traversed the southwestern 1,000 ft of the runway, the apron, and the access road from the city.

Immediately after the earthquake, the fissures were filled with pit-run gravel to provide minimum operating facilities. The fill material used for emergency repairs contained many cobbles and was not compacted in the fissures.

OEP entrusted the responsibility for the restoration of state-owned airport facilities to the Federal Aviation Agency (FAA). To eliminate competition for materials and labor between government agencies and duplication of government personnel in one locality, the design and the restoration of state-owned airports was transferred to the

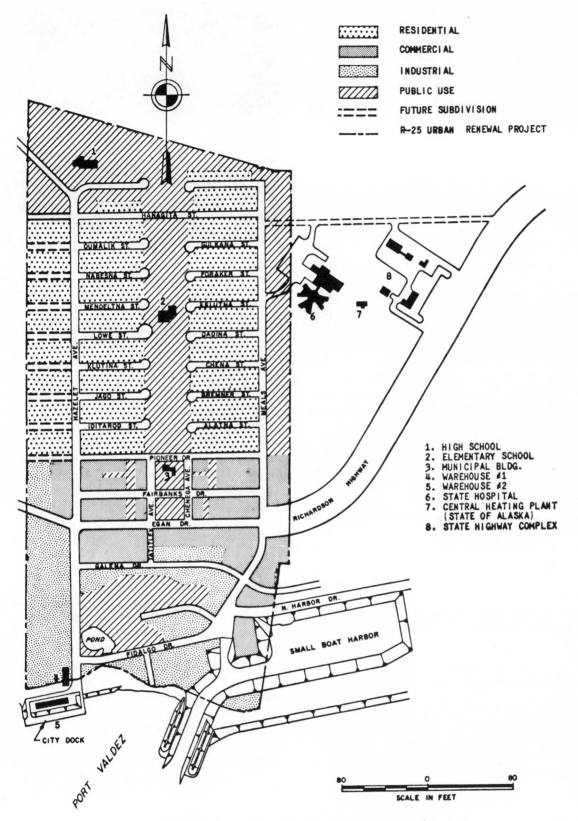

RESIDENTIAL
COMMERCIAL
INDUSTRIAL
PUBLIC USE
FUTURE SUBDIVISION
R-25 URBAN RENEWAL PROJECT

1. HIGH SCHOOL
2. ELEMENTARY SCHOOL
3. MUNICIPAL BLDG.
4. WAREHOUSE #1
5. WAREHOUSE #2
6. STATE HOSPITAL
7. CENTRAL HEATING PLANT
   (STATE OF ALASKA)
8. STATE HIGHWAY COMPLEX

SCALE IN FEET

FIGURE 20 Valdez–Mineral Creek townsite development plan.

Corps of Engineers in places where they were operating. The FAA retained the responsibility and authority for determining the scope of restoration required.

The restoration of the airport facilities required the excavation of all the fissures in the runway and apron to a depth of 4 ft.

Backfill material not susceptible to frost was placed and compacted in 8-in. lifts, the entire runway was shaped to grade, and a 6-in.-thick surface course of sandy gravel was placed and compacted.

RECONSTRUCTION EFFORT AT MINERAL CREEK TOWNSITE

The design and construction for the permanent restoration of Valdez at the Mineral Creek site began immediately after the decision to relocate the town. The Corps of Engineers was responsible for the planning and design of the waterfront facilities, the Alaska State Housing Authority for the overall planning of the municipal area, and the Alaska State Highway Department for the Richardson Highway extension into the townsite. The agencies involved cooperated to plan, design, and construct an entirely new city within the time allotted. The Mineral Creek townsite was donated to the city of Valdez by Owen Meals, a local pioneer and manager of the Valdez Power and Light Company. The criteria for the development of the city included utilities and streets for residential and commercial lots to accommodate a population of 1,000–1,500. A State of Alaska complex consisted of a psychiatric hospital, with beds for 150 mental and 15 emergency patients, and the highway district headquarters that included an office building, shop, service station, and materials laboratory. The waterfront was to have a dock capable of accommodating deep-draft vessels and associated cargo-storage warehouses; a small-boat basin was to be constructed, incorporating a ferry landing slip at the boat-harbor end of the entrance channel, small-boat slips, moorage area, and a boat-repair grid (Figure 20). The model prepared during the area-development study is shown in Figure 21.

DOCKING FACILITIES

The dock facilities destroyed by the earthquake were owned by the Valdez Dock Company. Although private businesses were not eligible for government financing for reconstruction, the docking facilities were considered an economic necessity; therefore, OEP authorized the design and construction of a deep-draft dock capable of accommodating one liberty-class vessel. The site selected for the dock was the only one available with ready and economical access to the town. The basic design criteria were as follows:

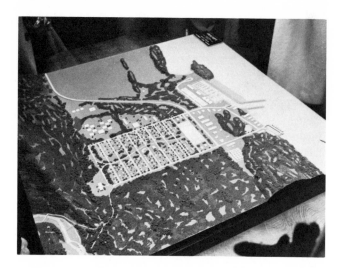

FIGURE 21   Model of the proposed development of the Mineral Creek townsite, as visualized in 1964.

- The water at the face of the dock must be 35 ft deep at mean lower low water.
- The dock must be 60 ft wide to permit limited cargo storage without interfering with the unloading equipment.
- Approaches must be adequate to accommodate loading and unloading traffic.
- The structure must be capable of supporting 600 psf live load and H20-S16 moving live load.
- The site should be large enough for construction of a 500-ft-long warehouse immediately shoreward of the dock. The site should also permit future expansion of the dock to accommodate three vessels simultaneously.

Originally, the dock was to be capable of handling both petroleum products and dry cargo. The requirements to handle petroleum products were subsequently deleted at the request of the local authorities.

Several types of dock construction were analyzed, including timber with wood deck, steel pile with reinforced concrete, concrete-encased steel pile and concrete deck, and prestressed concrete pile with concrete deck. Timber pile with wooden deck was found to be most economical on the basis of cost alone. The preliminary estimates indicated that the initial cost of a timber structure was approximately 25 percent less than the next most economical structure. A prestressed concrete-pile and concrete-deck structure would have been the most economical if the annual maintenance and replacement costs were considered. The timber structure, however, was selected to conform to the OEP requirements to provide a minimum facility at the lowest initial cost.

Because the need for docking facilities was urgent, the occupancy date was scheduled for November 30, 1964. In an effort to meet this schedule, the material for the dock was procured by the government while the design was being completed.

Construction of the dock began on August 20, 1964. By the middle of November, half the dock was available for the unloading of vessels, and the entire dock and approach facilities were completed by May 15, 1965 (Figure 22). Figure 20 shows the location of the dock and associated facilities.

WAREHOUSES

The construction of two warehouses was authorized by OEP to provide dry cargo storage near the docking facility. Warehouse 1 was placed near the east approach ramp with its long axis perpendicular to the dock to provide maneuvering room for vehicles unloading containerized cargo. Warehouse 2 was constructed between the dock access ramps on the fill that was placed adjacent to the dock (Figure 20).

OEP limited the facilities in the following ways:

• The warehousing area was to be adequate to handle the anticipated freight over the dock, but was not to exceed the original area existing before the earthquake.

• The type of structure was to be the most economical available that could perform the desired function.

• Limited office space was to be provided.

• Utilities, including electricity, were to be supplied.

• One warehouse was to be heated to provide warm storage.

The final design specified two preengineered metal buildings on concrete foundations. Both warehouses were approximately 60 ft wide; one was 200 ft long and the other about 300 ft long. Warehouse 2 was to be heated to provide storage for cargo susceptible to freezing.

FIGURE 22 An offshore view of the new city dock and east approach ramp constructed at the Mineral Creek townsite. Warehouse 1 is on the right and Warehouse 2 is on the left.

Storage facilities were to be available when the dock facilities were completed. Because the site for Warehouse 2 could not be prepared in time, a contract was awarded on August 14, 1964, for the construction of Warehouse 1. This contract was also to furnish the frame and siding of the preengineered building for Warehouse 2 in order to expedite its construction when the site was ready. Construction of Warehouse 1 progressed throughout the winter. The frozen ground was difficult to excavate; artificial heating was required to cure the foundation and floor-slab concrete, and bad weather caused some delay. Warehouse 1 was scheduled for completion in mid-May 1965, but was not finished until mid-June.

The construction of Warehouse 2 was scheduled for the summer of 1965 and was to be completed in December 1965. Delays in final siting and site preparation prevented construction from beginning until September 25, 1965. Warehouse 2 was designed to provide warm cargo storage, but the late construction start would not permit occupancy during the 1965–1966 winter. Temporary partitions and heat were therefore installed in Warehouse 1 to provide limited warm storage during that winter; the City of Valdez supplied the heat. Warehouse 2 was finally completed on July 1, 1966 (Figure 22).

SMALL-BOAT BASIN

The restoration of the small-boat basin was authorized partly under the Corps of Engineers disaster reconstruction authority and partly under the authority of OEP. Criteria for the siting and design were as follows:

• The project area was to be 4.7 acres.

• The site should permit future expansion.

• The depth was to be 12 ft below MLLW, sufficient to accommodate the vessels that were expected to use the basin.

• The boat basin should be rectangular in shape.

• The basin should be designed to limit the wave height to a maximum of 1 ft, or if possible, 6 in.

• The entrance-channel should have a minimum width of 100 ft to permit the passage of two large fishing boats traveling in opposite directions.

Two sites were examined for feasibility and cost. City Planning Associates, who had been engaged by the Alaska State Housing Authority to plan the Mineral Creek townsite, preferred one site, between two ribs of rock, that appeared to be the natural location for the basin.

Rock had been encountered within the project depth at this location, however, and the flat beaches would necessitate long breakwaters. These factors would increase the estimated construction costs to $1.5 million more than the cost at the alternate site. The Corps of Engineers therefore recommended construction of the boat basin at the alternate site just east of the dock facilities, and this site was finally approved on June 19, 1964, at a meeting attended by representatives of the federal and state commissions, participating federal agencies, city officials, and representatives of State of Alaska departments contributing to the development of the townsite.

Work began on the design of the basin as soon as the site had been approved. Two breakwaters, a west breakwater 625 ft long and an east breakwater 685 ft long, were needed to reduce the wave energy entering the basin. These breakwaters, constructed entirely of stone, were developed to resist the anticipated wave forces. The small-boat basin was made 12 ft deep below MLLW, 460 ft wide, and 1,270 ft long.

A two-lane boat-launching ramp was constructed at the northwest corner to serve trailer-transported boats, and a ferry-landing slip was constructed at the northwest corner of the entrance channel to provide easy access and turning room for the ferry *Chilkat*, which sails regularly between Valdez and Cordova.

The inner-harbor facilities were designed jointly by the State of Alaska and the Corps of Engineers. The state designed the float facility in accordance with its long-range development plan, although OEP limited the restoration of the facility to 168 individual stalls and a transit-vessel moorage area. The float system was provided with water, electricity, and fire-fighting equipment.

The replacement boat-repair grid, which facilitates minor maintenance of small boats during low tides, was authorized for construction by OEP. The grid was originally planned for the north bank of the small-boat basin, where it could be constructed most economically. The city officials objected to the location, mainly because the north side was more accessible from the town, and they thought that activities there should be associated with routine operation of boats. The city's harbor-development plan located the harbor-oriented light-industrial area at the south side of the harbor, which was the city's preferred location for the boat-repair grid. Although the government would not sanction the additional expenditure of funds to extend the water and electrical service lines from the north side of the harbor to accommodate the facility, the city decided to construct the boat-repair grid at the south side of the harbor, with utility service mains. Water and electrical services were installed on the grid, but the city was to be responsible for the extension of utility-service mains from the north side of the basin. Figure 20 shows the location of the boat basin and related inner-harbor facilities.

The basin was excavated from an area where an average elevation of about +12 ft MLLW allowed flooding at high tide. The cohesionless material excavated would provide an excellent fill for future foundations; it was placed alongside the basin to finished grade elevations between +21 and +23 ft MLLW and created an area suitable for the construction of onshore facilities and parking. Part of the excavated material was placed at the south side of the basin to prevent encroachment of waves from the port of Valdez. The south fill, 250 ft wide and to an elevation of +23 ft, provides usable land for light industrial development. Fill around the east end, which provides access to the south side of the basin, was also obtained from the basin excavation.

Construction began on August 17, 1964, and occupancy of the western 300 ft of the basin was scheduled for November 15, 1964, to provide safe anchorage for the boats remaining in Valdez. The contractor originally planned to excavate the basin with land-based equipment down to the water table and complete the excavation to the projected depth with a floating hydraulic dredge. The hydraulic dredge, however, could not excavate the material quickly enough, and the work was completed with land-based equipment. Water was withdrawn from the excavation with high-capacity pumps to the dredging depth of –14 ft MLLW. The dredge continued to excavate the entrance channel from the port of Valdez. Because of this, a plug had to be left at the throat of the entrance channel until the entire basin was excavated. The plug was then removed with a dragline and dredge. Because of these construction difficulties, the limited refuge area needed during the winter of 1964–1965 was not available until the excavation of the basin was completed in May 1965. Work on the ferry-landing dock was finished on June 21, 1965, and the inner-harbor facilities were ready on September 25, 1965, thereby providing a completed facility (Figure 23).

MUNICIPAL DEVELOPMENT

The development of the townsite planning and land acquisition was sponsored by the Urban Renewal Administration and was under the direction of the Alaska State Housing Authority. The authority engaged City Planning Associates, Inc., of Mishawaka, Indiana, to develop an integrated city plan (Figures 20 and 21). The commercial area of the town lies immediately north of the waterfront facilities. The Richardson Highway, an overland transportation tie with the interior of Alaska, enters the city from the east, passes through the commercial district, and continues south to the waterfront facilities. The residential area is north of the commercial district, where two main north–south streets run along the east and west boundaries of the project area. The residential lots are served with east–west streets that terminate in *culs-de-sac*. A north–south mall serves as a park and recreation area during the summer and in winter provides a storage place for snow, which may be as deep as 11 ft in the area. The grade school is in the mall, so that the children can

FIGURE 23 Northwesterly view of the Valdez small-boat basin and the Mineral Creek townsite during construction. Ferry-landing ramp is at left of harbor. Small-boat launching ramp is at northwest corner of basin, and small-boat floats are in center of basin, with access ramps extending to the north shore. The boat-repair grid is on the south shore. The land south and north of the basin was, for the most part, reclaimed by building it up with granular material excavated from the basin.

walk to school from anywhere in the residential area without crossing any streets; the high school is north of the area. The municipal water wells are north and west of the residential area, and the water-supply storage tank stands on a rock bench on the west flank of the mountain that overlooks the city.

The State of Alaska complex occupies the northeastern portion of the alluvial fan and is bordered on the west by the city and on the east by the Richardson Highway.

The coordinated plan and schedule established for the development of the new city was simple to formulate, but the execution was difficult and required close coordination of the agencies involved. The installation of all utilities and the construction of the base of the streets within the townsite were planned for 1964 and early 1965, to permit private construction during the normal 1965 construction season. To meet this goal, construction had to continue through the winter and all preliminary work had to be completed by October 1964. OEP authorized the Corps of Engineers to design the streets and utilities in accordance with the plan prepared under the direction of the Alaska State Housing Authority. The design progressed simultaneously with the development of the urban-renewal project, which also was scheduled for completion by October 1964. The development of the urban-renewal project, from its conception to the point of permitting construction, which could take several years under normal conditions, was accomplished in a few months with the coordination provided by the Federal Reconstruction Commission.

The Mineral Creek townsite was ideal for municipal development. The alluvial fan dips gently from northwest to southeast from an elevation of 60 ft to sea level. The north end of the fan terminates abruptly at the base of the steep mountain, and the port of Valdez borders the southern end of the fan. The entire area was usable because the part of the fan occupied by the city contained few gulleys or stream channels. The gentle overall southeasterly slope provided an ideal drainage pattern for both storm and sanitary sewers. The alluvial fan contained an adequate groundwater supply for the community, and a water-storage tank could be stationed on the mountain at the northern boundary at an elevation sufficient to supply the community by gravity.

Design of Streets and Utilities

The Corps of Engineers initiated the design of the new townsite by awarding a contract for a topographic survey sponsored by OEP. This survey supplied the Alaska State Housing Authority with the data to complete the plan and to design the streets and utilities. Because the Corps of Engineers and the Alaskan engineering firms had a tremendous workload throughout the areas affected by the earthquake, the firm of Cornell, Howland, Hayes, and Merryfield of Seattle, Washington, was engaged to design the streets and utilities and to prepare the contract documents. The features of the design are described by the firm's project engineer, James W. Poirot (1965).

The streets were designed for initial construction with a gravel surface, side ditches, and culverts. The plan and profile of the streets were designed to permit future construction of paving, curbs, gutters, sidewalks, and storm drains (Figure 24). The contract documents permitted the immediate advertising and award of contracts for street construction. OEP authorized the construction of a gravel-surfaced road, but could not authorize funds for paving or construction of curbs, sidewalks, and storm drains because few such improvements had existed at the old townsite. The improvements could not have been otherwise financed in time to permit their inclusion in the initial construction contract.

Pertinent design criteria for the construction included 6 ft of frost penetration (frost depths were calculated to extend to 9.3 ft under a cleared surface if the water table was below that depth); snow up to 11 ft deep, with an annual snowfall of up to 20 ft; and a rainfall intensity of 1 in. per hour. A runoff coefficient of 1 was used, on the assumption that the ground might be frozen at the time of the rain. Other general design criteria included a snow load of 80 psf, a wind load of 20 psf, an earthquake loading for seismic zone 3, a minimum temperature of –28 °F, and a mean annual precipitation of 62 in.

The design of the streets provided sufficient strength to accommodate the anticipated loads during the frost-melting periods and recognized that some frost heaving might occur.

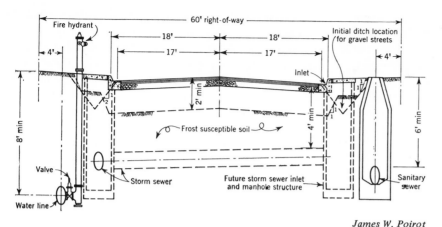

FIGURE 24 Typical relation of streets and utilities. The cross section shows the coordination between the gravel-surfaced street, water- and sewer-system design as originally awarded for construction, and the final arrangement of the paved streets, curbs, sidewalks, and storm-drain system, which were subsequently constructed, with the exception of the sidewalks in the residential area.

James W. Poirot

The reduced subgrade strength criteria required cohesionless soil, not susceptible to frost, to a depth of 2 ft below finished grade. In areas consisting of silts with high water table or organic soils, all the undesirable materials were excavated during construction and placed on the adjoining lots, with special precautions against piling the material around the large cottonwood trees that were scattered throughout the area. The townsite was covered with alders about 15 ft high and up to 6 in. in diameter; these were cleared from the residential area, and attractive lots were developed by grading them to drain down the natural southeast slope toward the waterfront.

Plans for drainage had to take into consideration that 15–20 ft of compacted snow would be stored on the mall at the *culs-de-sac*. The snow-storage areas were drained through a system of ditches, culverts, and catch basins. Rollover curbs at each *cul-de-sac* and in the residential streets facilitated crossing by snow-removal equipment and eliminated the need for driveway sections whose locations would not be known until the houses were planned. Vertical curb faces were used along the streets in the central business area.

The catch basins were designed as inlet manholes to allow for the flow of slush during thaws. The side inlet manholes left an open space 4 in. high and 3 ft long in the vertical face. Storm sewers were designed with a minimum cover of 4 ft to avoid conflict with water and sewer lines, which were designed with a minimum cover of 8 and 6 ft, respectively. The storm-sewer system was allowed to run within the frost zone because it requires the least reliability of the three systems. A typical cross section of the streets and their relation to the storm sewers is shown in Figure 24.

Water-Supply and Distribution Design

The two potential water-supply sources were Mineral Creek, which flowed along the west boundary of the townsite, and groundwater within the alluvial-fan deposit. The initial cost of construction and associated costs of water treatment

made the groundwater source attractive if sufficient quantities were available. Investigation of the characteristics of Mineral Creek water revealed that the flow from the glacier was extremely turbid during spring and summer; because treatment facilities would be needed, it would not be economical for use.

The Corps of Engineers drilled an 8-in. exploratory well to a depth of 90 ft during the summer of 1964, and a copious amount of water was encountered. They installed a 20-ft Johnson well screen; pump testing produced 340 gallons per minute (gpm) with a 2-ft drawdown. The engineers concluded that there was an extremely permeable aquifer that could produce flows up to 1,000 gpm. One pump station was therefore designed for a capacity of 400 gpm and another for a capacity of 600 gpm; the exploratory well was used as one of the permanent sources. Although the initial supply for the city was based on 300 gpm, the second well was included for standby capacity for fire control, future industrial growth, and domestic expansion. The second 12-in. well was to be drilled west of the exploration well. Each well was capable of producing at least 500 gpm with the present pumps.

A storage site to provide the proper flow of water by gravity was difficult to find, not because of a lack of high terrain, but because of the extremely steep slopes and solid rock of the mountains. An area was finally found that would ensure a minimum static pressure of 75 psi throughout the townsite. An access road to the reservoir has a grade of 25 percent at one point, but can be negotiated by vehicles with four-wheel drive. Reservoir capacity was established at 700,000 gallons, based on the total water demand, including that for fire control. The storage capacity was larger than was immediately required, but future expansion on the rock bench would have been extremely difficult because of the limited space available. OEP therefore approved the large tank on the basis of the engineering recommendations. Because a heat analysis indicated that ice could form on the inner wall of the steel tank and on the water surface, the tank was completely insulated with cellular glass 3 in. thick.

The piping system developed to transfer the water from the wells to the reservoir was a two-pipe supply system that permitted the use of either pipe in the event of an outage. The two pump stations operated alternately through an automatic control system based on the water level in the reservoir. The water supply is chlorinated, and metering facilities have been installed to maintain records of the water demand in the new town and of the performance of the wells.

Because an inspection of water-line damage in the Anchorage area revealed that gray cast-iron pipe had sustained less damage than asbestos-cement pipe, all water pipelines installed were to be of either ductile cast-iron or gray cast-iron. The Corps of Engineers sent their supply of cast-iron pipe to Valdez for installation during the winter of 1964–1965.

All water-distribution pipelines and sewer lines were laid between the sidewalk and the right-of-way line because the snow cover on adjacent property insulates the ground, making frost penetration there less than under the streets. Pipeline maintenance outside the sidewalks is also less costly because removal and replacement of pavement is not necessary.

Water-supply pipelines lie at a minimum depth of 8 ft. Electrical thaw wires are installed in each service connection to thaw frozen connections. The thaw wires are connected near the main and routed along the service pipe to the service stop at the property line (Figure 25). By connecting a welding generator to the wire and service pipe, heat can be generated from electrical current to thaw the line.

All fire hydrants are connected close to the mains, to prevent dead-end water lines. The connection consists of a tee off the water mains, a gate valve, and the fire hydrant (Figure 25). In the southeastern part of the site, where the water table is high, a copper pipe is connected to the bottom of each hydrant so that it can be dewatered below groundwater level. When compressed air is admitted to the hydrant, it forces the water to the surface through the copper tube. Without this feature, it would have been impossible to drain hydrants below the water table, and ice would then have developed inside the hydrants, making them inoperative during the winter season. Street lights, which were to be installed by the Copper Valley Electric Association, were to be placed near the fire hydrants, with a mark high up on appropriate poles to indicate, when the hydrants are covered with snow, that there is a fire hydrant at their base. Utility-service connections were installed at each lot. Because there is no permanent paving facility at Valdez, to bring paving equipment back into the area might have proved expensive. Service connections for water sewers were installed to all property lines during the initial construction so that future pavement removal and replacement would not be necessary.

Sewerage Facilities

A sewage-collection system for the new town was designed to serve all residential, commercial, and industrial areas, including waterfront facilities. The sewer lines were placed between the property line and the sidewalk on the south and east sides of the street rights-of-way; the water lines were on the opposite side.

Sewer lines were of asbestos-cement pipe with a minimum diameter of 8 in. This pipe was used because of its resistance to the high groundwater in some areas, because of the longer pipe lengths available with fewer joints, and because the asbestos-cement joints were watertight. A tight system was considered necessary because all water entering it would have to be treated at a proposed sewage-treatment plant, and a lower flow would result in lower operating costs. To prevent freezing, the sewer lines were placed at a minimum depth of 6 ft. The system was designed for gravity

James W. Poirot

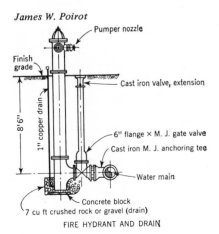

FIRE HYDRANT AND DRAIN

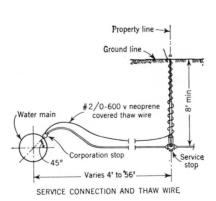

SERVICE CONNECTION AND THAW WIRE

FIGURE 25 Typical fire-hydrant and service-connection details.

operation until the sewage reaches the treatment plant, where a raw-sewage pumping station lifts it into the plant. The sanitary sewage facilities at the waterfront, however, need a pumping station to lift the sewage into the gravity system.

Although the source of funds for the construction of the sewage-treatment plant was uncertain, the facility was designed to provide continuity with the outfall system if or when funds became available.

The investigation of sewage-treatment facilities included a study of lagoons, primary treatment, and secondary treatment. The Alaska State Department of Health determined that facilities should provide at least primary treatment. Because of deep snows and high groundwater, a sewage lagoon was not economical. Although only primary sewage-treatment facilities were considered, an investigation indicated that extended-aeration package-treatment plants would be most desirable. This system produced almost no sludge, whereas a combined digester-clarifier primary-treatment plant would require sludge-disposal facilities. The higher degree of treatment in an extended aeration plant also minimized outfall constuction.

The sewage-treatment plant was designed to have a circular concrete tank, 39-ft in diameter, to house the treatment process. Because of extreme snow depths, it was necessary to construct a shed-type structure over the plant. The enclosure will be a glue-laminated beam, shed-type building, with one end open and both sides partly open to provide ventilation. The western end will be enclosed to house control facilities, a laboratory shop, and a heating system. The raw-sewage pumping station is designed as a packaged, buried structure with access through the floor of the control building. The architecture of the sewage-treatment plant conforms to the "little Switzerland" decor of the public facilities. The structure has a steep-pitched roof, covered with cedar shakes and resawn cedar siding.

In the activated-sludge-treatment facility, the sewage has to be heated to a minimum of 34 °F when the air temperature is –20 °F; this is done by a hot-water heating system with copper heating coils in the circular tank.

The partly buried concrete tank is designed with a 2-ft-thick concrete bottom slab to resist the buoyancy force from high groundwater. The part of the concrete tank above ground is insulated on the inside to minimize heat loss during periods of extreme cold.

The outfall line extends southward into the port of Valdez through a 16-in. cast-iron pipe with locking lugs. The outfall was constructed over a tideflat and into the water, to discharge at 5 ft below mean sea level.

A buried, packaged pump station is planned to serve the waterfront. This facility will be completely prefabricated, except for an A-frame shed constructed over the entrance hatch.

Construction History of Streets and Utilities

A contract was awarded on August 24, 1964, to clear the streets and residential areas of a thick growth of alders. The large cottonwood trees were not removed from the residential lots. The clearing contract was awarded before the completion of the street and utility design, to provide an area for the disposal of material excavated for the street subbase. The street and utility construction was thus greatly accelerated, and the contract was completed by October 7, 1964.

The initial contract for the construction of the streets and utilities was awarded September 29, 1964, before the completion of the design of the more complicated facilities, such as pumphouses, reservoirs, and sewage-treatment facilities, in an effort to allow as much time as possible for the installation of the underground facilities before the coming winter's freeze. The work included construction of the gravel-surfaced street network; construction of water lines to the two pumphouse locations, to the storage reservoir in the residential area, and to a point near Warehouse 1 on the waterfront; and the construction of the sewage-collection system for the residential area to the sewage lift station. Under this contract, water and sewage-collection mains were also extended into the state-complex area. The water and sewage-collection mains in the business district were not included in the contract because the planning for that area was not finished, and the construction schedule allowed for no delay. The initial phase of the work was completed with a minimum of conflict with private builders, during the following construction season. All construction ceased by December 19, 1964, because of frozen ground and high winds, but by then the majority of the streets and water lines were in place in the residential area. The contract was originally scheduled for completion on July 20, 1965, but because of the weather and of several modifications and the addition of part of the storm sewers to the contract, it was not completed until October 22, 1965. The initial contract for the streets and utilities was funded mainly by OEP within their authority to restore facilities similar to those in existence before the earthquake. The Urban Renewal Administration funded a small portion of the contract that was beyond the authority of OEP.

A second contract was awarded March 5, 1965, for the construction of the water-pump houses and water-storage tank, and a separate contract was awarded to drill the 12-in. well. With the completion of the contract on September 21, 1965, the city of Valdez had a reliable water supply and distribution system that satisfied its immediate needs and provided adequate water for future expansion.

Local, state, and federal agencies were unable to find funds with which the city could construct the sewage-treatment plant. It was therefore necessary to construct a sewage-lift station and outfall to the port of Valdez to temporarily provide a usable facility. The completion of this construction on November 12, 1965, provided the city with a usable sewage-disposal system.

The plan for the central business district was completed during the summer of 1965. A contract was awarded August 31, 1965, for the construction of the streets, parking areas, and utilities; the construction included only the base course and did not provide paving for the streets and parking areas. By July 1966, the network of water-distribution and sewer-collection lines for the townsite was completed, and all the street construction for the townsites, with the exception of pavement, curbs, and sidewalks, was finished.

Items, such as storm drains, not funded by OEP were funded by the Urban Renewal Administration.

During the spring of 1966, financing became available for the paving of all the municipal streets, the construction of curbs, the completion of the storm drain system, and the construction of sidewalks in the central business district and the main north and south residential access streets. A north-south asphaltic concrete sidewalk was also constructed through the mall, and sidewalks from each *cul-de-sac* to the central sidewalk facilitated pedestrian traffic to the central business district (Figure 26). All the facilities that were originally planned as reconstruction projects for the community were now completed. The construction of the side-walks in the residential area and of the sewage-treatment plant, and the integration of the waterfront sewage-

FIGURE 26 Southern view of the townsite completed to the extent permitted in 1966. The new Richardson Highway enters the city from the northeast (lower left) and terminates at the dock in the southwest (upper right). The state complex is seen at left. A petroleum-products dock, constructed with private funds, is situated between the dry-cargo dock and small-boat basin. The receiving tanks and pumping facilities are southeast of the city (upper right).

collection system with the municipal system, all of which required funding from sources not originally allocated for disaster relief, still remained to be accomplished. The completed facility closely resembled the model prepared by City Planning Associates (Figures 21 and 26). The Office of Emergency Planning authorized reconstruction at the Mineral Creek townsite of the municipal structures that had been owned by the city of Valdez before the earthquake. These structures included a consolidated junior and senior high school, an elementary school, and a municipal building that housed the city administration offices, firehouse, maintenance shop, and jail.

Junior and Senior High School

Construction of the junior and senior high school building received priority and was scheduled to be completed by the normal school opening date in September 1965. Work on the design was held up by delays in choosing the site at Mineral Creek and delays in the formulation of the design criteria. The city authorities of Valdez requested that a structure, similar in general arrangement and architectural appearance to the preearthquake structure, be constructed at the Mineral Creek site with a few minor floor-plan modifications. Time and money would be saved by using the existing plans. The floor plan was changed to run in the north–south direction to fit the new site at the northwest corner of the town (Figure 20).

Because the preearthquake school sustained only minor structural damage, the possibility of salvaging all usable structural members, windows, and siding was considered. Sufficient time was not available between the normal school closing date in May and the normal opening date in September to dismantle the existing structure and erect it at the Mineral Creek site. The school was therefore constructed entirely of new material.

The architect–engineer firm of Manley and Maher, Anchorage, designed the original school building and also adapted the plans to the Mineral Creek site. The school contained regular classrooms, a commercial room, a domestic science room, and a science room; a shop for manual training and a multipurpose room for physical training were also included. A portable stage and dressing rooms made it possible for the multipurpose room to be used as an auditorium. The structure also contained a library, administration offices, and storage areas.

The building was basically a wood-frame structure, with an exterior of prefinished metal siding and an interior finish of vinyl-covered gypsum board. The roof and ceiling are supported by open-web steel joists. A contract for the construction of the school was awarded on August 31, 1965, and scheduled for completion on January 19, 1966. The facility was actually transferred to the city for occupancy on January 17, 1966.

Elementary School

The Mineral Creek townsite elementary school, constructed in 1964, had no multipurpose room, although the school at the preearthquake townsite had included such a room. The City of Valdez requested that a similar room be added to the new elementary school. OEP authorized the design and construction of the addition with a stipulation that it be the same size as the preearthquake room. The preearthquake high school contained a small kitchen, and the city requested that the kitchen now be placed in the multipurpose area of the elementary school. The multipurpose addition has an area of approximately 4,640 ft^2, of which 3,360 ft^2 can be used for varied activities. The remainder of the area contains rest rooms and a kitchen. The mechanical room in the elementary school was modified to accommodate a boiler to supply the heat and hot water to the multipurpose room.

The construction of the addition was included in the contract for the construction of the junior–senior high school. The completed facility is shown in Figure 27.

Municipal Building

A municipal building to replace the preearthquake facilities was the last item constructed for the City of Valdez with PL 875 funds. The Office of Emergency Planning authorized the design and construction of a single structure to house the administration offices, fire station, and maintenance shop. The city authorities requested that two jail cells be incorporated in the structure and agreed to pay for the construction because no similar facilities existed in the preearthquake structure. The building was to be constructed in the central business district (Figure 20); work on the design was consequently delayed until the planning of that area was completed.

FIGURE 27   South and east elevation of the completed Valdez elementary school. The classrooms are in the left wing, and the multipurpose room is in the right wing.

FIGURE 28   South elevation of the Valdez municipal building. The west wing (left) houses the fire station and law-enforcement facilities. The portion of the east wing shown (right) is the main corridor for the administration offices and city council chambers.

The architect–engineer firm of Edwin Crittenden and Associates was retained by the Corps of Engineers to prepare a concept study. After approval of this study, the firm prepared the contract documents. The building is an L-shaped wood-frame structure; the service wing houses three fire-fighting vehicles and contains a stall for vehicle and equipment maintenance. The administration wing contains four offices, a conference room, and a city-council chamber. An office for the fire and police chiefs, two jail cells funded by the city, a rest room, a mechanical room, and storage facilities are situated at the juncture of the two wings. The architectural treatment is simple and blends well with the alpine setting of the townsite.

A contract was awarded on September 9, 1965, for the construction of the facility, which was completed for occupancy on January 12, 1966. The exterior painting and grading, which were deferred until the following summer, were completed July 9, 1966. A view of the completed structure is shown in Figure 28.

STATE OF ALASKA COMPLEX DEVELOPMENT

OEP authorized the relocation of all state-owned facilities that had existed before the earthquake. The state obtained land on the Mineral Creek fan east of the northeast corner of the townsite (Figure 20). The state-owned facilities, reconstructed with PL 875 disaster funds, consisted of a hospital for the mentally retarded and for acute patient care and a State Highway Department complex. The firm of Edwin Crittenden and Associates was awarded a contract to prepare a development plan for the entire state-complex area. The most important factor in the area development was to place the structures, utilities, and streets so as to create a physical and aesthetic separation between the hospital and highway complex, and yet to consolidate facilities to reduce initial and future maintenance costs. The highway complex was planned to the west of the area, with close access to the highway. The hospital was located adjacent to the city. A visual separation was obtained by selective clearing that utilized the thick growth of alder trees as a natural screen. The central-heating plant stands between the two areas and supplies heat and steam for hot water to the highway buildings and the hospital. Separate architect-engineer contracts were awarded for the design of the hospital, heating plant, and highway complex.

STATE PSYCHIATRIC HOSPITAL

According to the State of Alaska Department of Health officials, the city of Valdez was an ideal location for the State Psychiatric Hospital.

The preearthquake psychiatric hospital building was a series of single-story concrete-block structures originally constructed to be a motel. Several of the structures were extensively damaged by vibrations during the earthquake, although there was no injury or loss of life (Figures 12–14).

The City of Valdez owned and operated a relatively complete and modern hospital for the treatment of acute patients. The hospital was larger than the city needed and too expensive for it to run. Valdez and state officials agreed that a facility in which the equipment, service departments, and personnel for both types of hospital could be consolidated would be more economical and easier to operate. The state agreed to assume the ownership and operational responsibility of both facilities and to make the intensive-care section available to the public.

The psychiatric-hospital building in use before the earthquake was not designed to function as a hospital; the arrangement was not very efficient and in many cases was substandard. OEP therefore based the restoration criteria on the number of patients served, rather than on the replacement of the same area that had been available before the earthquake. The maximum number of patients was established at 150 mental patients and 15 intensive-care patients, and the design criteria were based on the minimum facilities established by the U.S. Public Health Service manuals to serve that number. Additional space for indoor recreation, however, was authorized because of the limited outdoor activity possible during the winter months. Additional storage area was also authorized because many items not locally available require long-term storage. All usable equipment from both the state and city hospital was to be moved into the new facilities. State Health Department and city officials estimated that intensive-care facilities for 15 patients would be adequate for the anticipated population of Valdez.

On the basis of these limitations, the State of Alaska Department of Health developed detailed design criteria and submitted them for review to the Corps of Engineers and to OEP.

When the design criteria for funding had been established, the architect–engineer firm of Narramore, Bain, Brady, and Johanson of Seattle, Washington, was engaged to prepare the plans and contract documents. Particular attention was given to the traffic flow in the development of the floor plan and in the consolidation of the various elements to minimize the number of personnel required to operate the hospital. The architect, who selected reinforced concrete as the primary building material, was instructed to arrange the basic facility to permit future expansion to twice the design population by a minimum amount of modifications to the basic structures. The psychiatric area was designed with an octagonal core, the center of which serves as a recreation and therapy area. A clerestory roof was provided over the recreation and therapy area to provide a well-lighted and relaxing environment. The outer perimeter of the center core contains the main hallway, central storage, offices, a dayroom for each ward, and nurse stations located in such a way that one nurse can survey two separate wards during periods of low activity. Six wards project from the sides of the center core, and a service area stood between each pair of wards. Each ward can accommodate 25 patients and was designed as an independent unit to permit the patients as much privacy as possible. Each ward also has access to the outdoors, with ample window area to relieve the feeling of confinement. The service area contains toilet, bathing, and storage facilities for each ward.

The intensive-care area, hospital administration, clinical area, and service areas are in a separate building, connected by a corridor to the psychiatric hospital. The medical consultants recommended separation of the psychiatric area from these facilities to minimize the confusion that might be generated by the activity associated with its normal operation. All the facilities within this structure serve both the psychiatric and intensive-care hospitals.

The building and all its parts were designed to support all dead, live, and lateral loads for seismic zone 3 design requirements. The structure, built entirely of reinforced concrete, provides a minimum fire-resistance of 1 hour, except where higher ratings are applicable. The roof is a one-way slab-and-beam design, with 4½-in.-thick slab. The walls are concrete shear with square reinforced-concrete tied columns. All floors are structural slabs over a 4½-ft crawl space that contains utility piping.

A contract was awarded on September 3, 1965, for the construction of the facility. Although originally to have been completed by November 7, 1966, it was not actually finished until February 1967 (Figure 29).

DEPARTMENT OF HIGHWAYS COMPLEX

Valdez is the headquarters of the Valdez District, State of Alaska Department of Highways, which is responsible for

FIGURE 29   Aerial view of the State of Alaska Hospital, Valdez.

the maintenance and engineering for approximately 900 mi of primary and secondary highways that run from the seaport cities into the interior of Alaska. The primary Richardson Highway crosses the rugged terrain of the Chugach Mountains, the flood plains of the Copper River, and the interior of Alaska. The Richardson Highway is the only overland tie that exists from the ice-free ports in the Prince William Sound area to the interior of Alaska.

The Department of Highways facilities that existed in Valdez before the earthquake were obtained from the Department of Commerce Bureau of Public Roads after Alaska became a state in 1959. The facilities consisted of an office building, materials, and a maintenance complex. The office building was a two-story wood-frame structure in the business district and contained about 10,000 ft^2 of floor space, which was occupied by the administrative and engineering staff of the Valdez Highway District. The earthquake damaged the structure to the extent that it became a hazard to public safety and was immediately demolished.

The major structure in the maintenance complex was a shop containing facilities for complete maintenance and rebuilding of the equipment used in the district. The building contained about 6,400 ft^2 of floor space and was constructed of steel and wood frame.

Four other structures on the site were used for storage and as a materials testing laboratory. These were wood-frame structures with corrugated metal siding that had been in a poor state of repair. They, however, did serve their function as indoor-storage areas necessary in an area of high snowfall. The complex also contained fuel-dispensing facilities.

The maintenance complex sustained only minor earthquake damage; the only damage reported resulted from a fissure that extended through a sand-storage shed and the maintenance shop. The fissure moved the columns and

threshold slab on the south side of the maintenance shop structure 2–3 in., leaving the south wall out of plumb. Relocation of the Department of Highway facilities at the Mineral Creek townsite was authorized by OEP. The possibility of moving the existing structures to the new location and of reusing salvageable material was studied and rejected as not economical. OEP therefore authorized the Corps of Engineers to replace the facilities in the Mineral Creek townsite with new structures, stipulating that the type of construction should be based on the least initial cost consistent with minimum code requirements and good engineering practices. The area of the buildings was not to exceed the preearthquake size.

The State of Alaska submitted definitive drawings of the structures they desired for review by OEP to determine the eligibility for PL 875 funds. The Corps of Engineers was then authorized to proceed with the design. Five buildings were to be constructed whose total area was not to exceed the preearthquake total. The buildings were to include an office building, soils and materials laboratory, a service station, storage building, and a maintenance shop. The State of Alaska was to supply all equipment required for proper functioning. The Corps of Engineers awarded an architect-engineer contract to Edwin Crittenden and Associates, of Anchorage, for the design of the highway complex whose location is shown in Figure 20.

A comparative-cost estimate to determine the most economical type of construction for the office building was required. Wood-frame construction was found to be the most economical. The one-story structure contained about 10,000 ft^2 of space, 5,500 ft^2 of which was occupied by administrative offices, and the remainder by an engineering office. The two areas were separated by the main entry (Figure 30).

The maintenance shop contained three stalls for the warm storage and maintenance of heavy equipment. Overhead doors were installed at both ends of each stall to eliminate the necessity of backing large equipment out of the

FIGURE 30   South and north elevation of the new State of Alaska Department of Highways office building.

FIGURE 31 South and east elevation of the State of Alaska Department of Highways vehicle maintenance shop (with attached lean-to) and the warehouse building at left.

stall and to permit more than one small vehicle to use a stall. Rails were embedded in the floor slab of one stall to eliminate floor damage caused by track vehicles. About 5,400 ft² of stall space were provided. The shop area was about 3,200 ft² and contained a machine and welding shop, a washroom, an engine room, an office, and a parts-storage area. The building (Figure 31) was constructed primarily with preengineered structural steel, with prefinished metal-panel exterior siding and insulated inner panels.

The warehouse building, adjacent to the maintenance shop, was connected to it by a covered corridor. A pre-engineered structural-steel building, about 3,200 ft² was planned. The building was to be used as a central warehouse for items required to operate the entire State of Alaska complex. Two supply offices were constructed in the building.

A laboratory for testing highway construction materials was constructed next to the administration building. The wood-frame building blended architecturally with the office building and covered an area of 2,000 ft². It contained a soils-testing laboratory, chemical and concrete laboratories, and office space (Figure 32).

The State of Alaska requested a service-station building, separate from the maintenance shop to minimize traffic congestion. OEP approved the request with the stipulation that the area of the service station be deducted from the area authorized in the maintenance shop. The service station was built with structural steel rigid frames, metal siding, and insulated inner panels. The building contains one stall with hydraulic lift for minor and preventative maintenance, a parts and storage area, and an office. A covered two-pump fuel-dispensing facility was also included. The steam for hot water and heat for the complete highway complex was supplied by the central heating plant. A contract for the construction of the highway-complex structures was awarded June 25, 1965, and construction was completed in June 1966.

The master plan for the state complex specified a central-heating plant that would serve all the buildings within the complex, thereby materially reducing maintenance and operating costs. The power plant stands between the Alaska State Hospital and the highway complex (Figure 20).

The architect–engineers designing the hospital and highway complex were asked to submit the steam demand for their structures as soon as the design had progressed to the stage where an accurate determination could be made. They indicated that 10,000 lb of steam an hour would be required to operate the hospital, and 2,300 lb of steam an hour would be required to operate the highway complex.

A warehouse for the hospital's bulk storage was also authorized, which was to be used not only for the maintenance of equipment but also for the manual training and recreation of the mental patients, for an office, and for a boiler room large enough to accommodate two boilers and two emergency electric generators. OEP could not authorize the installation of the emergency generators; therefore the state of Alaska funded a 100-kW generator capable of supplying the emergency demand of the hospital and boilers.

An architect–engineer contract was awarded to Ralph R. Stefano, Consulting Engineers, Fairbanks, Alaska, for the design of the heating plant and steam-distribution system throughout the complex. The architect–engineer submitted several alternatives, from which the state selected a structural-steel-frame building. Two 10,000 lb/hour boilers were provided to ensure adequate steam for the operation of the hospital in the case of a shutdown of one boiler. The oil-fired boilers were large enough to provide steam at 100 psi throughout the distribution system. The fuel-oil storage tanks were buried and can store a 1-month supply of fuel. Steam is distributed in a buried two-pipe conduit at 100 psi to the various buildings, where the pressure is reduced within the structures to 15 psi.

FIGURE 32 South and west elevation of the State of Alaska Department of Highways material testing laboratory (foreground). Office building is in the background.

FIGURE 33 South and east elevation of the central-heating plant that supplies steam for heating and domestic hot water for the entire State of Alaska complex.

A contract was awarded on August 10, 1965, for the construction of the heating plant and distribution system. The construction facility was completed on July 15, 1966 (Figure 33).

FINANCIAL PARTICIPATION BY FEDERAL AGENCIES

The economic survival of Valdez and of other earthquake-damaged communities would not have been possible without the financial aid of the federal government. Immediate financial aid for disaster relief and the winterization of the essential facilities in the earthquake-stricken site was given by OEP under the authority of Public Law 875.

The development of the new community and the acquisition of property in the stricken townsite were sponsored by the Urban Renewal Administration. OEP supplied most of the funds for the design and construction of the facilities required to provide an economic base for the new community. It also provided funds for the design and construction of the streets and utilities to permit private development and for the design and construction of publicly owned buildings.

The Corps of Engineers contributed funds for the small-boat basin expansion that was within the authority of the amendment to the Alaska Omnibus Bill.

The Farmers' Home Administration of the Department of Agriculture and the Small Business Administration (SBA) made available funds for private loans to build houses and reestablish the commercial base of the community. The Farmers' Home Administration financed the construction of 40 private dwellings. The SBA financed 44 businesses, including 10 or 11 commercial fishing boats, and the construction of 16 homes. Some of the businessmen who obtained loans did not relocate in Valdez.

Although the federal financial participation was the most significant, the city and the state also contributed funds within their capabilities for the reconstruction effort. Private concerns also were active in financing private establishments. A summary of federal expenditures required for the disaster relief and reconstruction program and for financing of private loans is shown in Table 1.

SUMMARY

The total funds provided by the federal government for the reconstruction of Valdez were $26,485,585—a per capita average of approximately $35,000 for a population of 750. This is the injection of capital required for the reconstruction. In addition, there were other homeowners who had to abandon old homes and build new ones. It is estimated that the cost of reconstructing Valdez was approximately $50,000 per capita.

The new city of Valdez was conceived, planned, designed, and constructed from March 27, 1964, to February 1967. This was made possible only by the money and assistance provided by the federal government. An important factor that contributed to the successful completion of this project was the close cooperation of the federal, state, and local agencies and the various authorities and personnel whose efforts were coordinated by the Federal Reconstruction Commission.

TABLE 1   Summary of Federal Financial Participation

Source	Purpose	Amount (in dollars)
Office of Emergency Planning (OEP)	City of Valdez (municipal)	$ 6,614,642
	State of Alaska facilities	5,253,639
	Ferry-landing ramp	153,353
	Airport rehabilitation	55,994
	Small-boat basin	1,583,924
	Inner harbor facilities	482,135
SUBTOTAL		$14,143,687
Urban Renewal Administration	R-22 Project (Stricken townsite)	3,127,011
	R-25 Project (Mineral Creek townsite)	1,592,887
SUBTOTAL		$ 4,719,898
Corps of Engineers	Small-boat basin expansion	476,000
Farmers' Home Administration	40 private dwelling loans	804,000
Small Business Administration	44 commercial loans	5,893,500
	16 private dwelling loans	448,500
SUBTOTAL		$ 7,622,000
TOTAL FEDERAL PARTICIPATION		$26,485,585

ACKNOWLEDGMENT

Except as otherwise noted, illustrations are credited to the U.S. Army Corps of Engineers.

REFERENCES

Coulter, Henry W., and Ralph R. Migliaccio, 1966. Effects of the earthquake of March 27, 1964, at Valdez, Alaska. U.S. Geological Survey Professional Paper 542-C. Washington: Government Printing Office. 36 p. Also *in* The Great Alaska Earthquake of 1964: Geology. NAS Pub. 1601. Washington: National Academy of Sciences, 1971. p. 359–394.

Poirot, James W., 1965. Utilities for a relocated town in Alaska. *Civil Engineering* (American Society of Civil Engineers), 35 (March), 50–53.

Shannon & Wilson, Inc., 1964. Report on subsurface investigation for Mineral Creek townsite, city of Valdez, Alaska, to U.S. Army Engineer District, Anchorage, Alaska. Seattle: Shannon & Wilson, Inc. 34 p.

Annotated
Bibliography

Alaska Department of Health and Welfare. Preliminary report of
earthquake damage to environmental health facilities and services in Alaska. Mimeographed Report of Alaska Department of
Health and Welfare, Division of Public Health. Juneau: Branch of
Environmental Health, 1964. 47 p.
Examines damage to water facilities, to sewerage, and to food, milk,
and medical supplies in communities affected by the March 1964
earthquake; describes the assistance in restoration of utilities that
was given by the Corps of Engineers.

Alaska Division of Mines and Minerals. The great Alaska earthquake,
March 27, 1964. Alaska Division of Mines and Minerals Miscellaneous Paper No. 1. Juneau: Alaska Division of Mines and Minerals, 1964. 4 p.
Gives preliminary data on the 1964 Alaska earthquake and attributes
principal damage to landslides and tsunamis.

Alaska Monthly Review of Business and Economic Conditions. The
economic impact of the Alaskan earthquake. College: University
of Alaska, Institute of Business, Economic and Government
Research. *Alaska Monthly Review of Business and Economic
Conditions*, 1 (May 1964), 1-8.
Describes economic effect of the 1964 earthquake on the Alaskan
Highway, the airports, and The Alaska Railroad, pointing up the
need for engineering know-how to prevent serious bottlenecks.

Alaska State Housing Authority. Earthquake damage to homes in
Alaska. Housing and Home Finance Agency–Alaska State Housing
Authority Damage Survey Report. Anchorage: Alaska State
Housing Authority [1964]. 19 p.
Evaluates damage sustained by residential properties in Anchorage,
Valdez, Seward, and Kodiak as a result of the 1964 earthquake, with
a view to determining possible repairs for damaged structures.

Alaskan Construction Consultant Committee. Reconstruction and
development survey of earthquake damages in Alaska. Committee Report prepared for the Federal Reconstruction and Development Planning Commission for Alaska. Washington: Federal
Reconstruction and Development Planning Commission for
Alaska [1964]. 98 p.
Recommends (1) competitive bidding as the proper method of
handling reconstruction after the Alaska earthquake; (2) a study of
the necessity for a sewage treatment plant in the Anchorage area;
(3) abandonment of the port at Whittier after completion of the
Seward docks and railroad; and (4) an engineering study of a cause-
way to the Kenai peninsula.

American Institute of Architects and Engineers Joint Council Committee. Report of the American Institute of Architects and the
Engineers Joint Council Committees on the Restoration and Development of Alaska. Anchorage: Federal Reconstruction and
Development Planning Commission for Alaska, 1964. 50 p.
Suggests that new generating equipment for Seward be ordered, that
research programs be initiated to develop designs and materials for
underground utility systems with increased resistance to earthquake
damage, and that there be better city enforcement of building code
regulations.

Anderson, L. O., and J. A. Liska. Wood structure performance in an
earthquake in Anchorage, Alaska, March 27, 1964. U.S. Department of Agriculture Forest Service Research Paper, Forest
Products Laboratory 16. Madison, Wisconsin: Forest Products
Laboratory, 1964. 12 p.
Finds that well-constructed light wood-frame buildings for the most
part resisted the forces of the Alaska earthquake and that vibrational damage to housing in the Anchorage area was superficial because the majority of homes there were of this type of construction.

Arno, Norman L., and Leonard F. McKinney. Harbor and waterfront
facilities *in* The Great Alaska Earthquake of 1964: Engineering.
NAS Pub. 1606. Washington: National Academy of Sciences,
1973.
Discusses the work of the U.S. Army Corps of Engineers in repairing
the harbors and waterfront communities of Anchorage, Cordova,
Homer, Kodiak, Seldovia, Seward, and Valdez after the 1964
Alaska earthquake.

Aspinall, Wayne N. Providing assistance to Alaska for reconstruction. *Congressional Record* (August 6, 1964), 17747-17748.
Submits conference report and statement on a bill (1) to amend the
Alaska Omnibus Act to provide assistance for urban renewal projects made necessary by the 1964 earthquake and (2) to extend the
term of home disaster loans for replacement or repair of damaged
or destroyed dwellings.

Atkinson, E. L. Transportation: Must for disaster recovery. *National Defense Transportation Journal*, 20 (July–August 1964), 42–45, 56, 58–59.
Reports on damages to surface transport links as a result of the great Alaska earthquake; indicates a need for reorganized planning to meet the transportation emergency.

Aune, Quintin A. Geologic hazards: Quick clays and California's clays: No quick solutions. *Mineral Information Service* (Publication of the California Division of Mines and Geology), 19 (August 1966), 119–123.
Defines quick clays such as were present in the Bootlegger Cove Clay in the Anchorage area at the time of the 1964 Alaska earthquake and draws a comparison to clay problems in California.

Ayres, J. Marx, Tseng-yao Sun, and Frederick R. Brown. Nonstructural damage to buildings *in* The Great Alaska Earthquake of 1964: Engineering. NAS Pub. 1606. Washington: National Academy of Sciences, 1973.
Studies the extensive earthquake damage to nonstructural elements of buildings such as facades, ceilings, partitions, elevators, lights, electrical systems, plumbing, ventilation and air-conditioning systems, heating systems, fire-protection systems, and communications systems.

Bartlett, E. L. Reconstruction of the State of Alaska. *Congressional Record*, 110 (April 8, 1964).
Comments on President Johnson's establishment of the Federal Reconstruction Development and Planning Commission and on the bill presented by Senator Jackson to provide aid for necessary reconstruction in Alaska due to the 1964 earthquake.

Becker, John C. Highway destruction in Alaska: Part II, Roadway damage. *American Highways*, 43 (January 1965), 27–29.
Reports on extensive subgrade and pavement damage throughout the 1964 Alaska earthquake area and on restoration of damaged highways there.

Belanger, David P. Port of Whittier *in* The Great Alaska Earthquake of 1964: Engineering. NAS Pub. 1606. Washington: National Academy of Sciences, 1973.
States that the port of Whittier, although close to the epicenter of the 1964 earthquake, did not sustain severe structural damage from ground shaking but received extensive damage from submarine landslides and tsunamis.

Benuska, K. Lee, and Ray W. Clough. Dynamic analysis of building failures *in* The Great Alaska Earthquake of 1964: Engineering. NAS Pub. 1606. Washington: National Academy of Sciences, 1973.
Analyzes by digital computer three Anchorage buildings, damaged during the 1964 Alaska earthquake, to correlate effects predicted by dynamic response theory with observed damages; concludes that the observed damage would have been expected even without construction deficiencies.

Berg, Glen V. Response of buildings in Anchorage *in* The Great Alaska Earthquake of 1964: Engineering. NAS Pub. 1606. Washington: National Academy of Sciences, 1973.
Examines behavior of Anchorage buildings significantly damaged by vibration and finds that most of the structural failures were associated with inadequate connections of structural members.

Berg, Glen V., and James L. Stratta. Anchorage and the Alaska earthquake of March 27, 1964. Report of the American Iron and Steel Institute. New York: American Iron and Steel Institute, 1964. 63 p. Abstract *in* Geophysical Abstracts 239: December 1966 (U.S. Department of the Interior Geological Survey). Washington: Government Printing Office, 1966. p. 1113.
Describes vibration damage to structures in the Anchorage area at the time of the 1964 Alaska earthquake, analyzes structural weaknesses, and stresses the importance of design, supervision, and inspection in earthquake zones.

Blume, John A., and Associates Research Division. Report on structural damage in Anchorage, Alaska, caused by the earthquake of March 27, 1964. Report prepared for Structural Response Program, Operational Safety Division, Nevada Operations Office, U.S. Atomic Energy Commission. San Francisco: John A. Blume and Associates Research Division, 1966. 91 p.
Evaluates the response of typical structures to ground motion caused by the Alaska earthquake in 1964 and analyzes structural and architectural damage from the standpoint of the causative mechanisms.

Bockstege, Herman H., Jr. Estimated damage to Anchorage Natural Gas Corporation and Alaska Pipeline Company facilities caused by earthquake on March 27, 1964 (Appendix A). Report of the Executive Vice President, April 24, 1964. Anchorage: Anchorage Natural Gas Corporation, 1964. 4 p.
Reports on damage to the natural gas facilities of the Anchorage Natural Gas Corporation as a result of the great Alaska earthquake and estimates the cost to repair and replace these facilities to be in excess of $1 million.

Brevdy, June. Target vulnerability studies, recovery research: Alaskan Project 1964. U.S. Naval Radiological Defense Laboratory Technical Report 751. San Francisco: U.S. Naval Radiological Defense Laboratory, 1964. 106 p.
Makes comparison between recovery from the results of the 1964 earthquake in Alaska and recovery from the effects of a nuclear attack, observing particularly the response of commercial structures to the shock.

Britt, R. H. Earthquake damage repair at Sitkinak Loran Station. *The Engineer's Digest* (U.S. Coast Guard), 133 (October–November–December 1965), 35–37.
Describes the postearthquake restoration of the Sitkinak Loran Station under a contract negotiated by the Civil Engineering Branch of the 17th Coast Guard District and completed by October 3, 1964, at a final cost of slightly more than $361,000.

Bruder, Wallace A. Earthquake changes Alaska shoreline (Abstract) *in* Science in Alaska, 1964: Proceedings Fifteenth Alaskan Science Conference, College, Alaska, August 31 to September 4, 1964. George Dahlgren, editor. College: Alaska Division American Association for the Advancement of Science, March 15, 1965. p. 284.
States that tectonic changes, landslides, and tsunamis, resulting from the 1964 earthquake, produced major shoreline changes.

Burdick, John L., editor. Profile of structural damage, Anchorage, Alaska, earthquake of 27 March 1964. [Fairbanks]: University of Alaska, Department of Civil Engineering [1964]. 4 p.
Presents the results of a house-to-house survey of all structures in a

two-block strip in Anchorage, recording the magnitude, type, and distribution of damage for a representative cross section of the city after the great Alaska earthquake.

Burton, Lynn R. Television examination of earthquake damage to underground communication and electrical systems in Anchorage *in* Effect of the earthquake of March 27, 1964, on the Eklutna Hydroelectric Project, Anchorage, Alaska. U.S. Geological Survey Professional Paper 545-A. Washington: Government Printing Office, 1967. p. 25–30.
Describes the use (by the U.S. Army Corps of Engineers) of a small-diameter, closed-circuit television camera to pass through the cable ducts, thereby examining earthquake damage to Anchorage's underground communication and electrical systems.

Campbell, Ian. Preparedness for disaster . . . The geologist's role. *Mineral Information Service* (Publication of the California Division of Mines and Geology), 18 (March 1965), 51–53.
Points out the fact that the hazard presented by the Bootlegger Cove Clay was ignored when some of Anchorage's most expensive residences were built in an extensive area of this clay and were therefore lost in the landslide resulting from the 1964 earthquake.

Century Film Productions. Alaska earthquake. 100-ft, 16-mm black and white film of Alaska damage [no sound]. Seattle: Century Film Productions [1964]. (Copy of one-page film list on file, Library, National Academy of Sciences–National Academy of Engineering, Washington, D.C.)
Presents views of the collapsed J. C. Penney store, wrecked buildings and sunken street (Fourth Avenue), and the Turnagain area in Anchorage, as well as debris in Seward, Kodiak, and Valdez–a graphic portrayal of the damage caused by the Alaska earthquake.

Christensen, Mark N., and Bruce A. Bolt. Earth movements: Alaskan earthquake, 1964. *Science*, 145 (September 11, 1964), 1207–1216.
Reports on conference at which K. V. Steinbrugge told of earthquake building code in Anchorage at the time of the 1964 earthquake and R. E. Goodman reported on his Alaskan field observations of the relation between soil mechanics and damage to structures.

Chugach Electric Association, Inc. Survey of damage caused by the great Alaska earthquake. Anchorage: Chugach Electric Association, Inc. [1964]. 34 p.
Analyzes the 1964 Alaska earthquake damage to the electrical distribution system, transmission line, and power plants and mentions long-range implications.

Clifton, Paul, Alvin L. Davis, and Austin D. Smart. Report of Alaskan earthquake disaster prepared by advisory team assigned to assist Alaska. Sacramento: California Department of Water Resources [1964]. 9 p.
Emphasizes the need for an engineering review of requested projects and for the appointment of an engineering coordinator to provide assistance to Alaska in reconstruction after the 1964 earthquake.

Clough, Ray W., and K. Lee Benuska. Earthquake performance of high-rise buildings: Digital computer investigation of the seismic response of a wide range of high-rise structural systems. A Report for Federal Housing Administration, Architectural Standards Division. Los Angeles: T. Y. Lin and Associates (Consulting Engineers), 1966. 367 p.

Investigates the structural performance of three buildings in Anchorage during the great Alaska earthquake and recommends design criteria for lateral earthquake forces in tall buildings.

Committee on Earthquake Engineering Research. Earthquake engineering research. A report to the National Science Foundation prepared by the Division of Engineering, National Academy of Engineering–National Research Council. Springfield, Virginia: Clearinghouse for Federal Scientific and Technical Information, 1969. 313 p.
Presents the engineering research point of view regarding structural dynamics analysis and structural synthesis and design in earthquakes such as the one in Alaska in 1964.

Committee on the Alaskan Earthquake. The Alaskan earthquake. California Department of Water Resources Bulletin No. 116-5. Sacramento: California Department of Water Resources, October 1965. 64 p.
Presents results of engineering investigations into structural failure, construction practices, and soil and foundation failures resulting from the 1964 Alaska earthquake.

Cook, Irvin P. 1964 earthquake damages to the Alaska Railroad. *AREA* [American Railway Engineering Association] *Bulletin*, 593 (June–July 1965), 750–755.
Describes the immobilization of 200 miles of The Alaska Railroad, damage to 110 bridges and to 225 pieces of rolling stock, and the sinking of 40 miles of roadbed from 4 to 10 feet into the Pacific Ocean, all as the result of the great Alaska earthquake.

Coulter, Henry W., and Ralph R. Migliaccio. Effects of the earthquake of March 27, 1964, at Valdez, Alaska. U.S. Geological Survey Professional Paper 542-C. Washington: Government Printing Office, 1966. 36 p. Also *in* The Great Alaska Earthquake of 1964: Geology. NAS Pub. 1601. Washington: National Academy of Sciences, 1971. p. 359–394.
States that fissures throughout the unconsolidated deposits at the head of the fiord, as well as the seismic shocks in March 1964, caused structural damage to many buildings in Valdez and destroyed the sewer and water systems; describes the relocation site for the town.

Cox, Doak C. Performance of the Seismic Sea Wave Warning System, 1948–1967. Report HIG-68-2. Honolulu: University of Hawaii, Institute of Geophysics, March 25, 1968. 79 p.
Explains the minimization of the hazards of tsunamis through the issuance of warnings (by the Seismic Sea Wave Warning System) based on seismic evaluation and marigraphic confirmation of tsunami generation.

Creisler, Joe. Tidal wave creates sanitation problems. *Public Works*, 95 (December 1964), 68–70, 138.
Details the sanitation program in Crescent City, California, necessitated by the tsunami resulting from the 1964 Alaska earthquake; states that the cleaning up was done in three phases: securing of the area and posting of quarantine signs, cleanup by local agencies, and final work by the U.S. Army Corps of Engineers.

Dobrovolny, Ernest, and Lidia Selkregg. Effects of the Good Friday earthquake on Anchorage, Alaska, and urban reconstruction (Abstract) *in* Science in Alaska, 1964: Proceedings Fifteenth Alaskan Science Conference, College, Alaska, August 31 to

September 4, 1964. George Dahlgren, editor. College: Alaska Division American Association for the Advancement of Science, March 15, 1965. p. 284.
Discusses the redevelopment plans in Anchorage after the 1964 earthquake and states that they were based on data supplied by a volunteer geologic evaluation group and on an extensive drilling, geophysical, and soil investigation by the U.S. Army Corps of Engineers.

Eckel, Edwin B. Effects of the earthquake of March 27, 1964, on air and water transport, communications, and utilities systems in south-central Alaska. U.S. Geological Survey Professional Paper 545-B. Washington: Government Printing Office, 1967. 27 p. Also *in* The Great Alaska Earthquake of 1964: Geology. NAS Pub. 1601. Washington: National Academy of Sciences, 1971. p. 705–731.
Notes that the great Alaska earthquake wrecked or severely hampered all forms of transportation, all utilities, and all communications systems over a large part of south central Alaska, but finds that temporary repairs were effected in a remarkably short time.

Engineering Geology Evaluation Group [Anchorage]. Geologic report: 27 March 1964 earthquake in Greater Anchorage area. Alaska State Housing Authority and City of Anchorage Report (unpublished). Anchorage: Alaska State Housing Authority and City of Anchorage, 1964. 47 p. plus maps and charts. (Copy on file, Library, National Academy of Sciences–National Academy of Engineering, Washington, D.C.)
Determines the effects of the 1964 earthquake geologically, recognizing areas of stability and instability around Anchorage, and provides background data for further engineering, geological, and soils studies and for the planning of proper land usage.

Federal Reconstruction and Development Planning Commission for Alaska. Response to disaster: Alaskan earthquake–March 27, 1964. Federal Reconstruction and Development Planning Commission Report. Washington: Government Printing Office, 1964. 84 p.
Details the 1964 postearthquake work of the scientific and engineering task force, along with the U.S. Army Corps of Engineers in Alaska, in recommending measures to reduce dangers in the event of another serious earthquake.

Fisher, Walter E., and Douglas H. Merkle. The great Alaska earthquake (2 vols.). Air Force Weapons Laboratory Technical Report AFWL-TR-65-92. Kirtland Air Force Base, New Mexico: Air Force Systems Command, Research and Technology Division, 1965. 100 p. (vol. I); 312 p. (vol. II).
Investigates the strengths and weaknesses of the many types of structures affected by the shocks of the 1964 earthquake.

Galliett, Harold H., George C. Silides, and Michael Baker, Jr. The Alaska Railroad, U.S. Department of the Interior: Proposal for investigation, report, and design of relocations and grade changes, Anchorage to Portage–A joint venture. Washington: U.S. Department of the Interior [1964]. 43 p.
Submits proposal for engineering studies necessary to make The Alaska Railroad operable between Mile 61.5 and Mile 104 through areas in which tide levels increased due to the 1964 earthquake displacement of the land.

Gardner, Thomas L., and Edmund J. McMahon. Assistance provided by the military bases *in* The Great Alaska Earthquake of 1964:
Engineering. NAS Pub. 1606. Washington: National Academy of Sciences, 1973.
Stresses the quick response of military bases in the region affected by the Alaska earthquake to the direct impact of the shock on their own territory and on the civilian communities in the area.

George, Warren. Introduction *in* The Great Alaska Earthquake of 1964: Engineering. NAS Pub. 1606. Washington: National Academy of Sciences, 1973.
Summarizes the studies of the 1964 earthquake damage and the analyses of its causes, which provide data of engineering significance that are valuable in prevention or mitigation of damage in future earthquakes.

George, Warren, Paul Knowles, John K. Allender, James F. Sizemore, and Duane E. Carson. Structures in Anchorage *in* The Great Alaska Earthquake of 1964: Engineering. NAS Pub. 1606. Washington: National Academy of Sciences, 1973.
Illustrates the performance of various types of structures in Anchorage during the 1964 earthquake and points out structural weaknesses.

George, Warren, Paul Knowles, John K. Allender, James F. Sizemore, and Duane E. Carson. Structures on military installations *in* The Great Alaska Earthquake of 1964: Engineering. NAS Pub. 1606. Washington: National Academy of Sciences, 1973.
Concludes that much of the damage to military installations in the Anchorage area at the time of the 1964 earthquake could have been avoided by better design and improved construction at little extra cost.

George, Warren, Paul Knowles, John K. Allender, James F. Sizemore, and Duane E. Carson. Structures in small communities *in* The Great Alaska Earthquake of 1964: Engineering. NAS Pub. 1606. Washington: National Academy of Sciences, 1973.
Finds that the modest buildings in small Alaskan communities in the 1964 earthquake were susceptible to damage that could have been avoided by better earthquake-resistant design and that some wood-frame buildings showed excellent resistance to ground shaking.

Goodman, Richard E., and H. Bolton Seed. Earthquake-induced displacements in sand embankments. *Journal of the Soil Mechanics and Foundations Division* (American Society of Civil Engineers), 92 (March 1966), 125–146.
States that, if a sand embankment is accelerated so that all points of the slope experience approximately the same acceleration at the same time, the result of overstressing is a surface slide involving a thin layer of soil, with the yield acceleration expressed in terms of the angle of friction and a shear strength intercept (functions of the cumulative downslope displacement).

Hadley, Homer M. The March 27 Alaskan earthquake–Effects on structures in Anchorage (discussion of the paper in June 1965 issue by Walter E. Kunze, John A. Sbarounis, and James E. Amrhein). *Journal of the American Concrete Institute*, 62 (December 1965), 1663–1670.
Expresses the reviewer's opinion (based on the results of the 1964 earthquake) that the only satisfactory nonskyscraper buildings (concrete or steel) are those that move bodily as a block or unit with the ground without major deformation.

Hansen, Wallace R. Effects of the earthquake of March 27, 1964, at

Anchorage, Alaska. U.S. Geological Survey Professional Paper 542-A. Washington: U.S. Government Printing Office, 1965. 68 p. Also *in* The Great Alaska Earthquake of 1964: Geology. NAS Pub. 1601. Washington: National Academy of Sciences, 1971. p. 289–357.
Analyzes the damage resulting from seismic vibration, ground cracks, and especially landslides in Anchorage at the time of the 1964 earthquake.

Hansen, Wallace R., Edwin B. Eckel, William E. Schaem, Robert E. Lyle, Warren George, and Genie Chance. The Alaska earthquake, March 27, 1964: Field investigations and reconstruction effort. U.S. Geological Survey Professional Paper 541. Washington: Government Printing Office, 1966. 111 p.
Summarizes the effects of the great Alaska earthquake and emphasizes field investigations made by the Geological Survey, the work of the Scientific and Engineering Task Force, and the reconstruction by the U.S. Army Corps of Engineers.

Hanson, Robert D. Behavior of liquid-storage tanks *in* The Great Alaska Earthquake of 1964: Engineering. NAS Pub. 1606. Washington: National Academy of Sciences, 1973.
Recommends that liquid-storage tanks be designed and constructed to resist realistic earthquake forces without significant uplift or that provisions be made to contain the contents of the tank after its collapse.

Harris, Leo. Foreman's report on earthquake, March 27, 1964 (unpublished). [Report of Valdez District Maintenance Foreman. Valdez: State of Alaska Department of Highways, 1964]. 4 p. (Copy on file, Library, National Academy of Sciences–National Academy of Engineering, Washington, D.C.)
Gives first-hand report of bridge and road damage, equipment problems, and cleanup work by the U.S. Army Corps of Engineers at Valdez after the 1964 earthquake.

Hauf, Harold D. Architectural factors in earthquake resistance *in* The Great Alaska Earthquake of 1964: Engineering. NAS Pub. 1606. Washington: National Academy of Sciences, 1973.
Emphasizes need for architectural plan to provide for reasonably symmetrical location of shear walls and for separations between dissimilar units or wings, as well as the need for a proper choice of building materials.

Housner, George W., and Paul C. Jennings. General introduction, conclusions, and recommendations *in* The Great Alaska Earthquake of 1964: Engineering. NAS Pub. 1606. Washington: National Academy of Sciences, 1973.
Stresses lessons to be learned by engineers from a study of the great Alaska earthquake and the data relating to the public safety and welfare during and after ground shaking.

Housner, George W., and Paul C. Jennings. Preface *in* The Great Alaska Earthquake of 1964: Engineering. NAS Pub. 1606. Washington: National Academy of Sciences, 1973.
Emphasizes the role of the U.S. Army Corps of Engineers in the reconstruction effort after the 1964 Alaska earthquake, as well as the ability of the Corps to assess the nature and cause of the damage.

Housner, George W., and Paul C. Jennings. Reconstituted earthquake ground motion at Anchorage *in* The Great Alaska Earthquake of 1964: Engineering. NAS Pub. 1606. Washington: National Academy of Sciences, 1973. (Copy of computer printout

for simulated horizontal ground acceleration for 240 seconds of ground shaking at Anchorage, Alaska, during the earthquake of March 27, 1964, on file, Library, National Academy of Sciences–National Academy of Engineering, Washington, D.C.)
Indicates, from the use of a simulated accelerogram of the ground motion at Anchorage during the 1964 earthquake, a maximum acceleration of approximately 15 percent of gravity, with strong ground shaking lasting about 1 minute and lesser shaking for about 3 minutes.

Housner, George W., and Paul C. Jennings. Rehabilitation of the Eklutna Project *in* The Great Alaska Earthquake of 1964: Engineering. NAS Pub. 1606. Washington: National Academy of Sciences, 1973.
Presents the first well-documented account of severe earthquake damage to an earth dam (during the 1964 earthquake) and of its rebuilding to raise the crest by 16 ft. Based on U.S. Bureau of Reclamation reports.

Hudson, Donald E., and William K. Cloud. Seismological background for engineering studies of the earthquake *in* The Great Alaska Earthquake of 1964: Engineering. NAS Pub. 1606. Washington: National Academy of Sciences, 1973.
Draws attention to the lack of any measurements of strong ground motion at the time of the 1964 Alaska earthquake because of the absence of suitable instrumentation in the area; assists in an engineering interpretation of the damage.

Jennings, Paul C. Response of coupled shear-wall structures *in* The Great Alaska Earthquake of 1964: Engineering. NAS Pub. 1606. Washington: National Academy of Sciences, 1973.
Analyzes coupled shear-wall idealizations of the Mt. McKinley and 1200 L Street apartment buildings in Anchorage (after the 1964 earthquake) to show that the distribution of failures in the spandrel beams and the fracturing of the shear walls in the two buildings are logical consequences of vibration in their fundamental modes.

Kachadoorian, Reuben. Effects of the earthquake of March 27, 1964, at Whittier, Alaska. U.S. Geological Survey Professional Paper 542-B. Washington: Government Printing Office, 1965. 21 p. Also *in* The Great Alaska Earthquake of 1964: Geology. NAS Pub. 1601. Washington: National Academy of Sciences, 1971. p. 439–459.
Describes 1964 earthquake damage at Whittier to part of The Alaska Railroad roadbed, the buildings of two lumber companies, the stub pier, the car-barge slip dock, several homes, fuel-storage tanks, and many buildings.

Kachadoorian, Reuben. Effects of the earthquake of March 27, 1964, on the Alaska highway system. U.S. Geological Survey Professional Paper 545-C. Washington: Government Printing Office, 1968. 66 p. Also *in* The Great Alaska Earthquake of 1964: Geology. NAS Pub. 1601. Washington: National Academy of Sciences, 1971. p. 641–703.
States that the chief engineering characteristics responsible for roadway and bridge damage in the 1964 Alaska earthquake include (1) thickness of roadway fills, (2) type of pile bents and masonry piers, (3) the weight ratio between the substructure and superstructure, and (4) the tie between the sub- and superstructure.

Kachadoorian, Reuben, and George Plafker. Effects of the earthquake of March 27, 1964, on the communities of Kodiak and nearby islands. U.S. Geological Survey Professional Paper 542-F.

Washington: Government Printing Office, 1967. 41 p. Abstract *in* The Great Alaska Earthquake of 1964: Geology. NAS Pub. 1601. Washington: National Academy of Sciences, 1971. p. 539–540.
Summarizes Kodiak property damage caused by tectonic subsidence and tsunamis resulting from the great Alaska earthquake; also gives information and property losses at Ouzinkie, Old Harbor, and Kaguyak.

Kerr, Paul F., and Isabella M. Drew. Quick clay movements, Anchorage, Alaska: A preliminary report. Air Force Cambridge Research Laboratories Scientific Report 5 (AFCRL-66-78). Bedford, Massachusetts: U.S. Air Force, Office of Aerospace Research, 1965. 133 p.
Indicates that quick clay initiated the slide action with deformation in overlying silts and gravel during the March 1964 earthquake in Alaska.

Kerr, Paul F., and Isabella Milling Drew. Quick clay slides in the U.S.A. *Engineering Geology* [Elsevier Publishing Company, Amsterdam], 2 (No. 4, 1968), 215–238.
Finds that the Anchorage quick clay (which caused landslides at the time of the 1964 earthquake) is apparently of glacial origin, formed at the coastline but subsequently elevated and leached of salt.

Kunze, Walter E., John A. Sbarounis, and James E. Amrhein. The March 27 Alaskan earthquake—Effects on structures in Anchorage. *Journal of the American Concrete Institute*, 62 (June 1965), 635–649.
Reviews requirements for earthquake-resistant structures, as indicated by an investigation of the damage in Anchorage resulting from the 1964 Alaska earthquake.

Lemke, Richard W. Effects of the earthquake of March 27, 1964, at Seward, Alaska. U.S. Geological Survey Professional Paper 542-E. Washington: Government Printing Office, 1967, 43 p. Also *in* The Great Alaska Earthquake of 1964: Geology. NAS Pub. 1601. Washington: National Academy of Sciences, 1971. p. 395–437.
Describes damage from submarine landsliding, tsunamis, and oil-tank fires in Seward as a result of the great Alaska earthquake.

Light, Herman Charles. Which buildings fail? *AIA* [American Institute of Architects] *Journal*, 42 (December 1964), 37–38.
States that the building ordinances in Anchorage had not been adhered to or adequately enforced prior to the 1964 Alaska earthquake and stresses the need for good structural design on stable soil.

Logan, Malcolm H. Effect of the earthquake of March 27, 1964, on the Eklutna Hydroelectric Project, Anchorage, Alaska *in* U.S. Geological Survey Professional Paper 545-A. Washington: Government Printing Office, 1967. p. 1–24. Abstract *in* The Great Alaska Earthquake of 1964: Geology. NAS Pub. 1601. Washington: National Academy of Sciences, 1971. p. 732.
Examines the 1964 Alaska earthquake damage to underground communication and electrical systems in Anchorage, as well as the repair of damaged facilities of the Eklutna Hydroelectric Project.

Long, Erwin L. Earth slides and related phenomena *in* The Great Alaska Earthquake of 1964: Engineering. NAS Pub. 1606. Washington: National Academy of Sciences, 1973.
States that some of the large destructive slides in the 1964 Alaska earthquake were the consequence of soil liquefaction, which caused a reduction in soil strength and was responsible for large soil movements.

Long, Erwin, and Warren George. Turnagain slide stabilization, Anchorage, Alaska. *Journal of the Soil Mechanics and Foundations Division* (American Society of Civil Engineers), 93 (July 1967), 611–627.
Recommends the protection of the seaward toe of the Turnagain slide against future erosion believed to be caused primarily by ice rafting of the soil.

McCulloch, David S. Slide-induced waves, seiching, and ground fracturing at Kenai Lake *in* The Great Alaska Earthquake of 1964: Hydrology. NAS Pub. 1603. Washington: National Academy of Sciences, 1968. p. 47–81.
Reports that deep lateral spreading of sediments toward delta margins displaced deeply driven railroad-bridge piles as a result of the great Alaska earthquake.

McCulloch, David S., and Manuel G. Bonilla. Effects of the earthquake of March 27, 1964, on The Alaska Railroad. U.S. Geological Survey Professional Paper 545-D. Washington: Government Printing Office, 1970. 161 p. Also *in* The Great Alaska Earthquake of 1964: Geology. NAS Pub. 1601. Washington: National Academy of Sciences, 1971. p. 543–640.
Analyzes the geologic controls of 1964 earthquake damage to The Alaska Railroad, with emphasis on damage caused by the mobilization of unconsolidated sediments.

Magoon, Orville T. Structural damage by tsunamis. Preliminary study presented at American Society of Civil Engineers Coastal Engineering Conference, Santa Barbara, California, October 11, 1965. 26 p.
Discusses damage to wood-frame structures of relatively light construction and to floating vessels at Crescent City, California, due to the tsunami resulting from the 1964 Alaska earthquake.

Martin, Kenneth K., and Charles A. Beasley. Post-earthquake attitudes on building materials *in* Science in Alaska, 1964: Proceedings Fifteenth Alaskan Science Conference, College, Alaska, August 31 to September 4, 1964. George Dahlgren, editor. College: Alaska Division American Association for the Advancement of Science, March 15, 1965. p. 280–283.
Deals with an investigation of the market potential for Alaskan clay products and with the effect of the 1964 earthquake in Alaska on basic attitudes toward building materials.

Mitchell, James K., William H. Houston, and George Yamane. Sensitivity and geotechnical properties of Bootlegger Cove Clay *in* The Great Alaska Earthquake of 1964: Engineering. NAS Pub. 1606. Washington: National Academy of Sciences, 1973.
Indicates that Bootlegger Cove Clay demonstrates no specific correlation between its mineralogical composition and its sensitivity.

National Board of Fire Underwriters and Pacific Fire Rating Bureau. The Alaska earthquake, March 27, 1964. San Francisco: The National Board of Fire Underwriters, 1964. 35 p.
Emphasizes the importance of the adoption and enforcement of an adequate building code, with consideration of soil conditions at the building site, as demonstrated by damage resulting from the 1964 Alaska earthquake.

O'Brien, Leo W. Amending the Alaska Omnibus Act to provide

assistance to the State of Alaska for the reconstruction of areas damaged by the earthquake of March 1964 and subsequent seismic waves. *Congressional Record* (July 21, 1964), 15909–15913.
Lists the items in the $275 million reconstruction program for Alaska after the 1964 earthquake, including restoration of public and federal facilities, highway repair, urban renewal projects, home disaster loans, civil works projects, and repurchase of home mortgages.

Oceanographic Services, Inc. Water level changes produced on the Pacific coasts of the United States and Canada by the Alaskan tsunami of 1964. Santa Barbara: Oceanographic Services, Inc., 1965. 14 p.
Comments on possible reasons for extremes in runup at Crescent City, California, and Alberni, British Columbia, in terms of water elevation, wave period, and sequence of wave amplitudes produced by the 1964 Alaska tsunami.

Office of Emergency Planning. The Alaska earthquake, a progress report—279 days of federal reconstruction effort. Office of Emergency Planning Progress Report. Washington: Office of Emergency Planning, 1964. 45 p.
Covers highlights of the response of federal departments and agencies, state and local governments, nongovernmental organizations, and the people themselves in the recovery program after the 1964 Alaska earthquake.

Office of Science and Technology. Earthquake prediction: A proposal for a ten year program of research. A report prepared by the *Ad Hoc* Panel on Earthquake Prediction. Office of Science and Technology, 1965. 136 p.
Recommends a ten-year research program calling for the development of a new generation of instruments for monitoring earthquake faults, for extensive surveys of fault zones, and for augmented research in earthquake engineering.

Osawa, Yutaka, Yukio Otsuki, Toshio Sato, Otohiko Suzuki, Hiroshi Tajimi, Kazuo Takahashi, and Kenzaburo Takeyama (Japanese Engineer Group). Earthquake damage survey in Anchorage area: Report of survey (Abstract) *in* Abstracts for 1964: GSA [Geological Society of America] Special Papers 82. New York: Geological Society of America, 1965. p. 359–360.
Discusses structural damage in the Anchorage area after the 1964 earthquake and finds that structures of short natural period underwent little damage, whereas those of longer period sustained more damage.

Pararas-Carayannis, George. A study of the source mechanism of the Alaska earthquake and tsunami of March 27, 1964: Part I, Water waves. *Pacific Science*, 21 (July 1967), 301–310. Also *in* The Great Alaska Earthquake of 1964: Seismology and Geodesy. NAS Pub. 1602. Washington: National Academy of Sciences, 1972. p. 249–258.
Determines the tsunami-generating area for the 1964 Alaska earthquake and discusses the extent of crustal displacement and the limits of the areas of subsidence and uplift.

Péwé, Troy L. Introduction: Avalanches *in* The Great Alaska Earthquake of 1964: Hydrology. NAS Pub. 1603. Washington: National Academy of Sciences, 1968. p. 351–354.
Summarizes studies of earthquake-triggered avalanches and the effects of avalanches on present and future glacier activity.

Plafker, George, Reuben Kachadoorian, Edwin B. Eckel, and Lawrence R. Mayo. Effects of the earthquake of March 27, 1964, on various communities. U.S. Geological Survey Professional Paper 542-G. Washington: Government Printing Office, 1969. 50 p. Also *in* The Great Alaska Earthquake of 1964: Geology. NAS Pub. 1601. Washington: National Academy of Sciences, 1971. p. 489–538.
Describes damage resulting primarily from tsunamis of diverse origins, displacements of the land relative to sea level, and seismic shaking in various Alaska communities in the 1964 earthquake.

Poirot, James W. Utilities for a relocated town in Alaska. *Civil Engineering*, 35 (March 1965), 50–53.
Gives details on street and storm-sewer construction, water facilities, use of cast-iron mains, sewerage, and sewage treatment facilities to be placed in the newly relocated town of Valdez after the 1964 earthquake by the U.S. Army Engineer District.

Powers, James R. An engineering glimpse of the Alaskan earthquake. *Air Force Civil Engineer*, 6 (February 1965), 2–5.
Stresses the concern of engineers about accelerations and periods of shock, resultant permanent land displacements, structural failures, and utilities damaged by the great Alaska earthquake.

Prestressed Concrete Institute. A report on the behavior of structures employing prestressed concrete during the Alaskan earthquake (Special Alaskan earthquake report). *PC Items*, 10 (June 1964), 2–7.
Emphasizes that, of the 28 Alaskan buildings using prestressed concrete at the time of the 1964 earthquake, only 5 collapsed totally or partially and their failure could not be attributed to the use of prestressed-concrete elements.

Public Administration Service. Report on a review of federal policy in grant, loan, and construction programs in areas of high risk of natural disaster damage. Chicago: Public Administration Service, 1965. 56 p.
Reports that federal agencies operating programs of a developmental nature in areas prone to floods, hurricanes, or earthquakes seek to avoid areas of high risk or, where such avoidance is impossible or not feasible, that they incorporate protective construction to counter the anticipated hazards.

Rice, E. F. The Alaska earthquake. *Civil Engineering*, 34 (May 1964), 52–56.
Deals with structural engineering problems caused by the 1964 earthquake and gives a critique of structural failures, as well as comments on damage to The Alaska Railroad, highways, port facilities, airports, and utilities.

Richardson, Claude B. Damage to utilities *in* The Great Alaska Earthquake of 1964: Engineering. NAS Pub. 1606. Washington: National Academy of Sciences, 1973.
States that damages to utilities owned by the state or municipalities were repaired by federal funds, with the major damage (to all utility systems) occurring in Anchorage due to earth slides set in motion by the 1964 earthquake.

Ross, Grant A., H. Bolton Seed, and Ralph R. Migliaccio. Performance of highway bridge foundations *in* The Great Alaska Earthquake of 1964: Engineering. NAS Pub. 1606. Washington: National Academy of Sciences, 1973.
Assesses the effects of foundation-support conditions, bridge and

channel configurations, and foundation displacements on bridge performance during the 1964 earthquake.

Rucker, Wheeler H., Jr. Report of physical damage and proposed order of repair of damage caused by earthquake of March 27, 1964. Report for the Port of Anchorage by Tippetts–Abbott–McCarthy–Stratton, Consulting Engineers & Architects (Seattle). Anchorage: Port of Anchorage, 1964. 20 p.
Gives itemized listing of 1964 earthquake damages to the municipal pier facility of the port of Anchorage.

Salley, Elsie M. Communications affected by earthquake (Chapter IX) in History of the Alaskan Communications Region, 1 January–30 June 1964. Elmendorf Air Force Base [Anchorage]: U.S. Air Force Communications Service [1964]. p. 78–102.
Discusses the instantaneous loss of all communications as a result of the 1964 earthquake, the rapid restoration of switchboard service, the slower restoration of teletype circuits, and the establishment of a temporary telegraph center at Anchorage.

Sawyer, Kenneth T. The Alaska earthquake: effects, reaction, and recovery. Military Engineer, 56 (July–August 1964), 246–249.
Describes assessment of damages and restoration of essential utilities and services on the army posts by the engineers of the Alaska District and the organization of three new resident engineer offices at Anchorage, Valdez, and Seward after the 1964 earthquake.

Schaem, William E. Structural design problems associated with the Alaskan earthquake in Science in Alaska, 1964: Proceedings Fifteenth Alaskan Science Conference, College, Alaska, August 31 to September 4, 1964. George Dahlgren, editor. College: Alaska Division American Association for the Advancement of Science, March 15, 1965. p. 253–258.
Outlines the responsibility of the structural engineer as to basic design and sound construction, as illustrated by errors brought to light by the 1964 Alaska earthquake.

Scientific and Engineering Task Force (Task Force No. 9). 30 Day Report of the Scientific and Engineering Task Force. Washington: Federal Reconstruction and Development Planning Commission for Alaska, 1964. 52 p.
Reviews the field investigations and actions by the U.S. Geological Survey, U.S. Coast and Geodetic Survey, and U.S. Army Corps of Engineers immediately after the 1964 earthquake and also covers the long-term scientific and engineering programs relating to engineering design.

Scott, Ronald F. Behavior of soils during the earthquake in The Great Alaska Earthquake of 1964: Engineering. NAS Pub. 1606. Washington: National Academy of Sciences, 1973.
Stresses that adverse behavior of soils during the 1964 earthquake caused extensive damage, that the present knowledge of soil behavior is not sufficient for future earthquake-resistant design, and that additional research on properties of soils is needed.

Scott, Ronald F., and Kenneth A. Zuckerman. Sandblows and liquefaction in The Great Alaska Earthquake of 1964: Engineering. NAS Pub. 1606. Washington: National Academy of Sciences, 1973.
Indicates that the presence of a finer-grained layer of soil overlying the liquefiable zone is necessary for the formation of sandblows which occur during some earthquakes such as that in Alaska in 1964.

Seed, H. Bolton. Landslides during earthquakes due to soil liquefaction. Journal of the Soil Mechanics and Foundations Division (American Society of Civil Engineers), 94, No. SM5 (September 1968), 1053–1122. Also in The Great Alaska Earthquake of 1964: Engineering. NAS Pub. 1606. Washington: National Academy of Sciences, 1973.
Points out the necessity for engineers to study the destructive landslides caused by soil liquefaction in the 1964 earthquake in order to evaluate complex situations in the future.

Seed, H. Bolton, and Clarence K. Chan. Clay strength under earthquake loading conditions. Journal of the Soil Mechanics and Foundations Division (American Society of Civil Engineers), 92 (March 1966), 53–78.
Describes procedure for determining the combinations of sustained stress and pulsating stress that will cause failure of a given soil and presents these data for three soil types.

Seed, H. Bolton, and Stanley D. Wilson. The Turnagain Heights landslide, Anchorage, Alaska. Journal of the Soil Mechanics and Foundations Division (American Society of Civil Engineers), 93 (July 1967), 325–353. Also in The Great Alaska Earthquake of 1964: Engineering. NAS Pub. 1606. Washington: National Academy of Sciences, 1973.
Studies the soil conditions in the Turnagain Heights area and analyzes the mechanics of the landslide development associated with the great Alaska earthquake.

Shannon & Wilson, Inc. Electro-osmosis field test section. Preliminary stabilization studies for the Turnagain buttress for U.S. Army Corps of Engineers, Alaska. Seattle: Shannon & Wilson, Inc., 1966. 153 p.
Reports that electroosmosis to stabilize the Turnagain area did not work when used in a field study and gives four possible reasons for the failure.

Shannon & Wilson, Inc. Preliminary report to U.S. Army Corps of Engineers on 4th Avenue slide, Anchorage, Alaska. Seattle: Shannon & Wilson, Inc., 1964. 10 p.
Presents preliminary findings from subsurface exploration, laboratory testing, and engineering studies of the Fourth Avenue slide, which occurred in Anchorage during the 1964 earthquake, along with conclusions regarding soil formation, mechanism of the landslide, and possible remedial measures.

Shannon & Wilson, Inc. Preliminary report to U.S. Army Corps of Engineers on Turnagain slide, Anchorage, Alaska. Seattle: Shannon & Wilson, Inc., 1964. 10 p.
Summarizes investigations, soil conditions in and adjacent to the slide area, and suggestions to improve the stability of the land behind the Turnagain slide area subsequent to the 1964 earthquake.

Shannon & Wilson, Inc. Remolding of Bootlegger Cove Clay with explosives. Preliminary stabilization studies for the Turnagain buttress for U.S. Army Corps of Engineers, Alaska. Seattle: Shannon & Wilson, Inc., 1965. 180 p.
Outlines the use of explosive charges to achieve stabilization of the Turnagain area by remolding the weak sensitive materials and allowing them to reconsolidate; suggests engineering design studies to evaluate the size and type of buttress required to stabilize the area.

Shannon & Wilson, Inc. Report on Anchorage area soil studies, Alaska, to U.S. Army Engineer District, Anchorage, Alaska.

Seattle: Shannon & Wilson, Inc., 1964. 300 p.
Describes engineering investigations and presents the results of studies and analyses of the earthquake-triggered landslides at Anchorage in 1964.

Shannon & Wilson, Inc. Report on subsurface investigation for Mineral Creek townsite, city of Valdez, Alaska, to U.S. Army Engineer District, Anchorage, Alaska. Seattle: Shannon & Wilson, Inc., 1964. 34 p.
Presents the results of exploration of the subsurface conditions of the Mineral Creek townsite, determines the suitability of the area for the new location of Valdez after the 1964 earthquake, and gives recommendations for construction of streets, utilities, and structure foundations.

Shannon & Wilson, Inc. Report on subsurface investigation for city of Seward, Alaska, and vicinity, to U.S. Army Engineer District, Anchorage, Alaska. Seattle: Shannon & Wilson, Inc., 1964. 77 p.
Determines the probable contributing factors responsible for the large submarine landslide at Seward during the 1964 earthquake and evaluates the present stability of this area.

Shannon, William L., and David E. Hilts. Submarine landslide at Seward in The Great Alaska Earthquake of 1964: Engineering. NAS Pub. 1606. Washington: National Academy of Sciences, 1973.
Indicates that the postearthquake stability of the Seward waterfront was unchanged from preearthquake conditions and that subaqueous landsliding may occur again in the event of another large earthquake.

Smith, Charles P. Highway destruction in Alaska: Part I, Alaska bridges experience an earthquake. *American Highways*, 43 (January 1965), 23–27.
Assesses highway bridge damage resulting from the 1964 earthquake in Alaska and tells of engineering plans for their temporary restoration with design for later permanent reconstruction.

Smith, Harold C. Anchorage–60 days after. *Modern Steel Construction* (Third Quarter 1964), 8–11.
Reports on the investigation (by two teams representing the steel industry) of structural behavior and of the progress and extent of repair and rehabilitation in Anchorage after the 1964 earthquake.

Sozen, Mete A. Lessons from an earthquake–A first-hand report from Anchorage. *Concrete Construction*, 9 (August 1964), 231–233.
Observes that the performance of reinforced-concrete structures in Anchorage at the time of the great Alaska earthquake underscored shortcomings in structural connections, openings in multistory shear walls, and inspection.

Sozen, Mete A., and N. Norby Nielsen. Analysis of the failure of the Anchorage International Airport control tower in The Great Alaska Earthquake of 1964: Engineering. NAS Pub. 1606. Washington: National Academy of Sciences, 1973.
Emphasizes the sources of ductility in reinforced-concrete connections by describing the observed damage to the Anchorage International Airport control tower after the 1964 earthquake.

Spaeth, Mark G., and Saul C. Berkman. The tsunami of March 28, 1964, as recorded at tide stations. ESSA [Environmental Science Services Administration]. Technical Report C&GS 33. Washington: Government Printing Office, 1967. 86 p. Also in The Great

Alaska Earthquake of 1964: Oceanography and Coastal Engineering. NAS Pub. 1605. Washington: National Academy of Sciences, 1972. p. 38–110.
Examines the damaging seiche action resulting from the 1964 tsunami, gives a history of the Tsunami Warning System, and tabulates fatality and damage figures.

Spreiregen, Paul. The Alaska earthquake: what the Task Force has to say. *AIA* [American Institute of Architects] *Journal*, 42 (December 1964), 35–37.
Describes a joint report made by a panel of non-Alaskan architects and engineers, with the architects recommending immediate restoration of essential facilities, prohibition of construction on unstable sites, study and recording of structural damage, and appointment of a committee of Alaskan architects to review all town or renewal plans.

Standard Oil Company of California. 1964 Alaskan earthquake damage (unpublished). Standard Oil Company of California Western Operations Report. San Francisco: Standard Oil Company of California, 1964. 10 p. (Copy on file, Library, National Academy of Sciences–National Academy of Engineering, Washington, D.C.)
Examines the extent of the damage to (1) Standard Oil Company marketing facilities at Anchorage, (2) crude-oil-producing facilities in the Swanson River Field on the Kenai Peninsula, (3) manufacturing facilities at the Alaskan refinery at Kenai, and (4) facilities of the Kenai Pipe Line Company.

Steinbrugge, Karl V. Engineering seismology aspects in Preliminary report–Prince William Sound, Alaskan earthquakes March–April 1964 (second printing). Seismology Division Report. Washington: U.S. Coast and Geodetic Survey, 1964. p. 58–72.
Reports on engineering survey of structural damage to Anchorage and vicinity after the 1964 earthquake and stresses the degree of earthquake bracing and the workmanship as qualifications to any broad classification of earthquake damage.

Steinbrugge, Karl V., and William K. Cloud. Prince William Sound, Alaska, March 28, 1964. *Bulletin of the Seismological Society of America*, 54 (August 1964), 1255–1256.
Points out that the selective damage to taller buildings in Anchorage during the 1964 earthquake was related to poor workmanship and design and to the predominant longer-period ground motions.

Stephenson, J. M. Cost may reach $8 million: Survey of quake damage at Anchorage produces valuable engineering data. *The Navy Civil Engineer*, 6 (May–June 1965), 11–16.
Emphasizes the importance of obtaining adequate knowledge of subsurface conditions and using it in the design of earthquake-resistant structures.

Stephenson, J. M. Earthquake damage to Anchorage area utilities–March 1964. U.S. Naval Civil Engineering Laboratory Technical Note N-607. Port Hueneme, California: U.S. Naval Civil Engineering Laboratory, 1964. 47 p.
Surveys the damage to utilities in Anchorage as a result of the great Alaska earthquake and finds that most of it, not being catastrophic, was restored within several days.

Stump, William J. Restoration of gas service after an earthquake. *Proceedings of the Pacific Coast Gas Association, Inc.*, 56 (1965), 123–126.

Analyzes the interruption of gas by the Anchorage Natural Gas Corporation after the 1964 earthquake, the damage to the system, and the use of a mobile leak detector.

Sturman, Gary G. The Alaska highway system *in* The Great Alaska Earthquake of 1964: Engineering. NAS Pub. 1606. Washington: National Academy of Sciences, 1973.
Describes the damage to Alaska roads and bridges due to subsidence, high tides, and soil movement on the stream embankments during the 1964 earthquake.

Sturman, Gary G. The Alaska Railroad *in* The Great Alaska Earthquake of 1964: Engineering. NAS Pub. 1606. Washington: National Academy of Sciences, 1973.
Assesses the severe damage to The Alaska Railroad in the 1964 earthquake and states that reconstruction of the facilities was completed in 2½ years at a cost of $22 million.

Tanaka, James M. Airports and air traffic control facilities *in* The Great Alaska Earthquake of 1964: Engineering. NAS Pub. 1606. Washington: National Academy of Sciences, 1973.
Stresses the importance of the Alaskan air-transportation system to the disaster-relief operations and its relatively low vulnerability compared to that of the highway and rail systems during the 1964 earthquake.

Tanaka, James M. Relocation of Valdez *in* The Great Alaska Earthquake of 1964: Engineering. NAS Pub. 1606. Washington: National Academy of Sciences, 1973.
Describes the rebuilding of Valdez (after the 1964 earthquake) on a new and less hazardous site at Mineral Creek, accomplished between March 1964 and February 1967 at a cost of $50,000 per capita for the population of 750 persons.

Tilgner, Edward E., and Jon R. Peterson. The Alaska Tsunami Warning System *in* Volume II-B,C: The Prince William Sound, Alaska, earthquake of 1964 and aftershocks. Environmental Science Services Administration, U.S. Coast and Geodetic Survey. Washington: Government Printing Office, 1969. p. 309–324.
Summarizes the seismograph components used in the Alaska Tsunami Warning System, describes the observatories, and gives information on data telemetry.

Transportation Consultants, Inc.–Wilbur Smith and Associates. Effects of the earthquake of 27 March 1964 on transportation in Alaska: An Interim Report of the Alaska Highway Study for the Bureau of Public Roads. Washington: Transportation Consultants, Inc., 1964. 27 p.
Recommends rehabilitation of all transport facilities and services in Alaska that were damaged by the 1964 earthquake and suggests the reopening of the railroad from Portage to Seward with a connection to the municipal dock.

Tudor, W. J. Tsunami damage at Kodiak, Alaska, and Crescent City, California, from Alaskan earthquake of 27 March 1964. U.S. Naval Civil Engineering Laboratory Technical Note N-622. Port Hueneme, California: U.S. Naval Civil Engineering Laboratory, 1964. 131 p.
Indicates light to moderate water-wave damage from 4- to 10-ft inundation and heavy damage from impact by wave-driven ships and debris at Kodiak, Alaska, and Crescent City, California, after the 1964 earthquake.

[U.S.] Alaskan Command. Operation helping hand: The armed forces react to earthquake disaster. Alaskan Command Publication. Seattle: Headquarters Alaskan Command [1964]. 83 p.
Outlines the assistance rendered to Alaskan civilians by the military forces in Alaska after the great earthquake there in 1964.

U.S. Army Engineer Division, Alaska District. After action report, Alaska Good Friday earthquake, 27 March 1964. Report prepared for U.S. Army Engineer Division, North Pacific. Anchorage: U.S. Army Corps of Engineers, January 1968. 76 p.
Provides a consolidated coverage of the disaster assistance given by the U.S. Army Engineers after the 1964 earthquake and includes cost summaries by agency, area, and type of restoration.

U.S. Army Engineering Division. Report on analysis of earthquake damage to military construction in Alaska, 27 March 1964. Washington: U.S. Army, Office Chief of Engineers, Directorate of Military Construction, 1964. 113 p.
Surveys the extent and type of damage to military construction in Alaska; reports on probable cause of failures, soils mechanics and foundation engineering, and damage to streets, roads, and bridges.

U.S. Bureau of Reclamation. Eklutna and the Alaska earthquake. A Report by the Alaska District Office of the Bureau of Reclamation. Juneau: U.S. Bureau of Reclamation, June 1966. 165 p.
Summarizes damage to the Eklutna power plant at the time of the 1964 Alaska earthquake, gives rehabilitation costs, and makes recommendations.

U.S. Bureau of Reclamation. Rehabilitation of Eklutna project features following earthquake of March 1964: A supplement to Eklutna Dam, tunnel and powerplant, technical record of design and construction, March 1958. A Water Resources Technical Publication. Denver: U.S. Bureau of Reclamation, June 1967. 111 p.
Deals with the replacement of the intake structure and the repair of the conduit for the Eklutna project and discusses the new dam and spillway.

U.S. Coast and Geodetic Survey. Preliminary report: Tidal datum plane changes, Prince William Sound, Alaskan earthquakes, March–April, 1964. Office of Oceanography Report. Rockville, Maryland: U.S. Coast and Geodetic Survey, 1964. 5 p.
Gives preliminary tidal datum plane changes for available locations in the Prince William Sound area for use in coastal engineering projects.

U.S. Coast and Geodetic Survey. Report on Tsunami Warning System in operation during the Alaskan earthquake of March 27, 1964, and how it should be improved, and recommendations for research in tsunami and earthquake forecasting. Washington: U.S. Coast and Geodetic Survey, 1964. 23 p.
Recommends improvements in the Tsunami Warning System existing at the time of the 1964 earthquake, estimates cost of improvement of the system, and suggests research on the prediction of earthquakes and resulting tsunamis.

U.S. Coast and Geodetic Survey. The Prince William Sound, Alaska, earthquake of 1964 and aftershocks. Fergus J. Wood, editor. Volume II-A: Research studies–Engineering seismology. Washington: Government Printing Office, 1967. 392 p.
Evaluates seismological effects of the great Alaska earthquake, in-

cluding earthquake engineering studies for the use of design and structural engineers and detailed appraisals of earthquake damage suffered by various types of structures.

U.S. Geological Survey. Color slides showing geologic effects and damage to the works of man caused by the great Alaska earthquake of March 27, 1964. Arthur Grantz, compiler and annotator. U.S. Geological Survey Photographic Library [Federal Center, Denver, Colorado] Annotated List of Slides. Washington: U.S. Geological Survey, 1965. 12 p. (Copy of list on file, Library, National Academy of Sciences–National Academy of Engineering, Washington, D.C.).
Lists captions of transparent slides that illustrate various kinds of earthquake effects, such as tectonic uplift and subsidence, faulting, fissuring, and lateral spreading of unconsolidated deposits weakened by seismic vibration. Slides are available from Photographic Library, U.S. Geological Survey, Denver Federal Center, Denver, Colorado 80225.

Van Dorn, William G. Source mechanism of the tsunami of March 28, 1964 in Alaska. Proceedings of the Ninth Conference (1964) on Coastal Engineering (Chapter 10). New York: American Society of Civil Engineers, 1965. p. 166–190. Also *in* The Great Alaska Earthquake of 1964: Oceanography and Coastal Engineering. NAS Pub. 1605. Washington: National Academy of Sciences, 1972. p. 140–146.
Suggests that the tsunami associated with the great Alaska earthquake was produced by a dipolar movement of the earth's crust and that the tilting of Prince William Sound to the northwest produced strong seiching action in the adjacent fiords.

Wallace, Robert E. Minimizing earthquake hazards–Part I, Geologic factors. *AIA* [American Institute of Architects] *Journal* (July 1968), 65–69.
Examines vital geologic considerations in minimizing the damage from future earthquakes and discusses faulting, failure of unstable ground under earthquake excitation, and the influence of the type and structure of ground on shaking.

White, W. R. H. The Alaska earthquake–Its effect in Canada. *Canadian Geographical Journal*, 72 (June 1966), 210–219.
Describes in detail the effects of earth movements and tsunamis (resulting from the 1964 Alaska earthquake) on such areas in Canada as Hot Springs Cove, Nootka Sound, Kyuquot Sound, Strait of Georgia–Juan de Fuca Strait, and Barkley Sound–Alberni Inlet.

Wiegel, Robert L. Earthquake engineering. Englewood Cliffs, New Jersey: Prentice-Hall, Inc., 1970. 518 p.
Summarizes data on earthquake-resistant structures and provides engineers with comprehensive coverage on this geological problem.

Wiegel, Robert L. Protection of Crescent City, California, from tsunami waves. Berkeley: The Redevelopment Agency of the City of Crescent City, March 5, 1965. 114 p.
Recommends (for the future protection of Crescent City from tsunamis) a reliance upon the Tsunami Warning System, the use of adequate fill to raise the land level, use of continuous reinforced concrete foundations, construction of a seawall, research on dock design, a model study on wave runup, and harbor dredging.

Wilson, Basil W., and Alf Tørum. The tsunami of the Alaskan earthquake, 1964: Engineering evaluation. Coastal Engineering Research Center Technical Memorandum No. 25. Washington: U.S. Army Corps of Engineers, May 1968. 444 p.
Provides an engineering view of the causes and effects of the 1964 Alaska tsunami and of future protective measures, with an engineering evaluation of severely damaged areas.

Contributors to This Volume

JOHN K. ALLENDER, Ellsworth Air Force Base, Rapid City, South Dakota 57706

NORMAN L. ARNO, U.S. Army Corps of Engineers, Washington, D.C. 20314

J. MARX AYRES, Ayres, Cohen & Hayakawa, Los Angeles, California 90035

DAVID P. BELANGER, U.S. Army Engineer District, Anchorage, Alaska 99501

K. LEE BENUSKA, Kinemetrics, San Gabriel, California 91776

GLEN V. BERG, University of Michigan, Ann Arbor, Michigan 48104

FREDERICK R. BROWN, Ayres, Cohen & Hayakawa, Los Angeles, California 90035

DUANE E. CARSON, U.S. Army Engineer District, Anchorage, Alaska 99501

WILLIAM K. CLOUD, University of California, Berkeley, California 94720

RAY W. CLOUGH, University of California, Berkeley, California 94720

THOMAS L. GARDNER, 3433 West 81st Avenue, Anchorage, Alaska 99502

WARREN GEORGE, U.S. Army Engineer District, Anchorage, Alaska 99501

ROBERT D. HANSON, University of Michigan, Ann Arbor, Michigan 48104

HAROLD D. HAUF, 13224–108th Drive, Sun City, Arizona 85351

DAVID E. HILTS, Shannon & Wilson, Inc., Spokane, Washington 99204

GEORGE W. HOUSNER, California Institute of Technology, Pasadena, California 91109

WILLIAM N. HOUSTON, University of California, Berkeley, California 94720

DONALD E. HUDSON, California Institute of Technology, Pasadena, California 91109

PAUL C. JENNINGS, California Institute of Technology, Pasadena, California 91109

PAUL KNOWLES, U.S. Army Engineer District, Walla Walla, Washington 99362

ERWIN L. LONG, U.S. Army Engineer District, Anchorage, Alaska 99501

LEONARD F. McKINNEY, Bureau of Land Management, Anchorage, Alaska 99501

EDMUND J. McMAHON, U.S. Army Engineer District, Anchorage, Alaska 99501

RALPH R. MIGLIACCIO, R&M Engineering and Geological Consultants, Fairbanks, Alaska 99701

JAMES K. MITCHELL, University of California, Berkeley, California 94720

N. NORBY NIELSEN, University of Hawaii, Honolulu, Hawaii 96822

CLAUDE B. RICHARDSON, U.S. Army Engineer District, Anchorage, Alaska 99501

GRANT A. ROSS, University of Calgary, Calgary 44, Alberta, Canada

RONALD F. SCOTT, California Institute of Technology, Pasadena, California 91109

H. BOLTON SEED, University of California, Berkeley, California 94720

WILLIAM L. SHANNON, Shannon & Wilson, Inc., Seattle, Washington 98103

JAMES F. SIZEMORE, Bureau of Land Management, Anchorage, Alaska 99501

METE A. SOZEN, University of Illinois, Urbana, Illinois 61801

GARY G. STURMAN, U.S. Army Engineer District, Anchorage, Alaska 99501

TSENG-YAO SUN, Ayres, Cohen & Hayakawa, Los Angeles, California 90035

JAMES M. TANAKA, Federal Aviation Administration, Anchorage, Alaska 99501

STANLEY D. WILSON, Shannon & Wilson, Inc., Seattle, Washington 98103

GEORGE YAMANE, Shannon & Wilson, Inc., Seattle, Washington 98103

KENNETH A. ZUCKERMAN, Zuckerman Building Company, Santa Monica, California 90403

English-Metric and Metric-English Conversion Tables

LENGTH

1 inch (in.)	=	2.54 centimeters (cm)
1 foot (ft) [12 in.]	=	30.48 cm
1 yard (yd) [3 ft]	=	91.44 cm
	=	0.914 meter (m)
1 mile (mi) [5280 ft]	=	1.610 kilometer (km)

AREA

1 square inch (in.²)	=	6.45 square centimeters (cm²)
1 square foot (ft²)	=	929.0 cm²
	=	0.0929 square meter (m²)
1 square yard (yd²)	=	0.836 m²
1 acre (a) [43560 ft²]	=	0.4047 hectare (ha)
1 square mile (mi²)	=	2.59 square kilometers (km²)

VOLUME

1 cubic inch (in.³)	=	16.4 cubic centimeters (cm³)
1 cubic foot (ft³)	=	28.3 × 10³ cm³
	=	0.0283 m³
1 cubic yard (yd³)	=	0.7646 cubic meter (m³)
1 cubic mile (mi³)	=	4.17 cubic kilometers (km³)
1 quart (qt) [0.25 U.S. gallon (gal)]	=	0.95 liter
1 gal [4 qt]	=	3.79 liter
1 bushel (bu) [U.S. dry]	=	35.24 liter

MASS

1 pound (lb) [16 ounces (oz)]	=	453.6 grams (g)
	=	0.4536 kilogram (kg)
1 U.S. ton (tn) [2000 lb]	=	907.2 kg
	=	0.9072 metric ton (MT)
1 long ton (LT) [2240 lb]	=	1.016 MT

PRESSURE

1 pound per square inch (lb/in.² or psi)	=	0.0704 kilogram per square centimeter (kg/cm²)
1 pound per square foot (lb/ft²)	=	4.8824 kilograms per square meter (kg/m²)
1 bar [1000 millibars (mb)]	=	1.020 kg/cm²

VELOCITY

1 foot per second (ft/s)	=	0.3048 meter per second (m/s)
	=	1.097 kilometer per hour (km/h)
	=	0.5925 international knot (kn)
1 mile per hour (mi/h)	=	1.609 km/h
	=	0.869 kn

LENGTH

1 millimeter (mm) [0.1 centimeter (cm)]	=	0.0394 inch (in.)
1 cm [10 mm]	=	0.3937 in.
1 meter (m) [100 cm]	=	39.37 in.
	=	3.28 feet (ft)
1 kilometer (km) [1000 m]	=	0.621 mile (mi)
1 international nautical mile [1852 m]	=	6076.1 ft

AREA

1 square centimeter (cm^2)	=	0.155 square inch (in.^{2})
1 square meter (m^2)	=	10.76 square feet (ft^2)
	=	1.196 square yards (yd^2)
1 hectare (ha)	=	2.4710 acres (a)
1 square kilometer (km^2)	=	0.386 square mile (mi^2)

VOLUME

1 cubic centimeter (cm^3)	=	0.0610 cubic inch (in.^{3})
1 cubic meter (m^3)	=	35.314 cubic feet (ft^3)
	=	1.31 cubic yards (yd^3)
1 cubic kilometer (km^3)	=	0.240 cubic mile (mi^3)
1 liter	=	1.06 quarts (qt)
	=	0.264 gallon (gal)

MASS

1 kilogram (kg) [1000 grams (g)]	=	2.20 pounds (lb)
	=	0.0011 ton
1 metric ton (MT) [1000 kg]	=	1.10 ton
	=	0.9842 long ton (LT)

PRESSURE

1 kilogram per square centimeter (kg/cm^2)	=	14.20 pounds per square inch (lb/in.^{2})
	=	2048 pounds per square foot (lb/ft^2)

VELOCITY

1 meter per second (m/s)	=	3.281 feet per second (ft/s)
1 kilometer per hour (km/h)	=	0.9113 ft/s
	=	0.621 mile per hour (mi/h)
1 knot (kn) [1852 m/h]	=	1.6878 ft/s
	=	1.151 mi/h

Index

Figures in italic indicate major discussion of topic.